A COURSE IN MODERN BUSINESS STATISTICS

SECOND EDITION

TERRY SINCICH

University of South Florida

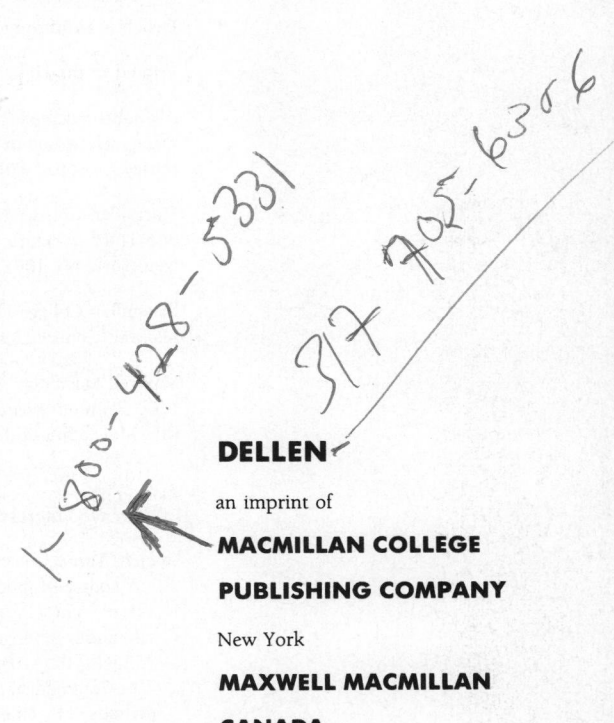

DELLEN

an imprint of

MACMILLAN COLLEGE PUBLISHING COMPANY

New York

MAXWELL MACMILLAN CANADA

Toronto

MAXWELL MACMILLAN INTERNATIONAL

New York   Oxford   Singapore   Sydney

On the cover: "Morning Mirror" is a bold acrylic on panel painting, 11 × 14 inches, by New York artist Gary Lang. His "mirror" is a complex composition of interwoven opaque, transparent, and fluorescent colors that vibrates with optical intensity.

Lang received a Master of Fine Arts degree from Yale University in 1975 and has been the focus of numerous one-man exhibitions throughout the United States and Europe. His work is included in the permanent collections of the Whitney Museum of American Art, New York City; the Museum of Contemporary Art, Los Angeles; the Madison Art Center, Madison, Wisconsin; and the Menil Collection, Houston, Texas. He is represented by Brian Gross Fine Art, San Francisco, and Michael Klein, Inc., New York City.

Editor: Don Dellen
Production supervisor: Phyllis Niklas
Text designer: Janet Bollow
Cover designer: John Williams
Cartoons: Tom Barnett
Technical illustrations: Folium

Copyright 1994 by Macmillan College Publishing Company, Inc.
Dellen is an imprint of Macmillan College Publishing Company.

Printed in the United States of America

Macmillan College Publishing Company
866 Third Avenue
New York, NY 10022

Macmillan College Publishing Company is part of the
Maxwell Communication Group of Companies.

Maxwell Macmillan Canada, Inc.
1200 Eglinton Avenue East, Suite 200
Don Mills, Ontario M3C 3N1

Library of Congress Cataloging-in-Publication Data

Sincich, Terry.
   A course in modern business statistics / Terry Sincich. —2nd ed.
      p.   cm.
   Includes bibliographical references and index.
   ISBN 0-02-410481-7
   1. Commercial statistics.   2. Social sciences—Statistical
methods.   I. Title.
   HF1017.S533   1994   93-39589
                                                              CIP

Printing: 1 2 3 4 5 6 7 8 9   Year: 4 5 6 7 8

CONTENTS

PREFACE

PEDAGOGY

A Course in Modern Business Statistics, Second Edition, is designed so that all major topics in introductory applied statistics can be covered in a single course. The prerequisite is only a high school background in mathematics.

The text incorporates American Statistical Association (ASA) guidelines developed from a series of conferences titled "Making Statistics More Effective in Schools of Business." At these annual conferences, there is a substantial consensus among the participants on the following points:

1. Students are most effectively motivated by seeing statistics at work in real applications, problems, cases, and projects.
2. Students should be provided with the opportunity to work with real data and to make serious use of statistical computations.
3. Formal training in probability needs to be downplayed in favor of intuitive concepts of probability.
4. We need to reduce our emphasis on the formal theory of statistics and increase emphasis on applications.

These ideas have culminated in a text that focuses on practical applications and interpretation of results, with less emphasis on calculations and probability.

FEATURES

Specifically, the main features of the text are:

1. An **early introduction to confidence intervals and hypothesis testing** (Chapter 5) familiarizes students with the basics of inferential statistics. This enables the instructor to cover all the fundamental statistical ideas and methods (eg, descriptive statistics, sampling distributions, interval estimation, hypothesis testing, control charts, and regression) in a single semester, if desired.
2. **Examples and problem sets are based on real data**. The data sets and problem ideas are extracted from academic journals, newspaper articles, and magazines. This practical orientation helps the student relate statistics to problems encountered in the real world and, hopefully, will develop a pattern of thought that will persist after the student begins his/her career.
3. **Case studies** detail interesting current problems in business. Each chapter ends with a case study that poses a series of questions for the student. The student is expected to solve the problem using the statistical concepts and methodology

presented in the chapter. Like the examples and problems, the cases are extracted from academic journals, newspaper articles, and magazines.

4. **Computer printouts** generated from three popular statistical software packages (**SAS, SPSS, MINITAB**) are presented throughout the text. This enables the instructor to emphasize interpretation of the statistical results rather than the computation of those results.

5. **Computer labs** appear throughout the text. These sections provide the SAS, SPSS, and MINITAB commands used to generate the computer printouts displayed in the chapter.

6. **Nonparametric and parametric statistical methods are integrated** throughout. Whenever a parametric technique is presented, a corresponding distribution-free (nonparametric) method is also discussed. This provides the student with an alternative method to solving a problem when, as often occurs in the real world, the parametric assumptions are violated.

7. **Chapter notes**, summarizing key ideas, definitions, formulas, and interpretations, are provided for the student at the end of each chapter.

8. **Key concepts are highlighted.** Throughout the text, definitions, formulas, steps to follow in performing a statistical procedure, and warnings (indicating a specific situation where a method is likely to be misused) are boxed and highlighted.

9. **Sample exam questions** are provided for logically grouped chapters. These give the student a feel for the types of questions that might be expected on an exam, and provides the instructor with sample questions that cover the material presented.

10. **Short answers to all problems** are provided at the back of the book. Answers to the case studies and sample exam questions are excluded so that they may be used for homework assignments, quizzes, etc.

REVISIONS

The second edition contains several substantial modifications, additions, and enhancements:

1. The material on **exploring and describing data is expanded and presented in two chapters:** Chapter 2 (qualitative data) and Chapter 3 (quantitative data). New sections in Chapter 2 cover summary frequency tables (Section 2.1) and cross-classification tables (Section 2.5). New sections added to Chapter 3 cover dot plots (Section 3.1) and sequence plots (Section 3.4).

2. The original chapter on **probability and statistical inference is split into two chapters:** Chapter 4 (basic concepts of probability) and Chapter 5 (introduction to statistical inference).

3. Ideas on **statistical process and quality control have been consolidated into a single chapter** (Chapter 9). New sections on total quality management (Section 9.1) and tolerance limits (Section 9.7) have been added.

4. Material on **regression analysis is expanded and presented in two parts:** Chapter 10 (part I) provides the basics of performing a regression analysis and presents several different types of linear models. Chapter 11 (part II) focuses on model building and model diagnostics. New sections in Chapter 11 cover variable transformations (Section 11.3) and influential observations (Section 11.7).

5. **Two new sections have been added to the time series chapter** (Chapter 12), one on index numbers (Section 12.3) and one on forecasting using lagged values of the dependent variable (Section 12.8).
6. A **new chapter on experimental design and analysis of variance** has been written (Chapter 13).
7. Several **new case studies** have been added.
8. **More problems** have been added to the problem sets in each chapter.

COURSE COVERAGE

Depending on the amount of material covered, the text can be used at either a 2-year junior college or 4-year institution, and at the undergraduate or graduate (ie, master's) level. For example, the text can be used in the following courses:

1. One-semester introductory statistics course at a 2-year junior college (suggested coverage: Chapters 1–6, 8).
2. One-semester introductory statistics course at a 4-year college or university (suggested coverage: Chapters 1–6, 8–10).
3. Two-semester introductory statistics course at a 4-year college or university (suggested coverage: Chapters 1–8 in semester 1; Chapters 9–13 in semester 2).
4. One-semester course in applied statistics for MBA students (suggested coverage: Chapters 1–10, 12).

At first glance, these multiple uses for the book may seem inconsistent. For example, how can a text be appropriate for both undergraduate and graduate business students? The answer lies in the content. In contrast to a course in statistical theory, the level of mathematical knowledge required for an applied statistics course is minimal. Consequently, the difficulty encountered in learning the mechanics is much the same for both undergraduate and graduate students. The challenge is in the application—diagnosing practical problems, deciding on the appropriate statistical method for a given situation, and knowing which inferential technique will answer a manager's practical question. This takes *experience*, and it explains why a student can take an undergraduate course in applied statistics and still benefit from covering some of the same ground in an MBA course.

SUPPLEMENTS

This text is accompanied by the following supplementary material:

1. **Student's Solutions Manual** (by Mark Dummeldinger). The manual contains the full solutions for the odd-numbered problems contained in the text.
2. **Instructor's Solutions Manual** (by Mark Dummeldinger). The manual contains the complete solutions to the even-numbered problems, case studies, and sample exam questions contained in the text.
3. **Data sets on diskette.** Several of the large data sets analyzed in examples and case studies are available (in ASCII format) on either a $3\frac{1}{2}$ or $5\frac{1}{4}$ inch IBM PC diskette. The data sets include the starting salaries of 2,000 college graduates, sale prices for 8,000 residential properties, costs of 300 HMO physicians, and low-bid prices for 300 bread contracts. The disk also includes data for all problem sets containing 20 or more observations.

4. **ASP statistical software diskette.** New to this edition, the text includes inside the back cover a $3\frac{1}{2}$ inch micro disk containing the ASP program, *A Statistical Package for Business, Economics, and the Social Sciences.* ASP, from DMC Software, Inc., is a user-friendly, totally menu-driven program that contains all the major statistical applications covered in the text, plus many more. ASP runs on any IBM-compatible PC with at least 512K of memory and two disk drives. With ASP, students with no knowledge of computer programming can create and analyze data sets easily and quickly. Appendix C contains start-up procedures and a short tutorial on the use of ASP. Full documentation is provided complimentary to adopters of the text.

5. **ASP Tutorial and Student Guide** (by George Blackford). Most students have little trouble learning to use ASP without documentation. Some, however, may want to purchase the *ASP Tutorial and Student Guide.* Book stores can order the tutorial from DMC Software, Inc., 6169 Pebbleshire Drive, Grand Blanc, MI, 48439.

6. **Test Bank Manual** (by Mark Dummeldinger). This manual provides a large number of test items utilizing real data.

7. **DellenTest software.** This unique computer-generated random test system is complimentary to adopters. Utilizing an IBM (or compatible) PC and printer, the system will generate an almost unlimited number of quizzes, chapter tests, final examinations, and drill exercises. At the same time, the system produces an answer key and student worksheet with an answer column that exactly matches the column on the answer key.

ACKNOWLEDGMENTS

Several individuals deserve special recognition upon completion of the second edition of this text. Don Dellen, my publisher, encouraged me to write the text and then provided all the necessary support to ensure the quality of the finished product. Joyce Curry-Daly (California Polytechnic Institute) provided a comprehensive and constructive review of the first edition; many of the changes you see in the text are due to her suggestions. Phyllis Niklas did an excellent job of supervising the production of the second edition. My wife, Faith Sincich, served in several capacities on both editions of the text, including word-processing specialist, proofreader, acquisition of permissions, moral supporter, and my toughest critic. Without Faith, this text could not have been completed. Finally, I thank my daughters, Kara and Kelly, for their love and understanding during those times when they failed to receive the attention they so richly deserved.

CHAPTER 1

INTRODUCTION: STATISTICS AND DATA

Can taking drugs improve your score on the Scholastic Aptitude Test (SAT)? Are the final outcomes of professional basketball games determined solely by what happens in the fourth quarter? How many job offers, on average, do graduating MBAs receive? Questions such as these can be answered if relevant data are collected. This chapter presents a general overview of the science of statistics and its value in extracting useful and reliable information from data.

WHAT IS STATISTICS?

1.1 Consider the following recent items from the news media:

The Wall Street Journal, July 14, 1992
Video card games (eg, video poker), once only legal in casinos, are now available for play in laundromats and grocery stores of states that have a lottery. These video card games are beginning to create adult addicts, many of them women, who gamble until they're broke and in debt. In a study of 52 women in Gamblers Anonymous, 90% were video poker players. After they became hooked on video poker, 75% exhausted their family savings, 33% embezzled from their employers, 25% declared bankruptcy, and 10% turned to prostitution to raise money.

Chance, Vol. 5, No. 3–4, 1992
Folk wisdom suggests that the final outcome of a professional basketball game is heavily dependent on what happens in the last quarter (final 12 minutes), if not the final 2 minutes, of playing time. Information for 189 National Basketball Association games was collected from the box scores reported in the *St. Louis Post-Dispatch*. In these games, the team leading after 3 quarters of play won 150 times and lost only 39 times—a "leader-win" percentage of almost 80%.

U.S. News & World Report, Mar. 22, 1993
According to *U.S. News'* fourth annual survey of "America's Best Graduate Schools," an MBA degree candidate received an average of only one job offer prior to graduation, compared to 3.8 job offers a decade ago. On some campuses last year, one in five MBA candidates had not received a single job offer by graduation.

Tampa Tribune, Jan. 10, 1990
A computer study conducted at Columbia University demonstrated that shuffling a deck of cards seven times prevents bettors from accurately predicting the next card in blackjack. Most Atlantic City casinos will continue with their customary two shuffles of the deck, however, since the extra 5 minutes it takes to perform the additional shuffles could result in a substantial profit loss.

Time, Jan. 22, 1990
Nissan's ad campaign for its Infiniti luxury cars was originally renowned for a novel gimmick: The autos were nowhere in sight. The Infiniti ads, which depicted lushly photographed trees, boulders, lightning bolts and ocean waves (but no cars), were found by a Gallup poll to be the best-recalled commercial on television. Unfortunately, Infiniti dealers in the United States sold only 32 cars a day during the last 2 months of the year, compared to the 134 cars per day sold by its archrival, the Toyota Lexus.

Every day we are inundated with bits of information—data—like those in the examples above, whether we are in the classroom, on the job, or at home. Many of you taking this course are studying to be (or may already be) managers of a business or firm. Some of you will be **data producers**, but most of you will be **data users**. As such, you will need to be able to make sense out of the mass of data that others produce for you. What specialized tools will enable you to become effective data users? The answer is **statistics**.

A common misconception is that a statistician is simply a "number cruncher," or a person who calculates and summarizes numbers, like baseball batting averages or unemployment rates. Statistics involves numbers, but there is much more to it than that.

According to *The Random House College Dictionary* (1988 ed.), statistics is "the science that deals with the collection, classification, analysis, and interpretation of numerical facts or data." In short, statistics is the **science of data**—a science that will enable you to be proficient data producers and efficient data users.

DEFINITION 1.1

Statistics is the science of data. This involves collecting, classifying, summarizing, organizing, analyzing, and interpreting data.

In this chapter we explore the different types of data that you will encounter in business and introduce you to some ideas on methods for collecting data. The various statistical methods for summarizing, analyzing, and interpreting data are presented in the chapters that follow.

TYPES OF DATA

1.2 Data are obtained by measuring some characteristic or property of the objects (usually people or things) of interest to us. These objects upon which the measurements (or observations) are made are called **experimental units**, and the properties being measured are called **variables** (since, in virtually all studies of interest, the property varies from one observation to another).

DEFINITION 1.2

An **experimental unit** is an object (person or thing) upon which we collect data.

DEFINITION 1.3

A **variable** is a characteristic (property) that differs, or varies, from one observation to the next.

All data (and consequently, the variables we measure) are either **quantitative** or **qualitative** in nature.* Quantitative data are data that can be measured on a numerical scale. In general, qualitative data take values that are nonnumerical; they can only be classified. The statistical tools that we use to analyze data depend on whether

---

* A finer breakdown of data types into nominal, ordinal, interval, and ratio data is possible. **Nominal** data are qualitative data with categories that cannot be meaningfully ordered. **Ordinal** data are also qualitative data, but a distinct ranking of the groups from high to low exists. **Interval** and **ratio** data are two different types of quantitative data. For most statistical applications (and all the methods presented in this introductory text), it is sufficient to classify data as either quantitative or qualitative.

the data are quantitative or qualitative. Thus, it is important to be able to distinguish between the two types of data.

DEFINITION 1.4

Quantitative data are observations measured on a numerical scale.

DEFINITION 1.5

Nonnumerical data that can only be classified into one of a group of categories are **qualitative data**.

To illustrate, consider the data in Table 1.1. This data set, obtained from *Business Week*'s 1993 "Executive Compensation Scoreboard," contains information on 10 of the 365 corporate executives who participated in the survey. In this example, the experimental units are the 10 corporate executives. For each executive (ie, each observation) five variables are recorded: (1) company, (2) industry group, (3) total 1992 pay (in thousands of dollars), (4) return to shareholders (in dollars) on a $100 investment made 3 years earlier, and (5) pay-for-performance rating measured on a scale of 1 (excellent) to 5 (poor).

The first two variables (company and industry group) are qualitative since the data they produce are values that are nonnumerical values; they can only be classified into categories or groups. The next two variables (total pay and shareholder return) are quantitative since they are measured on a numerical scale. The fifth variable (performance rating), although coded as a number (1–5), is really qualitative in nature. The performance categories are "excellent," "above average," "average," "be-

TABLE 1.1
Data on 10 CEOs in the 1993 Executive Compensation Scoreboard

CEO	(1) COMPANY	(2) INDUSTRY GROUP	(3) TOTAL PAY	(4) SHAREHOLDER RETURN	(5) PERFORMANCE RATING
C. Lazarus	Toys 'R' Us	Retailing	64,231	168	5
A. O'Reilly	Heinz	Food processing	36,918	135	5
W. Anders	General Dynamics	Aerospace	29,015	239	5
L. Bantle	UST Inc.	Tobacco	24,602	222	4
R. Allen	Delta	Airlines	2,740	80	2
H. Poling	Ford Motor	Automotive	6,167	113	3
D. Calloway	Pepsico	Beverages	15,984	201	3
A. Hirsig	Arco	Chemicals	1,950	141	1
P. Freiman	Syntex	Drugs	3,170	103	2
J. Marriott	Marriott	Food & lodging	3,421	65	4

Source: "Executive Pay: The Party Ain't Over Yet." *Business Week,* Apr. 26, 1993. Reprinted from Apr. 26, 1993 issue of *Business Week* by special permission, copyright © 1993 by McGraw-Hill, Inc. Used with permission.

low average," and "poor." For convenience, *Business Week* has chosen to assign numbers (ie, 1 for "excellent," 2 for "above average," etc.) to the categories to obtain a performance rating.* This does result in a meaningful variable, however, since the higher the rating, the poorer the executive's performance. In contrast, assigning numbers to industry group (eg, 1 for "aerospace," 2 for "airlines," etc.) would not result in a meaningful quantitative variable.

PROBLEMS

1.1 *Business Horizons* (Jan.–Feb. 1993) conducted a comprehensive study of 800 chief executive officers who run the country's largest global corporations. The purpose of the study was to build a profile of the CEOs based on their aggregate social background characteristics. Several of the variables measured for each CEO are listed below. Classify each variable as quantitative or qualitative.

   a. State of birth   **b.** Age   **c.** Education level
   d. Tenure with firm   **e.** Total compensation   **f.** Area of expertise

1.2 Marketers are keenly interested in the factors that motivate coupon usage by consumers. A study reported in the *Journal of Consumer Marketing* (Spring 1988) asked a sample of 290 shoppers to respond to the following questions:

   a. Do you collect and redeem coupons?
   b. Are you price-conscious while shopping?
   c. On average, how much time per week do you spend clipping and collecting coupons?

   Classify the responses to the questions as quantitative or qualitative data.

1.3 In Hawaii, condemnation proceedings have been underway since 1980 to enable private citizens to own the property that their homes are built on. (Prior to 1980, only estates were permitted to own land and homeowners leased the land from the estate.) The new law requires estates to sell land to homeowners at a fair market price. As part of a study to estimate the fair market value of its land (called the "leased fee" value), a large Hawaiian estate collected the data shown in the accompanying table for five properties.

PROPERTY	LEASED FEE VALUE Thousand Dollars	LOT SIZE 1,000 Square Feet	NEIGHBORHOOD	LOCATION OF LOT
1	70.7	13.5	Cove	Cul-de-sac
2	52.6	9.6	Highlands	Interior
3	87.1	17.6	Cove	Corner
4	43.2	7.9	Highlands	Interior
5	144.3	13.8	Golf course	Cul-de-sac

   a. Identify the experimental units.
   b. State whether each of the variables measured is quantitative or qualitative.

1.4 A study was conducted to examine the differences in job performance of white-collar workers with type A and type B behavior (*Journal of Human Stress*, Summer 1985). Type A workers exhibit on-the-job traits such as explosiveness, accelerated speech, ambitiousness, impatience, hostility, a tendency to challenge others, and the general appearance of tension; type B behavior is generally characterized by opposite attributes and qualities. The data for several workers

---

* To obtain the performance rating, *Business Week* compared an executive's return-to-pay ratio with those of others within the same industry group and assigned a rating of 1 to those executives with the highest ratios (relative to the others in the group), a rating of 2 to those with the next highest ratios, etc.

at a large Canadian manufacturing firm who took part in the study are given in the table. [*Note:* Job performance of each worker was measured on a 5 point scale (a higher score indicates better performance) based on ratings of immediate supervisors.]

WORKER	BEHAVIOR TYPE	AGE	MANAGERIAL LEVEL	NUMBER OF EMPLOYEES SUPERVISED	PERFORMANCE RATING
1	A	47	Upper	22	3
2	B	28	Middle	10	5
3	B	52	Upper	105	2
4	A	30	Lower	3	1

Source: Jamal, Muhammed, "Type A Behavior and Job Performance: Some Suggestive Findings." *Journal of Human Stress* (now *Behavioral Medicine*), Summer 1985, pp. 60–67. Reprinted with permission of the Helen Dwight Reid Educational Foundation. Published by Heldref Publications, 4000 Albemarle St., N.W., Washington, DC 20016. Copyright ©1985.

a. Identify the experimental units.
b. State whether each of the variables measured is quantitative or qualitative.

1.5 The data in the accompanying table were obtained from the Environmental Protection Agency (EPA) *1993 Gas Mileage Guide* for new automobiles.

MODEL NAME	MANUFACTURER	TRANSMISSION	ENGINE SIZE Liters	NUMBER OF CYLINDERS	ESTIMATED CITY MILES/GALLON	ESTIMATED HIGHWAY MILES/GALLON
NSX	Acura	Automatic	3.0	6	18	23
Colt	Dodge	Manual	1.5	4	32	40
318i	BMW	Automatic	1.8	4	22	30
Aerostar	Ford	Automatic	4.0	6	16	22
Camry	Toyota	Manual	2.2	4	22	30

Source: *1993 Gas Mileage Guide*, EPA Fuel Economy Estimates, Oct. 1992.

a. Identify the experimental units.
b. State whether each of the variables measured is quantitative or qualitative.

COMPUTER LAB 1

ENTERING AND LISTING DATA

In the Computer Lab sections in this text, we give the commands necessary to conduct a statistical analysis of data using any one of three statistical software packages—SAS, SPSS, and MINITAB. These three packages were selected because of their current popularity, ease of use, and availability at most university computing centers. In addition, all three packages have versions available both for large mainframe computers and for personal computers (PCs).

All three software packages utilize the following three basic types of instructions:

1. *Data entry commands.* Instructions on how the data will be entered
2. *Input data values.* The values of the variables in the data set
3. *Statistical analysis commands.* Instructions on what type of analysis is to be conducted on the data

In this section we give the **data entry commands** for each package. That is, we give the commands that will enable you to create a data set ready for analysis. (The appropriate statistical analysis commands are provided in the relevant sections of the text.) Assume the data set of interest contains sale prices for five residential properties sold in a midsized city; these are listed in Table 1.2.

NOTE   With few exceptions, the commands provided in the following sections are appropriate for the large mainframe and PC versions of the three software packages. When a mainframe computer is being used, however, these statements must be preceded by the job control language (JCL) commands required at your institution.

TABLE 1.2
Sales Information for Five Residential Properties

PROPERTY	SALE PRICE	APPRAISED LAND VALUE	APPRAISED VALUE OF IMPROVEMENTS	NEIGHBORHOOD
1	$ 81,300	$17,900	$ 60,200	A
2	154,100	32,500	110,500	B
3	96,900	20,200	75,200	B
4	72,900	17,600	51,000	A
5	51,200	13,800	39,200	B

SAS

Command
Line

```
 1    DATA SALES;
 2    INPUT SALEPRIC LANDVAL IMPROVAL NBRHOOD $;    } Data entry
 3    TOTVAL = LANDVAL + IMPROVAL;                       instructions
 4    SALTOAPR = SALEPRIC/TOTVAL;
 5    CARDS;
 6     81300   17900   60200   A
 7    154100  32500  110500   B
 8     96900  20200   75200   B    } Input data values
 9     72900  17600   51000   A      (1 observation per line)
10     51200  13800   39200   B
11    PROC PRINT;} Print instruction
```

COMMAND 1   SALES is an arbitrarily chosen name used to identify the data set. (Data set names are restricted to a maximum of eight characters in length.)

COMMAND 2   SALEPRIC, LANDVAL, IMPROVAL, and NBRHOOD are arbitrarily chosen names for the variables in the data set. (Variable names are also restricted to a maximum of eight characters in length.) A dollar sign ($) must follow the name of any nonnumeric variable in the data set.

COMMANDS 3–4   TOTVAL (total appraised value) is calculated as the sum of LANDVAL and IMPROVAL. SALTOAPR is calculated as the ratio of sale price to total appraised value. (The standard arithmetic operation symbols, $+$, $-$, $*$, and $/$, are used for addition, subtraction, multiplication, and division, respectively.)

COMMAND 5   CARDS signals SAS that the input data values are to follow.

COMMANDS 6–10   Each data line gives the values of the variables in the data set for a single observation (property) in the order in which the variables are listed in the INPUT command. Input data values must be separated by at least one blank space; commas are not permitted in numeric values.

COMMAND 11   The PRINT procedure (PROC) will produce a listing of the entire data set. In addition to the INPUT variables, the data set will contain any variables created using the standard arithmetic operations (eg, TOTVAL) in command line 3. The output from the SAS program is shown in Figure 1.1a.

FIGURE 1.1
Printouts of Data in Table 1.2

a. SAS

OBS	SALEPRIC	LANDVAL	IMPROVAL	NBRHOOD	TOTVAL	SALTOAPR
1	81300	17900	60200	A	78100	1.04097
2	154100	32500	110500	B	143000	1.07762
3	96900	20200	75200	B	95400	1.01572
4	72900	17600	51000	A	68600	1.06268
5	51200	13800	39200	B	53000	0.96604

b. SPSS

SALEPRIC	LANDVAL	IMPROVAL	NBRHOOD	TOTVAL	SALTOAPR
81300.00	17900.00	60200.00	A	78100.00	1.04
154100.0	32500.00	110500.0	B	143000.0	1.08
96900.00	20200.00	75200.00	B	95400.00	1.02
72900.00	17600.00	51000.00	A	68600.00	1.06
51200.00	13800.00	39200.00	B	53000.00	.97

c. MINITAB

ROW	SALEPRIC	LANDVAL	IMPROVAL	NBRHOOD	TOTVAL	SALTOAPR
1	81300	17900	60200	1	78100	1.04097
2	154100	32500	110500	0	143000	1.07762
3	96900	20200	75200	0	95400	1.01572
4	72900	17600	51000	1	68600	1.06268
5	51200	13800	39200	0	53000	0.96604

GENERAL   All SAS commands must end with a semicolon; the only exceptions to this rule are the input data values.

SPSS

Command
Line

```
 1     DATA LIST FREE/SALEPRIC LANDVAL IMPROVAL NBRHOOD (A1).⎫
 2     COMPUTE TOTVAL = LANDVAL + IMPROVAL.                   ⎬  Data entry
 3     COMPUTE SALTOAPR = SALEPRIC/TOTVAL.                    ⎭  instructions
 4     BEGIN DATA.
 5      81300   17900    60200   A⎫
 6     154100   32500   110500   B⎪
 7      96900   20200    75200   B⎬  Input data values
 8      72900   17600    51000   A⎪  (1 observation per line)
 9      51200   13800    39200   B⎭
10     END DATA.
11     LIST.⎬  Print instruction
```

COMMAND 1   SALEPRIC, LANDVAL, IMPROVAL, and NBRHOOD are arbitrarily chosen names for the variables in the data set. (Variable names are restricted to a maximum of eight characters in length.) An alphanumeric format of the form (A*n*) must be specified, in parentheses, after the name of any nonnumeric variable. For example, A1 specifies that the nonnumeric variable NBRHOOD will occupy one column in the input data lines.

COMMANDS 2–3   TOTVAL (total appraised value) is calculated as the sum of LANDVAL and IMPROVAL. SALTOAPR is calculated as the ratio of sale price to total appraised value. (The standard arithmetic operation symbols, $+$, $-$, $*$, and $/$, are used for addition, subtraction, multiplication, and division, respectively.)

COMMAND 4   BEGIN DATA signals SPSS that the input data values are to follow.

COMMANDS 5–9   Each data line gives the values of the variables in the data set for a single observation (property) in the order in which the variables are listed in the DATA LIST command. Values in the data list must be separated by at least one blank space; commas are not permitted in numeric values.

COMMAND 10   END DATA signals SPSS that all input data values have been entered.

COMMAND 11   The LIST command will produce a listing of the data for all the variables in the data set, including the variables created using COMPUTE commands. The output from the SPSS program is shown in Figure 1.1b.

GENERAL   In the PC environment, all SPSS commands must end with a command terminator (usually a period); the only exceptions to this rule are the input data values. Omit the periods when using mainframe SPSS.

MINITAB

Command
  Line
```
   1      READ C1 C2 C3 C4} Data entry instruction
   2       81300   17900    60200   1
   3      154100   32500   110500   0
   4       96900   20200    75200   0       Input data values
   5       72900   17600    51000   1       (1 observation per line)
   6       51200   13800    39200   0
   7      ADD C2 C3 PUT INTO C5
   8      DIVIDE C1 BY C5 PUT INTO C6}  Data entry instructions
   9      NAME C1 = 'SALEPRIC' C2 = 'LANDVAL' C3 = 'IMPROVAL' C4 = 'NBRHOOD'
  10      NAME C5 = 'TOTVAL' C6 = 'SALTOAPR'
  11      PRINT C1-C6}  Print instruction
  12      STOP
```

COMMAND 1   The four variables to be read onto the MINITAB "worksheet" are identified by the "columns" into which they are placed: C1, C2, C3, and C4. (MINITAB does not, in general, recognize variable names.) Thus, sale price will be read in column 1, land value in column 2, etc.

COMMANDS 2–6   Each data line gives the values of the variables read in the worksheet columns for a single observation (property). Input data values must be separated by at least one blank space; commas are not permitted. MINITAB also requires that all data used in statistical analysis be numerical. Thus, the values of the nonnumeric variable neighborhood are converted to numbers in C5. (Arbitrarily let 1 represent neighborhood A and 0 represent neighborhood B.)

COMMANDS 7–8   MINITAB uses the word commands ADD, SUBTRACT, MULTIPLY, and DIVIDE to perform the usual arithmetic operations on variables. The sum of land value (C2) and improvements value (C3) (ie, total appraised value) is stored in C5; the ratio of sale price (C1) to total appraised value (C5) is stored in C6.

COMMANDS 9–10   For labeling printed output, the NAME command can be used to give names to the variables stored in the worksheet columns. If the NAME command is omitted, the columns will be labeled C1, C2, etc., on the MINITAB printouts.

COMMAND 11   The PRINT command will produce a listing of the data in the MINITAB worksheet for the specified variables (columns). The output of the MINITAB program is shown in Figure 1.1c.

COMMAND 12 All MINITAB programs terminate with the STOP command.

GENERAL   MINITAB permits you to insert extraneous words within each command to help you follow the logic of the program. For example, command line 1 could be entered as follows:

```
READ PRICE IN C1, LANDVAL IN C2, IMPROVAL IN C3, NBHD IN C4
```

OPTIONAL: ACCESSING AN EXTERNAL DATA FILE

Data created by other software and saved in an external file as an ASCII data set also can be accessed and analyzed by the three statistical software packages. For example, the sales data of Table 1.2 are extracted from a much larger data set containing sales information for 8,313 residential properties. This data set is saved in an ASCII file called SALES.DAT on a floppy disk available from the publisher (see the Preface). The programs shown here give the appropriate commands for reading and listing the data on this external file.

SAS

Command
Line
```
1    DATA SALES;
2    INFILE 'SALES.DAT';
3    INPUT SALEPRIC LANDVAL IMPROVAL NBRHOOD $;    Data entry
4    TOTVAL = LANDVAL + IMPROVAL;                  instructions
5    SALTOAPR = SALEPRIC/TOTVAL;
6    PROC PRINT;}  Print instruction
```

SPSS

Command
Line
```
1    DATA LIST FILE='SALES.DAT' FREE
2              /SALEPRIC LANDVAL IMPROVAL NBRHOOD (A1),   Data entry
3    COMPUTE TOTVAL = LANDVAL + IMPROVAL,                 instructions
4    COMPUTE SALTOAPR = SALEPRIC/TOTVAL,
5    LIST,}  Print instruction
```

MINITAB

Command
Line
```
1    READ 'SALES.DAT' C1 C2 C3 C4
2    ADD C2 C3 PUT INTO C5               Data entry instructions
3    DIVIDE C1 BY C5 PUT INTO C6
4    NAME C1='SALEPRIC' C2='LANDVAL' C3='IMPROVAL' C4='NBRHOOD'
5    NAME C5='TOTVAL' C6='SALTOAPR'
6    PRINT C1-C6}  Print instruction
7    STOP
```

FUNDAMENTAL ELEMENTS OF A STATISTICAL ANALYSIS

1.3 When you examine a data set, you will be doing so because the data characterize some phenomenon of interest to you. In statistics, the data set that is the target of your interest is called a **population**. Notice that a statistical population does not refer to a group of people; it refers to a set of measurements. This data set, which is typically large, exists in fact or is part of an ongoing operation and hence is conceptual. Some examples of business phenomena and their corresponding populations are shown in Table 1.3.

DEFINITION 1.6

A **population** is a collection (or set) of data that describe some phenomenon of interest to you.

If you have the population in hand—that is, if you have every measurement in the population—then statistical methodology can help you describe the set of data. In this text we will present graphical and numerical ways to make sense out of a large mass of data. The branch of statistics devoted to this application is called **descriptive statistics**.

DEFINITION 1.7

The branch of statistics devoted to the organization, summarization, and description of data sets is called **descriptive statistics**.

Many populations are too large to measure each observation; others cannot be measured because they are conceptual. For example, population **a** in Table 1.3 cannot be measured since it would be impossible to identify all new residential

---

TABLE 1.3
Some Typical Populations

PHENOMENON	EXPERIMENTAL UNITS	POPULATION	TYPE
a. Current year, new residential construction prices	Residential properties sold this year	Set of prices of all new residential properties	Existing
b. Starting salary of a graduating MBA this year	MBAs graduating this year	Set of starting salaries of all MBAs who graduated this year	Existing
c. Profit per job in a construction company	Jobs	Set of profits for all jobs performed recently or to be performed in the near future	Part existing, part conceptual
d. Quality of items produced on an assembly line	Manufactured items	Set of quality measurements for all items manufactured over the recent past and in the future	Part existing, part conceptual

properties sold this year in the United States. Even if we could identify them, it would be too costly and time-consuming to research and record their sale prices. Population **d** in Table 1.3 cannot be measured because it is part conceptual. Even though we may be able to record the quality measurements of all items manufactured over the recent past, we cannot measure quality in the future. Because of this problem, we are required to select a subset of values from a population, called a **sample**.

DEFINITION 1.8
___

A **sample** is a subset of data selected from a population.

Numbers that summarize some particular characteristic of a population are called **parameters**; similarly, summary measures used to describe a sample are called **statistics**.

DEFINITION 1.9
___

A **parameter** is a numerical summary measure used to describe a characteristic of a population.

DEFINITION 1.10
___

A **statistic** is a numerical summary measure used to describe a characteristic of a sample.

In future chapters we will discover statistical methods that enable us to infer the nature of the population (for example, estimate the value of some unknown parameter) from the information in the sample. The branch of statistics devoted to this application is called **inferential statistics.** In addition, the methodology provides **measures of reliability** for each inference obtained from a sample. This last point is one of the major contributions of inferential statistics. Anyone can examine a sample and make a "guess" about the nature of the population. For example, we might estimate that the average price of new residential properties sold last year was $88,000. But statistical methodology enables us to go one step further. When the sample is selected in a specified way from the population, we can also say how accurate our estimate will be, that is, how close the estimate of $88,000 will be to the true average.

EXAMPLE 1.1   A University of Minnesota survey of brand names (eg, Levi's, Lee, Calvin Klein) and private labels manufactured for retail chains found a high percentage of jeans with incorrect waist and/or inseam sizes on the label. The researchers found that only 18 of 240 pairs, or 7.5%, of men's five-pocket, prewashed jeans sold in Minneapolis stores were correctly labeled—that is, came within a half inch of their label sizes (*Tampa Tribune,* May 20, 1991). In this study, identify:

a. The population   b. The sample
c. A parameter of interest   d. The inference made about the population

Solution
a. The researchers are interested in men's five-pocket, prewashed jeans manufactured for retail outlets in Minnesota. Consequently, the experimental units in the population are *all* pairs of men's five-pocket, prewashed jeans manufactured for retail outlets in Minnesota. The measurement (or variable) of interest is the label status of each pair of jeans—inseam and/or waist sizes labeled correctly or incorrectly. Note that this is a qualitative variable. In this example, the measurements could have been recorded as 1's and 0's, where a 1 would represent a correctly labeled inseam/waist size and a 0 would represent an incorrectly labeled inseam/waist size.
b. The sample consists of the collection of label status measurements (1's and 0's) for the 240 pairs of jeans examined in the study.
c. A parameter of interest to the researchers is the true percentage of jeans with correct inseam/waist sizes on the label.
d. Since 7.5% of the jeans in the sample had correct labels, the inference is that 7.5% of all jeans in the population have correct labels (ie, an estimate of the parameter of interest is 7.5%). This leads to the conclusion reached by the University of Minnesota researchers: A high percentage (over 90%) of the men's five-pocket, prewashed jeans manufactured for retail outlets in the state have incorrect inseam/waist size labels. Note that the researchers do not provide a measure of reliability for this inference. Enough information is available, however, to calculate such a measure. We will show in Chapter 8 that, with a high degree of "confidence," the estimate of 7.5% is within 3.4% of the true percentage. That is, the true percentage is no lower than 4.1% and no higher than 10.9%.

Statistical studies of the type described in Example 1.1 are also called **enumerative studies.** An enumerative study involves using samples to make inferences about some aspect of a population; the population is well-defined in this type of study, that is, it is possible to list (or count) all the experimental units in the population—hence, the name "enumerative."

> **DEFINITION 1.12**
>
> An **enumerative study** involves making inferences about a well-defined population based on sample data.

A second type of study, called an **analytic study**, involves analyzing and making inferences about **processes.** The main goal of an analytic study is to predict or improve process performance in the future.

> **DEFINITION 1.13**
>
> A **process** is a series of actions or operations that produces or generates data over time.

> **DEFINITION 1.14**
>
> An **analytic study** involves collecting and analyzing process data for the purpose of predictions or improving the future performance of the process.

EXAMPLE 1.2 Record orange juice production in Florida was expected to lower the average price of orange juice in 1993. As a result, sales of grapefruit juice declined. Table 1.4 lists annual sales of grapefruit juice (in millions of gallons) from 1987 to 1992. Suppose the Florida Citrus Department wants to use the data to predict grapefruit sales in 1993.

a. Describe the process of interest.
b. Identify the type of statistical study to be employed.
c. Is the data set, Table 1.4, a population or a sample?

Solution

a. The process of interest is the series of operations that grapefruit juice producers use to grow, produce, market, and sell their product. It is a process because it generates sales data (in gallons) over time—one observation per year.
b. Referring to Definition 1.14, this study is clearly analytic in nature since the Florida Citrus Department is interested in forecasting grapefruit juice sales in 1993.
c. In analytic studies, the data produced by a process are considered to be a sample. Since the Florida Citrus Department is ultimately interested in future grapefruit juice sales, the data of Table 1.4 represent a sample from a conceptual population consisting of grapefruit juice sales for all years, past and future.

TABLE 1.4
Annual Sales of Grapefruit Juice

YEAR	GALLONS Millions
1987	58.2
1988	54.1
1989	53.4
1990	48.0
1991	50.2
1992	45.6

Source: Florida Citrus Department

The tools used to conduct a statistical study will depend on whether the study is enumerative or analytic; thus, it is important to be able to distinguish between the two types of studies.

PROBLEMS

1.6 *Newsweek* (Nov. 16, 1987) reported on "a prescription drug that may help nervous test takers improve their Scholastic Aptitude Test (SAT) score." A researcher experimented with giving propranolol, one of the class of heart drugs called beta blockers, to nervous high school students prior to taking their SATs. The theory was that the same calming effect beta blockers provide heart patients could also be used to reduce anxiety in test takers. To test this theory, the researcher selected 22 high school juniors who had not performed as well on the SAT as they should have, based on IQs and other academic evaluations. One hour before the students repeated the test in their senior year, each student received a dosage of a beta blocker. Typically, students who retake the test without special preparations will increase their scores by an average of 38 points. These 22 students, however, improved their scores by an average of 120 points!

    a. Describe the population of interest to the researcher. (Give the precise statistical definition.)

    b. Describe the sample.

    c. Based on the sample results, what inference would you make about the use of beta blockers to increase SAT scores? (In Chapter 5 we show you how to assess the reliability of this type of inference.)

1.7 An assembly line that mass produces automobile gear shifts is monitored for quality. Each hour, quality control inspectors select 50 gear shifts from the production line and test for defects. The hourly proportion of defectives among the 50 tested serves as a measure of the quality of the process. If the percentage of defectives for any 1 hour exceeds a specified upper limit, adjustments will be made to the assembly line to improve future quality.

    a. Describe the process of interest to the manufacturer of the automobile gear shifts.

    b. Describe the sample.

1.8 Potential advertisers value television's well-known Nielsen ratings as a barometer of a TV show's popularity among viewers. The Nielsen rating of a certain TV program (eg, NBC's popular hit comedy series, *Seinfeld*) is an estimate of the proportion of viewers, expressed as a percentage, who tune their sets to the program on a given night at a given time. A typical Nielsen survey consists of 165 families selected nationwide who regularly watch television. Suppose we are interested in the Nielsen ratings for the latest episode of *Seinfeld*.

    a. Is the study enumerative or analytic?

    b. Identify the target population.

    c. Identify the sample.

1.9 The prime interest rates for the past 7 years are listed in the table. Suppose you are interested in using this information to forecast the prime interest rate in 1994.

YEAR	PRIME RATE %
1987	8.22
1988	9.32
1989	10.87
1990	10.01
1991	8.46
1992	6.25
1993	6.15

Source: U.S. Department of Labor, Federal Reserve Board

a. What type of statistical study is to be employed?
b. Identify the sample.
c. Describe the conceptual population of interest.

1.10   An enumerative study was conducted to explore the relationship of the personal trait of self-esteem and a positive inequity condition to on-the-job productivity (*Journal of Personality*, Dec. 1985). Eighty students enrolled in an industrial psychology course at a private New England university participated. All students were asked to complete a proofreading task and were compensated for their work on an hourly basis. However, some students were overpaid for each hour they worked (positive inequity condition), while the others were given fair compensation (equity condition). The results of the study revealed that individuals of high self-esteem were more productive (ie, completed more of the task) in the positive inequity condition than in the equity condition. However, the reverse was true for students of low self-esteem.

   a. In this study, we can envision four experimental conditions: (1) high self-esteem/positive inequity, (2) high self-esteem/equity, (3) low self-esteem/positive inequity, and (4) low self-esteem/equity. Describe the populations corresponding to the four conditions. (Recall that the variable of interest is productivity, measured as amount of the task completed.)
   b. Identify the samples. Assume that 20 students were assigned to each of the four experimental conditions.
   c. Do you think the samples adequately represent the populations described in part **a**?
   d. Do you think the results of the study were obtained by analyzing the data in the populations, or were they derived from sample information?

1.11   A study of merit raises at 16 U.S. corporations was conducted to discover the extent to which merit pay policies for employees are actually tied to performance (*Personnel Journal*, Mar. 1986). One phase of the study focused on the 3,990 merit raises (measured as percentage increases in salary) awarded during a year at one of the largest of the 16 firms. The analysis revealed that over half of the merit increases were between 7% and 10%.

   a. Identify the variable of interest. Is it quantitative or qualitative?
   b. Do the 3,990 merit raises represent a population or a sample? Explain.

COLLECTING DATA

ENUMERATIVE STUDIES

1.4

Enumerative studies, you will recall, involve sampling and using information in the sample to make inferences about a well-defined population. For these applications, it is essential that we obtain a **representative sample**.

DEFINITION 1.15

A **representative sample** exhibits characteristics similar to those possessed by the target population.

For example, consider the problem of estimating the average price of residential properties sold last year in the United States. It would be unwise to base our estimate on data collected for a sample of properties sold in Orange County, California, since this area has one of the highest priced housing markets in the United States. Our estimate would certainly be *biased* high, and, consequently, would not be very reliable.

The most common way to satisfy the requirement of "representative sample" in enumerative studies is to select a (simple) **random sample**.

> **DEFINITION 1.16**
>
> A **random sample** of n experimental units is one selected from the population in such a way that every different sample of size n has an equal probability (or chance) of selection.*

How can a random sample be generated? If the population is not too large, each observation may be recorded on a piece of paper and placed in a suitable container. After the collection of papers is thoroughly mixed, the researcher can remove n pieces of paper from the container; the elements named on these n pieces of paper are the ones to be included in the sample. Lottery officials utilize such a technique in generating the winning numbers for Florida's weekly 6/49 Lotto game. Forty-nine white Ping-Pong balls (the population), each identified from 1 to 49 in black numerals, are placed into a clear plastic drum and mixed by blowing air into the container. The Ping-Pong balls bounce at random until a total of six balls pop into a tube attached to the drum. The numbers on the six balls (the random sample) are the winning Lotto numbers.

This method of random sampling is fairly easy to implement if the population is relatively small. It is not feasible, however, when the population consists of a large number of observations. Since it is also very difficult to achieve a thorough mixing (recall the *Tampa Tribune* report on shuffling the deck of cards for blackjack), the procedure only approximates random sampling. Most scientific studies, however, rely on computers (with built-in random number generators) to automatically generate the random sample. Almost all of the commercial statistical software packages currently available (eg, SAS, SPSS, MINITAB) have procedures for generating random samples. We illustrate the use of a computer to generate a random sample in the following example.

EXAMPLE 1.3   Assume we have access to sales and appraisal information on 8,313 residential properties that sold in Tampa, Florida, in 1990. The information, supplied by the county property appraiser, includes the (1) location, (2) appraised land value, (3) appraised value of improvements, (4) sale price, and (5) home size for each of the 8,313 properties. Suppose, for this example, that our target population is the set of sale prices for the 8,313 properties. With a population this large, we will resort to sampling in order to make inferences about the population. Generate a random sample of 50 properties from the population.

Solution   Assuming that the property appraiser has numbered the properties consecutively from 1 to 8,313, our objective is to select 50 numbers at random from the 8,313. We will use the random number generator in SAS to produce the sample.†

---

* A more formal definition of probability will be provided in Chapter 4.

† Details on the SAS commands (and the equivalent commands in SPSS and MINITAB) used to generate the sample are given in Computer Lab 2.

FIGURE 1.2
SAS-Generated Random Sample,
Example 1.3

OBS	PROPERTY	OBS	PROPERTY	OBS	PROPERTY
1	297	18	3771	35	6467
2	452	19	3819	36	6556
3	508	20	3875	37	6746
4	514	21	4078	38	6999
5	837	22	4262	39	7106
6	1367	23	4322	40	7186
7	1426	24	4501	41	7310
8	1494	25	4877	42	7389
9	2201	26	4882	43	7520
10	2245	27	4954	44	7521
11	2367	28	5199	45	7607
12	2489	29	5268	46	8055
13	2625	30	5789	47	8123
14	2755	31	5795	48	8177
15	2770	32	6065	49	8306
16	2991	33	6327	50	8307
17	3204	34	6353		

The output from the SAS program is shown in Figure 1.2. The properties listed (ie, 297, 452, 508, etc.) are the properties that will be included in our random sample—that is, the properties for which we will obtain sales information from the property appraiser.

Although random sampling represents one of the simplest of the multitude of sampling techniques available for research, most of the statistical techniques presented in this introductory text assume that such a sample has been collected. We consider other, more sophisticated sampling methods in Chapter 13.

ANALYTIC STUDIES

Recall that analytic studies involve analyzing process data—that is, data collected sequentially over time. Sampling plans for process data are fairly easy to implement. For example, if we are interested in forecasting the annual price of gold, we might simply collect gold prices (in dollars per ounce) for each of the past 10 years. Then, our sample would consist of annual gold prices for the past 10 years. Or, if we are monitoring a manufacturing process (say, electronic components) to improve future quality, we might inspect one randomly selected item each hour for a period of 48 consecutive hours. The 48 quality measurements, recorded sequentially in time, represent our sample.

More information on sampling plans for process data is provided in Chapters 9 and 12.

PROBLEMS

1.12   Many opinion surveys are conducted by mail. In such a sampling procedure, a random sample of persons is selected from among a list of people who are supposed to constitute a target population (eg, purchasers of a product). Each is sent a questionnaire and is requested to complete and return the questionnaire to the pollster. Why might this type of survey yield a sample that would produce biased inferences?

1.13 Use a computer to generate a random sample of $n = 20$ observations from a population that contains 10,000 elements. (Refer to Computer Lab 2, which follows.)

1.14 Test marketing is used by companies to gauge consumer preferences for a new product. Conventional marketing tests usually involve sampling 3% of the target population over a 1 year period, a slow and expensive process to carry out. *Fortune* (Oct. 29, 1984) reports that many companies are turning to alternative methods that use a much smaller sample over a much shorter time span. One such method, called **simulated test marketing**, is described as follows: "A consumer recruited at a shopping center reads an ad for a new product and gets a free sample to take home. Later, she rates it in a telephone interview." The telephone responses are used by the test-marketing firm to predict potential sales volume. Simulated marketing tests appear to identify potential failures reasonably well, but "they don't do such a good job predicting the upside potential of products." Why might the sampling procedure yield a sample of consumer preferences that underestimates sales volume of a successful new product?

1.15 Refer to Problem 1.6 and the study on using beta blockers to improve SAT scores. The U.S. College Board (sponsors of the SAT) warns that "the findings have to be taken with a great deal of caution" and that they should not be interpreted to mean "that someone has discovered the magic pill that will unlock the SAT for thousands of teenagers who believe they do not do as well as they should because they're nervous."* Give several reasons for issuing such a warning. [*Hint:* Is the sample representative of the population referred to by the College Board?]

1.16 One of the most infamous examples of improper sampling was conducted in 1936 by the *Literary Digest* to determine the winner of the Landon–Roosevelt presidential election. The poll, which predicted Landon to be the winner, was conducted by sending ballots to a random sample of persons selected from among the names listed in the telephone directories of that year. In the actual election, Landon won in Maine and Vermont but lost in the remaining 46 states. The *Literary Digest*'s erroneous forecast is believed to be the major reason for its eventual failure. Give a plausible cause of the *Digest*'s erroneous forecast.

COMPUTER LAB 2

GENERATING A RANDOM SAMPLE

The computer commands for generating random numbers in the interval 0 to 1 (called **uniform random numbers**) are provided in this section. These random number generators can be used to select random samples from a population of known size. In each sample program, we select a sample of size $n = 50$ from a population with $N = 8,000$ elements. The values of n and N can be changed to fit the sampling situation for your particular application.

REMINDER   The commands given here are appropriate for both mainframe and PC versions of the three software packages, except where noted. When a mainframe computer is being used, however, these statements must be preceded by the JCL commands required at your computing center.

_____
* *Gainesville Sun*, Oct. 22, 1987.

SAS

Command Line		
1	`DATA SELECT;}`	Data entry instruction
2	`DO N= 1 to 50;`	
3	`NUMBER = 1 + 8000*RANUNI(0);`	Generates $n = 50$ random numbers between 1 and 8,000
4	`OUTPUT;`	
5	`END;`	
6	`PROC PRINT; VAR NUMBER;}`	Prints the random numbers

COMMAND 3 RANUNI is the uniform random number generator in SAS. The **seed**, that is, the value in parentheses following RANUNI, can be any integer value (including 0).

SPSS

Command Line		
1	`DATA LIST FREE/X.`	Data entry instructions
2	`COMPUTE NUMBER=1 + 8000*UNIFORM(1).`	Generates 50 random numbers between 1 and 8,000
3	`BEGIN DATA.`	
4	`1  2  3  4  5  6  7  8  9 10`	Input data values: One number for each observation in the sample, ending with $n = 50$
.	`.  .                       .`	
.	`.  .                       .`	
.	`.  .                       .`	
8	`41 42 43 44 45 46 47 48 49 50`	
9	`END DATA.`	
10	`LIST.}` Prints the random numbers	

COMMAND 2 UNIFORM(1) is the uniform random number generator in SPSS.

GENERAL Remember to omit the period at the end of each command when using mainframe SPSS.

MINITAB

Command Line		
1	`RANDOM 50 IN C1; UNIFORM.`	Data entry instructions
2	`MULTIPLY C1 BY 8000, PUT IN C2`	Generates $n = 50$ random numbers between 1 and 8,000
3	`NAME C2 = 'NUMBER'`	
4	`PRINT C2}` Prints the random numbers	

COMMAND 1   RANDOM is the random number generator in MINITAB. The UNI-
FORM subcommand generates uniform random numbers.

OVERVIEW OF THIS TEXT

1.5 Chapters 2–13 of this text describe and illustrate the many statistical
tools available for analyzing data. The proper choice will depend on
several factors, including the type of study (enumerative or analytic) you wish to
conduct, the goal (descriptive or inferential) of the study, and the type of data
(quantitative or qualitative) collected.

The flowchart in Figure 1.3 is provided as an outline of the remaining chapters
in the text and as a guide to selecting the statistical method appropriate for your

FIGURE 1.3

Choosing the Appropriate Statistical
Method

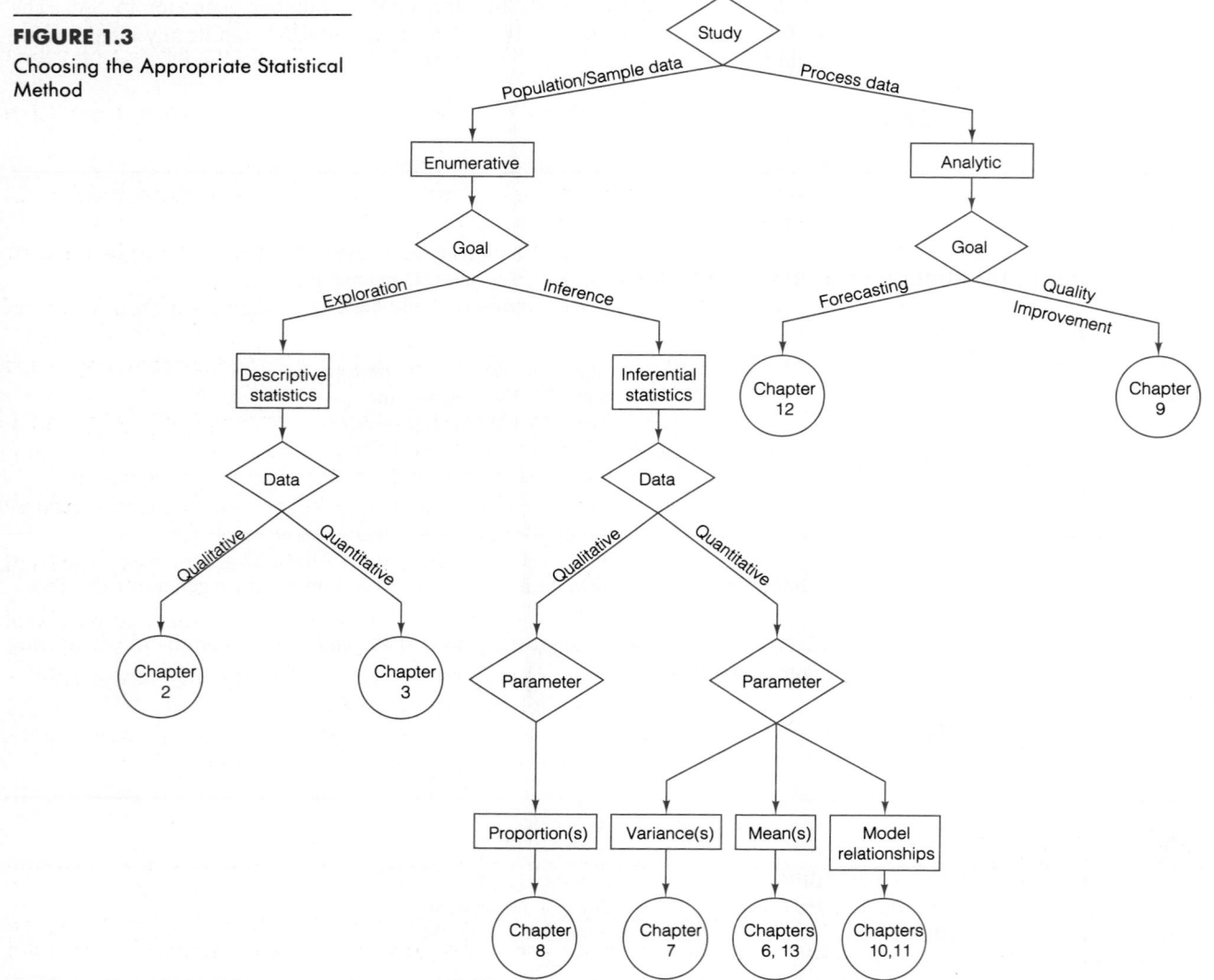

particular analysis. Note that Chapters 4 and 5 do not appear on Figure 1.3. These chapters, however, provide fundamental ideas that bridge the gap between descriptive and inferential statistics, and thus, are critical to building a firm foundation in statistics.

CHAPTER NOTES

- **Statistics** is the science of collecting, exploring, summarizing, analyzing, and interpreting the data.
- Data measured on a numerical scale are **quantitative**, while data that can only be classified into one of a group of categories are **qualitative**.
- **Experimental units** are the objects (eg, people or things) upon which we collect the measurements.
- A statistical **population** is a set of data (usually large) that we are interested in describing.
- A **sample** is a subset of data selected from the population.
- **Descriptive statistics** involves methods for organizing, summarizing, and describing data sets (either populations or samples).
- A **parameter** is a numerical summary measure used to describe a characteristic of a population.
- A **statistic** is a numerical summary measure used to describe a characteristic of a sample.
- **Inferential statistics** involves methods for making inferences about the population based on information in the sample.
- An **enumerative study** involves making inferences about a population of experimental units that can be listed or counted.
- A **process** is a series of actions or operations that produce data over time.
- An **analytic study** involves collecting and analyzing process data for the purpose of predicting or improving future performance of the process.
- Statistical methodology provides a **measure of reliability** for every statistical inference.
- For inferences about the population to be reliable, it is essential that we obtain a sample that is **representative** of the population.
- The most common way to satisfy the requirement of "representative sample" is to select a **random sample** from the population.
- **Random sampling** involves choosing a sample in such a way that every different sample of size n has an equal chance of selection from the population.

LOOKING AHEAD

In Chapters 2 and 3 we examine some basic statistical procedures for exploring and describing data sets. The method used will depend on whether the data are qualitative (Chapter 2) or quantitative (Chapter 3).

THE LATEST HITE REPORT—CONTROVERSY OVER THE NUMBERS

In 1968, researcher Shere Hite shocked conservative America with her now famous "Hite Report" on the permissive sexual attitudes of American men and women. Over 20 years later, Hite is surrounded by controversy again with her latest book, *Women and Love: A Cultural Revolution in Progress* (Knopf, 1988). In this latest Hite report, she reveals some startling statistics describing how women feel about contemporary relationships:

- 84% of women are not emotionally satisfied with their relationship.
- 95% of women report "emotional and psychological harassment" from their men.
- 70% of women married 5 years or more are having extramarital affairs.
- Only 13% of women married more than 2 years are "in love."

Hite conducted the survey by mailing out 100,000 questionnaires to women across the country over a 7 year period. Each questionnaire consisted of 127 open-ended questions, many with numerous subquestions and follow-ups. Hite's instructions read: "It is not necessary to answer every question! Feel free to skip around and answer those questions you choose." Approximately 4,500 completed questionnaires were returned for a response rate of 4.5%, and they form the data set from which the percentages above were determined. Hite claims that these 4,500 women are a representative sample of all women in the United States, and therefore, the survey results imply that vast numbers of women are "suffering a lot of pain in their love relationships with men." Many people disagree, however, saying that only unhappy women are likely to take the time to answer Hite's 127 essay questions, and thus her sample is representative only of the discontented.

The views of several statisticians and expert survey researchers on the validity of Hite's "numbers" were presented in a recent article in *Chance* magazine (Summer 1988). A few of the more critical comments follow.*

Hite used a combination of haphazard sampling and volunteer respondents to collect her [data]. First, Hite sent questionnaires to a wide variety of organizations and asked them to circulate the questionnaires to their members. She mentions that they included church groups, women's voting and political groups, women's rights organizations and counseling and walk-in centers for women. These groups would not seem to be representative of women in general; there is an over-representation of feminist groups and of women in troubled circumstances. In addition, the use of groups to distribute the questionnaires meant that gatekeepers had the power of assuring a zero response rate by not distributing the questionnaire, or conversely of greatly stimulating returns by endorsing the study in some fashion. Second, Hite also relied on volunteer respondents

* *Source:* Streitfeld, D. "Shere Hite and the Trouble with Numbers." *Chance: New Directions for Statistics and Computing*, Vol. 1, No. 3, Summer 1988, pp. 26–31. Springer-Verlag, © 1988, the *Washington Post*. Reprinted with permission.

who wrote in for copies of the questionnaire. These volunteers seem to have been recruited from readers of her past books and those who saw interviews on television and in the press. This type of volunteer respondent is the exact opposite of the randomly selected respondent utilized in standard survey research and even more potentially unrepresentative than the group samples cited above. (Tom Smith, National Opinion Research Center)

So few people responded, it's not representative of any group, except the odd group who agreed to respond. Hite has no assurance that even her claimed 4.5% response rate is correct. How do we know how many people passed their hands over these questionnaires? You don't want to fill it out, you give it to your sister, she gives it to a friend. You'll get one response, but that questionnaire may have been turned down by five people. (Donald Rubin, Professor and Chairman, Department of Statistics, Harvard University)

When you get instructions to only answer those questions you wish to, you're likely to skip some. Isn't it more likely that, for example, a woman who feels strongly about affairs would be more likely to answer questions on that subject than a woman who does not feel as strongly? Thus, her finding that 70% of all women married over five years are having affairs is meaningless because she does not report how many people answered each question. I cannot tell whether this means 70% of 1,000 women or 70% of 10 women. (Judith Tanur, Professor of Sociology and Statistical Specialist in Survey Methodology, State University of New York, Stony Brook)

Even in good samples, where you have a 50% or 70% response rate, you usually have some skews—say, with income, race, or region. If she can do a sample like this, she's got the Rosetta Stone, and I'll come study from her. (Martin Frankel, Professor of Statistics & CIS, Baruch College, commenting on Hite's claim that her sample matches the U.S. female population in terms of demographic balance)

According to Hite, whether you're 18 or 71, you're going to answer the questions the same way. Whether white, black, Hispanic, Middle Eastern, or Asian American, you're going to answer the same way. Whether you make $5,000 a year or over $75,000, you'll answer the questions the same way. I've never seen anything like this in my career—and the Kinsey Institute collects data from everybody. (June Reinisch, Director of Kinsey Institute, Indiana University, commenting on Hite's numbers showing that no matter what the demographic breakdown of the women married 5 years or more, about 70% are having extramarital affairs)

a. Identify the population of interest to Shere Hite. What are the experimental units?
b. Identify the variables of interest to Hite. Are they quantitative or qualitative variables?
c. Describe how Hite obtained her sample.
d. What inferences did Hite make about the population? Comment on the reliability of these inferences.
e. Discuss the difficulty in obtaining a representative sample of women across the United States to take part in a survey similar to the one conducted by Shere Hite.

Careers in Statistics. American Statistical Association and the Institute of Mathematical Statistics, 1974.

Cochran, W. G. *Sampling Techniques*, 2d ed. New York: Wiley, 1963.

MINITAB Primer: An Introduction to MINITAB Statistical Software. State College, PA: Minitab, Inc., 1986.

MINITAB Reference Manual, Release 8. State College, PA: Minitab, Inc., 1989.

MINITAB User Guide, DOS Microcomputer Version, Release 7. State College, PA: Minitab, Inc., 1989.

Norusis, M. J. *SPSS/PC+ 4.0 Base Manual*. Chicago: SPSS, Inc., 1990.

Ryan, B. F., Joiner, B. L., and Ryan, T. A. *Minitab Handbook*, 2d ed. Boston: PWS-Kent, 1990 (revised printing).

SAS Procedures Guide for Personal Computers, Version 6 ed. Cary, NC: SAS Institute, Inc., 1986.

SAS User's Guide: Basics, Version 6 ed. Cary, NC: SAS Institute, Inc., 1991.

Tanur, J. M., Mosteller, F., Kruskal, W. H., Link, R. F., Pieters, R. S., and Rising, G. R. (eds.). *Statistics: A Guide to the Unknown*, 3d ed. San Francisco: Holden-Day, 1989.

Yamane, T. *Elementary Sampling Theory*, 3d ed. Englewood Cliffs, NJ: Prentice-Hall, 1967.

CHAPTER 2   EXPLORING AND DESCRIBING QUALITATIVE DATA

Health-maintenance organizations (HMOs) periodically collect data such as gender, certification level, and primary specialty of participating physicians in their managed-care system. How can the HMO make sense out of this qualitative data? That is, how can the HMO organize and summarize the data to make it more comprehensible and meaningful? In this chapter, several basic statistical tools for describing qualitative data are presented. These involve graphs, charts, and tables that rapidly convey a visual picture of the data. The HMO data set is examined in detail in the chapter case study.

SUMMARY FREQUENCY TABLES

2.1 Qualitative data, you will recall, are nonnumerical in nature; the value of a qualitative variable can only be classified into one or more categories, called **classes**. The data can be summarized numerically by computing either the number of observations that fall into each class, called the **class frequency**, or the proportion of the total number of observations falling into each class, called the **class relative frequency**. The class frequencies and relative frequencies are displayed in table form.

DEFINITION 2.1

A **class** is one of the categories into which qualitative data can be classified.

DEFINITION 2.2

The **frequency** for a particular class is the number of observations in the data set falling in that class.

DEFINITION 2.3

The **relative frequency** for a particular class is equal to the class frequency divided by the total number of observations in the data set.

To illustrate, consider a problem of interest to the Business Economics Division (BED) of the U.S. Department of Labor. Each year, the BED monitors business failures and classifies each failure into one of the following six categories: (1) lack of experience in the production line, (2) lack of managerial experience, (3) unbalanced experience, (4) incompetence, (5) other causes (such as neglect, fraud, natural disaster), and (6) unknown reasons. These classifications are based on the opinions of informed creditors and information in BED reports. Recently, the BED determined the cause of 1,463 failures of construction enterprises. The variable of interest to the BED is "underlying cause" of a construction business failure; it is a qualitative variable, since its values can only be classified into one of the six classes.

The individual measurements (ie, underlying causes) for each of the 1,463 construction failures are summarized in Table 2.1. The summary table gives both the frequency (number of failures) and the relative frequency (proportion of the 1,463 failures) in each class. Note that the sum of the class frequencies equals the total number of experimental units (failures), 1,463.

From Definition 2.3, the class relative frequency is calculated by dividing the class frequency by the total number of observations in the data set. Thus, the relative frequency for the class "lack of line experience" in Table 2.1 is $\frac{111}{1,463} = .076$, the relative frequency for "lack of managerial experience" is $\frac{236}{1,463} = .161$, etc. Note that

TABLE 2.1

Summary Table for 1,463 Construction Failures (As Determined by the BED)

CLASS Underlying Cause	FREQUENCY Number of Failures	RELATIVE FREQUENCY Proportion
Lack of line experience	111	.076
Lack of managerial experience	236	.161
Unbalanced experience	314	.215
Incompetence	698	.477
Other causes	21	.014
Reason unknown	83	.057
Totals	1,463	1.000

Source: Business Economics Division, U.S. Department of Labor.

the most frequent cause of construction failure is "incompetence"—nearly half (47.7%) of the failures were due to this reason.

Frequency tables such as Table 2.1 summarize the values of a single qualitative variable numerically. The next three sections illustrate ways to summarize the data graphically.

PROBLEMS

2.1   A recent study by the Wheat Industry Council indicates that the majority of American consumers purchase white loaf bread from the supermarket shelf. In a survey, 3,368 people were asked where they purchase their white bread. The breakdown of the responses by store type is given in the table.

STORE TYPE	FREQUENCY
Convenience store	236
Day-old/Thrift store	404
Neighborhood bakery	101
Supermarket in-store bakery	269
Supermarket shelf	2,257
Other	101
Total	3,368

Source: "Food, Nutrition, and Dieting: A Comprehensive Study of American Attitudes, Habits, Perceptions and Myths." Wheat Industry Council, Universal Foods Corp., 1983.

a. Identify the qualitative variable described in the table.
b. Calculate the relative frequencies for each category of the table.

2.2   During August 1980, hundreds of thousands of Poland's workers walked off the job, protesting the country's poor labor conditions. One of their demands, eventually negotiated with the government through the independent Polish labor union Solidarity, was the reduction of a mandatory 6 day, 48 hour work week to a 5 day, 40 hour work week. In the United States, many corporations are considering instituting a 4 day, 40 hour work week or a 3 day, 40 hour work week. Suppose a company surveyed its employees concerning the type of work week they would prefer; a 6 day, 48 hour work week; a 5 day, 40 hour work week; a 4 day, 40 hour work week; or a 3 day, 40 hour work week. Suppose 25 employees responded as shown in the table at the top of the next page.

EMPLOYEE	WORK WEEK	EMPLOYEE	WORK WEEK	EMPLOYEE	WORK WEEK
1	5 day, 40 hour	10	5 day, 40 hour	18	5 day, 40 hour
2	5 day, 40 hour	11	4 day, 40 hour	19	5 day, 40 hour
3	3 day, 40 hour	12	5 day, 40 hour	20	4 day, 40 hour
4	6 day, 48 hour	13	4 day, 40 hour	21	3 day, 40 hour
5	4 day, 40 hour	14	4 day, 40 hour	22	5 day, 40 hour
6	4 day, 40 hour	15	6 day, 48 hour	23	3 day, 40 hour
7	5 day, 40 hour	16	4 day, 40 hour	24	4 day, 40 hour
8	3 day, 40 hour	17	5 day, 40 hour	25	5 day, 40 hour
9	6 day, 48 hour				

a. Identify the type of variable measured. **b.** Identify the classes.
c. Compute the frequency of each class. **d.** Compute the relative frequency of each class.

2.3   The *Journal of Consumer Marketing* (Summer 1992) reported on a study of company responses to letters of consumer complaints. Marketing students at a large midwest public university "were asked to write letters of complaint to companies whose products legitimately caused them to be dissatisfied." Of the 750 students in the class, 286 wrote letters of complaint. The table shows the type of responses received from the companies and the number of each type. Summarize the results with a relative frequency table.

TYPE OF RESPONSE	NUMBER
Letter and product replacement	42
Letter and good coupon	36
Letter and cents off coupon	29
Letter and refund check	23
Letter, refund check, and coupon	13
Letter only	76
No response	67
Total	286

Source: Clark, G. L., Kaminski, P. F., and Rink, D. R. "Consumer Complaints: Advice on How Companies Should Respond Based on an Empirical Study." *Journal of Consumer Marketing,* Vol. 9, No. 3, Summer 1992, p. 8 (Table 1).

BAR GRAPHS

2.2

Although class (relative) frequencies adequately describe qualitative data, graphical presentation is often desired. One of the most widely used graphical methods for describing qualitative data is a **bar graph**. Bar graphs, constructed either by hand or computer, visually show class frequencies or class relative frequencies.

Figure 2.1 is the SAS bar graph showing the frequencies of construction failures for the six categories of Table 2.1. Notice that the figure contains a rectangle, or **bar**, for each "underlying cause" (shown on the horizontal axis), and that the height of a particular bar is proportional to the number, or frequency, of failures (shown on the vertical axis) for its corresponding category.

It is also common to reverse the axes of a bar graph and display the bars in a horizontal fashion. Figure 2.2 is the SPSS horizontal bar graph that displays the data of Table 2.1.

Relative frequency bar graphs can also be constructed by making the bar heights proportional to the class relative frequencies; as the next example illustrates.

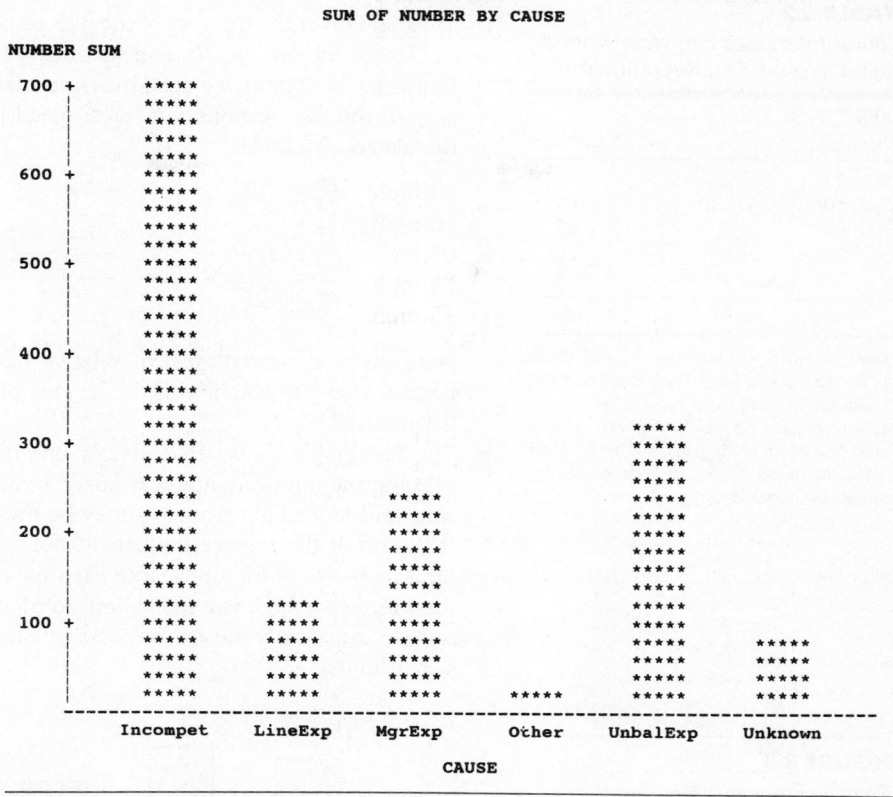

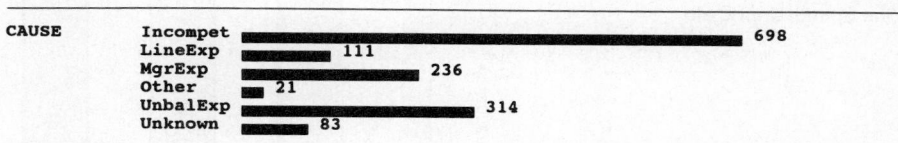

EXAMPLE 2.1 Over the past decade, federal and state governments have proposed and implemented several new programs designed to improve automobile and highway safety standards. These include stricter drunken driving laws and mandatory-use seat belt laws in many states, and federal guidelines related to air bags in new automobiles. Three Northeastern University professors conducted a survey of 328 U.S. residents "in an attempt to gauge their opinions concerning existing and proposed automobile safety standards" (*Transportation Journal*, Summer 1986). It was hoped that the results of the survey would aid federal and state government officials in the planning and design of automobile safety programs. One question put to the respondents was "What interstate highway speed limit would you recommend?" A numerical summary of the 328 responses is given in Table 2.2.

a. Construct a relative frequency bar graph for the data.

b. Interpret the graph.

TABLE 2.2
What Interstate Highway Speed
Limit Would You Recommend?

RESPONSE mph	NUMBER
55	102
60	105
65	95
70	20
75	6
Total	328

Source: Lieb, R. C., Wiseman, F., and Moore, T. E. "Automobile Safety Programs: The Public Viewpoint." *Transportation Journal,* Vol. 25, No. 4, Summer 1986, pp. 22–30. Reprinted with express permission of the publisher, the American Society of Transportation and Logistics, Inc., for educational purposes only.

Solution

a. Table 2.2 gives the number of the 328 responses falling in each of five categories or classes: 55, 60, 65, 70, and 75 miles per hour (mph). To construct a relative frequency bar graph, we need the class relative frequencies—that is, the percentages of the 328 responses in each speed-limit category. These percentages are calculated as follows:

55 mph: $\frac{102}{328} = .31$
60 mph: $\frac{105}{328} = .32$
65 mph: $\frac{95}{328} = .29$
70 mph: $\frac{20}{328} = .06$
75 mph: $\frac{6}{328} = .02$

Note that the percentages, or relative frequencies, sum to 1. Figure 2.3 is a hand-drawn bar graph with the heights of the bars proportional to the relative frequencies.

b. The bar graph shows that almost one-third (31%) of the respondents favor keeping the interstate highway speed limit at 55 mph. Even more important to state and federal governments may be the fact that only 8% of the respondents (the sum of the relative frequencies for the last two bars) recommend a speed limit in excess of 65 mph. Since the time of the study, several states have raised their interstate highway speed limit to 65 mph. Based on the information in this sample, apparently most drivers are satisfied with the current interstate highway speed limits.

FIGURE 2.3
Relative Frequency Bar Graph for the Speed-Limit Data

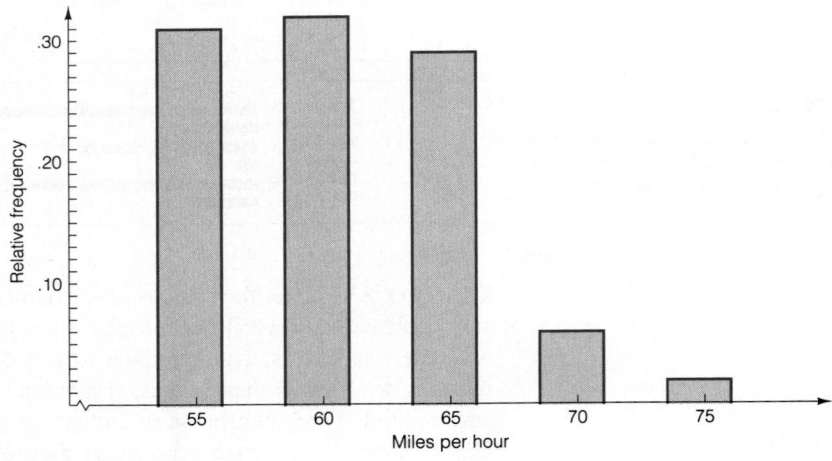

CONSTRUCTING A BAR GRAPH

STEP 1   Summarize the data in a frequency table. The table should contain the frequency and relative frequency for each class (or category) of the qualitative variable.

STEP 2   Draw horizontal and vertical axes on graph paper. The vertical axis can represent either class frequency or class relative frequency. The classes (or categories) of the qualitative variable should be marked under the horizontal axis.

STEP 3   Draw in the bars for each class (or category). The height of the bar should be proportional to either the class frequency or class relative frequency.

Note: The commands for generating bar graphs using a computer are given in the Computer Lab section of this chapter.

PROBLEMS

2.4   The Wheat Industry Council survey data from Problem 2.1 are reproduced below.

a. Use the appropriate graphical method to describe the data.

b. Comment on the Wheat Industry Council's statement that the majority of consumers purchase their bread off the supermarket shelf.

STORE TYPE	FREQUENCY
Convenience store	236
Day-old/Thrift store	404
Neighborhood bakery	101
Supermarket in-store bakery	269
Supermarket shelf	2,257
Other	101
Total	3,368

Source: "Food, Nutrition, and Dieting: A Comprehensive Study of American Attitudes, Habits, Perceptions and Myths." Wheat Industry Council, University Foods Corp., 1983.

2.5   Refer to the *Journal of Consumer Marketing* study of company responses to consumer complaints, Problem 2.3. The data are reproduced below for convenience.

a. Display the study results in a relative frequency bar graph.

b. What percentage of consumers received a response to their letter of complaint?

TYPE OF RESPONSE	NUMBER
Letter and product replacement	42
Letter and good coupon	36
Letter and cents off coupon	29
Letter and refund check	23
Letter, refund check, and coupon	13
Letter only	76
No response	67
Total	286

Source: Clark, G. L., Kaminski, P. F., and Rink, D. R. "Consumer Complaints: Advice on How Companies Should Respond Based on an Empirical Study." *Journal of Consumer Marketing,* Vol. 9, No. 3, Summer 1992, p. 8 (Table 1).

2.6 PepsiCo, Inc., through mergers and acquisitions, now owns and operates all Pizza Hut, Taco Bell, and Kentucky Fried Chicken (KFC) restaurant chains. Operating nearly 23 million restaurants worldwide, this makes PepsiCo the world's largest restaurant system. The accompanying bar graph, extracted from PepsiCo's 1992 annual report, shows the number of restaurant units operated by the eight largest worldwide restaurant systems. Interpret the results.

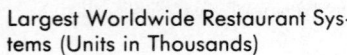

Largest Worldwide Restaurant Systems (Units in Thousands)

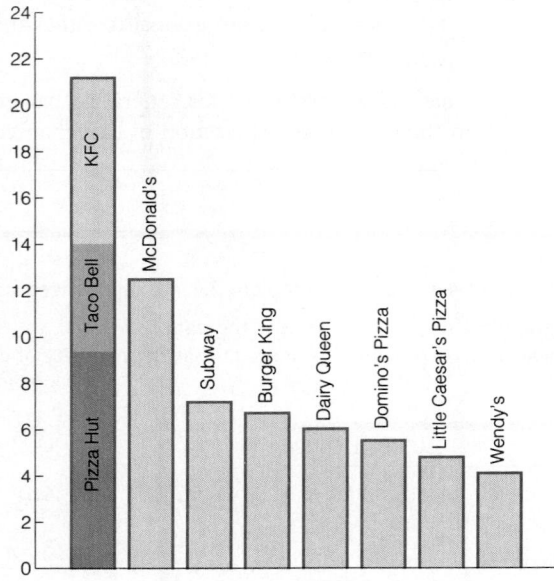

Source: Courtesy, PepsiCo, Inc. © 1993.

2.7 In Florida, civil engineers are designing roads with the latest safety-oriented construction methods in response to the fact that in 1988 more people in Florida were killed by bad roads than by guns. A total of 135 traffic accidents that occurred during the year have been attributed to poorly constructed roads (*Tampa Tribune,* Nov. 14, 1989). A breakdown of the poor road conditions that caused the accidents is shown in the table. Construct and interpret a frequency bar graph for the data.

POOR ROAD CONDITION	NUMBER OF FATALITIES
Obstructions without warning	7
Road repairs/under construction	39
Loose surface material	13
Soft or low shoulders	20
Holes, ruts, etc.	8
Standing water	25
Worn road surface	6
Other	17
Total	135

Source: Florida Department of Highway Safety and Motor Vehicles, 1989.

2.8 Some scientists claim that global climate warming—caused by smoke stacks, gas-powered automobiles, power-generating stations, forest fires, etc.—will threaten the habitability of the Earth by the end of the twentieth century. *Scientific American* (July 1990) reported on computer models designed to assess the causes of global warming. The accompanying horizontal relative frequency bar chart shows a breakdown of the potential causes of global warming into five general categories: (1) energy use and production, (2) chlorofluorocarbons, (3) agriculture, (4) land-use modification, and (5) other industrial causes. Interpret the bar chart.

Human Activities That May Cause Global Warming

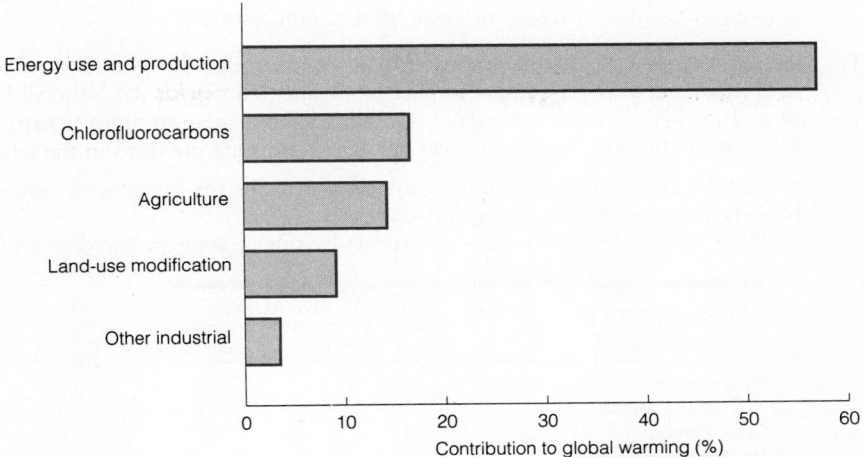

2.9   Refer to the *Business Horizons* study of 800 CEOs, Problem 1.1. A summary of the birth regions of the CEOs is displayed in the table. Illustrate the data with a bar graph.

REGION OF BIRTH	PERCENT OF CEOS
Northeast	37
South	18
Midwest	32
West	7
Outside U.S.A.	6
	100

2.10   Researchers have been creating thin films of tiny diamonds since the early 1950's, but industry has only recently utilized diamond thin films in the manufacture of such products as cutting tools, stereo loudspeaker tweeters, heat sinks, sunglasses, and components for scientific instruments. According to the Philadelphia Institute for Scientific

COUNTRY	NUMBER OF PAPERS ON DIAMOND THIN-FILM RESEARCH
United States	105
Japan	63
United Kingdom	20
Germany	17
Italy	7
Others	39
Total	251

Information (ISI), the United States and Japan are preeminent in current research on diamond thin films. Each of 251 published papers was categorized according to the author's country of residence. The results are shown in the table. Use an appropriate graphical technique to summarize the data. Do you agree with ISI's assessment of the United States and Japan with regard to diamond thin-film research?

2.11 Casual restaurants—eateries featuring basic entrees, relaxed decors, and moderate prices—will be the major trend for restaurants in the 1990's, according to a Gallup survey for the National Restaurant Association (*Tampa Tribune*, Mar. 10, 1990). Gallup surveyed 1,000 adults about their attitudes toward casual and fine dining. One question asked how often the respondents eat out. The results are provided in the table.

a. Use the appropriate graphical technique to describe the frequency of eating out at casual restaurants.
b. Repeat part **a** for fine dining restaurants.
c. Place the graphs from parts **a** and **b** side-by-side to compare the distributions at the two types of restaurants.

FREQUENCY OF EATING OUT	TYPE OF RESTAURANT	
	Casual (%)	Fine (%)
Once a week	29	4
2–3 times a month	24	9
Once a month	17	12
Once every few months	12	16
Once every 6 months	6	13
Once a year	4	15
Less than once a year	8	31
Totals	100	100

Source: 1990 National Restaurant Association Gallup Survey.

PIE CHARTS

2.3 Another popular graphical method for describing qualitative data is a **pie chart**. Pie charts, like bar graphs, display the different classes of the qualitative variable; however, pie charts usually show only the relative frequency in each class. Figure 2.4 is a hand-drawn pie chart for the construction failure data of Table 2.1. The total number of failures for the six cause categories (the pie) is split

FIGURE 2.4
Pie Chart Showing Relative Frequencies of Construction Failures for Six Underlying Causes

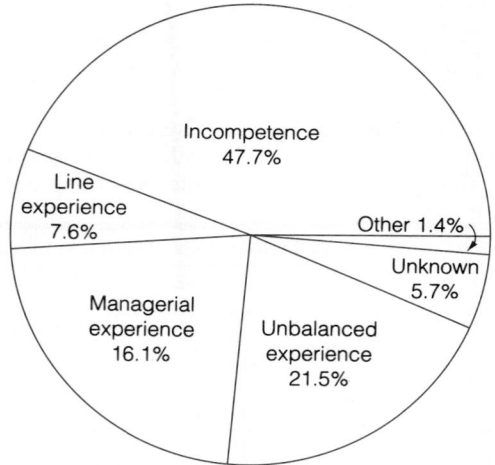

into six pieces. The size (angle) of the slice assigned to an underlying cause is proportional to the relative frequency for that category. For example, since a circle spans 360°, the slice assigned to the category "incompetence" is 47.7% of 360°, or

$$(.477)(360°) = 171.7°$$

It is common to show the percentage of measurements in each class on the pie chart as displayed in Figure 2.4.

CONSTRUCTING A PIE CHART

STEP 1   Summarize the data in a frequency table. The table should contain the frequency and relative frequency for each class (or category) of the qualitative variable.

STEP 2   Draw a circle (360°) on a sheet of paper.

STEP 3   Calculate the size (angle) of each class (or category) by multiplying the class relative frequency by 360°.

STEP 4   Draw the sections of the pie using the angles computed in step 3. Label each section by its class (or category) name. You may want to mark the class relative frequency (or percentage) on each slice.

Note: The commands for generating pie charts using a computer are given in the Computer Lab section.

PROBLEMS

2.12   Real estate investment trusts (REITs) are corporations or trusts that sell stock and combine capital from investors to buy properties or make real estate loans. Since REITs must meet federal guidelines and are regulated by the Internal Revenue Service, only a limited number exist. Currently, there are 219 REITs operating nationwide. The major type of properties owned by these 219 REITs are summarized in the table.

a. Display the data with a pie chart.
b. Interpret the pie chart.
c. Does the pie chart describe population or sample data? Explain.

TYPE OF PROPERTY	PERCENT OF REITS
Health care	17
Hotels	2
Industrial	11
Office	20
Residential	15
Retail	21
Other	14
Total	100

Source: *Chicago Tribune*, Sept. 1992.

2.13   The pie chart describes the fate of the (estimated) 242 million automobile tires that are scrapped in the United States each year.

    a. Interpret the pie chart.
    b. Convert the pie chart into a relative frequency bar chart.
    c. Convert the pie chart into a frequency bar chart.

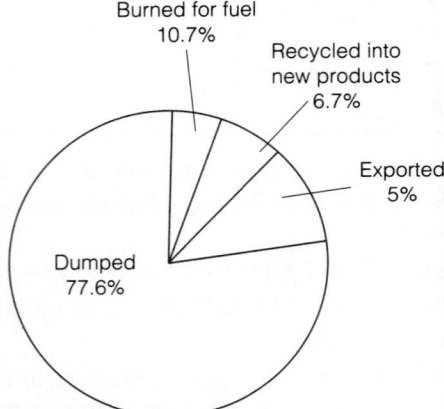

Source: U.S. Environmental Protection Agency and National Solid Waste Management Association. *Tampa Tribune,* June 29, 1992.

2.14   The University of Miami recently conducted a study for the U.S. Department of Labor concerning barriers to women's upward mobility in the workplace. General characteristics of the 176 female executives throughout the country who participated in the survey are illustrated in the pie charts. Use this information to describe the typical woman executive.

INDUSTRY
Industry of respondent's current employer:

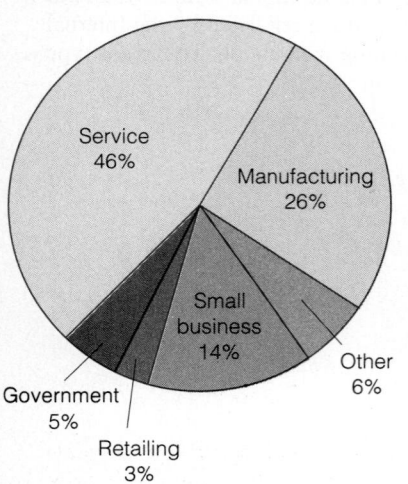

EDUCATION

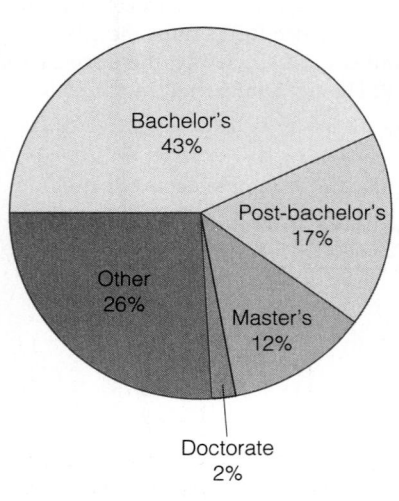

MARITAL STATUS

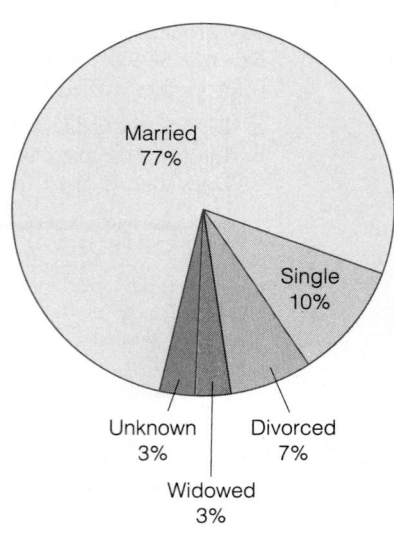

Source: Miami Herald, Apr. 12, 1993.

2.15 Professional purchasers are now getting tougher on their suppliers. According to *Purchasing* (Jan. 17, 1991), "suppliers are being subjected to formal and detailed monthly or quarterly performance surveys by purchasing-led teams of auditors on everything from product quality and delivery schedules to receipt of technical data sheets and timely billing paperwork." A recent survey of supplier performance evaluations revealed the results shown in the table. Summarize the data with a pie chart. Interpret the chart.

PRIMARY REASON SUPPLIERS ARE EVALUATED	RELATIVE FREQUENCY
Quality	.42
Technical expertise	.11
Price	.12
Service	.13
Delivery	.22
Total	1.00

Source: Stundza, T. "Suppliers on the Hot Seat." *Purchasing,* Jan. 17, 1991, p. 92.

2.16 H. J. Heinz, the Pittsburgh-based food processor, regularly captures over 50% of the annual market share of ketchup sales. The pie chart describes the U.S. ketchup market, based on number of sales, in 1993.

a. Identify the qualitative variable summarized in the pie chart.
b. Use the information in the pie chart to form a relative frequency bar chart.

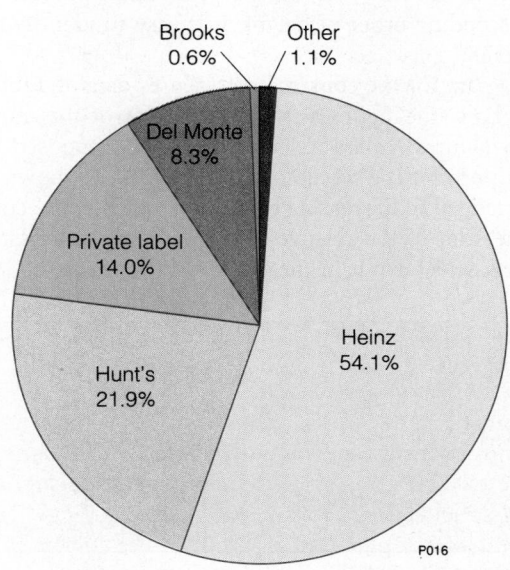

KETCHUP

Brooks 0.6%
Other 1.1%
Del Monte 8.3%
Private label 14.0%
Hunt's 21.9%
Heinz 54.1%

P016

Source: *Investor's Business Daily,* Apr. 13, 1993.

2.17 Most emergency-care patients in Florida use some type of insurance coverage, public or private, to pay for treatment. Surprisingly, over 20% of these patients have no insurance coverage of any kind to help pay emergency-care costs (*Annals of Emergency Medicine,* Oct. 1992). Data collected on 1,645 emergency-care patients treated at Florida hospitals were classified according to primary party responsible for payment. The data are summarized in the table. Construct and interpret a pie chart for the data.

PRIMARY INSURANCE	NUMBER OF PATIENTS
Self-responsible	339
Medicare	288
Medicaid	120
Commercial	526
HMO/PPO	238
Workers Compensation	134
Total	1,645

Source: Mitchell, T. A., and Remmel, R. J. "Level of Uncompensated Care Delivered by Emergency Physicians in Florida." *Annals of Emergency Medicine*, Vol. 21, No. 10, Oct. 1992, p. 55 (Table 2).

PARETO DIAGRAMS

2.4 Vertical bar graphs like those in Figures 2.1 and 2.3 can be enhanced by rearranging the bars on the graph in the form of a **Pareto diagram**. A Pareto diagram (named for the Italian economist Vilfredo Pareto) is a frequency bar graph with the bars displayed in order of height, starting with the tallest bar on the left. Pareto diagrams are popular graphical tools in process and quality control, where the heights of the bars often represent frequencies of problems (eg, defects, accidents, breakdowns, failures, etc.) in the production process. Because the bars are arranged in descending order of height, it is easy to identify the areas with the most severe problems.

Figure 2.5 is a Pareto diagram for the construction failures data of Table 2.1. In addition to reordering the bars, the figure also shows a plot of the **cumulative proportion** of construction failures (called a "cum" line) superimposed over the bars. The cumulative proportions for the six classes of Table 2.1 are shown in Table 2.3. When the classes are arranged in decreasing order of frequency, the cumulative proportion for a class is the sum of the relative frequency for that class plus the relative frequencies for all classes above it in the table.

DEFINITION 2.4

When the classes are arranged in decreasing order of frequency and listed in a table, the **cumulative proportion** (or **cumulative relative frequency**) for a particular class is equal to the class relative frequency plus the sum of the class relative frequencies for all classes above it.

The cum line scale appears on the right side of the Pareto diagram. From Figure 2.5, you can see that almost 70% of the construction failures are due to the first two causes, incompetence and unbalanced experience.

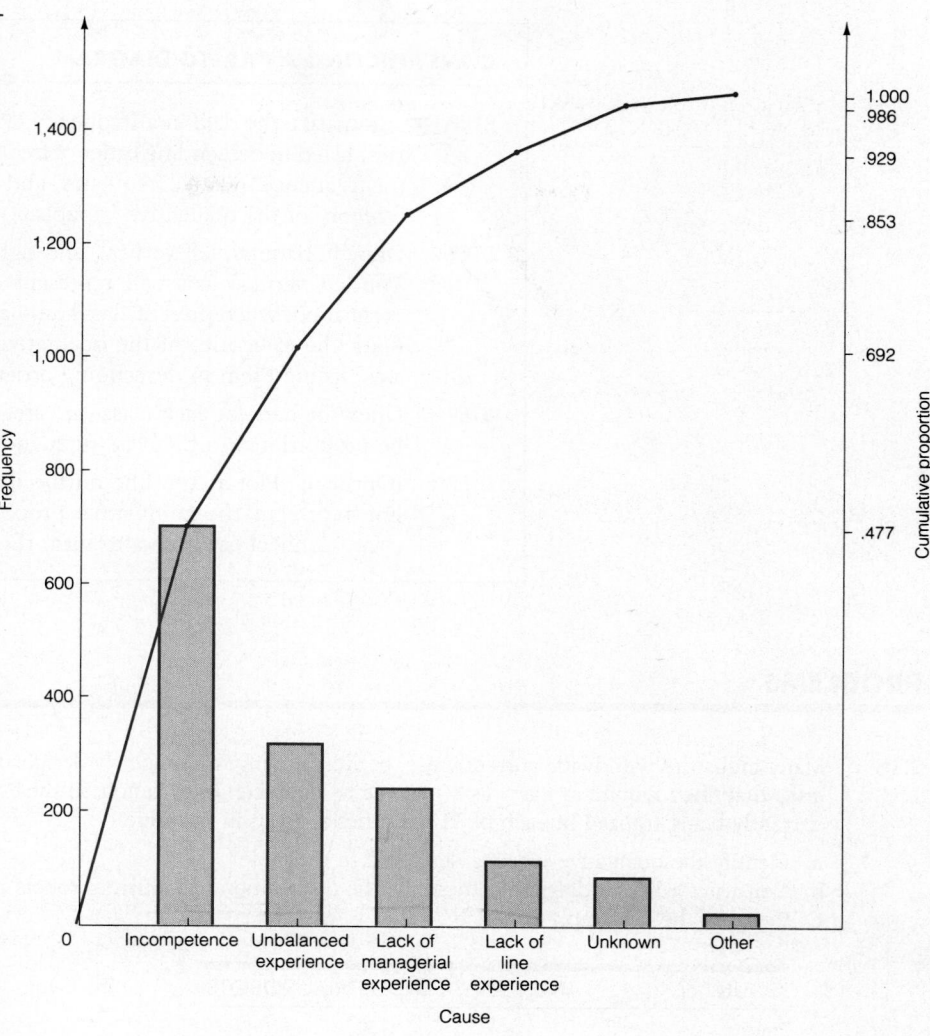

TABLE 2.3
Reasons for 1,463 Construction Failures Rearranged
in Order of Frequency, with Cumulative Proportions

UNDERLYING CAUSE	FREQUENCY	RELATIVE FREQUENCY	CUMULATIVE PROPORTION
Incompetence	698	.477	.477
Unbalanced experience	314	.215	.692
Lack of managerial experience	236	.161	.853
Lack of line experience	111	.076	.929
Reason unknown	83	.057	.986
Other causes	21	.014	1.000
Totals	1,463	1.000	

CONSTRUCTING A PARETO DIAGRAM

STEP 1   Summarize the data in a frequency table, with the classes (or categories) listed in descending order of frequency. The table should contain the frequency, relative frequency, and cumulative percentage for each category of the qualitative variable.

STEP 2   Draw horizontal, left vertical, and right vertical axes on graph paper. The left vertical axis will represent class frequency, and the right vertical axis will represent class cumulative proportion (or percentage). Mark the categories of the qualitative variable under the horizontal axis, listing them in descending order of frequency.

STEP 3   Draw the bars for each class (or category). The height of the bar will be proportional to the class frequency (marked on the left).

STEP 4   (Optional) Plot a cum line on the diagram. The points on the cum line represent the cumulative proportion (or percentage) for each class. Connect the points to form the cum line.

PROBLEMS

2.18   Many industries worldwide currently use, or are planning to use, newly designed robots to perform certain assembly tasks that often require as many as 10 people to complete. Information on the estimated number of industrial robots currently being utilized in each of 11 countries is given in the table.

   a. Identify the qualitative variable described in the table.
   b. Construct a Pareto diagram to describe the distribution of industrial robots in the 11 countries.
   c. Interpret the bar graph in part **b**.

COUNTRY	NUMBER OF INDUSTRIAL ROBOTS
Finland	130
France	200
Great Britain	185
Italy	500
Japan	10,000
Norway	200
Poland	360
Sweden	600
United States	3,000
Russia	25
Germany	850
Total	16,050

2.19   A study was conducted to examine the stock return behavior around the time a bond rating change was announced by Moody's Bond Service (*Quarterly Journal of Business and Economics*, Summer 1987). The table gives the frequency distribution of the lag (in trading days) between the wire service announcement of the bond rating and the later publication of the rating in *Moody's Bond Survey* for a sample of 162 firms—93 with bond downgrades and 69 with bond upgrades. Describe the data using a Pareto diagram for each type of bond, upgraded, downgraded, and total number.

TRADING DAYS FROM WIRE SERVICE TO PUBLICATION	NUMBER OF UPGRADED BONDS	NUMBER OF DOWNGRADED BONDS	TOTAL NUMBER OF BONDS
0	13	9	22
1	2	11	13
2	10	20	30
3	19	15	34
4	12	20	32
5	9	15	24
6	1	1	2
7	2	1	3
8	0	0	0
9	1	0	1
15	0	1	1
Totals	69	93	162

Source: Glascock, J. L., Davidson, W. N., and Henderson, G. V. "Announcement Effects of Moody's Bond Rating Changes on Equity Returns." *Quarterly Journal of Business and Economics,* Vol. 26, No. 3, Summer 1987, p. 75.

2.20 The data from the *Journal of Consumer Marketing* study, Problems 2.3 and 2.5, are reproduced below. Use the information to construct a Pareto diagram for the data. Interpret the results.

TYPE OF RESPONSE	NUMBER
Letter and product replacement	42
Letter and good coupon	36
Letter and cents off coupon	29
Letter and refund check	23
Letter, refund check, and coupon	13
Letter only	76
No response	67
Total	286

Source: Clark, G. L., Kaminski, P. F., and Rink, D. R. "Consumer Complaints: Advice on How Companies Should Respond Based on an Empirical Study." *Journal of Consumer Marketing,* Vol. 9, No. 3, Summer 1992, p. 8 (Table 1).

CROSS-CLASSIFICATION (TWO-WAY) TABLES

2.5 Experimental units in a study are often simultaneously categorized according to two qualitative variables. For example, consider a recent study in the *Journal of Education for Business* concerning whether a firm would give hiring preference to business majors knowledgeable in foreign languages.

Personnel directors of both domestic and foreign businesses were mailed questionnaires, and a total of 215 responses were returned. Thus, each director was categorized according to type of business, U.S. or foreign. In addition, the directors responded to the question "Would you give hiring preference to business majors knowledgeable in foreign languages?" Responses were either "yes," "no," or "neutral." Therefore, the study involved classification of personnel directors according to each of two qualitative variables: type of business (two categories) and hiring preference (three categories). The frequencies of directors falling into each of the $2 \times 3 = 6$ combined categories are shown in the **cross-classification table**, Table 2.4.

Examining Table 2.4, we see that 50 of the 215 directors who work for U.S. firms definitely have a preference for hiring business majors with a knowledge of foreign languages (ie, 50 fall in the U.S./Yes cell of the table). Similarly, 57 directors of U.S. firms are neutral regarding hiring majors with foreign language knowledge, and 19 U.S. directors have no preference for hiring majors with foreign language knowledge, etc.

TABLE 2.4
Cross-Classification Table for *Journal of Education for Business* Study

FIRM TYPE	FOREIGN LANGUAGE HIRING PREFERENCE			Totals
	Yes	Neutral	No	
U.S.	50	57	19	126
Foreign	60	22	7	89
Totals	110	79	26	215

Source: Cornick, M. F., et al. "The Value of Foreign Language Skills for Accounting and Business Majors." *Journal of Education for Business,* Jan./Feb. 1991, p. 162 (Table 2).

The cross-classification table shown in Table 2.4 is also known as a **two-way contingency table**, because one objective of the study is to investigate whether the percentages of directors who respond "yes," "no," or "neutral" to the foreign language hiring question depend (or are *contingent*) on firm type.

To explore a possible pattern, or relationship between the two qualitative variables (firm type and foreign language hiring preference), it is useful to compute the relative frequency for each cell. One way to obtain these relative frequencies is to divide each cell frequency by the corresponding total for the row in which the cell appears.* For example, consider the U.S./Yes cell category. From Table 2.4, the observed frequency is 50 and the total for the U.S. row is 126; thus, the relative frequency for U.S./Yes is $\frac{50}{126} = .397$. Similarly, the relative frequency for Foreign/Yes is 60 (the observed frequency) divided by 89 (the total for the Foreign row), or $\frac{60}{89} = .674$. The relative frequencies for all six cells, based on row totals, are displayed in Table 2.5. Note that the relative frequencies in each row sum to 1.

The relative frequencies of Table 2.5 can be visually displayed using bar charts. Since the cross-classification table contains two rows (U.S. and Foreign), we form one bar chart for U.S. firms and one for foreign firms, and then place them side-by-side for comparison purposes. This side-by-side bar chart is shown in Figure 2.6.

---

* Alternatively, the relative frequencies can be obtained by dividing the frequencies by either their overall total (in this case, 215) or the corresponding column totals. The choice of divisor will depend on the objective of the analysis.

TABLE 2.5
Relative Frequencies for Table 2.4 Based on Row Totals

| FIRM TYPE | FOREIGN LANGUAGE HIRING PREFERENCE | | | |
	Yes	Neutral	No	Totals
U.S.	.397	.452	.151	1.000
Foreign	.674	.247	.079	1.000
Totals	.512	.367	.121	1.000

From Figure 2.6 we notice that the Yes bar for foreign firms is nearly twice as high as the Yes bar for U.S. firms. Numerically, these relative frequencies (from Table 2.5) are .674 and .397, respectively. That is, for foreign firms, about 67% of the personnel directors prefer hiring business majors with foreign language skills. In contrast, only about 40% of U.S. personnel directors prefer hiring business majors with foreign language skills. Consequently, it appears that the foreign language skill hiring preferences of the personnel directors in the sample does depend on whether the firm is foreign or domestic.

Cross-classification tables and side-by-side bar graphs are useful methods for describing the simultaneous occurrence of two qualitative variables, and can be used to make inferences about whether or not the two variables are related. However, no measure of reliability can be attached to such an inference without a more sophisticated numerical analysis. In Chapter 8 we present a formal inferential method for analyzing cross-classification (two-way contingency) tables.

FIGURE 2.6

Side-by-Side Bar Chart for the Data in Table 2.5

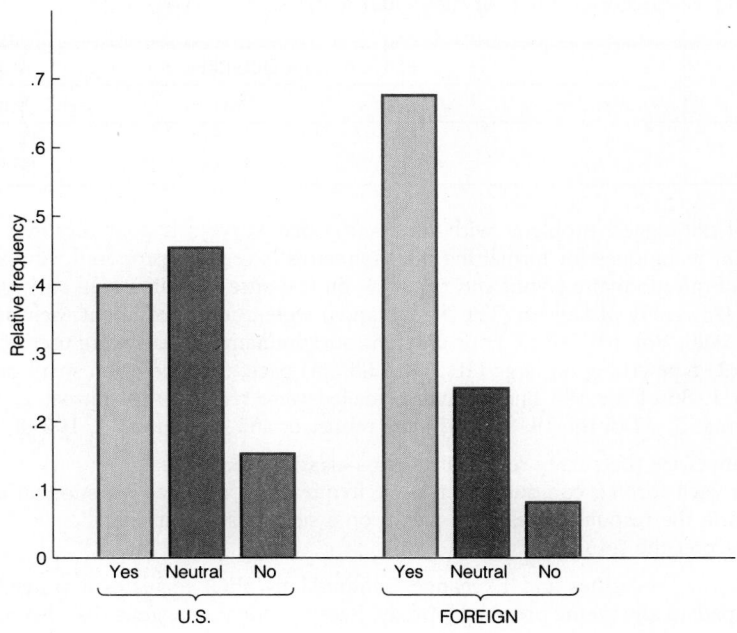

PROBLEMS

2.21   *Toehold acquisition* is a term used by financial analysts to describe the purchase of a relatively small proportion (often less than 10%) of the shares of a corporation by a corporate raider whose ultimate objective is to take over control of the firm. For each toehold acquisition, the potential raider of the firm must report the transaction to the Securities and Exchange Commission by filing Form 13D. Experts hypothesize that the filing of Form 13D provides a clear signal to investors of the corporate raiders' intention. To test this theory, a sample of 461 transactions was drawn from a list of firms in which corporate raiders acquired at least 5% of the outstanding shares (*Akron Business and Economic Review*, Spring 1990). A contingency table relating transaction type and transaction timing for the 461 transactions is shown below.

TRANSACTION TYPE	TIME RELATIVE TO FORM 13D FILING	
	Before	After
Purchase	184	83
Sale	105	89

a. If, in fact, the experts' theory is true, describe the relationship between transaction type and transaction timing.
b. For each transaction type, calculate the relative frequencies associated with the two transaction timings.
c. Display the relative frequencies from part **b** in a side-by-side bar chart.
d. Does it appear that the two variables, transaction type and transaction timing, are related?

2.22   The *Journal of Cash Management* (Nov./Dec. 1988) reported on a survey of 582 corporate financial executives. The questionnaire covered four areas: compensation, job description, career preparation, and demographic information. In the area of career preparation, an important question pertained to level of education. Each corporate executive in the sample was classified according to sex and highest degree attained. The results are displayed in the contingency table. Use the technique described in this section to explore whether the percentages of corporate executives in the four degree categories differ for males and females.

SEX	EDUCATION DEGREE			
	Associate	Bachelor's	Master's	PhD/Other
Male	6	210	171	14
Female	18	89	56	18

2.23   One of the biggest problems with conducting mail surveys is poor response rates. To reduce nonresponse, several different techniques for formatting questionnaires have been proposed. An experiment was conducted to study the effect of questionnaire layout and page size on response rates in a mail survey. Approximately 850 students enrolled at the University of Leyden (The Netherlands) were questioned about their attitudes toward suicide (*Perceptual and Motor Skills*, Vol. 61, 1985). Four different questionnaire formats were used: (1) typewriting on small (15 × 21 cm) page; (2) typewriting on large (18.5 × 25.5 cm) page; (3) typeset on small page; and (4) typeset on large page. For format 1, 86 of the 143 questionnaires mailed were returned; for format 2, 191 of the 288 mailed were returned; for format 3, 72 of the 141 mailed were returned; and, for format 4, 192 of the 284 mailed were returned.

a. Summarize the survey results in a cross-classification table.
b. For each format, compute the relative frequency of returned questionnaires, that is, the response rate.
c. Graph the response rates from part **b** on a side-by-side bar chart.
d. Interpret the results.

2.24   By law, the Securities and Exchange Commission (SEC) regulates a system by which a firm's shareholders may participate in any voting process by proxy. Recent evidence suggests that this proxy voting process dissuades dissident shareholders from challenging the goals of the firm's management. One study investigated 142 New York Stock Exchange (NYSE) and American Stock Exchange (AMEX) firms involved in proxy contests for minority or majority board of directors representation (*Financial Management,* Autumn 1992). Of the 142 firms in the sample, 95 conducted full-control contests for board seats and 47 conducted partial-control contests. In the full-control contests, dissident shareholders were successful in winning board seats for 32 firms; in the partial-control contests, dissidents were successful for 28 firms.

a. Identify the two qualitative variables measured for each of the 142 firms in the sample.
b. Construct a cross-classification table for the data.
c. Use a side-by-side bar chart to summarize the data graphically.
d. Interpret the results of the study.

COMPUTER LAB

DESCRIBING QUALITATIVE DATA SETS

The SAS, SPSS, and MINITAB commands for exploring and describing qualitative data are provided in this section. For purposes of illustration, consider a data set containing the following information on 1,795 recent University of Florida graduates: college, gender, and degree. The first 50 observations (graduates) in the data set are shown in Table 2.6.

TABLE 2.6
Data on University of Florida Graduates with Jobs

GRADUATE	COLLEGE	GENDER	DEGREE	GRADUATE	COLLEGE	GENDER	DEGREE
1	Business Adm	F	Masters	26	Lib Arts/Sciences	M	Masters
2	Engineering	M	Bachelor	27	Lib Arts/Sciences	F	Bachelor
3	Engineering	M	Bachelor	28	Engineering	M	Bachelor
4	Lib Arts/Sciences	F	Masters	29	Engineering	M	Bachelor
5	Engineering	M	Masters	30	Engineering	M	Bachelor
6	Engineering	M	Bachelor	31	Engineering	M	Bachelor
7	Lib Arts/Sciences	M	Bachelor	32	Nursing	F	Masters
8	Engineering	M	PhD	33	Engineering	M	Masters
9	Engineering	M	Masters	34	Engineering	M	PhD
10	Engineering	F	Bachelor	35	Business Adm	M	Bachelor
11	Lib Arts/Sciences	M	Masters	36	Lib Arts/Sciences	F	Masters
12	Engineering	M	Bachelor	37	Engineering	M	Masters
13	Journalism/Comm	F	Bachelor	38	Lib Arts/Sciences	F	Bachelor
14	Engineering	M	Masters	39	Journalism/Comm	F	Bachelor
15	Lib Arts/Sciences	M	Bachelor	40	Lib Arts/Sciences	M	Masters
16	Business Adm	M	Bachelor	41	Lib Arts/Sciences	M	Masters
17	Business Adm	M	Bachelor	42	Engineering	M	Masters
18	Engineering	M	Bachelor	43	Engineering	M	Bachelor
19	Lib Arts/Sciences	F	Masters	44	Business Adm	M	Bachelor
20	Business Adm	F	Masters	45	Lib Arts/Sciences	F	Masters
21	Journalism/Comm	F	Bachelor	46	Business Adm	M	Bachelor
22	Lib Arts/Sciences	M	Bachelor	47	Engineering	M	Bachelor
23	Business Adm	F	Bachelor	48	Lib Arts/Sciences	M	Masters
24	Engineering	F	Masters	49	Lib Arts/Sciences	M	Masters
25	Engineering	M	Bachelor	50	Business Adm	M	Masters

Source: Career Resource Center, University of Florida.

In particular, the programs below will produce (1) a frequency table for college, (2) a frequency bar graph for gender, (3) a relative frequency bar graph for degree, (4) a pie chart for degree (if available), and (5) a cross-classification table for gender × degree.

SAS

```
Command
Line
  1        DATA GRADS;                                    ⎫  Data entry
  2        INPUT COLLEGE $ GENDER $ DEGREE $;             ⎬  instructions
  3        CARDS;                                         ⎭
           BUS F MASTERS      ⎫
           ENG M BACHELOR     ⎪
           ENG M BACHELOR     ⎪
             •   •   •   •    ⎬   Input data values
             •   •   •   •    ⎪   (1 observation per line)
             •   •   •   •    ⎪
           BUS M MASTERS      ⎭
  4        PROC FREQ;                                     ⎫  Frequency table
  5        TABLES COLLEGE;                                ⎭
  6        PROC CHART;                   ⎫  Frequency bar graph
  7        HBAR GENDER;                  ⎭
  8        PROC CHART;                              ⎫  Relative frequency bar graph
  9        VBAR DEGREE/TYPE=PERCENT;                ⎭
 10        PROC CHART;            ⎫  Pie chart
 11        PIE DEGREE;            ⎭
 12        PROC FREQ;                               ⎫  Cross-classification table
 13        TABLES GENDER*DEGREE;                    ⎭
```

COMMANDS 4–5, 12–13 The FREQ procedure produces summary frequency tables for qualitative data. The qualitative variable is specified after the TABLES command. If a single variable is specified, a one-way table is produced; if two variables are specified (separated by an asterisk), a two-way contingency table is produced.

COMMANDS 6–9 The CHART procedure produces vertical and horizontal bar graphs. The command VBAR followed by the variable name produces a vertical frequency bar graph. Replace VBAR with HBAR to produce a horizontal bar graph. The option TYPE=PERCENT requests a relative frequency bar graph.

COMMANDS 10–11 The CHART procedure with the PIE command produces a pie chart for the qualitative variable specified.

NOTE The output for the SAS program is displayed in Figure 2.7.

FIGURE 2.7
Output for the SAS Program

COLLEGE	Frequency	Percent	Cumulative Frequency	Cumulative Percent
BUS	9	18.0	9	18.0
ENG	22	44.0	31	62.0
JRN	3	6.0	34	68.0
LAS	15	30.0	49	98.0
NUR	1	2.0	50	100.0

```
                          FREQUENCY OF GENDER

GENDER                                              CUM              CUM
                                         FREQ      FREQ   PERCENT  PERCENT

F          |***************                15        15    30.00    30.00

M          |**********************************      35        50    70.00   100.00
           -----+----+----+----+----+----+----+
                5   10   15   20   25   30   35
                            FREQUENCY
```

```
                        PERCENTAGE OF DEGREE

PERCENTAGE
           |       *****
           |       *****
           |       *****
       50 +|       *****
           |       *****
           |       *****
           |       *****        *****
       40 +|       *****        *****
           |       *****        *****
           |       *****        *****
           |       *****        *****
           |       *****        *****
       30 +|       *****        *****
           |       *****        *****
           |       *****        *****
           |       *****        *****
           |       *****        *****
       20 +|       *****        *****
           |       *****        *****
           |       *****        *****
           |       *****        *****
           |       *****        *****
       10 +|       *****        *****
           |       *****        *****
           |       *****        *****
           |       *****        *****        *****
           |       *****        *****        *****
           ---------------------------------------------
                 BACHELOR    MASTERS      PHD
                            DEGREE
```

(continued)

FIGURE 2.7 (*Continued*)
Output for the SAS Program

FREQUENCY OF DEGREE

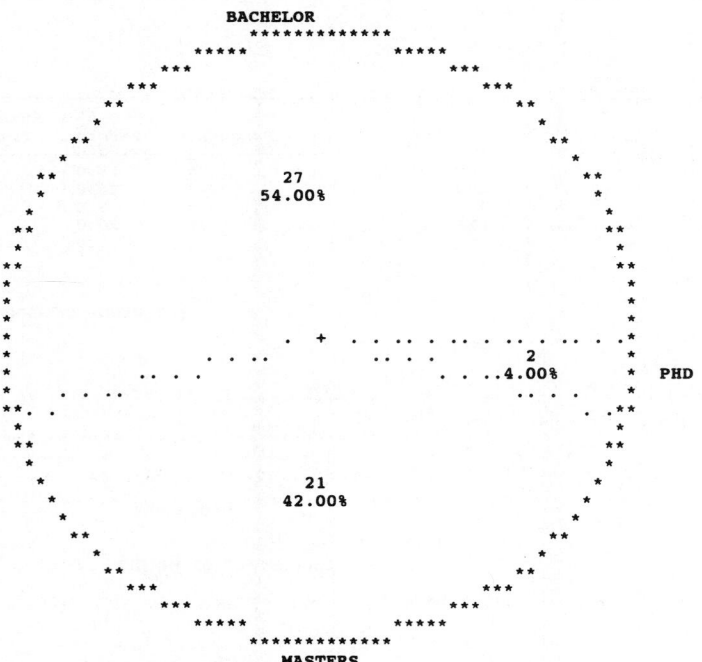

TABLE OF GENDER BY DEGREE

GENDER   DEGREE

Frequency Percent Row Pct Col Pct	BACHELOR	MASTERS	PHD	Total
F	7 14.00 46.67 25.93	8 16.00 53.33 38.10	0 0.00 0.00 0.00	15 30.00
M	20 40.00 57.14 74.07	13 26.00 37.14 61.90	2 4.00 5.71 100.00	35 70.00
Total	27 54.00	21 42.00	2 4.00	50 100.00

SPSS

```
1    DATA LIST FREE/COLLEGE (A3) GENDER (A1) DEGREE (A8).⎫  Data entry
                                                          ⎭  instruction
2    BEGIN DATA.
     BUS F MASTERS   ⎫
     ENG M BACHELOR  ⎪
     ENG M BACHELOR  ⎪
       .   .   .   . ⎬  Input data values
       .   .   .   . ⎪  (1 observation per line)
       .   .   .   . ⎪
     BUS M MASTERS   ⎭
3    END DATA.
4    FREQUENCIES VARIABLES=COLLEGE.}  Frequency table
5    FREQUENCIES VARIABLES=GENDER DEGREE/⎫
6              BARCHART.                 ⎭  Frequency bar graphs
7    CROSSTABS TABLES=GENDER BY DEGREE.}  Cross-classification table
```

COMMANDS 4–6   The FREQUENCIES command produces summary frequency tables for the qualitative variables specified. The BARCHART subcommand will also produce a frequency bar graph. (Relative frequency bar graphs and pie charts are not available in SPSS.)

COMMAND 7   The CROSSTABS command will generate a cross-classification table for the variables specified after the keyword TABLES=. The variable names must be separated by the keyword, BY.

NOTE   The output for the SPSS program is displayed in Figure 2.8 (p. 52).

MINITAB

```
1    READ C1 C2 C3}  Data entry instruction
     1  0  2 ⎫
     2  1  1 ⎪
     2  1  1 ⎪
     .  .  . ⎬  Input data values
     .  .  . ⎪  (1 observation per line)
     .  .  . ⎪
     1  1  2 ⎭
2    NAME C1='COLLEGE' C2='GENDER' C3='DEGREE'}  Data entry instruction
3    TALLY C1}  Frequency table
4    HISTOGRAM C2 C3}  Frequency bar graph
5    TABLES C2 C3}  Cross-classification table
6    STOP
```

FIGURE 2.8
Output for the SPSS Program

COLLEGE

Value Label	Value	Frequency	Percent	Valid Percent	Cum Percent
	BUS	9	18.0	18.0	18.0
	ENG	22	44.0	44.0	62.0
	JRN	3	6.0	6.0	68.0
	LAS	15	30.0	30.0	98.0
	NUR	1	2.0	2.0	100.0
		-------	-------	-------	
	Total	50	100.0	100.0	

Valid cases   50   Missing cases   0

GENDER

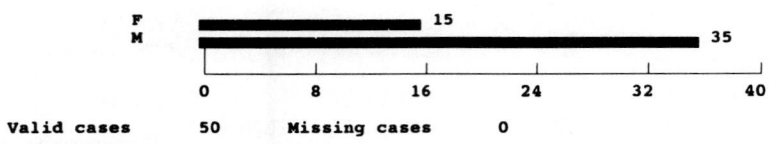

Valid cases   50   Missing cases   0

DEGREE

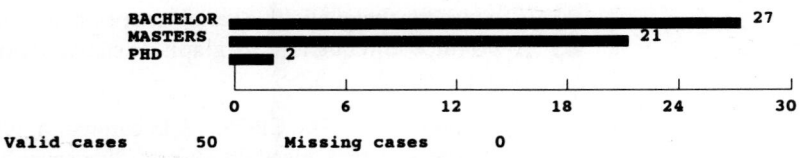

Valid cases   50   Missing cases   0

GENDER by DEGREE

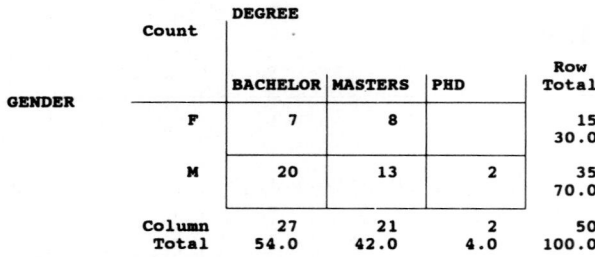

		DEGREE			
	Count				Row Total
GENDER		BACHELOR	MASTERS	PHD	
	F	7	8		15 30.0
	M	20	13	2	35 70.0
	Column Total	27 54.0	21 42.0	2 4.0	50 100.0

Number of Missing Observations: 0

INPUT DATA VALUES   All qualitative data must be entered as numeric values. For C1, we arbitrarily use 1 for BUS, 2 for ENG, 3 for LAS, 4 for JRN, and 5 for NUR. For C2, we use 0 for F and 1 for M. For C3, we use 1 for BACHELOR, 2 for MASTERS, and 3 for PHD.

COMMAND 3   The TALLY command will produce a summary frequency table for the qualitative data in the specified column(s).

COMMAND 4   The HISTOGRAM command produces horizontal frequency bar graphs for the qualitative data in the specified column(s). (Relative frequency bar graphs and pie charts are not available in MINITAB.)

COMMAND 5   The TABLES command produces a cross-classification table for the variables in the specified columns.

NOTE   The output for the MINITAB program is displayed in Figure 2.9.

FIGURE 2.9
Output for the MINITAB Program

```
COLLEGE   COUNT
    1        9
    2       22
    3       15
    4        3
    5        1
   N=       50
```

```
Histogram of GENDER    N = 50

Midpoint   Count
    0        15    **************
    1        35    ***********************************
```

```
Histogram of DEGREE    N = 50

Midpoint   Count
    1        27    ***************************
    2        21    *********************
    3         2    **
```

```
ROWS:  GENDER      COLUMNS: DEGREE

             1          2          3        ALL

 0           7          8          0        15
 1          20         13          2        35
ALL         27         21          2        50

   CELL  CONTENTS --
                 COUNT
```

CHAPTER NOTES

- A **class** is one of the possible categories into which qualitative data can be classified.
- Qualitative data are summarized numerically by computing the **frequency** and **relative frequency** of observations falling into each class.
- **Bar graphs** and **pie charts** are graphical displays of the (relative) frequencies of the classes of a qualitative variable.

- A **Pareto diagram** is a vertical frequency bar graph with the bars displayed in decreasing order of height. The diagram may be enhanced by superimposing **cumulative proportions** over the bars.
- **Cross-classification** (or **contingency**) **tables** are used to summarize data that are simultaneously classified according to two qualitative variables.

LOOKING AHEAD

In Chapter 3 we will learn how to explore and summarize data that are quantitative in nature.

CASE STUDY

CHARACTERISTICS OF HMO PHYSICIANS

During the past 20 years, health-care costs have escalated at a rapid rate. In an attempt to make health care more affordable, health-maintenance organizations (HMOs) have designed insurance packages that allow patients to obtain as much service as possible at low or minimal personal expense. An HMO is usually made up of an independent group of physicians who provide primary and special health care to patients in a geographical area. Since most HMOs are unmanaged, they provide only marginally beneficial services and are usually not cost-effective.

In contrast, the object of a managed health-care system is to provide patients with care that is genuinely needed, not what the patients think they want or the physician wants to provide. A case manager authorizes any unusual testing, referral to physicians other than the primary-care physician, and referral to a hospital for admission. Most experts view primary-care physicians (eg, general practitioners, family physicians, general internists, pediatricians) as the best case managers by virtue of their generalized professional training.

A study was conducted by a network of private practicing physicians in Florida, called the Tampa Bay Area Doctors (TBAD). The study had two major goals: (1) to describe the characteristics of the HMO physicians in the group, and (2) to investigate the cost-effectiveness of the physicians. For this case study, consider the first goal.

Table 2.7 lists the data collected by the researchers.* For each of the 186 physicians in the HMO, the following variables were measured:

1. Primary specialty: general practice (GP), internal medicine (IM), pediatrics (PD), family practice (FP), obstetrics (OB), or other (OT)
2. Secondary specialty: yes (Y) or no (N)
3. Certification level: 0, 1, or 2

---

* *Source:* Lane, W., and Sincich, T. "Selection of Cost-Effective Primary-Care Physician Case Managers." *Medical Interface,* Oct. 1992.

TABLE 2.7
Characteristics of HMO Physicians

(1)	(2)	(3)	(4)	(5)	(6)	(7)	(8)	(9)	(1)	(2)	(3)	(4)	(5)	(6)	(7)	(8)	(9)
PD	N	1	M	USA	USA	37	47.6	2108	PD	N	1	M	USA	USA	39	18.2	74
PD	Y	1	M	FOR	USA	35	25.9	18	IM	N	1	M	USA	USA	13	83.5	1117
PD	N	2	M	FOR	USA	0	53.7	430	FP	N	1	M	USA	USA	22	61.7	5459
PD	N	1	F	FOR	USA	21	74.1	255	FP	N	2	M	USA	FOR	31	45.5	1345
IM	N	1	M	FOR	USA	8	18.2	12	GP	N	0	M	FOR	FOR	0	136.5	76
OT	N	0	M	FOR	FOR	0	141.4	707	IM	N	1	M	FOR	FOR	28	61.2	1160
IM	N	0	M	FOR	FOR	38	8.0	71	FP	N	2	M	FOR	FOR	27	122.5	654
FP	N	1	M	USA	FOR	22	20.5	88	PD	N	1	M	USA	USA	10	47.7	432
PD	N	1	M	USA	FOR	23	21.6	1001	OB	N	1	F	USA	USA	18	1104.3	6
PD	N	1	F	FOR	USA	0	32.0	577	IM	N	2	F	FOR	USA	14	75.5	3305
IM	N	1	M	FOR	USA	20	45.1	650	PD	N	0	M	FOR	FOR	0	79.1	103
OB	N	1	M	USA	USA	14	8.9	18	FP	N	1	M	USA	USA	18	54.5	568
IM	N	1	M	USA	FOR	41	56.3	344	PD	Y	1	M	USA	USA	41	117.3	534
FP	N	1	M	USA	USA	24	1.8	38	GP	N	0	M	FOR	FOR	0	53.9	2822
PD	N	1	M	FOR	USA	13	137.2	80	PD	N	1	F	FOR	USA	27	35.9	322
PD	N	1	F	FOR	FOR	26	12.1	427	FP	N	1	M	USA	USA	9	39.0	898
GP	N	0	M	FOR	FOR	32	20.0	69	PD	N	1	M	USA	FOR	9	35.7	129
FP	N	1	M	USA	FOR	30	71.3	507	GP	N	2	M	FOR	FOR	0	18.2	181
FP	N	1	F	FOR	FOR	0	69.7	123	FP	N	1	M	FOR	FOR	0	69.3	1237
FP	N	1	M	USA	USA	8	67.0	563	FP	N	1	M	USA	USA	8	42.9	1771
FP	N	2	M	FOR	USA	45	45.1	958	OB	N	1	M	FOR	USA	30	25.5	3
PD	N	0	M	FOR	USA	0	7.7	82	FP	N	1	M	FOR	USA	0	80.8	431
IM	N	1	M	FOR	USA	12	79.9	397	IM	N	2	M	USA	USA	6	77.7	1260
PD	N	1	F	USA	USA	14	14.3	243	PD	N	1	M	USA	USA	13	33.1	20
IM	N	1	M	USA	USA	16	103.7	1779	FP	N	1	M	USA	USA	29	140.3	1049
OT	Y	1	M	USA	USA	45	105.0	1036	PD	N	1	M	FOR	FOR	13	59.5	759
PD	N	1	M	USA	USA	12	39.3	511	PD	N	1	M	FOR	USA	29	2.1	36
OB	N	1	M	USA	USA	9	413.3	7	GP	N	1	M	FOR	FOR	11	61.0	763
PD	N	1	M	USA	USA	47	14.5	235	GP	Y	2	M	FOR	USA	0	45.9	21
FP	N	1	M	FOR	FOR	28	48.9	3047	OT	Y	1	M	FOR	USA	40	81.5	2
IM	N	1	M	USA	USA	14	24.2	37	PD	N	1	F	USA	USA	13	16.5	18
PD	N	1	M	USA	USA	29	50.6	103	GP	Y	0	M	FOR	FOR	0	67.7	558
PD	N	0	M	FOR	FOR	0	12.0	11	PD	N	2	F	FOR	USA	8	60.2	12
IM	N	1	M	USA	USA	9	78.5	538	GP	Y	0	M	FOR	FOR	0	47.2	30
PD	N	0	M	FOR	FOR	0	37.3	344	FP	N	1	M	USA	USA	11	34.9	176
FP	N	1	M	USA	USA	16	66.8	679	FP	N	1	M	FOR	FOR	12	431.2	36
OB	N	1	M	USA	USA	9	14.3	4	FP	N	1	M	USA	USA	34	18.9	565
FP	N	2	M	FOR	USA	26	9.8	199	GP	Y	0	M	FOR	FOR	0	195.4	337
FP	N	1	M	FOR	USA	0	74.1	515	PD	N	2	M	FOR	USA	3	80.3	13
GP	Y	0	M	FOR	USA	30	11.4	56	IM	N	0	M	FOR	FOR	0	41.9	319
GP	N	0	M	FOR	USA	27	51.7	262	IM	N	2	M	FOR	USA	16	56.7	357
FP	N	1	M	FOR	FOR	38	154.3	1255	FP	N	1	M	USA	FOR	25	44.0	6716
OT	N	1	M	FOR	FOR	0	58.1	218	FP	N	1	M	USA	FOR	35	24.1	471
FP	N	1	M	USA	FOR	33	71.8	1835	IM	Y	1	M	USA	USA	6	169.1	733
PD	Y	0	M	FOR	FOR	0	79.1	561	OB	N	1	M	FOR	USA	24	24.6	2
FP	N	1	M	USA	USA	19	242.0	18	OB	N	1	M	USA	USA	20	65.9	3
PD	N	1	M	USA	USA	6	116.0	282	OB	N	1	M	USA	USA	20	58.5	7
PD	N	2	M	FOR	USA	30	13.6	369	PD	N	1	M	USA	USA	14	53.4	211
IM	N	2	M	FOR	FOR	11	47.3	226	FP	N	1	M	USA	USA	19	56.0	1141
PD	N	1	M	USA	USA	38	22.2	78	IM	Y	1	M	USA	USA	22	66.1	795
OT	Y	1	M	USA	USA	18	29.7	396	OT	N	2	M	FOR	FOR	16	126.7	2
PD	N	1	M	FOR	USA	18	63.8	422	FP	N	1	M	FOR	USA	12	11.1	152
IM	N	1	M	FOR	USA	0	27.1	111	GP	N	2	M	USA	FOR	32	47.6	1558
GP	N	0	F	FOR	FOR	0	61.3	8	GP	Y	0	M	USA	USA	32	3.1	71

(continued)

TABLE 2.7 (*Continued*)

(1)	(2)	(3)	(4)	(5)	(6)	(7)	(8)	(9)	(1)	(2)	(3)	(4)	(5)	(6)	(7)	(8)	(9)
FP	N	1	M	FOR	FOR	39	135.3	70	PD	N	2	F	FOR	USA	15	34.2	849
PD	N	1	M	USA	USA	34	52.4	387	PD	Y	1	M	USA	USA	25	159.6	276
PD	N	1	M	FOR	USA	16	32.7	975	PD	N	1	F	FOR	USA	0	24.3	262
OT	Y	0	M	FOR	USA	28	32.8	85	PD	N	1	M	USA	USA	15	111.7	164
IM	N	2	M	USA	USA	6	140.2	111	FP	N	1	M	FOR	USA	13	35.8	845
OT	N	2	M	FOR	FOR	21	8.2	14	IM	N	1	F	FOR	USA	14	55.1	417
IM	N	1	M	FOR	USA	13	33.5	424	PD	N	0	M	FOR	FOR	0	23.4	81
FP	N	0	M	USA	FOR	11	47.7	1412	GP	Y	2	M	FOR	USA	0	69.3	74
IM	N	1	M	USA	USA	22	117.5	354	IM	N	1	M	USA	USA	15	93.5	2250
PD	Y	1	M	FOR	USA	0	24.5	157	PD	N	2	M	USA	USA	37	42.5	520
FP	N	1	M	USA	USA	11	57.6	2648	FP	N	1	M	USA	USA	12	32.7	320
IM	N	1	M	USA	USA	17	52.9	476	PD	N	1	F	USA	USA	12	10.4	324
PD	N	1	F	FOR	USA	17	30.6	490	OB	N	2	M	FOR	FOR	18	133.9	2
IM	N	2	M	FOR	USA	16	135.9	291	FP	N	1	M	USA	FOR	29	64.1	2646
FP	N	1	M	USA	USA	13	31.0	1413	IM	N	1	M	USA	USA	38	50.0	982
IM	N	1	M	USA	USA	47	151.1	971	OT	Y	1	M	FOR	USA	0	113.7	22
IM	Y	2	M	FOR	USA	0	17.1	48	FP	N	0	M	FOR	FOR	22	46.1	181
PD	N	2	M	USA	USA	46	10.4	363	PD	N	1	F	USA	USA	11	35.9	977
FP	N	1	M	USA	FOR	40	52.7	958	FP	N	1	M	USA	FOR	30	32.7	4
IM	N	2	M	FOR	USA	8	16.8	21	PD	N	1	M	USA	USA	27	80.8	261
PD	Y	1	M	FOR	USA	0	29.6	194	FP	N	1	M	USA	USA	12	30.4	87
FP	N	2	M	FOR	FOR	43	51.3	1969	PD	N	2	F	FOR	USA	33	35.1	360
FP	N	1	M	USA	USA	12	14.8	1	PD	N	1	M	USA	USA	23	31.6	1066
IM	N	2	M	USA	USA	38	66.0	517	IM	N	2	M	FOR	USA	18	144.7	765
PD	N	1	M	FOR	USA	0	112.2	65	FP	N	1	M	USA	USA	42	18.4	220
PD	N	1	F	USA	FOR	12	24.7	218	OT	Y	1	M	FOR	FOR	14	37.8	42
OT	Y	0	M	USA	USA	24	817.3	32	FP	N	1	M	FOR	USA	0	52.2	2359
FP	N	2	M	USA	USA	21	52.5	1265	IM	N	1	F	USA	USA	15	225.9	451
GP	Y	1	M	FOR	FOR	0	33.4	103	OT	Y	1	M	USA	USA	16	4725.2	1
FP	N	1	M	USA	FOR	35	24.5	560	IM	N	2	F	USA	USA	6	86.0	889
FP	N	1	M	FOR	USA	20	27.2	128	PD	N	2	F	FOR	USA	0	59.4	157
GP	N	0	M	FOR	FOR	0	30.1	1568	PD	N	2	M	FOR	USA	15	59.6	602
PD	N	1	M	FOR	USA	26	21.0	143	FP	N	0	F	USA	USA	6	78.6	1702
GP	N	0	M	USA	FOR	0	43.2	187	FP	N	1	M	USA	FOR	9	42.6	928
IM	N	0	M	USA	USA	6	40.6	51	OT	Y	1	M	USA	FOR	32	28.6	740
FP	Y	1	M	USA	USA	31	105.7	459	FP	N	1	M	USA	USA	16	36.2	1039
OB	N	2	M	USA	USA	10	1121.0	5	IM	N	2	M	FOR	FOR	0	94.6	212
GP	Y	1	M	FOR	FOR	0	164.1	190	OT	Y	2	M	FOR	USA	15	169.8	65
FP	N	1	M	FOR	FOR	23	1.7	41	IM	N	1	M	USA	USA	13	50.5	435

4. Gender: male (M) or female (F)
5. Country of medical school: (USA) or foreign (FOR)
6. Country of medical residency: (USA) or foreign (FOR)
7. Years of experience
8. Total costs accrued per patient per month
9. Total patient–months

a. Identify the qualitative variables in the data set.
b. Summary frequency tables for each of the qualitative variables, produced using

FIGURE 2.10
SAS Frequency Tables for Qualitative Variables

PRIMSPEC	Frequency	Percent	Cumulative Frequency	Cumulative Percent
FP	52	28.0	52	28.0
GP	19	10.2	71	38.2
IM	36	19.4	107	57.5
OB	10	5.4	117	62.9
OT	14	7.5	131	70.4
PD	55	29.6	186	100.0

SECSPEC	Frequency	Percent	Cumulative Frequency	Cumulative Percent
N	157	84.4	157	84.4
Y	29	15.6	186	100.0

CERTLEV	Frequency	Percent	Cumulative Frequency	Cumulative Percent
0	27	14.5	27	14.5
1	122	65.6	149	80.1
2	37	19.9	186	100.0

GENDER	Frequency	Percent	Cumulative Frequency	Cumulative Percent
F	23	12.4	23	12.4
M	163	87.6	186	100.0

MEDSCHL	Frequency	Percent	Cumulative Frequency	Cumulative Percent
FOR	93	50.0	93	50.0
USA	93	50.0	186	100.0

MEDRES	Frequency	Percent	Cumulative Frequency	Cumulative Percent
FOR	59	31.7	59	31.7
USA	127	68.3	186	100.0

SAS, are displayed in Figure 2.10. Display this information using one of the graphical methods discussed in this chapter.

c. A cross-classification table, produced using SAS, for the two qualitative variables, secondary specialty and country of medical residency, is displayed in Figure 2.11. Interpret the results. Does it appear that the two variables are related?

d. Use a computer to generate cross-classification tables for all remaining pairs of qualitative variables. Interpret the results.

FIGURE 2.11
SAS Contingency Table

```
          TABLE OF SECSPEC BY MEDRES

SECSPEC        MEDRES

Frequency|
Percent  |
Row Pct  |
Col Pct  |FOR      |USA      |   Total
---------+---------+---------+
N        |      51 |     106 |     157
         |   27.42 |   56.99 |   84.41
         |   32.48 |   67.52 |
         |   86.44 |   83.46 |
---------+---------+---------+
Y        |       8 |      21 |      29
         |    4.30 |   11.29 |   15.59
         |   27.59 |   72.41 |
         |   13.56 |   16.54 |
---------+---------+---------+
Total           59       127        186
             31.72     68.28     100.00
```

REFERENCES

Agresti, A. *A Categorical Data Analysis.* New York: Wiley, 1990.

Chambers, J. M., Cleveland, W. S., Kleiner, B., and Tukey, P. A. *Graphical Methods for Data Analysis.* Belmont, CA: Wadsworth, 1983.

McClave, J. T., and Dietrich, F. *A First Course in Statistics,* 4th ed. San Francisco: Dellen, 1992.

CHAPTER 3

EXPLORING AND DESCRIBING QUANTITATIVE DATA

CONTENTS

The *U.S. News & World Report* annually conducts a survey of MBAs to determine the top 25 graduate schools of business. One variable of interest to prospective MBAs is the acceptance rate at these schools. How could you describe the quantitative variable, acceptance rate, for the sample of 25 business schools? This chapter presents several basic tools for describing quantitative data. As in Chapter 2, these techniques include graphs and plots that rapidly convey a visual picture of the data. In addition, powerful numerical measures that describe certain features of a quantitative data set are presented. The analysis of the quantitative data in the MBA survey is discussed in Problems 3.5, 3.11, 3.24, and 3.35.

3.1 For small quantitative data sets, the simplest graph is the **dot plot**. A dot plot is constructed by first drawing a horizontal scale that spans the range of the data. The numerical values of the observations are located on the horizontal scale by placing a dot over the appropriate value. If data values repeat, then the dots are placed on top of each other, forming a pile at that particular numerical location.

To illustrate, consider the data set in Table 3.1. The data represent a sample of 20 starting salaries of recent University of Florida graduates selected from a larger data set of 1,795 starting salaries.* Figure 3.1 is a hand-drawn plot for the data. Since the smallest measurement in the data set is 18 (ie, $18,000) and the largest is 50 (ie, $50,000), the horizontal axis is drawn to span this range.

TABLE 3.1
Starting Salaries of 20 Recent University of Florida Graduates

GRADUATION DATE	DEGREE	STARTING SALARY Thousand Dollars	GRADUATION DATE	DEGREE	STARTING SALARY Thousand Dollars
Fall 1989	PhD	28.0	Fall 1989	Masters	32.0
Fall 1989	Bachelor	28.0	Fall 1989	PhD	24.0
Fall 1989	Bachelor	33.0	Spring 1990	Bachelor	25.1
Spring 1990	Bachelor	27.6	Fall 1990	Bachelor	18.5
Spring 1990	Masters	49.0	Fall 1990	Bachelor	23.0
Spring 1990	Bachelor	21.1	Fall 1990	Bachelor	21.2
Spring 1990	Bachelor	27.5	Spring 1991	PhD	35.0
Fall 1990	Bachelor	23.0	Spring 1991	Bachelor	21.0
Spring 1991	PhD	50.0	Spring 1991	Bachelor	18.0
Spring 1991	Bachelor	30.0	Spring 1991	Bachelor	20.0

CONSTRUCTING A DOT PLOT

STEP 1   Examine the data set to determine the smallest and largest measurements.

STEP 2   Draw a horizontal scale that spans the range of the data.

STEP 3   Place a dot over the appropriate value on the scale for each measurement in the data set. If data values repeat, the dots are placed on top of each other.

FIGURE 3.1
Hand-Drawn Dot Plot for Starting Salary Data in Table 3.1

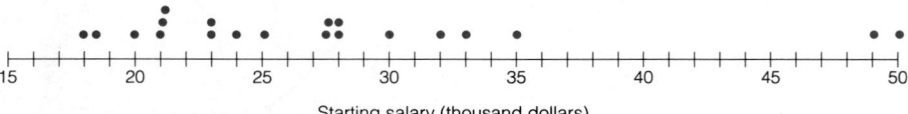
Starting salary (thousand dollars)

* The data were obtained from the University of Florida's Career Resource Center (CRC) for graduates who earned their degree between 1989 and 1991.

For small data sets such as the one in Table 3.1, the dot plot provides a quick and easy way to obtain a visual picture of how the data are distributed along the horizontal scale. Figure 3.1 shows that most of the starting salaries lie between $20,000 and $30,000, and that two extreme values ($49,000 and $50,000) occur. Note that these extreme salaries belong to graduates with advanced (Masters or PhD) degrees. (See Table 3.1.)

Dot plots also can be generated by computer. Figure 3.2 is a MINITAB dot plot for the data in Table 3.1. As an option, we requested MINITAB to produce two starting salary dot plots, one for the 14 Bachelor degree graduates (Degree = 0) and one for the 6 advanced degree (Masters or PhD) graduates in the sample (Degree = 1).* Figure 3.2 shows clearly that the largest starting salaries in the data set belong to advanced degree graduates (ie, those identified by Degree = 1).

FIGURE 3.2

MINITAB Dot Plots for Starting Salary Data

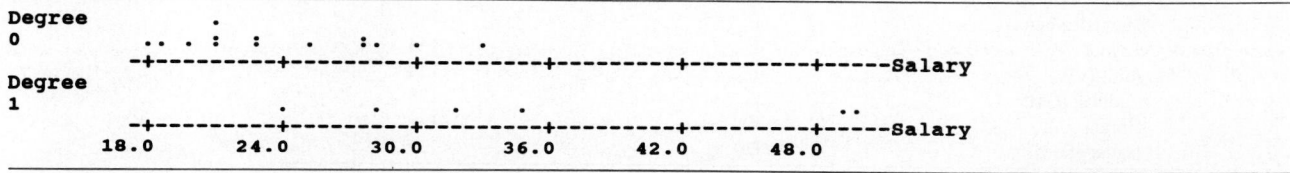

PROBLEMS

3.1 According to one study, "The majority of people who die from fire and smoke in compartmented fire-resistive buildings—the type used for hotels, motels, apartments, and other health care facilities—die in the attempt to evacuate" (*Risk Management*, Feb. 1986). The accompanying data represent the number of victims who attempted to

FIRE	NUMBER OF VICTIMS
Las Vegas Hilton (Las Vegas)	5
Inn on the Park (Toronto)	5
Westchase Hilton (Houston)	8
Holiday Inn (Cambridge, Ohio)	10
Conrad Hilton (Chicago)	4
Providence College (Providence)	8
Baptist Towers (Atlanta)	7
Howard Johnson (New Orleans)	5
Cornell University (Ithaca, New York)	9
Westport Central Apartments (Kansas City, Missouri)	4
Orrington Hotel (Evanston, Illinois)	0
Hartford Hospital (Hartford, Connecticut)	16
Milford Plaza (New York)	0
MGM Grand (Las Vegas)	36

Source: Macdonald, J. N. "Is Evacuation a Fatal Flaw in Fire Fighting Philosophy?" *Risk Management*, Vol. 33, No. 2, Feb. 1986, p. 37.

---

* The commands for generating the MINITAB dot plots are provided in Computer Lab 1, following Section 3.4.

evacuate for a sample of 14 recent fires in compartmented fire-resistive buildings reported in the study. Construct a dot plot for the data. Interpret the plot.

3.2 The Customer Satisfaction Index, compiled monthly by J. D. Powers & Associates, is designed to measure customer satisfaction with new automobiles in the areas of repair, reliability, and experience at the dealership. The index is based on questionnaires completed by drivers 1 year after they bought their cars. In 1992, an index of 129 was considered average, with ratings above 129 considered above average and ratings below 129 considered below average in terms of overall customer satisfaction. The table lists the 1992 Customer Satisfaction Index for the top 10 rated automobiles. Use a dot plot to describe the data.

AUTO (MANUFACTURER)	FOREIGN (F) OR DOMESTIC (D)	CUSTOMER SATISFACTION INDEX
Lexus (Toyota)	F	179
Infiniti (Nissan)	F	167
Saturn (GM)	D	160
Acura (Honda)	F	148
Mercedes-Benz	F	145
Toyota	F	144
Audi (VW)	F	139
Cadillac (GM)	D	138
Honda	F	138
Jaguar (Ford)	D	137

Source: J. D. Powers and Associates, 1992. Customer Satisfaction StudySM.

3.3 What are the top corporate executives being paid? To answer this question, *Business Week* magazine conducts a survey of U.S. corporate executives (CEOs) each year, called the "Executive Compensation Scoreboard." The 1993 survey of 365 corporations revealed a 2% decrease in CEO salary and bonuses from 1991 to 1992. The top 20 CEOs and their 1992 total cash compensations (salary plus bonus plus long-term compensation, in thousands of dollars) are listed in the table. A MINITAB dot plot for the data is also shown. Interpret the graph.

CEO	COMPANY	TOTAL PAY
T. Frist, Jr.	HCA	127,002
S. Weill	Primerica	67,635
C. Lazarus	Toys 'R' Us	64,231
L. Hirsch	U.S. Surgical	62,171
S. Wynn	Mirage Resorts	38,005
A. O'Reilly	H. J. Heinz	36,918
M. Wygod	Medco Containment	30,207
W. Anders	General Dynamics	29,015
R. Richey	Torchmark	26,568
L. Bantle	UST Inc.	24,602
R. Mark	Colgate-Palmolive	22,818
W. Sanders III	Advanced Micro Devices	22,356
J. Welch, Jr.	General Electric	17,970
L. Iacocca	Chrysler	16,908
E. Grisanti	Int'l Flavors	16,475
A. Greenberg	Bear Stearns	15,832
R. Goizueta	Coca-Cola	15,218
W. Bartlett	Multimedia	14,822
C. Mathewson	Int'l Game Tech	14,795
P. Rooney	Wheelabrator Tech	11,216

Source: "Executive Compensation Scoreboard." *Business Week*, Apr. 26, 1993. Reprinted from Apr. 26, 1993 issue of *Business Week* by special permission, copyright © 1993 by McGraw-Hill, Inc. Used with permission.

Dot Plot for Problem 3.3

```
                                      :.
                          .  :: :..:  :           ...                          .
         +---------+---------+---------+---------+---------+-------TotalPay
                   0       25000     50000     75000    100000    125000
```

3.4 The *Tampa Bay Business Journal* recently surveyed the 25 largest certified public accountant (CPA) firms in the Tampa, Florida, area. The data in the table give the number of CPAs employed by each firm. Summarize the data with a dot plot. Interpret the results.

110	60	102	86	106	63	24	29	16	16
20	28	25	25	20	18	14	8	6	16
12	11	10	11	6					

Source: Tampa Bay Business Journal, Mar. 8–14, 1991.

3.5 If you are an undergraduate student in business, are you thinking about going to graduate school and obtaining your MBA? If so, you will want answers to several questions before you make your decision. To provide prospective students with "as much comparative educational information as possible beyond the adjective burdened generalizations offered by college marketing brochures," *U.S. News & World Report* each year conducts its Survey of America's Best Graduate and Professional Schools. The table lists the top 25 business schools according to this survey. The data

SCHOOL	OVERALL SCORE	TUITION	GMAT	ACCEPTANCE RATE %	STARTING SALARY
Harvard University	100.0	$16,400	644[a]	15.0[a]	$63,000[a]
Stanford University	97.9	16,575	665[a]	10.2[a]	60,500
University of Pennsylvania (Wharton)	92.7	16,500	644	19.4	55,000[a]
Northwestern University (Kellogg)	91.1	16,650	640[a]	22.6	54,000[a]
Massachusetts Institute of Technology (Sloan)	89.8	17,250	650	21.3	59,000
University of Chicago	87.8	16,700	632[a]	30.0[a]	54,500[a]
Duke University (Fuqua)	86.0	16,200	630	18.2	51,000
Dartmouth College (Tuck)	85.6	16,500	649	13.4	57,000
University of Virginia (Darden)	85.4	11,700	630	23.0	55,269
University of Michigan	85.2	15,700	620	32.4	53,300
Columbia University	84.5	16,300	635	37.1	52,000[a]
Cornell University (Johnson)	81.1	16,100	648	14.9	50,700
Carnegie Mellon University	78.5	16,500	630	31.2	52,050
University of North Carolina (Chapel Hill)	78.3	5,600	625	15.4	50,800
University of California at Berkeley (Haas)	77.4	7,800	634	24.7	50,000
University of California at Los Angeles (Anderson)	76.7	8,135	640	20.7	51,494
University of Texas at Austin	76.2	3,648	612	28.1	43,985
Indiana University at Bloomington	76.1	8,175	600	29.0	44,119
New York University (Stern)	74.6	15,490	610	35.0	53,161
Purdue University (Krannert)	73.4	6,764	595	26.8	43,500
University of Southern California	71.7	14,378	610	31.9	49,080
University of Pittsburgh (Katz)[b]	68.7	16,860	605	33.0	43,500
Georgetown University[b]	68.7	14,500	617	31.7	45,156
University of Maryland at College Park	67.7	7,139	593	28.1	42,925
University of Rochester (Simon)	67.2	14,700	605	35.9	44,499

Source: "The Best Graduate Schools." U.S. News & World Report, Apr. 29, 1991, p. 68.
[a] *U.S. News estimates.*   [b] Indicates a tie.

include each school's overall score (based on a weighted average of rankings in five areas), out-of-state tuition costs, average GMAT scores of entering MBAs, acceptance rate, and average starting salary of MBAs who obtained employment. MINITAB dot plots for the five quantitative variables listed in the table are also shown. Interpret the results.

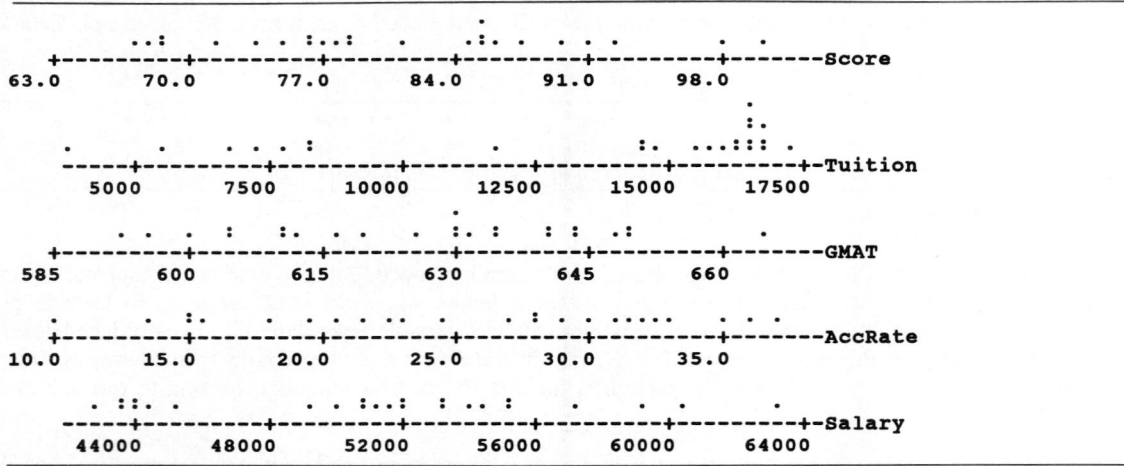

Dot Plots for Problem 3.5

STEM-AND-LEAF DISPLAYS

3.2 A **stem-and-leaf display** is another popular graphical method for describing quantitative data sets. For small to moderately sized data sets (say, 30 or fewer observations) that consist of measurements with only a few digits, stem-and-leaf displays can be constructed easily and quickly by hand. Like the bar graphs and pie charts of Chapter 2, these displays show the number of observations that fall into each class. The difference is that the classes represent values of a quantitative variable rather than categories of a qualitative variable.

To illustrate, suppose you are interested in describing and summarizing recent sales of residential properties in a particular neighborhood. The sale prices (in hundreds of dollars) of 25 recently sold (and randomly selected) properties in the neighborhood are listed in Table 3.2.

To construct a stem-and-leaf display, first break each measurement into a **stem** and a **leaf**. One or more of the digits will make up the stem, while the remaining digits (or digit) will be the leaf. Since the stems will represent the classes in the graph, it is best to choose the stem so that more than just a few classes are represented.

TABLE 3.2

Sale Prices for a Random Sample of 25 Residential Properties

| | SALE PRICE | | | |
	Hundred Dollars			
660	595	1,060	500	630
899	1,295	749	820	843
710	950	720	575	760
1,090	770	682	1,016	650
425	367	1,480	945	1,120

For this data set, the best choice is a one-digit or two-digit stem, with the last two digits representing the leaf. So, for the first number, 660 (representing a sale price of $66,000), the stem is 6 and the leaf is 60, as illustrated here:

STEM	LEAF
6	60

Now, list all stem possibilities in a column, starting with the smallest stem and ending with the largest. For this data set, the smallest stem is 3 (corresponding to the number 367) and the largest stem is 14 (corresponding to the number 1,480), as shown in Figure 3.3. The final step is to place the leaf of each measurement in the row of the display corresponding to the measurement's stem. For example, for the number 660, the leaf 60 is placed in the stem row 6. After the leaves of the 25 measurements are placed in the appropriate stem rows (and, optionally, arranged in order of magnitude), the completed stem-and-leaf display will appear as shown in Figure 3.3.

You can see that the stem-and-leaf display in Figure 3.3 partitions the data set into 12 categories (or classes) corresponding to the 12 stems. The class corresponding to the stem 3 would contain all measurements from 300 to 399; the class corresponding to the stem 4 would contain all measurements from 400 to 499; etc. The number of leaves in each class gives the class frequency. From Figure 3.3, we notice that the class corresponding to the stem 7 has the largest frequency—namely, 5 sale prices. Thus, 5 out of the 25 residential properties in the sample, or 20%, had sale prices between $70,000 and $79,999.

A computer-generated (MINITAB) stem-and-leaf display for the data of Table 3.2 is shown in Figure 3.4.* Note that the second column of the MINITAB printout gives the stems 3, 4, 5, ..., 14; and the third column gives the leaves. Note also that MINITAB uses only a single digit—the number in the tens place—to represent the leaf.† Thus, the leaf 6 in stem row 3 of Figure 3.4 represents the value 367 in Table 3.2; the leaf 2 in stem row 4 represents the value 425; etc.‡

STEM	LEAF
3	67
4	25
5	00 75 95
6	30 50 60 82
7	10 20 49 60 70
8	20 43 99
9	45 50
10	16 60 90
11	20
12	95
13	
14	80

FIGURE 3.3

Stem-and-Leaf Display for the Sale Price Data in Table 3.2

---

* The MINITAB commands for generating stem-and-leaf displays are provided in Computer Lab 1, following Section 3.4.

† In MINITAB, the leaf will always be the digit immediately to the right of the stem.

‡ The numbers in the first column of the MINITAB printout give the cumulative number of observations from the stem row to the nearest end of the distribution.

FIGURE 3.4

MINITAB Stem-and-Leaf Display for
Sale Prices in Table 3.2

```
Stem-and-leaf of salepric   N = 25
Leaf Unit = 1.0

    1      3  6
    2      4  2
    5      5  079
    9      6  3568
  (5)      7  12467
   11      8  249
    8      9  45
    6     10  169
    3     11  2
    2     12  9
    1     13
    1     14  8
```

Like the dot plot, a stem-and-leaf display gives a visual description of the distribution of a data set. From either Figure 3.3 or Figure 3.4, it is clear that a majority of residential properties in the neighborhood sold between $50,000 and $100,000, with the typical sale price around $70,000.

CONSTRUCTING A STEM-AND-LEAF DISPLAY

STEP 1   Decide how the stems and leaves will be defined.

STEP 2   List the stems in order in a column, starting with the smallest stem and ending with the largest.

STEP 3   Proceed through the data set, placing the leaf for each observation in the appropriate stem row. (You may want to place the leaves of each stem in increasing order.)

PROBLEMS

3.6   Construct a stem-and-leaf display for the Customer Satisfaction Index data given in Problem 3.2. Circle the index values for the foreign auto makers on the graph. Are customers more satisfied with foreign auto makers?

3.7   Under a voluntary cooperative inspection program, all passenger cruise ships arriving at U.S. ports are subject to unannounced inspections. The purpose of these inspections is to achieve levels of sanitation that will minimize the potential for gastrointestinal disease outbreaks on these ships. Ships are rated on a 0 to 100 point scale, depending on how well they meet the Center for Disease Control sanitation standards. In general, the lower the score, the lower the level of sanitation. The table lists the sanitation inspection scores for 91 international cruise ships during 1992.

a. A MINITAB stem-and-leaf display of the data is shown on p. 67. Identify the stems and leaves of the graph.
b. A score of 86 or higher at the time of inspection indicates the ship is providing an accepted standard of sanitation. Use the MINITAB graph to estimate the proportion of ships that have an accepted sanitation standard.
c. Locate the inspection score of 70 (Pacific Star) on the stem-and-leaf display.

Data for Problem 3.7

SHIP	SCORE	SHIP	SCORE	SHIP	SCORE
Americana	89	Hanseatic Renaissance	82	Sea Princess	88
Amerikanis	97	Holiday	91	Seabourn Spirit	92
Azure Seas	83	Horizon	94	Seabourn Pride	99
Britanis	93	Island Princess	87	Seabreeze I	96
Caribbean Prince	84	Jubilee	89	Seaward	89
Caribe 1	90	Mardi Gras	92	Sky Princess	97
Carla C	90	Meridian	95	Society Explorer	66
Carnivale	92	Nantucket Clipper	89	Song of America	95
Celebration	95	New Shoreham II	95	Song of Flower	99
Club Med 1	94	Nieuw Amsterdam	97	Song of Norway	92
Costa Classica	91	Noordam	92	Southward	89
Costa Marina	91	Nordic Empress	93	Sovereign of the Seas	93
Costa Riviera	91	Nordic Prince	92	Star Princess	94
Crown Monarch	94	Norway	84	Starship Atlantic	87
Crown Odyssey	88	Pacific Princess	88	Starship Majestic	94
Crown Princess	88	Pacific Star	70	Starship Oceanic	97
Crystal Harmony	99	Queen Elizabeth 2	98	Starward	96
Cunard Countess	96	Regent Sea	87	Stella Solaris	94
Cunard Princess	89	Regent Star	74	Sun Viking	90
Daphne	86	Regent Sun	95	Sunward	95
Dawn Princess	86	Rotterdam	92	Triton	86
Discovery I	93	Royal Princess	93	Tropicale	93
Dolphin IV	96	Royal Viking Sun	86	Universe	92
Ecstasy	94	Sagafjord	89	Victoria	96
Emerald Seas	95	Scandinavian Dawn	87	Viking Princess	90
Enchanted Isle	86	Scandinavian Song	90	Viking Serenade	96
Enchanted Seas	96	Scandinavian Sun	89	Vistafjord	94
Fair Princess	87	Sea Bird	86	Westerdam	91
Fantasy	97	Sea Goddess I	97	Wind Spirit	96
Festivale	94	Sea Lion	91	Yorktown Clipper	92
Golden Odyssey	89				

Source: Center of Environmental Health and Injury Control, Miami, FL (reported in *Tampa Tribune*, May 17, 1992).

```
Stem-and-leaf of SanLevel   N = 91
Leaf Unit = 1.0


      1     6  6
      1     6
      2     7  0
      2     7
      3     7  4
      3     7
      3     7
      3     8
      5     8  23
      7     8  44
     18     8  66666677777
     31     8  8888999999999
     42     9  00000111111
    (15)    9  222222222333333
     34     9  4444444445555555
     18     9  66666666777777
      4     9  8999
```

3.8 Multinational corporations are firms with both domestic and foreign assets/investments. The foreign revenue (as a percentage of total revenue) generated by each of the top 20 U.S.-based multinationals is listed in the table.

Exxon	73.2	Procter & Gamble	39.9
IBM	58.9	Philip Morris	19.6
GM	26.6	Eastman Kodak	40.9
Mobil	64.7	Digital	54.1
Ford	33.2	GE	12.4
Citicorp	52.3	United Technologies	32.9
EI duPont	39.8	Amoco	26.1
Texaco	42.3	Hewlitt-Packard	53.3
ITT	43.3	Xerox	34.6
Dow Chemical	54.1	Chevron	20.5

Source: *Forbes,* July 23, 1990, pp. 362–363. Used by permission. © Forbes Inc., 1990.

a. Construct a stem-and-leaf display for the data.
b. Interpret the display obtained in part **a**.
c. What proportion of the 20 multinational firms generated at least 50% of their revenue from foreign investments/ sales?

3.9 How strong an effect do characteristics such as brand name or store name have on a buyer's perception of the quality of a product? Numerous studies have been conducted to investigate this phenomenon, but the results seem to vary depending on the method used to analyze the data, type of product, price, etc. An article in the *Journal of Marketing Research* (Aug. 1989) summarized the results of 15 studies that investigated the effect of brand name on product quality and 17 studies that examined the effect of store name on quality. In all studies (the experimental units), an effect size index was computed. The index ranges from 0 to 1.00; values closer to 0 indicate small effects and values near 1 indicate the presence of large effects. Stem-and-leaf displays of the effect size index for the two groups of studies are shown here. Compare and contrast the two displays. Which variable, brand name or store name, seems to have the stronger effect on perceived quality? Explain.

BRAND NAME 15 Studies		STORE NAME 17 Studies	
STEM	LEAF	STEM	LEAF
.6	0	.6	
.5	7	.5	
.4		.4	3 4
.3	4	.3	
.2	5 5	.2	
.1	0 1 1 2 4	.1	2
.0	3 3 5 5 7	.0	0 0 0 1 1 2 2 3 3 4 6 7 8 8

Source: Rao, A. R., and Monroe, K. B. "The Effect of Price, Brand Name, and Store Name on Buyers' Perceptions of Product Quality: An Integrative Review." *Journal of Marketing Research,* Vol. 26, Aug. 1989, p. 354 (Table 2). Reprinted with permission from *Journal of Marketing Research,* published by the American Marketing Association, Chicago, IL.

3.10 Construct a stem-and-leaf display for the CEO salary data given in Problem 3.3. Compare your display to the MINITAB dot plot in Problem 3.3.

3.11 Refer to the data given in Problem 3.5 on the top 25 graduate business schools. MINITAB stem-and-leaf displays for each of the five quantitative variables measured are shown below. Interpret the results.

```
Stem-and-leaf of Score      N = 25
Leaf Unit = 1.0

    4     6  7788
    7     7  134
   (6)    7  666788
   12     8  14
   10     8  555679
    4     9  12
    2     9  7
    1    10  0


Stem-and-leaf of Tuition    N = 25
Leaf Unit = 1000

    1     0  3
    2     0  5
    5     0  677
    7     0  88
    8     1  1
    8     1
   (5)    1  44455
   12     1  666666666667


Stem-and-leaf of GMAT       N = 25
Leaf Unit = 1.0

    2    59  35
    5    60  055
    9    61  0027
   11    62  05
   (6)   63  000245
    8    64  004489
    2    65  0
    1    66  5
```

```
Stem-and-leaf of AccRate    N = 25
Leaf Unit = 1.0

    1     1  0
    2     1  3
    5     1  455
    5     1
    7     1  89
    9     2  01
   11     2  23
   12     2  4
   (1)    2  6
   12     2  889
    9     3  0111
    5     3  23
    3     3  55
    1     3  7


Stem-and-leaf of Salary     N = 25
Leaf Unit = 1000

    4     4  2333
    7     4  445
    7     4
    8     4  9
   (5)    5  00011
   12     5  2233
    8     5  4455
    4     5  7
    3     5  9
    2     6  0
    1     6  3
```

HISTOGRAMS

3.3 A third way of visually portraying the distribution of a quantitative data set is to construct a **histogram**. Histograms (or **relative frequency distributions**) are similar to the bar graphs of Chapter 2 except that the classes represent intervals of values of the quantitative data. Although dot plots and stem-and-leaf displays are well-suited for small data sets, histograms are better for the description of large data sets, and they permit greater flexibility in the choice of the classes.

To illustrate, consider a sample of 50 of the 1,795 recent University of Florida graduates. The starting salaries for these 50 graduates are shown in Table 3.3.

The first step in constructing the histogram is to define the **class intervals** (categories) into which the data will fall. Note that the smallest and largest starting salaries in the data set are $9,000 and $41,900, respectively. Since we want the smallest salary to fall within the lowest class interval and the largest salary to fall within the highest class interval, the class intervals must span starting salaries ranging from $9,000 to $41,900.

TABLE 3.3
Starting Salaries for 50 University of Florida Graduates

$28,000	$18,600	$30,400	$12,200	$13,700
23,200	24,100	28,300	18,400	36,900
20,800	18,400	15,400	28,900	27,400
13,300	22,400	30,700	21,200	21,100
32,600	29,400	20,100	24,700	31,100
24,600	34,700	20,800	19,400	14,800
18,700	41,900	23,200	24,700	38,500
9,000	34,600	26,200	24,300	18,100
19,500	18,500	23,600	22,900	18,000
18,400	35,500	26,700	11,200	26,300

Source: Career Resource Center, University of Florida.

The second step is to choose the **class interval width**, and this will depend on how many intervals we want to use to span the starting salary range. The starting salary range is equal to

$$\text{Range} = \text{Largest measurement} - \text{Smallest measurement}$$
$$= \$41,900 - \$9,000 = \$32,900$$

Suppose we choose to use 11 class intervals. Then the class interval width should approximately equal

$$\text{Class interval width} \approx \frac{\text{Range}}{\text{Number of class intervals}}$$
$$\approx \frac{32,900}{11} \approx 2,990.9 \approx \$3,000$$

Start the first class slightly below the smallest observation ($9,000), and choose the starting point so that no observation can fall on a class boundary. Since starting salaries are recorded to the nearest hundred dollars, we can do this simply by choosing the lower class boundary of the first class interval to be $8,950.* Then the class intervals will be $8,950 to $11,950, $11,950 to $14,950, and so on. The 11 class intervals are shown in the second column of Table 3.4.

The third step in constructing a histogram is to obtain each class frequency. This is done by examining each starting salary in Table 3.3 and recording by tally (as shown in the third column of Table 3.4) the class in which it falls. The tally for

---

* We could just as easily have chosen $8,955, $8,975, $8,990, or any one of many other points below and near $9,000.

TABLE 3.4
Tabulation of Data for the Starting Salaries of Table 3.3

CLASS	CLASS INTERVAL	TALLY	CLASS FREQUENCY	CLASS RELATIVE FREQUENCY
1	8,950–11,950	||	2	.04
2	11,950–14,950	||||	4	.08
3	14,950–17,950	|	1	.02
4	17,950–20,950	⫴⫴ |||	13	.26
5	20,950–23,950	⫴ ||	7	.14
6	23,950–26,950	⫴ |||	8	.16
7	26,950–29,950	⫴	5	.10
8	29,950–32,950	||||	4	.08
9	32,950–35,950	|||	3	.06
10	35,950–38,950	||	2	.04
11	38,950–41,950	|	1	.02
		Totals	50	1.00

each class gives the class frequency shown in column 4 of Table 3.4. Finally, we calculate the class relative frequency as

$$\text{Class relative frequency} = \frac{\text{Class frequency}}{\text{Total number of observations}}$$
$$= \frac{\text{Class frequency}}{50}$$

These values are shown in the fifth column of Table 3.4.

The final step is to draw the graph. Mark the class intervals along a horizontal line, as shown in Figure 3.5. Then construct over each class interval a bar with the height proportional to either the class frequency (a **frequency histogram**) or the class relative frequency (a **relative frequency histogram**). Figure 3.5 is a relative frequency histogram since the bars are proportional to the class relative frequency.

How do we interpret the histogram in Figure 3.5? Remember, a histogram (like a dot plot and stem-and-leaf display) conveys a visual picture of the distribution of the data. In particular, the histogram will identify the range of values where most of the data fall. You can see from Figure 3.5 that most of the 50 starting salaries fall between $17,950 and $32,950. The five classes (bars) associated with this interval have relative frequencies of .26, .14, .16, .10, and .08, respectively. The sum of these relative frequencies is .74. Thus, 74% of the graduates in the sample had starting salaries between $17,950 and $32,950.

Note also that none of the starting salaries was less than $8,950, but several high salaries caused the distribution to tail out to the right. We say that such a distribution is **rightward skewed** (or **positively skewed**). Similarly a **leftward** (or **negatively**) **skewed** distribution has a histogram that tails out to the left because of several unusually small values. Illustrations of rightward and leftward skewed distributions, as well as a **nonskewed (symmetric)** distribution, are shown in Figure 3.6.

FIGURE 3.5
Relative Frequency Histogram for
the Data of Table 3.3

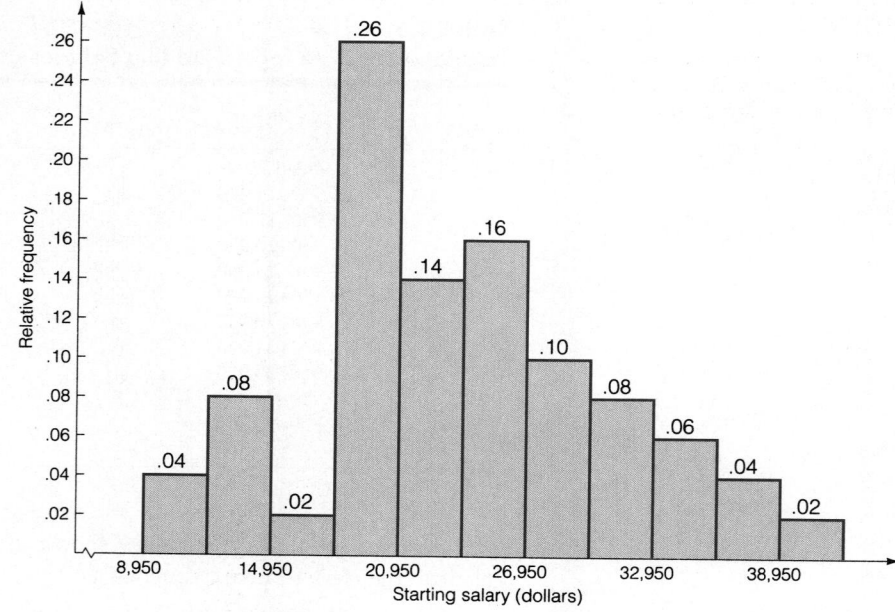

FIGURE 3.6
Skewed and Symmetric Distributions

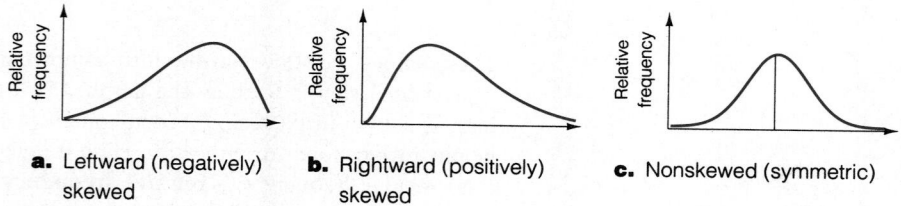

a. Leftward (negatively) skewed   b. Rightward (positively) skewed   c. Nonskewed (symmetric)

EXAMPLE 3.1 Figure 3.7 is a computer-generated (SAS) relative frequency histogram of the starting salaries for all recent University of Florida graduates who responded to the Career Resource Center salary questionnaire (1,795 graduates).*

a. Interpret the graph.
b. Visually estimate the proportion of graduates with starting salaries that lie between $18,000 and $38,000.

---

* The SAS commands (as well as SPSS and MINITAB) for generating histograms are provided in Computer Lab 1, following Section 3.4.

FIGURE 3.7

A Relative Frequency Distribution for the 1,795 Starting Salaries of University of Florida Graduates

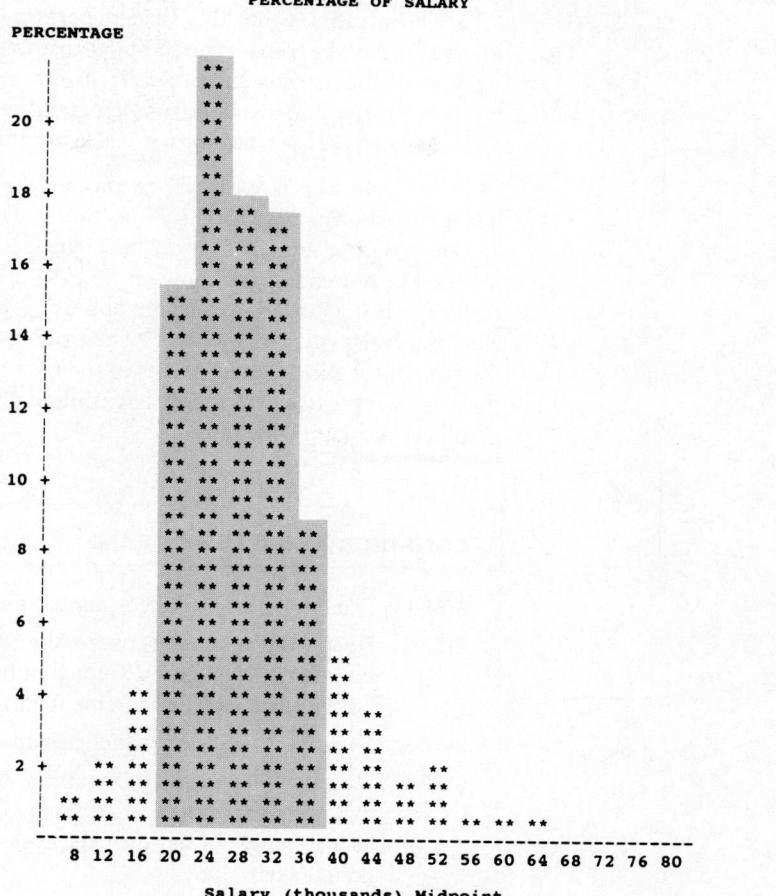

Solution

a. Note that the classes are marked off in intervals of $4,000 along the horizontal axis of the SAS histogram in Figure 3.7, with the midpoint (rather than the lower and upper boundaries) of each interval shown.* You can see that the starting salaries tend to pile up near $24,000—that is, the class from $22,000 to $26,000 has the greatest relative frequency (or percentage). Since the histogram tails out to the right, the data are rightward skewed.

---

* Note that the SAS-generated relative frequency histogram leaves gaps between the bars. However, the resulting figure should not be confused with a bar graph for qualitative data. When drawn by hand, the bars of a histogram are adjacent, with no gaps. (See Figure 3.5.)

3.3 HISTOGRAMS

73

b. The bars that fall in the interval from $18,000 to $38,000 are shaded in Figure 3.7. You can see that this shaded portion represents approximately .80 of the total area of the bars for the complete distribution. This tells us that approximately 80% of the starting salaries were in the interval from $18,000 to $38,000. A more precise (but less rapid) answer could be obtained by recording and summing the relative frequencies for the classes in the interval from $18,000 to $38,000.

[*Note:* No bars appear above the last four classes of the relative frequency histogram shown in Figure 3.7 (ie, the classes 66,000–70,000; 70,000–74,000; 74,000–78,000; and 78,000–82,000). In fact, there are starting salaries in these ranges, but not enough to show on the SAS printout due to spacing limitations. To make the histogram more visually appealing, we may choose to represent the last class interval as "Over $66,000." Then the bar over this interval would represent the sum of the relative frequencies of the four classes mentioned above. By allowing the classes at the two extremes to have different widths, we obtain a more informative graphical display of the data.]

CONSTRUCTING A HISTOGRAM

STEP 1   Examine the data to determine the smallest and largest measurements.

STEP 2   Divide the interval between the smallest and largest measurements into between 5 and 20 equal subintervals called **classes** (see next box) so that each measurement falls into one and only one subinterval.

STEP 3   Compute the class frequencies and/or the class relative frequencies.

STEP 4   Using a vertical axis of about three-quarters the length of the horizontal axis, plot each relative frequency (or frequency) on the vertical axis as a rectangle or bar over the corresponding subinterval on the horizontal axis.

RULE OF THUMB FOR DETERMINING THE NUMBER OF CLASSES IN A HISTOGRAM

NUMBER OF OBSERVATIONS IN A DATA SET	NUMBER OF CLASSES
Less than 25	5 or 6
25–50	7–14
More than 50	15–20

PROBLEMS

3.12   A study was conducted to evaluate the advertisement awareness and sales effectiveness of advertising campaigns for 18 confectionery brands (*Journal of the Market Research Society*, Jan. 1986). For each brand, an ad awareness index (maximum = 100) was determined from a consumer survey, while a sales effectiveness index (maximum = 100) was estimated from market shares. The frequency histograms shown here were used to summarize the data.

Distribution of 18 Campaigns by Ad Awareness (Maximum = 100)

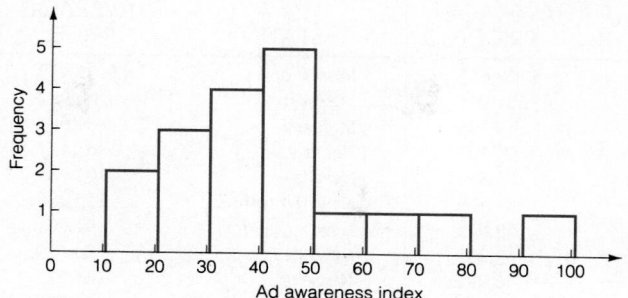

Distribution of 18 Campaigns by Sales Effectiveness (Maximum = 100)

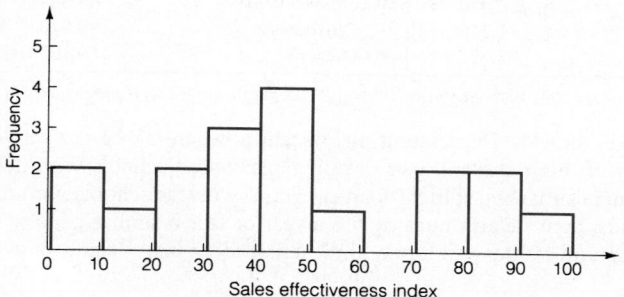

Source: Broadbent, S., and Colman, S. "Advertising Effectiveness: Across Brands." *Journal of the Market Research Society*, Vol. 28, No. 1, 1986, pp. 15–23.

a. How many of the 18 brands had an ad awareness index of 40 or less?
b. How many of the 18 brands had a sales effectiveness index of 70 or more?
c. Use the information provided by the frequency histogram to construct a relative frequency histogram for the 18 ad awareness indexes. Interpret the graph.
d. Use the information provided by the frequency histogram to construct a relative frequency histogram for the 18 sales effectiveness indexes.

3.13   Century 21 Real Estate compiled data on more than 600,000 sales of single-family homes in the United States in 1990. Based on the average price, the realty company found that Hawaii has the most expensive homes (average price of $281,042) and North Dakota is the least expensive (average price of $51,334). The average prices of single-family homes for all 50 states are listed in the table.

a. Construct a histogram for the data.
b. Are the data on average prices skewed right, skewed left, or symmetric?

STATE	1990 AVERAGE PRICE	STATE	1990 AVERAGE PRICE	STATE	1990 AVERAGE PRICE
Alabama	$ 64,734	Arkansas	$ 53,750	Connecticut	$152,157
Alaska	86,215	California	166,423	Delaware	95,504
Arizona	82,514	Colorado	70,879	Florida	77,785

(continued)

Data for Problem 3.13 (Continued)

STATE	1990 AVERAGE PRICE	STATE	1990 AVERAGE PRICE	STATE	1990 AVERAGE PRICE
Georgia	$ 78,655	Mississippi	$ 59,413	Pennsylvania	$ 88,510
Hawaii	281,042	Missouri	60,992	Rhode Island	127,628
Idaho	59,328	Montana	60,607	South Carolina	72,614
Illinois	94,707	Nebraska	61,157	South Dakota	54,346
Indiana	73,593	Nevada	101,784	Tennessee	63,953
Iowa	51,478	New Hampshire	115,288	Texas	65,638
Kansas	58,075	New Jersey	141,701	Utah	60,122
Kentucky	64,205	New Mexico	73,449	Vermont	96,538
Louisiana	56,991	New York	124,245	Virginia	98,708
Maine	90,972	North Carolina	77,077	Washington	86,667
Maryland	114,074	North Dakota	51,334	West Virginia	58,667
Massachusetts	168,840	Ohio	68,569	Wisconsin	64,666
Michigan	71,246	Oklahoma	49,828	Wyoming	62,728
Minnesota	67,357	Oregon	69,133		

Source: USA Today, Mar. 22, 1991. Copyright 1991, USA TODAY. Reprinted with permission.

3.14   Beginning in 1991, the U.S. Department of Education began taking corrective and punitive actions against colleges and universities with high student-loan default rates. Those schools with default rates above 60% face suspension from the government's massive student-loan program, whereas schools with default rates between 40% and 60% are mandated to reduce their default rates by 5% a year or face a similar penalty (*Tampa Tribune,* June 21, 1989). A list of 66 colleges and universities in Florida and their student-loan default rates is provided in the table.

COLLEGE/UNIVERSITY	DEFAULT RATE (%)	COLLEGE/UNIVERSITY	DEFAULT RATE (%)
Florida College of Business	76.2	Pasco-Hernando CC	13.5
Ft. Lauderdale College	48.5	Orlando College	13.5
Florida Career College	48.3	Jones College	13.1
United College	46.8	Webber College	11.8
Florida Memorial College	46.2	Warner Southern College	11.8
Bethune Cookman College	43.0	Central Florida CC	11.8
Edward Waters College	38.3	Indian River CC	11.8
Florida College of Medical and Dental Careers	32.6	St. Petersburg CC	11.3
International Fine Arts College	26.5	Valencia CC	10.8
Tampa College	23.9	Florida Southern College	10.3
Miami Technical College	23.3	Lake City CC	9.8
Tallahassee CC	20.6	Brevard CC	9.4
Charron Williams College	20.2	College of Boca Raton	9.1
Florida CC	19.1	Florida International University	8.7
Miami-Dade CC	19.0	Santa Fe CC	8.6
Broward CC	18.4	Edison CC	8.5
Daytona Beach CC	16.9	Palm Beach Junior College	8.0
Lake Sumter CC	16.7	Eckerd College	7.9
Florida Technical College	16.6	University of Tampa	7.6
Florida A&M University	15.8	Lakeland College of Business	7.2
Prospect Hall College	15.1	Pensacola Junior College	6.8
Hillsborough CC	14.4	University of Miami	6.7

(*continued*)

M = 1.5 Max 76.2 $\bar{X}$ = 14.07   STD = ~~36~~ 14.14

COLLEGE/UNIVERSITY	DEFAULT RATE (%)	COLLEGE/UNIVERSITY	DEFAULT RATE (%)
Florida Institute of Technology	6.7	Southern College	5.3
University of West Florida	6.3	Flagler College	4.7
Palm Beach Atlantic College	6.0	Florida Atlantic University	4.4
University of Central Florida	5.7	University of South Florida	4.2
Seminole CC	5.6	Manatee Junior College	4.1
Polk CC	5.6	Florida State University	4.0
Phillips Junior College	5.6	University of North Florida	3.9
Nova University	5.5	Barry University	3.1
Rollins College	5.5	University of Florida	3.1
St. Leo College	5.5	Stetson University	2.9
Gulf Coast CC	5.4	Jacksonville University	1.5

2 x STD = 28.28   3 x STD = 42.42

a. Construct a relative frequency histogram for the data using 12 classes to span the range.

b. Repeat part **a**, but use only three classes to span the range. Compare the result with the relative frequency distribution you constructed in part **a**. Which is more informative? Why does an inadequate number of classes limit the information conveyed by the relative frequency distribution?

c. Repeat part **a**, but use 25 classes. Comment on the information provided by this graph as compared with that of part **a**.

d. Refer to the histogram constructed in part **a**. Estimate the proportion of Florida colleges and universities with a default rate of 40% or higher. Shade the bars in the histogram corresponding to this area.

e. Note that Florida College of Business has a default rate nearly 30% higher than the next highest rate. Omit the value for Florida College of Business from the data set and reconstruct the histogram.

f. Compare the histograms constructed in parts **a** and **e**. Which graph is more informative? Explain.

3.15 The SAS relative frequency histogram on p. 78 describes the 8,313 sale prices (in thousands of dollars) of residential properties sold in Tampa, Florida, in 1990.

a. Are the data skewed? If so, in what direction?

b. Visually estimate the proportion of the total number of sale prices that lie between $42,500 and $102,500.

3.16 A study of merit raises at 16 U.S. corporations was conducted in an effort to discover the extent to which merit pay policies for employees are actually tied to performance (*Personnel Journal*, Mar. 1986). One phase of the study focused on the distribution of merit raises (measured as percentage increase in salary) awarded at the companies. The frequency histogram of the 3,990 merit increases awarded at one of the largest firms in the study is reproduced on p. 78.

a. Approximately how many of the firm's employees were awarded merit increases between 6% and 10%?

b. Approximately what proportion of the 3,990 merit increases were less than 5%?

c. Is the distribution skewed? If so, is it skewed right or left?

3.17 Are major colleges and universities lax in hiring minorities to fill top positions in their athletic programs? A *USA Today* survey of 62 division I schools found that only 12.5% of the jobs in the athletic departments were held by minorities (African Americans, Hispanics, Native Americans, and Asians). In contrast, the 1990 Census shows minorities represent 19.7% of the U.S. population (*USA Today*, Mar. 19, 1991). The results of the survey are reproduced in the table on p. 79. The 62 schools were selected based on the top 25 polls for men's and women's basketball during the 1989–1990 season and the final 1990 top 25 football poll. (Northwestern declined to respond, and Seton Hall did not supply figures.)

a. Do the data represent a sample or a population? Explain.

b. Describe the data on percentage of minority positions in the athletic departments of the 60 colleges and universities that responded to the survey using a graphical technique. Interpret the graph.

PERCENTAGE OF SALEPRIC

```
PERCENTAGE
    |                ***
    |                ***
20 +                ***
    |                ***
    |                ***
    |                ***
18 +                ***
    |                ***
    |                ***
16 +                ***
    |                ***
    |            *** *** ***
    |        *** *** *** ***
14 +        *** *** *** ***
    |        *** *** *** ***
    |        *** *** *** ***
    |        *** *** *** *** ***
12 +        *** *** *** *** ***
    |        *** *** *** *** ***
    |    *** *** *** *** *** ***
    |    *** *** *** *** *** ***
10 +    *** *** *** *** *** ***
    |    *** *** *** *** *** ***
    |    *** *** *** *** *** ***
 8 +    *** *** *** *** *** ***
    |    *** *** *** *** *** ***
    |    *** *** *** *** *** ***
    |    *** *** *** *** *** ***
 6 +    *** *** *** *** *** *** ***
    |    *** *** *** *** *** *** ***
    |    *** *** *** *** *** *** ***
    |    *** *** *** *** *** *** ***
 4 +    *** *** *** *** *** *** *** ***
    |    *** *** *** *** *** *** *** ***
    |    *** *** *** *** *** *** *** *** ***
    |    *** *** *** *** *** *** *** *** ***
 2 +    *** *** *** *** *** *** *** *** ***                                     ***
    |    *** *** *** *** *** *** *** *** *** *** ***                            ***
    |    *** *** *** *** *** *** *** *** *** *** *** ***                        ***
    |    *** *** *** *** *** *** *** *** *** *** *** *** *** *** *** *** *** *** ***
   ---------------------------------------------------------------------------------
        20  35  50  65  80  95 110 125 140 155 170 185 200 215 230 245 260 275
                             SALEPRIC MIDPOINT
```

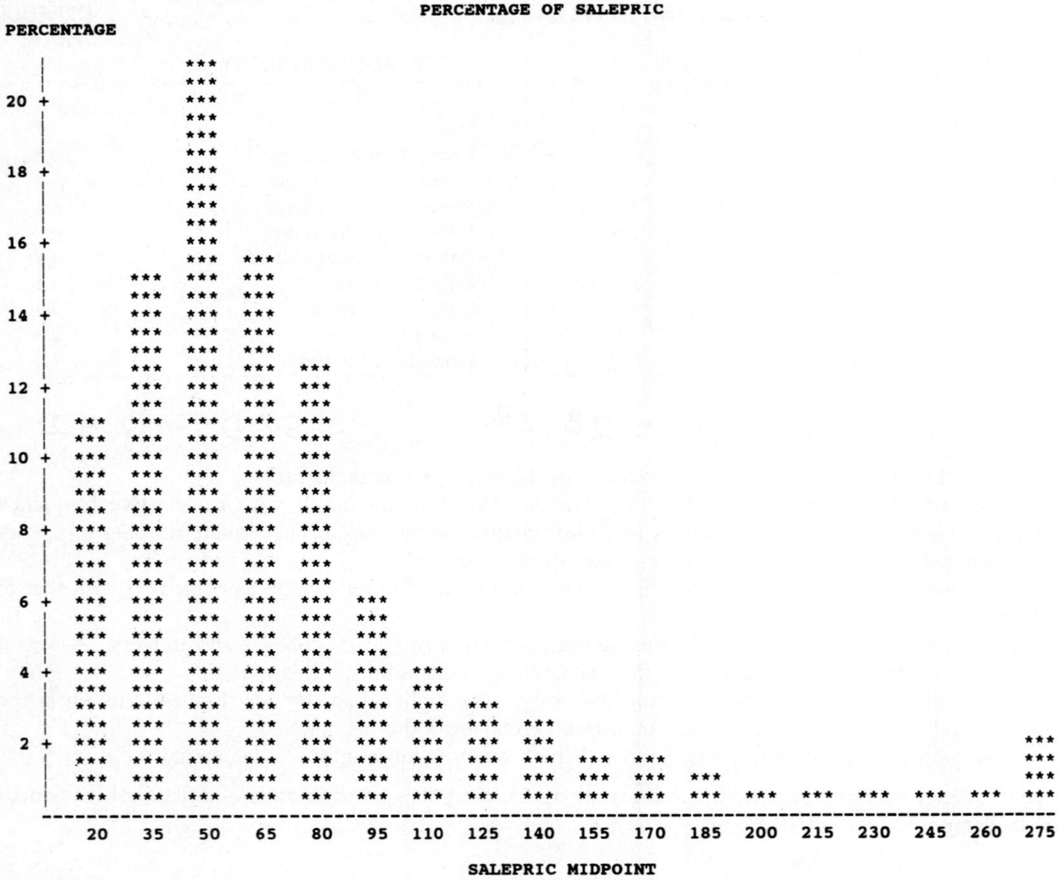

Frequency Histogram for
Problem 3.16

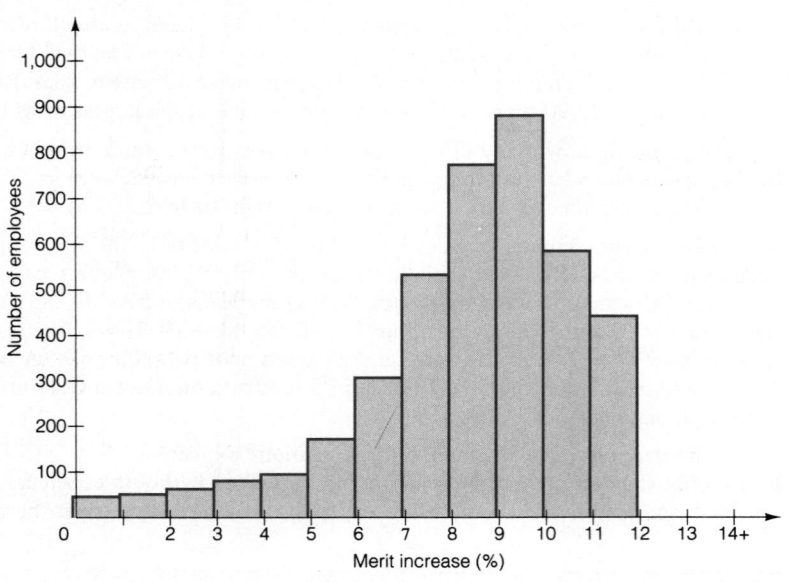

Data for Problem 3.17

SCHOOL	TOTAL POSITIONS	POSITIONS HELD BY MINORITY	PERCENT MINORITY	SCHOOL	TOTAL POSITIONS	POSITIONS HELD BY MINORITY	PERCENT MINORITY
Georgetown	30	8	26.7	Syracuse	52	6	11.5
Houston	43	11	25.6	Arkansas	44	5	11.4
Miami	55	14	25.5	Northern Illinois	53	6	11.3
Arizona	67	15	22.4	Alabama	54	6	11.1
Long Beach State	53	11	20.8	Western Kentucky	18	2	11.1
USC	65	13	20.0	University of	55	6	10.9
Pittsburgh	54	10	18.5	Nevada, Las Vegas			
Oklahoma State	34	6	17.6	Connecticut	37	4	10.8
Oklahoma	63	11	17.5	South Carolina	49	5	10.2
Washington	63	11	17.5	East Tennessee State	30	3	10.0
Southern Mississippi	35	6	17.1	Texas—El Paso	30	3	10.0
Stanford	71	12	16.9	Rutgers	42	4	9.5
Iowa	72	12	16.7	North Carolina State	44	4	9.1
Georgia Tech	52	8	15.4	Texas[a]	67	6	9.0
Michigan State	60	9	15.0	Michigan	58	5	8.6
Illinois	54	8	14.8	Penn State	82	7	8.5
Kentucky	54	8	14.8	St. John's	60	5	8.3
Ohio State	64	9	14.1	Nebraska	64	5	7.8
Colorado	43	6	14.0	Mississippi State	52	4	7.7
LSU	59	8	13.6	Providence	13	1	7.7
Purdue	53	7	13.2	Mississippi	40	3	7.5
New Mexico State	38	5	13.2	Florida State	53	4	7.5
UCLA	84	11	13.1	Indiana	57	4	7.0
Clemson	48	6	12.5	Tennessee[a]	73	5	6.8
North Carolina	57	7	12.3	Duke	45	3	6.7
Kansas	49	6	12.2	Virginia	60	4	6.7
Utah	33	4	12.1	BYU	51	3	5.9
Louisville	34	4	11.8	Princeton	44	2	4.5
Georgia	60	7	11.7	Notre Dame	47	2	4.3
Florida	61	7	11.5	Stephen F. Austin	27	1	3.7
Louisiana Tech	26	3	11.5				

Source: USA Today, Mar. 19, 1991. Copyright 1991, USA TODAY. Reprinted with permission.

[a] Numbers combined from separate men's/women's athletic programs.

SEQUENCE PLOTS

3.4

The graphical methods illustrated in the previous three sections—dot plots, stem-and-leaf displays, and histograms—are useful for describing quantitative data distributions. These methods are usually employed in enumerative studies, where the objective is to describe population (or sample) data. Analytic studies, on the other hand, involve collecting process data sequentially over time. A basic graphical tool for describing process data is a **sequence plot**. Sequence plots are simple two-dimensional graphs with time displayed on the horizontal axis and some numeric quantity (a measure of quality or some other process variable) plotted on the vertical axis.

To illustrate, consider the grapefruit juice sales data introduced in Example 1.2. The data, in millions of gallons, are reproduced in Table 3.5. A sequence plot for the data, with annual sales on the vertical axis and time (year) on the horizontal

FIGURE 3.8
Sequence Plot of Annual Grapefruit
Juice Sales

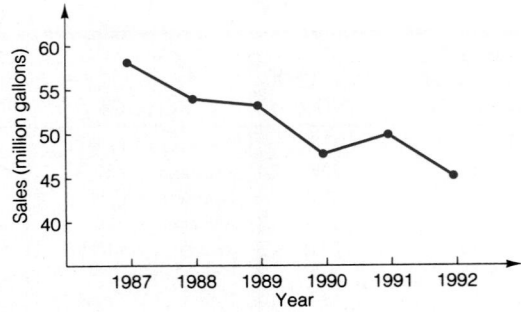

TABLE 3.5
Annual Sales of Grapefruit Juice

YEAR	GALLONS Millions
1987	58.2
1988	54.1
1989	53.4
1990	48.0
1991	50.2
1992	45.6

Source: Florida Citrus Department.

axis, is shown in Figure 3.8. As an option, the points (dots) on the plot are connected by lines to highlight the time trend.

Figure 3.8 shows a clear downward trend in annual grapefruit juice sales from 1987 to 1992, leading us to conclude that grapefruit juice sales in 1993 will likely be less than 45.6 million gallons, the 1992 sales value. (We will learn how to attach a measure of reliability to such a forecast in Chapter 12.)

In addition to predicting future behavior of a process, sequence plots can help us detect changes or problems in the process. The next example illustrates this point.

EXAMPLE 3.2   Consider a manufacturing process in which coil springs are produced on an assembly line. According to specifications, the springs should lengthen between .3 and .7 millimeter (mm) for each gram of pull. To monitor the process, each day a quality control engineer records the elongation for 30 springs randomly selected and tested in order of manufacture. The data for one particular day are listed in Table 3.6.

a. Display the data with a sequence plot.
b. Interpret the results.

TABLE 3.6
Coil Spring Elongation Data for One Day's Production

SPRING NUMBER	ELONGATION READING mm	SPRING NUMBER	ELONGATION READING mm	SPRING NUMBER	ELONGATION READING mm
1	.65	11	.61	21	.50
2	.68	12	.57	22	.47
3	.60	13	.50	23	.46
4	.55	14	.53	24	.42
5	.66	15	.49	25	.41
6	.58	16	.52	26	.43
7	.57	17	.45	27	.38
8	.52	18	.48	28	.40
9	.51	19	.56	29	.32
10	.53	20	.54	30	.30

FIGURE 3.9

Sequence Plot for the Data of Table 3.6

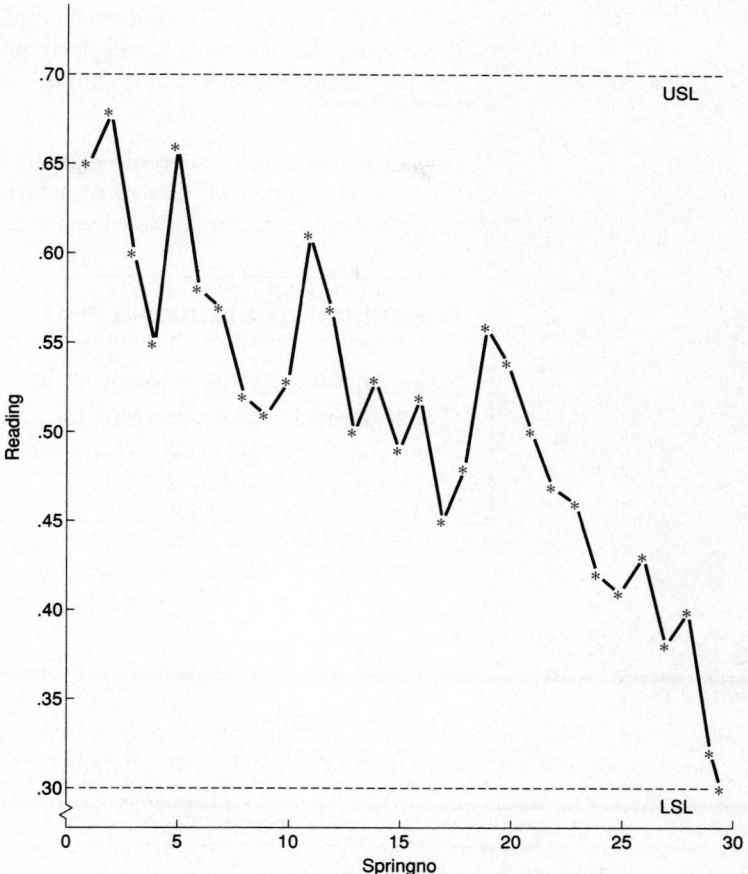

Solution

a. Since the coil springs are selected and tested in order of manufacture, the spring number represents the time variable to be plotted on the horizontal axis of the sequence plot and the elongation reading is the process variable on the vertical axis. A computer-generated (SAS) sequence plot for the data is shown in Figure 3.9.*

b. The specification limits of .3 and .7 mm are also shown on the sequence plot. Note that all 30 elongation readings fall within these limits, tempting one to conclude that no problems exist with the process. However, the sequence plot exhibits a strong downward trend in elongation readings. Coils manufactured early in the day have higher readings than coils manufactured later in the day. In fact, the latest readings border on the lower specification limit of .3 mm.

---

* The computer commands (SAS, SPSS, and MINITAB) for generating sequence plots are provided in Computer Lab 1.

This time trend signals a potential problem with the manufacturing process.*
If not corrected, the process will likely produce coil springs in the future that
will fall outside the specification limits.

Despite their simplicity, sequence plots are powerful graphical tools for exploring
and describing quantitative data in an analytic type of study. Sequence plots will
form the basis of more sophisticated analyses in Chapters 9 and 12.

CONSTRUCTING A SEQUENCE PLOT

STEP 1   Form a horizontal axis with time as the variable.

STEP 2   Form a vertical axis using the numerical process variable of interest.

STEP 3   Plot the data points on the two-dimensional graph. As an option,
connect the dots with lines.

PROBLEMS

3.18   The prices of gold (dollars per ounce) from 1971 to 1990 are shown in the table. Use a sequence plot to graphically
display the data. Do you detect any trends in the gold prices over time?

YEAR	PRICE	YEAR	PRICE	YEAR	PRICE
1971	$ 41.25	1978	$193.50	1985	$317.30
1972	58.61	1979	307.80	1986	367.87
1973	97.81	1980	606.01	1987	408.91
1974	159.70	1981	450.63	1988	436.93
1975	161.40	1982	374.18	1989	381.28
1976	124.80	1983	449.03	1990	384.07
1977	148.30	1984	360.29		

Source: *Survey of Current Business*, U.S. Department of Commerce.

3.19   A rheostat knob, produced by molding plastic, contains a metal insert. The fit of this knob into its assembly is
determined by the distance from the back of the knob to the far side of a pin hole. To monitor the molding operation,
one knob from each hour's production was randomly sampled and the dimension measured on each. The table gives
the distance measurements (in inches) for the first 27 hours the process was in operation.

---

* In the actual study on which this example is based, an assembly line operator noticed the trend and
found the source of the trouble to be a thermocouple that permitted the temperature to drift during the
annealing of the springs. (See Tanur, J., et al., Eds. *Statistics: A Guide to the Unknown*. San Francisco:
Holden-Day, 1978, pp. 279–281.)

HOUR	DISTANCE MEASUREMENT	HOUR	DISTANCE MEASUREMENT	HOUR	DISTANCE MEASUREMENT
1	.140	10	.142	19	.142
2	.138	11	.137	20	.136
3	.139	12	.137	21	.142
4	.143	13	.142	22	.139
5	.142	14	.137	23	.140
6	.136	15	.144	24	.134
7	.142	16	.140	25	.138
8	.143	17	.137	26	.140
9	.141	18	.137	27	.145

a. Use a sequence plot to graphically display the process data.

b. Specifications require that the knob distances fall between .135 and .145 inch. Does the process appear to be producing rheostat knobs that meet specifications?

3.20 Ameritech is one of the world's largest providers of full-service telephone communications. The data in the table are the total number of telephone lines (residential and business) serviced by Ameritech from 1984 to 1992.

a. Describe the data in the table with a graph.

b. Connect the points on the graph from part **a**. Do you detect a trend in the annual number of telephone lines serviced by Ameritech?

YEAR	NUMBER OF LINES Millions	YEAR	NUMBER OF LINES Millions
1984	14.3	1989	16.0
1985	14.6	1990	16.4
1986	14.8	1991	16.6
1987	15.2	1992	17.0
1988	15.5		

Source: Ameritech Annual Report, 1992.

3.21 Each month the quality control engineer at a bottle manufacturing company randomly samples one finished bottle from the production process at 20 points in time (days) and records the weight of each bottle (in ounces). The data for last month's inspection are provided in the table.

a. Describe the data in the table with a graph.

b. Do you detect any trends in the bottle weights over time?

c. The manufacturer requires that the bottle weights deviate no more than .5 ounce from the machine setting weight of 6.0 ounces. Check to see whether the bottles sampled meet these specifications.

DAY	BOTTLE WEIGHT	DAY	BOTTLE WEIGHT	DAY	BOTTLE WEIGHT	DAY	BOTTLE WEIGHT
1	5.6	6	6.0	11	6.2	16	5.8
2	5.7	7	5.8	12	5.9	17	6.1
3	6.1	8	5.8	13	5.2	18	6.2
4	6.3	9	6.4	14	6.0	19	5.3
5	5.2	10	6.0	15	6.3	20	6.0

DESCRIBING QUANTITATIVE DATA GRAPHICALLY

In this section we give the SAS, SPSS, and MINITAB commands for producing graphical descriptions of quantitative data. In particular, the programs will produce (1) a dot plot (if available), (2) a stem-and-leaf display, (3) a box plot,* and (4) a histogram for the 50 starting salaries in Table 3.3; and (5) a sequence plot for the coil spring data in Table 3.6.

[*Note:* As in all Computer Lab sections, the commands given below are (unless otherwise noted) appropriate for both mainframe and personal computers. However, programs run on mainframe computers require JCL instructions. See your instructor for the appropriate JCL commands to use at your computing center.]

SAS

Command
Line

```
 1    DATA GRADS;                         ⎫ Data entry instructions
 2    INPUT SALARY @@;                    ⎭
 3    CARDS;
      28000  18600  30400  12200  13700  ⎫
      23200  24100  28300  18400  36900  ⎪
        .      .      .      .      .     ⎬ Input data values
        .      .      .      .      .     ⎪ (5 observations per line)
        .      .      .      .      .     ⎪
      18400  35500  26700  11200  26300  ⎭
 4    PROC CHART;                         ⎫ Relative frequency histogram
 5    VBAR SALARY/TYPE=PERCENT;           ⎭
 6    PROC UNIVARIATE PLOT;               ⎫ Stem-and-leaf display, box plot
 7    VAR SALARY;                         ⎭
 8    DATA COILS;                         ⎫ Data entry instructions
 9    INPUT SPRINGNO READING;             ⎭
10    CARDS;
       1 .65                              ⎫
       2 .68                              ⎪
       .  .                               ⎬ Input data values
       .  .                               ⎪ (1 observation per line)
       .  .                               ⎪
      30 .30                              ⎭
11    PROC PLOT;                          ⎫ Sequence plot
12    PLOT READING*SPRINGNO;              ⎭
```

---

* Box plots are described in Section 3.9.

COMMAND 2   The symbol @@ placed at the end of the INPUT statement allows multiple observations of the variable SALARY to be entered on each data line as long as the values are separated by blank spaces.

COMMANDS 4–5   The CHART procedure produces relative frequency and frequency histograms for quantitative data. The key word VBAR followed by the variable name (eg, SALARY) produces a frequency histogram. Relative frequency histograms are produced by adding the option TYPE=PERCENT. SAS will automatically select suitable class intervals for the histogram.*

COMMANDS 6–7   The UNIVARIATE procedure with the PLOT option will produce a stem-and-leaf display and a box plot for the variable specified in the VAR statement (eg, SALARY). [For large data sets (approximately 50 or more observations), a horizontal bar chart is produced rather than a stem-and-leaf display.]

COMMANDS 11–12   The PLOT procedure produces two-dimensional plots. The two variables plotted are specified on the PLOT command line, separated by an asterisk. (The variable to the left of the asterisk is plotted on the vertical axis; the variable to the right on the horizontal axis.) When a time-ordered variable (eg, SPRINGNO) is used on the horizontal axis, a sequence plot is generated.

GENERAL   Dot plots are not available in SAS.

NOTE   The output for this SAS program is displayed in Figure 3.10 (p. 88).

SPSS

Command Line		
1	`DATA LIST FREE/SALARY.`}	Data entry instruction
2	`BEGIN DATA.`	

```
      28000   18600   30400   12200   13700
      23200   24100   28300   18400   36900
        .       .       .       .       .
        .       .       .       .       .
      18400   35500   26700   11200   26300
```
Input data values (5 observations per line)

3	`END DATA.`	
4	`EXAMINE VARIABLES=SALARY.`}	Stem-and-leaf display/box plot
5	`FREQUENCIES VARIABLES=SALARY/`	
6	`          HISTOGRAM=PERCENT.`	Relative frequency histogram

(continued)

---

* The MIDPOINTS option allows the user to select the class intervals. Consult the SAS references for details on how to use the MIDPOINTS option in PROC CHART.

```
7    DATA LIST FREE/SPRINGNO READING.⎤
8    BEGIN DATA.                      ⎦ Data entry instructions
       1 .65⎤
       2 .68⎥
       .  . ⎬ Input data values
       .  . ⎥ (1 observation per line)
       .  . ⎥
      30 .30⎦
9    END DATA.
10   PLOT PLOT=READING WITH SPRINGNO.} Sequence plot
```

COMMAND 4   The EXAMINE command produces a stem-and-leaf display and a box plot for the variable specified (eg, SALARY).

COMMANDS 5–6   The FREQUENCIES command produces histograms for quantitative variables. The subcommand HISTOGRAM will produce a frequency histogram for the variable specified in the VARIABLES subcommand (eg, SALARY). Relative frequency histograms are generated by adding the PERCENT option to the HISTOGRAM subcommand. SPSS will automatically select suitable class intervals for the histogram.*

COMMAND 10   The PLOT command produces two-dimensional plots. The variables to be plotted are given in the PLOT subcommand. The variable on the vertical axis (eg, READING) is specified to the left of the key word WITH; the variable on the horizontal axis (eg, SPRINGNO) is specified to the right. Since the horizontal axis variable is time-ordered, a sequence plot is generated.

GENERAL   Dot plots are not available in SPSS.

NOTE   The output for this SPSS program is displayed in Figure 3.11 (p. 89).

MINITAB

Command
Line
```
1    SET C1  Data entry instruction
     28000  18600  30400  12200  13700⎤
     23200  24100  28300  18400  36900⎥
       .      .      .      .      .  ⎬ Input data values
       .      .      .      .      .  ⎥ (5 observations per line)
       .      .      .      .      .  ⎥
     18400  35500  26700  11200  26300⎦
```

* The INCREMENT option allows the user to select the width of the class intervals. Consult the SPSS references for details on how to use the INCREMENT option in FREQUENCIES.

```
Command
  Line
    2     NAME C1='SALARY'
    3     DOTPLOT C1    Dot plot
    4     HISTOGRAM C1    Relative frequency histogram
    5     STEM-AND-LEAF C1    Stem-and-leaf display
    6     BOXPLOT C1    Box plot
    7     READ C1 C2    Data entry instruction
          1  .65 ⎞
          2  .68 ⎟
          .   . ⎬  Input data values
          .   . ⎟  (1 observation per line)
          .   . ⎟
         30  .30 ⎠
    8     NAME C1='SPRINGNO' C2='READING'
    9     PLOT C2 C1    Sequence plot
```

COMMAND 1   The SET command allows multiple observations of the column specified to be entered on the input data lines, as long as the numeric values are separated by blanks.

COMMAND 3   The DOTPLOT command produces a dot plot for the column (variable) specified.

COMMAND 4   The HISTOGRAM command will generate horizontal frequency histograms for qualitative data. MINITAB will automatically select suitable class intervals for the frequency histogram of the column (variable) specified.*

COMMANDS 5–6   The STEM-AND-LEAF and BOXPLOT commands produce a stem-and-leaf display and a box plot, respectively, for the column (variable) specified.

COMMAND 9   The PLOT command produces two-dimensional plots for the two columns (variables) listed. The first variable is plotted on the vertical axis; the second on the horizontal axis. When the variable on the horizontal axis is time-ordered, a sequence plot is generated.

NOTE   The output for this MINITAB program is displayed in Figure 3.12 (p. 91).

---

* The optional commands INCREMENT and START allow the user to select the class intervals. Consult the MINITAB references for details on how to use these HISTOGRAM options.

FIGURE 3.10
Output from SAS Program

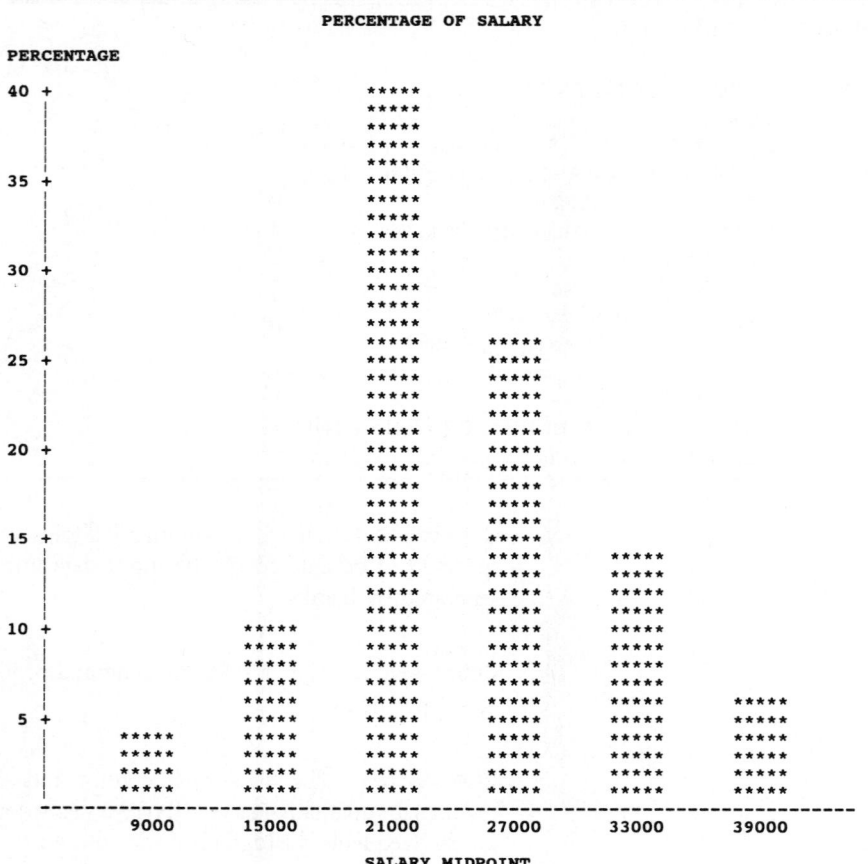

PERCENTAGE OF SALARY

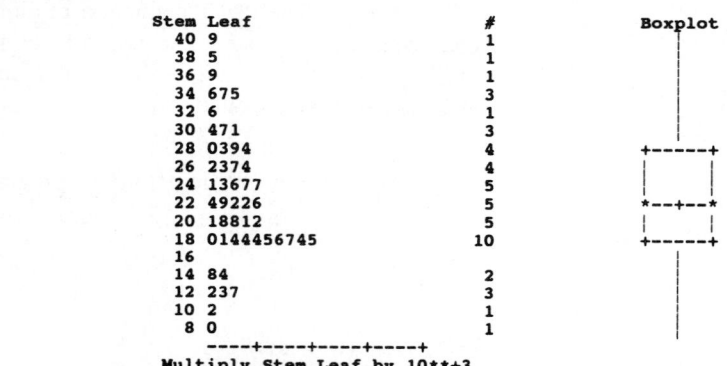

Variable=SALARY

Stem	Leaf	#	Boxplot
40	9	1	
38	5	1	
36	9	1	
34	675	3	
32	6	1	
30	471	3	
28	0394	4	+-----+
26	2374	4	
24	13677	5	
22	49226	5	*--+--*
20	18812	5	
18	0144456745	10	+-----+
16			
14	84	2	
12	237	3	
10	2	1	
8	0	1	

Multiply Stem.Leaf by 10**+3

(continued)

FIGURE 3.10 (*Continued*)

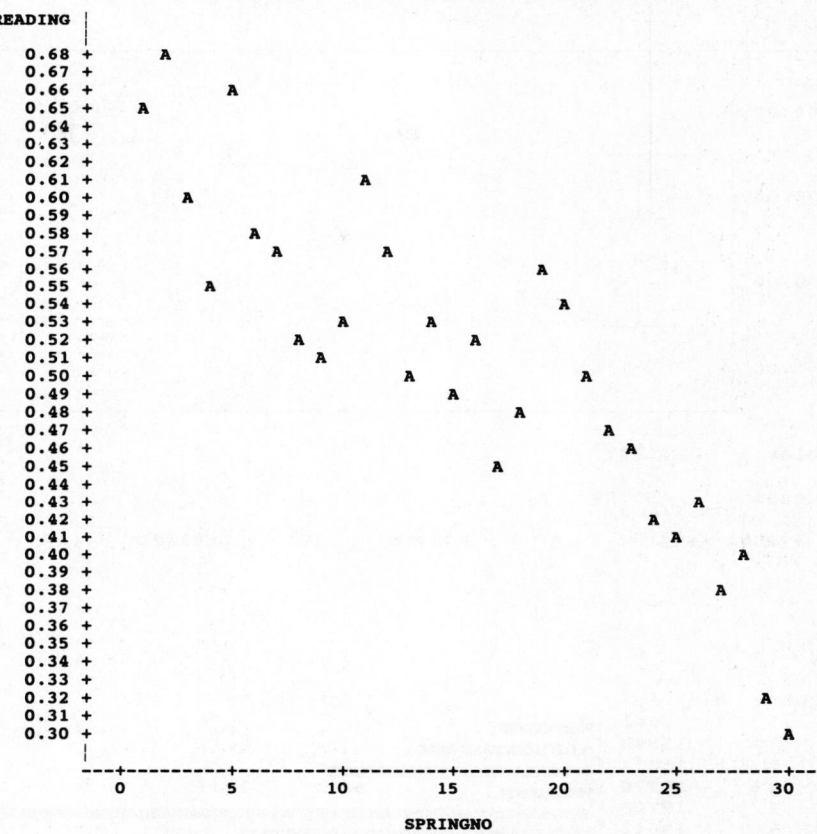

Plot of READING*SPRINGNO.   Legend: A = 1 obs, B = 2 obs, etc.

FIGURE 3.11
Output from SPSS Program

SALARY

Frequency	Stem &	Leaf
1.00	0 .	9
5.00	1 *	12334
11.00	1 .	58888888899
15.00	2 *	000112233344444
8.00	2 .	66678889
6.00	3 *	001244
3.00	3 .	568
1.00	4 *	1

Stem width: 10000.00
Each leaf: 1 case(s)

COMPUTER LAB 1
89

FIGURE 3.11 (*Continued*)

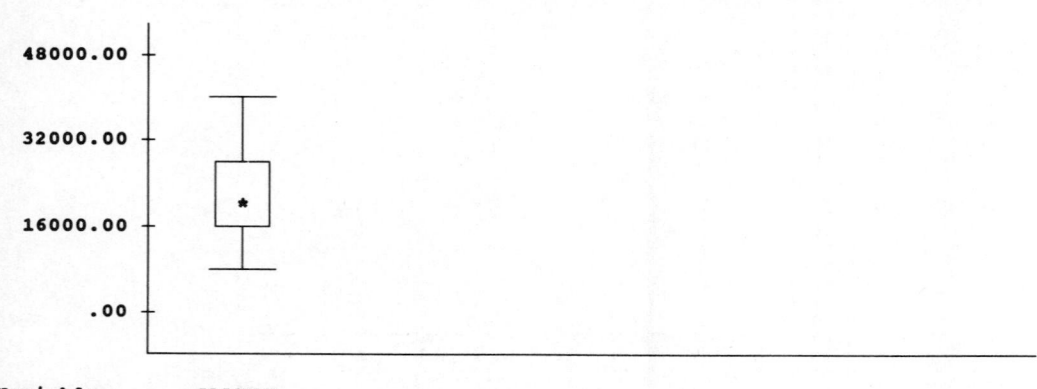

Variables	SALARY
N of Cases	50.00

Symbol Key: *****   - Median   **(O)** - Outlier   **(E)** - Extreme

SALARY

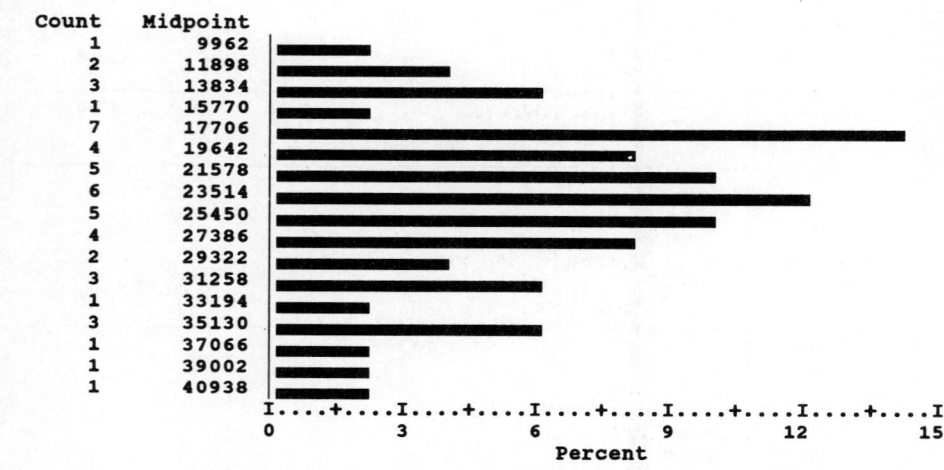

Count	Midpoint
1	9962
2	11898
3	13834
1	15770
7	17706
4	19642
5	21578
6	23514
5	25450
4	27386
2	29322
3	31258
1	33194
3	35130
1	37066
1	39002
1	40938

(*continued*)

FIGURE 3.11 (*Continued*)

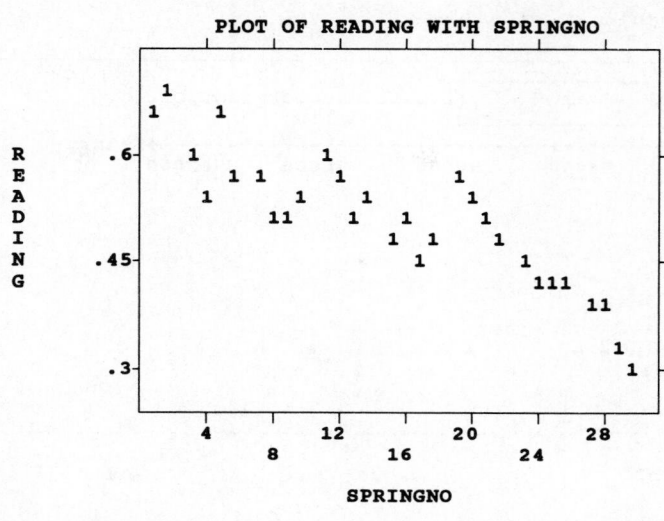

PLOT OF READING WITH SPRINGNO

SPRINGNO

FIGURE 3.12
Output from MINITAB Program

```
Histogram of Salary    N = 50

Midpoint    Count
  10000        3    ***
  15000        4    ****
  20000       16    ****************
  25000       13    *************
  30000        7    ******
  35000        5    *****
  40000        2    **


Stem-and-leaf of Salary    N = 50
Leaf Unit = 1000

     1      0 9
     2      1 1
     5      1 233
     7      1 45
     7      1
    17      1 8888888899
    22      2 00011
   (5)      2 22333
    23      2 44444
    18      2 6667
    14      2 8889
    10      3 001
     7      3 2
     6      3 445
     3      3 6
     2      3 8
     1      4 1
```

(continued)

FIGURE 3.12 (*Continued*)

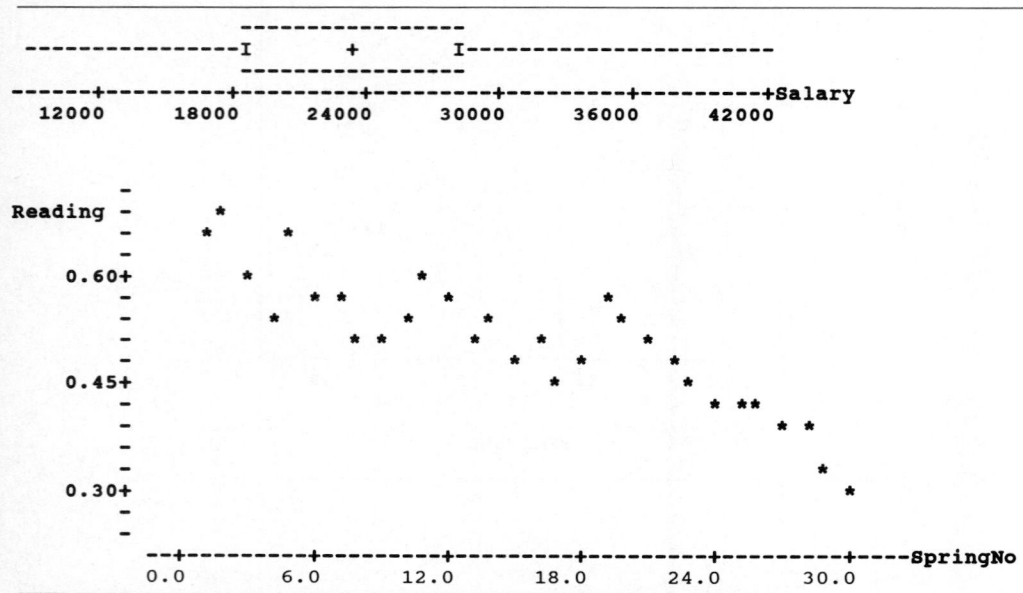

DESCRIPTIVE STATISTICS: CENTRAL TENDENCY

3.5

It is probably true that a picture is worth a thousand words, and it is certainly true when the goal is to describe a quantitative data set. But sometimes distribution plots (eg, stem-and-leaf displays or histograms) do not completely describe the data. When this situation occurs, we seek a few summarizing numbers, called **numerical descriptive measures** (or **descriptive statistics**), that help us describe the data. The measures discussed in this text are of two types: (1) **measures of central tendency**, which locate the "center" of the data set, and (2) **measures of variation**, which describe the "spread" of the data. In this section, we discuss how to calculate and interpret numerical measures of central tendency for a population or a sample.

DEFINITION 3.1

Numerical descriptive measures (or **descriptive statistics**) are numbers that summarize certain features of a quantitative data set.

DEFINITION 3.2

Measures of central tendency are numbers that are located near the center of the distribution of data.

> **DEFINITION 3.3**
>
> **Measures of variation** are numbers that measure the spread of the distribution.

MEAN

The most common measure of central tendency (the one that you are probably most familiar with) is the **mean**, or arithmetic average, of the data set. The **sample mean** and **population mean** are defined as follows:

> **DEFINITION 3.4**
>
> Let $x_1, x_2, ..., x_n$ denote a sample of n measurements. Then the **sample mean** is denoted by the symbol $\bar{x}$ (read "x-bar") and is computed as
>
> $$\bar{x} = \frac{\text{Sum of the } x \text{ values}}{\text{Number of observations}} = \frac{\Sigma x}{n}$$
>
> *Note:* The symbol Σ is read "summation" and instructs you to sum all the values of the variable shown to the right of the symbol.

> **DEFINITION 3.5**
>
> Let $x_1, x_2, ..., x_N$ denote all N measurements in a population. Then the **population mean** is denoted by the symbol μ and is computed as
>
> $$\mu = \frac{\Sigma x}{N}$$

For example, consider the sample data set containing the following five measurements: 5, 1, 6, 2, 4. Then the sample mean is

$$\bar{x} = \frac{\Sigma x}{n} = \frac{5 + 1 + 6 + 2 + 4}{5} = \frac{18}{5} = 3.6$$

The sample mean tells us that, on average, the values in the sample equal 3.6. You can see that 3.6 falls near the center of the five values when they are listed in order of magnitude: 1, 2, 4, 5, 6.

MEDIAN

A second measure of central tendency for a data set is the **median**. The median is a number chosen so that half the measurements in the data set are less than the median and half are larger. Since the areas of the bars used to construct a histogram are proportional to the relative frequency of observations falling within the classes, it follows that the median is a number that divides the histogram into two equal

FIGURE 3.13

The Median Divides the Distribution of Data in Half

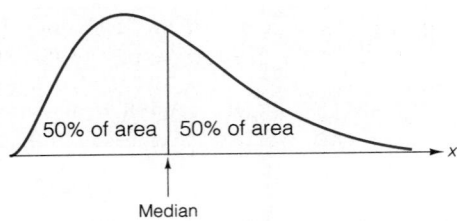

proportions. Half the area will lie to the left of the median (see Figure 3.13) and half will lie to the right. The sample and population median are defined as follows:

DEFINITION 3.6

Let $x_1, x_2, ..., x_n$ denote a sample of n measurements. Then the **sample median** M of the n observations is defined as follows:

If n is odd: The middle observation when the data are arranged in order

If n is even: The number halfway between the two middle observations—that is, the mean of the two middle observations—when the data are arranged in order [The two middle observations are the numbers in the $n/2$ and $(n/2) + 1$ positions.]

DEFINITION 3.7

Let $x_1, x_2, ..., x_N$ denote all N measurements in a population. Then the **population median**, denoted by the symbol η, is the number that divides the distribution of data exactly in half.

For example, the median for the sample of the five measurements above is determined as follows. First, arrange the data in increasing (or decreasing) order:

1   2   4   5   6

Since we have an odd number of measurements, the sample median is the middle observation, $M = 4$.

Now suppose we have an even number of measurements in the sample— say, 5, 7, 3, 1, 4, 6. To find the median, we again arrange the data in order:

1   3   4   5   6   7

The two middle observations are 4 and 5. Thus, the sample median is

$$M = \frac{4 + 5}{2} = 4.5$$

MODE

A third measure of central tendency is the **mode**. The mode is the measurement that occurs with the greatest frequency in the data (see Figure 3.14). If the data have been grouped into classes in a histogram, the **modal class** is defined as the class with the largest frequency.

FIGURE 3.14

The Mode Is the Measurement That Occurs with Greatest Frequency

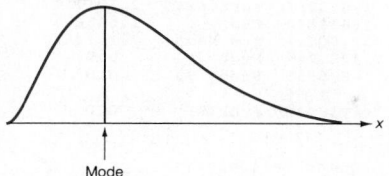

Mode

DEFINITION 3.8

The population (or sample) **mode** is the measurement x_i that occurs with the greatest frequency in the data set. If the actual data points are not available, but are summarized in a histogram, the **modal class** is the class with the largest frequency.

EXAMPLE 3.3 Consider the sample data set containing the starting salaries for 1,795 recent University of Florida graduates. (These were University of Florida graduates who responded to a Career Resource Center questionnaire and indicated they had secured a job at the time of graduation.) Calculate the mean, median, and mode for this data set. Interpret the results.

Solution   Although this data set represents a sample (since not all University of Florida graduates responded to the CRC survey), it is extremely large. Consequently, we will use a computer to calculate the three measures of central tendency. Figure 3.15 (p. 96) is the SAS printout of the analysis.* From Figure 3.15, the values of the sample mean, median, and mode (shaded) are $28,474.83, $27,000, and $20,000, respectively. The mean indicates that the average starting salary of the 1,795 graduates in the sample was $28,474.83. Fifty percent (or about 900) of the graduates in the sample had starting salaries below the median of $27,000, and 50% had salaries above $27,000. The starting salary that occurred most frequently in the sample was the mode, $20,000.

---

* The computer commands for generating descriptive statistics are given in Computer Lab 2, following Section 3.10.

```
                         UNIVARIATE PROCEDURE

          Variable=SALARY

                              Moments

          N               1795    Sum Wgts       1795
          Mean         28474.83    Sum        51112325
          Std Dev      9369.484    Variance   87787229
          Skewness     1.093351    Kurtosis   2.301454
          USS          1.613E12    CSS         1.575E11
          CV           32.90444    Std Mean   221.1482
          T:Mean=0      128.759    Prob>|T|        0.0
          Sgn Rank       805955    Prob>|S|        0.0
          Num ^= 0         1795
          W:Normal     0.934422    Prob<W          0.0


                          Quantiles(Def=5)

          100% Max       80000       99%       60000
           75% Q3        33000       95%       46000
           50% Med       27000       90%       40000
           25% Q1        22000       10%       19000
            0% Min        7100        5%       16000
                                      1%       10000

          Range          72900
          Q3-Q1          11000
          Mode           20000


                             Extremes

          Lowest     Obs      Highest     Obs
           7100(    1003)     66000(     532)
           7200(    1603)     70000(     557)
           8000(    1776)     70000(     711)
           8000(     920)     70000(     884)
           8000(     849)     80000(    1433)
```

The mean, median, and mode of Example 3.3 are shown on the histogram for the 1,795 starting salaries, Figure 3.16. Which is the best measure of central tendency for this data set? The answer is that it depends on the type of descriptive information you want. If you desire the "average" salary, then, of course, the mean is the best measure. If your notion of a typical, or "central," starting salary is one that is larger than half the salaries and less than the remainder, then you will prefer the median. The mode is rarely the choice measure of central tendency since the measurement that occurs most often does not necessarily lie in the center of the distribution of data. There are situations, however, where the mode is preferred. For example, if the relative frequency of occurrence of values of starting salaries can be viewed as a measure of employer perception of a college graduate's first-year value (eg, the greatest frequency of starting salaries occurred in the $22,000–$26,000 class), then the mode might be the preferred measure of central tendency. More realistically, a retailer of women's shoes would be interested in the modal shoe size of potential customers.

In making your decision, you should know that the **mean is sensitive to very large or very small measurements**. Consequently, the mean will shift away from the median toward the direction of skewness and may be a misleading measure of central tendency in some situations. You can see from Figure 3.16 that the mean falls to the right of the median and that the starting salaries are skewed to the right. The high starting salaries of relatively few graduates will influence the mean much more than the median. For this reason the median is sometimes called a **resistant**

FIGURE 3.16

Locations of the Mean, Median, and Mode for the Starting Salary Data

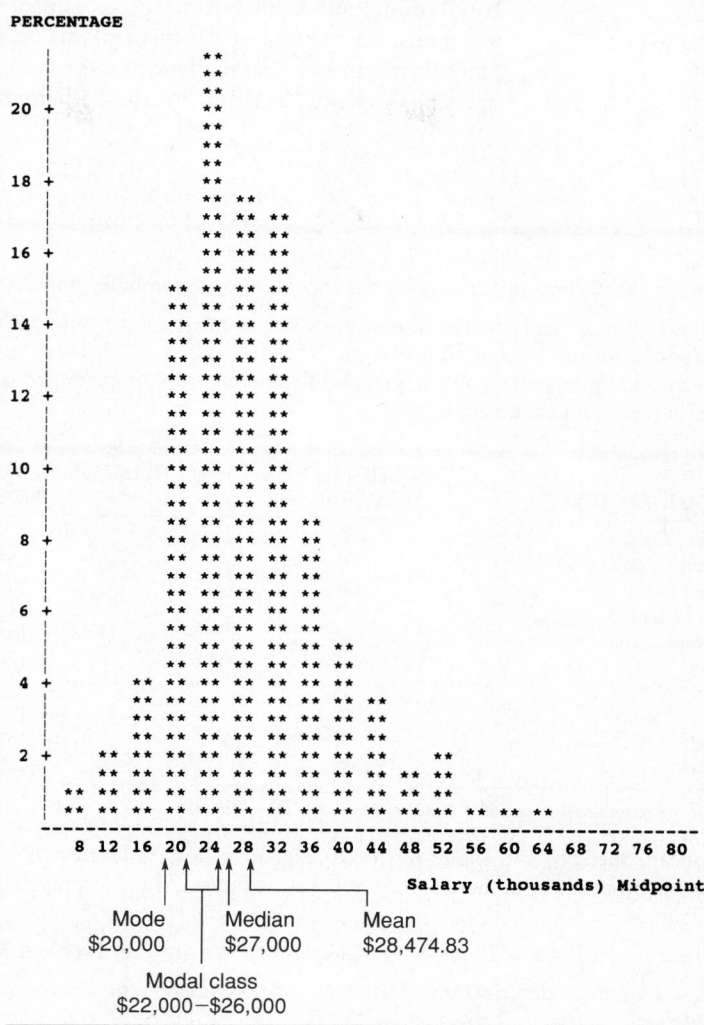

measure of central tendency, since it, unlike the mean, is resistant to the influence of extreme measurements. For data sets that are extremely skewed, the median would better represent the center of the distribution of data.

WARNING

For data sets that are extremely skewed, be wary of using the mean as a measure of the center of the distribution. In this situation, a more meaningful measure of central tendency may be the median, which is more resistant to the influence of extreme measurements.

Most of the inferential statistical methods discussed in this text are theoretically based on mound-shaped distributions of data with little or no skewness. For these situations, the mean and the median will be, for all practical purposes, the same. Since the mean has nicer mathematical properties than the median, it is the preferred measure of central tendency for these inferential techniques.

PROBLEMS

3.22 The Customer Satisfaction Index data for the top 10 rated automobiles in 1992 (Problem 3.2) are reproduced below.

   a. Compute the mean and median of the index values for domestic auto makers.
   b. Repeat part **a** for the foreign auto makers.
   c. Use the results from parts **a** and **b** to make an inference about customer satisfaction with the two groups of auto makers, foreign and domestic.

AUTO (MANUFACTURER)	FOREIGN (F) OR DOMESTIC (D)	CUSTOMER SATISFACTION INDEX
Lexus (Toyota)	F	179
Infiniti (Nissan)	F	167
Saturn (GM)	D	160
Acura (Honda)	F	148
Mercedes-Benz	F	145
Toyota	F	144
Audi (VW)	F	139
Cadillac (GM)	D	138
Honda	F	138
Jaguar (Ford)	D	137

Source: J. D. Powers and Associates, 1992. Customer Satisfaction StudySM.

3.23 Find the mean, median, and mode of the 20 executive salaries listed in Problem 3.3 (p. 62). Which of the three measures of central tendency best describes the distribution of total compensations for the top corporate executives in 1992? Explain.

3.24 Refer to the data on the top 25 graduate business schools given in Problem 3.5 (p. 63).

   a. Calculate numerical descriptive measures of central tendency for out-of-state tuition costs. (Use a computer if you wish.)
   b. Based on the results in part **a**, make a statement about the type of skewness present in the distribution of out-of-state tuition costs.

3.25 Refer to the Center for Disease Control study of sanitation levels for 91 international cruise ships, Problem 3.7. A MINITAB printout of the descriptive statistics for the data is shown below. (Recall that sanitation scores range from 0 to 100.) Interpret the numerical descriptive measures of central tendency displayed in the printout.

	N	MEAN	MEDIAN	TRMEAN	STDEV	SEMEAN
sanlevel	91	91.044	92.000	91.580	5.566	0.583

	MIN	MAX	Q1	Q3		
sanlevel	66.000	99.000	89.000	95.000		

3.26   Refer to the data set containing 8,313 residential property sale prices, Problem 3.15 (p. 77). The SAS printout giving descriptive statistics for the data is shown here.

```
                    UNIVARIATE PROCEDURE

                    Variable=SALEPRIC

                        Moments

N                 8313    Sum Wgts            8313
Mean          77158.19    Sum             6.4142E8
Std Dev       72576.43    Variance        5.2673E9
Skewness       5.98757    Kurtosis        75.10215
USS           9.327E13    CSS             4.378E13
CV            94.06186    Std Mean        796.0067
T:Mean=0      96.93158    Prob>|T|             0.0
Sgn Rank      17278571    Prob>|S|             0.0
Num ^= 0          8313


                    Quantiles(Def=5)

100% Max       1593900         99%        365000
 75% Q3          86900         95%        191000
 50% Med         59900         90%        140000
 25% Q1          41800         10%         25000
  0% Min          5500          5%         17000
                                1%          8800
Range          1588400
Q3-Q1            45100
Mode             50000


                        Extremes

Lowest       Obs       Highest      Obs
   5500(    7997)    1100000(     3611)
   5500(    7638)    1100000(     3612)
   5500(    6928)    1225000(     4982)
   5500(    6705)    1565000(     5208)
   5500(    6640)    1593900(      132)
```

a. Find the values of the mean, median, and mode in the printout. Interpret these values.

b. Locate the values of the mean, median, and mode from part **a** in the SAS histogram shown in Problem 3.15. Which measure of central tendency best describes the residential sale prices?

DESCRIPTIVE STATISTICS: SPREAD

3.6   Just as measures of central tendency locate the center of a distribution of data, measures of variability measure its spread. The three most common measures of spread are the (1) **range**, (2) **variance**, and (3) **standard deviation**.

RANGE

The simplest of the three measures to compute is the **range**.

DEFINITION 3.9

The **range** of a quantitative data set (population or sample) is equal to the difference between the largest and smallest measurements in the set.

For example, consider the sample data set: 3, 7, 2, 1, 8. The largest measurement is 8 and the smallest is 1; hence, the range is

$$\text{Range} = \text{Largest measurement} - \text{Smallest measurement}$$
$$= 8 - 1 = 7$$

The range of a data set is easy to calculate, but it is an insensitive measure of variation and is not very informative. To illustrate, consider the two distributions of data shown in Figure 3.17. Both data sets have the same range, but it is clear that the distribution in Figure 3.17b is much less variable than the distribution in Figure 3.17a. Most of the observations in Figure 3.17b lie close to the mean. In contrast, most of the data in Figure 3.17a deviate substantially from the center of the distribution. The problem is that the range quantifies the spread of the *extreme* largest and smallest measurements in the data and, thus, is insensitive to the variability of the remaining measurements.

FIGURE 3.17
Two Data Distributions with Equal Ranges but Differing Patterns of Variation

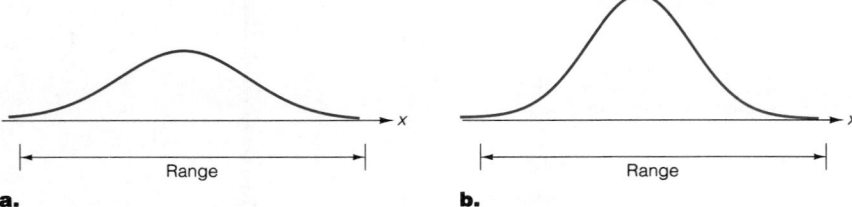

VARIANCE

A more useful measure of spread is one that is sensitive to all observations in the data set. One such measure is the **variance**. The variance of a data set is based on how much the observations deviate from their mean. The deviation between an observation x and the mean is the difference

$$(x - \text{Mean})$$

Then the variance is equal to the average of the squared deviations of all observations in the data set.

DEFINITION 3.10

Let $x_1, x_2, ..., x_n$ denote the n measurements in a sample. The **sample variance**, s^2, is equal to the sum of the squares of deviations of the measurements about their mean, divided by $(n - 1)$:

$$s^2 = \frac{\Sigma(x - \bar{x})^2}{n - 1}$$

Note: A shortcut formula for calculating the numerator of s^2 is

$$\Sigma(x - \bar{x})^2 = \Sigma x^2 - \frac{(\Sigma x)^2}{n}$$

In the formulas you will note that we divide by $(n - 1)$ rather than n to obtain the sample variance. Statistical theory shows that dividing by $(n - 1)$ makes the sample variance s^2 a mathematically good estimate of the population variance, σ^2.*

The larger the variance of a data set, the more spread out the data are; the smaller the variance, the less spread out the data are. Consequently, the variance for the data set portrayed in Figure 3.17a will be larger than the variance for the data set portrayed in Figure 3.17b.

The calculation of the sample variance for a small data set is illustrated in the following example.

EXAMPLE 3.4   Find the variance for the sample measurements: 3, 7, 2, 1, 8.

Solution   The five observations are listed in the first column of Table 3.7. You can see that $\Sigma x = 21$ and, therefore,

$$\bar{x} = \frac{\Sigma x}{n} = \frac{21}{5} = 4.2$$

This value of $\bar{x}$, 4.2, is subtracted from each observation to determine how much each observation deviates from the mean. These deviations are shown in the second column of Table 3.7. A **negative deviation** means that the observation fell *below*

TABLE 3.7
Data and Computation Table for Example 3.4

OBSERVATION x	$x - \bar{x}$	$(x - \bar{x})^2$
3	−1.2	1.44
7	2.8	7.84
2	−2.2	4.84
1	−3.2	10.24
8	3.8	14.44
Totals 21	0	38.80

* When n is used in the denominator of the formula for s^2, the value of s^2 tends to underestimate σ^2. Dividing by $(n - 1)$ adjusts for the underestimation problem.

the mean; a **positive deviation** indicates that the observation fell *above* the mean. Notice that the sum of the deviations equals 0. This will be true for all data sets.

The squares of the deviations are shown in the third column of Table 3.7. The total at the bottom of the column gives the sum of squares of deviations:

$$\Sigma(x - \bar{x})^2 = 38.8$$

Then the sample variance is

$$s^2 = \frac{\Sigma(x - \bar{x})^2}{n - 1} = \frac{38.8}{4} = 9.7$$

TABLE 3.8
Table for Calculating a Sample Variance; Shortcut Procedure

OBSERVATION	
x	x^2
3	9
7	49
2	4
1	1
8	64
Totals 21	127

Note: For larger data sets, the procedure for calculating a variance shown in Example 3.4 is tedious and often leads to rounding errors in finding the sum of squares of deviations, $\Sigma(x - \bar{x})^2$. The shortcut procedure given in Definition 3.10 provides an easy way to compute $\Sigma(x - \bar{x})^2$, the numerator of the sample variance. Instead of calculating the deviation of each measurement from the mean, we calculate the squares of the observations, as shown in Table 3.8. Substituting the sum of squares Σx^2 and the sum Σx of the observations into the shortcut formula, Definition 3.10, we obtain

$$\Sigma(x - \bar{x})^2 = \Sigma x^2 - \frac{(\Sigma x)^2}{n}$$

$$= 127 - \frac{(21)^2}{5}$$

$$= 127 - 88.2 = 38.8$$

This is exactly the same total that we obtained for the sum of squares of deviations in Table 3.7, Example 3.4.

How can we interpret the value of the sample variance calculated in Example 3.4? We know that data sets with large variances are more variable (ie, more spread out) than data sets with smaller variances. But what information can we obtain from the number, $s^2 = 9.7$? One interpretation is that the average squared deviation of the sample measurements from their mean is 9.7. However, a more practical interpretation can be obtained by calculating the square root of this number.

STANDARD DEVIATION

A third measure of data variation, the **standard deviation**, is obtained by taking the square root of the variance. This results in a number with units of measurement equal to the units of the original data. That is, if the units of measurement for the sample observations are feet, dollars, or hours, the standard deviation of the sample is measured in feet, dollars, or hours (instead of feet^2, dollars^2, or hours^2).

Like the variance, the standard deviation measures the amount of spread in a quantitative data set. As we will see in the following chapters, we use the sample standard deviation s to estimate the standard deviation of the population, denoted by σ.

The standard deviation of the five sample measurements in Example 3.4 is

$$s = \sqrt{s^2} = \sqrt{9.7} = 3.1$$

We develop the interpretation of this number in the next section. As we will see:

When combined with the mean, the standard deviation gives us a range within which most of the data fall.

SOME RULES FOR DESCRIBING QUANTITATIVE DATA

3.7 In this section, we give two rules for describing quantitative data sets: (1) the **Empirical Rule** and (2) **Tchebysheff's theorem**. Both rules use the mean and standard deviation of a data set to determine an interval of values within which most of the measurements fall. For samples, the intervals take the form

$$\bar{x} \pm (k)s$$

where k is any positive constant (usually 1, 2, or 3). For populations, the intervals take the form

$$\mu \pm (k)\sigma$$

The particular rule you apply will depend on the shape of the relative frequency distribution for the data set.

EMPIRICAL RULE

Consider again the sample data set that contains the 1,795 starting salaries for recent University of Florida graduates. A portion of the SAS printout that gives numerical descriptive measures for the data is reproduced in Figure 3.18. The mean and standard deviation of the sample are

$$\bar{x} = \$28,475 \qquad s = \$9,369 \quad \text{Rounded to the nearest dollar}$$

These values are shaded in the printout, Figure 3.18.

FIGURE 3.18

SAS Printout: Descriptive Statistics for Starting Salaries

```
Variable=SALARY

          Moments

N                1795   Sum Wgts           1795
Mean         28474.83   Sum            51112325
Std Dev      9369.484   Variance       87787229
Skewness     1.093351   Kurtosis       2.301454
USS          1.613E12   CSS            1.575E11
CV           32.90444   Std Mean       221.1482
T:Mean=0      128.759   Prob>|T|            0.0
Sgn Rank       805955   Prob>|S|            0.0
Num ^= 0         1795
W:Normal     0.934422   Prob<W              0.0
```

Now, we'll form an interval by measuring 1 standard deviation on each side of the mean, that is, $\bar{x} \pm s$:

$$\bar{x} \pm s = 28{,}475 \pm 9{,}369$$
$$= (28{,}475 - 9{,}369, + 28{,}475 + 9{,}369)$$
$$= (19{,}106, + 37{,}844)$$

The intervals $\bar{x} \pm 2s$ and $\bar{x} \pm 3s$ are calculated in a similar fashion:

$$\bar{x} \pm 2s = 28{,}475 \pm 2(9{,}369) \qquad \bar{x} \pm 3s = 28{,}475 \pm 3(9{,}369)$$
$$= 28{,}475 \pm 18{,}738 \qquad\qquad = 28{,}475 \pm 28{,}107$$
$$= (9{,}737, + 47{,}213) \qquad\qquad = (368, + 56{,}582)$$

These three intervals are shown on the SAS relative frequency histogram for the data in Figure 3.19. You can visually estimate from the figure that (1) about 70% of the starting salaries fall in the $\bar{x} \pm s$ interval, (2) approximately 95% fall in the $\bar{x} \pm 2s$ interval, and (3) nearly 100% fall in the $\bar{x} \pm 3s$ interval. Statisticians have verified empirically that these percentages hold true, in general, for distributions of data that look similar to Figure 3.19 (ie, *mound-shaped* distributions of data with *little or moderate skewness*). This rule of thumb is commonly known as the **Empirical Rule**.

EMPIRICAL RULE

For a mound-shaped distribution of data (population or sample), apply the following rules to estimate the proportions of observations falling within the three specified intervals:

SAMPLE	POPULATION	PROPORTION
$\bar{x} \pm s$	$\mu \pm \sigma$	About 70%
$\bar{x} \pm 2s$	$\mu \pm 2\sigma$	Approximately 95%
$\bar{x} \pm 3s$	$\mu \pm 3\sigma$	Near 100%

Note: The percentages may vary from these amounts for skewed distributions.

FIGURE 3.19
Location of Intervals $\bar{x} \pm s$, $\bar{x} \pm 2s$, and $\bar{x} \pm 3s$ for Starting Salary Data

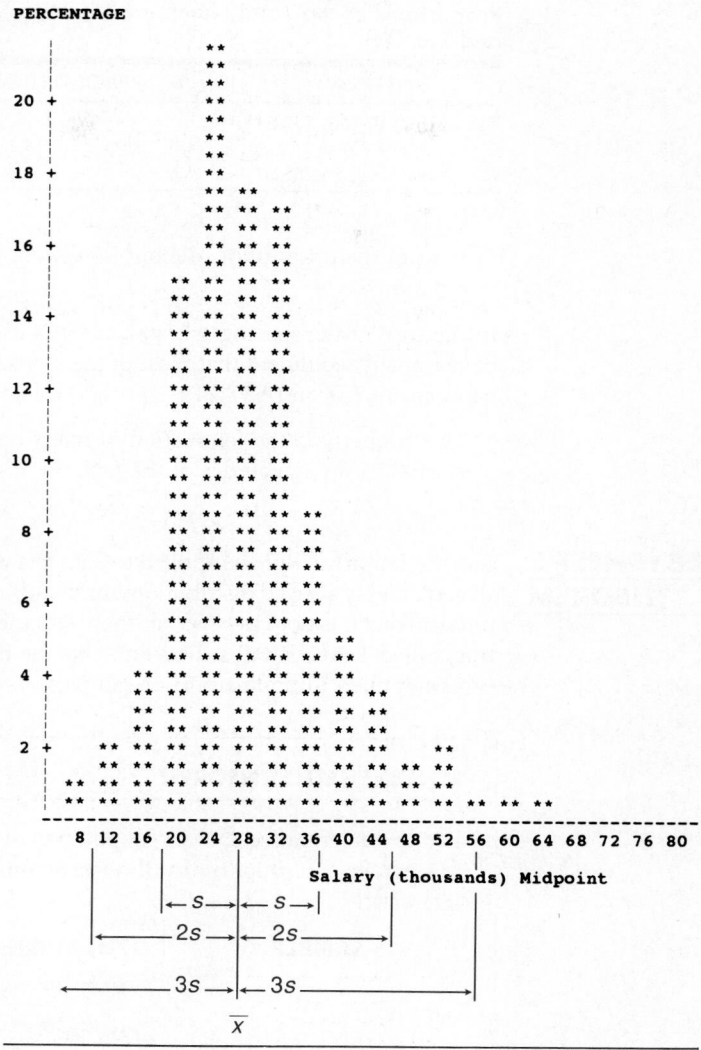

To verify that the Empirical Rule holds for the starting salary data, we used a computer to calculate the proportions of the total number of starting salaries falling within the three intervals. The results are shown in Table 3.9. You can see that the proportions agree with the Empirical Rule.

For any mound-shaped data set (population or sample) that is not too highly skewed, the Empirical Rule provides a very good rule of thumb for forming a mental image of the distribution of data when you know the mean and standard deviation. In particular, we know that:

TABLE 3.9

Proportions of the Total Number of Starting Salaries in Intervals $\bar{x} \pm s$, $\bar{x} \pm 2s$, and $\bar{x} \pm 3s$

INTERVAL	PROPORTION IN INTERVAL
$\bar{x} \pm \ \ s$ or ($19,106, $37,844)	.758
$\bar{x} \pm 2s$ or ($9,737, $47,213)	.947
$\bar{x} \pm 3s$ or ($368, $56,582)	.986

Most of the observations (about 95%) will fall within 2 standard deviations of the mean.

In the case of the starting salary data set, with knowledge of only $\bar{x}$ and s, we can be reasonably confident that most of the University of Florida graduates had salaries between $9,737 and $47,213.

This property is the foundation of many of the inferential techniques that we discuss in the remainder of the text.

TCHEBYSHEFF'S THEOREM

Can the Empirical Rule be applied to data sets with distributions that are not mound-shaped, highly skewed distributions, or distributions of unknown shape? The answer, unfortunately, is no. However, in these situations we can apply a more conservative rule, called **Tchebysheff's theorem**. Like the Empirical Rule, Tchebysheff's theorem can be applied to populations or samples.

TCHEBYSHEFF'S THEOREM

For any quantitative data set (population or sample), apply the following rules to estimate the proportions of observations falling within the two* specified intervals:

SAMPLE	POPULATION	PROPORTION
$\bar{x} \pm 2s$	$\mu \pm 2\sigma$	At least 75%
$\bar{x} \pm 3s$	$\mu \pm 3\sigma$	At least 89%

Note that Tchebysheff's theorem applies to any set of measurements, regardless of the shape of the relative frequency distribution. The rule is conservative in the sense that the specified percentage for any interval is a *lower bound* on the actual percentage of measurements falling in that interval. For example, the theorem states that at least 75% of the starting salaries in the sample of 1,795 University of Florida

---

* Formally, the theorem states that at least $(1 - 1/k^2)$ of the total number of observations will fall within k standard deviations of the mean. For $k = 1$, $1 - 1/k^2 = 1 - 1/(1)^2 = 0$. Thus, Tchebysheff's theorem states that at least 0% of the observations fall within $\bar{x} \pm s$ or $\mu \pm \sigma$. Consequently, no useful information is provided about the interval.

graduates will fall in the interval $\bar{x} \pm 2s$. We know (from Table 3.9) that the actual percentage (94.7%) is closer to the Empirical Rule's value of 95%. Consequently, whenever you know that a distribution of data is mound-shaped and nonskewed, the Empirical Rule will give a more precise estimate of the true proportion falling within a specified interval.

EXAMPLE 3.5 Travelers who have no intention of showing up often fail to cancel their hotel reservations in a timely manner. These travelers are known, in the parlance of the hospitality trade, as "no-shows." To protect against no-shows and late cancellations, hotels invariably overbook rooms. A study reported in the *Journal of Travel Research* examined the problem of overbooking rooms in the hotel industry. The data in Table 3.10, extracted from the study, represent daily numbers of late cancellations and no-shows for a random sample of 30 days at a large (500 room) hotel. Based on this sample, how many rooms, at minimum, should the large hotel overbook each day?

TABLE 3.10

Hotel No-Shows for a Sample of 30 Days

18	16	16	16	14	18	16	18	14	19	15	19	9	20	15
10	10	12	14	18	12	14	14	17	12	18	13	15	13	19

Source: Toh, R. S. "An Inventory Depletion Overbooking Model for the Hotel Industry." *Journal of Travel Research*, Vol. 23, No. 4, Spring 1985, p. 27. The *Journal of Travel Research* is published by the Travel and Tourism Research Association (TTRA) and the Business Research Division, University of Colorado at Boulder.

Solution To answer this question, we need to know a range of values where most of the daily numbers of no-shows fall. This requires that we compute $\bar{x}$ and s, and examine the shape of the relative frequency distribution for the data.

Figure 3.20 is a MINITAB printout that shows a stem-and-leaf display and descriptive statistics of the sample data. Notice from the stem-and-leaf display that the distribution of daily no-shows is mound-shaped, and only slightly skewed on

FIGURE 3.20

MINITAB Printout: Describing the No-Show Data

```
Stem-and-leaf of noshows   N  = 30
Leaf Unit = 0.10

    1     9  0
    3    10  00
    3    11
    6    12  000
    8    13  00
   13    14  00000
   (3)   15  000
   14    16  0000
   10    17  0
    9    18  00000
    4    19  000
    1    20  0
```

	N	MEAN	MEDIAN	TRMEAN	STDEV	SEMEAN
noshows	30	15.133	15.000	15.231	2.945	0.538

	MIN	MAX	Q1	Q3
noshows	9.000	20.000	13.000	18.000

the low (top) side. Thus, the Empirical Rule should give a good estimate of the percentage of days that fall within 1, 2, and 3 standard deviations of the mean.

The mean and standard deviation of the sample data, shaded in the MINITAB printout, are $\bar{x} = 15.133$ and $s = 2.945$. From the Empirical Rule, we know that about 95% of the daily number of no-shows fall within 2 standard deviations of the mean, that is, within the interval

$$\bar{x} \pm 2s = 15.133 \pm 2(2.945)$$
$$= 15.133 \pm 5.890$$

or between 9.243 and 21.023 no-shows. (If we count the number of measurements in this data set, we find that actually 29 out of 30, or 96.7%, fall in this interval.)

From this result, the large hotel can infer that there will be at least 9.243 (or, rounding up, 10) no-shows per day. Consequently, the hotel can overbook at least 10 rooms per day and still be highly confident that all reservations can be honored.

PROBLEMS

3.27 The fire victim data from Problem 3.1 are reproduced in the table.

FIRE	NUMBER OF VICTIMS
Las Vegas Hilton (Las Vegas)	5
Inn on the Park (Toronto)	5
Westchase Hilton (Houston)	8
Holiday Inn (Cambridge, Ohio)	10
Conrad Hilton (Chicago)	4
Providence College (Providence)	8
Baptist Towers (Atlanta)	7
Howard Johnson (New Orleans)	5
Cornell University (Ithaca, New York)	9
Westport Central Apartments (Kansas City, Missouri)	4
Orrington Hotel (Evanston, Illinois)	0
Hartford Hospital (Hartford, Connecticut)	16
Milford Plaza (New York)	0
MGM Grand (Las Vegas)	36

Source: Macdonald, J. N. "Is Evacuation a Fatal Flaw in Fire Fighting Philosophy?" *Risk Management*, Vol. 33, No. 2, Feb. 1986, p. 37.

a. Find the mean of the sample data.
b. Find the range, variance, and standard deviation of the sample data.
c. What percentage of measurements would you expect to find in the interval $\bar{x} \pm 2s$?
d. Determine the percentage of measurements that actually fall within the interval of part c. Compare this result with your answer to part c.
e. Repeat parts a–d, omitting the data for the MGM Grand fire (36 victims) from the analysis.

3.28 Refer to the data given in Problem 3.14 on student-loan default rates for 66 Florida colleges. An SPSS printout giving descriptive statistics for the data set is displayed at the top of the next page.

a. Locate the mean default rate in the printout.
b. Locate the variance and standard deviation of the default rates in the printout.

```
Number of Valid Observations (Listwise) =        66.00

Variable  DEFRATE

Mean              14.682           S.E. Mean         1.741
Std Dev           14.141           Variance        199.974
Kurtosis           5.427           S.E. Kurt          .582
Skewness           2.204           S.E. Skew          .295
Range             74.700           Minimum           1.50
Maximum           76.20            Sum             969.000

Valid Observations -        66      Missing Observations -        0
```

c. What proportion of measurements would you expect to find within 2 standard deviations of the mean?

d. Determine the proportion of measurements (default rates) that actually fall within the interval of part **c**. Compare this result with your answer to part **c**.

e. Suppose the college with the highest default rate (Florida College of Business, 76.2%) was omitted from the analysis. Would you expect the mean to increase or decrease? Would you expect the standard deviation to increase or decrease?

f. Calculate the mean and standard deviation for the data set with Florida College of Business excluded. Compare these results with your answer to part **e**.

g. Answer parts **c** and **d** using the recalculated mean and standard deviation.

3.29 Refer to the SAS printout describing the residential sale price data in Problem 3.26 (p. 99). Use the information in the printout to find an interval of values where most of the sale prices fall.

3.30 Periodically, the Federal Trade Commission (FTC) ranks domestic cigarette brands according to tar, nicotine, and carbon monoxide content. The test results are obtained by using a sequential smoking machine to "smoke" cigarettes to a 23 millimeter butt length. The tar, nicotine, and carbon monoxide concentration (rounded to the nearest milligram) in the residual "dry" particulate matter of the smoke are then measured.

a. An SPSS histogram of the tar contents of 372 cigarettes tested in 1991 is shown below.* Which rule would best describe the distribution of tar contents, the Empirical Rule or Tchebysheff's theorem?

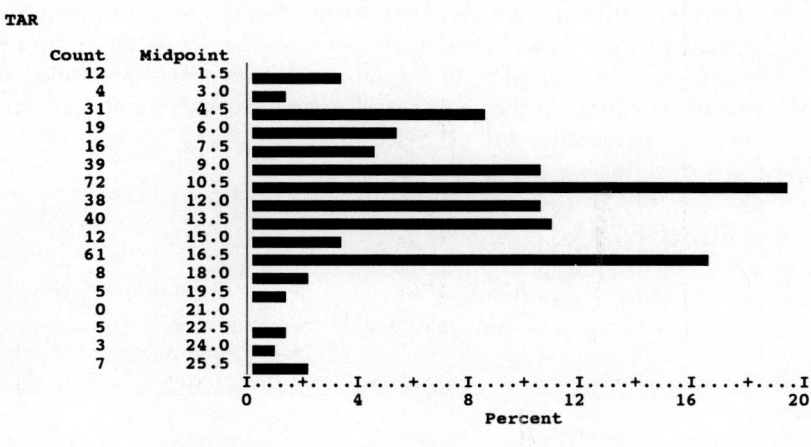

---

* Source: "Tar, Nicotine, and Carbon Monoxide of the Smoke of 475 Varieties of Domestic Cigarettes."
Federal Trade Commission report, 1991.

b. The mean and standard deviation of the 372 tar contents are 11.60 mg and 4.97 mg, respectively. Use this information to form a 2 standard deviation interval around the mean.

c. Based on your answer to part **a**, estimate the percentage of cigarettes with tar contents in the interval formed in part **b**.

d. Use the information in the SPSS histogram to determine the actual percentage of tar contents that fall within the interval formed in part **b**. Does your answer agree with your estimate of part **c**?

3.31 Nevada continues to be the leading gold producer in the United States. According to the U.S. Bureau of Mines, it ranks among the top four regional producers worldwide (trailing South Africa, Russia, and Australia). The data in the table represent the production (in thousands of ounces) for the top 30 gold mines in the state.

1,467.8	228.0	111.3	76.0	55.1	40.0
318.0	222.6	89.1	72.5	54.1	32.4
296.9	214.6	82.0	66.0	50.0	30.9
256.0	207.3	81.5	60.4	50.0	30.3
254.5	120.7	78.8	60.0	44.5	30.0

Source: *Engineering & Mining Journal*, June 1990, p. 38.

a. Summarize the data using a graphical technique.

b. Calculate the mean, median, and standard deviation of the data.

c. What proportion of Nevada mines have production values that lie within 2 standard deviations of the mean?

d. Note the extremely large production value, 1,467.8, for the first mine listed in the table. Recalculate the mean, median, and standard deviation with the production measurement for this mine deleted.

e. Explain how the three numerical descriptive measures (mean, median, and standard deviation) are affected by the deletion of the measurement, 1,467.8.

DESCRIPTIVE STATISTICS: RELATIVE STANDING

3.8

In some situations, you may want to describe the relative position of a particular measurement in a quantitative data set. For example, suppose a college graduate in the data set containing 1,795 salaries has a starting salary of $46,000. You might want to know whether this is a relatively low or high starting salary, etc. What percentage of the starting salaries were less than $46,000; what percentage were higher? Descriptive measures that locate the relative position of a measurement—in relation to the other measurements—are called **measures of relative standing**. In this section, we present two such numerical descriptive measures: (1) **percentiles** and (2) **z-scores**.

> **DEFINITION 3.13**
>
> A **measure of relative standing** is a numerical descriptive measure that locates the position of a measurement in a data set relative to the other measurements in the data set.

PERCENTILES

A measure that expresses the relative position of a quantitative observation in terms of a percentage is called a **percentile** for the data set. The starting salary of $46,000 mentioned above falls at the 95th percentile of the starting salary data.

This tells you that 95% of the 1,795 starting salaries were less than \$46,000 and $(100 - 95)\% = 5\%$ were greater.

DEFINITION 3.14

Let x_1, x_2, ..., x_n be a set of n measurements arranged in increasing (or decreasing) order. The **pth percentile** is a number x such that $p\%$ of the measurements fall below the pth percentile and $(100 - p)\%$ fall above it.

The median, by definition, is the 50th percentile. The 25th percentile, the median, and the 75th percentile are often used to describe a data set because they divide the data set into four groups, with each group containing one-fourth (25%) of the observations. They also divide the relative frequency distribution for a data set into four parts, each containing the same area (.25), as shown in Figure 3.21. Consequently, the 25th percentile, the median, and the 75th percentile are called the **lower quartile**, **mid-quartile**, and **upper quartile**, respectively, for a data set.

FIGURE 3.21

Locations of the Lower and Upper Quartiles

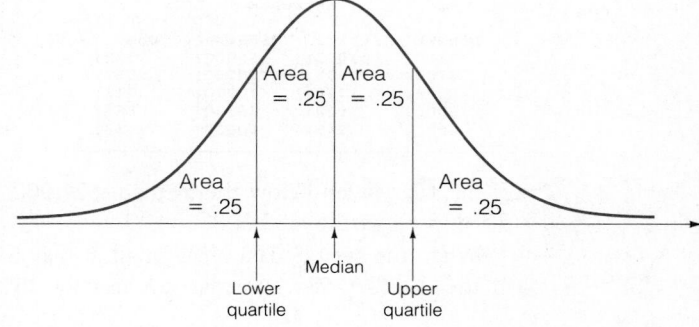

DEFINITION 3.15

The **lower quartile** for a data set is the 25th percentile and is denoted by the symbol Q_L (or Q_1).

The **mid-quartile** (median) for a data set is the 50th percentile and is denoted by the symbol M (or Q_2).

The **upper quartile** for a data set is the 75th percentile and is denoted by the symbol Q_U (or Q_3).

Although, for large data sets, quartiles can be found by locating the corresponding areas under the relative frequency distribution, they are usually found via the computer. Figure 3.22 is a reproduction of the SAS printout describing the starting salary data with the values of Q_L, M, and Q_U shaded. From these values we know that 25% of the 1,795 starting salaries fall below the lower quartile, \$22,000; 50%

FIGURE 3.22

SAS Printout: Quartiles for Starting
Salary Data Set

UNIVARIATE PROCEDURE

Variable=SALARY

Moments

N	1795	Sum Wgts	1795
Mean	28474.83	Sum	51112325
Std Dev	9369.484	Variance	87787229
Skewness	1.093351	Kurtosis	2.301454
USS	1.613E12	CSS	1.575E11
CV	32.90444	Std Mean	221.1482
T:Mean=0	128.759	Prob>|T|	0.0
Sgn Rank	805955	Prob>|S|	0.0
Num ^= 0	1795		
W:Normal	0.934422	Prob<W	0.0

Quantiles(Def=5)

100% Max	80000	99%	60000
75% Q3	33000	95%	46000
50% Med	27000	90%	40000
25% Q1	22000	10%	19000
0% Min	7100	5%	16000
		1%	10000
Range	72900		
Q3-Q1	11000		
Mode	20000		

Extremes

Lowest	Obs	Highest	Obs
7100(	1003)	66000(	532)
7200(	1603)	70000(	557)
8000(	1776)	70000(	711)
8000(	920)	70000(	884)
8000(	849)	80000(	1433)

of the salaries fall below the median, $27,000; and 75% of the salaries fall below the upper quartile, $33,000.

When the sample data set is small, it may be impossible to find a measurement in the data set that exceeds, say, exactly 25% of the remaining measurements.

FINDING QUARTILES (AND PERCENTILES) WITH SMALL DATA SETS

STEP 1   Rank the n measurements in the data set in increasing order of magnitude.

STEP 2   Calculate the quantity $\frac{1}{4}(n + 1)$ and round to the nearest integer. The measurement with this rank represents the lower quartile, or 25th percentile. [*Note:* If $\frac{1}{4}(n + 1)$ falls halfway between two integers, round up.]

STEP 3   Calculate the quantity $\frac{3}{4}(n + 1)$ and round to the nearest integer. The measurement with this rank represents the upper quartile, or 75th percentile. [*Note:* If $\frac{3}{4}(n + 1)$ falls halfway between two integers, round down.]

GENERAL   To find the pth percentile, calculate the quantity $p(n + 1)/100$ and round to the nearest integer. The measurement with this rank is the pth percentile.

Consequently, the lower and upper quartiles for small data sets are not well-defined. The box describes an approximate procedure for finding quartiles and other percentiles with small-sample data sets.

One advantage of a stem-and-leaf display is that the display makes it easy to locate the median and the upper and lower quartiles for a small data set. This is illustrated in the next example.

EXAMPLE 3.6 Find the lower quartile, the median, the upper quartile, and the 90th percentile for the 25 residential property sale prices in Table 3.2 (p. 65).

Solution The stem-and-leaf display for the data of Table 3.2 is reproduced for convenience in Figure 3.23. Since there are 25 observations in the data set, $\frac{1}{4}(n + 1) = \frac{1}{4}(26) = 6.5$. Since this value is halfway between 6 and 7, we round up to 7. Thus, the lower quartile Q_L will be the 7th observation when the data are arranged in order from smallest to largest. We can locate Q_L by proceeding down the stem-and-leaf display until we reach the stem (6) that contains the 7th leaf. Of the leaves in this stem, the value 50 represents the 7th leaf; therefore, $Q_L = 650$ (corresponding to \$65,000).

The median of the data set is the 13th observation when the data are arranged in order. Counting leaves from the top of the display, you can see that the 13th leaf is the next-to-largest entry in stem 7—namely, 60. Therefore, the median is $M = 760$ (or \$76,000).

To find the upper quartile, we compute $\frac{3}{4}(n + 1) = \frac{3}{4}(26) = 19.5$. Since this value is halfway between 19 and 20, we round down to 19. Thus, the upper quartile is the 19th leaf from the top (or the 7th leaf from the bottom) of the display, the leaf 50 in stem 9. Therefore, $Q_U = 950$ (or \$95,000).

Finally, we find the 90th percentile by computing $90(n + 1)/100 = 23.4$ (or 23, after rounding). Thus, the 90th percentile is the 23rd leaf from the top (or the third leaf from the bottom) of the stem-and-leaf display. This value is 1,120 (or \$112,000).

Recall that knowing the relation of the mean to the median aids in determining the type of skewness present in a data set. When a data set is large, the locations of the quartiles relative to the median also help us detect possible skewness in the distribution for a data set. For example, if Q_L is farther away from the median than Q_U, then the distribution is likely to be skewed to the left. If Q_U is farther away from the median than Q_L, then the distribution is likely to be skewed to the right. Lack of skewness is suggested when Q_L and Q_U are approximately equidistant from the median. These three types of skewness are depicted in Figure 3.24.

FIGURE 3.23

Stem-and-Leaf Display for the Data of Table 3.2

STEM	LEAF
3	67
4	25
5	00 75 95
6	30 50 60 82
7	10 20 49 60 70
8	20 43 99
9	45 50
10	16 60 90
11	20
12	95
13	
14	80

FIGURE 3.24

Locations of the Quartiles and Median for Various Types of Skewness

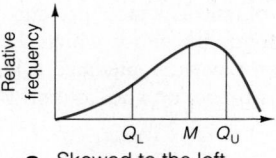
a. Skewed to the left

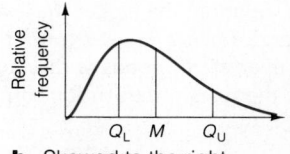
b. Skewed to the right

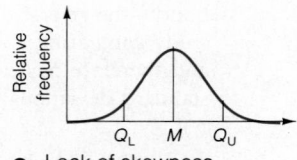
c. Lack of skewness

z-SCORES   Another measure of relative standing is the **z-score** for a measurement. For example, suppose you were told that $42,000 lies 1.44 standard deviations above the mean of the 1,795 starting salaries of University of Florida graduates discussed in earlier examples. Knowing that most of the starting salaries will be less than 2 standard deviations from the mean and almost all will be within 3, you would have a good idea of the relative standing of the $42,000 starting salary. The distance that a measurement x lies above or below the mean of a data set, measured in units of the standard deviation, is called the z-score for the measurement. A negative z-score indicates that the observation lies to the left of the mean; a positive z-score indicates that the observation lies to the right of the mean.

DEFINITION 3.16

The **z-score** for the sample measurement x is

$$z = \frac{x - \bar{x}}{s}$$

When the mean and standard deviation of the population are known, the z-score is

$$z = \frac{x - \mu}{\sigma}$$

We have noted that the sample mean and sample standard deviation for the 1,795 starting salaries are $\bar{x} = \$28{,}475$ and $s = \$9{,}369$, respectively (see Figure 3.22). Then, the z-score for a starting salary of, say, $42,000 is:

$$z = \frac{x - \bar{x}}{s} = \frac{42{,}000 - 28{,}475}{9{,}369}$$

$$= 1.44$$

Since the z-score is positive, we conclude that the $42,000 starting salary lies a distance of 1.44 standard deviations above (to the right of) the mean of $28,475.

In the next section we discuss how percentiles and z-scores can be used to detect unusual observations in a data set.

PROBLEMS

3.32   The variation of the rate of return on a bond is often used to measure the level of risk associated with buying the bond—the greater the variation, the higher the level of risk. The table presents a portion of the results of a simulation study comparing the performance of zero-coupon bonds (those for which the interest coupons have been removed and therefore pay no interest) to bonds with coupon payments attached. The simulation study yielded means and standard deviations of the rates of return for both zero-coupon and coupon bonds at a fixed interest rate.

	ZERO-COUPON BONDS	COUPON-ATTACHED BONDS
Mean	12.48%	12.48%
Standard deviation	20.80%	14.56%

Source: Potter, T. "Your Finances." *American Bar Association Journal,* Aug. 1984. Reprinted with permission from the August 1984 issue of the ABA Journal, The Lawyer's Magazine, published by the American Bar Association.

a. Use the Empirical Rule to sketch the relative frequency distributions for the rates of return of both zero-coupon bonds and coupon-attached bonds.

b. Compute the z-score for a zero-coupon bond with a rate of return of -20%. Interpret this value.

c. Compute the z-score for a coupon-attached bond with a rate of return of -20%. Interpret this value.

3.33 The hotel no-show data presented in Example 3.5 is reproduced here.

18	16	16	16	14	18	16	18	14	19	15	19	9	20	15
10	10	12	14	18	12	14	14	17	12	18	13	15	13	19

Source: Toh, R. S. "An Inventory Depletion Overbooking Model for the Hotel Industry." *Journal of Travel Research,* Vol. 23, No. 4, Spring 1985, p. 27. The *Journal of Travel Research* is published by the Travel and Tourism Research Association (TTRA) and the Business Research Division, University of Colorado at Boulder.

a. Use the stem-and-leaf display shown in Figure 3.20 (p. 107) to compute the values of Q_L, M, and Q_U.

b. Interpret the results from part **a**.

c. Compute and interpret the 90th percentile for the data.

3.34 Many Vietnam veterans have dangerously high levels of the dioxin 2,3,7,8-TCDD in blood and fat tissue as a result of their exposure to the defoliant Agent Orange. A study published in *Chemosphere* (Vol. 20, 1990) reported on the TCDD levels of 20 Massachusetts Vietnam veterans who possibly were exposed to Agent Orange. The data on TCDD levels in the plasma and fat tissue of the 20 Vietnam veterans is reproduced below.

TCDD LEVELS IN PLASMA			TCDD LEVELS IN FAT TISSUE		
2.5	3.1	2.1	4.9	5.9	4.4
3.5	3.1	1.8	6.9	7.0	4.2
6.8	3.0	36.0	10.0	5.5	41.0
4.7	6.9	3.3	4.4	7.0	2.9
4.6	1.6	7.2	4.6	1.4	7.7
1.8	20.0	2.0	1.1	11.0	2.5
2.5	4.1		2.3	2.5	

Source: Schecter, A., et al. "Partitioning of 2,3,7,8-Chlorinated Dibenzo-*p*-dioxins and Dibenzofurans Between Adipose Tissue and Plasma Lipid of 20 Massachusetts Vietnam Veterans." *Chemosphere,* Vol. 20, Nos. 7–9, 1990, pp. 954–955 (Tables I, II).

a. Calculate $\bar{x}$ and s for the TCDD levels in plasma.

b. Calculate $\bar{x}$ and s for the TCDD levels in fat tissue.

c. Calculate the z-score for a TCDD level in plasma of 20.

d. Calculate the z-score for a TCDD level in fat tissue of 20.

e. Based on the results of parts **c** and **d**, is a TCDD level of 20 more likely to occur in plasma or fat tissue? Explain.

3.35 Refer to the data given in Problem 3.5 (p. 63) on the top 25 graduate business schools. Descriptive statistics for the acceptance rate variable are shown in the SPSS printout at the top of the next page.

```
ACCRATE

Mean          25.160    Std err       1.552    Median    26.800
Mode          28.100    Std dev       7.760    Variance  60.214
Kurtosis      -1.056    S E Kurt       .902    Skewness   -.286
S E Skew        .464    Range        26.900    Minimum   10.200
Maximum       37.100    Sum         629.000

Percentile    Value     Percentile    Value    Percentile    Value

  25.00      18.800       75.00      31.800       90.00      35.360
```

a. Locate the measures of relative standing in the printout, and interpret their values.

b. Calculate a measure of relative standing for Stanford University's acceptance rate. Interpret this value.

3.36 Refer to the SAS printout describing the 8,313 residential property sale prices, Problem 3.26 (p. 99).

a. Locate the lower quartile in the printout, and interpret its value.

b. Locate the upper quartile in the printout, and interpret its value.

c. Locate the 95th percentile in the printout, and interpret its value.

d. One property in the sample sold for $80,000. Give a measure of relative standing for this property.

DETECTING UNUSUAL OBSERVATIONS: OUTLIERS

3.9 Sometimes extreme and unusual observations are included in a data set. For example, when we discuss starting salaries of college graduates with bachelor's degrees, we generally think of traditional college graduates—those near 22 years of age with 4 years of college education. But suppose one of the graduates is a 34-year-old PhD accountant who has returned to the university to obtain a bachelor's degree in marketing. Clearly, the starting salary for this graduate could be much higher than the other starting salaries because of the graduate's additional education and experience, and we probably would not want to include it in the data set. Such an unusual observation, which lies outside the range of the data values we want to describe, is called an **outlier**.

Outliers are often attributable to one of several causes. First, the measurement associated with the outlier may be invalid. For example, the experimental procedure used to generate the measurement may have malfunctioned, the experimenter may have misrecorded the measurement, or the data might have been coded incorrectly

---

DEFINITION 3.17

An observation (or measurement) that is unusually large or small relative to the other values in a data set is called an **outlier**. Outliers typically are attributable to one of the following causes:

1. The measurement is observed, recorded, or entered into the computer incorrectly.

2. The measurement comes from a different population.

3. The measurement is correct, but represents a rare (chance) event.

---

into the computer. Second, the outlier may be the result of a misclassified measurement. That is, the measurement is not from the population from which the rest of the sample was drawn, as in the case of the accountant's salary described in the preceding paragraph. Finally, the measurement associated with the outlier may be recorded correctly and from the same population as the rest of the sample, but it may represent a rare (chance) event. Such outliers occur most often when the distribution of the data is extremely skewed, because such a distribution has a tendency to include extremely large or small observations relative to the others in the data set.

Two methods for detecting outliers involve using (1) z-scores and (2) box plots.

z-SCORE METHOD

Both the Empirical Rule and Tchebysheff's theorem (Section 3.7) tell us that most of the observations in a data set will fall within 2 standard deviations of their mean, and almost all within 3 standard deviations. Since a z-score measures the distance of an observation from its mean in units of the standard deviation, it is obvious that z-scores are useful tools for detecting outliers. For mound-shaped distributions with little skewness, observations with z-scores greater than 3 in absolute value are highly unlikely and are considered outliers. For some highly skewed distributions, observations with z-scores greater than 2 in absolute value can be outliers. The cutoff you use will depend on the shape of the relative frequency distribution of the data you are analyzing, as illustrated in the next example.

EXAMPLE 3.7 Each county in the state of Florida negotiates an annual contract for bread to supply the county's public schools. Sealed bids are submitted by vendors, and the lowest bid (price per pound of bread) is selected as the bid winner. This process works extremely well in competitive markets, but it has the potential to increase the cost of purchasing if the markets are noncompetitive or if collusive practices are present. The latter occurred in the early 1980's in the Florida bread market. In several markets the suppliers of white bread were found guilty of price-fixing, that is, setting the price of bread several cents above the fair, or competitive, price.

For this example, we have obtained the winning (or low) bid prices for a random sample of 303 white bread contracts awarded in eight geographic markets over a 6 year period in Florida. (For confidentiality, the specific years and markets are not identified.) Descriptive statistics and a histogram for the data are shown in the SAS printouts in Figures 3.25a and 3.25b. Use the information provided in the printouts to identify any outliers in the bid price data.

Solution The mean and standard deviation of the sample bid prices are shaded in the SAS printout shown in Figure 3.25a. To check for outliers we would use these values, $\overline{x} = .243$ and $s = .052$, to calculate z-scores for all $n = 303$ bid prices in the data set. For the purposes of this example, we'll focus on only the highest bid prices in the sample. Notice that the five highest prices are given at the bottom of the printout, in the section titled "Extremes." The z-scores for these five prices (corresponding to contracts 17, 303, 233, 224, and 295) are computed as follows:

$$x_{17} = .364: \qquad z = \frac{.364 - .243}{.052} = 2.33$$

$$x_{303} = .375: \qquad z = \frac{.375 - .243}{.052} = 2.54$$

$$x_{233} = .405: \qquad z = \frac{.405 - .243}{.052} = 3.12$$

$$x_{224} = .410: \qquad z = \frac{.410 - .243}{.052} = 3.21$$

$$x_{295} = .440: \qquad z = \frac{.440 - .243}{.052} = 3.79$$

All five prices have z-scores that exceed 2; the prices for contracts 233, 224, and 295 have z-scores that exceed 3.

Which of these cutoffs, 2 or 3, should be used with this data set? Since the shape of the (horizontal) histogram shown in Figure 3.25b is mound-shaped and only slightly skewed to the high side, the Empirical Rule best describes the distribution of bid prices. Thus, we expect nearly all the bid prices to fall within 3 standard deviations of the sample mean. Those falling beyond this range are considered outliers and should be investigated for cause. In this example, the bid prices corresponding to contracts 233, 224, and 295 are outliers. Further investigation of these bread contacts may reveal that they were not from the population of competitively bid prices, but were fixed during collusion.

FIGURE 3.25a
SAS Printout: Descriptive Statistics for Bid Price Data

```
Variable=PRICE

                      Moments

N                303    Sum Wgts          303
Mean        0.242777    Sum          73.56131
Std Dev     0.051701    Variance     0.002673
Skewness    0.674997    Kurtosis     0.243131
USS         18.66622    CSS          0.807249
CV          21.29577    Std Mean      0.00297
T:Mean=0    81.73874    Prob>|T|       0.0001
Sgn Rank       23028    Prob>|S|       0.0001
Num ^= 0         303
W:Normal    0.948543    Prob<W         0.0001


                 Quantiles(Def=5)

 100% Max      0.44      99%       0.375
  75% Q3     0.2793      95%    0.328889
  50% Med      0.23      90%       0.312
  25% Q1     0.2052      10%    0.186667
   0% Min     0.145       5%    0.173333
                          1%    0.153333
Range         0.295
Q3-Q1        0.0741
Mode            0.2


                   Extremes

   Lowest     Obs      Highest      Obs
   0.145(     145)     0.364(       17)
0.150267(      1)      0.375(      303)
0.153333(    288)  0.405333(      233)
0.153333(    282)      0.41(      224)
0.153333(    193)      0.44(      295)
```

FIGURE 3.25b

SAS Printout: Histogram and Box
Plot for Bid Price Data

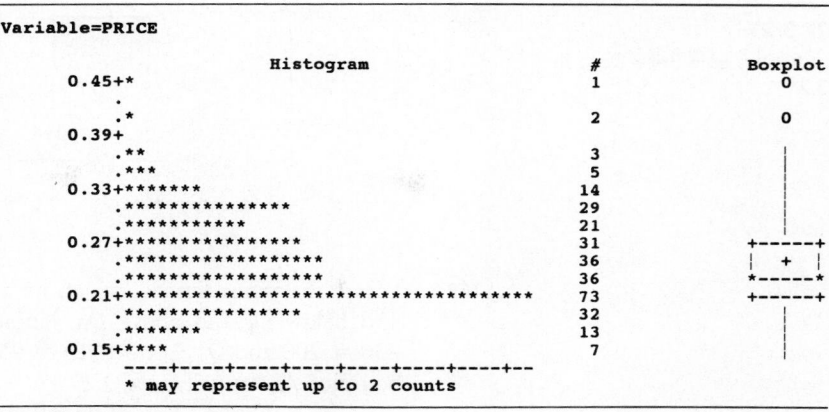

```
Variable=PRICE

                    Histogram                                #        Boxplot
    0.45+*                                                    1           0
       .
       .*                                                     2           0
    0.39+
       .**                                                    3
       .***                                                   5
    0.33+*******                                             14
       .***************                                      29
       .**********                                           21
    0.27+****************                                    31       +-----+
       .******************                                   36       |     |
       .******************                                   36       *-----*
    0.21+*****************************************           73       +-----+
       .****************                                     32
       .*******                                              13
    0.15+****                                                 7
       ----+----+----+----+----+----+----+--
    * may represent up to 2 counts
```

BOX-PLOT METHOD

Another procedure for detecting outliers is to construct a **box plot** of the data. With this method, we construct intervals similar to the $\bar{x} \pm 2s$ and $\bar{x} \pm 3s$ intervals of the Empirical Rule; however, the intervals are based on a quantity called the **interquartile range** instead of the standard deviation s.

DEFINITION 3.18

The **interquartile range**, **IQR**, is the distance between the upper and lower quartiles:

$$IQR = Q_U - Q_L$$

FIGURE 3.26

The Interquartile Range

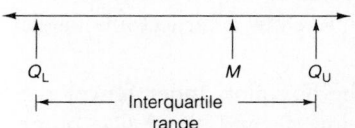

You can see from Figure 3.26 that the interquartile range is a measure of data variation. The larger the interquartile range, the more variable the data tend to be.

The box-plot procedure is especially easy to use for small data sets because the quartiles and the interquartile range can be quickly determined. We will illustrate the procedure in Example 3.8.

EXAMPLE 3.8   Refer to the residential property sale price data of Table 3.2 (p. 65). Construct a box plot for the data and check for outliers.

Solution

STEP 1   Find M, Q_L, Q_U, and IQR. From Example 3.6, $M = 760$, $Q_L = 650$, and $Q_U = 950$; therefore, the interquartile range for the data set is

$$IQR = Q_U - Q_L = 950 - 650 = 300$$

STEP 2   Construct a box with Q_L and Q_U located at the lower corners (see Figure 3.27). The base width will then be equal to the interquartile range.

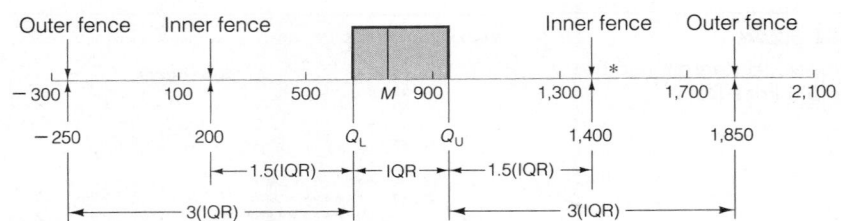

FIGURE 3.27

Box Plot for the Sale Price Data in Table 3.2

STEP 3   Locate the **inner fences**, which lie a distance of $1.5(\text{IQR}) = 1.5(300) = 450$ below Q_L and above Q_U. These values, $Q_L - 1.5(\text{IQR}) = 650 - 450 = 200$ and $Q_U + 1.5(\text{IQR}) = 950 + 450 = 1{,}400$, are located in the box plot shown in Figure 3.27.

STEP 4   Locate the **outer fences**, which lie a distance of $1.5(\text{IQR}) = 450$ below the lower inner fence and above the upper inner fence. Thus, the outer fences for this data set are located at -250 and $1{,}850$, as indicated in the figure.

STEP 5   Observations that fall between the inner and outer fences (usually indicated by asterisks) are deemed to be **suspect outliers**. Observations falling outside the outer fences (usually indicated by small circles) are judged **highly suspect outliers**. Checking the data set in Table 3.2, you can see that only the measurement 1,480 (representing a sale price of $148,000) falls outside the inner fences. Since it lies within the outer fences, it would be judged a suspect outlier and is located on the box plot with an asterisk (∗).

STEPS TO FOLLOW IN CONSTRUCTING A BOX PLOT

STEP 1   Calculate the median, M, lower and upper quartiles, Q_L and Q_U, and the interquartile range, IQR, for the measurements in a data set.

STEP 2   Construct a box with Q_L and Q_U located at the lower corners. The base width will then be equal to IQR. Draw a vertical line inside the box to locate the median, M.

STEPS 3–4   Construct two sets of limits on the box plot. **Inner fences** are located a distance of $1.5(\text{IQR})$ below Q_L and above Q_U; **outer fences** are located a distance of $3(\text{IQR})$ below Q_L and above Q_U.

STEP 5   Observations that fall between the inner and outer fences are called **suspect outliers**. Locate the suspect outliers on the box plot using asterisks (∗). Observations that fall outside the outer fences are called **highly suspect outliers**. Use small circles (∘) to locate highly suspect outliers.

For large data sets, box plots can be constructed using an available statistical software package. A MINITAB box plot for the data in Table 3.2 is shown in Figure

FIGURE 3.28
MINITAB Box Plot for the Sale Price
Data in Table 3.2

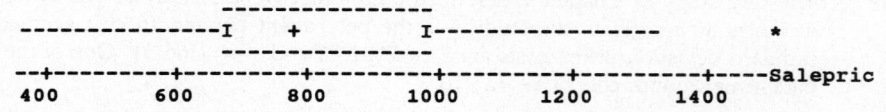

3.28. Note that Q_L and Q_U are indicated in the box plot with the symbol I (called a **hinge**). The plus (+) symbol locates the median in the box plot, and the asterisk (∗) identifies the suspect outlier at 1,480. To further highlight extreme values, MINITAB adds dashed lines (called **whiskers**) to the box plot of Figure 3.28. The left whisker extends to the smallest sale price in the region between Q_L and the lower inner fence, while the right whisker extends to the largest sale price in the region between Q_U and the upper inner fence.

The SAS box plot for the bid price data set of Example 3.7 is shown in Figure 3.25b. Like the MINITAB box plot, the plus (+) symbol locates the median bid price. However, SAS uses zeros (0) to locate suspect outliers. You can see from the box plot in Figure 3.25b that the two largest bid prices are identified as suspect outliers.

The z-score and box-plot methods both establish rules of thumb for limits outside of which a measurement is deemed to be an outlier (see the box below). Usually, the two methods produce similar results. However, the presence of one or more outliers in a data set can inflate the computed value of s (or σ). Consequently, it would be less likely that an errant observation would have a z-score larger than 3 in absolute value. In contrast, the values of the quartiles used to calculate the intervals for a box plot are not affected by the presence of outliers.

RULES OF THUMB FOR DETECTING OUTLIERS

---

1. *z-Scores:* Observations with z-scores greater than 3 in absolute value are considered **outliers**. (For some highly skewed data sets, observations with z-scores greater than 2 in absolute value may be outliers.)

2. *Box Plots:* Observations falling between the inner and outer fences are deemed **suspect outliers**. Observations falling beyond the outer fences are deemed **highly suspect outliers**.

The z-score method for detecting outliers is a popular tool in monitoring the quality of a production process. We discuss the idea of quality control in Chapter 9.

PROBLEMS

3.37   Refer to the hotel no-show data of Example 3.5 and Problem 3.33.

   a. Use the stem-and-leaf display (Figure 3.20) and the results of Problem 3.33 to form a box plot for the data.
   b. How would you classify the observations that lie between the inner and outer fences of the box plot?
   c. How would you classify the observations that lie outside the outer fences of the box plot?
   d. Use z-scores to detect suspect outliers in the data. Do your results agree with the box plot? Explain.

3.38   The case study of Chapter 2 described a cost-effectiveness study of 186 HMO physicians. One of the quantitative variables of interest in the study was the per patient per month cost accrued by each physician. The mean and standard deviation of the costs are $\bar{x} = \$102.96$ and $s = \$366.31$. One of the physicians in the data set had a per patient per month cost of $\$4,725.10$.

a. Calculate and interpret the z-score for this physician's cost. Is the observation an outlier?

b. A careful examination of this physician's data reveals a total patient–month value of 1. In other words, the physician treated only a single patient during a single month of the year at a cost of $\$4,725.10$. Based on this information, how would you classify this outlier?

3.39   The data in the table represent sales (in thousands of dollars per week) for a random sample of 24 fast-food outlets located in four cities. A MINITAB box plot for the data follows.

CITY	WEEKLY SALES Thousand Dollars
A	6.3, 6.6, 7.6, 3.0, 9.5, 5.9, 6.1, 5.0, 3.6
B	2.8, 6.7, 5.2
C	82.0, 5.0, 3.9, 5.4, 4.1, 3.1, 5.4
D	8.4, 9.5, 8.7, 10.6, 3.3

```
          ---
        -I+I--                                        0
          ---
    +---------+---------+---------+---------+---------+------Sales
    0        15        30        45        60        75
```

a. Examine the box plot. Do you detect any outliers? If so, identify the city and the weekly sales measurement associated with the outlier(s).

b. Calculate $\bar{x}$ and s for the sample data. Then use this information to compute the z-score for the outlier(s) identified in part **a**. Is the result consistent with the box plot constructed in part **a**? Explain.

c. A careful check of the sales records revealed that the weekly sales value for the first fast-food outlet in city C was actually 8.2, but was incorrectly recorded as 82.0. When this recording error is corrected, the MINITAB box plot appears as shown below. Repeat parts **a** and **b** for the corrected sales data set.

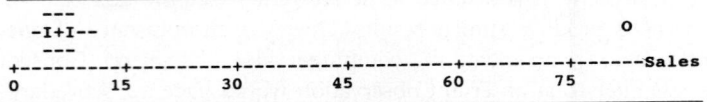

```
              -------------------------
      --------I           +            I------------------
              -------------------------
    ----+---------+---------+---------+---------+---------+--Sales
        3.0       4.5       6.0       7.5       9.0      10.5
```

3.40   Refer to the salary data for the top 20 corporate executives, Problem 3.3. The data are reproduced here.

CEO	COMPANY	TOTAL PAY
T. Frist, Jr.	HCA	127,002
S. Weill	Primerica	67,635
C. Lazarus	Toys 'R' Us	64,231
L. Hirsch	U.S. Surgical	62,171
S. Wynn	Mirage Resorts	38,005
A. O'Reilly	H. J. Heinz	36,918
M. Wygod	Medco Containment	30,207
W. Anders	General Dynamics	29,015
R. Richey	Torchmark	26,568
L. Bantle	UST Inc.	24,602
R. Mark	Colgate-Palmolive	22,818

(continued)

CEO	COMPANY	TOTAL PAY
W. Sanders III	Advanced Micro Devices	22,356
J. Welch, Jr.	General Electric	17,970
L. Iacocca	Chrysler	16,908
E. Grisanti	Int'l Flavors	16,475
A. Greenberg	Bear Stearns	15,832
R. Goizueta	Coca-Cola	15,218
W. Bartlett	Multimedia	14,822
C. Mathewson	Int'l Game Tech	14,795
P. Rooney	Wheelabrator Tech	11,216

Source: "Executive Compensation Scoreboard." *Business Week*, Apr. 26, 1993. Reprinted from Apr. 26, 1993 issue of *Business Week* by special permission, copyright © 1993 by McGraw-Hill, Inc. Used with permission.

a. Compute and interpret the values of Q_L, M, and Q_U. **b.** Construct a box plot for the data.
c. Use the box plot to detect any outliers.
d. Use the z-score method to detect any outliers. Compare to the results obtained in part **c.**

3.41 The data on TCDD levels in plasma of Vietnam veterans from Problem 3.34 are reproduced here. Use the methods of this section to check for outliers in the data set.

TCDD LEVELS IN PLASMA									
2.5	3.1	2.1	3.5	3.1	1.8	6.8	3.0	36.0	4.7
6.9	3.3	4.6	1.6	7.2	1.8	20.0	2.0	2.5	4.1

Source: Schecter, A., et al. "Partitioning of 2,3,7,8-Chlorinated Dibenzo-*p*-dioxins and Dibenzofurans Between Adipose Tissue and Plasma Lipid of 20 Massachusetts Vietnam Veterans." *Chemosphere*, Vol. 20, Nos. 7–9, 1990, pp. 954–955 (Table I).

DETECTING BIVARIATE RELATIONSHIPS

3.10 The procedures discussed in the previous sections were concerned with describing the measurements on a single variable x. Another important concern may be the relationship between two different quantitative variables, x and y, known as a **bivariate relationship**. For example, a real estate appraiser may be interested in the relationship between the appraised value of a property, x, and its sale price, y; or a marketer may be interested in the relationship between the price of a product, x, and the demand for the product, y; or a concessions manager at a major league baseball stadium may be interested in the relationship between the total attendance, x, at a game and the number of hot dogs purchased, y; and so on.

DEFINITION 3.19

A **bivariate relationship** describes the relationship between two quantitative variables, x and y.

How can we describe bivariate relationships? That is, how can we assess the degree and strength of the relationship between two variables, x and y? In this section we consider two methods, one graphical and one numerical.

The simplest and most appealing method of describing a bivariate relationship is a graphical one, as illustrated in Figure 3.29. These graphs, called **scattergrams**, are constructed by plotting pairs of observations (x, y) associated with the experimental units on graph paper. Typically, x-values are plotted on the horizontal axis and y-values on the vertical axis. Scattergrams often reveal a pattern that clearly indicates how the variables are related.

Figure 3.29a is a scattergram showing a **positive association** between the two variables. That is, small y-values tend to be associated with small x-values, and large

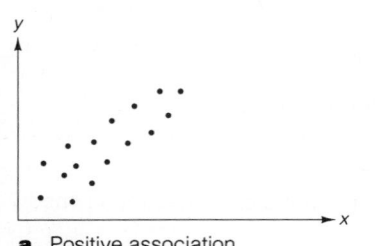

a. Positive association

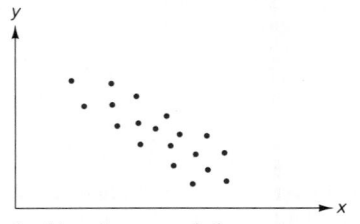

b. Negative association

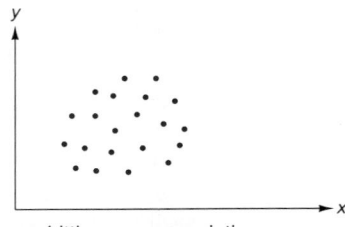

c. Little or no association

FIGURE 3.29
Scattergrams for Three Data Sets

TABLE 3.11
Data for EPA Study

BAY	STATE	PCB CONCENTRATION 1984	PCB CONCENTRATION 1985	BAY	STATE	PCB CONCENTRATION 1984	PCB CONCENTRATION 1985
Casco Bay	ME	95.28	77.55	Mississippi River Delta	LA	34	30.14
Merrimack River	MA	52.97	29.23	Barataria Bay	LA	0	0
Salem Harbor	MA	533.58	403.1	San Antonio Bay	TX	0	0
Boston Harbor	MA	17,104.86	736	Corpus Christi Bay	TX	0	0
Buzzards Bay	MA	308.46	192.15	San Diego Harbor	CA	422.1	531.67
Narragansett Bay	RI	159.96	220.6	San Diego Bay	CA	6.74	9.3
East Long Island Sound	NY	10	8.62	Dana Point	CA	7.06	5.74
West Long Island Sound	NY	234.43	174.31	Seal Beach	CA	46.71	46.47
Raritan Bay	NJ	443.89	529.28	San Pedro Canyon	CA	159.56	176.9
Delaware Bay	DE	2.5	130.67	Santa Monica Bay	CA	14	13.69
Lower Chesapeake Bay	VA	51	39.74	Bodega Bay	CA	4.18	4.89
Pamlico Sound	NC	0	0	Coos Bay	OR	3.19	6.6
Charleston Harbor	SC	9.1	8.43	Columbia River Mouth	OR	8.77	6.73
Sapelo Sound	GA	0	0	Nisqually Beach	WA	4.23	4.28
St. Johns River	FL	140	120.04	Commencement Bay	WA	20.6	20.5
Tampa Bay	FL	0	0	Elliott Bay	WA	329.97	414.5
Apalachicola Bay	FL	12	11.93	Lutak Inlet	AK	5.5	5.8
Mobile Bay	AL	0	0	Nahku Bay	AK	6.6	5.08
Round Island	MS	0	0				

Source: Environmental Quality, 1987–1988.

y-values tend to be associated with large *x*-values. Stated another way, *y* tends to *increase* as *x* increases. We would expect appraised value (*x*) of a property and its sale price (*y*) to be positively related. Alternatively, the scattergram in Figure 3.29b reveals a **negative association** between *y* and *x*; *y* tends to *decrease* as *x* increases. We would expect the demand (*y*) for a product to be negatively related to its price (*x*). No distinct pattern is revealed by the scattergram in Figure 3.29c. Consequently, we say there is little or no association between *y* and *x* in this data set. That is, as *x* increases (or decreases), there is no definite trend in the values of *y*.

To illustrate with real data, consider an Environmental Protection Agency (EPA) study of PCBs in water specimens collected at each of 37 U.S. bays and estuaries. The PCB level (in parts per billion) was measured in 1984 and 1985. The data for the two quantitative variables, 1984 PCB level (*x*) and 1985 PCB level (*y*), are given in Table 3.11. A scattergram for the data is shown in Figure 3.30.

FIGURE 3.30

Scattergram for EPA Study Data

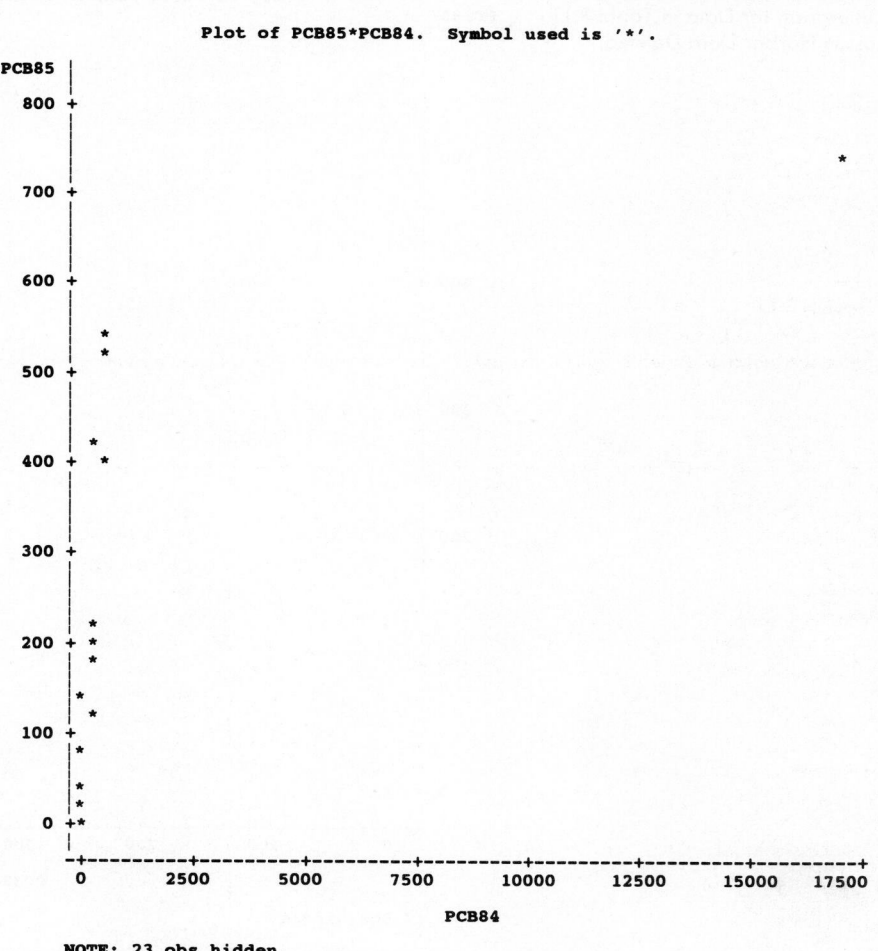

From the scattergram it is difficult to detect a relationship between *x* and *y*. We are tempted to say that little or no association exists between the 1984 and 1985 PCB levels. Before we make such an inference, however, we should examine the data set for outliers. Notice that the 1984 PCB level (*x*-value) of Boston Harbor is extremely large relative to the other *x*-values in the sample. (In fact, the *z*-score for this *x*-value is 5.91, implying that the 1984 PCB level in Boston Harbor falls nearly 6 standard deviations above the mean 1984 PCB level for the sample.) If we delete the (*x*, *y*) data point for Boston Harbor from the scattergram, we may get a clearer picture of the relationship between the two variables. This scattergram is shown in Figure 3.31. The plot reveals what now clearly appears to be a strong positive association between the 1984 and 1985 PCB levels. That is, large PCB levels in 1984 tended to be associated with large PCB levels in 1985.

FIGURE 3.31

Scattergram for Data in Table 3.11 (Boston Harbor Data Deleted)

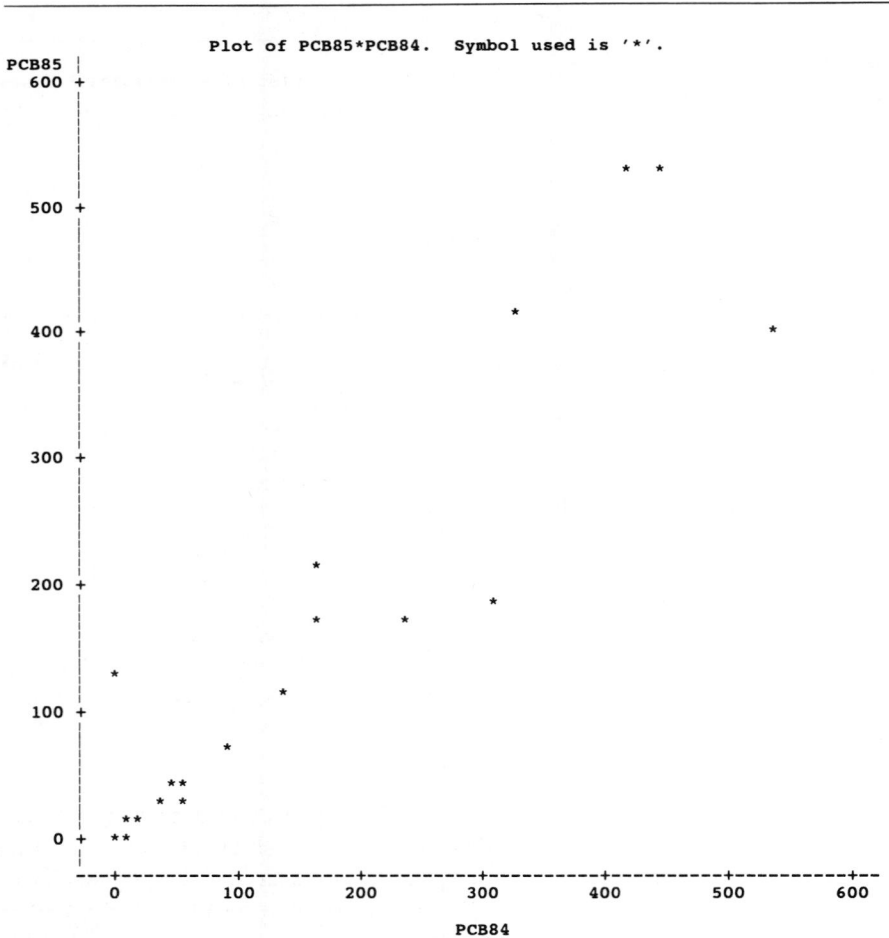

CORRELATION

Scattergrams represent a graphical method of detecting relationships between variables. The strength of the relationship is often expressed numerically through the concept of **correlation**. For example, we often hear that the crime rate and the unemployment rate are "highly correlated." Another popular belief is that the gross national product and the rate of inflation are "correlated." In the following example we show how to calculate a numerical descriptive measure of the correlation between two variables, x and y, in a sample.

EXAMPLE 3.9 Each year, *Fortune* ranks the top American cities according to their ability to provide high-quality, low-cost labor for companies that are relocating. One important measure used to form the rankings is the *labor market stress index* (y), which indicates the availability of workers in the city. (The higher the index, the tighter the labor market.) A second important variable is the *unemployment rate* (x). The values of these two variables for each of the top 10 cities in 1990 are listed in Table 3.12. Calculate a numerical descriptive measure of the correlation between the unemployment rate, x, and the labor market stress index, y, for the 10 cities in the sample.

TABLE 3.12
Data for Example 3.9

RANK	CITY	LABOR MARKET STRESS INDEX y	UNEMPLOYMENT RATE x, %
1	Salt Lake City	107	4.5
2	Minneapolis–St. Paul	107	3.8
3	Atlanta	100	5.1
4	Sacramento	100	4.9
5	Austin (Texas)	80	5.4
6	Columbus (Ohio)	100	4.8
7	Dallas/Fort Worth	100	5.5
8	Phoenix	93	4.3
9	Jacksonville (Florida)	87	5.7
10	Oklahoma City	80	4.6

Source: Fortune, Oct. 22, 1990, pp. 58–63. FORTUNE © 1990 Time Inc. All rights reserved.

Solution The first step in computing a measure of correlation between x and y for the $n = 10$ pairs of observations is to find the sums of the x-values ($\Sigma\, x$) and y-values ($\Sigma\, y$), the squares of the x-values ($\Sigma\, x^2$), the squares of the y-values ($\Sigma\, y^2$), and the cross-products of the corresponding x- and y-values ($\Sigma\, xy$). As an aid in finding these quantities, construct a **sums of squares table** of the type shown in Table 3.13. Notice that the quantities $\Sigma\, x$, $\Sigma\, y$, $\Sigma\, x^2$, $\Sigma\, y^2$, and $\Sigma\, xy$ appear in the bottom row of the table.

TABLE 3.13

Sums of Squares for Data of Example 3.9

x	y	x^2	y^2	xy
4.5	107	20.25	11,449	481.5
3.8	107	14.44	11,449	406.6
5.1	100	26.01	10,000	510.0
4.9	100	24.01	10,000	490.0
5.4	80	29.16	6,400	432.0
4.8	100	23.04	10,000	480.0
5.5	100	30.25	10,000	550.0
4.3	93	18.49	8,649	399.9
5.7	87	32.49	7,569	495.9
4.6	80	21.16	6,400	368.0
Totals $\Sigma x = 48.6$	$\Sigma y = 954$	$\Sigma x^2 = 239.30$	$\Sigma y^2 = 91,916$	$\Sigma xy = 4,613.9$

The second step is to calculate the quantities SS_{xy}, SS_{xx}, and SS_{yy}, as shown below:

$$SS_{xy} = \Sigma xy - \frac{(\Sigma x)(\Sigma y)}{n} = 4,613.9 - \frac{(48.6)(954)}{10} = -22.54$$

$$SS_{xx} = \Sigma x^2 - \frac{(\Sigma x)^2}{n} = 239.30 - \frac{(48.6)^2}{10} = 3.104$$

$$SS_{yy} = \Sigma y^2 - \frac{(\Sigma y)^2}{n} = 91,916 - \frac{(954)^2}{10} = 904.4$$

Finally, compute the **measure of correlation**, denoted by the symbol, r, as follows:

$$r = \frac{SS_{xy}}{\sqrt{SS_{xx}SS_{yy}}} = \frac{-22.54}{\sqrt{(3.104)(904.4)}} = -.425$$

The formal name given to r is the **Pearson product moment coefficient of correlation**. It can be shown (proof omitted) that r is scaleless—that is, it is not measured in dollars or pounds, etc., but always assumes a value between -1 and $+1$ regardless of the units of measurement of the variables x and y. More importantly, the correlation coefficient r is a measure of the strength of the **linear** (ie, straight-line) relationship between x and y in the sample. We can gain insight into this interpretation by reexamining the scattergrams presented in Figure 3.29.

Consider first the scattergram in Figure 3.29c. The correlation coefficient r for this set of points is near 0, implying little or no linear association between x and y. In contrast, positive values of r imply a positive linear association between y and x. Consequently, the value of r for the data illustrated in Figure 3.29a is positive. Similarly, a negative value of r implies a negative linear association between y and x (see Figure 3.29b). A perfect linear relationship exists when all the (x, y) points fall exactly along a straight line. A value of $r = +1$ implies a perfect positive linear relationship between y and x, and a value of $r = -1$ implies a perfect negative linear relationship between y and x.

DEFINITION 3.20

The **Pearson product moment coefficient of correlation**, r, is computed as follows for a sample of n measurements x and y:

$$r = \frac{SS_{xy}}{\sqrt{SS_{xx}SS_{yy}}}$$

where

$$SS_{xy} = \Sigma\, xy - \frac{(\Sigma\, x)(\Sigma\, y)}{n}$$

$$SS_{xx} = \Sigma\, x^2 - \frac{(\Sigma\, x)^2}{n}$$

$$SS_{yy} = \Sigma\, y^2 - \frac{(\Sigma\, y)^2}{n}$$

It is a measure of the strength of the *linear* relationship between two random variables x and y. Values of r near $+1$ imply a strong positive linear association between the variables; values of r near -1, a strong negative linear association; and values of r near 0, little or no linear association.

In Example 3.9, we calculated the coefficient of correlation as $r = -.425$. How should *Fortune* interpret this value of r? Since r is both negative and moderate in magnitude (absolute value), the implication is that a moderately negative association between labor market stress index (y) and unemployment rate (x) exists for the 10 cities in the sample. We can see this moderate negative linear relationship in the scattergram for the data of Table 3.12 shown in Figure 3.32 (p. 130).

EXAMPLE 3.10   Refer to the PCB data in Table 3.11. Calculate and interpret the coefficient of correlation r between 1984 PCB level (x) and 1985 PCB level (y) of U.S. bays and estuaries, excluding Boston Harbor.

Solution   The data were analyzed by computer using SAS software. The sample correlation coefficient r is shaded in the SAS printout shown in Figure 3.33. You can see that $r = .947$. (You should be able to verify this number using the computing formulas given in the box.) The positive sign and the large magnitude (absolute value) of r imply that there is a strong positive association between the 1984 and 1985 PCB levels in the sample. Note that this interpretation agrees with our interpretation of the scattergram, Figure 3.31.

In concluding this discussion of correlation, three important points need to be made. First, the correlation coefficient r measures the strength of only the *linear* relationship between x and y. Consequently, the value of r may be misleading when

FIGURE 3.32
Scattergram for Example 3.9

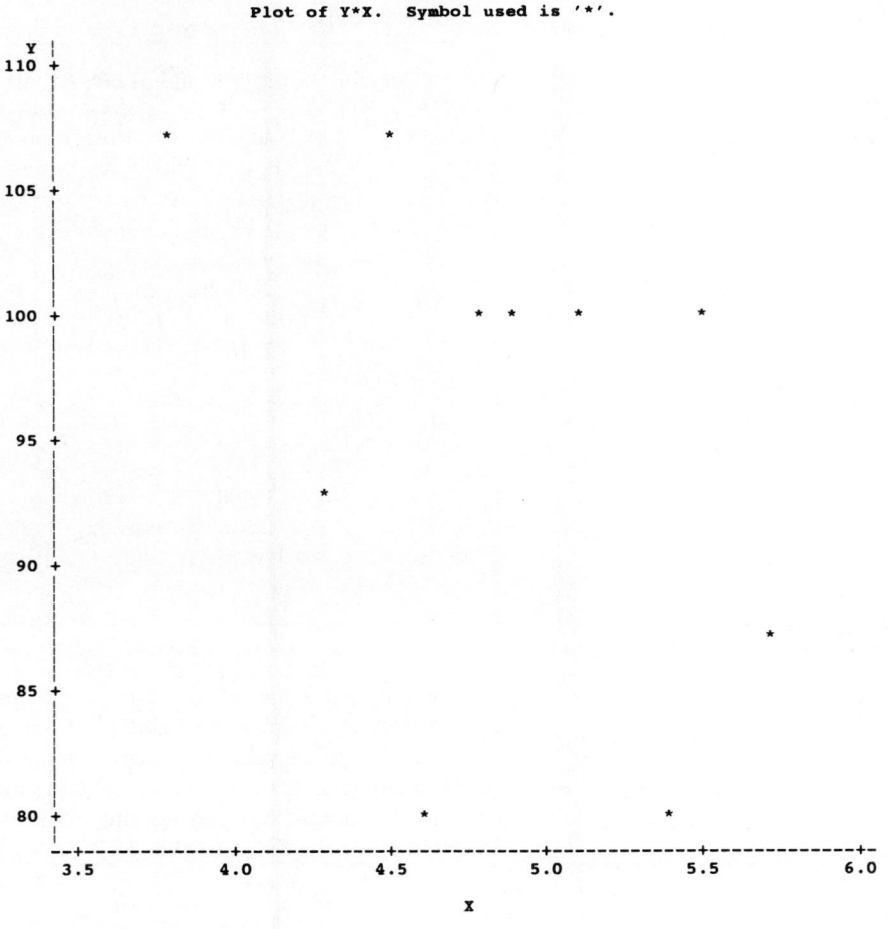

Plot of Y*X.   Symbol used is '*'.

FIGURE 3.33
SAS Printout of Correlation Analysis for Example 3.10

CORRELATION ANALYSIS

2 'VAR' Variables: PCB84   PCB85

Pearson Correlation Coefficients / Prob > |R| under Ho: Rho=0 / N = 36

	PCB84	PCB85
PCB84	1.00000	0.94728
	0.0	0.0001
PCB85	0.94728	1.00000
	0.0001	0.0

the relationship is more complex than a straight line. Figure 3.34 shows a very strong *curvilinear* relationship between the variables, and yet the value of r is near 0.

When interpreting r, be sure to restrict your inferences to the linear relationship between x and y.

FIGURE 3.34

A Curvilinear Relationship Between y
and x; r Is Near 0

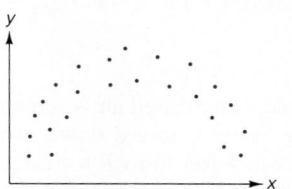

Second, r is only a sample statistic, that is:

It measures the correlation in the sample only, not the population.

A measure of correlation in the population from which the sample of (x, y) data points was selected is called the **population correlation coefficient**, and is denoted by the symbol ρ (rho). Our interpretation of ρ is analogous to that of r: The population coefficient of correlation measures the strength of the linear relationship between x-values and y-values in the entire population. Statistical methods for making inferences about the population correlation coefficient based on the value of r are presented in Chapter 10.

Finally, we conclude with a warning.

WARNING

High correlation *does not imply causality*. If a large positive or negative value of the sample correlation coefficient r is observed, it is incorrect to conclude that a change in x causes a change in y. The only valid conclusion is that a linear trend may exist between x and y.

PROBLEMS

3.42 An automated system for marking large numbers of student computer programs, called AUTOMARK, has been used successfully at McMaster University in Ontario, Canada. AUTOMARK takes into account both program correctness and program style when marking student assignments. AUTOMARK was used to grade the FORTRAN77 assignments of a class of 33 students. To evaluate the effectiveness of the automated system, these grades were compared to the grades assigned by the instructor. The results are shown in the table.

AUTOMARK GRADE	INSTRUCTOR GRADE	AUTOMARK GRADE	INSTRUCTOR GRADE	AUTOMARK GRADE	INSTRUCTOR GRADE
x	y	x	y	x	y
12.2	10	18.2	15	19.0	17
10.6	11	15.1	16	19.3	17
15.1	12	17.2	16	19.5	17
16.2	12	17.5	16	19.7	17
16.6	12	18.6	16	18.6	18
16.6	13	18.8	16	19.0	18
17.2	14	17.8	17	19.2	18
17.6	14	18.0	17	19.4	18
18.2	14	18.2	17	19.6	18
16.5	15	18.4	17	20.1	18
17.2	15	18.6	17	19.2	19

Source: Redish, K. A., and Smyth, W. F. "Program Style Analysis: A Natural By-Product of Program Compilation." *Communications of the Association for Computing Machinery*, Vol. 29, No. 2, Feb. 1986, p. 32 (Fig. 4).

a. Construct a scattergram for the data. After examining the scattergram, do you think that x and y are correlated? If correlation is present, is it positive or negative?

b. Find the correlation coefficient r and interpret its value.

3.43 To examine potential gender differences in the industrial sales force, a sample of 244 males and a sample of 153 females were administered a questionnaire (*Journal of Personal Selling & Sales Management*, Summer 1990). All respondents were either sales managers or salespeople at one of 16 industrial firms located in the southeastern United States. Two variables of interest to the researchers were level of organizational commitment (y) and total months experience in sales (x). For the 244 males in the study, the coefficient of correlation between x and y was $r_{\text{Males}} = -.35$. For the 153 females in the study, the correlation coefficient was $r_{\text{Females}} = -.06$.

  a. Interpret the value of r_{Males}.   **b.** Interpret the value of r_{Females}.

3.44 Two processes for hydraulic drilling of rock are dry drilling and wet drilling. In a dry hole, compressed air is forced down the drill rods in order to flush the cuttings and drive the hammer; in a wet hole, water is forced down. An experiment was conducted to determine whether the time y it takes to dry drill a distance of 5 feet in rock increases with depth x (*The American Statistician*, Feb. 1991). The results for one portion of the experiment are shown in the table.

DEPTH WHERE DRILLING BEGINS x, feet	TIME TO DRILL 5 FEET y, minutes	DEPTH WHERE DRILLING BEGINS x, feet	TIME TO DRILL 5 FEET y, minutes
0	4.90	225	8.28
25	7.41	250	4.84
50	6.19	275	8.29
75	5.57	300	8.91
100	5.17	325	8.54
125	6.89	350	11.79
150	7.05	375	12.12
175	7.11	395	11.02
200	6.19		

Source: Penner, R., and Watts, D. G. "Mining Information." *The American Statistician*, Vol. 45, No. 1, Feb. 1991, p. 6 (Table 1). Reprinted with permission from *The American Statistician*. Copyright 1991 by the American Statistical Association. All rights reserved.

  a. Construct a scattergram for the data. After examining the scattergram, do you think that x and y are correlated? If correlation is present, is it positive or negative?
  b. Find the correlation coefficient r and interpret its value.

3.45 In the business world, the term *Machiavellian* is often used to describe those who employ aggressive, manipulative, exploitive, and devious moves in order to achieve personal and corporate objectives. A *Journal of Marketing* (Summer 1984) study investigated Machiavellian tactics in marketing. One question concerned the relationship between age and Machiavellianism. Do young marketers tend to be more Machiavellian than older marketers? A sample of 1,076 members of the American Marketing Association were given a questionnaire that measured tendency toward Machiavellianism. (The higher the score, the greater the tendency toward Machiavellianism.) The sample correlation coefficient between age and Machiavellianism score was found to be $r = -.20$. Interpret this value of r.

3.46 For a company to maintain a competitive edge in the marketplace, spending on research and development (R&D) is essential. To determine the optimum level for R&D spending and its effect on a company's value, a simple linear regression analysis was performed (*Research Management*, Sept./Oct. 1986). Data collected for the largest R&D spenders (based on 1981–1982 averages) were used to fit a straight-line model relating y to x, where

$$y = \text{Price/earnings (P/E) ratio}$$
$$x = \text{R\&D expenditures/sales (R/S) ratio}$$

The data for 20 of the companies used in the study are provided in the table.

COMPANY	P/E RATIO y	R/S RATIO x	COMPANY	P/E RATIO y	R/S RATIO x
1	5.6	.003	11	8.4	.058
2	7.2	.004	12	11.1	.058
3	8.1	.009	13	11.1	.067
4	9.9	.021	14	13.2	.080
5	6.0	.023	15	13.4	.080
6	8.2	.030	16	11.5	.083
7	6.3	.035	17	9.8	.091
8	10.0	.037	18	16.1	.092
9	8.5	.044	19	7.0	.064
10	13.2	.051	20	5.9	.028

Source: Wallin, C. C., and Gilman, J. J. "Determining the Optimum Level for R&D Spending." *Research Management*, Vol. 14, No. 5, Sept./Oct. 1986, pp. 19–24 (adapted from Fig. 1, p. 20).

a. Construct a scattergram for the data. After examining the scattergram, do you think that x and y are correlated? If correlation is present, is it positive or negative?

b. Find the correlation coefficient r and interpret its value.

3.47 Refer to *Business Week's* "Executive Compensation Scoreboard," discussed in Problem 3.3. In addition to total 1992 CEO compensation, *Business Week* also measured the return to shareholders on a $100 investment made 3 years earlier in each CEO's firm. The data for these two variables, total pay (x) and shareholder return (y), for the top 20 CEOs in 1992 are shown in the table. Use the methods of this section to identify the nature of the bivariate relationship between total CEO pay (x) and shareholder return (y).

CEO	COMPANY	TOTAL PAY x	SHAREHOLDER RETURN y
T. Frist, Jr.	HCA	127,002	—
S. Weill	Primerica	67,635	175
C. Lazarus	Toys 'R' Us	64,231	168
L. Hirsch	U.S. Surgical	62,171	508
S. Wynn	Mirage Resorts	38,005	—
A. O'Reilly	H. J. Heinz	36,918	135
M. Wygod	Medco Containment	30,207	518
W. Anders	General Dynamics	29,015	239
R. Richey	Torchmark	26,568	162
L. Bantle	UST Inc.	24,602	222
R. Mark	Colgate-Palmolive	22,818	185
W. Sanders III	Advanced Micro Devices	22,356	230
J. Welch, Jr.	General Electric	17,970	142
L. Iacocca	Chrysler	16,908	181
E. Grisanti	Int'l Flavors	16,475	172
A. Greenberg	Bear Stearns	15,832	199
R. Goizueta	Coca-Cola	15,218	224
W. Bartlett	Multimedia	14,822	—
C. Mathewson	Int'l Game Tech	14,795	1,573
P. Rooney	Wheelabrator Tech	11,216	211

Source: "Executive Compensation Scoreboard." *Business Week*, Apr. 26, 1993. Reprinted from Apr. 26, 1993 issue of *Business Week* by special permission, copyright © 1993 by McGraw-Hill, Inc. Used with permission.

DESCRIBING QUANTITATIVE DATA NUMERICALLY

The SAS, SPSS, and MINITAB commands for producing numerical descriptive measures of quantitative data (eg, mean, median, standard deviation, percentiles) and the sample coefficient of correlation are presented in this section. For the purpose of illustration, the data in Table 3.11 (with the observation for Boston Harbor omitted) are used to produce descriptive statistics for the two quantitative variables, PCB levels in 1984 and 1985, and to examine the correlation between the two variables.

[*Note:* As in all Computer Lab sections, the commands given below (unless otherwise noted) are appropriate for both mainframe and personal computers. However, programs run on mainframe computers require JCL instructions. See your instructor for the appropriate JCL commands for your computing center.]

SAS

```
Command
Line
  1      DATA EPA;                        ⎫ Data entry instructions
  2      INPUT BAY $ PCB84 PCB85;         ⎭
  3      CARDS;
         CASCO        95.28    77.55 ⎫
         MERRIMACK    52.97    29.23 ⎪
            •            •        •   ⎬ Input data values
            •            •        •   ⎪ (1 observation per line)
            •            •        •   ⎪
         NAHKU         6.60     5.08 ⎭
  4      PROC UNIVARIATE; ⎫ Descriptive statistics
  5      VAR PCB84 PCB85; ⎭
  6      PROC PLOT;            ⎫ Scattergram
  7      PLOT PCB84*PCB85;     ⎭
  8      PROC CORR;            ⎫ Correlation coefficient
  9      VAR PCB84 PCB85;      ⎭
```

COMMANDS 4–5   The UNIVARIATE procedure produces descriptive statistics for each of the variables specified in the VAR statement. The summary measures printed include the mean, median, mode, variance, standard deviation, lower quartile, upper quartile, 90th, 95th, and 99th percentiles.

COMMANDS 6–7   The PLOT procedure will produce a scattergram for bivariate data. The variable on the vertical axis (in this case, PCB84) appears to the left of the asterisk in the PLOT statement; the variable on the horizontal axis (in this case, PCB85) to the right.

COMMANDS 8–9   The CORR procedure calculates correlation coefficients for each pair of variables listed on the VAR statement.

NOTE   The output for this SAS program is displayed in Figure 3.35 (p. 137).

SPSS

```
Command
  Line
   1    DATA LIST FREE/BAY (A10) PCB84 PCB85.⎫
   2    BEGIN DATA.                          ⎬ Data entry instructions
        CASCO       95.28  77.55⎫
        MERRIMACK   52.97  29.23⎪
           .          .      .  ⎪ Input data values
           .          .      .  ⎬ (1 observation per line)
           .          .      .  ⎪
        NAHKU        6.60   5.08⎭
   3    END DATA.
   4    FREQUENCIES VARIABLES=PCB84 PCB85/⎫
   5                STATISTICS=ALL/        ⎬ Descriptive statistics
   6                PERCENTILES=25 75 90.  ⎭
   7    PLOT PLOT=PCB84 WITH PCB85.  Scattergram
   8    CORRELATIONS VARIABLES=PCB84 PCB85.  Correlation coefficient
```

COMMANDS 4–6   The FREQUENCIES command computes descriptive statistics for the quantitative variables listed in the VARIABLES subcommand. The STATISTICS=ALL option computes the mean, median, mode, variance, and standard deviation. The PERCENTILES subcommand calculates all percentiles specified (eg, 25) after the equals sign.

COMMAND 7   The PLOT command produces bivariate scattergrams. The variable on the vertical axis (in this case, PCB84) is specified to the left of the key word WITH; the variable on the horizontal axis (in this case, PCB85) to the right.

COMMAND 8   The CORRELATIONS command calculates correlation coefficients for each pair of variables listed in the VARIABLE subcommand.

NOTE   The output for this SPSS program is displayed in Figure 3.36 (p. 139).

```
Command
  Line
   1      READ  C1  C2   Data entry instruction
           95.28   77.55
           52.97   29.23
              .        .        Input data values
              .        .        (1 observation per line)
              .        .
            6.60     5.08
   2      NAME  C1='PCB84'  C2='PCB85'    Data entry instruction
   3      DESCRIBE  C1  C2   Descriptive statistics
   4      PLOT  C1  C2   Scattergram
   5      CORRELATION  C1  C2    Correlation coefficient
```

COMMAND 3 The DESCRIBE command produces descriptive statistics (mean, median, standard deviation, lower quartile, and upper quartile) for each column (variables) specified.

COMMAND 4 The PLOT command produces a scattergram for bivariate data. The column (variable) listed first is placed on the vertical axis; the column (variable) listed second is placed on the horizontal axis.

COMMAND 5 The CORRELATION command calculates correlation coefficients for each pair of columns (variables) listed.

NOTE The output for this MINITAB program is displayed in Figure 3.37 (p. 140).

FIGURE 3.35

SAS Output for Computer Lab 2

```
                    UNIVARIATE PROCEDURE
Variable=PCB84
                    Moments

N                    36    Sum Wgts              36
Mean            86.84389   Sum              3126.38
Std Dev         145.1213   Variance         21060.2
Skewness        1.874029   Kurtosis        2.550049
USS              1008614   CSS               737107
CV               167.106   Std Mean        24.18689
T:Mean=0        3.590536   Prob>|T|          0.0010
Sgn Rank             203   Prob>|S|          0.0001
Num ^= 0              28


                 Quantiles(Def=5)

  100% Max     533.58        99%     533.58
   75% Q3      117.64        95%     443.89
   50% Med       9.55        90%     329.97
   25% Q1       2.845        10%          0
    0% Min          0         5%          0
                              1%          0

  Range        533.58
  Q3-Q1       114.795
  Mode             0

                    Extremes

    Lowest    Obs      Highest     Obs
        0(     22)     308.46(      4)
        0(     21)     329.97(     34)
        0(     20)      422.1(     23)
        0(     18)     443.89(      8)
        0(     17)     533.58(      3)


Variable=PCB85
                    Moments

N                    36    Sum Wgts              36
Mean             89.665    Sum              3227.94
Std Dev         151.105    Variance        22832.73
Skewness        1.996359   Kurtosis        3.097108
USS              1088579   CSS             799145.6
CV               168.5218  Std Mean        25.18417
T:Mean=0        3.560371   Prob>|T|          0.0011
Sgn Rank             203   Prob>|S|          0.0001
Num ^= 0              28


                 Quantiles(Def=5)

  100% Max     531.67        99%     531.67
   75% Q3     125.355        95%     529.28
   50% Med    10.615         90%      403.1
   25% Q1      4.585         10%          0
    0% Min         0          5%          0
                              1%          0

  Range        531.67
  Q3-Q1       120.77
  Mode             0

                    Extremes

    Lowest    Obs      Highest     Obs
        0(     22)      220.6(      5)
        0(     21)      403.1(      3)
        0(     20)      414.5(     34)
        0(     18)     529.28(      8)
        0(     17)     531.67(     23)
```

(continued)

FIGURE 3.35 (*Continued*)

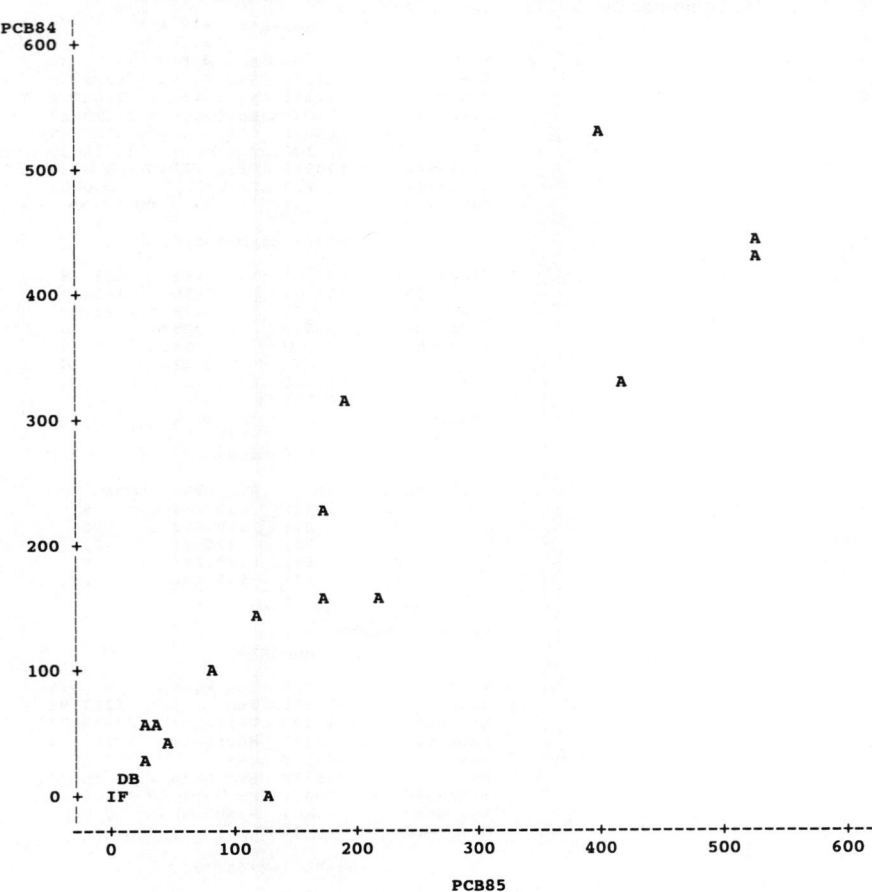

Plot of PCB84*PCB85.   Legend: A = 1 obs, B = 2 obs, etc.

CORRELATION ANALYSIS

Pearson Correlation Coefficients / Prob > |R| under Ho: Rho=0 / N = 36

	PCB84	PCB85
PCB84	1.00000	0.94728
	0.0	0.0001
PCB85	0.94728	1.00000
	0.0001	0.0

FIGURE 3.36

SPSS Output for Computer Lab 2

PCB84

Mean	86.844	Std err	24.187	Median	9.550
Mode	.000	Std dev	145.121	Variance	21060.201
Kurtosis	2.550	S E Kurt	.768	Skewness	1.874
S E Skew	.393	Range	533.580	Minimum	.000
Maximum	533.580	Sum	3126.380		

Percentile	Value	Percentile	Value	Percentile	Value
25.00	2.673	75.00	128.820	90.00	357.609

Valid cases   36   Missing cases   0

PCB85

Mean	89.665	Std err	25.184	Median	10.615
Mode	.000	Std dev	151.105	Variance	22832.732
Kurtosis	3.097	S E Kurt	.768	Skewness	1.996
S E Skew	.393	Range	531.670	Minimum	.000
Maximum	531.670	Sum	3227.940		

Percentile	Value	Percentile	Value	Percentile	Value
25.00	4.433	75.00	128.012	90.00	406.520

Valid cases   36   Missing cases   0

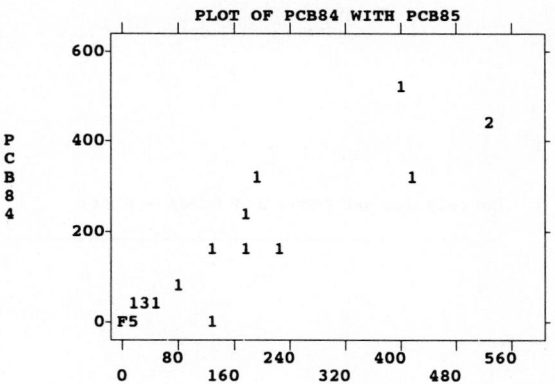

Correlations: PCB84   PCB85

PCB84	1.0000	.9473**
PCB85	.9473**	1.0000

N of cases: 36   1-tailed Signif: * - .01   ** - .001

FIGURE 3.37

MINITAB Output for Computer
Lab 2

	N	MEAN	MEDIAN	TRMEAN	STDEV	SEMEAN
PCB84	36	86.8	9.6	67.2	145.1	24.2
PCB85	36	89.7	10.6	67.7	151.1	25.2

	MIN	MAX	Q1	Q3
PCB84	0.0	533.6	2.7	128.8
PCB85	0.0	531.7	4.4	128.0

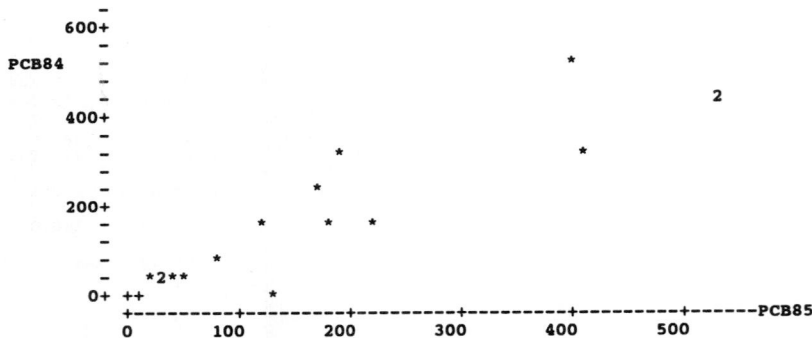

Correlation of PCB84 and PCB85 = 0.947

CHAPTER NOTES

- **Dot plots, stem-and-leaf displays**, and **histograms** are graphical displays of the distribution of a quantitative variable.
- Distributions of data that are spread unusually far to the right or left (ie, with elongated "tails") are called **skewed** distributions.
- **Positively skewed** distributions are skewed to the right, while **negatively skewed** distributions are skewed to the left.
- **Sequence plots** are plots of quantitative process data collected sequentially over time.
- **Numerical descriptive measures** (or **descriptive statistics**) are numbers that summarize certain features of a quantitative data set.
- The **mean**, **median**, and **mode** are numerical descriptive measures of **central tendency** for quantitative data.

- The **sample mean**, $\bar{x}$, is the average of all the measurements in the sample:

$$\bar{x} = \frac{\sum x}{n}$$

- The **population mean**, μ, is the average of all the measurements in the population.
- The **population median**, η, is the measurement that divides the distribution of data into two equal proportions. Half the measurements fall below η and half exceed η.
- The **sample median**, M, is the middle observation (or average of the two middle observations) when the sample data are arranged in order of magnitude.
- The median is a **resistant** measure of central tendency. It is less sensitive to extreme measurements than the mean.
- The **mode** is the measurement that occurs most often.
- The **range**, **variance**, and **standard deviation** are numerical descriptive measures of **spread** for quantitative data.
- The **range** is the difference between the largest and smallest measurement in the data set.
- The **sample variance**, s^2, is the sum of squared deviations of the sample measurements about their mean, divided by $(n - 1)$:

$$s^2 = \frac{\sum(x - \bar{x})^2}{n - 1} = \frac{\sum x^2 - \frac{(\sum x)^2}{n}}{n - 1}$$

- The **population variance**, σ^2, is the sum of squared deviations of the population measurements about their mean, divided by N:

$$\sigma^2 = \frac{\sum(x - \mu)^2}{N}$$

- The **sample standard deviation**, s, is the square root of the sample variance, s^2.
- The **population standard deviation**, σ, is the square root of the population variance, σ^2.
- Two rules for describing (population or sample) quantitative data sets are the **Empirical Rule** and **Tchebysheff's theorem**. The Empirical Rule can be applied when the distribution of data is mound-shaped and not highly skewed. Tchebysheff's theorem can be applied to any data set.
- The percentages of measurements that fall within 1, 2, and 3 standard deviations of the mean under each rule are given below:

	EMPIRICAL RULE	**TCHEBYSHEFF'S THEOREM**
Mean $\pm$ 1 st. dev.:	About 70%	At least 0%
Mean $\pm$ 2 st. dev.:	Approx. 95%	At least 75%
Mean $\pm$ 3 st. dev.:	Near 100%	At least 89%

- Numerical descriptive measures that locate the relative position of a measurement in a data set are called measures of **relative standing**.
- Two measures of relative standing are **percentiles** and **z-scores**.
- The **pth percentile** is a number such that $p\%$ of the measurements in the data set fall below it and $(100 - p)\%$ fall above it.

- The **lower quartile** (Q_L), **mid-quartile** (M), and **upper quartile** (Q_U) represent the 25th, 50th (median), and 75th percentiles, respectively.
- The **interquartile range**, **IQR**, is the distance between the upper and lower quartiles:

$$IQR = Q_U - Q_L$$

- **Box plots** describe a distribution of data by locating two sets of limits: **inner fences** and **outer fences**. Inner fences lie a distance of 1.5(IQR) below Q_L and above Q_U. Outer fences lie a distance of 3(IQR) below Q_L and above Q_U.
- The **z-score** for a measurement x is the distance that x falls above (or below) its mean, measured in units of standard deviations:

$$\text{Samples:} \quad z = \frac{x - \bar{x}}{s} \qquad \text{Populations:} \quad z = \frac{x - \mu}{\sigma}$$

- **Outliers** are unusually large or small measurements relative to the others in a data set. Outliers can be detected using either z-scores or box plots:

	z-SCORES	**BOX PLOT**
Suspect outliers:	$2 < |z| < 3$	Observations between inner and outer fences
Highly suspect outliers:	$|z| > 3$	Observations beyond outer fences

- The relationship between two quantitative variables x and y is called a **bivariate relationship**.
- A **scattergram** is a plot of the pairs of bivariate data points (x, y).
- Two variables x and y are **positively associated** if y tends to increase as x increases; x and y are **negatively associated** if y tends to decrease as x increases.
- A numerical descriptive measure of the strength of the **linear** association between two variables x and y in the sample is the **sample correlation coefficient, r**:

$$r = \frac{SS_{xy}}{\sqrt{SS_{xx}SS_{yy}}}$$

where

$$SS_{xy} = \Sigma \, xy - \frac{(\Sigma \, x)(\Sigma \, y)}{n}$$

$$SS_{xx} = \Sigma \, x^2 - \frac{(\Sigma \, x)^2}{n}$$

$$SS_{yy} = \Sigma \, y^2 - \frac{(\Sigma \, y)^2}{n}$$

- Values of r near $+1$ imply a **strong positive linear association** between the variables; values of r near -1, a **strong negative linear association**; and values of r near 0, **little or no linear association**.
- The **population correlation coefficient, ρ**, measures the strength of the linear association between two variables x and y in the population.

In Chapter 4 we discuss some basic concepts of probability and probability distributions. This knowledge will enable us to construct confidence intervals and perform statistical tests of hypotheses for population parameters. Confidence intervals and hypothesis tests, introduced in Chapter 5, are the two major tools of statistical inference.

CASE STUDY

FUDGING THE DATA

Statistics plays a key role in monitoring the quality of manufactured products and in controlling the quality of products shipped to consumers (see Chapter 9). In his essay "Making Things Right," W. Edwards Deming gave several illustrations of statistical control of quality drawn from the production line.* In one example, Deming examined the quality control process for a manufacturer of steel rods. Rods produced with diameters smaller than the **lower specification limit (LSL)** of 1 centimeter fit too loosely in their bearings and ultimately must be rejected (thrown out). To determine if the diameter setting of the machine that produces the rods is correct, 500 rods are selected from the day's production and their diameters are recorded. The 500 diameters for one day's production are provided in Table 3.14.

a. Use one or more of the methods discussed in this chapter to completely describe and summarize the data.†

b. The manufacturing process is out of control if more than 10% of the rods produced have diameters below the LSL. Use your results from part **a** to determine whether the process is out of control.

c. There has been speculation that some of the inspectors are unaware of the trouble that an undersized rod diameter would cause later on in the manufacturing process. Consequently, these inspectors may be passing rods with diameters that are barely below the LSL and recording them as 1.000 centimeter. Is there any evidence to support the claim that the inspectors "fudged" the data? Explain.

d. The inspectors admitted that they were, in fact, passing rods barely below the LSL and fudging the diameters. When the inspection process was corrected for the next day's sample of 500 rods, 105 were found to be defective. Based on this new and more accurate information, is the process out of control? [*Note:* This new information led to a finding of an incorrect machine setting on the production line. When the setting was corrected, the process was back in control.]

---

* From Tanur, J., et al. (Eds.). *Statistics: A Guide to the Unknown.* Pacific Grove, CA: Brooks/Cole, 1978, pp. 279–281.

† The data are available on floppy disk from the publisher.

TABLE 3.14
Diameters of 500 Steel Rods from One Day's Production

1.000	1.005	1.002	1.003	1.001	1.002	1.000	1.005	1.001	1.001
1.003	1.000	1.000	1.001	1.004	1.000	1.002	1.005	1.004	1.000
1.003	1.001	1.001	1.002	1.004	1.006	1.003	1.002	1.006	1.000
.997	1.003	1.000	1.004	1.000	1.002	.998	1.007	.998	1.004
1.000	1.004	1.002	1.002	1.002	1.005	.997	1.005	1.003	1.003
1.004	1.000	1.000	1.003	1.002	1.000	1.006	1.002	1.004	1.006
1.001	1.004	1.002	1.007	1.001	1.004	1.004	1.003	1.000	1.005
1.005	.997	1.001	1.005	1.002	1.003	1.000	1.003	1.003	1.003
1.000	.998	1.001	1.004	.997	1.003	1.005	.998	1.000	1.000
1.002	1.004	1.004	1.004	1.005	1.000	1.001	1.002	1.004	1.003
1.002	1.005	1.004	1.003	1.001	1.005	1.000	1.004	1.000	1.003
1.001	1.005	1.001	1.002	1.006	1.004	1.005	1.002	1.002	1.004
1.003	1.005	1.001	1.004	1.003	1.003	1.002	1.004	1.007	1.002
.997	1.007	1.002	1.003	1.000	1.001	.998	1.000	1.001	1.003
1.003	1.002	1.000	1.001	1.002	1.004	1.003	1.006	1.005	1.006
1.003	1.003	1.007	1.006	1.000	1.002	1.002	1.002	1.003	.997
1.002	1.005	1.002	1.002	1.005	1.002	1.002	1.002	1.002	1.000
1.003	1.004	1.001	.998	1.002	1.001	.998	1.001	1.003	1.000
1.001	1.002	.998	1.002	1.003	1.004	1.001	1.000	1.003	1.002
1.004	1.002	.998	1.005	1.005	1.004	1.004	1.005	1.003	1.002
1.001	1.002	1.004	1.004	1.003	1.004	1.002	1.003	1.004	1.002
1.005	1.004	1.000	.998	1.003	1.003	1.000	1.002	1.001	1.001
1.006	1.006	1.006	1.000	1.004	1.002	1.004	1.001	1.000	1.000
1.001	1.001	1.002	1.001	1.001	1.003	1.005	1.002	1.002	1.006
1.001	1.007	.998	1.000	1.003	1.003	1.001	1.001	1.001	1.003
1.003	1.002	1.000	1.004	1.000	1.003	1.003	1.002	1.003	.998
1.004	1.001	1.002	1.002	1.002	1.001	1.000	1.003	.997	1.004
1.005	1.006	1.002	1.000	1.002	1.002	1.002	1.001	.998	1.002
.998	1.001	1.003	1.005	1.004	1.003	1.006	1.000	1.003	.998
1.004	1.003	1.003	1.000	1.001	1.002	1.004	1.004	1.002	1.001
1.000	1.001	1.002	1.004	.997	1.001	1.000	1.001	1.005	.998
1.003	1.001	1.001	1.005	1.004	1.004	1.003	1.006	1.000	1.000
1.001	1.003	1.000	1.000	1.002	.998	1.006	1.004	1.000	1.005
1.002	1.004	1.001	1.003	1.002	1.002	1.001	1.001	1.002	1.002
1.002	1.002	1.000	.998	1.005	1.007	1.002	1.002	1.003	1.001
1.000	1.002	1.005	.998	1.002	1.002	1.000	.997	1.003	1.001
.998	1.007	1.003	1.002	1.001	1.003	1.001	1.004	1.002	1.006
1.004	1.000	1.000	1.000	1.005	1.000	1.007	1.004	1.007	1.001
.997	1.001	1.005	1.000	1.002	.998	1.004	1.003	1.004	1.002
1.004	1.004	1.000	1.004	1.000	1.003	1.005	1.000	1.004	1.003
1.000	1.007	1.004	1.004	1.003	1.003	1.002	1.002	1.002	1.000
1.003	1.001	1.002	1.002	1.003	1.003	1.001	.998	1.006	1.004
1.002	1.001	1.000	1.001	1.004	.998	1.000	1.000	1.002	1.003
1.006	1.002	1.005	1.000	1.003	1.003	1.002	1.003	.998	1.002
.998	1.000	1.000	1.002	1.000	1.000	1.005	1.006	1.003	1.003
1.000	1.002	1.000	1.002	1.001	1.003	1.001	1.005	1.001	1.003
1.002	.998	1.003	1.001	1.004	1.003	1.001	1.005	1.001	1.003
1.004	1.004	.998	1.000	.998	1.003	1.003	1.005	1.004	1.006
1.000	1.003	1.000	1.004	1.001	1.003	1.001	1.000	1.005	1.002
1.005	1.004	1.002	1.002	1.003	1.000	1.004	.998	1.000	.998

Note: The data were simulated based on information provided in the essay.

REFERENCES

Freedman, D., Pisani, R., and Purves, R. *Statistics*. New York: Norton, 1978.
McClave, J. T., and Benson, P. G. *A First Course in Business Statistics*, 5th ed. San Francisco: Dellen, 1992.
Mendenhall, W. *Introduction to Probability and Statistics*, 8th ed. Boston: Duxbury, 1990.
Tukey, J. *Exploratory Data Analysis*. Reading MA: Addison-Wesley, 1977.

SAMPLE EXAM QUESTIONS: CHAPTERS 1–3

(1–14)   A Purdue University study was recently conducted to examine the reasons why individual investors select certain investment portfolios (*Quarterly Review of Economics & Business*, Autumn 1989). A list of 3,000 accounts was obtained, at random, from the computerized customer records of a large nationwide financial brokerage house, and each individual investor on the list was mailed a lengthy questionnaire. A total of 972 completed questionnaires were returned with information on the (1) sex, (2) marital status, (3) age, (4) annual income, (5) education, and (6) occupation of the individual investors. The data were tabulated to form an investor profile. The number of investors in each category of the six variables is shown in the table.

(1) SEX		(2) MARITAL STATUS		(3) AGE		
Male	782	Married	784	21–25	1	
Female	190	Unmarried	188	26–34	29	
				35–44	117	
				45–54	274	
				55–64	252	
				65 & over	299	

(4) ANNUAL INCOME[a]		(5) EDUCATION		(6) OCCUPATION			
Under $5,000	1	High school diploma	225	Professional & technical	265	Farm owner	15
$5,000–9,999	80	Bachelor degree	526	Managerial	157	Service worker	5
$10,000–14,999	148	Master's degree	90	Proprietor	124	Clerical	23
$15,000–19,999	129	Law degree	63	Sales	53	Craftsman	18
$20,000–24,999	173	PhD	28	Housewife	69	Retired	217
$25,000–49,999	251	Medical degree	40	Operative & laborer	8	Unemployed	18
$50,000–99,999	132						
$100,000–149,000	27						
$150,000 & over	15						

Source: Krehbiel, T. L., and McCarthy, P. "An Analysis of the Determinants of Portfolio Selection." *Quarterly Review of Economics & Business*, Vol. 29, No. 3, 1989, p. 46.
[a] Sixteen investors did not report their annual income.

1. Identify the type (quantitative or qualitative) of each variable measured.
2. Identify the population of interest to the researchers.
3. Identify the sample of interest to the researchers.
4. Comment on how representative the sample is.
5. Describe each variable with the appropriate graphical technique.

Two quantitative variables of interest to the researchers were x_1 = dollar value of portfolio and x_2 = number of securities held by each of the 972 investors. Descriptive statistics for these variables are provided in the table.

	MEAN	STANDARD DEVIATION	MEDIAN	MODE	90th PERCENTILE
DOLLAR VALUE OF PORTFOLIO x_1	$35,007	$64,699	$24,255	$30,000	$1,205,000
NUMBER OF SECURITIES HELD x_2	17.7	5.0	21	5	31

6. Interpret the mean of the x_1-values.
7. Interpret the median of the x_2-values.
8. Interpret the standard deviation of the x_1-values.
9. Give an interval of x_2-values within which approximately 95% of the investors fall. (Assume the distribution of x_2-values is mound-shaped and symmetric.)
10. Interpret the mode of the x_1-values.
11. Interpret the 90th percentile of the x_2-values.
12. Explain how the researchers could describe the bivariate relationship between x_1 and x_2.
13. Would you expect to observe an investor with a portfolio dollar value of $x_1 = \$2,000,000$? Explain.
14. Would you expect to observe an investor who holds $x_2 = 14$ securities? Explain.

(15–20)   One way in which stock market analysts measure the price volatility of an individual stock relative to the market is to compute the stock's **beta value**. Beta values greater than 1 indicate that the stock's price has changed faster than the average market price, while beta values less than 1 indicate that the stock's price has changed slower than the average market price. The table lists the ticker abbreviations and beta values for a sample of 23 Standard & Poor's 500 stocks.

TICKER	BETA	TICKER	BETA	TICKER	BETA
AL	1.489	ID	1.187	S	.688
BX	.987	JCP	.561	TL	1.137
CMK	.746	KO	.548	UPJ	.951
DOC	1.220	LIT	1.502	VO	1.317
ECH	.907	MAT	1.662	WEN	1.731
FNC	.859	NSM	2.014	XON	.980
GS	.722	PRD	1.358	ZE	1.304
HIA	1.736	REV	.879		

Source: Standard & Poor's, "Inside S&P 500 Stock Index Futures." Index & Option Market.

15. Construct a stem-and-leaf display for the data.
16. Compute and interpret a useful descriptive measure of central tendency for the data.
17. Compute and interpret a useful descriptive measure of variation for the data.
18. Compute and interpret a useful descriptive measure of relative standing for the data.
19. Do you detect any outliers in the data?
20. Suppose you were to delete the outliers from the data set and recalculate the descriptive statistics. How will the recalculated numerical descriptive measures compare to the original values?

(21–22)   One of the operations in a plant consists of thread-grinding a fitting for an aircraft hydraulic system. To monitor the process, a production supervisor randomly selects one fitting each hour, for a period of 20 hours, and measures the pitch diameter of each thread. The 20 time-ordered measurements, expressed in units of .0001 inch in excess of .4000 inch, are given in the table at the top of the next page. (For example, the value 36 represents .4036 inch.)

HOUR	DIAMETER	HOUR	DIAMETER	HOUR	DIAMETER
1	36	8	23	15	30
2	31	9	43	16	28
3	30	10	36	17	33
4	32	11	34	18	27
5	32	12	36	19	35
6	32	13	36	20	33
7	33	14	36		

21. Construct a plot that will enable the supervisor to detect time-order trends in the data.
22. When the process is in control, all the hourly readings will fall within the control limits. Assuming the process is in control, compute the appropriate control limits from the data.

(23–25) Recently, federal government outlays for elementary, secondary, and vocational education were cut, yet Scholastic Aptitude Test (SAT) scores increased. Has such a relationship existed in the past? According to *Fortune* (Oct. 29, 1984), "federal spending on education is strongly and negatively correlated with both verbal and math SAT scores" over the past decade.

23. Based on *Fortune's* claim, sketch the bivariate relationship between federal spending on education and SAT scores.
24. *Fortune* reports that the sample correlation coefficient between verbal SAT scores and federal spending on education was $r = -.92$, while the correlation between math SAT scores and federal spending was $r = -.71$. Do these results support *Fortune's* claim?
25. Comment on the statement, "the results imply that a reduction of federal spending on education will cause higher SAT scores."

CHAPTER 4

PROBABILITY AND PROBABILITY DISTRIBUTIONS

CONTENTS

Now would you like to win a state lottery, choose the grand prize in "Let's Make a Deal," or obtain a winning edge in blackjack? What do each of these ventures have to do with statistics? The answer is *uncertainty*. The return in real dollars on most investments cannot be predicted with certainty. Neither can we be certain that an inference about a population, based on the partial information contained in a sample, will be correct. In this chapter we learn how probability can be used to measure uncertainty and take a brief glimpse at its role in assessing the reliability of statistical inferences. An illustration of how managers use probability to aid in cost decisions is presented in the chapter case study.

BASIC CONCEPTS OF PROBABILITY

4.1 If you play blackjack, a popular casino gambling game, you know that whether you win in any one game is an outcome that is very uncertain. Similarly, investing in bonds, stock, or a new business is a venture whose success is subject to uncertainty.

Much like playing blackjack and investing, making inferences based on sample data is also subject to uncertainty. A sample rarely tells a perfectly accurate story about the population from which it was selected. There is always a margin of error (as the pollsters tell us) when sample data are used to estimate the proportions of people in favor of a particular political candidate, some consumer product, or some political or social issue. There is always uncertainty about how far the sample estimate will depart from the true population proportion of affirmative answers that you are attempting to estimate. Consequently, a measure of the amount of uncertainty associated with an estimate (which we called the **reliability of an inference** in Chapter 1) plays a major role in statistical inference.

How do we measure the uncertainty associated with events? Anyone who has observed a daily television newscast can answer that question. The answer is **probability**. For example, it may be reported that the probability of rain on a given day is 20%. Such a statement acknowledges that the forecaster is uncertain whether it will rain on the given day and measures the likelihood of the occurrence as 20%. In this section we will examine the meaning of probability and study some basic properties of probability useful in the study of statistics.

EXPERIMENTS, EVENTS, AND PROBABILITY

In the language employed in a study of probability, the word **experiment** has a very broad meaning—it is a process of making an observation. For example, suppose you are dealt a single card from a standard 52-card bridge deck. Observing the outcome (ie, the number and suit of the card) could be viewed as an experiment. Counting the number of defective light bulbs produced per hour in a manufacturing process is an experiment. Similarly, recording the annual sales of a corporation is an experiment. Note that most experiments result in outcomes, or **events**, that cannot be predicted with certainty in advance.

DEFINITION 4.1

The process of making an observation is called an **experiment**.

DEFINITION 4.2

Outcomes of experiments are called **events**. [*Note:* To simplify our discussion, we will use capital letters, *A*, *B*, *C*, ..., to denote specific events.]

Suppose we perform the following experiment: Toss a coin and observe whether the upside of the coin is a head or a tail. Define the event H by

H: Observe a head.

You know that the probability of H, denoted by $P(H)$, is equal to $\frac{1}{2}$. This does not mean, however, that exactly half of a number of tosses will result in heads. (For example, we do not expect to observe *exactly* 1 head in 2 tosses of a coin or exactly 5 heads in 10 tosses of a coin.) Rather, it means that in a very long series of tosses, we believe that approximately half would result in a head. Therefore, the number $\frac{1}{2}$ measures the likelihood of observing a head on a single toss of the coin. This property is illustrated in the graph in Figure 4.1.

Figure 4.1 shows the proportion of heads observed after $n = 25, 50, 75, 100, 125, \ldots, 1,450, 1,475,$ and $1,500$ computer-simulated repetitions of a coin-tossing experiment. The number of tosses is marked along the horizontal axis of the graph and the corresponding proportion of heads is plotted along the vertical axis above the values of n. The points are connected by line segments to emphasize the fact that the proportion of heads moves closer and closer to .5 as n gets larger (as you move to the right on the graph).

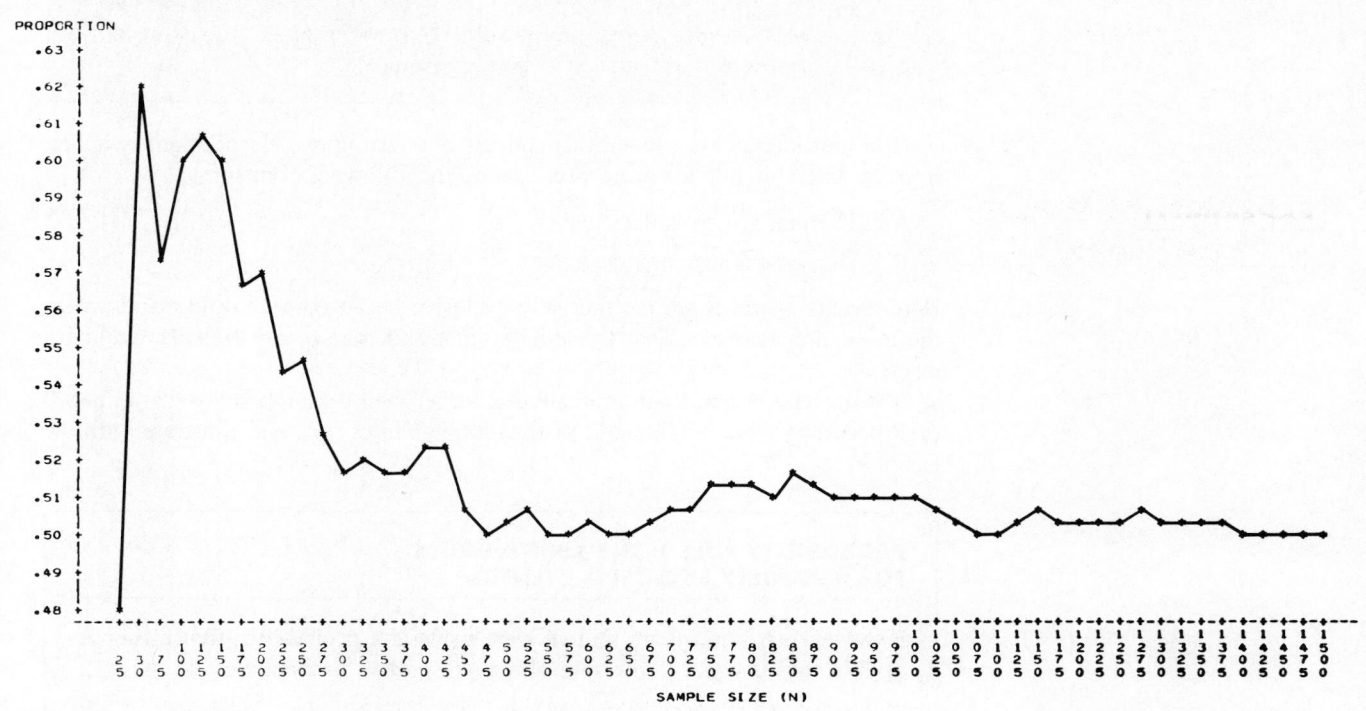

FIGURE 4.1

The Proportion of Heads in n Tosses of a Coin

The **probability of an event A**, denoted by $P(A)$, is the proportion of times that A is observed when the experiment is repeated a very large number of times.

Certain types of events have special properties that enable us to form rules for calculating their probabilities. Two of these are **mutually exclusive** and **complementary events**.

MUTUALLY EXCLUSIVE EVENTS

Two events, A and B, are said to be **mutually exclusive** if, when A occurs, B cannot occur, and vice versa. For example, you cannot toss a coin and observe H (a head) while at the same time observing T (a tail). Therefore, we say that the events H and T are mutually exclusive.

DEFINITION 4.4

Two events are said to be **mutually exclusive** if, when one of the two events occurs in an experiment, the other cannot occur.

Now consider an experiment that consists of selecting two electric light switches from an assembly line for inspection. Define the following events:

A: The first switch is defective.

B: The second switch is defective.

Here, events A and B are *not* mutually exclusive because both could occur when the inspection is made. That is, both the first and the second switches could be defective.

If two events A and B are mutually exclusive, then the probability that either A or B occurs is equal to the sum of their probabilities. We will illustrate with an example.

PROBABILITY RULE 1: THE ADDITIVE RULE FOR MUTUALLY EXCLUSIVE EVENTS

If two events A and B are mutually exclusive, the **probability that either A or B occurs** is equal to the sum of their respective probabilities:

$P(\text{Either } A \text{ or } B \text{ occurs}) = P(A) + P(B)$

In general, the probability that any one of k mutually exclusive events, A_1, A_2, ..., A_k, occurs is the sum of their respective probabilities:

$P(\text{Either } A_1 \text{ or } A_2 \text{ or ... or } A_k) = P(A_1) + P(A_2) + \cdots + P(A_k)$

EXAMPLE 4.1 Environmental engineers classify U.S. consumers into five mutually exclusive groups based on the consumers' feelings about environmentalism:

1. *Basic browns* claim they don't have the knowledge to understand environmental problems.
2. *True-blue greens* use biodegradable products.
3. *Greenback greens* support requiring new cars to run on alternative fuel.
4. *Sprouts* recycle newspapers regularly.
5. *Grousers* believe industries, not individuals, should solve environmental problems.

[In theory, a consumer may use biodegradable products (true-blue green) and also recycle newspapers regularly (sprout). However, for practical reasons, environmentalists classify each consumer into a single group based on their strongest feelings about the environment.]

The probability that a consumer is classified into any one of the five groups is shown in the table. Suppose a U.S. consumer is selected at random and questioned about environmentalism. Find the probability that the consumer supports environmentalism in some fashion (ie, is either a true-blue green, greenback green, or sprout).

	EVENT	PROBABILITY
A:	Basic brown	.28
B:	True-blue green	.11
C:	Greenback green	.11
D:	Sprout	.26
E:	Grouser	.24

Source: The Orange County (CA) Register, Aug. 7, 1990.

Solution The event of interest, that the consumer supports environmentalism, will occur if either event B, C, or D occurs. Since the events are mutually exclusive, we apply Probability Rule 1, to find

$$P(\text{Either } B \text{ or } C \text{ or } D \text{ occurs}) = P(B) + P(C) + P(D)$$
$$= .11 + .11 + .26 = .48$$

Probability Rule 1 is modified when an experiment can result in one and only one of a number of equally likely (equiprobable), mutually exclusive events.

PROBABILITY RULE 2: THE PROBABILITY RULE FOR AN EXPERIMENT THAT RESULTS IN ONE OF A NUMBER OF EQUALLY LIKELY, MUTUALLY EXCLUSIVE EVENTS

Suppose an experiment can result in one and only one of M equally likely, mutually exclusive events and that m of these events result in event A. Then the probability of event A is

$$P(A) = \frac{m}{M}$$

EXAMPLE 4.2 A box contains three fuses, one good and two defective. Two fuses are drawn in sequence, first one and then the other. What is the probability that the second fuse drawn is defective?

Solution   We will denote the good fuse by G and the two defective fuses as D_1 and D_2. If the fuses are drawn at random from the box, the six possible orders of selection are

     D_1, G (D_1, D_2) D_2, G

STEP 1   Since these six mutually exclusive events are equally likely and comprise all possible outcomes of the draw, we have $M = 6$.

STEP 2   Next, we must find the number of selections in which a defective fuse is selected in the second draw. You can see from the listed draws that $m = 4$ (these are the circled pairs).

STEP 3   Using Probability Rule 2, we conclude that the probability of obtaining a defective fuse on the second draw is

$$P(\text{Defective fuse on second draw}) = \frac{m}{M} = \frac{4}{6} = \frac{2}{3}$$

Examples 4.1 and 4.2 identify the properties of the probabilities of all events, as summarized in the box.

PROPERTIES OF PROBABILITIES

1. The probability of an event always assumes a value between 0 and 1.
2. If two events A and B are mutually exclusive, then the probability that either A or B occurs is equal to $P(A) + P(B)$.
3. If we list all possible mutually exclusive events associated with an experiment, then the sum of their probabilities will always equal 1.

COMPLEMENTARY EVENTS

In the coin-tossing experiment we noted that events H (observe a head) and T (observe a tail) are mutually exclusive events. Further, T is the event that H *does not occur*, and $P(T) + P(H) = 1$. When these properties hold, we say that the events T and H are **complementary events**.

DEFINITION 4.5

The **complement** of an event A, denoted by the symbol $\overline{A}$, is the event that A does not occur.

Complementary events are important because sometimes it is difficult to find the probability of an event A, but easy to find the probability of its complement $\overline{A}$. In this case, we can find $P(A)$ using the relationship stated in the box. To illustrate, define A as the event that the second fuse drawn in Example 4.2 is defective. Then, the probability that the second fuse drawn is nondefective is $1 - P(A) = 1 - \frac{2}{3} = \frac{1}{3}$.

PROBABILITY RELATIONSHIP FOR COMPLEMENTARY EVENTS

$$P(A) = 1 - P(\overline{A})$$

CONDITIONAL PROBABILITIES AND INDEPENDENCE

The event probabilities we have discussed thus far give the relative frequencies of occurrence of the events when an experiment is repeated a very large number of times. They are called **unconditional probabilities** because no special conditions are assumed other than those that define the experiment.

Sometimes we may want to revise the probability of an event when we have additional knowledge that might affect its outcome. To give a simple example, the probability of observing a sum of 7 when two dice are tossed is $\frac{1}{6}$. But suppose you are given the information that the sum of the two numbers showing on the dice is even. Would you still believe that the probability of observing a 7 on that particular toss is $\frac{1}{6}$? Intuitively, you will realize that the probability of observing a 7 is now 0. Since you know that an even number occurred, the outcome 7 cannot have occurred (because 7 is an odd number). The probability of observing a 7, *given that you know some other event has already occurred*, is called the **conditional probability** of the event.

DEFINITION 4.6

The probability of an event A, given that an event B has occurred, is called the **conditional probability of A given B** and is denoted by the symbol

$P(A|B)$

Note: The vertical bar between A and B is read "given."

EXAMPLE 4.3 Refer to Example 4.2, where we drew two fuses in sequence from a box containing one good and two defective fuses. What is the probability that the second fuse drawn is defective if you know for certain that the first fuse drawn is defective?

Solution The probability of observing a defective fuse on the second draw, given that you have observed a defective fuse on the first draw, is the conditional probability $P(A|B)$, where

A: Observe a defective fuse on the second draw.

B: Observe a defective fuse on the first draw.

If the first fuse drawn from the box is defective, then the box now contains only two fuses, one defective and one nondefective. This means that there is a 50% chance of drawing a defective fuse on the second draw, given that a defective fuse has already been drawn. That is,

$$P(A|B) = \frac{1}{2}$$

Note that the probability obtained in Example 4.2, the *unconditional* probability of event A, was equal to $\frac{2}{3}$. Example 4.3 clearly shows that the probability of event A has changed when we know that event B has occurred. However, if the probability of one event does not depend on whether a second event has occurred, then the events are said to be **independent**.

DEFINITION 4.7

Two events A and B are said to be **independent** if

$P(A|B) = P(A)$ or if $P(B|A) = P(B)$

Note: If one of these equalities is true, then the other will also be true.

The notion of independence is particularly important when we want to find the probability that both of two events will occur. When the events are independent, the probability that both events will occur is equal to the product of their unconditional probabilities.

**PROBABILITY RULE 3: THE MULTIPLICATIVE
RULE FOR INDEPENDENT EVENTS**

If two events A and B are independent, then the **probability that both A and B occur** is equal to the product of their respective unconditional probabilities:

$P(\text{Both } A \text{ and } B \text{ occur}) = P(A)P(B)$

In general, the probability that all of k independent events, A_1, A_2, ..., A_k, occur simultaneously is the product of their respective probabilities:

$P(A_1 \text{ and } A_2 \text{ and } ... \text{ and } A_k \text{ occur}) = P(A_1) \cdot P(A_2) \cdot \cdots \cdot P(A_k)$

Probability Rule 3 can be applied to any number of independent events. For example, if A, B, and C are independent events, then

$$P(\text{All of the events, } A, B, \text{ and } C, \text{ occur}) = P(A)P(B)P(C)$$

EXAMPLE 4.4   We now consider a problem in statistical inference. Experience has shown that a manufacturing operation produces, on the average, only 1 defective unit in 10. These are removed from the production line, repaired, and returned to the warehouse. Suppose that during a given period of time you observe 5 defective units emerging in sequence from the production line.

a. If prior history has shown that defective units usually emerge randomly from the production line, what is the probability of observing a sequence of 5 consecutive defective units?
b. If the event in part **a** really occurred, what would you conclude about the process?

Solution

a. If the defective units really occur randomly, then whether any one unit is defective should be independent of whether the others are defective. Second, the unconditional probability that any one unit is defective is known to be $\frac{1}{10}$. We will define the following events:

D_1:   The first unit is defective.

D_2:   The second unit is defective.

> .   .
> .   .
> .   .

D_5:   The fifth unit is defective.

Then,

$$P(D_1) = P(D_2) = P(D_3) = P(D_4) = P(D_5) = \frac{1}{10}$$

Now we apply Probability Rule 3 to compute the probability that all 5 are defective:

$$P(\text{All 5 are defective}) = P(D_1)P(D_2)P(D_3)P(D_4)P(D_5)$$

$$= \left(\frac{1}{10}\right)\left(\frac{1}{10}\right)\left(\frac{1}{10}\right)\left(\frac{1}{10}\right)\left(\frac{1}{10}\right) = \frac{1}{100,000}$$

b. We do not need a knowledge of probability to know that something must be wrong with the production line. Intuition would tell us that observing 5 defectives in sequence is highly improbable (given past history), and we would immediately infer that past history no longer describes the condition of the process. In fact, we would infer that something is disturbing the stability of the process.

Example 4.4 illustrates how you can use your knowledge of probability and the probability of a sample event to make an inference about some population. The technique, called the **rare-event approach**, is summarized in the box.

PROBLEMS

4.1   During the 1989 U.S. Open, four professional golfers (Doug Weaver, Jerry Pate, Nick Price, and Mark Wiebe) made holes in one (aces) on the sixth hole at Oak Hill Country Club—all on the same day! How unlikely is such a feat? According to *Golf Digest* (Mar. 1990), the probability of a Professional Golf Association (PGA) tour pro making an ace on a given hole is approximately $\frac{1}{3,000}$. The estimate is based on the ratio of the number of aces made on the PGA tour to the total number of rounds played.

    a. Interpret the probability of $\frac{1}{3,000}$.

    b. *Golf Digest* also estimates that the probability of any four players getting aces on the same hole on the same day during the next U.S. Open as $\frac{1}{150,000}$. Interpret this probability.

4.2   After Evelyn Marie Adams won the New Jersey weekly lottery twice within a 4-month period in 1986, the event was widely reported as an amazing feat that beat the odds of 1 in 17 trillion. Although the probability of the event, $\frac{1}{17,000,000,000,000}$, is technically correct, it does not take into account a fundamental law of statistics called "the law of very large numbers." In the words of Harvard statisticians Perci Diaconis and Frederick Mosteller (*Journal of the American Statistical Association*, Dec. 1989), the law states that "with a large enough sample, any outrageous thing is apt to happen." Diaconis and Mosteller go on to explain that "one in 17 trillion is the odds that a given person (eg, Ms. Adams) who buys a single ticket for exactly two New Jersey lotteries will win both times." The true question, they say, is "What is the chance that some person, out of all the millions and millions who buy lottery tickets in the United States, hits a lottery twice in a lifetime?" Based on a 7 year study of state lottery winners, Purdue statisticians Stephen Samuels and George McCabe estimated the "odds are better than even that there will be a double lottery winner somewhere in the United States" (*The Wall Street Journal*, Feb. 27, 1990). Let A be the event that you buy a New Jersey lottery ticket for exactly two different weeks and win both times. Let B be the event that any person wins a state lottery twice.

    a. Are the events A and B mutually exclusive?

    b. What is the probability of A?

    c. What is the probability of B?

    d. Explain why the probabilities in parts **b** and **c** are so drastically different.

4.3   Local area merchants often use scratch-off tickets with promises of grand prize giveaways to entice customers to visit their stores. One such game, called Jackpot, was recently used in Tampa, Florida. Residents were mailed game tickets with 10 "play squares" and the instructions: "Scratch off your choice of ONLY ONE Jackpot Play Square. If you reveal any 3-OF-A-KIND combination, you WIN. Call NOW to make an appointment to claim your prize." All 10 play squares, of course, have winning 3-of-a-kind combinations. On one such ticket, three cherries (worth up to $1,000 in cash or prizes) appeared in play squares numbered 1, 2, 3, 4, 5, 6, 7, and 9; three lemons (worth a 10-piece microwave cookware set) appeared in play square number 8; and three 7's (worth a whirlpool spa) appeared in play square 10.

a. If you play Jackpot, what is the probability that you win a whirlpool spa?

b. If you play Jackpot, what is the probability that you win $1,000 in cash or prizes?

4.4   International commercial banks that loan money to developing countries always run the risk of the country rescheduling its debt. Consequently, it is important that the bank be able to distinguish between countries that have a tendency to reschedule their debts and countries that do not. A study was conducted to investigate the incidence of debt rescheduling of developing countries (*Journal of International Business Statistics*, Summer 1986). During the 1960's and early 1970's, there were only 21 incidents of debt reschedulings out of a sample of 238 observations. (Here, an observation consists of a year–country combination. That is, for a particular country in a particular year, it was determined whether the country rescheduled its debt.) In contrast, a study of 30 developing countries over the 8 year period 1975–1982 (ie, 30 × 8 = 240 observations) found 40 incidents of debt rescheduling.

a. Suppose you select one of the sample of 238 year–country observations during the 1960's and early 1970's. What is the estimated probability that the developing country rescheduled its debt during the year?

b. Answer part **a** assuming that you select one of the sample of 240 year–country observations during 1975–1982.

c. Compare the probabilities obtained in parts **a** and **b**. In which of the two periods is a rescheduled debt more likely?

4.5   "Employee Burnout: America's Newest Epidemic" is the name of a 1991 survey of American workers commissioned by Northwestern National Life Insurance Company. The main topic of the study was job-related stress. The origins of job stress, according to the responses of 600 workers, are summarized in the pie chart:

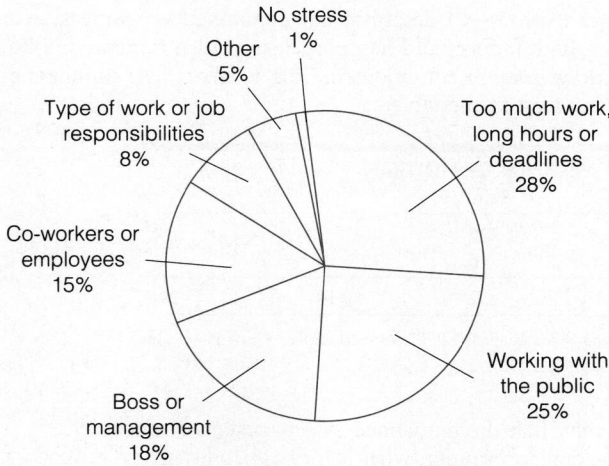

Source: *Tampa Tribune*, May 8, 1991.

Suppose one of the 600 workers in the survey is selected at random.

a. What is the probability that the worker attributes on-the-job stress to his or her "boss or management"?

b. What is the probability that the worker attributes on-the-job stress to "too much work, long hours, or deadlines"?

c. What is the probability that the worker has on-the-job stress?

d. What is the probability that the worker attributes on-the-job stress to people (eg, coworkers, employees, boss, management, or the public)?

4.6 The YES/MVS (Yorktown Expert System/MVS Manager) is an experimental expert system designed to exert active control over a computer system and provide advice to computer operators. YES/MVS is designed with a knowledge base consisting of 548 rules that are triggered in response to messages or queries from the computer operator. The table gives the number of rules allocated to different subdomains of the operator's actions. Periodically, the rules in the YES/MVS knowledge base are tested and, if necessary, adjusted. Suppose a rule is selected at random for testing and its type (operator action/query) noted.

OPERATOR'S ACTION/QUERY	NUMBER OF RULES
Batch scheduling	139
JES queue space	104
C-to-C links	68
Hardware errors	87
SMF management	25
Quiesce and IPL	52
Performance	41
Background monitor	32
Total	548

Source: Ennis, R. L., et al. "A Continuous Realtime Expert System for Computer Operations." *IBM Journal of Research and Development*, Vol. 30, No. 1, Jan. 1986, p. 19. Copyright 1986, International Business Machines Corporation; reprinted with permission.

a. List the outcomes for this experiment.
b. Assign probabilities to the outcomes based on the information contained in the table.
c. What is the probability the rule is a C-to-C link or hardware error rule?
d. What is the probability the rule is not a performance rule?

4.7 An article in *IEEE Computer Applications in Power* (Apr. 1990) describes "an unmanned watching system to detect intruders in real time without spurious detections, both indoors and outdoors, using video cameras and microprocessors." The system was tested outdoors under various weather conditions in Tokyo, Japan. The numbers of intruders detected and missed under each condition are provided in the table.

	WEATHER CONDITION				
	Clear	Cloudy	Rainy	Snowy	Windy
Intruders Detected	21	228	226	7	185
Intruders Missed	0	6	6	3	10
Totals	21	234	232	10	195

Source: Kaneda, K., et al. "An Unmanned Watching System Using Video Cameras." *IEEE Computer Applications in Power*, Apr. 1990, p. 24.

a. Under cloudy conditions, what is the probability that the unmanned system detects an intruder?
b. Given that the unmanned system missed detecting an intruder, what is the probability that the weather condition was snowy?

4.8 Market researchers are keenly interested in consumer preferences for the various benefits offered by a product. Researchers at the University of Pennsylvania conducted a study of consumer preferences for shampoo benefits (*Journal of the Market Research Society*, Jan. 1984). Part of the study involved a survey of 186 undergraduate business students. Each respondent was shown a list of 13 benefits and asked to select up to four benefits that he or she most strongly desires in a shampoo. The group of benefits selected by a respondent is termed a *benefit bundle*. The 13 benefits are listed below:

Body	Thickness	Contains protein
Bounciness	Softness	Natural ingredients
Control	Manageability	Repairs split ends
Luster	Gentle action	Conditions hair
Protection against dandruff		

a. Suppose a respondent is permitted to select two benefits from those listed in the first column. List the outcomes for this experiment.

b. Assuming that the benefit bundles from part **a** are equally likely, what is the probability that a respondent will select the {Body, Luster} bundle as most desirable?

c. Assuming the benefit bundles from part **a** are equally likely, what is the probability that a respondent will select Control as one of the two benefits?

4.9 In 1987, Congress enacted the Surface Transportation and Uniform Act, which allowed states to increase the speed limit to 65 miles per hour (mph) on interstate highways located outside an urban area of 50,000 or more persons. In a study of traffic fatalities on interstate highways, the Fatal Accident Reporting System discovered that 96% of the interstate highway miles eligible to be posted at 65 mph are rural interstates, and 97% of these eligible miles were actually posted at 65 mph (*American Journal of Public Health*, Oct. 1989).

a. For a particular 1 mile stretch of interstate highway eligible to be posted at 65 mph, estimate the probability that the 1 mile stretch is posted at 65 mph.

b. For a particular 1 mile stretch of interstate highway eligible to be posted at 65 mph, estimate the probability that the 1 mile stretch is not rural.

c. Are the events in parts **a** and **b** mutually exclusive? Explain.

4.10 According to the National Highway Traffic Safety Administration, "as many as nine out of ten heavily used cars, such as those from the leasing companies, may have had their mileage rolled back when resold" (*Orlando Sentinel*, Apr. 13, 1984). Officials estimate that an altered odometer adds $750 to the price of a used car. Suppose you are considering buying a used car from an auto-leasing company that has three cars available. Assume also that 9 out of every 10 used cars sold by the company have falsified odometer readings and that the 3 available cars represent a random sample of used cars sold by the company.

a. What is the probability that all 3 cars have falsified odometer readings?

b. What is the probability that none of the 3 cars has a falsified odometer reading?

c. Suppose a salesperson claims that none of the 3 cars has a falsified odometer reading. What would you infer about the claim?

4.11 Periodically, magazine publishers promote their products by mailing "sweepstakes" packets to consumers. These packets offer the chance to win a grand prize of $1 million or more, with no obligation to purchase any of the advertised products. Despite the low odds of winning, marketing experts have found that the sweepstakes contests dramatically increase consumer interest and orders. Recently, the U.S. government investigated the legitimacy of popular sweepstakes conducted by Publishers Clearing House, American Family Publishers, and Reader's Digest. On a nationwide basis, the odds of winning the grand prize are 1 in 181,795,000 for the current Publishers Clearing House sweepstakes, 1 in 200,000,000 for the American Family Publishers sweepstakes, and 1 in 84,000,000 for the Reader's Digest sweepstakes (*Gainesville Sun*, Jan. 24, 1985).

a. Calculate the probability of winning the grand prize in the Publishers Clearing House sweepstakes.

b. Repeat part **a** for the American Family Publishers sweepstakes.

c. Repeat part **a** for the Reader's Digest sweepstakes.

4.12 Refer to Problem 4.11. Suppose you enter all three of the sweepstakes contests.

  a. What is the probability that you win the grand prize in all three contests?
  b. What is the probability that you do not win any of the three grand prizes?
  c. Use the probability computed in part **b** to calculate the probability of winning at least one of the three grand prizes.

4.13 Nightmares about exams appear to be common among college graduates. In a recent survey of 30- to 45-year-old graduates from Transylvania University, 50 of 188 respondents admitted they had recurring dreams about college exams (*Tampa Tribune*, Dec. 12, 1988). Of these 50, 47 felt distress, anguish, fear, or terror in their dreams. (For example, some dreamers "couldn't find the building or they walked in and all the students were different." Other dreamers either overslept or didn't realize they were enrolled in the class.)

  a. Calculate the approximate probability that a 30- to 45-year-old graduate of Transylvania University has recurring dreams about college exams. Why is this probability approximate?
  b. Refer to part **a**. Given that the graduate has recurring dreams, what is the approximate probability that the dreams are unpleasant (ie, that the graduate feels distress, anguish, fear, or terror in the dreams)?
  c. Are the events {Graduate has recurring dreams} and {Dreams are unpleasant} independent?

4.14 Managers of oil exploration portfolios make decisions on which prospects to pursue based, in part, on the level of risk associated with each venture. The problem of risk analysis in oil exploration was recently examined using the outcomes and associated probabilities for a single prospect shown in the table.

OUTCOME Barrels	PROBABILITY
0 (dry hole)	.60
50,000	.10
100,000	.15
500,000	.10
1,000,000	.05
Total	1.00

Source: Kinchen, A. L. "Projected Outcomes of Exploration Programs Based on Current Program Status and the Impact of Prospects Under Consideration." *Journal of Petroleum Technology*, Vol. 38, No. 4, Apr. 1986, pp. 461–467. Copyright 1986, Society of Petroleum Engineers.

  a. What is the probability that a single oil well prospect will result in no more than 100,000 barrels of oil?
  b. What is the probability that a single oil well prospect will strike oil?
  c. Now consider two identical oil well prospects. List the possible outcomes if the two wells are drilled. Assume that the outcomes listed in the table are the only possible outcomes for any one well. [*Hint:* One possible outcome is two dry holes.]
  d. Use the information in the table to calculate the probabilities of the outcomes listed in part **c**. (Assume that the individual outcomes of the two wells are independent of each other.)
  e. Refer to part **d**. Find the probability that at least one of the two oil prospects strikes oil.

RANDOM VARIABLES

4.2

In a practical business setting, an experiment involves selecting a sample of data consisting of one or more observations on some variable. For example, we might survey 1,000 consumers concerning their preferences for toothpaste, and record x, the number who prefer a particular brand. Or we might randomly select a single property from all residential properties in a county and record its total appraised value, x. Since we can never know with certainty in advance the exact value we will observe when we record x for a single performance of the experiment, we call x a **random variable**.

DEFINITION 4.8

A **random variable** is a variable that assumes numerical values associated with events of an experiment

---

The random variables described above are examples of two different types of random variables—**discrete** and **continuous**. The number x of consumers in a sample of 1,000 who prefer a particular brand of toothpaste is a discrete random variable, because it can assume only a countable number of values—namely, 0, 1, 2, 3, ..., 999, 1,000. Note that this discrete random variable results from observing and counting qualitative outcomes (ie, prefer or not prefer the brand of toothpaste) on the experimental units (ie, consumers).

In contrast, the appraised value of a property is a continuous random variable, because it could theoretically assume any one of an infinite number of quantitative values—namely, any value from $0 upward. Of course, in practice, we record appraised value to the nearest dollar but, in theory, the appraised value of a property could assume any value, say, $51,144.13471.

A good way to distinguish between discrete and continuous random variables is to imagine the values they may assume as points on a line. Discrete random variables may assume any one of a countable number (say, 10, 21, or 100) of values corresponding to points on a line. In contrast, a continuous random variable can theoretically assume any value corresponding to the points in one or more intervals on a line. For example, the appraised value of a property could be represented by any of the infinitely large number of points on some portions of the positive half of a line.

DEFINITION 4.9

A **discrete random variable** is one that can assume only a countable number of values.

DEFINITION 4.10

A **continuous random variable** can assume any value in one or more intervals on a line.

EXAMPLE 4.5 Suppose you randomly select a student attending your college or university. Classify each of the following random variables as discrete or continuous:

a. Number of credit hours taken by the student this semester
b. Current grade-point average of the student

Solution

a. The number of credit hours taken by the student this semester is a discrete random variable, because it can assume only a countable number of values (eg, 15, 16, 17, etc.). It is not continuous, since the number of credit hours cannot assume values such as 15.2062, 16.1134, and 17.0398 hours.
b. The grade-point average for the student is a continuous random variable, since it could theoretically assume any value (eg, 2.87355) corresponding to the points on the line interval from 0 to 4.

PROBABILITY MODELS

4.3

We learned in Section 4.1 that we make inferences based on the probability of observing a particular sample outcome. Since we never know the *exact* probability of some event, we must construct **probability models** for the values assumed by random variables. The form of the probability model (or **probability distribution**) for a random variable depends on whether the variable is discrete or continuous.

The probability distribution for a discrete random variable x is a table, formula, or graph that gives the probability of observing each value of x.

DEFINITION 4.11

The **probability distribution for a discrete random variable** x is a table, graph, or formula that gives the probability of observing each value of x. If we denote the probability of x by the symbol $p(x)$, the probability distribution has the following properties:

1. $0 \leq p(x) \leq 1$ for all values of x
2. $\Sigma\, p(x) = 1$

EXAMPLE 4.6 Consider the following sampling situation: Draw a random sample of $n = 5$ physicians from a very large number—say, 10,000—and record the number x of physicians who favor aspirin brand A. Suppose that 2,000 of the physicians actually prefer brand A. Replace the 5 physicians in the population and randomly draw a new sample of $n = 5$ physicians. Record the value of x again. Repeat this process over and over again 100,000 times.

---

a. We simulated (on a computer) the drawing of 100,000 samples of $n = 5$ physicians from 10,000. Table 4.1 gives the possible values of x (0, 1, 2, 3, 4, and 5), the frequency, and the relative frequency for each of these values. Construct a relative frequency histogram for the 100,000 values of x.

b. Assuming that the relative frequencies listed in Table 4.1 are good approximations to the probabilities of x, show that the properties of a probability distribution are satisfied.

TABLE 4.1
Relative Frequencies for 100,000 Observations on x, the Number of Physicians in a Sample of $n = 5$ Who Prefer Aspirin Brand A

x	FREQUENCY	RELATIVE FREQUENCY
0	32,807	.32807
1	40,949	.40949
2	20,473	.20473
3	5,122	.05122
4	645	.00645
5	4	.00004

Solution

a. The relative frequency histogram for the values of x is shown in Figure 4.2. This figure provides a very good approximation to the probability distribution for x, the number of physicians in a sample of $n = 5$ who prefer brand A (assuming that 20% of the physicians in the population prefer brand A).

FIGURE 4.2
Relative Frequency Histogram for Example 4.6

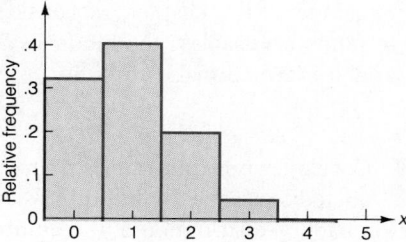

b. We use the relative frequencies of Table 4.1 as approximations to the probabilities of $x = 0$, $x = 1$, ..., $x = 5$. Note that each probability (relative frequency) is between 0 and 1. Summing these probabilities, we obtain

$$.32807 + .40949 + .20473 + .05122 + .00645 + .00004 = 1$$

Thus, the properties of a discrete probability distribution are satisfied.

Since continuous random variables can assume an infinitely large number of values in an interval, we are unable to represent the probability distribution with a table as in Example 4.6. Instead, a probability model for a continuous random variable is a smooth curve that represents the hypothetical relative frequency distribution of

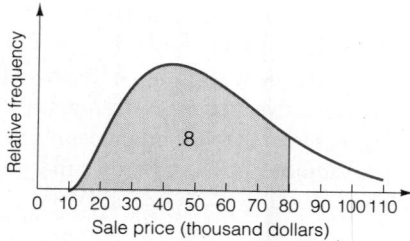

the random variable.* The area under the smooth curve that falls over a particular interval represents the probability that the random variable x falls in that interval. For example, the shaded area under the curve in Figure 4.3 is the probability that a sale price of a property falls below $80,000.

DEFINITION 4.12

The **probability distribution for a continuous random variable** x is a smooth curve that represents the relative frequency distribution of x. The probability distribution has the following properties:

1. $P(a < x < b)$ is equal to the area under the curve between the points $x = a$ and $x = b$.

2. The area under the entire curve equals 1.

In the remainder of this chapter, we consider two useful probability models, one for discrete random variables (the binomial distribution) and one for continuous random variables (the normal distribution).

THE BINOMIAL DISTRIBUTION FOR DISCRETE DATA

4.4 Consumer preferences and opinion polls (ie, sample surveys) are conducted so frequently in business and industry that it is useful for us to know the probability distribution of the number x in a random sample of n experimental units (ie, people) who prefer some specific proposition. This probability distribution, known as a **binomial probability distribution**, is applicable when the sample size n is small relative to the number N of experimental units in the population.

Strictly speaking, the binomial probability distribution applies only to sampling that satisfies the conditions of a **binomial experiment** listed in the box on p. 167.

In real life, there are probably few experiments that satisfy exactly the conditions for a binomial experiment. However, there are many that satisfy these conditions approximately, at least for all practical purposes. Consider, for example, a sample survey. As suggested above, when the number N of elements in the population is

---

* The probability distribution for a continuous random variable also can be represented by a formula, denoted $f(x)$, called a *probability density function*. When graphed, the probability density function forms the smooth curve of the relative frequency distribution.

large and the sample size n is small relative to N, the sampling satisfies, approximately, the conditions of a binomial experiment.

CONDITIONS REQUIRED FOR A BINOMIAL EXPERIMENT

1. A sample of n experimental units is selected from the population **without replacement** (ie, once an experimental unit is selected, it cannot be selected again).
2. Each experimental unit possesses one of two mutually exclusive characteristics. We conventionally call the characteristic of interest a **success** and the other a **failure**.
3. The probability that a single experimental unit possesses the success characteristic is equal to π. This probability is the same for all experimental units.
4. The outcome for any one experimental unit is independent of the outcome for any other experimental unit (ie, the draws are independent).
5. The random variable x counts the number of successes in n trials.

THE BINOMIAL PROBABILITY DISTRIBUTION

$$p(x) = \binom{n}{x} \pi^x (1 - \pi)^{n-x} \qquad x = 0, 1, 2, ..., n$$

where

n = Sample size (number of trials)

x = Number of successes in n trials

π = Probability of success on a single trial

$$\binom{n}{x} = \frac{n!}{x!(n-x)!}$$

Assumption: The sample size n is small relative to the number N of elements in the population (say, n/N smaller than $1/20$).

Note: $x! = x(x-1)(x-2)(x-3) \cdot \cdots \cdot (3)(2)(1)$, and $0! = 1$.

EXAMPLE 4.7 Verify that the physician survey described in Example 4.6 is a binomial experiment. Then use the binomial probability distribution to calculate the probabilities of $x = 0$, $x = 1$, ..., $x = 5$.

Solution The sample survey satisfies the five requirements for a binomial experiment given in the box:

---

1. A sample of $n = 5$ physicians (experimental units) is selected from a population.
2. Each physician surveyed possesses one of two mutually exclusive characteristics: favors aspirin brand A (a *success*) or does not favor aspirin brand A (a *failure*).
3. The proportion of physicians in the population who prefer aspirin brand A is .2; thus, the probability of a success is $\pi = .2$. Since the sample size $n = 5$ is small relative to the population size $N = 10,000$, this probability remains the same for all trials.
4. The response for any one physician is independent of the response for any other physician.
5. We are counting $x = $ the number of physicians in the sample who favor aspirin brand A.

To calculate the binomial probabilities, we will substitute the values of $n = 5$ and $\pi = .2$ and each value of x into the formula for $p(x)$:

$$p(x) = \binom{n}{x}\pi^x(1 - \pi)^{n-x} = \frac{n!}{x!(n - x)!}\pi^x(1 - \pi)^{n-x}$$

Thus, remembering that $0! = 1$, we have

$$P(x = 0) = p(0) = \binom{5}{0}(.2)^0(.8)^5$$

$$= \frac{5!}{0!5!}(.2)^0(.8)^5 = (1)(1)(.32768)$$

$$= .32768$$

Similarly,

$$P(x = 1) = p(1) = \binom{5}{1}(.2)^1(.8)^4 = \frac{5!}{1!4!}(.2)^1(.8)^4 = .40960$$

$$P(x = 2) = p(2) = \binom{5}{2}(.2)^2(.8)^3 = \frac{5!}{2!3!}(.2)^2(.8)^3 = .20480$$

$$P(x = 3) = p(3) = \binom{5}{3}(.2)^3(.8)^2 = \frac{5!}{3!2!}(.2)^3(.8)^2 = .05120$$

$$P(x = 4) = p(4) = \binom{5}{4}(.2)^4(.8)^1 = \frac{5!}{4!1!}(.2)^4(.8)^1 = .00640$$

$$P(x = 5) = p(5) = \binom{5}{5}(.2)^5(.8)^0 = \frac{5!}{5!0!}(.2)^5(.8)^0 = .00032$$

Note that these probabilities are approximately equal to the relative frequencies reported in Table 4.1.

EXAMPLE 4.8   Refer to Example 4.7. Find the probability that 3 or more physicians in the sample prefer brand A.

Solution   The values that a random variable x can assume are always mutually exclusive events—that is, you could not observe $x = 2$ and, at the same time, observe $x = 3$. Therefore, the event "x is 3 or more" (the event that $x = 3$ or $x = 4$ or $x = 5$) can be found using Probability Rule 1 (Section 4.1). Thus,

$$P(x = 3 \text{ or } x = 4 \text{ or } x = 5) = P(x = 3) + P(x = 4) + P(x = 5)$$
$$= p(3) + p(4) + p(5)$$

Substituting the probabilities found in Example 4.7, we obtain

$$P(x = 3 \text{ or } x = 4 \text{ or } x = 5) = .05120 + .00640 + .00032 = .05792$$

In some situations we will want to compare an observed value of x obtained from an opinion poll (or other binomial experiment) with some theory or claim associated with the sampled population. In particular, we will want to see if the observed value of x represents a rare event, assuming that the claim is true.

EXAMPLE 4.9   Are today's college graduates willing to work long, hard hours on the job? According to the College Placement Council, 90% of college students indicated they would, in fact, work long hours on the job (*Personnel Journal*, July 1984). Suppose we interview 10 randomly selected college students and find that only 5 would work long, hard hours on the job. Is this sample outcome highly improbable (ie, does it represent a rare event) if in fact the College Placement Council's claim is true?

Solution   If π is in fact equal to .90 (or some larger value), then observing a small number, x, of college students willing to work long, hard hours on the job would represent a rare event. Since we observed $x = 5$, we want to know the probability of observing a value of $x = 5$ or some other value of x even more contradictory to the Council's claim; that is, we want to find the probability that $x = 0$ or $x = 1$ or $x = 2$ or ... or $x = 5$. Using the additive rule for values of $p(x)$, we obtain

$$P(x = 0 \text{ or } x = 1 \text{ or } x = 2 \text{ or ... or } x = 5)$$
$$= p(0) + p(1) + p(2) + p(3) + p(4) + p(5)$$

As you saw in Example 4.7, the calculation of the binomial probabilities in the sum can be very tedious. In practice, we refer to one of the many tables that give partial sums of the values of $p(x)$, called **cumulative probabilities**, for a wide range of values of n and π. Table 1 in Appendix A includes cumulative binomial tables for $n = 5, 6, 7, 8, 9, 10, 15, 20,$ and 25. A reproduction of the cumulative binomial probability table for $n = 10$ is shown in Table 4.2.

DEFINITION 4.13

A **cumulative probability** $P(x \leq k)$ for a discrete random variable x is the sum of the values of $p(x)$ from $x = 0$ to $x = k$ for some value k.

$$P(x \leq k) = p(0) + p(1) + p(2) + \cdots + p(k)$$

TABLE 4.2
Reproduction of a Portion of Table 1, Appendix A: Cumulative Binomial Probabilities, $n = 10$

x	.01	.05	.1	.2	.3	.4	π .5	.6	.7	.8	.9	.95	.99
0	.9044	.5987	.3487	.1074	.0282	.0060	.0010	.0001	.0000	.0000	.0000	.0000	.0000
1	.9957	.9139	.7361	.3758	.1493	.0464	.0107	.0017	.0001	.0000	.0000	.0000	.0000
2	.9999	.9885	.9298	.6778	.3828	.1673	.0547	.0123	.0016	.0001	.0000	.0000	.0000
3	1.0000	.9990	.9872	.8791	.6496	.3823	.1719	.0548	.0106	.0009	.0000	.0000	.0000
4	1.0000	.9999	.9984	.9672	.8497	.6331	.3770	.1662	.0473	.0064	.0001	.0000	.0000
5	1.0000	1.0000	.9999	.9936	.9527	.8338	.6230	.3669	.1503	.0328	.0016	.0001	.0000
6	1.0000	1.0000	1.0000	.9991	.9894	.9452	.8281	.6177	.3504	.1209	.0128	.0010	.0000
7	1.0000	1.0000	1.0000	.9999	.9984	.9877	.9453	.8327	.6172	.3222	.0702	.0115	.0001
8	1.0000	1.0000	1.0000	1.0000	.9999	.9983	.9893	.9536	.8507	.6242	.2639	.0861	.0043
9	1.0000	1.0000	1.0000	1.0000	1.0000	.9999	.9990	.9940	.9718	.8926	.6513	.4013	.0956

In general, to find the sum of the binomial probabilities $p(x)$ for $x = 0, 1, 2,$ ..., a using Table 1, Appendix A, locate the entry corresponding to the row $x = a$ under the appropriate column for π. The cumulative sum of probabilities for this example is given in the column corresponding to $\pi = .9$ and the row corresponding to $x = 5$. Therefore,

$$P(x \leq 5) = p(0) + p(1) + p(2) + p(3) + p(4) + p(5) = .0016$$

This small probability (shaded in Table 4.2) tells us that observing as few as 5 out of 10 college students who would be willing to work long, hard hours on the job is indeed a rare event, if the Council's claim is true. Such a sample result suggests either that the College Placement Council's claim is false or that the 10 college students interviewed do not represent a random sample from the population.

In addition to binomial probabilities, formulas are also available for calculating the mean and variance of the binomial random variable. For large samples, the mean and the variance of the binomial probability distribution (shown in the box) also can be used to make inferences about the sampled population, as illustrated in the next example.

**MEAN, VARIANCE, AND STANDARD DEVIATION
FOR A BINOMIAL PROBABILITY DISTRIBUTION**

$$\mu = n\pi \qquad \sigma^2 = n\pi(1 - \pi) \qquad \sigma = \sqrt{n\pi(1 - \pi)}$$

where

n = Sample size

π = Probability of success on a single trial

  = Proportion of experimental units in a large population
    that are successes

EXAMPLE 4.10 People who work at high-stress jobs frequently develop stress-related physical problems (eg, high blood pressure, ulcers, and irritability). In a recent study it was found that 40% of the large number of business executives surveyed have symptoms of stress-induced problems. Consider a group of 1,500 randomly selected business executives and assume that the probability of an executive with stress-induced problems is $\pi = .40$. Let x be the number of business executives in the sample of 1,500 who develop stress-related problems.

a. What are the mean and standard deviation of x?

b. Based on the Empirical Rule, within what range of values would you expect x to fall?

c. Suppose you observe $x = 800$ executives with symptoms of stress-induced problems. What can you infer about the value of π?

Solution

a. Since $n = 1,500$ executives in the sample is small relative to the large number of business executives in the population, the number x of executives with stress-induced problems is a binomial random variable with $\pi = .4$. We use the formulas for μ and σ given in the box to obtain the mean and standard deviation of this binomial distribution:

$$\mu = n\pi = (1,500)(.4) = 600$$
$$\sigma = \sqrt{n\pi(1 - \pi)} = \sqrt{(1,500)(.4)(.6)} = \sqrt{360} = 18.97$$

b. According to the Empirical Rule, most (about 95%) of the x-values will fall within 2 standard deviations of the mean. Thus, we would expect the number of sampled executives with stress-induced problems to fall in the interval from

$$\mu - 2\sigma = 600 - 2(18.97) = 562.06$$

to

$$\mu + 2\sigma = 600 + 2(18.97) = 637.94$$

c. Using the rare-event approach of Chapter 3, we want to determine whether observing $x = 800$ executives with stress-induced problems is unusual, assuming $\pi = .40$. You can see that this value of x is highly improbable when $\pi = .40$, since it lies a long way outside the interval $\mu \pm 2\sigma$. The z-score for this value of x is

$$z = \frac{x - \mu}{n} = \frac{800 - 600}{18.97} = 10.54$$

Clearly, if $\pi = .40$, the probability that the number x of executives with stress-induced problems in the sample is 800 or larger is almost 0. Therefore, we are inclined to believe (based on the sample value of $x = 800$) that the proportion of executives with stress-induced problems is much higher than $\pi = .40$.

PROBLEMS

4.15 A study of 5 year trends in the logistics information systems of various industries found that the greatest computerization advances were in the transportation industry (*Industrial Engineering*, July 1990). Currently, 90% of all industries contain shipping open-order files in their computerized database. In a random sample of 10 industries, let x equal the number that include shipping open-order files in their computerized database.

    a. Verify that the probability distribution of x can be modeled using the binomial distribution.
    b. Find $P(x = 7)$.
    c. Find $P(x > 5)$.

4.16 *Organic Gardening* magazine recently conducted a poll to determine whether consumers would prefer organically grown fruits and vegetables over those grown with fertilizers and pesticides (*New York Times*, Mar. 21, 1989). If the costs of the two food types were the same, 85% said they would prefer the organic food. Surprisingly, 50% said they would prefer the organic food even if they had to pay more for it. Consider the preferences of a random sample of $n = 25$ consumers.

    a. Assuming the percentages in the poll are reflective of the population, find the probability that at least 20 of the 25 consumers would prefer the organically grown food if the costs were the same.
    b. Assuming the percentages in the poll are reflective of the population, find the probability that at least 20 of the 25 consumers would prefer the organically grown food if the costs were higher than food grown with fertilizers and pesticides.

4.17 According to the American Hotel and Motel Association, women are expected to account for half of all business travelers by the year 2000. To attract these women business travelers, hotels are providing more amenities that women particularly like, such as shampoo, conditioner, and body lotion. A recent survey of American hotels found that 86% now offer shampoo in their guest rooms (*The Wall Street Journal*, Oct. 14, 1988). Consider a random sample of 5 hotels and let x be the number that provide shampoo as a guest-room amenity.

    a. To a reasonable degree of approximation, is this a binomial experiment?
    b. What is a success in the context of this experiment?
    c. What is the value of π?
    d. Find the probability that $x = 4$.
    e. Find the probability that $x \geq 4$.

4.18 In a recent study, *Consumer Reports* (Feb. 1992) found widespread contamination and mislabeling of seafood in supermarkets in New York City and Chicago. One alarming statistic: 40% of the swordfish pieces available for sale had a mercury level above the Food and Drug Administration (FDA) minimum amount. In a random sample of 3 swordfish pieces, what is the probability that:

    a. All 3 swordfish pieces have mercury levels above the FDA minimum?
    b. Exactly 1 swordfish piece has a mercury level above the FDA minimum?
    c. At most 1 swordfish piece has a mercury level above the FDA minimum?

4.19 When you graduate, will you find a job of your own choosing? A recent Gallup survey for the National Occupational Information Coordinating Committee revealed that only 40% of American workers hold the types of jobs they had planned to have (*Tampa Tribune*, Jan. 12, 1990). The majority of those employed attribute their job to simple chance or lack of choice. Let x be the number of American workers in a sample of $n = 250$ who consciously chose their job or career.

    a. Is this a binomial experiment? Explain.
    b. What is π, the probability of success?
    c. What is the mean of x?
    d. Within what limits would you expect x to fall?
    e. Give a value of x that would contradict the findings that 40% of American workers hold jobs they had planned for. Explain.

4.20 Electrical engineers recognize that high neutral current in computer power systems is a potential problem. A recent survey of computer power system load currents at U.S. sites found that 10% of the sites had high neutral to full load current ratios (*IEEE Transactions on Industry Applications*, July/Aug. 1990). In a sample of 20 computer power systems selected from the large number of sites in the country, let x be the number with high neutral to full-load current ratios.

    a. Find and interpret the mean of x.
    b. Find and interpret the standard deviation of x.

4.21 *The Wall Street Journal* (Nov. 2, 1983) reported on a survey conducted to evaluate the public's opinion concerning the honest and ethical behavior of business executives. The survey included a representative sample of 1,558 adults selected from all the adults in the United States. Each person in the sample was asked to respond "yes" or "no" to each of a series of questions.

    a. If this sample were randomly selected from all the adults in the United States, would the number x responding "yes" to a particular question possess (approximately) a binomial probability distribution? Explain.
    b. The survey found that 20% of the general public rates business executives as possessing either low or very low honesty and ethical standards. Suppose you were to randomly select 25 adults from the general public, and let x represent the number of people in the sample of 25 who believe that business executives possess either low or very low honesty and ethical standards. Find $P(x \geq 10)$, assuming $\pi = .2$.
    c. Using the information in part **b**, find $P(x \leq 5)$.
    d. Using the information in part **b**, find $P(x \geq 7)$.

4.22 Travelers who fail to cancel their hotel reservations when they have no intention of showing up are commonly referred to as *no-shows*. In anticipation of no-shows and late cancellations, most hotels overbook (ie, accept reservations for more rooms than the number of rooms in their inventory). (See Example 3.5.) The *Journal of Travel Research* (Spring 1985) reported that six major hotels in the Seattle area had a no-show rate of 10%. Consider a random sample of 200 travelers with reservations at one of these six Seattle hotels. Let x equal the number of no-shows.

    a. Find the mean of x.
    b. Find the standard deviation of x.
    c. Within what limits would you expect x to fall?
    d. Use your answer to part **c** to assess the likelihood of observing 30 or more no-shows in the sample of 200.

4.23 In an interesting and easily readable article, James S. Trefil writes on the role of probabilities and expected values in our everyday lives. Trefil illustrates expected value theory by applying it to junk-mail contests, ploys used by advertisers to interest readers in their products. He writes:*

> If you are on a junk-mail list, you probably get regular notices announcing that "You may have already won the $10,000 jackpot!" Is it really worth answering the ad? Well, suppose the mailing went to 100,000 people. Your chances of winning are then 1 in 100,000. Over many contests, therefore, you would expect to win an average of $10,000 \times (1/100,000)$, or ten cents per game.... You will note that the expected [winnings] in this case is less than the price of the postage stamp you need to enter the contest. In fact, you can expect to lose ten cents every time you play, so the reaction "it's not worth answering this" is correct.

Suppose you randomly select $n = 10$ junk-mail contests to enter, each offering a $10,000 jackpot if you win. Assume that the probability of your winning any one contest is 1 in 100,000, or .00001. Let x be the number of contests you win.

    a. Is this a binomial experiment? Explain.
    b. What is the value of π?

---

* Trefil, J. S. "Odds Are Against Your Breaking That Law of Averages." *Smithsonian*, Vol. 15, No. 6, Sept. 1984, pp. 66–75.

c. Find the mean of x. (This is also known as the **expected value** of x.)

d. Now let y be the amount of money you win on any one contest. In Trefil's illustration, either $y = \$10,000$ (ie, you win the contest) or $y = 0$ (ie, you lose the contest). In this particular case, it can be shown that the mean of y is $\mu_y = \$10,000(\mu_x)$. Find your mean (or expected) winnings, μ_y.

e. Find μ_y if you enter only a single contest (ie, $n = 1$). Does this value agree with Trefil's "ten cents" per game?

4.24   As a college student, are you frequently depressed and overwhelmed by the pressure to succeed? According to the American Council on Education (ACE), the level of stress among first-year college students is rising rapidly. In a 1988 survey of 308,007 full-time first-year college students conducted for the ACE by UCLA's Higher Education Research Institute, more than 10% reported frequently "feeling depressed," compared with 8.2% in 1985 (*Tampa Tribune*, Jan. 9, 1989).

a. On average, how many of the 308,007 first-year students surveyed would you expect to report frequent feelings of depression if the true percentage in the population is 8.2% (the 1985 figure)?

b. Find the standard deviation of the number of the 308,007 first-year students surveyed who frequently feel depressed if the true percentage is 8.2%.

c. Suppose that 30,800 of the first-year students surveyed reported frequent feelings of depression. (This number, 30,800, is approximately the number observed in the actual study.) Calculate the z-score for 30,800.

d. Based on the result in part **c**, what would you infer about the true percentage of first-year college students in 1988 who frequently feel depressed? Explain.

THE NORMAL DISTRIBUTION FOR CONTINUOUS DATA

4.5   One of the most useful models for continuous population relative frequency distributions is the **normal distribution** shown in Figure 4.4.* The normal distribution (often called the **normal curve**) is mound-shaped and symmetric about its mean μ; its spread is determined by the value of its standard deviation. Three normal curves with different means and standard deviations are shown in Figure 4.5.

FIGURE 4.4
The Normal Curve

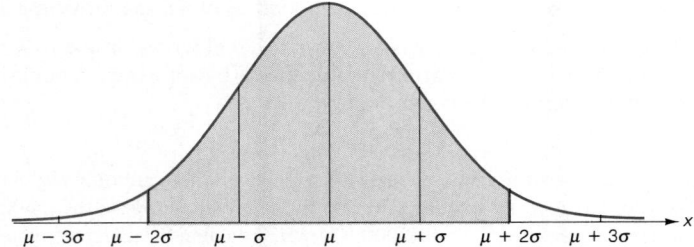

Furthermore, approximately 68% of the area under a normal curve lies within the interval $\mu \pm \sigma$; approximately 95% of the area lies within the interval $\mu \pm 2\sigma$ (shaded in Figure 4.4); and almost all (99.7%) lies within the interval $\mu \pm 3\sigma$. Note that the percentages agree with the Empirical Rule of Section 3.7. (This is

---

* The formula for the normal curve, denoted $f(x)$ and called the **normal probability density function**, is

$$f(x) = \frac{1}{\sigma\sqrt{2\pi}} e^{-(1/2)[(x-\mu)/\sigma]^2}$$

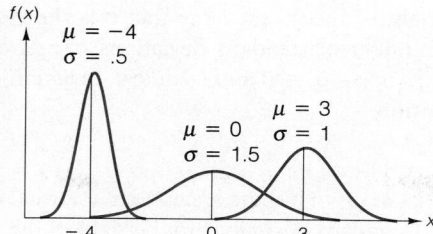

because the Empirical Rule is based on data that can be modeled by a normal distribution.)

Computing the area over an interval under the normal probability distribution can be a difficult task.* Consequently, we will use the computed areas listed in Table 2 of Appendix A; a partial reproduction of this table is shown in Table 4.3. As you can see from the normal curve above the table, the entries give areas under the normal curve between the mean of the distribution and a standardized distance,

$$z = \frac{x - \mu}{\sigma}$$

TABLE 4.3
Reproduction of Part of Table 2, Appendix A: Normal Curve Areas

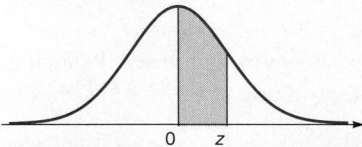

z	.00	.01	.02	.03	.04	.05	.06	.07	.08	.09
0.0	.0000	.0040	.0080	.0120	.0160	.0199	.0239	.0279	.0319	.0359
0.1	.0398	.0438	.0478	.0517	.0557	.0596	.0636	.0675	.0714	.0753
0.2	.0793	.0832	.0871	.0910	.0948	.0987	.1026	.1064	.1103	.1141
0.3	.1179	.1217	.1255	.1293	.1331	.1368	.1406	.1443	.1480	.1517
0.4	.1554	.1591	.1628	.1664	.1700	.1736	.1772	.1808	.1844	.1879
0.5	.1915	.1950	.1985	.2019	.2054	.2088	.2123	.2157	.2190	.2224
0.6	.2257	.2291	.2324	.2357	.2389	.2422	.2454	.2486	.2517	.2549
0.7	.2580	.2611	.2642	.2673	.2704	.2734	.2764	.2794	.2823	.2852
0.8	.2881	.2910	.2939	.2967	.2995	.3023	.3051	.3078	.3106	.3133
0.9	.3159	.3186	.3212	.3238	.3264	.3289	.3315	.3340	.3365	.3389
1.0	.3413	.3438	.3461	.3485	.3508	.3531	.3554	.3577	.3599	.3621
1.1	.3643	.3665	.3686	.3708	.3729	.3749	.3770	.3790	.3810	.3830
1.2	.3849	.3869	.3888	.3907	.3925	.3944	.3962	.3980	.3997	.4015
1.3	.4032	.4049	.4066	.4082	.4099	.4115	.4131	.4147	.4162	.4177
1.4	.4192	.4207	.4222	.4236	.4251	.4265	.4279	.4292	.4306	.4319
1.5	.4332	.4345	.4357	.4370	.4382	.4394	.4406	.4418	.4429	.4441

* Students with knowledge of calculus should note that the probability that x assumes a value in the interval $a < x < b$ is $P(a < x < b) = \int_a^b f(y)\, dy$, assuming the integral exists. The value of this definite integral can be obtained to any desired degree of accuracy by approximation procedures. For this reason, it is tabulated for the user.

to the right of the mean. Note that z is the z-score discussed in Section 3.8, that is, the number of standard deviations σ between μ and x. The distribution of z, which has mean $\mu = 0$ and standard deviation $\sigma = 1$, is called a **standard normal distribution**.

FIGURE 4.6

The Tabulated Area Corresponding to $z = 1.26$

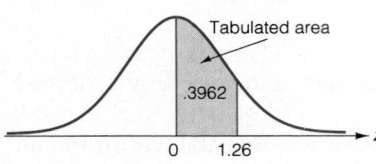

EXAMPLE 4.11 Find the area under a normal curve between the mean and a point $z = 1.26$ standard deviations to the right of the mean; that is, find $P(0 \leq z \leq 1.26)$.

Solution   To locate the proper entry in Table 4.3, proceed down the left (z) column of the table to the row corresponding to $z = 1.2$. Then move across the top of the table to the column headed .06. The intersection of the .06 column and the 1.2 row (shaded in Table 4.3) contains the desired area, .3962, as shown in Figure 4.6.

EXAMPLE 4.12 Use Table 2, Appendix A, to determine the area to the right of the z-score 1.64 for the standard normal distribution. That is, find $P(z \geq 1.64)$.

Solution   The probability that a normal random variable will fall more than 1.64 standard deviations to the right of its mean is indicated in Figure 4.7. Because the normal distribution is symmetric, half of the total probability (.5) lies to the right of the mean and half to the left. Therefore, the desired probability is

$$P(z > 1.64) = .5 - A$$

where A is the area between $\mu = 0$ and $z = 1.64$, as shown in Figure 4.7. Referring to Table 2, Appendix A, we find that the area A corresponding to $z = 1.64$ is .4495. So,

$$P(z \geq 1.64) = .5 - A = .5 - .4995 = .0505$$

FIGURE 4.7

Normal Curve Sketch for Example 4.12

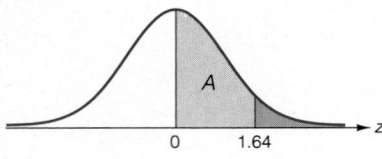

Many distributions of data that occur in the real world are approximately normal, but few are *standard* normal. In the next example, we show you how to use the standard normal table to solve problems involving any normal distribution.

EXAMPLE 4.13 Value Line is an advisory service that provides investors with forecasts of the movement of the stock market. Each week Value Line selects one stock that it believes has the highest probability of moving upward in the coming months. Over a certain 3 year period, Value Line's stock selection strategy was highly successful. However, its selections the following year performed below par, according to Value Line's *Selection & Opinion*, which listed the performance of the stock selections to date. Performance was measured as the percentage change in stock price since the date of recommendation. The mean percentage change of the stocks was -19.9, and the standard deviation was 18.6. Assume that the percentage change in stock price over the period of interest can be modeled by a normal probability distribution.

a. What is the probability that the percentage change of a stock recommended by Value Line over the period is greater than 0? (This is the probability that the stock will gain, or move upward.)

b. For this period, 10% of the stocks recommended by Value Line had percentage changes below what value?

c. Would you expect to observe a stock recommended by Value Line that doubled in price during the below par year?

Solution

a. The percentage change, x, of Value Line's stocks is assumed to be approximately normal with $\mu = -19.9$ and standard deviation $\sigma = 18.6$. We want to find the probability that x exceeds 0, that is, $P(x > 0)$. This is the area P shaded under the normal curve in Figure 4.8a. To use the standard normal tables, we must find this probability on the standard normal curve (Figure 4.8b). This amounts to finding the z-value corresponding to 0%. Substituting $x = 0$, $\mu = -19.9$, and $\sigma = 18.6$ into the formula for z, we obtain

$$z = \frac{x - \mu}{\sigma} = \frac{0 - (-19.9)}{18.6} = \frac{19.9}{18.6} = 1.07$$

Thus, we have $P(x > 0) = P(z > 1.07)$. Therefore, $P(z > 1.07) = (.5 - A)$, where A is the area between $\mu = 0$ and $z = 1.07$. This area, given in Table 2, Appendix A, is .3577. It follows that

$$P(x > 0) = P(z > 1.07) = .5 - A = .5 - .3577 = .1423$$

FIGURE 4.8

Normal Curve Sketches for Example 4.13a

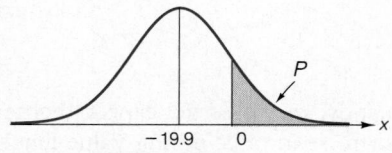 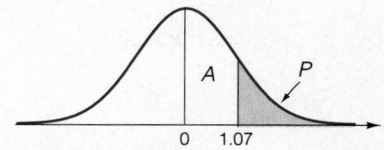

a. Percentage change, x **b.** Standard normal, z

b. We want to find a value x_0 of the normal random variable x, percentage change, such that $P(x < x_0) = .10$. Unlike part **a**, where we were given a value of x and asked to find a corresponding probability, here we are given a probability (.10) and asked to locate the corresponding value of x. Notice that x_0 must be located to the left of (ie, below) the mean for $P(x < x_0)$ to be so small. (See Figure 4.9.)

FIGURE 4.9

Normal Curve Areas for Example 4.13b

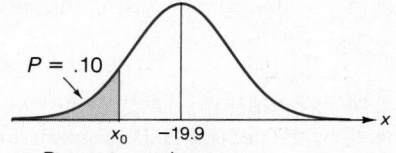 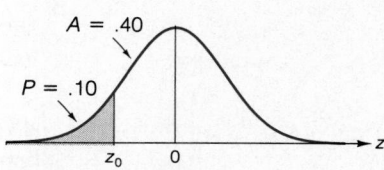

a. Percentage change, x **b.** Standard normal, z

To find the value of x_0, we first must find its corresponding z-value, z_0, where

$$z_0 = \frac{x_0 - \mu}{\sigma} = \frac{x_0 - (-19.9)}{18.6}$$

Once we locate z_0, we can use the equivalent relation

$$x_0 = \mu + z_0(\sigma) = -19.9 + z_0(18.6)$$

to find x_0.

You can see from Figure 4.9b that z_0 is the z-value that corresponds to the area $A = .40$ in Table 2, Appendix A. In the body of the table, we see that the value closest to .40 is .3997. The z-value corresponding to this area is $z_0 = -1.28$. (Note that z_0 is negative since it lies to the left of 0.) Substituting into the formula above, we have

$$x_0 = -19.9 + z_0(18.6) = -19.9 + (-1.28)(18.6) = -43.71$$

Thus, 10% of the stocks recommended by Value Line had percentage changes below -43.71.

c. The percentage change of a stock that doubles in price is $x = 100$ (ie, a 100% increase in price). The likelihood of observing at least a 100% increase in price is

$$P(x \geq 100) = P\left(z \geq \frac{100 - \mu}{\sigma}\right)$$

$$= P\left(z \geq \frac{100 - (-19.9)}{18.6}\right)$$

$$= P(z \geq 6.45) \approx 0$$

Consequently, we would not expect to observe a recommended stock with such a large increase in price during Value Line's below par year.

The preceding examples deal with cases in which we know that the relative frequency distribution for the population is normal, and they help us understand the use of the standard normal table. In the sections and chapters that follow, we will learn how to make inferences about the population based on the information in a sample. Several of these techniques are based on the assumption that the population is approximately normally distributed. Consequently, it will be important to determine whether the sample data come from a normal population before we can properly apply these inferential methods.

Several descriptive techniques can be used to check for normality. These are summarized in the box at the top of the next page and illustrated in the next example.

EXAMPLE 4.14   Consider the data set consisting of the tar contents of 372 cigarette brands collected by the Federal Trade Commission. Numerical and graphical descriptive measures for the data are shown in the SAS printouts, Figures 4.10a–c. Determine whether the tar contents have an approximate normal distribution.

Solution   As a first check, we examine the horizontal frequency histogram of the data shown in Figure 4.10b. Clearly, the tar contents fall in an approximately mound-shaped, symmetric distribution centered around the mean of 11.60 milligrams. Thus, from check 1 in the box, the data appear to be approximately normal.

Check 2 in the box requires that we find the interquartile range (ie, the difference between the 75th and 25th percentiles) and the standard deviation of the data set,

---

FIGURE 4.10a

SAS Descriptive Statistics for Tar Contents

UNIVARIATE PROCEDURE

Variable=TAR

Moments

N	372	Sum Wgts	372
Mean	11.60215	Sum	4316
Std Dev	4.966089	Variance	24.66204
Skewness	0.247064	Kurtosis	0.301387
USS	59224.5	CSS	9149.618
CV	42.80318	Std Mean	0.25748
T:Mean=0	45.06044	Prob>|T|	0.0001
Sgn Rank	34689	Prob>|S|	0.0001
Num ^= 0	372		

Quantiles(Def=5)

100% Max	26	99%	25
75% Q3	15	95%	19
50% Med	11	90%	17
25% Q1	9	10%	5
0% Min	0.5	5%	4
		1%	0.5
Range	25.5		
Q3-Q1	6		
Mode	9		

Extremes

Lowest	Obs	Highest	Obs
0.5(	250)	25(	258)
0.5(	249)	25(	276)
0.5(	61)	25(	298)
0.5(	59)	26(	255)
0.5(	57)	26(	271)

FIGURE 4.10b

SAS Histogram and Box Plot for Tar Contents

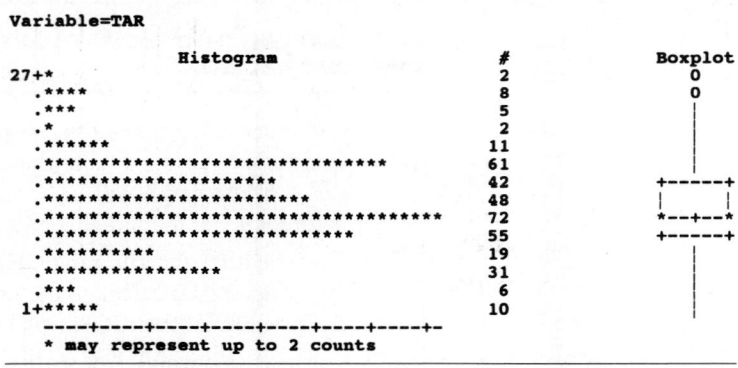

```
Variable=TAR
                      Histogram                    #        Boxplot
27+*                                               2          0
  .****                                            8          0
  .***                                             5          |
  .*                                               2          |
  .******                                         11          |
  .********************************               61          |
  .*********************                          42       +-----+
  .************************                       48       |     |
  .*********************************************  72       *--+--*
  .***************************                    55       +-----+
  .**********                                     19          |
  .****************                               31          |
  .***                                             6          |
1+*****                                           10          |
  ----+----+----+----+----+----+----+-
   * may represent up to 2 counts
```

FIGURE 4.10c

SAS Normal Probability Plot for Tar Contents

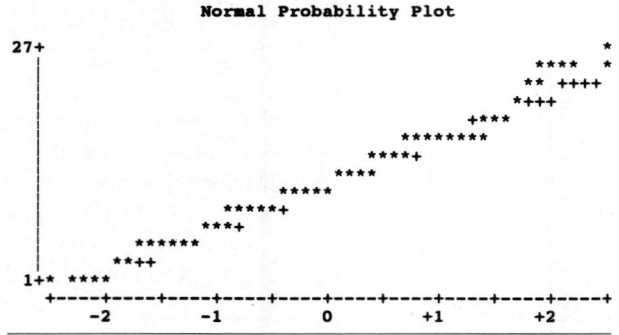

```
                  Normal Probability Plot
27+                                               *
                                         ****  *
                                         **  ++++
                                         *+++
                                     +***
                                 ********
                             ****+
                         ****
                     *****
               *****+
            ***+
         ******
      **++
1+*  ****
   +----+----+----+----+----+----+----+----+----+----+
       -2        -1         0        +1        +2
```

and compute the ratio of these two numbers. The ratio IQR/s for a sample from a normal distribution will approximately equal 1.3.* The values of IQR and s, shaded in Figure 4.10a, are IQR = $Q_U - Q_L$ = 6 and s = 4.966. Then the ratio is

$$\frac{\text{IQR}}{s} = \frac{6}{4.966} = 1.21$$

Since this value is approximately equal to 1.3, we have further confirmation that the data are approximately normal.

A third descriptive technique for checking normality is a **normal probability plot**. In a normal probability plot, the observations in the data set are ordered and then plotted against the standardized expected values of the observations under the assumption that the data are normally distributed. When the data are, in fact, normally distributed, an observation will approximately equal its expected value. Thus, a linear (straight-line) trend in the normal probability plot suggests that the data are from an approximate normal distribution, while a nonlinear trend indicates that the data are nonnormal.

---

* You can see that this property holds for normal distributions by noting that the z-values (obtained from Table 2, Appendix A) corresponding to the 75th and 25th percentiles are .67 and $-.67$, respectively. Since $\sigma = 1$ for a standard normal (z) distribution, IQR/σ = [.67 $- (-.67)$]/1 = 1.34.

Normal probability plots can be constructed by hand, as shown in the next box. However, it is easier to generate these plots by computer. The SAS normal probability plot for the 372 tar measurements is shown in Figure 4.10c. Notice that the ordered measurements (represented by the plotting symbol "*") fall reasonably close to a straight line (plotting symbol "+"). Thus, check 3 also suggests that the data are likely to be approximately normally distributed.

CONSTRUCTING A NORMAL PROBABILITY PLOT FOR A DATA SET

STEP 1   List the observations in the sample data set in ascending order, where x_i represents the ith ordered value.

STEP 2   For each observation, calculate the corresponding tail area of the standard normal (z) distribution,

$$A = \frac{i - .375}{n + .25}$$

where n is the sample size.

STEP 3   Calculate the estimated expected value of x_i under normality using the following formula:

$$E(x_i) = (s)[Z(A)]$$

where s is the sample standard deviation and $Z(A)$ is the z-value that cuts off an area A in the lower tail of the standard normal distribution.

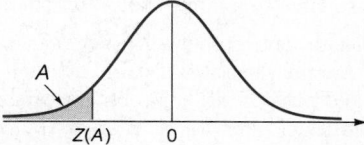

STEP 4   Plot the ordered observations, x_i, on the vertical axis and the corresponding estimated expected values, $E(x_i)$, on the horizontal axis.

The checks for normality given in the box are simple yet powerful techniques to apply, but they are only descriptive in nature. It is possible (although unlikely) that the data are nonnormal even when all three checks are reasonably satisfied. Thus, we should be careful not to claim that the 372 tar measurements are, in fact, normally distributed. We can only state that it is reasonable to believe that the data are from a normal distribution.*

---

* Statistical tests of normality that provide a measure of reliability for the inference are available. However, these tests tend to be very sensitive to slight departures from normality; that is, they tend to reject the hypothesis of normality for any distribution that is not perfectly symmetrical and mound-shaped. Consult the references if you want to learn more about these tests.

PROBLEMS

4.25 Pacemakers are used to control the heartbeat of cardiac patients, with over 120,000 of the devices implanted each year. A single pacemaker is made up of several biomedical components that must be of a high quality for the pacemaker to work. It is vitally important for manufacturers of pacemakers to use parts that meet specifications. One particular plastic part, called a connector module, mounts on the top of the pacemaker. Connector modules are required to have a length between .304 and .322 inch to work properly. Any module with a length outside these limits is considered *out-of-spec*. *Quality* (Aug. 1989) reported on one supplier of connector modules that had been shipping out-of-spec parts to the manufacturer for 12 months.

    a. The lengths of the connector modules produced by the supplier were found to follow an approximate normal distribution with mean $\mu = .3015$ inch and standard deviation $\sigma = .0016$ inch. Use this information to find the probability that the supplier produces an out-of-spec part.

    b. Once the problem was detected, the supplier's inspection crew began to employ an automated data-collection system designed to improve product quality. After 2 months, the process was producing connector modules with mean $\mu = .3146$ inch and standard deviation $\sigma = .0030$ inch. Find the probability that an out-of-spec part will now be produced. Compare your answer to part **a**.

4.26 "Cents off" coupons have been traditionally viewed by economists as price discriminators between two segments of the product's customers: loyal consumers with a high value of time who choose not to use the coupon (and pay full price), and customers with a low value of time who redeem the coupon to realize a lower price. In contrast, marketers view "cents off" coupons simply as a form of advertisement or promotion of a product; very few customers are expected to take advantage of the reduced price. A study was conducted to investigate these two competing interpretations of "cents off" coupons (*Quarterly Journal of Business and Economics*, Autumn 1986). Price comparisons of a particular brand of paper towels purchased with and without coupons resulted in a mean difference of 2.75¢ and a standard deviation of 3.45¢. Assume that the price difference x (in cents) is normally distributed.

    a. Find $P(x > 9)$.   **b.** Find $P(x > 5)$.   **c.** Find $P(x < 0)$.

    d. The upper and lower quartiles of the price differences were found to be 5.11¢ and .42¢. Use this information to determine whether it is reasonable to assume the price differences are normally distributed.

4.27 It is well-known that children with developmental delays (i.e., mild mental retardation) are slower cognitively than normally developing children. Are their social skills also lacking? A study compared the social interactions of the two groups of children in a controlled playground environment (*American Journal on Mental Retardation*, Jan. 1992). One variable of interest was the number of intervals of "no play" by each child. Children with developmental delays had a mean of 2.73 intervals of "no play" and a standard deviation of 2.58 intervals. Based on this information, is it possible for the variable of interest to be normally distributed? Explain.

4.28 The U.S. Department of Agriculture (USDA) has patented a process that uses a bacterium for removing bitterness from citrus juices (*Chemical Engineering*, Feb. 3, 1986). In theory, almost all the bitterness could be removed by the process, but for practical purposes the USDA aims at 50% overall removal. Suppose a USDA spokesperson claims that the percentage of bitterness removed from an 8 ounce glass of freshly squeezed citrus juice is normally distributed with mean 50.1 and standard deviation 10.4. To test this claim, the bitterness removal process is applied to a randomly selected 8 ounce glass of citrus juice.

    a. Find the probability that the process removes less than 33.7% of the bitterness.

    b. Refer to your answer to part **a**. If the test on the single glass of citrus juice yielded a bitterness removal percentage of 33.7%, would you tend to doubt the USDA spokesperson's claim?

4.29 The metropolitan airport commission is considering the establishment of limitations on the extent of noise pollution around a local airport. At the present time the noise level per jet takeoff in one neighborhood near the airport is approximately normally distributed with a mean of 100 decibels and a standard deviation of 6 decibels.

    a. What is the probability that a randomly selected jet will generate a noise level greater than 108 decibels in this neighborhood?

b. What is the probability that a randomly selected jet will generate a noise level of exactly 100 decibels?

c. Suppose a regulation is passed that requires jet noises in this neighborhood to be lower than 105 decibels 95% of the time. Assuming the standard deviation of the noise distribution remains the same, how much will the mean noise level have to be lowered to comply with the regulations?

4.30 One common ploy of advertisements for new automobiles is to list the Environmental Protection Agency (EPA) estimated miles per gallon (mpg) for the make of car being advertised. For example, the Plymouth Voyager minivan has an EPA estimated miles per gallon of 28. The EPA tests cars under conditions (weather, brand of gasoline, speed, terrain, etc.) ideally suited for maximum mileage performance. Nevertheless, even under identical conditions, it is unreasonable and impractical to assume that all Plymouth Voyager minivans tested will obtain the same gas mileage. It is most likely that the 28 mpg figure is the average miles per gallon obtained by the sample of minivans tested. Let us assume that the EPA estimated miles per gallon for this type of car is accurate, that is, that the true mean miles per gallon obtained under ideal conditions for all Plymouth Voyager minivans is, in fact, 28. Also, suppose the distribution of miles per gallon is approximately normal with a standard deviation of 2.

a. What proportion of all Plymouth Voyager minivans tested under ideal conditions will obtain at least 32 mpg?

b. What is the probability that a Plymouth Voyager minivan tested under ideal conditions will obtain less than 20 mpg?

c. Fifteen percent of all Plymouth Voyager minivans tested will obtain a miles per gallon rating above a particular value. Find this value.

d. Suppose you test your new Plymouth Voyager minivan under ideal conditions and find that your car obtains 20 mpg. Does this result imply that you have bought a "lemon," or is it more likely that the EPA estimated figure of 28 mpg is too high? [*Hint:* Use your answer to part **b**.]

4.31 Foresters collected data on trembling aspen trees in British Columbia's boreal forest. The diameters at breast height (in meters) for a sample of 28 trembling aspen trees are listed in the table. Determine whether the sample data are from an approximately normal distribution.

12.4	17.3	27.3	19.1	16.9	16.2	20.0
16.6	16.3	16.3	21.4	25.7	15.0	19.3
12.9	18.6	12.4	15.9	18.8	14.9	12.8
24.8	26.9	13.5	17.9	13.2	23.2	12.7

Source: Scholz, H. "Fish Creek Community Forest: Exploratory Statistical Analysis of Selected Data." Working paper, Northern Lights College, British Columbia, Canada.

4.32 Behaviorists have developed an instrument designed to measure the maturity of small groups of people. The 10 item questionnaire is based on the assumptions that a mature group is able to function independently of its leader, is active, is organized, and has an established working history, while an immature group has the opposite attributes. Krayer divided a class of undergraduate college students into two groups, mature and immature, based on their answers to the 10 item questionnaire. A final project was assigned and, at the end of the semester, student performances were evaluated. A summary of the grades on the project for the two groups is provided in the table. Assume these represent population means and standard deviations.

GROUP	MEAN GRADE	STANDARD DEVIATION
Mature	91.50	8.48
Immature	84.20	6.98

Source: Krayer, K. J. "Exploring Group Maturity in the Classroom." *Small Group Behavior*, Vol. 19, No. 2, May 1988, p. 268.

a. Assuming the population of project grades for the mature group is approximately normal, find the probability that a mature student will score below 80 on the final project.

b. Repeat part **a** for the immature group.

c. Why might the assumption of normality in parts **a** and **b** be suspect? [*Hint:* Consider the fact that the highest grade that can be assigned to a project is 100.]

d. A stem-and-leaf display and normal probability plot for each of the two groups are shown in the accompanying SAS printouts. Based on these graphs, assess whether the grade distributions are approximately normal.

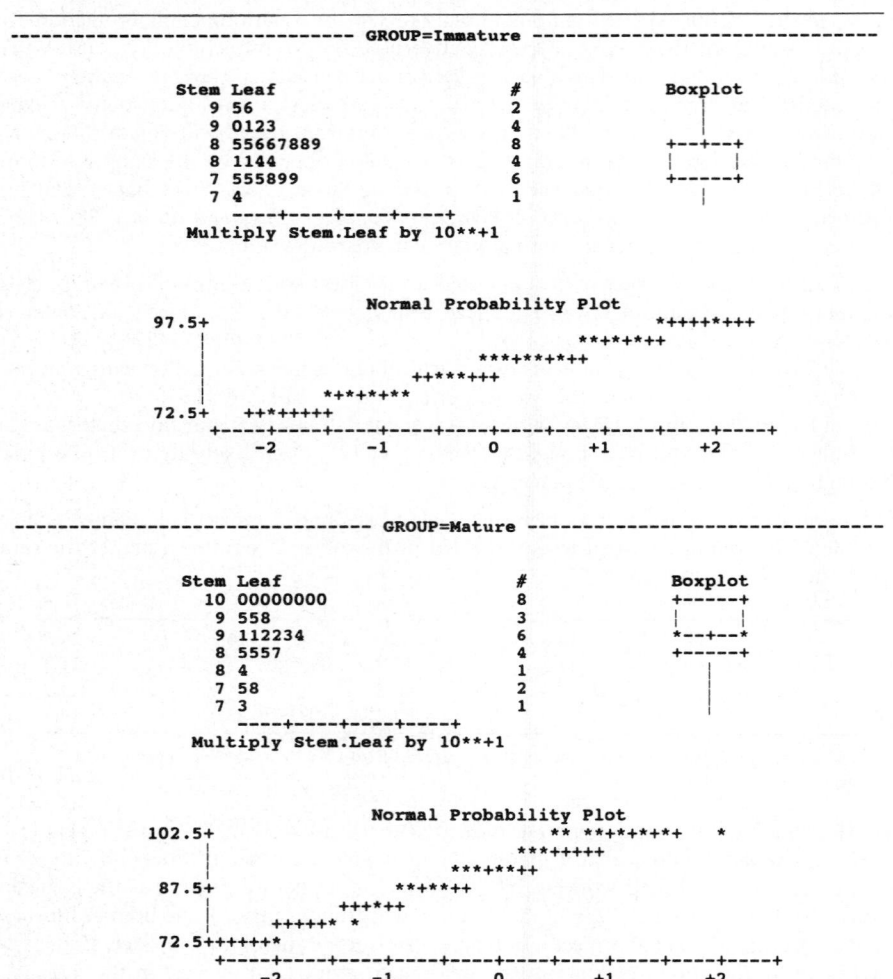

4.33 How does the stock market react when a firm announces its stock earnings in *The Wall Street Journal*? To examine this issue, a comprehensive study of 240 stocks was conducted over a 10 year period (*The Accounting Review*, Jan. 1991). One of the variables used to measure market reaction was excess trading volume. Excess trading volume is defined as the difference between the percentage of shares traded on the day of the earnings announcement and the average percentage of shares traded for a 3 day period prior to the announcement. The researcher assumes that excess trading volume, when standardized, has an approximate standard normal distribution. Let x equal the standardized excess trading volume for a particular stock.

a. What is the mean of x?

b. What is the standard deviation of x?

c. Find the median (50th percentile) of x.

d. Find the lower quartile (25th percentile) of x.

e. Find the upper quartile (75th percentile) of x.

4.34 Refer to Exercise 4.33. Using simulation, the researcher found that standardized excess trading volume x is approximately normal, but with mean $\mu = -1.767$ and standard deviation $\sigma = .956$.

a. Find $P(x < 0)$.

b. Find $P(x < Q_L)$, where Q_L is the lower quartile of a standard normal (z) distribution.

c. Find $P(x < Q_U)$, where Q_U is the upper quartile of a standard normal (z) distribution.

d. Based on the results in parts **a–c**, how well does the standard normal (z) distribution approximate the true distribution of x?

COMPUTER LAB

NORMAL PROBABILITY PLOTS

All three statistical software packages (SAS, SPSS, and MINITAB) have routines for producing a normal probability plot. To illustrate, we show how to obtain a normal probability plot for the tar contents of the 372 cigarette brands examined by the Federal Trade Commission.*

SAS

```
Command
  Line
   1      DATA FTC;        ⎫ Data entry instructions
   2      INPUT TAR @@;    ⎭
   3      CARDS;
        17   15    9    9   15 ⎫
        10   16   16   12   12 ⎪
         •    •    •    •    •  ⎬ Input data values
         •    •    •    •    •  ⎪ (5 observations per line)
         •    •    •    •    •  ⎪
        10   10    5    5   10 ⎭
   4      PROC UNIVARIATE PLOT; ⎫ Normal probability plot
   5      VAR TAR;              ⎭
```

COMMANDS 4–5 The UNIVARIATE procedure with the PLOT option will produce a normal probability plot for the variable (eg, TAR) specified.

NOTE Use the NORMAL option to compute a test statistic for the hypothesis that the data come from a normal distribution.

NOTE The SAS printout is shown in Figure 4.10c (p. 180).

---

* The full data set, in an ASCII file, is available on micro (or floppy) diskette from the publisher (see the Preface).

SPSS

```
Command
  Line
   1     DATA LIST FREE/TAR.⎤
   2     BEGIN DATA.          ⎬  Data entry instructions

         17   15    9    9   15⎤
         10   16   16   12   12│
          .    .    .    .    .⎬  Input data values
          .    .    .    .    .│  (5 observations per line)
          .    .    .    .    .│
         10   10    5    5   10⎦
   3     END DATA.
   4     EXAMINE VARIABLES=TAR/PLOT=NPPLOT.   Normal probability plot
```

COMMAND 4   The EXAMINE command with the PLOT=NPPLOT subcommand will produce a normal probability plot for the variable (eg, TAR) specified.

NOTE   PLOT=NPPLOT will also produce a test statistic for the normal distribution hypothesis.

NOTE   The output of the SPSS program is displayed in Figure 4.11.

MINITAB

```
Command
  Line
   1     SET C1   Data entry instruction
         17   15    9    9   15⎤
         10   16   16   12   12│
          .    .    .    .    .⎬  Input data values
          .    .    .    .    .│  (5 observations per line)
          .    .    .    .    .│
         10   10    5    5   10⎦
   2     NSCORES C1 C2                          ⎤
   3     NAME C1='TAR' C2='EXPECTED'           ⎬ Normal probability plot
   4     PLOT C1 C2                             ⎦
```

COMMAND 2   To generate a normal probability plot in MINITAB, first create "normal scores" for the data in C1 using the NSCORES command. These normal scores (saved in C2) are the standard expected values of the data points, assuming the data are normally distributed.

COMMAND 4   The PLOT command produces the normal probability plot by plotting the actual data in C1 on the vertical axis and the normal scores in C2 on the horizontal axis.

NOTE   The MINITAB printout is displayed in Figure 4.12.

FIGURE 4.11

SPSS Output for the Federal Trade Commission Data

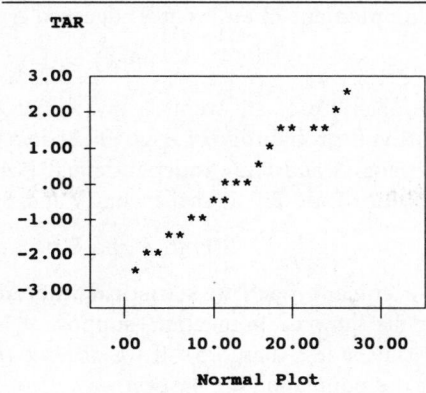

	Statistic	df	Significance
K-S (Lilliefors)	.0896	372	.0000

FIGURE 4.12

MINITAB Output for the Federal Trade Commission Data

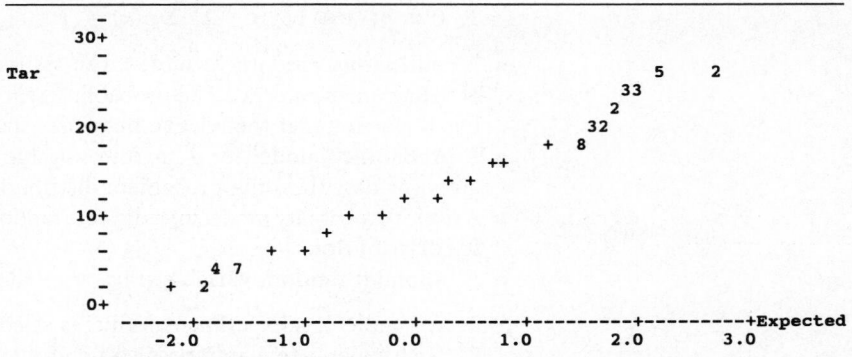

CHAPTER NOTES

- The process of making an observation is called an **experiment**.
- Outcomes of experiments are called **events**.
- The **probability** of an event is the proportion of times the event is observed when the experiment is repeated a very large number of times. All probabilities must lie between 0 and 1.
- **Mutually exclusive** events are events that cannot occur at the same time.
- **Probability Rule 1:** If events A and B are mutually exclusive, then

$$P(\text{Either } A \text{ or } B \text{ occurs}) = P(A) + P(B)$$

- **Probability Rule 2:** If an experiment results in one and only one of M equally likely mutually exclusive events, and m of these events result in event A, then

$$P(A) = \frac{m}{M}$$

- The **complement** of an event A, denoted $\overline{A}$, is the event that A does not occur;

$$P(\overline{A}) = 1 - P(A)$$

- The probability of an event A, given that event B has occurred, is called the **conditional probability of A given B**, and is denoted $P(A \mid B)$.
- Two events A and B are **independent** if $P(A \mid B) = P(A)$ or if $P(B \mid A) = P(B)$.
- **Probability Rule 3:**   If two events A and B are independent, then

$$P(\text{Both } A \text{ and } B \text{ occur}) = P(A)P(B)$$

- **Rare-event approach to statistical inference:**   Based on certain assumptions about the sampled population, suppose A is a **rare event**, that is, $P(A) = p$ is small (say, p less than .05). If we observe that A occurs, then our assumptions about the population are suspect.
- A **random variable** is a variable that assumes numerical values associated with events of an experiment.
- A **discrete random variable x** can assume only a countable number of possible values, and has the following properties:

1. $0 \leq p(x) \leq 1$ **2.** $\Sigma\, p(x) = 1$

- A **continuous random variable x** can assume any of the infinitely large number of values in an interval. The probability that x falls between two numbers a and b is the area under the relative frequency distribution for x between a and b.
- A **probability model** for a random variable x is a table, formula, or graph that gives (or describes) the probability distribution of x.
- A useful probability model for a discrete random variable is the **binomial probability distribution**.
- A **binomial random variable x** has the following properties:

1. A sample of n experimental units is selected from a population.
2. Each experimental unit possesses one of two characteristics, **success** or **failure**.
3. $P(\text{Success}) = \pi$ and $P(\text{Failure}) = (1 - \pi)$ are the same for all experimental units.
4. The outcome for any one experimental unit is independent of the outcome for any other experimental unit (ie, the draws are independent in a probabilistic sense).
5. $x = $ Number of successes in n trials
6. $p(x) = \binom{n}{x} \pi^x (1 - \pi)^{n-x}$ $(x = 0, 1, 2, ..., n)$,   where $\binom{n}{x} = \dfrac{n!}{x!(n - x)!}$
7. $\mu = n\pi$, $\sigma = \sqrt{n\pi(1 - \pi)}$

- A useful probability model for a continuous random variable is the **normal probability distribution**. The theoretical relative frequency histogram for the normal distribution (ie, the **normal curve**) is mound-shaped and symmetric about its mean μ, and its spread is determined by its standard deviation σ.
- The **standard normal (z) distribution** is a normal distribution with mean $\mu = 0$ and standard deviation $\sigma = 1$. If x is normally distributed with mean μ and standard deviation σ, then $z = (x - \mu)/\sigma$ is standard normal.

- Perform one or more of the following checks to determine whether a data set is from an approximately normal distribution:

1. Compare a stem-and-leaf display or histogram of the data to the normal curve.
2. Calculate the ratio IQR/s for the data and compare to 1.3.
3. Construct a **normal probability plot** for the data and compare to a straight line.

LOOKING AHEAD

In Chapter 5 we will learn more about the role of probability in assessing the reliability of statistical inferences. We will use our knowledge of probability distributions to construct confidence intervals and perform statistical tests of hypotheses for population parameters—the two major tools of statistical inference.

CASE STUDY

BREAK-EVEN ANALYSIS—WHEN TO MARKET A NEW PRODUCT

The inherent risk involved with marketing a new product is a key consideration for market researchers. How much will it cost to produce the product? Should the product be marketed? And if marketed, what should be the price of the new product? Will it be profitable? Various statistical models have been developed to aid speculators and businesses in making such decisions. Typically, these decision models are based on the assumption that production costs and selling price are known, and that the quantity produced is determined without knowledge of the demand for the product.

One area of marketing research that uses decision models is called *break-even analysis*. The underlying assumption of break-even analysis is that the demand for a product is normally distributed, with known mean μ and standard deviation σ. Of interest is the relationship between actual demand D and the break-even point BE, where the break-even point is defined as the number of units of the product the company must sell in order to break even on the investment.

Shih (1981) developed two practical decision criteria using break-even analysis.* Both decision rules require knowledge of probability and the normal distribution.

DECISION RULE A

Market the new product if the chance is better than 50% that demand D will exceed the break-even point BE—that is, market the product if

$$P(D \geq BE) > .5$$

---

* Shih, W. "A General Decision Model for Cost–Volume–Profit Analysis Under Uncertainty: A Reply." *The Accounting Review*, Vol. 56, No. 2, 1981, pp. 404–408.

Under the assumption that demand is normally distributed, decision rule A is equivalent to marketing the product when $\mu \geq BE$. Thus, no knowledge of σ is needed to arrive at a decision.

The probability $P(D \geq BE)$ is often called the *level of risk*. Shih's second decision criterion "allows top management to vary the level of risk it could tolerate [for each new product] in light of its outlook on the uncertainty."

DECISION RULE B
_____

For a specified level of risk $p(0 \leq p \leq 1)$, market the new product if

$P(D \geq BE) > p$

Under the normality assumption, decision rule B can be implemented in either of two ways:

1. Given the values of μ and σ, calculate $P(D \geq BE)$ using the standard normal probability table. Then compare this probability to the specified level of risk p. If $P(D \geq BE) > p$, market the new product.
2. Calculate the *break-even average demand M*, such that the probability of breaking even or better is equal to the specified level of risk p. That is, compute

$$M = BE - z_p\sigma$$

where $P(z > z_p) = p$. Market the new product if $\mu \geq M$.

Suppose a company wants to decide whether to market a new type of ceiling fan. From past experience, the company knows that the number of ceiling fans of this type sold per year follows a normal distribution with a mean of 4,000 and a standard deviation of 500. Marketing researchers have also determined that the company needs to sell 3,500 units in order to break even for the year.

a. According to decision rule A, should the company market the new ceiling fans?
b. Use a sketch of the normal distribution to show that if $P(D \geq BE) > .5$, then it must be true that $\mu \geq BE$.
c. Suppose that the minimum level of risk the company is willing to tolerate is $p = .8$. Use decision rule B to arrive at a decision. Show that the two ways of implementing the rule lead to the same decision.

REFERENCES

Hogg, R. V., and Craig, A. T. *Introduction to Mathematical Statistics*, 4th ed. New York: Macmillan, 1978.

Mendenhall, W., Wackerly, D., and Scheaffer, R. *Mathematical Statistics with Applications*, 4th ed. Boston: PWS-Kent, 1989.

Snedecor, G. W., and Cochran, W. G. *Statistical Methods*, 7th ed. Ames: Iowa State University Press, 1980.

CHAPTER 5

INTRODUCTION TO STATISTICAL INFERENCE

E ach year, *Business Week* reports on the salaries of CEOs at major U.S. companies in its "Executive Compensation Scoreboard." In order to determine whether CEOs are worth their pay, a ratio of shareholder return to salary is calculated for each CEO. How can we use the sample information provided by *Business Week* to estimate the average ratio for all CEOs in the United States? In this chapter we bridge the gap between probability and statistical inference. The basic tools of statistical inference—confidence intervals and tests of hypothesis—are discussed. You'll apply one of these tools to answer the question posed above in Problem 5.16.

5.1

Recall from Chapter 1 that one of the main objectives of statistics in enumerative studies is to make inferences about a population parameter based on the value of a sample statistic. The value of a population parameter (eg, the mean μ) is constant (although it is usually unknown to us); its value does not vary from sample to sample. However, the value of a sample statistic (eg, the sample mean, $\bar{x}$) is highly dependent on the particular sample selected. Since statistics vary from sample to sample, any inferences based on them will necessarily be subject to some uncertainty. How, then, do we judge the reliability of a sample statistic as a tool in making an inference about the corresponding population parameter? Fortunately, the uncertainty of a statistic generally has characteristic properties known to us and reflected in its **sampling distribution**. Knowledge of the sampling distribution of a particular statistic provides us with information about its performance over the long run.

DEFINITION 5.1

The **sampling distribution** of a sample statistic (based on n observations) is the relative frequency distribution of the values of the statistic theoretically generated by taking repeated random samples of size n and computing the value of the statistic for each sample.

To illustrate the notion of a sampling distribution, consider the population of 1,795 starting salaries of University of Florida graduates described in earlier chapters. (Although the true value of μ, the mean of these 1,795 observations, is already known to us from Example 3.3, this example will illustrate the concepts.) How can we generate the sampling distribution of $\bar{x}$, the mean of a random sample of $n = 5$ observations from the population of starting salaries? According to Definition 5.1, the sampling distribution can be generated in the following manner. Select a random sample of five measurements from the population of 1,795 observations on starting salary; compute and record the value of $\bar{x}$ for this sample. Now return these five measurements to the population and repeat the procedure; that is, draw another random sample of measurements and repeat the process. If this sampling procedure could be repeated an infinite number of times, as shown in Figure 5.1, the infinite number of values of $\bar{x}$ obtained could be summarized in a relative frequency distribution, called the **sampling distribution of $\bar{x}$**.

The task described above, which may seem impractical if not impossible, is not performed in actual practice. Instead, the sampling distribution of a statistic is obtained by applying mathematical theory or computer simulation, as illustrated below.

EXAMPLE 5.1   Use computer simulation to find the approximate sampling distribution of $\bar{x}$, the mean of a random sample of n observations from the population of 1,795 starting salaries, for:

FIGURE 5.1

Generating the Theoretical Sampling Distribution of the Sample Mean, $\bar{x}$

Select sample of size $n = 5$ salaries from target population

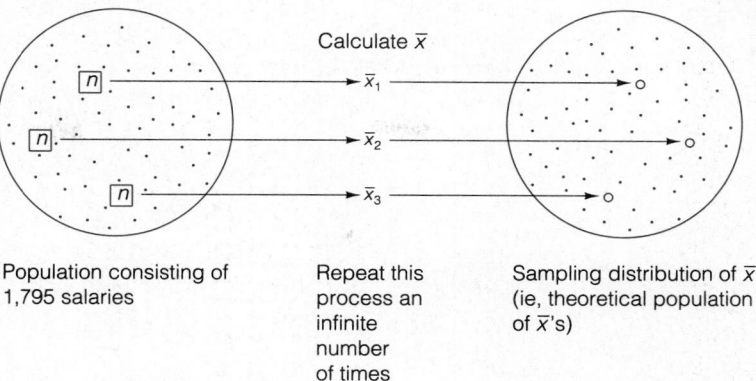

Calculate $\bar{x}$

| Population consisting of 1,795 salaries | Repeat this process an infinite number of times | Sampling distribution of $\bar{x}$ (ie, theoretical population of $\bar{x}$'s) |

a. $n = 5$

b. $n = 25$

c. Compare and contrast the two distributions with the relative frequency distribution of the actual population, reproduced in Figure 5.2 (p. 194).

Solution

a. We obtained 100 computer-generated random samples of size $n = 5$ from the target population. The first 10 of these samples are presented in Table 5.1.

For example, the first computer-generated sample contained the measurements: 27,000, 28,100, 34,500, 10,000, 25,500. The corresponding value of the sample mean is

$$\bar{x} = \frac{\Sigma x}{n} = \frac{27,000 + 28,100 + 34,500 + 10,000 + 25,500}{5} = \$25,020$$

For each sample of five observations, the sample mean $\bar{x}$ was computed. The 100 values of $\bar{x}$ are summarized in the SAS relative frequency histogram shown in Figure 5.3.

TABLE 5.1

First 10 Samples of $n = 5$ Starting Salaries

SAMPLE	STARTING SALARIES (DOLLARS)				
1	27,000	28,100	34,500	10,000	25,500
2	23,000	23,600	26,000	23,000	20,000
3	35,000	24,000	30,900	38,000	36,000
4	38,000	35,000	20,000	25,000	33,000
5	41,100	20,000	20,000	24,000	16,000
6	15,000	30,000	24,000	26,000	30,000
7	34,900	26,400	18,000	22,000	26,400
8	26,400	20,000	15,000	26,000	22,500
9	30,900	28,000	12,000	26,400	24,000
10	18,700	35,000	40,000	30,000	16,000

FIGURE 5.2

Relative Frequency Histogram of
Population of 1,795 Starting Salaries

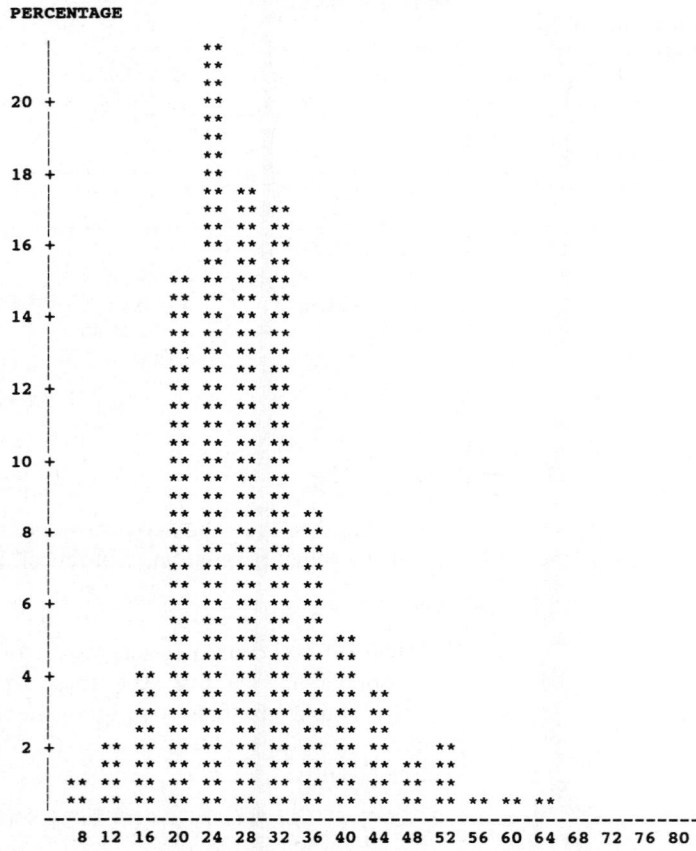

FIGURE 5.3

Sampling Distribution of $\bar{x}$: Relative
Frequency Histogram of $\bar{x}$ Based on
100 Samples of $n = 5$

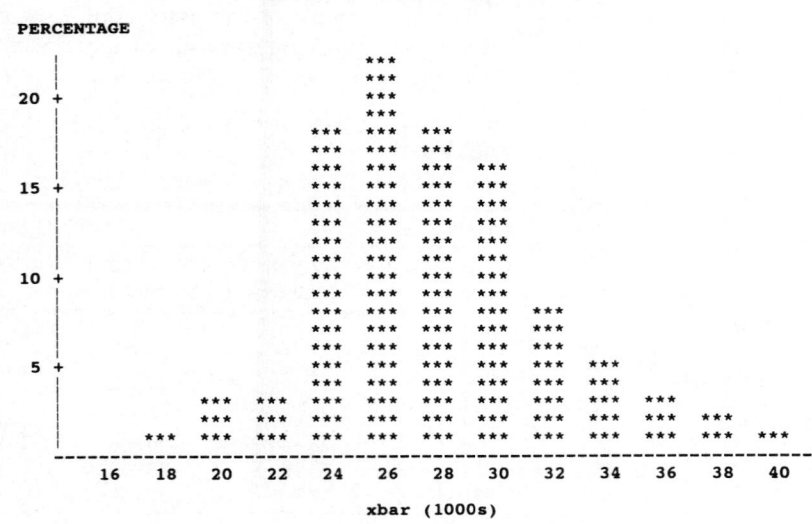

b. Using the method of part **a**, we obtained 100 computer-generated random samples of size $n = 25$ from the target population. The SAS relative frequency histogram for the 100 corresponding values of $\bar{x}$ is shown in Figure 5.4.

FIGURE 5.4

Relative Frequency Histogram of $\bar{x}$ Based on 100 Samples of Size $n = 25$

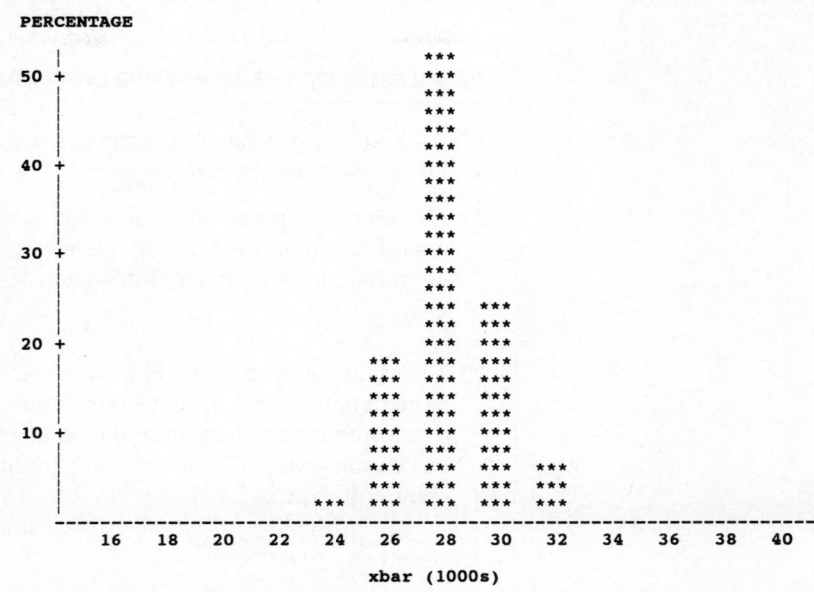

c. Comparing the two sampling distributions for $\bar{x}$ (Figures 5.3 and 5.4) with the relative frequency distribution for the population shown in Figure 5.2, note that (1) the values of $\bar{x}$ in Figures 5.3 and 5.4 tend to cluster around the population mean, $\mu = \$28,475$; and (2) the values of the sample mean are less spread out (ie, they have less variation) than the population values shown in Figure 5.2. These two observations are borne out by comparing the means and standard deviations of the three sets of observations, as shown in Table 5.2. Note also that the variation of the $\bar{x}$-values about their mean, based on samples of size $n = 25$ (Figure 5.4), is less than the variation in the values of $\bar{x}$ based on samples

TABLE 5.2

Comparison of the Population Distribution and the Approximate Sampling Distribution of $\bar{x}$, Based on 100 Samples of Size $n = 5$ and $n = 25$

	MEAN	STANDARD DEVIATION
Population of 1,795 starting salaries (Figure 5.2)	$\mu = \$28,475$	$\sigma = \$9,369$
100 values of $\bar{x}$ based on samples of size $n = 5$ (Figure 5.3)	$27,891	$4,152
100 values of $\bar{x}$ based on samples of size $n = 25$ (Figure 5.4)	$28,349	$1,564

of size $n = 5$ (Figure 5.3). From Table 5.2 we observe that, as the sample size increases, there is less variation in the sampling distribution of $\bar{x}$; that is, the values of $\bar{x}$ tend to cluster more closely about the population mean as n gets larger. This intuitively appealing result is stated formally in the box.

PROPERTIES OF THE SAMPLING DISTRIBUTION OF $\bar{x}$

If $\bar{x}$ is the mean of a random sample of size n from a population with mean μ and standard deviation σ, then:

1. The sampling distribution of $\bar{x}$ has a mean equal to the mean of the population from which the sample was selected. That is, if we let $\mu_{\bar{x}}$ denote the mean of the sampling distribution of $\bar{x}$, then

$$\mu_{\bar{x}} = \mu$$

2. The sampling distribution of $\bar{x}$ has a standard deviation equal to the standard deviation of the population from which the sample was selected, divided by the square root of the sample size. That is, if we let $\sigma_{\bar{x}}$ denote the standard deviation of the sampling distribution of $\bar{x}$ (also called the **standard error of $\bar{x}$**), then

$$\sigma_{\bar{x}} = \frac{\sigma}{\sqrt{n}}$$

The following theorem, of fundamental importance in statistics, provides information about the actual sampling distribution of $\bar{x}$.

THE CENTRAL LIMIT THEOREM

If the sample size is sufficiently large, then the mean $\bar{x}$ of a random sample from a population has a sampling distribution that is approximately normal, **regardless of the shape of the relative frequency distribution of the target population.** The larger the sample size, the better the normal approximation to the sampling distribution.

EXAMPLE 5.2 In Example 5.1, we obtained repeated random samples of sizes $n = 5$ and $n = 25$ from the population of starting salaries of University of Florida graduates. For this target population, we know the values of the parameters μ and σ:

Population mean: $\mu = \$28{,}475$

Population standard deviation: $\sigma = \$9{,}369$

Show that the empirical evidence obtained in Example 5.1 supports the Central Limit Theorem and the two properties of the sampling distribution of $\bar{x}$.

Solution In Figures 5.3 and 5.4, we noted that the values of $\bar{x}$ tend to cluster about the population mean, $\mu = \$28,475$. This is guaranteed by property 1, which implies that, in the long run, the average of *all* values of $\bar{x}$ that would be generated in infinite repeated sampling would be equal to μ.

We also observed, from Table 5.2, that the standard deviation of the sampling distribution of $\bar{x}$ decreases as the sample size increases from $n = 5$ to $n = 25$. Property 2 quantifies the decrease and relates it to the sample size. For example, note that, for our approximate (simulated) sampling distribution based on samples of size $n = 5$, we obtained a standard deviation of $\$4,152$, whereas property 2 tells us that, for the actual sampling distribution of $\bar{x}$, the standard deviation is equal to

$$\sigma_{\bar{x}} = \frac{\sigma}{\sqrt{n}} = \frac{\$9,369}{\sqrt{5}} = \$4,190$$

Similarly, for samples of size $n = 25$, the sampling distribution of $\bar{x}$ actually has a standard deviation of

$$\sigma_{\bar{x}} = \frac{\sigma}{\sqrt{n}} = \frac{\$9,369}{\sqrt{25}} = \$1,874$$

The value we obtained by simulation was $\$1,564$.

Finally, for sufficiently large samples, the Central Limit Theorem guarantees an approximately normal distribution for $\bar{x}$, regardless of the shape of the original population. In our examples, the population from which the samples were selected is seen in Figure 5.2 to be moderately skewed to the right. Note from Figures 5.3 and 5.4 that, although the sampling distribution of $\bar{x}$ tends to be mound-shaped in each case, the normal approximation improves when the sample size is increased from $n = 5$ (Figure 5.3) to $n = 25$ (Figure 5.4).

EXAMPLE 5.3 The rash of recent incidents of unethical business tactics has organizations searching for ways to dissuade unethical behavior. But how much will a company's stated concern for ethical conduct influence the behavior of its decision-makers? To answer this question, researchers at Marquette University presented MBA students (believed to be representative of entry-level managers) with decision-making situations that were clearly unethical in nature (*Journal of Business Ethics*, Vol. 6, 1987). Each subject's decisions were then rated on a scale of 1 ("definitely unethical") to 5 ("definitely ethical"). When no references to ethical concern by the "company" were explicitly stated, the ratings had a mean of 3.00 and a standard deviation of 1.03. Assume that these values represent the population mean and standard deviation, respectively, under the condition "no reference to ethical concern."

a. Suppose we present a random sample of 30 entry-level managers with a similar situation and record the ratings of each. Find the probability that $\bar{x}$, the sample mean rating, is greater than 3.55.

b. Refer to part **a**. Prior to making their decisions, the 30 entry-level managers were read a statement from the president of the "company" concerning the company's code of business ethics. The code advocates socially responsible behavior by all employees. The researchers theorize that the population mean rating of the managers under this condition will be larger than for the condition "no reference to ethical concern." (A higher mean indicates a more ethical response.) If the sample mean, $\bar{x}$, is 3.55, what can you infer about the population mean under the "stated concern" condition?

Solution

a. Although we have no information about the shape of the relative frequency distribution of the ratings, we can apply the Central Limit Theorem to conclude that the sampling distribution of the sample mean rating, based on 30 observations, is approximately normally distributed. In addition, the mean, $\mu_{\bar{x}}$, and the standard deviation, $\sigma_{\bar{x}}$, of the sampling distribution are given by

$$\mu_{\bar{x}} = \mu = 3.00 \quad \text{and} \quad \sigma_{\bar{x}} = \frac{\sigma}{\sqrt{n}} = \frac{1.03}{\sqrt{30}} = .188$$

assuming that $\mu = 3$ and $\sigma = 1.03$ under the condition "no reference to ethical concern." Then $P(\bar{x} \geq 3.55)$, the probability of observing a mean rating of 3.55 or more in the sample of 30 ratings, is equal to the shaded area shown in Figure 5.5.

FIGURE 5.5

Sampling Distribution of $\bar{x}$

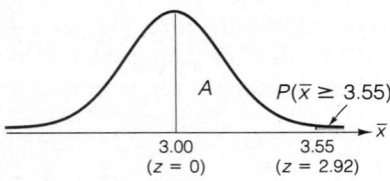

$$A \qquad P(\bar{x} \geq 3.55)$$

3.00	3.55
($z = 0$)	($z = 2.92$)

Since the sampling distribution is approximately normal, with mean and standard deviation as obtained above, we can compute the desired area by obtaining the z-score for $\bar{x} = 3.55$:

$$z = \frac{\bar{x} - \mu_{\bar{x}}}{\sigma_{\bar{x}}} = \frac{3.55 - 3.00}{.188} = 2.92$$

Thus, $P(\bar{x} \geq 3.55) = P(z \geq 2.92)$, and this probability (area) may be found using Table 2, Appendix A, and the methods of Section 4.5:

$$P(\bar{x} \geq 3.55) = P(z \geq 2.92)$$
$$= .5 - A \qquad \text{See Figure 5.5}$$
$$= .5 - .4982 = .0018$$

b. The probability that we would obtain a sample rating of 3.55 or greater is only .0018 if the mean rating μ under the "stated concern" condition is the same as under the "no reference to ethical concern" condition. According to the rare-event approach discussed in Section 4.1, the occurrence of this unlikely event leads us to conclude that the mean rating μ under the "stated concern" condition is larger than $\mu = 3.00$. The reliability of our inference is measured by the probability .0018—only about 2 times out of 1,000 would we observe a sample mean this large when $\mu = 3.00$.

In the next two sections we show how the Central Limit Theorem can be used to form confidence intervals for (Section 5.2) and conduct tests of hypotheses about

(Section 5.3) population parameters. As was noted earlier, we will not be required to obtain sampling distributions by simulation or by mathematical arguments. Rather, for all the statistics to be used in this course, the sampling distribution and its properties (which are a matter of record) will be presented as the need arises.

PROBLEMS

5.1   The table contains 50 random samples of $n = 5$ measurements selected from a population with $\mu = 4.5$ and $\sigma^2 = 8.25$.

SAMPLE				
1, 8, 0, 6, 6	1, 6, 0, 0, 9	3, 6, 4, 2, 0	4, 5, 3, 4, 8	2, 3, 7, 6, 3
2, 1, 7, 2, 9	6, 8, 5, 2, 8	1, 5, 0, 5, 8	5, 6, 7, 8, 2	2, 0, 6, 3, 3
4, 5, 7, 7, 1	2, 4, 9, 4, 6	4, 6, 2, 6, 2	3, 8, 6, 0, 1	1, 9, 0, 3, 2
3, 6, 1, 8, 1	6, 7, 0, 4, 3	1, 8, 8, 2, 1	1, 4, 4, 9, 0	8, 9, 2, 7, 0
9, 8, 6, 2, 9	0, 5, 9, 9, 6	9, 0, 6, 1, 7	7, 7, 9, 8, 1	1, 5, 0, 5, 1
6, 8, 8, 3, 5	4, 4, 7, 5, 6	3, 7, 3, 4, 3	9, 2, 9, 8, 7	7, 8, 7, 7, 6
9, 5, 7, 7, 9	6, 6, 5, 5, 6	4, 5, 2, 6, 6	6, 8, 9, 6, 0	9, 3, 7, 3, 9
7, 6, 4, 4, 7	5, 0, 6, 6, 5	9, 3, 7, 1, 3	3, 4, 6, 7, 0	5, 1, 1, 4, 0
6, 5, 6, 4, 2	3, 0, 4, 9, 6	1, 9, 6, 9, 2	8, 4, 7, 6, 9	2, 5, 7, 7, 9
8, 6, 8, 6, 0	3, 0, 7, 4, 1	5, 1, 2, 3, 4	6, 9, 4, 4, 2	3, 0, 6, 9, 7

a. Calculate $\bar{x}$ for each of the 50 samples.
b. Construct a relative frequency histogram for the 50 sample means. This figure represents an approximation to the sampling distribution of $\bar{x}$ based on samples of size $n = 5$.
c. Compute the mean and standard deviation for the 50 sample means. Locate these values on the histogram of part b. Note how the sample means cluster about $\mu = 4.5$.

5.2   Refer to Problem 5.1. Combine pairs of samples (moving down the columns of the table) to obtain 25 samples of $n = 10$ measurements.

a. Calculate $\bar{x}$ for each of the 25 samples.
b. Construct a relative frequency histogram for the 25 sample means. This figure represents an approximation to the sampling distribution of $\bar{x}$ based on samples of size $n = 10$. Compare with the figure constructed in Problem 5.1.
c. Compute the mean and standard deviation for the 25 sample means, and locate them on the relative frequency histogram. Note how the sample means cluster about $\mu = 4.5$.
d. Compare the standard deviations of the two sampling distributions in Problems 5.1 and 5.2. Which sampling distribution has less variation?

5.3   Let $\bar{x}_{25}$ represent the mean of a random sample of size 25 obtained from a population with mean $\mu = 17$ and standard deviation $\sigma = 10$. Similarly, let $\bar{x}_{100}$ represent the mean of a random sample of size 100 selected from the same population.

a. Describe the sampling distribution of $\bar{x}_{25}$.
b. Describe the sampling distribution of $\bar{x}_{100}$.
c. Which of the probabilities, $P(15 < \bar{x}_{25} < 19)$ or $P(15 < \bar{x}_{100} < 19)$, would you expect to be larger?
d. Calculate the two probabilities in part c. Was your answer to part c correct?

5.4   The National Institute for Occupational Safety and Health (NIOSH) recently completed a study to evaluate the level of exposure of workers to the chemical dioxin, 2,3,7,8-TCDD. The distribution of TCDD levels (in parts per trillion, ppt) among production workers at a Newark, New Jersey, chemical plant had a mean of 293 ppt and a standard deviation of 847 ppt (*Chemosphere*, Vol. 20, 1990). A graph of the distribution is shown here:

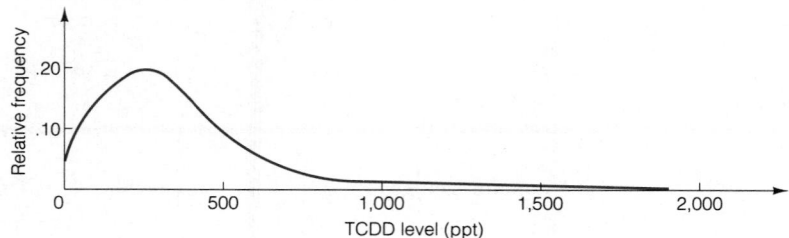

In a random sample of $n = 50$ workers selected at the Newark plant, let $\bar{x}$ represent the sample mean TCDD level.

a. Find the mean and standard deviation of the sampling distribution of $\bar{x}$.
b. Draw a sketch of the sampling distribution of $\bar{x}$. Locate the mean on the graph.
c. Find the probability that $\bar{x}$ exceeds 550 ppt.

5.5 Many firms are using research and development limited partnerships (R&D LPs) as innovative fund-raising vehicles. According to the Securities and Exchange Commission (SEC), funds raised through an R&D LP should be reported as debt on the firm's balance sheet. Most firms, however, violate this policy. To gain more insight on this problem, the *Accounting Review* (Jan. 1991) investigated the financial statements of firms with R&D LPs. The mean and standard deviation of the population, consisting of present values of all R&D LPs, were estimated to be $\mu = \$28.5$ million and $\sigma = \$51.8$ million. Consider a random sample of $n = 75$ R&D LPs selected from the population.

a. Describe the sampling distribution of $\bar{x}$, the mean present value of the sample of 75 R&D LPs.
b. What is the probability that $\bar{x}$ falls between \$25.2 and \$36.6 million?
c. What is the probability that $\bar{x}$ is less than \$30 million?

5.6 *Cost estimation* is the term used to describe the process by which engineers estimate the cost of work contracts (eg, road construction, building construction) that are to be awarded to the lowest bidder. An engineer's estimate is the baseline against which the low (winning) bid is compared. A recent study investigated the factors that affect the accuracy of engineers' estimates (*Cost Engineering*, Oct. 1988), where accuracy is measured as the percentage difference between the low bid and an engineer's estimate. One of the most important factors is number of bidders—the more bidders on the contract, the more likely the engineers are to overestimate the cost. For building contracts with 5 bidders, the mean percentage error was -7.02 and the standard deviation was 24.66. Consider a sample of 50 building contracts, each with 5 bidders.

a. Describe the sampling distribution of $\bar{x}$, the mean percentage difference between the low bid and an engineer's estimate, for the 50 contracts.
b. Find $P(\bar{x} < 0)$. (This is the probability of an overestimate.)
c. Suppose you observe $\bar{x} = -17.83$ for a sample of 50 building contracts. Based on the information above, are all these contracts likely to have 5 bidders? Explain.

5.7 By definition, an entrepreneur is "one who undertakes to start and conduct an enterprise or business, assuming full control and risks" (Funk & Wagnall's *Standard Dictionary*). Thus, a distinguishing characteristic of entrepreneurs is their propensity for taking risks. R. H. Brockhaus used a choice dilemma questionnaire (CDQ) to measure the risk-taking propensities of successful entrepreneurs (*Academy of Management Journal*, Sept. 1980). He found that the CDQ scores of entrepreneurs had a mean of 71 and a standard deviation of 12. (Lower scores are associated with a greater propensity for taking risks.) Let x be the mean CDQ score for a random sample of $n = 50$ entrepreneurs.

a. Describe the sampling distribution of $\bar{x}$.
b. Find $P(69 \leq \bar{x} \leq 72)$.

c. Find $P(\bar{x} \le 67)$.

d. Would you expect to observe a sample mean CDQ score of 67 or lower?

5.8 As part of industrial quality control programs, it is common practice to monitor the quality characteristics of a product. For example, the amount of alkali in soap might be monitored by randomly selecting from the production process and analyzing $n = 30$ test quantities twice each day. If the sample mean, $\bar{x}$, falls within specified control limits, the process is deemed to be in control. If $\bar{x}$ is outside the limits, the monitor flashes a warning signal and suggests that something is wrong with the process. Suppose the lower and upper control limits are located, respectively, $3\sigma_{\bar{x}}$ below and above μ, the true mean amount of alkali in the soap.

a. For the soap process, experience has shown that $\mu = 2\%$ and $\sigma = 1\%$. Specify the lower and upper control limits for the process. [*Hint:* Calculate $\mu - 3\sigma_{\bar{x}}$ and $\mu + 3\sigma_{\bar{x}}$.]

b. If the process is in control, what is the probability that $\bar{x}$ falls outside the control limits? Use the fact that the probability that $\bar{x}$ falls outside the control limits is given by

$$1 - P(\text{Process is in control}) = 1 - P(\mu - 3\sigma_{\bar{x}} < \bar{x} < \mu + 3\sigma_{\bar{x}})$$

5.9 Engineers responsible for the design and maintenance of aircraft pavements traditionally use pavement-quality concrete or Marshall asphalt surfaces. A study was conducted at Luton Airport (United Kingdom) to assess the suitability of concrete blocks as a surface for aircraft pavements (*Proceedings of the Civil Engineers*, Apr. 1986). The original pavement-quality concrete of the western end of the runway was overlaid with concrete blocks 80 mm thick, and a series of plate-bearing tests was carried out to determine the load classification number (LCN)—a measure of breaking strength—of the surface. Let x represent the mean LCN of a sample of 25 concrete block sections on the western end of the runway.

a. Prior to resurfacing, the mean LCN of the original pavement-quality concrete of the western end of the runway was $\mu = 60$. Assume the standard deviation was $\sigma = 10$. If the mean strength of the new concrete block surface is no different from that of the original surface, find the probability that $\bar{x}$, the sample mean LCN of the 25 concrete block sections, exceeds 65.

b. The plate-bearing tests on the new concrete block surface resulted in $\bar{x} = 73$. Based on this result, what can you infer about the true mean LCN of the new surface?

LARGE-SAMPLE CONFIDENCE INTERVALS

5.2 We can make an inference about a population parameter in two ways: (1) estimate its value and (2) make a decision about its value (ie, test a hypothesis about its value). In this section we will illustrate the concepts involved in estimation, using the estimation of a population mean as an example. Tests of hypotheses will be discussed in Section 5.3.

PROPERTIES OF ESTIMATORS

To estimate a population parameter, we choose a sample statistic computed from the observations in a sample. The sample statistic is often called a **point estimator** since it represents a single value (or point) used to estimate the population parameter. If the mean of the sampling distribution of a statistic equals the parameter we are estimating, we say that the statistic is an **unbiased estimator** of the parameter. If not, we say that it is **biased**.

Ideally, we want to choose an unbiased estimator since its sampling distribution will center around the parameter we are trying to estimate. In addition, we want the standard deviation of the sampling distribution (ie, the **standard error**) to be small. The smaller the standard error, the more likely our estimate will be close to the true parameter value. The statistic that has these two properties—unbiased estimator and smallest variance—is called the **minimum variance unbiased estimator (MVUE)**.

DEFINITION 5.2

A **point estimate** of a parameter is a statistic, a single value computed from the observations in a sample, used to estimate the value of the target parameter.

DEFINITION 5.3

An estimator of a parameter is **unbiased** if the mean of the sampling distribution of the estimator is equal to the parameter value. If not, the estimator is **biased**.

DEFINITION 5.4

The **standard error** of an estimator is the standard deviation of the sampling distribution of the estimator.

DEFINITION 5.5

The **minimum variance unbiased estimator (MVUE)** of a parameter is the estimator that has the smallest variance (ie, smallest standard error) of all unbiased estimators.

FIGURE 5.6

Sampling Distribution of $\bar{x}$

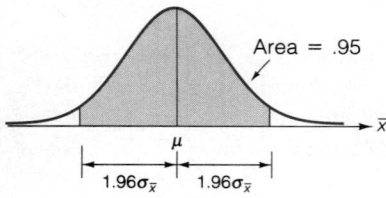

FIGURE 5.7

Sampling Distribution of $\bar{x}$ for 95% Confidence Interval

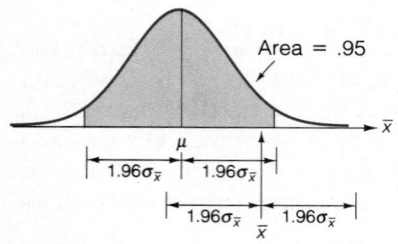

In Section 5.1 we noted that the sampling distribution of the sample mean is approximately normally distributed for moderate to large sample sizes and that it possesses a mean, μ, and a standard error, $\sigma/\sqrt{n}$. Therefore, as shown in Figure 5.6, $\bar{x}$ is an unbiased estimator of the population mean, μ, and (proof omitted) $\bar{x}$ has the smallest standard error of all unbiased estimators. Consequently, $\bar{x}$ is the MVUE for μ and is considered the "best" estimate of μ.

Since the distribution of $\bar{x}$ is normal when n is large, we can form an interval estimate for μ. The probability that $\bar{x}$ will fall within $1.96\sigma_{\bar{x}} = 1.96\sigma/\sqrt{n}$ of the true value of μ is approximately .95. Since $\bar{x}$ will fall within $1.96\sigma_{\bar{x}}$ of μ approximately 95% of the time, it follows that the interval

$$\bar{x} - 1.96\sigma_{\bar{x}} \qquad \text{to} \qquad \bar{x} + 1.96\sigma_{\bar{x}}$$

will enclose μ approximately 95% of the time in repeated sampling (see Figure 5.7). This interval is called a 95% **confidence interval** for μ.

For example, suppose that a random sample of $n = 100$ observations from the population of starting salaries discussed earlier yielded the following sample statistics:

$$\bar{x} = \$27,800 \qquad s = \$8,850$$

A 95% confidence interval for μ, the population mean starting salary, based on a sample of size $n = 100$, is given by

$$\bar{x} \pm 1.96\sigma_{\bar{x}} = \bar{x} \pm \left(\frac{\sigma}{\sqrt{n}}\right)$$

$$= 27,800 \pm 1.96\left(\frac{\sigma}{\sqrt{100}}\right)$$

In most practical applications, the value of the population standard deviation σ will be unknown. However, for large samples, the sample standard deviation s provides a good approximation to σ. For the purpose of illustration, we will use s in place of σ in the formula for the confidence interval.* In this case, the approximate 95% confidence interval is

$$27,800 \pm 1.96\left(\frac{8,850}{\sqrt{100}}\right) = 27,800 \pm 1,735$$

or (26,065, 29,535). Hence, we estimate that the population starting salary falls within the interval from $26,065 to $29,535.

How much confidence do we have that the interval ($26,065, $29,535) contains μ, the true population mean starting salary? Although we cannot be certain whether the sample interval contains μ (unless we calculate the true value of μ for all 1,795 observations), we can be reasonably sure that it does. This confidence is based on the interpretation of the confidence interval procedure: If we were to select repeated random samples of size $n = 100$ starting salaries, and form a 1.96 standard deviation interval around $\bar{x}$ for each sample, then approximately 95% of the intervals constructed in this manner would contain μ. Thus, we are 95% confident that the particular interval ($26,065, $29,535) contains μ, and this is our measure of the reliability of the point estimate $\bar{x}$.

To illustrate this classical interpretation of a confidence interval, we generated 40 random samples, each of size $n = 100$, from the population of 1,795 starting salaries. We then constructed the 95% confidence interval for μ using the information from each sample. The results are shown in Table 5.3. Recall that for the target population of 1,795 starting salaries, we had previously obtained the population mean value $\mu = \$28,475$. In the 40 repetitions of the confidence interval procedure, only two of the intervals (those based on samples 14 and 30, indicated by asterisks

---

* In Section 5.4 we present an alternative procedure to use when σ is unknown.

TABLE 5.3

95% Confidence Intervals for μ for 40 Random Samples of 100 Starting Salaries

SAMPLE	$\bar{x}$	LOWER CONFIDENCE LIMIT	UPPER CONFIDENCE LIMIT	SAMPLE	$\bar{x}$	LOWER CONFIDENCE LIMIT	UPPER CONFIDENCE LIMIT
1	28,965	27,129	30,801	21	29,551	27,715	31,387
2	28,692	26,856	30,528	22	29,210	27,374	31,046
3	27,816	25,980	29,652	23	28,203	26,367	30,039
4	29,760	27,924	31,596	24	27,844	26,008	29,680
5	27,469	25,633	29,305	25	29,280	27,444	31,116
6	28,334	26,498	30,170	26	29,365	27,529	31,201
7	30,234	28,398	32,070	27	29,044	27,208	30,880
8	29,592	27,756	31,428	28	29,336	27,500	31,172
9	29,194	27,358	31,030	29	28,769	26,933	30,605
10	29,436	27,600	31,272	30	26,581	24,745	28,417*
11	27,962	26,126	29,798	31	28,498	26,662	30,334
12	28,299	26,463	30,135	32	28,521	26,685	30,357
13	29,210	27,374	31,046	33	27,085	25,249	28,921
14	30,355	28,519	32,191*	34	27,151	25,315	28,987
15	29,304	27,468	31,140	35	29,749	27,913	31,585
16	28,538	26,702	30,374	36	28,567	26,731	30,403
17	29,068	27,232	30,904	37	28,120	26,284	29,956
18	26,705	24,869	28,541	38	28,356	26,520	30,192
19	27,721	25,885	29,557	39	27,918	26,082	29,754
20	28.161	26,325	29,997	40	29,512	27,676	31,348

Note: Asterisks (*) identify the intervals that do not contain μ = $28,475.

in the table) do not contain the value of μ, whereas the remaining 38 intervals (or 95% of the 40 intervals) do contain the true value of μ. This proportion, .95, is called the **confidence coefficient** for the interval.

> **DEFINITION 5.7**
>
> The **confidence coefficient** (or **confidence level**) is the proportion of times that a confidence interval encloses the true value of the population parameter if the confidence interval procedure is repeated a very large number of times.

Keep in mind that in actual practice you would not know the true value of μ, and you would not perform this repeated sampling; rather, you would select a single random sample and construct the associated 95% confidence interval. Although the one confidence interval you form may or may not contain μ, it is very likely that it does because of your "confidence" in the statistical procedure (the basis for which is illustrated in Table 5.3).

Confidence intervals based on the normal distribution can be constructed using any desired confidence coefficient. For example, if we define $z_{\alpha/2}$ to be the value of a standard normal variable that places the area $\alpha/2$ in the right-hand tail of the z

FIGURE 5.8

Locating $z_{\alpha/2}$ on the Standard Normal Curve

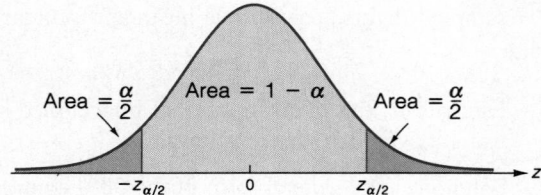

Area = $\frac{\alpha}{2}$ Area = $1 - \alpha$ Area = $\frac{\alpha}{2}$

$-z_{\alpha/2}$ 0 $z_{\alpha/2}$ z

distribution (see Figure 5.8), then a $(1 - \alpha)100\%$ confidence interval for μ, based on large samples, is given in the box.

LARGE-SAMPLE $(1 - \alpha)100\%$ CONFIDENCE INTERVAL FOR A POPULATION MEAN, μ

$$\bar{x} \pm z_{\alpha/2}\sigma_{\bar{x}} = \bar{x} \pm z_{\alpha/2}\left(\frac{\sigma}{\sqrt{n}}\right)$$

where $z_{\alpha/2}$ is the z-value that locates an area of $\alpha/2$ to its right, σ is the standard deviation of the population from which the sample was selected, n is the sample size, and $\bar{x}$ is the value of the sample mean.

Assumption: A large random sample (usually, $n \geq 30$) is selected.

Note: When the value of σ is unknown (as will usually be the case), the sample standard deviation s may be used to approximate σ in the formula for the confidence interval. The approximation is generally quite satisfactory for large samples.

Typical confidence coefficients and corresponding values of $z_{\alpha/2}$ are shown in Table 5.4.

TABLE 5.4

Commonly Used Confidence Coefficients and Associated z-Values

CONFIDENCE COEFFICIENT $(1 - \alpha)$	$\alpha/2$	$z_{\alpha/2}$
.90	.05	1.645
.95	.025	1.96
.98	.01	2.33
.99	.005	2.58

EXAMPLE 5.4 Unoccupied seats on flights cause airlines to lose revenue. Suppose a large airline wants to estimate the mean number of unoccupied seats per flight over the past year. To accomplish this, the records of 225 flights are randomly selected from the files, and the number of unoccupied seats is noted for each of the

sampled flights. The sample mean and standard deviation are

$$\bar{x} = 11.6 \text{ seats} \qquad s = 4.1 \text{ seats}$$

Estimate μ, the mean number of unoccupied seats per flight during the past year, using a 90% confidence interval.

Solution   The general form of the 90% confidence interval for a population mean is

$$\bar{x} \pm z_{\alpha/2}\sigma_{\bar{x}} = \bar{x} \pm z_{.05}\sigma_{\bar{x}}$$
$$= \bar{x} \pm 1.645\left(\frac{\sigma}{\sqrt{n}}\right)$$

For the 225 records sampled, we have

$$11.6 \pm 1.645\left(\frac{\sigma}{\sqrt{225}}\right)$$

Since we do not know the value of σ (the standard deviation of the number of unoccupied seats per flight for all flights during the year), we use our best approximation, the sample standard deviation s. Then the 90% confidence interval is, approximately,

$$11.6 \pm 1.645\left(\frac{4.1}{\sqrt{225}}\right) = 11.6 \pm .45$$

or from 11.15 to 12.05. That is, the airline can be 90% confident that the mean number of unoccupied seats per flight was between 11.15 and 12.05 during the sampled year.

In some cases, the calculated confidence interval may be too wide to be of use in a practical setting. For example, suppose a 95% confidence interval for the mean sale price of homes in your neighborhood is ($82,000, $157,000). The interval is really too wide to be of much use to potential home buyers or to you as a potential seller. Ideally, you would like to obtain a much narrower confidence interval for the mean sale price. The following example illustrates two ways in which you can reduce the width of a confidence interval.

EXAMPLE 5.5   Refer to the 90% confidence interval for μ, the mean number of unoccupied seats per flight, Example 5.4.

a. Using the sample information provided in Example 5.4, construct a 95% confidence interval for μ. For a fixed sample size, how is the width of the confidence interval related to the confidence coefficient?

b. Assume that the given values of $\bar{x}$ and s were based on a sample of size $n = 100$ instead of a sample of size $n = 225$. Construct a 90% confidence interval for μ. For a fixed confidence coefficient, how is the width of the confidence interval related to the sample size?

c. Based on the results from parts **a** and **b**, give two ways in which you can reduce the width of a confidence interval.

Solution

a. The form of a large-sample 95% confidence interval for a population mean μ is

$$\bar{x} \pm 1.96\left(\frac{\sigma}{\sqrt{n}}\right) \approx \bar{x} \pm 1.96\left(\frac{s}{\sqrt{n}}\right)$$

$$\approx 11.6 \pm 1.96\left(\frac{4.1}{\sqrt{225}}\right)$$

$$\approx 11.6 \pm .54$$

or (11.06, 12.14). Recall that the 90% confidence interval for μ was determined in Example 5.4 to be (11.15, 12.05). The 95% confidence interval, based on the same sample information, is wider than the 90% confidence interval. This relationship holds in general.

b. Substitution of the values of the sample statistics into the general formula for a 90% confidence interval for μ yields

$$\bar{x} \pm 1.645\left(\frac{\sigma}{\sqrt{n}}\right) \approx 11.6 \pm 1.645\left(\frac{4.1}{\sqrt{100}}\right)$$

$$\approx 11.6 \pm .67$$

or (10.93, 12.27). The 90% confidence interval based on a sample of size $n = 100$ is wider than the 90% confidence interval based on a sample of size $n = 225$ constructed in Example 5.4. This will also hold true in general.

c. The results in parts **a** and **b** imply that we can reduce the width of a confidence interval in one of two ways: (1) *decrease* the confidence coefficient $(1 - \alpha)$ or (2) *increase* the sample size n. Our preference is to increase n, if possible, rather than give up any degree of confidence in the procedure.

RELATIONSHIP BETWEEN WIDTH OF CONFIDENCE INTERVAL AND CONFIDENCE COEFFICIENT

For a given sample size, the width of the confidence interval for a parameter increases as the confidence coefficient increases. Intuitively, the interval must become wider for us to have greater confidence that it contains the true parameter value.

RELATIONSHIP BETWEEN WIDTH OF CONFIDENCE INTERVAL AND SAMPLE SIZE

For a fixed confidence coefficient, the width of the confidence interval decreases as the sample size increases. In other words, larger samples generally provide more information about the target population than do smaller samples.

In this section, we have introduced the concepts of point and interval estimation of the population mean μ, based on large samples. The general theory appropriate for the estimation of μ also carries over to the estimation of other population parameters.

In general, the formula for a large-sample confidence interval for any population parameter based on a normal sampling distribution is shown in the next box.

A LARGE-SAMPLE $(1 - \alpha)100\%$ CONFIDENCE INTERVAL FOR A POPULATION PARAMETER BASED ON A NORMAL DISTRIBUTION

(Point estimate) $\pm$ $(z_{\alpha/2})$(Standard error)

Assumption: The sample size is large enough to apply the Central Limit Theorem.

In subsequent chapters, we specify the point estimate of the population parameter, its standard error, and the large-sample properties of its sampling distribution. When the sampling distribution is normal (as is usually the case), the above formula is used to construct the confidence interval.

PROBLEMS

5.10   Give a precise interpretation of the statement, "We are 95% confident that the interval estimate contains μ."

5.11   In a large-sample confidence interval for a population mean, what does the confidence coefficient represent?

5.12   Refer to the data on physician costs in the Case Study of Chapter 2. The president of the health maintenance organization (HMO) wants to estimate the average per-member per-month cost of the physicians in the HMO.

    a. Use the method of Section 1.4 to select a random sample of 30 physician costs.
    b. Use the data from part **a** to construct a 97% confidence interval for the true average physician cost of this HMO.
    c. What is the confidence coefficient for the interval of part **b**? Interpret this value.
    d. Based on your interval obtained in part **b**, would you expect the true mean physician cost to exceed $200 per member per month?

5.13   What do college recruiters believe are the most important topics to be covered in a job interview? To answer this and other questions, a recent study elicited the opinions of recruiters interviewing at a small midwestern college and a large midwestern university (*Journal of Occupational Psychology*, Vol. 57, 1984). Recruiters were asked to rate the importance of each of 25 interview topics on a 105 point scale [where 0 = least important (ie, can often be omitted without hurting the interview), 52.5 = average importance (ie, can sometimes be omitted without hurting the interview), and 105 = most important (ie, can never be omitted without hurting the interview)]. The topic concerning "applicant's skill in communicating ideas to others" received the highest ratings of the $n = 58$ college recruiters who returned the questionnaire. The sample mean rating and sample standard deviation for this topic were $\bar{x} = 84.84$ and $s = 15.67$, respectively.

    a. Give a point estimate for the true mean rating of "applicant's skill in communicating ideas to others" by all college recruiters.
    b. Use the sample information to construct a 95% confidence interval for the true mean rating.
    c. What is the confidence coefficient for the interval of part **b**? Interpret this value.

5.14 A study was conducted to investigate the perceived unit effectiveness of purchasing companies (*Journal of Applied Behavioral Science*, Vol. 22, 1986). The researchers define unit effectiveness as "the relative ability of the members of a unit (eg, office) to mobilize their centers of power to produce, adapt, and handle temporarily unpredicted overloads of work." A sample of 115 purchasing agents participated in the study by responding to questionnaires on the organizational effectiveness of their offices. Each agent rated each of eight effectiveness items on a scale of 1 to 5 (where 1 = not effective and 5 = very effective). The sum of the eight values was used as a measure of perceived unit effectiveness. The results were

$$\bar{x} = 29.07 \qquad s = 4.68$$

Construct a 95% confidence interval for the true mean "perceived unit effectiveness" rating of all purchasing agents. Interpret the interval.

5.15 Adult students are enrolling in colleges and universities in ever-increasing numbers, and many are majoring in marketing. Recently, a study was conducted to determine the attitudes of marketing faculty toward the adult students in their classes (*Journal of Marketing Education*, Summer 1987). A sample of 290 faculty, drawn at random from the American Marketing Association's membership directory, responded to a series of attitudinal statements, the first of which was, "Adult students (ie, undergraduates 24 years or older) participate more actively in classroom discussions than do younger students." Attitudes were measured using a 5 point Likert scale (1 = strongly agree, 2 = agree, 3 = no opinion, 4 = disagree, and 5 = strongly disagree). For the participation statement, the mean attitudinal score for the sample was 1.94 and the standard deviation was .92.

a. Estimate the true mean attitudinal score of marketing faculty with regard to classroom participation of adult students using a 98% confidence interval. Interpret the result.
b. How could you reduce the width of the confidence interval in part **a**?

5.16 Each year *Business Week*'s "Executive Compensation Scoreboard" reports on the salaries of CEOs at major U.S. companies. A measure of a CEO's worth is the ratio of shareholder return (on a $100 investment made 3 years earlier) to the executive's salary. A random sample of 50 return-to-pay ratios selected from the 1992 "Executive Compensation Scoreboard" are shown in the table. A MINITAB printout showing descriptive statistics for the sample and a 95% confidence interval for the mean return-to-pay ratio of all CEOs is also shown.

0.03	0.021	0.033	0.086	0.041	0.062	0.029	0.072	0.005	0.047
0.051	0.206	0.005	0.025	0.112	0.037	0.042	0.023	0.026	0.086
0.049	0.122	0.091	0.033	0.029	0.032	0.036	0.02	0.032	0.005
0.01	0.049	0.048	0.081	0.051	0.122	0.019	0.047	0.031	0.031
0.02	0.025	0.206	0.091	0.14	0.017	0.026	0.02	0.018	0.02

Source: Business Week, Apr. 26, 1993. Reprinted from Apr. 26, 1993 issue of *Business Week* by special permission, copyright © 1993 by McGraw-Hill, Inc. Used with permission.

	N	MEAN	STDEV	SE MEAN	95.0 PERCENT C.I.
ratio	50	0.05120	0.04530	0.00641	(0.03832, 0.06408)

a. Use the data in the table to verify the 95% confidence interval shown in the MINITAB printout.
b. Interpret the interval.
c. How could you reduce the width of the confidence interval? Are there any drawbacks to reducing the interval width? Explain.

LARGE-SAMPLE TESTS OF HYPOTHESIS

5.3 In this section we turn our attention to another method of inference making called **hypothesis testing**. These procedures are useful in situations where we are interested in making a decision about a parameter value, rather than obtaining an estimate of its value. Every statistical test of hypothesis consists of five key elements: (1) null hypothesis, (2) alternative hypothesis, (3) test statistic, (4) rejection region, and (5) conclusion.

NULL AND ALTERNATIVE HYPOTHESES

When a researcher in any field sets out to test a new theory, he/she first formulates a hypothesis, or claim, which is believed to be true. In statistical terms, the hypothesis that the researcher tries to establish is called the **alternative hypothesis**, or **research hypothesis**. The alternative hypothesis is paired with the **null hypothesis**, which is the "opposite" of the alternative hypothesis. In this way, the null and alternative hypotheses, both stated in terms of the appropriate population parameters, describe two possible states of nature that are mutually exclusive (ie, they cannot simultaneously be true). When the researcher begins to collect information about the phenomenon of interest, he/she generally tries to present evidence that lends support to the alternative hypothesis. As you will learn, we take an indirect approach to obtaining support for the alternative hypothesis: Instead of trying to show that the alternative hypothesis is true, we attempt to produce evidence to show that the null hypothesis (which may often be interpreted as "no change from the status quo") is false.

DEFINITION 5.8

A statistical **hypothesis** is a statement about the value of a population parameter.

DEFINITION 5.9

The hypothesis against which we hope to gather evidence is called the **null hypothesis** and is denoted by H_0.

DEFINITION 5.10

The hypothesis for which we wish to gather supporting evidence is called the **alternative hypothesis** and is denoted by H_a.

EXAMPLE 5.6 A metal lathe is checked periodically by quality control inspectors to determine if it is producing machine bearings with a mean diameter of .5 inch. If the mean diameter of the bearings is larger or smaller than .5 inch, then the process is out of control and needs to be adjusted. Formulate the null and alternative hypotheses that could be used to test whether the bearing production process is out of control.

Solution   We define the parameter

μ = True mean diameter (in inches) of all bearings produced by the lathe

If either $\mu > .5$ or $\mu < .5$, then the production process is out of control. Since we wish to be able to detect either possibility, the null and alternative hypotheses are

H_0: $\mu = .5$ The process is in control
H_a: $\mu \neq .5$ The process is out of control

EXAMPLE 5.7   Since 1970, cigarette advertisements have been required by law to carry the following statement: "Warning: The surgeon general has determined that cigarette smoking is dangerous to your health." However, this warning is often located in inconspicuous corners of the advertisements and printed in very small type. Consequently, a spokesperson for the Federal Trade Commission (FTC) believes that over 80% of those who read cigarette advertisements fail to see the warning. Specify the null and alternative hypotheses that would be used in testing the spokesperson's theory.

Solution   The FTC spokesperson wants to make an inference about π, the true population proportion of all readers of cigarette advertisements who fail to see the surgeon general's warning. In particular, the FTC spokesperson wishes to collect evidence to support the claim that π is greater than .80; thus, the null and alternative hypotheses are

H_0: $\pi = .80$
H_a: $\pi > .80$

Observe that the statement of H_0 in these examples, and in general, is written with an equality ($=$) sign. In Example 5.7 we could have formulated the null hypothesis as H_0: $\pi \leq .80$. However, since the alternative of interest is that $\pi > .80$, then any evidence that would lead to a rejection of the null hypothesis H_0. $\pi = .80$ in favor of H_a: $\pi > .80$ would also lead to a rejection of H_0: $\pi = \pi'$, for any value of π' that is less than .80. In other words, H_0: $\pi = .80$ represents the worst possible case, from the FTC spokesperson's point of view, if the alternative hypothesis is not correct. Thus, for mathematical ease, we combine all possible situations for describing the opposite of H_a into one statement involving an equality.

An alternative hypothesis may hypothesize a change from H_0 in a particular direction, or it may merely hypothesize a change without specifying a direction. In Example 5.7 we are interested in detecting a departure from H_0 in one particular direction: whether the proportion of cigarette advertisement readers who fail to see the surgeon general's warning is greater than .80. This test is a **one-tailed** (or **one-sided**) **test**. In contrast, Example 5.6 illustrates a **two-tailed** (or **two-sided**) **test** in which we are interested in whether the mean diameter of the machine bearings differs in either direction from .5 inch, that is, whether the process is out of control.

DEFINITION 5.11

A **one-tailed test** of hypothesis is one in which the alternative hypothesis is directional and includes either the symbol "<" or ">."

DEFINITION 5.12

A **two-tailed test** of hypothesis is one in which the alternative hypothesis does not specify departure from H_0 in a particular direction; such an alternative is written with the symbol "$\neq$."

The goal of any hypothesis testing situation is to make a decision; in particular, we will decide whether to reject the null hypothesis H_0 in favor of the alternative hypothesis H_a. Although we would always like to be able to make a correct decision, we must remember that the decision will be based on sample information and, thus, we are subject to making one of two types of error, as defined in the following boxes.

DEFINITION 5.13

A **Type I error** occurs if we reject a null hypothesis when it is true. The probability of committing a Type I error is usually denoted by α.

DEFINITION 5.14

A **Type II error** occurs if we accept a null hypothesis when it is false. The probability of making a Type II error is usually denoted by β.

The null hypothesis can be either true or false; further, we will make a decision either to reject or accept the null hypothesis. Thus, there are four possible situations that may arise in testing a hypothesis. These are summarized in Table 5.5.

Note that we risk a Type I error only if the null hypothesis is rejected, and we risk a Type II error only if the null hypothesis is accepted. Thus, we may make no error, or we may make either a Type I error (with probability α) or a Type II error (with probability β), but not both. There is an intuitively appealing relationship between the probabilities for the two types of error: As α increases, β decreases; similarly, as β increases, α decreases. The only way to reduce α and β simultaneously

TABLE 5.5
Conclusions and Consequences for Testing a Hypothesis

	TRUE STATE OF NATURE	
DECISION	H_0 True (H_a False)	H_0 False (H_a True)
Accept H_0	Correct decision	Type II error
Reject H_0	Type I error	Correct decision

is to increase the amount of information available in the sample, that is, to increase the sample size.

In Example 5.6, a Type I error would occur if we concluded that the process is out of control when in fact the process is in control, that is, if we concluded that $\mu \neq .5$ inch, when in fact $\mu = .5$ inch. The consequence of making such an error would be that unnecessary time and effort would be expended to repair the metal lathe. On the other hand, a Type II error would occur if we concluded that the process is in control ($\mu = .5$ inch), when in fact it is out of control ($\mu \neq .5$ inch). The practical significance of making a Type II error is that the metal lathe would not be repaired, when it should be to bring the process in control.

Subsequently, we will see that the probability of making a Type I error is controlled by the researcher; thus, it is often used as a measure of the reliability of the conclusion and is called the **significance level** of the test.

DEFINITION 5.15

The probability, α, of making a Type I error is called the **level of significance** (or **significance level**) for a hypothesis test.

EXAMPLE 5.8   The logic used in hypothesis testing has often been likened to that used in the courtroom in which a defendant is on trial for committing a crime.

a. Formulate appropriate null and alternative hypotheses for judging the guilt or innocence of the defendant.
b. Interpret the Type I and Type II errors in this context.
c. If you were the defendant, would you want α to be small or large? Explain.

Solution

a. Under our judicial system, a defendant is "innocent until proven guilty." That is, the burden of proof is not on the defendant to prove his or her innocence; rather, the court must collect sufficient evidence to support the claim that the defendant is guilty. Thus, the null and alternative hypotheses would be

H_0:   Defendant is innocent.

H_a: Defendant is guilty.

TABLE 5.6
Conclusions and Consequences in Example 5.8

| | TRUE STATE OF NATURE | |
DECISION OF COURT	Defendant Is Innocent	Defendant Is Guilty
Defendant Is Innocent	Correct decision	Type II error
Defendant Is Guilty	Type I error	Correct decision

b. The four possible outcomes are shown in Table 5.6. A Type I error would be to conclude that the defendant is guilty, when in fact he or she is innocent; a Type II error would be to conclude that the defendant is innocent, when in fact he or she is guilty.

c. Most would probably agree that in this situation the Type I error is by far the more serious. Thus, we would want α, the probability of committing a Type I error, to be very small indeed.

TEST STATISTICS AND REJECTION REGIONS

Once we have formulated the null and alternative hypotheses, we are ready to carry out the test. For example, suppose we want to test the hypotheses

$$H_0: \quad \mu = \mu_0$$
$$H_a: \quad \mu > \mu_0$$

where μ_0 is some fixed value of the population mean. The general format for carrying out a statistical test of hypothesis consists of several steps.

STEP 1   Obtain a random sample from the population of interest. The information provided by this sample, in the form of a sample statistic, will help us decide whether to reject the null hypothesis. The sample statistic upon which we base our decision is called the **test statistic**.

> **DEFINITION 5.16**
>
> The **test statistic** is a sample statistic, computed from the information provided by the sample, upon which the decision concerning the null and alternative hypotheses is based.

STEP 2   Determine a test statistic that is reasonable in the context of a given hypothesis test. For this example, we are hypothesizing about the value of the population mean, μ. Since our best guess about the value of μ is the sample mean, $\bar{x}$, it seems reasonable to use $\bar{x}$ as a test statistic. In general, when the hypothesis test involves a specific population parameter, the test statistic to be used is the conventional point estimate of that parameter in standardized form. Standardizing $\bar{x}$, we obtain the test statistic

$$z = \frac{\bar{x} - \mu_0}{\sigma_{\bar{x}}}$$

STEP 3   Specify the range of possible computed values of the test statistic for which the null hypothesis will be rejected. That is, what specific values of the test statistic will lead us to reject the null hypothesis in favor of the alternative hypothesis? These specific values are known collectively as the **rejection region** for the test.

DEFINITION 5.17

The **rejection region** is the set of possible computed values of the test statistic for which the null hypothesis will be rejected.

The logic used to decide whether sample data disagree with the null hypothesis can be seen by viewing the sampling distribution of $\bar{x}$ shown in Figure 5.9. If the population mean μ is equal to μ_0 (ie, if the null hypothesis is true), then the mean $\bar{x}$ calculated from a sample should fall, with high probability, within $2\sigma_{\bar{x}}$ of μ_0. If $\bar{x}$ falls too far away from μ_0 on the high side, or if the standardized distance

$$z = \frac{\bar{x} - \mu_0}{\sigma_{\bar{x}}}$$

is too large, we conclude that the data disagree with our hypothesis, and we reject the null hypothesis.

If we want to detect the alternative hypothesis that $\mu > \mu_0$, we locate the boundary of the rejection region in the upper tail of the z distribution at the point z_α, as shown in Figure 5.10a. The value z_α is called the **critical value** of the test, and we will reject H_0 if $z > z_\alpha$.

Similarly, to detect $\mu < \mu_0$, we place the rejection region in the lower tail of the z distribution and reject H_0 if $z < -z_\alpha$, as shown in Figure 5.10b. To detect either $\mu > \mu_0$ or $\mu < \mu_0$, that is, $\mu \neq \mu_0$, we split α equally between the two tails of the z distribution and reject the null hypothesis if $z > z_{\alpha/2}$ or $z < -z_{\alpha/2}$, as shown in Figure 5.10c.

You can see that to fully specify the rejection region, we must decide on the value of α, the level of significance. Some guidelines for step 3 are provided in the box.

FIGURE 5.9

Sampling Distribution of $\bar{x}$ for $\mu = \mu_0$

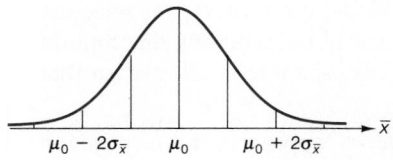

FIGURE 5.10

Location of the Rejection Region for Various Alternative Hypotheses

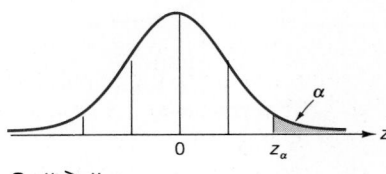

a. $\mu > \mu_0$

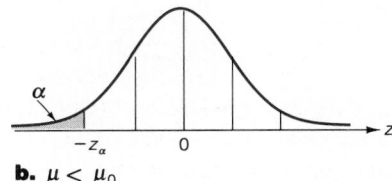

b. $\mu < \mu_0$

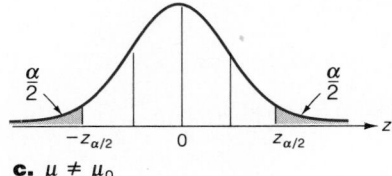

c. $\mu \neq \mu_0$

GUIDELINES FOR SETTING UP TEST STATISTICS AND REJECTION REGIONS FOR HYPOTHESIS TESTING

1. The value of α, the probability of a Type I error, is specified in advance by the researcher. It can be made as small or as large as desired; typical values are $\alpha = .01, .02, .05$, and $.10$. For a fixed sample size, the size of the rejection region decreases as the value of α decreases (see Figure 5.11). That is, for smaller values of α, more extreme departures of the test statistic from the null hypothesized parameter value are required to permit rejection of H_0.

2. The test statistic (ie, the point estimate of the target parameter) is standardized to provide a measure of how far it departs from the null hypothesized value of the parameter. The standardization is based on the sampling distribution of the point estimate, assuming H_0 is true. (It is through the standardization that the rejection rule takes into account the sample sizes.)

$$\text{Test statistic} = \frac{\text{Point estimate} - \text{Hypothesized value}}{\text{Standard error of point estimate}}$$

3. The location of the rejection region depends on whether the test is one-tailed or two-tailed, and on the prespecified significance level, α.

   a. For a one-tailed test in which the symbol ">" occurs in H_a, the rejection region consists of values in the upper tail of the sampling distribution of the standardized test statistic. The critical value is selected so that the area to its right is equal to α.

   b. For a one-tailed test in which the symbol "<" appears in H_a, the rejection region consists of values in the lower tail of the sampling distribution of the standardized test statistic. The critical value is selected so that the area to its left is equal to α.

   c. For a two-tailed test in which the symbol "$\neq$" occurs in H_a, the rejection region consists of two sets of values. The critical values are selected so that the area in each tail of the sampling distribution of the standardized test statistic is equal to $\alpha/2$.

FIGURE 5.11

Size of the Upper-Tail Rejection Region for Different Values of α

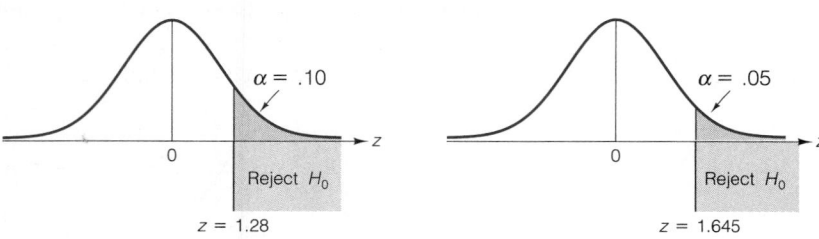

STEP 4 Use the data in the sample to compute the value of the test statistic.

STEP 5 Make a decision by observing whether the computed value falls within the rejection region. If the computed value falls within the rejection region, we reject the null hypothesis; otherwise, we do not reject the null hypothesis.

The z test, which is summarized in the next box, is appropriate when the sample size is large; consequently, it is called a **large-sample test**. The large sample size enables us to use the standard normal (z) distribution for finding the rejection region and, in the case of the population mean, the sample standard deviation, s, as an approximation to the usually unknown value of σ.

**LARGE-SAMPLE TEST OF HYPOTHESIS
ABOUT A POPULATION PARAMETER**

H_0: Parameter = Hypothesized value

ONE-TAILED TEST   **TWO-TAILED TEST**

H_a: Parameter < Hypothesized value H_a: Parameter $\neq$
        [or H_a: Parameter >   Hypothesized value
                Hypothesized value]

$$\text{Test statistic:} \quad \frac{\text{Point estimate} - \text{Hypothesized value}}{\text{Standard error of point estimate}}$$

Rejection region: *Rejection region:*
$z < -z_\alpha$ [or $z > z_\alpha$] $z < -z_{\alpha/2}$ or $z > z_{\alpha/2}$
where z_α is chosen so that   where $z_{\alpha/2}$ is chosen so that
$P(z > z_\alpha) = \alpha$ $P(z > z_{\alpha/2}) = \alpha/2$

We illustrate the z test for a population mean with an example.

EXAMPLE 5.9 Building specifications in a certain city require that the average breaking strength of residential sewer pipe be more than 2,400 pounds per foot of length (ie, per lineal foot). A sampling of the strengths of 70 sections of pipe produced by a manufacturer yielded a sample mean and standard deviation of

$$\bar{x} = 2,430 \qquad s = 190$$

Do these statistics, calculated from the sample data, present sufficient evidence to indicate that the manufacturer's pipe meets the city's specifications? Test at a significance level of $\alpha = .05$.

Solution   Since we wish to determine whether $\mu > 2{,}400$, the elements of the test are

$$H_0: \quad \mu = 2{,}400$$
$$H_a: \quad \mu > 2{,}400$$

Test statistic: $z = \dfrac{\bar{x} - 2{,}400}{\sigma_{\bar{x}}} = \dfrac{\bar{x} - 2{,}400}{\sigma/\sqrt{n}} \approx \dfrac{\bar{x} - 2{,}400}{s/\sqrt{n}}$

Rejection region: $z > 1.645$ for $\alpha = .05$ See Figure 5.12

See Figure 5.12

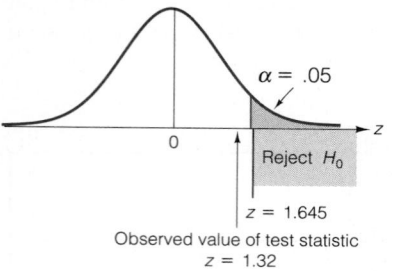

FIGURE 5.12

Location of Rejection Region and Test Statistic

$\alpha = .05$

Reject H_0

$z = 1.645$

Observed value of test statistic
$z = 1.32$

Substituting the sample statistics into the test statistic, we have

$$z \approx \frac{\bar{x} - 2{,}400}{s/\sqrt{n}} = \frac{2{,}430 - 2{,}400}{190/\sqrt{70}} = 1.32$$

The sample mean of 2,430, although greater than 2,400, is only $1.32\sigma_{\bar{x}}$ above that value. Therefore, the sample does not provide sufficient evidence at $\alpha = .05$ to conclude that the sewer pipe meets the city's strength specifications.

POWER OF A TEST

In Example 5.9, note that we have carefully avoided stating a decision in terms of "accept the null hypothesis H_0." Instead, if the sample does not provide enough evidence to support the alternative hypothesis H_a, we prefer to state the decision as "do not reject H_0," "fail to reject H_0," or "insufficient evidence to reject H_0." This is because, if we were to "accept H_0," the reliability of the conclusion would be measured by β, the probability of a Type II error. Unlike α, the value of β is typically not controlled by the researcher, and, in most testing situations, is very difficult to calculate. Consequently, when the test statistic does not fall in the rejection region, we state our conclusion as "do not reject H_0" rather than risk making a Type II error with unknown probability of occurrence.

In certain situations, however, it is possible to calculate β for a specified value of the parameter in H_a, as the following example illustrates.

EXAMPLE 5.10   Suppose we want to conduct the test of hypothesis of Example 5.9, where

$$H_0: \quad \mu = 2{,}400$$
$$H_a: \quad \mu > 2{,}400$$

at a significance level $\alpha = .05$. Recall that the test was based on a random sample of $n = 70$ measurements, with $\bar{x} = 2{,}430$ and $s = 190$. Calculate the value of β if the value of μ in H_a is $\mu_a = 2{,}420$.

Solution

STEP 1   The first step is to find the value of $\bar{x}$ on the border between the rejection region and the acceptance region. From Example 5.9, the rejection region is $z > 1.645$. Since the test statistic is calculated as

$$z = \frac{\bar{x} - 2,400}{\sigma/\sqrt{n}}$$

we can write the rejection region in terms of $\bar{x}$:

$$\frac{\bar{x} - 2,400}{\sigma/\sqrt{n}} > 1.645$$

or

$$\bar{x} > 2,400 + 1.645\left(\frac{\sigma}{\sqrt{n}}\right)$$

Substituting $n = 70$ and $s = 190$ (as an approximation for σ) into the expression for the rejection region, we obtain

$$\bar{x} > 2,400 + 1.645\left(\frac{190}{\sqrt{70}}\right) = 2,437.4$$

Thus, at $\alpha = .05$, we will reject H_0 if the sample mean $\bar{x}$ exceeds 2,437.4. Or equivalently, we will accept H_0 if $\bar{x} < 2,437.4$. These rejection and acceptance regions are illustrated in Figure 5.13.

STEP 2   The next step is to write β as a probability statement involving $\bar{x}$:

$$\beta = P(\text{Type II error})$$
$$= P(\text{Accept } H_0 \text{ when } H_0 \text{ is false})$$
$$= P(\bar{x} < 2,437.4 \text{ when } \mu_a = 2,420)$$

[Note that we have substituted $\mu_a = 2,420$ for "H_0 is false," because this is the value of μ specified in H_a.] This probability is shown in Figure 5.14.

STEP 3   The final step is to calculate β using the standard normal (z) table (Table 2, Appendix A):

$$\beta = P(\bar{x} < 2,437.4 \text{ when } \mu = 2,420)$$
$$= P\left(\frac{\bar{x} - \mu}{\sigma/\sqrt{n}} < \frac{2,437.4 - 2,420}{\sigma/\sqrt{n}}\right)$$
$$= P\left(z < \frac{2,437.4 - 2,420}{190/\sqrt{70}}\right)$$
$$= P(z < .76)$$
$$= .5 + .2764 = .7764$$

Thus, the probability that the test procedure will lead us to incorrectly accept H_0: $\mu = 2,400$ when $\mu = 2,420$ is approximately .78. This probability is so large that it will be difficult to detect departures from H_0 for values of μ close, but not equal, to 2,400.

FIGURE 5.13

Rejection and Acceptance Regions in Terms of $\bar{x}$

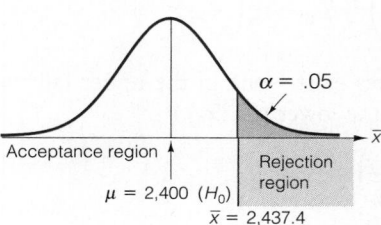

FIGURE 5.14

Value of β When $\mu_a = 2,420$

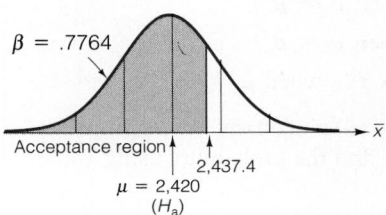

**GUIDELINES FOR CALCULATING β FOR
A LARGE-SAMPLE TEST ABOUT μ**

Consider a large-sample test of H_0: $\mu = \mu_0$ at significance level α. The value of β for a specific value of the alternative, $\mu = \mu_a$, is calculated as follows:

STEP 1 For one-tailed tests, find the value of $\bar{x}$ corresponding to the border of the rejection region. The calculation of this value, $\bar{x}_0$, depends on whether the test is upper-tailed or lower-tailed.

Upper-tailed test: $\quad \bar{x}_0 = \mu_0 + z_\alpha\left(\dfrac{\sigma}{\sqrt{n}}\right) \approx \mu_0 + z_\alpha\left(\dfrac{s}{\sqrt{n}}\right)$

Lower-tailed test: $\quad \bar{x}_0 = \mu_0 - z_\alpha\left(\dfrac{\sigma}{\sqrt{n}}\right) \approx \mu_0 - z_\alpha\left(\dfrac{s}{\sqrt{n}}\right)$

For two-tailed tests, two border values exist—one in the upper tail of the distribution ($\bar{x}_{0,U}$) and one in the lower tail ($\bar{x}_{0,L}$):

Two-tailed test: $\quad \bar{x}_{0,U} \approx \mu_0 + z_{\alpha/2}\left(\dfrac{s}{\sqrt{n}}\right)$

$\qquad\qquad\qquad\quad \bar{x}_{0,L} \approx \mu_0 - z_{\alpha/2}\left(\dfrac{s}{\sqrt{n}}\right)$

STEP 2 Write β as a probability involving the border value(s) of $\bar{x}$ and the alternative value of μ:

Upper-tailed test: $\quad \beta = P(\bar{x} < \bar{x}_0 \text{ when } \mu = \mu_a)$
Lower-tailed test: $\quad \beta = P(\bar{x} > \bar{x}_0 \text{ when } \mu = \mu_a)$
Two-tailed test: $\quad \beta = P(\bar{x}_{0,L} < \bar{x} < \bar{x}_{0,U} \text{ when } \mu = \mu_a)$

STEP 3 Convert the border value(s) of $\bar{x}$ to z-value(s) in the appropriate probability statement of step 2. Then find the probability using Table 2, Appendix A.

Upper-tailed test: $\quad P\left(z < \dfrac{\bar{x}_0 - \mu_a}{s/\sqrt{n}}\right)$

Lower-tailed test: $\quad P\left(z > \dfrac{\bar{x}_0 - \mu_a}{s/\sqrt{n}}\right)$

Two-tailed test: $\quad P\left(\dfrac{\bar{x}_{0,L} - \mu_a}{s/\sqrt{n}} < z < \dfrac{\bar{x}_{0,U} - \mu_a}{s/\sqrt{n}}\right)$

EXAMPLE 5.11 Refer to Example 5.10. Calculate the value of β when the value of μ in H_a is $\mu_a = 2,500$.

FIGURE 5.15

Value of β When $\mu_a = 2,500$

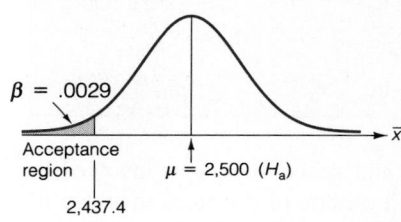

$\beta = .0029$

Acceptance region

2,437.4

$\mu = 2,500 \ (H_a)$

Solution From step 1 of Example 5.10, we know that the "acceptance region" for the test with $\alpha = .05$ is $\bar{x} < 2,437.4$. Then, for $\mu_a = 2,500$, we have

$$\beta = P(\text{Accept } H_0 \text{ when } H_0 \text{ is false})$$
$$= P(\bar{x} < 2,437.4 \text{ when } \mu_a = 2,500)$$
$$= P\left(\frac{\bar{x} - \mu_a}{\sigma/\sqrt{n}} < \frac{2,437.4 - 2,500}{190/\sqrt{70}}\right)$$
$$= P(z < -2.76)$$

From Table 2, Appendix A, this probability is

$$\beta = .5 - .4971 = .0029 \quad \text{See Figure 5.15}$$

Examples 5.10 and 5.11 illustrate an important property of the statistical test of hypothesis: The value of β decreases as the true value of μ departs from the value hypothesized in H_0. In other words, the farther away the true value of μ lies from μ_0, the less likely you will be to incorrectly accept H_0, or, equivalently, the more likely you will be to correctly reject H_0. Also, it can be easily shown that β decreases as α increases for fixed n, or as n increases for fixed α. These properties of β are summarized in the next box.

PROPERTIES OF β FOR A TEST OF HYPOTHESIS ABOUT μ

1. β decreases as the distance between μ_0 and μ_a increases.
2. For fixed sample size n, β decreases as α increases.
3. For fixed significance level α, β decreases as n increases.

In practice, it is useful to interpret the value of $(1 - \beta)$, which is known as the **power of the test**. Since β and $(1 - \beta)$ are complementary probabilities, the power represents the probability that you will reject H_0 when H_0 is false, that is:

The power of the test is the probability that you detect a departure from H_0 for a specific value of μ in H_a.

For example, the power of the test for $\mu_a = 2,500$ in Example 5.11 is

$$\text{Power} = 1 - \beta = 1 - .0029 = .9971$$

Thus, the test is highly likely (probability of about .997) to lead to a rejection of $H_0: \mu = 2,400$ in favor of the alternative $H_a: \mu > 2,400$ when the true value of μ is $\mu_a = 2,500$. The greater the power, the more powerful the test is for the particular alternative value of μ. All the testing procedures we will discuss in the following chapters have been shown to be most powerful for a general set of alternatives.

In this chapter we have introduced the logic and general concepts involved in the statistical procedure of hypothesis testing. An outline of the steps involved in conducting a statistical test is provided in the box. The techniques will be illustrated more fully with practical applications in the relevant chapters.

OUTLINE FOR TESTING A HYPOTHESIS

___

STEP 1   State the hypothesis you want to support as the **alternative hypothesis, H_a**.

STEP 2   The **null hypothesis, H_0**, will be the opposite of H_a and will contain an equality sign.

STEP 3   Obtain a random sample from the population(s) of interest.

STEP 4   Determine a standardized **test statistic** that is reasonable in the context of the given hypothesis test.

STEP 5   Specify the **rejection region**, the range of possible computed values of the test statistic for which the null hypothesis will be rejected. The rejection region will depend on the value of α selected by the researcher.

STEP 6   Use the data in the sample to compute the value of the test statistic.

STEP 7   Make a conclusion by observing whether the computed value of the test statistic lies within the rejection region. If so, reject the null hypothesis; otherwise, do not reject the null hypothesis. The measure of reliability of the test is the value of α, the probability of a Type I error.

PROBLEMS

5.17   Formulate the appropriate null and alternative hypotheses for each of the following problems. [*Note:*   Use the symbol μ to represent a population mean, π to represent a population proportion, $(\mu_1 - \mu_2)$ to represent the difference between two population means, and $(\pi_1 - \pi_2)$ to represent the difference between two population proportions.]

   a. A *Harvard Business Review* (Sept.–Oct. 1985) survey was conducted to determine whether a difference exists between the proportions of male executives and female executives who agree with the statement, "A woman executive is invariably paid less than her male counterpart."

b. Kimberly-Clark Corporation, the maker of Kleenex, periodically conducts market surveys to determine the average number of tissues used by people when they have a cold. Currently, the company puts 60 tissues in a box. Suppose marketing experts at the company want to test whether the mean number of tissues used by people with colds exceeds 60. [*Note:* This test is carried out in Problem 5.20.]

c. A study reported in the *Academy of Management Journal* (Mar. 1982) investigated whether the mean performance appraisal of "leavers" at a large national oil company is less than the mean performance appraisal of "stayers."

d. Cannibalism among chickens is common when the birds are confined in small areas. A breeder and seller of live chickens wants to test whether the mortality rate due to cannibalism is less than .04 for a certain breed of chickens.

e. A management consultant who has worked for both Japanese and American organizations wants to compare the average motivational levels of Japanese and American managers.

5.18 State whether each of the tests in Problem 5.17 is one-tailed or two-tailed.

5.19 Why do we avoid stating a decision in terms of "accept the null hypothesis H_0"?

5.20 How do the makers of Kleenex know how many tissues to put in a box? According to *The Wall Street Journal* (Sept. 2, 1984), the marketing experts at Kimberly-Clark Corporation have "little doubt that the company should put 60 tissues in each pack." The researchers determined that 60 is "the average number of times people blow their nose during a cold" by asking hundreds of customers to keep count of their Kleenex use in diaries. Suppose a random sample of 250 Kleenex users yielded the following summary statistics on the number of times they blew their noses when they had a cold: $\bar{x} = 57$, $s = 26$.

a. Is this sufficient evidence to dispute the researchers' claim? Test at $\alpha = .05$.

b. Specify the Type I and Type II errors for this problem.

5.21 Every so often, one of the major U.S. car manufacturers announces a recall of some of its automobiles that have been found to be defective. A study was conducted to investigate the impact of automobile recall announcements on the equity holders of the manufacturer's competitors (*Quarterly Journal of Business and Economics*, Autumn 1986). For each of a sample of 112 recalls that were severe in nature (eg, problems that possibly could result in engine compartment and fuel tank fires, loss of steering or brake control, and repeated engine stalling), the researchers measured the abnormal rate of return for competitors' stocks 2 days after the recall was announced. (The abnormal return rate is the difference between the actual rate of return and the expected return that would have transpired in the absence of a recall.) A summary of the results is given below:

$$\bar{x} = .0050 \qquad s = .0233$$

a. Is there sufficient evidence to conclude (at significance level $\alpha = .05$) that the average abnormal rate of return 2 days after the recall announcement exceeds 0? (If the average abnormal return rate is greater than 0, the researchers will conclude that the recall announcement had a positive impact on competitors' car sales.)

b. Calculate the power of the test if the true mean abnormal rate of return is $\mu_a = .0025$. Interpret this result.

5.22 External organization development (OD) professionals provide consulting services in such areas as human resources, training, planning, skills education, industrial psychology, and organizational behavior. The *Training and Development Journal* (Feb. 1984) conducted a survey of OD professionals. A random sample of 440 external OD consultants yielded the following summary statistics on daily fees charged:

$$\bar{x} = \$720 \qquad s = \$275$$

Suppose it is known that other management consultants charge, on average, $800 per day. Do the data provide sufficient evidence to indicate that the mean daily fee charged by external OD consultants is less than $800? Test using $\alpha = .10$.

5.23 Most supermarket chains give each store manager a detailed plan showing exactly where each product belongs on each shelf. Since more products are picked up from shelves at eye level than from any others, the most profitable and fastest-moving items are placed at eye level to make them easy for shoppers to reach. Traditionally, the eye-level shelf has been slightly under 5 feet from the floor—just the right height for the average female shopper, who is 5 feet 4 inches tall. But nowadays more men are shopping than ever before. Since the average male shopper is 5 feet 10 inches tall, how will this affect the eye-level shelf? To investigate this, a random sample of 100 supermarkets from across the country were selected and the height of the eye-level shelf (ie, the shelf with the most popular products) was recorded for each. The results were:

$$\bar{x} = 62 \text{ inches} \qquad s = 3 \text{ inches}$$

a. Is there evidence that the average height of the eye-level shelf at supermarkets is now higher than 60 inches from the floor (ie, higher than the traditional height of 5 feet)? Test using $\alpha = .01$.
b. Specify Type I and Type II errors in terms of this problem.
c. What is the probability of a Type I error?
d. What is the probability of a Type II error when the true mean is 61 inches?
e. What is the power of the test when the true mean is 63 inches?

INFERENCES BASED ON SMALL SAMPLES

5.4

In the previous two sections, we discussed confidence intervals and hypothesis tests for a population mean based on large random samples. However, time or cost limitations may often restrict the number of sample observations that may be obtained, so that the inferential procedures of Sections 5.2 and 5.3 would not be applicable.

With small samples the following two problems arise:

1. Since the Central Limit Theorem applies only to large samples, we are not able to assume that the sampling distribution of $\bar{x}$ is approximately normal. For small samples, the sampling distribution of $\bar{x}$ depends on the particular form of the relative frequency distribution of the population being sampled.
2. The sample standard deviation s may not be a satisfactory approximation to the population standard deviation σ if the sample size is small. Thus, replacing σ with s in the large-sample formula given in Section 5.2 is not appropriate.

Fortunately, we may proceed with estimation techniques based on small samples if we can make the following assumption:

ASSUMPTION REQUIRED FOR ESTIMATING μ BASED ON SMALL SAMPLES

The population from which the sample is selected has an approximate normal distribution.

If this assumption is valid, then we may again use $\bar{x}$ as a point estimate for μ, and the general form of a small-sample confidence interval and small-sample test statistic for μ are:

SMALL-SAMPLE INFERENCES FOR μ

CONFIDENCE INTERVAL

$$\bar{x} \pm (t_{\alpha/2})\left(\frac{s}{\sqrt{n}}\right)$$

TEST STATISTIC

$$t = \frac{\bar{x} - \mu_0}{s/\sqrt{n}}$$

where the distribution of t is based on $(n - 1)$ degrees of freedom.

Upon comparing these formulas to the large-sample formulas, you will observe that the sample standard deviation s replaces the population standard deviation σ. Also, the sampling distribution upon which the inferences are based is known as a **Student's t distribution.*** Consequently, we must replace the value of $z_{\alpha/2}$ used in a large-sample confidence interval and the value of z_α used in a large-sample rejection region by a value obtained from the t distribution.

The t distribution is very much like the z distribution. In particular, both are symmetric, mound-shaped, and have a mean of 0. However, the t distribution is flatter, that is, more variable (see Figure 5.16, p. 226). Also, the distribution of t depends on a quantity called its **degrees of freedom (df)**, which is equal to $(n - 1)$ when estimating a population mean based on a small sample of size n. Intuitively, we can think of the number of degrees of freedom as the amount of information available for estimating, in addition to μ, the unknown quantity σ^2. Table 3, Appendix A, gives the values of t_α that locate an area of α in the upper tail of the t distribution for various values of α and for degrees of freedom ranging from 1 to 120. A portion of this table is reproduced in Table 5.7.

TABLE 5.7

Reproduction of a Portion of Table 3, Appendix A: Critical Values for Student's t

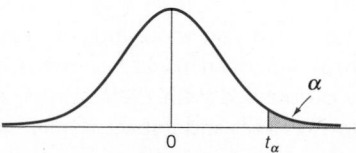

DEGREES OF FREEDOM	$t_{.100}$	$t_{.050}$	$t_{.025}$	$t_{.010}$	$t_{.005}$	$t_{.001}$	$t_{.0005}$
1	3.078	6.314	12.706	31.821	63.657	318.31	636.62
2	1.886	2.920	4.303	6.965	9.925	22.326	31.598
3	1.638	2.353	3.182	4.541	5.841	10.213	12.924
4	1.533	2.132	2.776	3.747	4.604	7.173	8.610
5	1.476	2.015	2.571	3.365	4.032	5.893	6.869
6	1.440	1.943	2.447	3.143	3.707	5.208	5.959
7	1.415	1.895	2.365	2.998	3.499	4.785	5.408
8	1.397	1.860	2.306	2.896	3.355	4.501	5.041
9	1.383	1.833	2.262	2.821	3.250	4.297	4.781
10	1.372	1.812	2.228	2.764	3.169	4.144	4.587
11	1.363	1.796	2.201	2.718	3.106	4.025	4.437
12	1.356	1.782	2.179	2.681	3.055	3.930	4.318
13	1.350	1.771	2.160	2.650	3.102	3.852	4.221
14	1.345	1.761	2.145	2.624	2.977	3.787	4.140
15	1.341	1.753	2.131	2.602	2.947	3.733	4.073

* The result was first published in 1908 by W. S. Gosset, who wrote under the pen name of Student. Thereafter, the distribution became known as Student's t.

FIGURE 5.16

Comparison of the *z* Distribution to the *t* Distribution

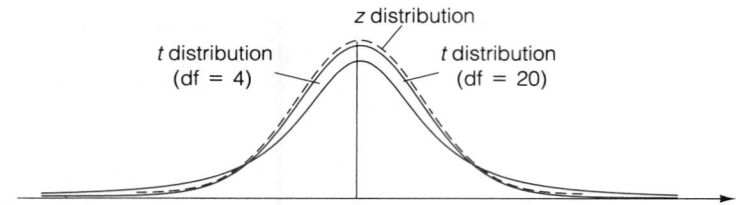

z distribution

t distribution
(df = 4)

t distribution
(df = 20)

CHARACTERISTICS OF STUDENT'S *t* DISTRIBUTION

1. Symmetric distribution
2. Mean of 0
3. More variable (flatter) than the standard normal (*z*) distribution
4. Depends on a quantity called **degrees of freedom (df)**
5. For large samples (ie, large df values), the *t* and *z* distributions are nearly equivalent.

EXAMPLE 5.12 Each year thousands of manufacturers' sales promotions are conducted by North American packaged goods companies, but promotion managers are frequently dissatisfied with their results. An exploratory study was conducted to examine the objectives and impact of such sales promotions (*Journal of Marketing*, July 1986). A sample of Canadian packaged goods companies provided information on examples of past sales promotions, including trade promotions. For the 21 successful trade promotions (where "success" is determined by the company managers) identified in the sample, the mean incremental profit was $53,000 and the standard deviation was $95,000.* Find a 95% confidence interval for the true mean incremental profit of successful trade promotions.

Solution   Since we must base our estimation procedure on a small sample ($n = 21$), it is necessary to assume that the population of incremental profits of all successful trade promotions has a relative frequency distribution that is approximately normal.

The desired confidence interval is based on a *t* distribution with $(n - 1) = (21 - 1) = 20$ degrees of freedom; we obtain the value of $t_{\alpha/2} = t_{.025} = 2.086$ from Table 3, Appendix A. A 95% confidence interval for μ is

$$\bar{x} \pm t_{.025}\left(\frac{s}{\sqrt{n}}\right) = 53{,}000 \pm 2.086\left(\frac{95{,}000}{\sqrt{21}}\right)$$

$$= 53{,}000 \pm 43{,}244$$

---

* Hardy, K. G. "Key Success Factors for Manufacturers' Sales Promotions in Package Goods." *Journal of Marketing*, Vol. 50, No. 7, July 1986, p. 16. Reprinted with permission from *Journal of Marketing*, published by the American Marketing Association, Chicago, IL.

or (9,756, 96,244). Thus, we are 95% confident that the interval from $9,756 to $96,244 contains the true mean incremental profit of the successful trade promotions. Note that the interval is extremely wide; thus, it may not be of much use in practice.

Before concluding this section, two comments are necessary. The first concerns the assumption that the sampled population is normally distributed. In the real world we rarely know whether a sampled population has an exact normal distribution. However, empirical studies indicate that moderate departures from this assumption do not seriously affect the confidence coefficients for small-sample confidence intervals. For example, if the population of incremental profits of the promotions of Example 5.12 has a distribution that is mound-shaped but nonnormal, it is likely that the actual confidence coefficient for the 95% confidence interval will be close to .95—at least close enough to be practical. As a consequence, the small-sample confidence interval given in the box on p. 224 is frequently used by experimenters when estimating the population mean of a nonnormal distribution, as long as the distribution is mound-shaped and only moderately skewed. For populations that depart greatly from normality, however, other inferential techniques are recommended. (We introduce one of these techniques in Section 5.6.)

The second comment focuses on whether σ is known or unknown. It can be shown (proof omitted) that when σ is known and the sampled population is normally distributed, the sampling distribution of $\bar{x}$ is normal regardless of the size of the sample. That is, if you know the value of σ and you know that the sample comes from a normal population, then you can use the z distribution rather than the t distribution to form confidence intervals and rejection regions. In reality, however, σ is rarely (if ever) known. Consequently, you will always be using s in place of σ in the confidence interval and test statistic formulas, and the sampling distribution of $\bar{x}$ will be a t distribution. This is why the formulas for a large-sample confidence interval and test of hypothesis given in Sections 5.2 and 5.3, respectively, are only approximate; in the large-sample case, $t \approx z$. Many statistical software packages give the results for *exact* confidence intervals and statistical tests when σ is unknown; thus, these results are based on the t distribution. For practical reasons, however, we will continue to distinguish between z and t tests (or confidence intervals) based on whether the sample size is large or small.

PROBLEMS

5.24   Give two reasons why the interval estimation procedure of Section 5.2 may not be applicable when the sample size is small, that is, when $n < 30$.

5.25   How does lack of sleep have an impact on one's creative ability? A British study, believed to be the first to measure systematically the effect of sleep loss on divergent thinking, found that loss of sleep sabotages creative faculties and the ability to deal with unfamiliar situations (*Sleep*, Jan. 1989). In the study, 12 healthy college students, deprived of one night's sleep, received an array of tests intended to measure thinking time, fluency, flexibility, and originality of thought. The overall test scores of the sleep-deprived students were compared to the average score expected from students who received their accustomed sleep. Suppose the overall scores of the 12 sleep-deprived students had a mean of $\bar{x} = 63$ and a standard deviation of 17. (Lower scores are associated with a decreased ability to think creatively.)

a. Test the hypothesis that the true mean score of sleep-deprived subjects is less than 80, the mean score of subjects who received sleep prior to taking the test. Use $\alpha = .05$.

b. What assumption is required for the hypothesis test of part **a** to be valid?

5.26 Refer to the *Risk Management* study on fires in compartmented fire-resistive buildings, Problem 3.1. The data are repeated here for convenience. The table gives the number of victims who died attempting to evacuate (for a sample of 14 fires).

FIRE	NUMBER OF VICTIMS
Las Vegas Hilton (Las Vegas)	5
Inn on the Park (Toronto)	5
Westchase Hilton (Houston)	8
Holiday Inn (Cambridge, Ohio)	10
Conrad Hilton (Chicago)	4
Providence College (Providence)	8
Baptist Towers (Atlanta)	7
Howard Johnson (New Orleans)	5
Cornell University (Ithaca, New York)	9
Westport Central Apartments (Kansas City, Missouri)	4
Orrington Hotel (Evanston, Illinois)	0
Hartford Hospital (Hartford, Connecticut)	16
Milford Plaza (New York)	0
MGM Grand (Las Vegas)	36

Source: Macdonald, J. N. "Is Evacuation a Fatal Flaw in Fire Fighting Philosophy?" *Risk Management,* Vol. 33, No. 2, Feb. 1986, p. 37.

a. State the assumption, in terms of the problem, that is required for a small-sample confidence interval technique to be valid. Is it satisfied?

b. Construct a 98% confidence interval for the true mean number of victims per fire who die attempting to evacuate compartmented fire-resistive buildings.

c. Interpret the interval constructed in part **b**.

5.27 Refer to the *Journal of Marketing Research* study of the effect of brand name and store name on product quality, Problem 3.9. The stem-and-leaf displays showing the distribution of effect size (an index ranging from 0 to 1) for the 15 brand name studies and 17 store name studies are reproduced below.

BRAND NAME 15 Studies		STORE NAME 17 Studies	
STEM	LEAF	STEM	LEAF
.6	0	.6	
.5	7	.5	
.4		.4	3 4
.3	4	.3	
.2	5 5	.2	
.1	0 1 1 2 4	.1	2
.0	3 3 5 5 7	.0	0 0 0 1 1 2 2 3 3 4 6 7 8 8

Source: Rao, A. R., and Monroe, K. B. "The Effect of Price, Brand Name, and Store Name on Buyers' Perceptions of Product Quality: An Integrative Review." *Journal of Marketing Research,* Vol. 26, Aug. 1989, p. 354 (Table 2). Reprinted with permission from *Journal of Marketing Research,* published by the American Marketing Association, Chicago, IL.

a. Use the method of this section to find a 95% confidence interval for the mean effect size for all brand name studies. Interpret the result.

b. Repeat part **a** for the store name studies.

c. Why might the validity of the confidence intervals from parts **a** and **b** be suspect?

5.28 The effect of machine breakdowns on the performance of a manufacturing system was investigated using computer simulation (*Industrial Engineering*, Aug. 1990). The simulation study focused on a single machine tool system with several characteristics, including a mean interarrival time of 1.25 minutes, a constant processing time of 1 minute, and a machine that breaks down 10% of the time. After $n = 5$ independent simulation runs of length 160 hours, the mean throughput per 40 hour week was $\bar{x} = 1,908.8$ parts. For a system with no breakdowns, the mean throughput for a 40 hour week will be equal to 1,920 parts. Assuming the standard deviation of the 5 sample runs was $s = 18$ parts per 40 hour week, test the hypothesis that the true mean throughput per 40 hour week for the system is less than 1,920 parts. Test using $\alpha = .05$.

5.29 Scientists have labeled benzene, a chemical solvent commonly used to synthesize plastics, as a possible cancer-causing agent. Studies have shown that people who work with benzene more than 5 years have 20 times the incidence of leukemia in the general population. As a result, the federal government has lowered the maximum allowable level of benzene in the workplace from 10 parts per million (ppm) to 1 ppm (reported in *Florida Times-Union*, Apr. 2, 1984). Suppose a steel manufacturing plant, which exposes its workers to benzene daily, is under investigation by the Occupational Health and Safety Commission. Twenty air samples, collected over a period of 1 month and examined for benzene content, yielded the following summary statistics:

$$\bar{x} = 2.1 \text{ ppm} \qquad s = 1.7 \text{ ppm}$$

a. Is the steel manufacturing plant in violation of the new government standards? Test the hypothesis that the mean level of benzene at the steel manufacturing plant is greater than 1 ppm, using $\alpha = .05$.

b. What assumption is required for the hypothesis test to be valid?

REPORTING TEST RESULTS: *p*-VALUES

5.5

The statistical hypothesis testing technique we have developed in Sections 5.3 and 5.4 requires us to choose the significance level α (ie, the maximum probability of a Type I error that we are willing to tolerate) before obtaining the data and computing the test statistic. By choosing α a priori, we in effect fix the rejection region for the test. Thus, no matter how large or how small the observed value of the test statistic, our decision regarding H_0 is clear-cut: Reject H_0 (ie, conclude that the test results are statistically significant) if the observed value of the test statistic falls into the rejection region, and do not reject H_0 (ie, conclude that the test results are insignificant) otherwise. This "fixed" significance level, α, then serves as a measure of the reliability of our inference. However, there is one drawback to a test conducted in this manner—namely, a measure of the *degree* of significance of the test results is not readily available. If the value of the test statistic falls into the rejection region, we have no measure of the extent to which the data disagree with the null hypothesis.

To illustrate, suppose a large-sample test of H_0: $\mu = 80$ versus H_a: $\mu > 80$ is to be conducted at a fixed significance level of $\alpha = .05$. Consider the following possible values of the computed test statistic:

$$z = 1.82 \qquad z = 5.66$$

Which of the above values of the test statistic do you think provides stronger evidence for the rejection of H_0? The appropriate rejection region for this test at $\alpha = .05$ is given by

$$z > z_{.05} = 1.645$$

Clearly, for either of the test statistic values given above, $z = 1.82$ or $z = 5.66$, we will reject H_0; hence, the result in each case is statistically significant. Recall, however, that the appropriate test statistic for a large-sample test concerning μ is simply the z-score for the observed sample mean, $\bar{x}$, calculated by using the hypothesized value of μ in H_0 (in this case, $\mu = 80$). The larger the z-score, the greater the distance (in units of standard deviations) that $\bar{x}$ is from the hypothesized value of $\mu = 80$. Thus, a z-score of 5.66 would present stronger evidence that the true mean is larger than 80 than would a z-score of 1.82. This reasoning stems from our knowledge of the sampling distribution of $\bar{x}$; if in fact $\mu = 80$, we would certainly not expect to observe an $\bar{x}$ with a z-score as large as 5.66.

One way of measuring the amount of disagreement between the observed data and the value of μ in the null hypothesis is to calculate the probability of observing a value of the test statistic equal to or greater than the actual computed value, if in fact H_0 were true. That is, if z_c is the computed value of the test statistic, calculate $P(z \geq z_c)$ assuming the null hypothesis is true. This "disagreement" probability, or **p-value**, is calculated below for each of the computed test statistics, $z = 1.82$ and $z = 5.66$, using Table 2, Appendix A:

$$P(z \geq 1.82) = .5 - .4656 = .0344$$
$$P(z \geq 5.66) = .5 - .5 \approx 0$$

You can see that the smaller the p-value, the greater the extent of disagreement between the data and the null hypothesis—that is, the more significant the result. For this reason, the p-value is often referred to as the **observed significance level** of the test.

DEFINITION 5.19

The **observed significance level**, or **p-value**, of a test is the probability of observing a value of the test statistic that is at least as contradictory to the null hypothesis, H_0, as the actual computed value.

In general, p-values are computed as shown in the box at the top of the next page. Notice that the p-value of a two-tailed test is twice the probability for the one-tailed test. This is because the disagreement between the data and H_0 can be in two directions.

When publishing the results of a statistical test of hypothesis in journals, case studies, reports, etc., many researchers make use of p-values. Instead of selecting α a priori and then conducting a test as outlined in this chapter, the researcher will compute and report the value of the appropriate test statistic and its associated p-value. It is left to the reader of the report to judge the significance of the result; the reader must determine whether to reject the null hypothesis in favor of the alternative, based on the reported p-value. Usually, the null hypothesis will be rejected if the p-value is *less* than the fixed significance level, α, chosen by the reader. The inherent advantages of reporting test results in this manner are twofold: (1) Each reader is permitted to select the maximum value of α that he or she would

---

MEASURING THE DISAGREEMENT BETWEEN THE DATA AND H_0: *p*-VALUES

Upper-tailed test: *p*-value $= P(z \geq z_c)$

Lower-tailed test: *p*-value $= P(z \leq z_c)$

Two-tailed test: *p*-value $= 2P(z \geq |z_c|)$

where z_c is the computed value of the large-sample test statistic.

Note: For a small-sample test, replace z_c in the above probabilities with t_c, the computed value of the *t* statistic.

---

be willing to tolerate in carrying out a standard test of hypothesis in the manner outlined in this chapter; and (2) a measure of the degree of significance of the result (ie, the *p*-value) is provided.

REPORTING TEST RESULTS AS *p*-VALUES: HOW TO DECIDE WHETHER TO REJECT H_0

---

1. Choose the maximum value of α that you are willing to tolerate.

2. If the observed significance level (*p*-value) of the test is less than the maximum value of α, then reject the null hypothesis.

EXAMPLE 5.13   In Example 5.9 we tested the null hypothesis H_0: $\mu = 2{,}400$ against H_a: $\mu > 2{,}400$, to determine whether the manufacturer's pipe meets specifications. Compute the *p*-value of the test and interpret its value.

Solution   In this large-sample test, the computed value of the test statistic was $z_c = 1.32$. Since the test is one-tailed, the associated *p*-value is given by

$$P(z \geq z_c) = P(z \geq 1.32)$$
$$= .5 - .4066 = .0934$$

Thus, the *p*-value of the test is .0934. To reject the null hypothesis H_0: $\mu = 2{,}400$, we would have to be willing to risk a Type I error probability, α, of at least .0934. Since the city wants to test at $\alpha = .05$, the result is insignificant (ie, there is insufficient evidence to reject H_0). However, if the city is willing to risk a Type I error probability of $\alpha = .10$, the null hypothesis can be rejected since $p = .0934$ is less than $\alpha = .10$.

Since most statistical software packages automatically compute and report the *p*-value for a test of hypothesis, we will rely less on the rejection region approach

---

and more on the p-value approach for conducting tests in the following chapters. Whether we conduct a test using p-values or the rejection region approach, our choice of a maximum tolerable Type I error probability becomes critical to the decision concerning H_0 and should not be made hastily. In either case, care should be taken to weigh the seriousness of committing a Type I error in the context of the problem.

PROBLEMS

5.30   For a large-sample test of

H_0: $\mu = 10$
H_a: $\mu > 10$

compute the p-value associated with each of the following computed test statistic values:

a. $z_c = 1.96$ **b.** $z_c = 1.645$ **c.** $z_c = 2.67$ **d.** $z_c = 1.25$

5.31   Give the approximate observed significance level of the test of H_0: $\mu = 16$ against H_a: $\mu \neq 16$ for each of the following combinations of test statistic value and sample size:

a. $t = 3.25$, $n = 10$ **b.** $t = -1.58$, $n = 15$ **c.** $t = 2.20$, $n = 12$ **d.** $t = -2.97$, $n = 5$

5.32   Refer to Problem 5.17 (p. 222). For each problem, the p-value and the value of α for the appropriate test are given below. State the conclusions in the words of each problem.

a. p-value $= .217$, $\alpha = .10$ **b.** p-value $= .033$, $\alpha = .05$ **c.** p-value $= .001$, $\alpha = .05$
d. p-value $= .866$, $\alpha = .01$ **e.** p-value $= .025$, $\alpha = .01$

5.33   Refer to Problem 5.20 (p. 223). Compute the observed significance level (p-value) of the test. Interpret the result.

5.34   Refer to Problem 5.21 (p. 223). Compute the observed significance level (p-value) of the test. Interpret the result.

5.35   Refer to Problem 5.29 (p. 229). Compute the observed significance level (p-value) of the test. Interpret the result.

DISTRIBUTION-FREE TESTS: NONPARAMETRICS

5.6   Confidence intervals and tests of hypothesis based on the t distribution are unsuitable for some types of data that fall into one of two categories. The first are data sets that do not satisfy the assumptions upon which the t test is based. For example, when making inferences about a population mean using small samples (Section 5.4), we assume that the random variable being measured has a normal probability distribution. Yet in practice, the population may be decidedly nonnormal. For example, the distribution might be very flat, peaked, or strongly skewed to the right or left. (See Figure 5.17.) When the normality assumption required for the t test is seriously violated, the computed t statistic may not follow the Student's t distribution. If this is true, the tabulated values of t given in Table 3, Appendix A, are not applicable, the correct value of α for the test (or confidence interval) is unknown, and the t test (or confidence interval) is of dubious value.

The second type of data for which it is inappropriate to apply the t distribution consist of responses that are not susceptible to measurement but can be *ranked in order of magnitude*. For example, suppose we want to compare the ease of operation of a new type of computer software against some industry standard based on subjective evaluations of trained observers. Although we cannot give an exact value to the variable "Ease of operation of the software package," we may be able to decide that the new software package is better than the standard. If the new software

FIGURE 5.17
Some Nonnormal Distributions for Which the *t* Statistic Is Invalid

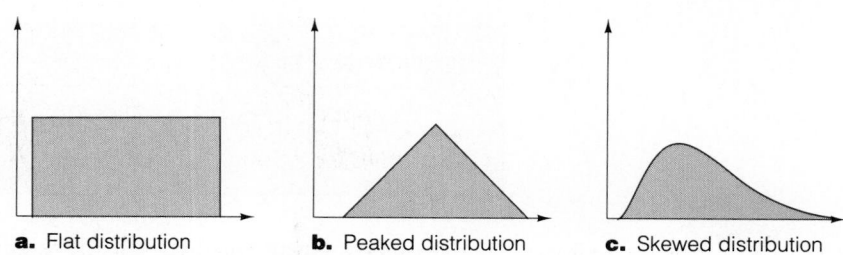

a. Flat distribution   **b.** Peaked distribution   **c.** Skewed distribution

package is evaluated by each of 10 observers, we have the problem of comparing the mean ease of operation of the new software package, μ, to the known mean, μ_0, of the industry standard. But the *t* test of Section 5.4 would be inappropriate, because the only data that can be recorded are preferences—each observer decides either that the new software is better than the standard or vice versa.

Consider another example of this type of data. Most firms that plan to purchase a new product first test the product to determine its acceptability. For a computer, an automobile, or some other piece of equipment, this may involve tests in which engineers rank the new product in order of preference with respect to one or more currently popular product types or makes. An engineer probably has a preference for each product, but the strength of the preference is difficult, if not impossible, to measure. Consequently, the best we can do is to have each engineer examine the new product along with a few established products and rank them according to preference: 1 for the product that is most preferred, 2 for the product with the second greatest preference, and so on.

A host of **nonparametric** techniques are available for analyzing data that do not follow a normal distribution. Nonparametric tests do not depend on the distribution of the sampled population; hence, they are also called **distribution-free tests**. Also, nonparametric methods focus on the location of the probability distribution of the sampled population, rather than specific parameters of the population such as the mean (hence, the name "nonparametrics"). For example, if it can be inferred that the distribution of preferences for a new product lies above (to the right of) the others, as illustrated in Figure 5.18, the implication is that the engineers tend to prefer the new product to the other products.

DEFINITION 5.20

Distribution-free tests are statistical tests that do not rely on any underlying assumptions about the probability distribution of the sampled population.

FIGURE 5.18
Probability Distributions of Strengths of Preference Measurements (New Product is Preferred)

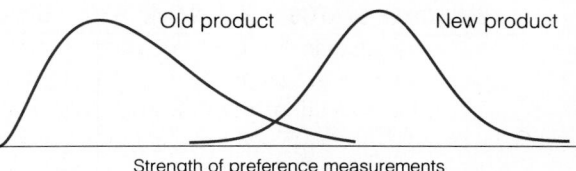

Old product   New product

Strength of preference measurements

Many nonparametric methods use the **relative ranks** of the sample observations rather than their actual numerical values. These tests are particularly valuable when we are unable to obtain numerical measurements of some phenomenon but are able to rank the measurements relative to each other. Statistics based on the ranks of measurements are called **rank statistics**.

EXAMPLE 5.14   Studies have shown that in a nonbusiness (eg, academic) setting, those who tend to have job mobility are generally better performers. A 15 year study was conducted to examine the performance turnover relationship in a business setting (*Academy of Management Journal*, Mar. 1982). A company's employees were divided into two groups, "stayers" (those employees who stayed with the company during the 15 year period) and "leavers" (those former employees who left the company at varying points during the 15 year period). The company's annual performance appraisals corresponding to the initial years of service were used to rank all past and current employees. Table 5.8 gives the rank of each of a sample of 10 employees, 5 stayers and 5 leavers, where the best performer receives rank 1; the next best, rank 2; etc.

a. From this information calculate the sum of the ranks of the stayers and the sum of the ranks of the leavers.
b. Explain how the rank sums from part **a** might be used to draw inferences about the two groups of employees.

TABLE 5.8
Performance Ranks for Stayers and Leavers

EMPLOYEE STATUS	RANK	EMPLOYEE STATUS	RANK
Stayer	1	Leaver	6
Stayer	2	Stayer	7
Leaver	3	Leaver	8
Stayer	4	Leaver	9
Stayer	5	Leaver	10

Solution

a. The sum of the ranks for stayers, denoted R_S, is

$$R_S = 1 + 2 + 4 + 5 + 7 = 19$$

Similarly, the rank sum for leavers, denoted R_L, is

$$R_L = 3 + 6 + 8 + 9 + 10 = 36$$

b. Note that the rank sum for leavers, R_L, is nearly twice as large as the rank sum for stayers, R_S. The implication is that leavers are more likely to have higher ranks (and, consequently, lower performance ratings) than stayers. Thus, the rank sums can be used to make inferences about the two populations of performance ratings, one for leavers and one for stayers. (In Chapter 6 we will demonstrate how to attach a measure of reliability to inferences derived from rank statistics used to compare two populations.)

In the chapters that follow, we present the parametric and nonparametric methods appropriate for making inferences about the population(s) of interest. For convenience, both methods will be presented in the same section so that you can compare and contrast the results. As you will see subsequently, nonparametrtic tests most often reach the same conclusions as their parametric counterparts and do so with no underlying assumptions about the distributions of the sampled populations.

CHAPTER NOTES

- The **sampling distribution** of a sample statistic (based on n observations) is the relative frequency distribution of the values of the statistic theoretically generated by taking repeated random samples of size n and computing the value of the statistic for each sample.
- If $\bar{x}$ is the mean of a random sample of size n from a population with mean μ and standard deviation σ, then the **sampling distribution of $\bar{x}$** has the following properties:

  1. Approximate normal distribution for large n (the Central Limit Theorem)
  2. $\mu_{\bar{x}} = \mu$
  3. $\sigma_{\bar{x}} = \sigma/\sqrt{n}$

- If a random sample of size n is selected from a normal population, then the statistic

$$t = \frac{\bar{x} - \mu}{s/\sqrt{n}}$$

has a **Student's t distribution** with $(n - 1)$ **degrees of freedom**.
- An estimator of a parameter is **unbiased** if the mean of the sampling distribution of the estimator is equal to the parameter value. If not, the estimator is **biased**.
- The **standard error** of the estimator is the standard deviation of the sampling distribution of the estimator.

- The **minimum variance unbiased estimator (MVUE)** of a parameter is the estimator that has the smallest variance of all unbiased estimators.
- A **confidence interval** for a parameter is an interval of numbers within which we expect the true value of the parameter to be contained.
- The **confidence coefficient** $(1 - \alpha)$ is the proportion of times that a confidence interval encloses the true value of the parameter if the sampling procedure is repeated a very large number of times.
- A **large-sample** $(1 - \alpha)100\%$ **confidence interval** for a parameter (eg, the population mean) is

$$\text{Estimator} \pm (z_{\alpha/2})\text{Standard error}$$

- A **small-sample** $(1 - \alpha)100\%$ **confidence interval** for a parameter (eg, the mean) of a normal population is

$$\text{Estimator} \pm (t_{\alpha/2})\text{Estimated standard error}$$

- For a given sample size n, the width of the confidence interval increases as the confidence coefficient $(1 - \alpha)$ increases. For a fixed confidence coefficient $(1 - \alpha)$, the width of the interval decreases as the sample size n increases.
- The **null hypothesis (H_0)** is usually a hypothesis about a population parameter that we hope to gather evidence against.
- The **alternative hypothesis (H_a)** is usually the hypothesis about a population parameter that we hope to gather supporting evidence for.
- A **one-tailed test of hypothesis** is one in which the alternative hypothesis is directional and includes either the symbol "<" or ">" (eg, H_a: $\mu > 5$).
- A **two-tailed test of hypothesis** is one in which the alternative hypothesis does not specify departure from H_0 in a particular direction and includes the symbol "$\neq$" (eg, H_a: $\mu \neq 5$).
- A **Type I error** occurs if we reject H_0 when H_0 is true. The probability of a Type I error, denoted by α, is called the **significance level** of the test and is controlled (selected) by the researcher.
- A **Type II error** occurs if we accept H_0 when H_0 is false. The probability of a Type II error, denoted by β, is rarely known (although it can be estimated for particular values of the parameter in H_a).
- The **power of a test** is the probability of rejecting H_0 when H_0 is true and is calculated as $(1 - \beta)$. For fixed α, the power of the test increases as the sample size n increases.
- The **test statistic** is the estimator of the parameter in standardized form:

$$\text{Test statistic} = \frac{\text{Estimator} - \text{Hypothesized value of parameter in } H_0}{\text{Standard error of estimator}}$$

- The test statistics appropriate for testing a population mean μ are:

Large sample: $\quad z = \dfrac{\bar{x} - \mu_0}{\sigma/\sqrt{n}} \approx \dfrac{\bar{x} - \mu_0}{s/\sqrt{n}}$

Small sample: $\quad t = \dfrac{\bar{x} - \mu_0}{s/\sqrt{n}}$

(assuming the sample is selected from a normal population).

- The **rejection region** is the set of possible computed values of the test statistic for which H_0 will be rejected. If the test statistic falls into the rejection region, then "reject H_0" with measure of reliability α; otherwise, "fail to reject H_0." Because β is usually unknown, we avoid "accepting H_0."
- The **observed significance level (*p*-value)** of the test is the probability of observing a value of the test statistic that is at least as contradictory to the null hypothesis, H_0, as the computed value. Reject H_0 if the *p*-value is less than the value of α chosen a priori.
- The *p*-value for a one-tailed test is half the *p*-value for a two-tailed test.
- **Nonparametric methods** do not rely on any underlying assumptions about the probability distribution of the sampled population; hence, they are called **distribution-free tests**.

LOOKING AHEAD

In Chapters 6–8 we apply our newfound knowledge of confidence intervals and tests of hypotheses to make inferences about various population parameters. We present both parametric and nonparametric methods for making inferences about population means for quantitative data (Chapter 6), population variances for quantitative data (Chapter 7), and population proportions for qualitative data (Chapter 8).

CASE STUDY

A DECISION PROBLEM FOR FINANCIAL MANAGERS: WHEN TO INVESTIGATE COST VARIANCES

Financial managers are faced daily with the job of controlling costs, and several useful management techniques for implementing that control are available. In this case study we focus on a method that has been received favorably in the health-care field—**cost variance analysis**.

In variance analysis actual performance (usually measured as either cost or level of activity) is compared to some standard of expected performance. The difference between the two measures of performance is called a *variance.** These differences, or variances, can direct managers to potential problem areas or situations where costs are out of control. The question is, which variances should the manager investigate? When is the deviation between the expected and the actual results large enough to warrant an expensive investigation?

W. A. Robbins and F. A. Jacobs† discuss the relevant issues surrounding the cost variance investigation decision problem. They illustrate the problem as follows:

---

* The word *variance* is used loosely here. Students should not confuse its meaning with the statistical definition of variance given in Section 3.6.

† Robbins, W. A., and Jacobs, F. A. *Healthcare Financial Management*, Sept. 1985, pp. 36–41.

Suppose a laboratory technician is able to perform a given test in 45 minutes, "on average," and management observes the test performed during the previous week took 60 minutes, on average, to perform. An investigation of this 15-minute unfavorable variance might reveal the technicians are being poorly supervised, resulting in an inefficient use of their time. On the other hand, management might find newly installed laboratory testing equipment is more sophisticated and requires a longer set-up time than originally anticipated, perhaps an additional 15 minutes on average. The investigation in this latter situation may result in management changing their expectation (standard) of efficient performance to 60 minutes or to some other new time dictated by the new technology.

In either instance, the variance has directed attention to a problem that can be corrected upon investigation.

Robbins and Jacobs developed a statistical model for the cost variance investigation decision problem. "The model," they write, "is based on the concept that a standard [usually the mean or average of an activity distribution] is best described by a band or area of acceptability, rather than a single point. The UCL and LCL [upper and lower control limits] form the bounds on the area of acceptability. Any variations falling within this area are considered to be due to random causes and do not require investigation. If a variance falls outside these limits, it is deemed to have a controllable source (nonrandom) and should be considered for possible investigation." The decision model is illustrated in Figure 5.19.

The control limits of the decision model can be either arbitrarily selected by management or mathematically calculated. For the purposes of this case study, consider the following three decision rules, each with a different method of calculating LCL and UCL:

RULE 1 $LCL = \mu - p\mu$ and $UCL = \mu + p\mu$

where

μ = Mean (or expected) level of activity

p = Percentage of mean $(0 < p < 1)$

$\bar{x}$ = Actual mean activity level of a sample of n observations

Acceptable area: $(\mu - p\mu) < \bar{x} < (\mu + p\mu)$ Do not investigate

FIGURE 5.19
Decision Model for Case Study

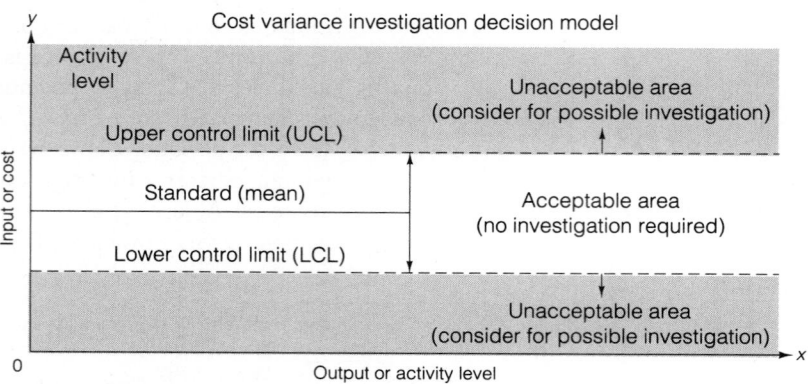

RULE 2 $LCL = \mu - 2\sigma$ and $UCL = \mu + 2\sigma$

where

μ = Mean (or expected) level of activity

σ = Standard deviation of distribution of activity levels

$\bar{x}$ = Actual mean activity level of a sample of n observations

Acceptable area: $(\mu - 2\sigma) < \bar{x} < (\mu + 2\sigma)$ Do not investigate

RULE 3 $LCL = \mu - \dfrac{2\sigma}{\sqrt{n}}$ and $UCL = \mu + \dfrac{2\sigma}{\sqrt{n}}$

where

μ = Mean (or expected) level of activity

σ = Standard deviation of distribution of activity levels

$\bar{x}$ = Actual mean activity level of a sample of n observations

Acceptable area: $\left(\mu - \dfrac{2\sigma}{\sqrt{n}}\right) < \bar{x} < \left(\mu + \dfrac{2\sigma}{\sqrt{n}}\right)$ Do not investigate

To illustrate the differences among the three rules, we use a variation of a problem proposed by Robbins and Jacobs. Suppose the time required to fill a certain type of prescription in a hospital pharmacy is expected to have a probability distribution with $\mu = 24$ minutes and $\sigma = 2.7$ minutes. As a check on the prescription-filling process, the manager of the pharmacy sampled $n = 30$ prescriptions of this type and recorded the time it took to fill each prescription. If the sample mean, $\bar{x}$, falls outside the control limits, the manager will conduct a costly investigation of the prescription-filling process.

a. Suppose the process is out of control, that is, the mean time required to fill the prescription is greater than the expected mean of $\mu = 24$. Assuming the actual mean is $\mu = 26$, describe the sampling distribution of the sample mean, $\bar{x}$.

b. Using the expected mean ($\mu = 24$), calculate LCL and UCL for rule 1 when $p = .10$. (This is a situation in which management believes a time variance of 10%, greater than or less than the mean, is significant enough to warrant an investigation.) Assuming the process is out of control (ie, $\mu = 26$), what is the probability that $\bar{x}$ falls outside the control limits? This can be viewed as the probability that the manager will proceed with an investigation when, in fact, the process is out of control. [*Hint:* Use the sampling distribution from part **a** to calculate the probability.]

c. Using the expected mean ($\mu = 24$), calculate LCL and UCL for rule 2. Assuming the process is out of control (ie, $\mu = 26$), what is the probability that $\bar{x}$ falls outside the control limits?

d. Using the expected mean ($\mu = 24$), calculate LCL and UCL for rule 3. Assuming the process is out of control (ie, $\mu = 26$), what is the probability that $\bar{x}$ falls outside the control limits?

e. Based on the three probabilities computed in parts **b–d**, which decision rule would you recommend? Explain.

REFERENCES

Hollander, M., and Wolfe, D. A. *Nonparametric Statistical Methods*. New York: Wiley, 1973.

McClave, J. T., and Benson, P. G. *A First Course in Business Statistics*, 5th ed. San Francisco: Dellen, 1992.

Mendenhall, W., Wackerly, D., and Scheaffer, R. *Mathematical Statistics with Applications*, 4th ed. Boston: PWS-Kent, 1989.

Snedecor, G. W., and Cochran, W. G. *Statistical Methods*, 7th ed. Ames: Iowa State University Press, 1980.

SAMPLE EXAM QUESTIONS: CHAPTERS 4–5

(1–4)   A daily newspaper operates with two high-speed presses (press 1 and press 2). The manufacturer of these high-speed presses claims that, when operating properly, press 1 and press 2 shut down for repairs on only 1% and 2%, respectively, of all operating days. Also, the presses operate independently—that is, the chance of one press breaking down is in no way influenced by the current operating condition of the other. One operating day is randomly selected and the performance of the presses is observed.

   1. What is the probability that press 1 will be shut down for repairs?
   2. What is the probability that press 2 will operate successfully?
   3. What is the probability that both presses will be shut down for repairs?
   4. Suppose that both presses actually do need to be shut down for repairs during the operating day. What would you infer about the manufacturer's claim?

(5–7)   In a national study, it was discovered that 4 out of every 10 full-time employees claim they participate in their companies' purchasing decisions on a regular basis (*Journal of Advertising Research*, Aug./Sept. 1984). Let x be the number of full-time employees in a sample of $n = 500$ who regularly participate in their companies' purchasing decisions.

   5. What is the mean of x?
   6. What is the standard deviation of x?
   7. Would the value $x = 185$ contradict the statement that 4 out of every 10 employees regularly participate in their firms' buying decisions?

(8–9)   Studies show that the differences between the actual and scheduled arrival times for trains in an underground rapid transit system (URTS) are normally distributed with a mean of 5 minutes and a standard deviation of 11 minutes.

   8. Find the probability that the URTS train will be at least 10 minutes late.
   9. The management of the URTS wants to adjust the scheduled arrival times of the trains so that the system appears to be operating more efficiently. How many minutes should they add to the current scheduled time of arrival so that only 10% of the trains would arrive late?

(10–12)   The manufacturer of a new instant-picture camera claims that its product has "the world's fastest-developing color film by far." Extensive laboratory testing has shown that the relative frequency distribution for the time it takes the new instant camera to begin to reveal the image after shooting has a mean of 9.8 seconds and a standard deviation of .55 second. Suppose 50 of these cameras are randomly selected from the production line and tested. The time until the image is first revealed, x, is recorded for each camera.

   10. Describe the sampling distribution of $\bar{x}$, the mean time it takes the sample of 50 cameras to begin to reveal the image.
   11. Find $P(\bar{x} < 9.55)$.

12. If the mean and standard deviation of the population relative frequency distribution for the times until the cameras begin to reveal the image are correct, would you expect to observe a value of $\bar{x}$ less than 9.55 seconds?

(13–16) The manager of the County Property Appraisers Office wants to assess the collective ability of the county's real-estate appraisers. The manager collected a random sample of 20 properties and recorded the ratio of sale price to appraised value for each. Summary statistics for the data are:

$$\bar{x} = 1.506 \qquad s = .462$$

13. Construct a 90% confidence interval for the mean ratio of sale price to appraised value for the county's properties.
14. Give both a practical and theoretical interpretation of the interval.
15. Give a situation when this interval would be invalid.
16. How could the manager decrease the width of the interval?

(17–20) Recently, Fiat Motors of North America has been advertising its new 5 year, 50,000 mile warranty. The extended warranty covers the engine, transmission, and drivetrain of all new Fiat-made cars for up to 5 years or 50,000 miles, whichever comes first. However, one Fiat dealer believes the 5 year portion of the warranty is unnecessary since the mean number of miles driven by Fiat owners in 5 years exceeds 50,000 miles. A sample of 52 new Fiat owners produced the following summary statistics on number of miles driven after 5 years:

$$\bar{x} = 51,117 \qquad s = 1,866$$

17. Test the dealer's claim using $\alpha = .01$.
18. Describe a Type I error and a Type II error in terms of the problem.
19. Calculate the power of the test when the true mean is 56,000 miles.
20. Calculate the p-value of the test and interpret the result.

(21–25) Transportation researchers investigated the frequency of safety seat-belt usage among automobile owners. Each in a sample of 387 drivers was classified according to frequency of use (always, frequently, infrequently, and never) and state of residence (states with mandatory safety seat-belt laws, states with pending mandatory laws, and states without mandatory laws). The results are shown in the table:

STATE OF RESIDENCE	SEAT-BELT USAGE				
	Always	Frequently	Infrequently	Never	Totals
Mandatory Seat-Belt Law	67	24	18	19	128
Pending Mandatory Seat-Belt Law	27	20	23	8	78
No Mandatory Seat-Belt Law	63	42	38	38	181
Totals	157	86	79	65	387

Source: Lieb, R. C., Wiseman, F., and Moore, T. E. "Automobile Safety Programs: The Public Viewpoint." *Transportation Journal,* Vol. 25, No. 4, Summer 1986, p. 25. Reprinted with express permission of the publisher, the American Society of Transportation and Logistics, Inc., for educational purposes only.

Suppose we select one of the 387 drivers in the study.

21. Find the probability that the driver uses safety seat belts infrequently.
22. Find the probability that the driver resides in a state with a pending mandatory seat-belt law and never uses seat belts.
23. Find the probability that the driver either resides in a state with a mandatory seat-belt law or always uses seat belts.
24. Given that the driver never uses seat belts, what is the probability that the driver resides in a state with no mandatory seat-belt law?
25. Given that the driver resides in a state with a pending mandatory seat-belt law, what is the probability that the driver frequently uses seat belts?

CHAPTER 6

ONE-SAMPLE AND TWO-SAMPLE INFERENTIAL METHODS FOR QUANTITATIVE DATA: MEANS

CONTENTS

According to a researcher, a dose of the heart drug propranolol 1 hour before taking the Scholastic Aptitude Test (SAT) will lead to an improved performance. Suppose you wanted to determine whether the drug does, in fact, increase the mean SAT score. In this chapter we apply the two inferential techniques of Chapter 5—confidence intervals and tests of hypothesis—to population means of quantitative data. The results of the SAT–heart drug study are presented and discussed in the chapter case study.

6.1 Recall that data can be classified as quantitative or qualitative. In this chapter we present methods for making inferences about means of quantitative data sets. Specifically, we will consider two population parameters: the mean μ of a single population (Section 6.2), and $\mu_1 - \mu_2$, the difference between the means of two populations (Sections 6.3 and 6.4).

In Section 5.1 we learned that the best estimator of μ is $\bar{x}$, the mean of the sample. Likewise, the best estimator of $\mu_1 - \mu_2$ is $\bar{x}_1 - \bar{x}_2$, the difference between the sample means. For large samples, both $\bar{x}$ and $\bar{x}_1 - \bar{x}_2$ have sampling distributions that are approximately normal. Consequently, large-sample confidence intervals and test statistics for μ and $\mu_1 - \mu_2$ have the general forms presented in Sections 5.2 and 5.3:

Confidence interval: Estimator $\pm$ ($z_{\alpha/2}$)Standard error of estimator

Test statistic: $z = \dfrac{\text{Estimator} - \text{Hypothesized value in } H_0}{\text{Standard error of estimator}}$

The estimators and standard errors of the estimators for these two parameters are listed in Table 6.1.

TABLE 6.1
Estimators and Standard Errors for Population Means

PARAMETER	ESTIMATOR	STANDARD ERROR	ESTIMATED STANDARD ERROR
μ	$\bar{x}$	$\sigma/\sqrt{n}$	$s/\sqrt{n}$
$\mu_1 - \mu_2$	$\bar{x}_1 - \bar{x}_2$	$\sqrt{\dfrac{\sigma_1^2}{n_1} + \dfrac{\sigma_2^2}{n_2}}$	$\sqrt{\dfrac{s_1^2}{n_1} + \dfrac{s_2^2}{n_2}}$

To construct a large-sample confidence interval or test statistic for means, first determine the parameter of interest (either μ or $\mu_1 - \mu_2$). Then substitute the appropriate estimator and standard error into the general formulas given above.

Small-sample inferences utilize the same general formula, except that we substitute the t statistic for the z statistic. Also, the population variances are usually unknown, so we use the estimated standard errors shown in the last column of Table 6.1. For small samples, the general formulas take the form:

Confidence interval: Estimator $\pm$ ($t_{\alpha/2}$)Estimated standard error of estimator

Test statistic: $t = \dfrac{\text{Estimator} - \text{Hypothesized value in } H_0}{\text{Estimated standard error of estimator}}$

Certain assumptions also must be satisfied in order to properly apply these small-sample methods. Details are provided in the relevant sections of this chapter.

INFERENCES ABOUT A SINGLE POPULATION MEAN

6.2 Confidence intervals and tests of hypothesis about μ based on the z and t distributions were first presented in Chapter 5. A summary of these parametric techniques is provided in the box. Note that these formulas are obtained by substituting the estimator, $\bar{x}$, standard error, $\sigma/\sqrt{n}$, and estimated standard error, $s/\sqrt{n}$, into the general formulas provided in Section 6.1.

PARAMETRIC METHODS

PARAMETRIC METHODS FOR INFERENCES ABOUT A POPULATION MEAN, μ

CONFIDENCE INTERVALS

LARGE SAMPLE

$$\bar{x} \pm z_{\alpha/2}\left(\frac{\sigma}{\sqrt{n}}\right)$$

Note: When the value of σ is unknown (as will usually be the case), use s to approximate σ.

SMALL SAMPLE

$$\bar{x} \pm t_{\alpha/2}\left(\frac{s}{\sqrt{n}}\right)$$

where the distribution of t is based on $(n - 1)$ degrees of freedom.

Assumption: Sampled population is approximately normal.

TESTS OF HYPOTHESIS

ONE-TAILED TEST

H_0: $\mu = \mu_0$
H_a: $\mu < \mu_0$
      [or H_a: $\mu > \mu_0$]

TWO-TAILED TEST

H_0: $\mu = \mu_0$
H_a: $\mu \neq \mu_0$

LARGE SAMPLE

Test statistic: $z_c = \dfrac{\bar{x} - \mu_0}{\sigma/\sqrt{n}}$

Rejection region: $z_c < -z_\alpha$
                    [or $z_c > z_\alpha$]

p-Value: $p = P(z < z_c)$
          [or $p = P(z > z_c)$]

Rejection region: $|z_c| > z_{\alpha/2}$

p-Value: $p = 2P(z > |z_c|)$

Note: When the value of σ is unknown (as will usually be the case), use s to approximate σ.

(continued)

SMALL SAMPLE

$$\text{Test statistic:} \quad t_c = \frac{\bar{x} - \mu_0}{s/\sqrt{n}}$$

Rejection region: $t_c < -t_\alpha$
                   [or $t_c > t_\alpha$]

Rejection region: $|t_c| > t_{\alpha/2}$

p-Value: $p = P(t < t_c)$
            [or $p = P(t > t_c)$]

p-Value: $p = 2P(t > |t_c|)$

where the distribution of t is based on $(n - 1)$ degrees of freedom.

Assumption: Sampled population is approximately normal.

EXAMPLE 6.1   The Geothermal Loop Experimental Facility, located in the Salton Sea in southern California, is a U.S. Department of Energy operation for studying the feasibility of generating electricity from the hot brines of the Salton Sea. Operating experience has shown that the saline water leaves silica scale deposits on metallic plant piping, causing excessive plant outages. Researchers have reported that scaling can be reduced somewhat by adding chemical solutions to the brine.* In one screening experiment, each of five antiscalants was added to an aliquot of brine, and the solutions were filtered. A silicon determination (parts per million of silicon dioxide) was made on each filtered sample after a holding time of 24 hours, with the following results:

229   255   280   203   229

a. Compute $\bar{x}$ and s for the sample.
b. Make an inference about μ, the mean amount of silicon dioxide present in an aliquot of brine treated with antiscalant solutions. [*Note:* $\mu = 300$ is the mean amount of silicon present in an aliquot of brine without antiscalant solutions.]
c. What assumption is required for the procedure of part **b** to be valid?

Solution
a. The data were entered into a computer, and descriptive statistics were generated using MINITAB. The MINITAB printout is shown in Figure 6.1. You can see that the values of the sample mean and standard deviation (shaded) are:

$$\bar{x} = 239.2 \qquad s = 29.3$$

b. Since $\mu = 300$ ppm is the mean amount of silicon present in an aliquot of brine *without* antiscalants, one useful inference is to determine whether the true mean

---

* Jacobsen, W., Rogers, A., Schoepflin, F., and Henry, P. "Scale and Corrosion Parameters at a Geothermal Loop Experimental Facility." *Journal of Testing and Evaluation*, Vol. 9, No. 2, Mar. 1981, pp. 82–92. Copyright ASTM. Reprinted with permission.

FIGURE 6.1
MINITAB Descriptive Statistics for Example 6.1

	N	MEAN	MEDIAN	TRMEAN	STDEV	SEMEAN
ppm	5	239.2	229.0	239.2	29.3	13.1

	MIN	MAX	Q1	Q3
ppm	203.0	280.0	216.0	267.5

for brine *with* antiscalants differs from 300. This inference can be made by constructing a confidence interval for μ or by testing the hypothesis:

H_0: $\mu = 300$

H_a: $\mu \neq 300$

Since the sample is small, both the test and the confidence interval are based on the t statistic. For example, the test statistic is computed as follows:

$$t = \frac{\bar{x} - \mu_0}{s/\sqrt{n}} = \frac{239.2 - 300}{29.3/\sqrt{5}} = -4.64$$

This value is shaded on the MINITAB printout of the test results shown in Figure 6.2. In addition, the printout gives the observed significance level (*p*-value) for a two-tailed test. Note that this value is .0097. This implies that, for an α value of .01 or larger, we can reject H_0. That is, there is sufficient evidence (at $\alpha \geq .01$) to say that the mean amount of silicon dioxide present in the treated brine solution differs from 300 ppm.

FIGURE 6.2
MINITAB Printout: Test and Confidence Interval

TEST OF MU = 300.000 VS MU N.E. 300.000

	N	MEAN	STDEV	SE MEAN	T	P VALUE
ppm	5	239.200	29.295	13.101	-4.64	0.0097

	N	MEAN	STDEV	SE MEAN	99.0 PERCENT C.I.	
ppm	5	239.2	29.3	13.1	(178.9,	299.5)

The same conclusion can be obtained by interpreting a 99% confidence interval for μ, shaded in the MINITAB printout shown in Figure 6.2. The interval ranges from 178.9 to 299.5. Since all values are less than 300, we can be 99% confident that μ falls below 300.

c. The procedure requires the assumption that the relative frequency distribution of the silicon amounts present in all aliquots of brine treated with antiscalant solutions is approximately normal.

NONPARAMETRIC METHODS

Suppose the researchers in Example 6.1 know from experience that the silicon measurements come from a nonnormal population. Then the t test is not valid, and we must resort to a nonparametric procedure. The simplest nonparametric technique to apply in this situation is the **sign test**. The sign test is specifically designed for testing hypotheses about the median of any continuous population. Like the mean, the median measures, or locates, the center of the distribution; consequently, the sign test is sometimes referred to as a **test for location**.

Consider a population with unknown population median η, and suppose we want to test the null hypothesis H_0: $\eta = 100$ against the one-sided alternative H_a: $\eta > 100$. We know that the median is a number such that half the area under the probability distribution lies to the left of η and half lies to the right (see Figure 6.3). Therefore, the probability that an x-value selected from the population is larger than η is .5, that is, $P(x_i > \eta) = .5$. If, in fact, the null hypothesis is true, then we would expect to observe approximately half the sample x-values greater than $\eta = 100$.

FIGURE 6.3

Location of the Population Median, η

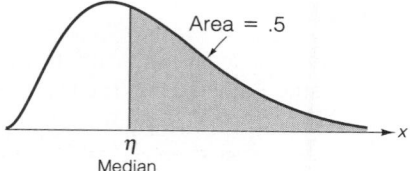

The sign test utilizes the test statistic, S, where

$$S = \text{Number of sample observations } (x\text{'s}) \text{ that exceed } 100$$

Notice that S depends only on the *sign* (positive or negative) of the difference between each sample value x_i and 100. That is, we are simply counting the number of positive (+) signs among the sample differences $(x_i - 100)$. If S is "too large" (ie, if we observe an unusual number of x_i's exceeding 100), then we will reject H_0 in favor of the alternative H_a: $\eta > 100$.

The p-value for the sign test is derived as follows: Let each sample difference $(x_i - 100)$ denote the outcome of a single trial in an experiment consisting of n identical trials. If we call a positive difference a success and a negative difference a failure, then S is the number of successes in n trials. Under H_0 the probability of observing a success on any one trial is

$$\pi = P(\text{Success}) = P(x_i - 100 > 0)$$
$$= P(x_i > 100)$$
$$= .5$$

Since the trials are independent, the properties of a binomial experiment, listed in Section 4.4, are satisfied. Therefore, S has a binomial distribution with parameters n and $\pi = .5$. We can use this fact to calculate the p-value of the sign test, as illlustrated in the following example.

EXAMPLE 6.2   The Environmental Protection Agency (EPA) sets certain pollution guidelines for major industries. The EPA criterion for a particular company that discharges waste into a nearby river is that the median amount of pollution in water samples collected from the river may not exceed 5 parts per million (ppm). Responding to numerous complaints, the EPA takes 10 water samples from the river at the discharge point and measures the pollution level in each sample. The results (in ppm) are as follows:

| 5.1 | 4.3 | 5.3 | 6.2 | 5.6 | 4.7 | 8.4 | 5.9 | 6.8 | 3.0 |

Do the data provide sufficient evidence to indicate that the median pollution level in water discharged at the plant exceeds 5 ppm? Test using $\alpha = .05$.

Solution   We want to test

$$H_0: \quad \eta = 5$$
$$H_a: \quad \eta > 5$$

using the sign test. The test statistic is

$$S = \text{Number of sample observations that exceed } 5$$
$$= 7$$

where S has a binomial distribution with parameters $n = 10$ and $\pi = .5$.

We know that the observed significance level (p-value) of the test is the probability that we observe a value of the test statistic S that is at least as contradictory to the null hypothesis as the computed value. For this one-sided case, the p-value is the probability that we observe a value of S greater than or equal to 7. We find the probability using the binomial table for $n = 10$ and $\pi = .5$ in Table 1, Appendix A:

$$p\text{-Value} = P(S \geq 7) = 1 - P(S \leq 6)$$
$$= 1 - .8281$$
$$= .1719$$

The p-value is also shown (shaded) in the MINITAB printout of the analysis shown in Figure 6.4. Since $p = .1719$ is larger than $\alpha = .05$, we cannot reject the null hypothesis. That is, there is insufficient evidence to indicate that the median pollution level of water discharged from the plant exceeds 5 ppm.

FIGURE 6.4
MINITAB Printout for Example 6.2

```
SIGN TEST OF MEDIAN = 5.000 VERSUS  G.T.   5.000

            N   BELOW  EQUAL  ABOVE  P-VALUE   MEDIAN
pollevel   10     3      0      7    0.1719    5.450
```

A summary of the nonparametric sign test for one-sided and two-sided alternatives is provided in the box. For a two-tailed test, you may calculate the test statistic as either

$$S_1 = \text{Number of sample observations greater than } \eta_0$$
$$= \text{Number of successes in } n \text{ trials}$$

or

$$S_2 = \text{Number of sample observations less than } \eta_0$$
$$= \text{Number of failures in } n \text{ trials}$$

Note that $S_1 + S_2 = n$; therefore, $S_2 = n - S_1$. In either case, the p-value of the test is double the corresponding one-sided p-value.

PROBLEMS

6.1   When a university professor attempts to publish a research article in a professional journal, the manuscript goes through a rigorous review process. Usually, anywhere from three to five reviewers read and critique the article, then pass judgment on whether or not the article should be published. Recently, a study was undertaken to seek information on how reviewers for research journals pursue their activities (*Academy of Management Journal*, Mar. 1989). A sample of 73 reviewers for the Academy of Management's *Journal* (*AMJ*) and *Review* (*AMR*) were asked how many hours they spent per paper for a typical complete review process. The sample mean and standard deviation were computed to be $\bar{x} = 5.4$ hours and $s = 3.6$ hours.

   a. Find a point estimate for μ, the true mean number of hours spent by a reviewer in conducting a complete review of a paper submitted to *AMJ* or *AMR*.
   b. Compute a 99% confidence interval for μ.
   c. Interpret the interval from part **b**.

6.2   Many Vietnam veterans have dangerously high levels of the dioxin 2,3,7,8-TCDD in blood and fat tissue as a result of their exposure to the defoliant Agent Orange. A study published in *Chemosphere* (Vol. 20, 1990) reported on the TCDD levels of 20 Massachusetts Vietnam veterans who were possibly exposed to Agent Orange. The amounts of TCDD (measured in parts per trillion) in blood plasma drawn from each veteran are shown in the table.

VETERAN	TCDD LEVELS IN PLASMA	VETERAN	TCDD LEVELS IN PLASMA
1	2.5	11	6.9
2	3.1	12	3.3
3	2.1	13	4.6
4	3.5	14	1.6
5	3.1	15	7.2
6	1.8	16	1.8
7	6.0	17	20.0
8	3.0	18	2.0
9	36.0	19	2.5
10	4.7	20	4.1

Source: Schecter, A., et al. "Partitioning of 2,3,7,8-Chlorinated Dibenzo-*p*-dioxins and Dibenzofurans Between Adipose Tissue and Plasma Lipid of 20 Massachusetts Vietnam Veterans." *Chemosphere*, Vol. 20, Nos. 7–9, 1990, pp. 954–955 (Table I).

    a. Construct a 90% confidence interval for the true mean TCDD level in plasma of all Vietnam veterans exposed to Agent Orange.

    b. Interpret the interval from part **a**.

    c. What assumption is required for the interval estimation procedure to be valid?

    d. Use one of the methods of Section 4.5 to determine whether the assumption in part **c** is approximately satisfied.

6.3 Refer to Problem 5.16 and the random sample of 50 return-to-pay ratios of CEOs selected from *Business Week*'s 1992 "Executive Compensation Scoreboard." The data are reproduced here for convenience. The SAS printout for testing the null hypothesis that the true mean return-to-pay ratio of CEOs is equal to .10 is displayed below. Interpret the results.

0.03	0.021	0.033	0.086	0.041	0.062	0.029	0.072	0.005	0.047
0.051	0.206	0.005	0.025	0.112	0.037	0.042	0.023	0.026	0.086
0.049	0.122	0.091	0.033	0.029	0.032	0.036	0.02	0.032	0.005
0.01	0.049	0.048	0.081	0.051	0.122	0.019	0.047	0.031	0.031
0.02	0.025	0.206	0.091	0.14	0.017	0.026	0.02	0.018	0.02

Source: *Business Week*, Apr. 26, 1993. Reprinted from Apr. 26, 1993 issue of *Business Week* by special permission, copyright © 1993 by McGraw-Hill, Inc. Used with permission.

```
Analysis Variable : RATIO_01 (Ratio minus .1)

N Obs        Mean        Std Dev      Std Error         T    Prob>|T|
-----------------------------------------------------------------------
  50       -0.0488000    0.0452977    0.0064061    -7.6177919   0.0001
-----------------------------------------------------------------------
```

6.4 Refer to the *Risk Management* study on victims who attempted to evacuate fires at compartmented fire-resistive buildings, described in Problem 3.1 (p. 61). The data are repeated here for convenience. The table at the top of the next page gives the number of victims who died attempting to evacuate for a sample of 14 fires.

    a. In Problem 3.1, you constructed a dot plot for the data. Does it appear that the sample data are from a normally distributed population?

    b. Based on your answer to part **a**, why is a nonparametric test for location preferred over a parametric test? Explain.

    c. Conduct a test to determine whether the median number of victims who attempt to evacuate fires at compartmented fire-resistive buildings differs from 6. Test using $\alpha = .01$.

Data for Problem 6.4

FIRE	NUMBER OF VICTIMS
Las Vegas Hilton (Las Vegas)	5
Inn on the Park (Toronto)	5
Westchase Hilton (Houston)	8
Holiday Inn (Cambridge, Ohio)	10
Conrad Hilton (Chicago)	4
Providence College (Providence)	8
Baptist Towers (Atlanta)	7
Howard Johnson (New Orleans)	5
Cornell University (Ithaca, New York)	9
Westport Central Apartments (Kansas City, Missouri)	4
Orrington Hotel (Evanston, Illinois)	0
Hartford Hospital (Hartford, Connecticut)	16
Milford Plaza (New York)	0
MGM Grand (Las Vegas)	36

Source: Macdonald, J. N. "Is Evacuation a Fatal Flaw in Fire Fighting Philosophy?" *Risk Management,* Vol. 33, No. 2, Feb. 1986, p. 37.

6.5 Refer to the data given in Problem 3.14 (p. 76) on student-loan default rates for 66 Florida colleges. A MINITAB printout showing descriptive statistics for the sample data and a 95% confidence interval for the mean student-loan default rate is displayed below.

	N	MEAN	STDEV	SE MEAN	95.0 PERCENT C.I.
defrate	66	14.68	14.14	1.74	(11.20, 18.16)

a. Use the descriptive statistics in the MINITAB printout to verify the 95% confidence interval shown in the printout.
b. Interpret the interval.
c. How could you reduce the width of the confidence interval? Are there any drawbacks to reducing the interval width? Explain.
d. Would you feel comfortable using the 95% confidence interval to make an inference about the true mean student-loan default rate of all U.S. colleges? Explain.

6.6 Farm and power equipment dealers are typically dependent on a primary supplier organization for many of their business needs. These suppliers often demand control over many of the dealers' decisions. To determine the degree to which dealers are dependent on suppliers, a national survey of 226 farm and power equipment dealers was conducted. The study revealed the following summary statistics on the total number of suppliers engaged by the dealers:

$$\bar{x} = 3.12 \qquad s = 1.91$$

(*Academy of Management Journal,* Mar. 1989). Use this information to test the hypothesis that the true mean number of suppliers engaged by farm and power equipment dealers exceeds 2. Compute the p-value of the test and interpret the result.

6.7 Refer to the data on the total 1992 compensations (in thousands of dollars) for the top 20 corporate executives (as determined by *Business Week*) discussed in Problems 3.3 and 3.10. The data are reproduced in the table.

a. Refer to the stem-and-leaf display for the data, which you constructed in Problem 3.10 (p. 68). Based on the graph, would you be willing to assume that the sample data come from a normal population?
b. Test the hypothesis that the median total 1992 compensation of the highest-paid corporate executives in the United States exceeds $15 million. Use $\alpha = .10$.

6.8 Refer to the *U.S. News & World Report* (Apr. 29, 1991) survey of the top 25 business schools given in Problem 3.5 (p. 63). A MINITAB printout showing 95% confidence intervals for the means of the five variables measured in the study (overall score, tuition, GMAT, acceptance rate, and starting salary) is displayed on p. 253.

Data for Problem 6.7

CEO	COMPANY	TOTAL PAY
T. Frist, Jr.	HCA	127,002
S. Weill	Primerica	67,635
C. Lazarus	Toys 'R' Us	64,231
L. Hirsch	U.S. Surgical	62,171
S. Wynn	Mirage Resorts	38,005
A. O'Reilly	H. J. Heinz	36,918
M. Wygod	Medco Containment	30,207
W. Anders	General Dynamics	29,015
R. Richey	Torchmark	26,568
L. Bantle	UST Inc.	24,602
R. Mark	Colgate-Palmolive	22,818
W. Sanders III	Advanced Micro Devices	22,356
J. Welch, Jr.	General Electric	17,970
L. Iacocca	Chrysler	16,908
E. Grisanti	Int'l Flavors	16,475
A. Greenberg	Bear Stearns	15,832
R. Goizueta	Coca-Cola	15,218
W. Bartlett	Multimedia	14,822
C. Mathewson	Int'l Game Tech	14,795
P. Rooney	Wheelabrator Tech	11,216

Source: "Executive Compensation Scoreboard." *Business Week*, Apr. 26, 1993. Reprinted from Apr. 26, 1993 issue of *Business Week* by special permission, copyright © 1993 by McGraw-Hill, Inc. Used with permission.

a. Interpret the confidence intervals shown in the printout.

b. What assumption is required for the confidence intervals to be valid?

c. In Problem 3.11 (p. 69), MINITAB stem-and-leaf displays were given for each variable. Use this information to comment on the validity of the assumption made in part **b**.

	N	MEAN	STDEV	SE MEAN	95.0 PERCENT C.I.	
Score	25	80.89	9.25	1.85	(77.07,	84.71)
Tuition	25	13290.6	4384.4	876.9	(11480.3,	15100.8)
GMAT	25	626.52	19.16	3.83	(618.61,	634.43)
AccRate	25	25.16	7.76	1.55	(21.96,	28.36)
Salary	25	51181.5	5615.1	1123.0	(48863.2,	53499.9)

6.9 *Scram* is the term used by nuclear engineers to describe a rapid emergency shutdown of a nuclear reactor. The nuclear industry has made a concerted effort to reduce significantly the number of unplanned scrams each year. The number of unplanned scrams at each of a random sample of 20 nuclear reactor units in a recent year are given below:

1	8	0	3	3	9	1	2	4	5
4	3	1	2	7	10	2	6	3	0

Test the hypothesis (at $\alpha = .10$) that the median number of unplanned scrams at nuclear reactor plants is less than 5. Use the SPSS printout shown at the top of the next page to make your conclusion.

```
- - - - - Sign Test

    SCRAMS
with MED


    Cases

    5   - Diffs (MED Lt SCRAMS)
    14  + Diffs (MED Gt SCRAMS)        (Binomial)
    1     Ties                          2-tailed P =      .0636
    --
    20    Total
```

COMPARING TWO POPULATION MEANS: INDEPENDENT SAMPLES

6.3 We now consider how to use the information in two samples to infer the nature of the difference between two population means ($\mu_1 - \mu_2$). For example, we may want to compare the mean starting salaries for bachelor's degree graduates of the University of Florida in the colleges of Engineering and Journalism, or the mean gasoline consumptions that may be expected this year for drivers in two areas of the country, or the mean sales of Pepsi and Coke.

PARAMETRIC METHODS

The parametric techniques to be presented are a straightforward extension of those used for a single population mean, and are based on the assumption that we have selected *independent* random samples from the two populations.

As noted in Section 6.1, we use the difference between the sample means $(\bar{x}_1 - \bar{x}_2)$ as our point estimate of the differences between the population means $(\mu_1 - \mu_2)$. The properties of the point estimate $(\bar{x}_1 - \bar{x}_2)$ are summarized by its sampling distribution, shown in the box and illustrated in Figure 6.5.

FIGURE 6.5
Sampling Distribution of $(\bar{x}_1 - \bar{x}_2)$

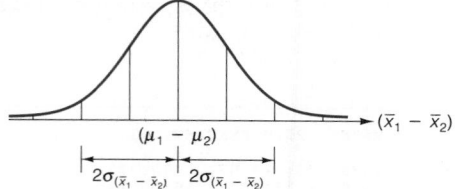

SAMPLING DISTRIBUTION OF $(\bar{x}_1 - \bar{x}_2)$

For sufficiently large sample sizes, the sampling distribution of $(\bar{x}_1 - \bar{x}_2)$, based on independent random samples from two populations, is approximately normal with

Mean: $\mu_{(\bar{x}_1 - \bar{x}_2)} = (\mu_1 - \mu_2)$

Standard error: $\sigma_{(\bar{x}_1 - \bar{x}_2)} = \sqrt{\dfrac{\sigma_1^2}{n_1} + \dfrac{\sigma_2^2}{n_2}}$

where σ_1^2 and σ_2^2 are the variances of the two populations from which the samples were selected.

As was the case with large-sample estimation of a single population mean, the requirement of large sample sizes enables us to apply the Central Limit Theorem to obtain the sampling distribution of $(\bar{x}_1 - \bar{x}_2)$; it also justifies the use of s_1^2 and s_2^2 as approximations to the respective population variances, σ_1^2 and σ_2^2. Substituting the estimator, $\bar{x}_1 - \bar{x}_2$, and the standard error, $\sqrt{\sigma_1^2/n_1 + \sigma_2^2/n_2}$, into the general large-sample formulas of Section 6.1, we obtain the following working formulas:

LARGE-SAMPLE PARAMETRIC INFERENCES FOR $(\mu_1 - \mu_2)$

CONFIDENCE INTERVAL

$$(\bar{x}_1 - \bar{x}_2) \pm z_{\alpha/2}\sigma_{(\bar{x}_1 - \bar{x}_2)} = (\bar{x}_1 - \bar{x}_2) \pm z_{\alpha/2}\sqrt{\frac{\sigma_1^2}{n_1} + \frac{\sigma_2^2}{n_2}}$$

$$\approx (\bar{x}_1 - \bar{x}_2) \pm z_{\alpha/2}\sqrt{\frac{s_1^2}{n_1} + \frac{s_2^2}{n_2}}$$

Note: We have used the sample variances s_1^2 and s_2^2 as approximations to the corresponding population parameters.

TESTS OF HYPOTHESES

ONE-TAILED TEST   **TWO-TAILED TEST**

H_0: $(\mu_1 - \mu_2) = D_0$ H_0: $(\mu_1 - \mu_2) = D_0$

H_a: $(\mu_1 - \mu_2) > D_0$ H_a: $(\mu_1 - \mu_2) \neq D_0$

[or H_a: $(\mu_1 - \mu_2) < D_0$]

$$\text{Test statistic:} \quad z = \frac{(\bar{x}_1 - \bar{x}_2) - D_0}{\sigma_{(\bar{x}_1 - \bar{x}_2)}} \approx \frac{(\bar{x}_1 - \bar{x}_2) - D_0}{\sqrt{\dfrac{s_1^2}{n_1} + \dfrac{s_2^2}{n_2}}}$$

Rejection region: $z > z_\alpha$ *Rejection region:* $|z| > z_{\alpha/2}$

[or $z < -z_\alpha$]

Note: D_0 is our symbol for the particular numerical value specified for $(\mu_1 - \mu_2)$ in the null hypothesis. In many practical applications, we wish to hypothesize that there is no difference between the population means; in such cases, $D_0 = 0$.

Assumption: The two random samples are selected in an independent manner from the target populations. That is, the choice of elements in one sample does not affect, and is not affected by, the choice of elements in the other sample.

EXAMPLE 6.3 The personnel manager for a large steel company suspects there is a difference between the mean amounts of work time lost due to sickness for blue-collar and white-collar workers at the plant. She randomly sampled the records of

TABLE 6.2

Comparison of Lost Sick Days

	BLUE-COLLAR	WHITE-COLLAR
Sample size	$n_1 = 45$	$n_2 = 38$
Sample mean	$\bar{x}_1 = 10.76$	$\bar{x}_2 = 7.95$
Sample standard deviation	$s_1 = 11.79$	$s_2 = 5.72$

45 blue-collar workers and 38 white-collar workers and recorded the number of days lost due to sickness within the past year. Summary statistics were computed, with the results shown in Table 6.2. Estimate $(\mu_1 - \mu_2)$, the difference between the population mean times lost to sickness for blue-collar and white-collar workers at the steel company last year, using a 90% confidence interval. Interpret the result.

Solution The general form of a large-sample 90% confidence interval for $(\mu_1 - \mu_2)$ is

$$(\bar{x}_1 - \bar{x}_2) \pm z_{.05}\sqrt{\frac{\sigma_1^2}{n_1} + \frac{\sigma_2^2}{n_2}}$$

Substitution of the sample variances, s_1^2 and s_2^2, for the corresponding population values, σ_1^2 and σ_2^2, with $z_{.05} = 1.645$ and the statistics provided in Table 6.2 yields the 90% confidence interval

$$(10.76 - 7.95) \pm 1.645\sqrt{\frac{(11.79)^2}{45} + \frac{(5.72)^2}{38}} = 2.81 \pm 3.27 \quad \text{or} \ (-.46, 6.08)$$

Thus, we conclude that the interval from $-.46$ to 6.08 contains $(\mu_1 - \mu_2)$, the difference between the mean days lost to sickness for the two groups of workers, with 90% confidence. In other words, we estimate (with 90% confidence) that μ_2, the mean days lost to sickness for white-collar workers, could be larger than μ_1, the mean days lost to sickness for blue-collar workers, by as much as .46, or it could be less than μ_1 by as much as 6.08. Since the interval contains the value 0, we are unable to conclude that there is a real difference between the mean number of sick days lost by the two groups. If such a difference exists, we would have to increase the sample sizes to be able to detect it. This would reduce the width of the confidence interval and provide more information about the phenomenon under investigation.

EXAMPLE 6.4 Refer to Example 6.3. Use a statistical test of hypothesis to analyze the data in Table 6.2. Test using $\alpha = .10$.

Solution Since the personnel manager suspects there is a difference between the mean amounts of work time lost due to sickness for the two groups of workers, she wants to test

$H_0: \ \mu_1 - \mu_2 = 0$

$H_a: \ \mu_1 - \mu_2 \neq 0$

FIGURE 6.6
SAS Printout

```
                          TTEST PROCEDURE
Variable: DAYS

SAMPLE          N                Mean          Std Dev        Std Error
-----------------------------------------------------------------------
BlueColl        45         10.75555556     11.79398066       1.75814283
WhitColl        38          7.94736842      5.72310334       0.92840996

Variances       T         DF     Prob>|T|
-----------------------------------------
Unequal       1.4124     65.9     0.1625
Equal         1.3397     81.0     0.1841
```

The raw data (not shown in Table 6.2) are entered into the computer and analyzed using SAS. From the printout in Figure 6.6, we see that the value of the test statistic (for the unequal variances case) is $t = 1.4124$, and the two-tailed p-value of the test is $p = .1625$. [*Note:* SAS uses the t distribution rather than the z distribution to compute the p-value of the test. This is because the true population variances, σ_1^2 and σ_2^2, are unknown. However, we know that for large samples, the t and z distributions are nearly equivalent.] Since this large p-value exceeds $\alpha = .10$, there is insufficient evidence to reject H_0. That is, we are unable to conclude that a difference between the two population means exists. Note that this conclusion is identical to that derived from the confidence interval in Example 6.3.

Examples 6.3 and 6.4 illustrate an important point. A confidence interval for $(\mu_1 - \mu_2)$ and a two-tailed test of $H_0: (\mu_1 - \mu_2) = 0$ will lead to the same result if the value of α is the same for both. If all we want to know is whether the two population means differ, there is no advantage to using either method. If a difference is detected, however, the confidence interval provides some additional information—an estimate of the magnitude of the difference. Consequently, confidence intervals are preferred over tests when the alternative is nondirectional (ie, two-tailed).

When estimating or testing the difference between two population means, based on small samples from each population, we must make specific assumptions about the relative frequency distributions of the two populations, as indicated in the box.

ASSUMPTIONS REQUIRED FOR SMALL-SAMPLE INFERENCES ABOUT $(\mu_1 - \mu_2)$

1. Both of the populations from which the samples are selected have relative frequency distributions that are approximately normal.
2. The variances σ_1^2 and σ_2^2 of the two populations are equal.
3. The random samples are selected in an independent manner from the two populations.

Figure 6.7 illustrates the form of the population distributions implied by assumptions 1 and 2. Observe that both populations have relative frequency distributions

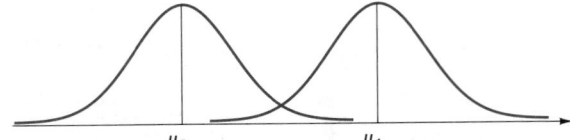

that are approximately normal. Although the means of the two populations may differ, we require the variances σ_1^2 and σ_2^2, which measure the spread of the two distributions, to be equal. When these assumptions are satisfied, we employ the Student's t distribution to construct a confidence interval and test $(\mu_1 - \mu_2)$, based on small samples from the respective populations. Since we assume that the two populations have equal variances (ie, $\sigma_1^2 = \sigma_2^2 = \sigma^2$), we construct an estimate of σ^2 based on the information contained in *both* samples. This **pooled estimate**, denoted by s_p^2, is a weighted average of the two sample estimates, s_1^2 and s_2^2, where the weights are the sample sizes n_1 and n_2. The formula for computing s_p^2 is shown in the box on the next page.

EXAMPLE 6.5 A key aspect of organizational buying is negotiation. S. W. Clopton investigated several issues pertaining to buyer–seller negotiations (*Journal of Marketing Research*, Feb. 1984). One aspect of the analysis involved a comparison of two types of bargaining strategies—competitive bargaining and coordinative bargaining. A *competitive strategy* is characterized by inflexible behavior aimed at forcing concessions, while a *coordinative strategy* involves a problem-solving orientation to negotiations with a high degree of trust and cooperation. A sample of organizational buyers were recruited to participate in a particular negotiation experiment. In one negotiation setting where the maximum profit was fixed, eight buyers used the competitive bargaining strategy and eight buyers used the coordinative bargaining strategy. The individual savings for the two groups of buyers are provided in Table 6.3. In theory, the mean buyer savings for the competitive strategy will be less than the corresponding mean for the coordinative strategy. Test the theory using $\alpha = .025$.

TABLE 6.3
Data for Example 6.5

COMPETITIVE BARGAINING	COORDINATIVE BARGAINING
$1,857	$1,544
1,700	2,640
1,829	1,645
2,644	2,275
1,566	2,137
663	2,327
1,712	2,152
1,679	2,130

Source: Clopton, S. W. "Seller and Buying Firm Factors Affecting Industrial Buyers' Negotiation Behavior and Outcomes." *Journal of Marketing*, Feb. 1984, pp. 39–53, published by the American Marketing Association.

SMALL-SAMPLE PARAMETRIC INFERENCES FOR $(\mu_1 - \mu_2)$

CONFIDENCE INTERVAL

$$(\bar{x}_1 - \bar{x}_2) \pm t_{\alpha/2} \sqrt{\frac{s_p^2}{n_1} + \frac{s_p^2}{n_2}}$$

where

$$s_p^2 = \frac{(n_1 - 1)s_1^2 + (n_2 - 1)s_2^2}{n_1 + n_2 - 2}$$

and the value of $t_{\alpha/2}$ is based on $(n_1 - 1) + (n_2 - 1)$ degrees of freedom.

TESTS OF HYPOTHESES

ONE-TAILED TEST	TWO-TAILED TEST

H_0: $(\mu_1 - \mu_2) = D_0$ $\qquad\qquad\qquad$ H_0: $(\mu_1 - \mu_2) = D_0$

H_a: $(\mu_1 - \mu_2) > D_0$ $\qquad\qquad\qquad$ H_a: $(\mu_1 - \mu_2) \neq D_0$

[or H_a: $(\mu_1 - \mu_2) < D_0$]

$$\text{Test statistic:}\quad t = \frac{(\bar{x}_1 - \bar{x}_2) - D_0}{\sqrt{\frac{s_p^2}{n_1} + \frac{s_p^2}{n_2}}}$$

Rejection region: $t > t_\alpha$ $\qquad\qquad\qquad$ Rejection region: $|t| > t_{\alpha/2}$

[or $t < -t_\alpha$]

where

$$s_p^2 = \frac{(n_1 - 1)s_1^2 + (n_2 - 1)s_2^2}{n_1 + n_2 - 2}$$

and the distribution of t is based on $(n_1 - 1) + (n_2 - 1)$ degrees of freedom.

Assumption: See previous box.

Solution   We want to test the following hypotheses:

H_0: $(\mu_1 - \mu_2) = 0$ No difference in mean buyer savings

H_a: $(\mu_1 - \mu_2) < 0$ The mean buyer savings for competitive strategy is less than the mean for coordinative strategy

where μ_1 and μ_2 are the true mean savings of buyers using the competitive and coordinative bargaining strategies, respectively. Since the samples selected for the study are small ($n_1 = n_2 = 8$), the following assumptions are required:

1. The populations of buyer savings under the competitive and coordinative strategies both have approximately normal distributions.

---

2. The variances of the populations of buyer savings for the two bargaining strategies are equal.
3. The samples were independently and randomly selected.

If these three assumptions are valid, the test statistic will have a t distribution with $(n_1 - 1) + (n_2 - 1) = 7 + 7 = 14$ degrees of freedom. With a significance level of $\alpha = .025$, the rejection region is given by

$$t < t_{.025} = -2.145 \quad \text{See Figure 6.8}$$

To compute the test statistic, we need to find $\bar{x}_1$, $\bar{x}_2$. and s_p. These summary statistics are given in the MINITAB printout shown in Figure 6.9 as $\bar{x}_1 = 1,706$, $\bar{x}_2 = 2,106$, and $s_p = 457$ (given as POOLED STDEV).

Using the pooled sample standard deviation in the computation of the test statistic, we obtain

$$t = \frac{(\bar{x}_1 - \bar{x}_2) - D_0}{\sqrt{\frac{s_p^2}{n_1} + \frac{s_p^2}{n_2}}} = \frac{(1,706 - 2,106) - 0}{\sqrt{\frac{(457)^2}{8} + \frac{(457)^2}{8}}} = -1.75$$

Since the computed value of t does not fall within the rejection region, we fail to reject the null hypothesis at $\alpha = .025$. There is insufficient evidence (at $\alpha = .025$) that the mean savings of bargainers using the competitive strategy is less than the corresponding mean for bargainers using the coordinative strategy.

The analysis of the data in Table 6.3 could be performed using the t test procedure available in a statistical software package. The MINITAB analysis is shown at the bottom of Figure 6.9. The p-value of the two-tailed test, shaded on the printout, is .10; hence, the p-value of the one-tailed test is

$$p = \frac{.10}{2} = .05$$

Since this one-tailed p-value exceeds $\alpha = .025$, we cannot reject H_0.

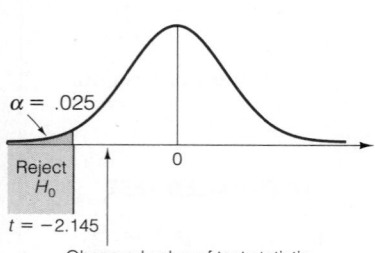

FIGURE 6.8

Rejection Region

$\alpha = .025$

Reject H_0

$t = -2.145$

Observed value of test statistic
$t = -1.75$

FIGURE 6.9

MINITAB Printout for Example 6.5

```
TWOSAMPLE T FOR Compete VS Coordin
             N      MEAN      STDEV    SE MEAN
Compete    8       1706      538      190
Coordin    8       2106      357      126

95 PCT CI FOR MU Compete - MU Coordin: (-890, 90)

TTEST MU Compete = MU Coordin (VS NE): T= -1.75   P=0.10   DF=  14

POOLED STDEV =          457
```

As with the one-sample case, the assumptions required for confidence intervals and tests of $(\mu_1 - \mu_2)$ with small samples do not have to be satisfied exactly for the inferences to be useful in practice. Slight departures from these assumptions do not seriously affect the level of confidence in the procedure. For example, when the variances σ_1^2 and σ_2^2 of the sampled populations are unequal, researchers have found that the formulas for small-sample confidence intervals and tests for $(\mu_1 - \mu_2)$ will still yield valid results in practice, as long as the two populations are normal and the sample sizes are equal, that is, $n_1 = n_2$.

This situation occurs in Example 6.5. The sample standard deviations given in Figure 6.9 are 538 and 357. Thus, it is very likely that the population standard deviations (and variances) are unequal.* However, since $n_1 = n_2 = 8$, the inference derived from the test is still valid if we use s_1^2 and s_2^2 as estimates for the population variances (rather than using the pooled sample variance s_p^2). In the case where $\sigma_1^2 \neq \sigma_2^2$ and $n_1 \neq n_2$, approximate confidence intervals and tests for $(\mu_1 - \mu_2)$ can be performed by modifying the degrees of freedom associated with the t distribution and, again, substituting s_1^2 for σ_1^2 and s_2^2 for σ_2^2. These modifications are shown in the box.

APPROXIMATE SMALL-SAMPLE INFERENCES
FOR $(\mu_1 - \mu_2)$ WHEN $\sigma_1^2 \neq \sigma_2^2$

To obtain approximate confidence intervals and tests for $(\mu_1 - \mu_2)$ when $\sigma_1^2 \neq \sigma_2^2$, make the following modifications to the degrees of freedom ν used in the t distribution and the estimated standard error:

$$n_1 = n_2 = n: \quad \nu = n_1 + n_2 - 2 = 2(n - 1) \qquad \hat{\sigma}_{\bar{x}_1 - \bar{x}_2} = \sqrt{\frac{1}{n}(s_1^2 + s_2^2)}$$

$$n_1 \neq n_2: \quad \nu = \frac{(s_1^2/n_1 + s_2^2/n_2)^2}{\dfrac{(s_1^2/n_1)^2}{n_1 - 1} + \dfrac{(s_2^2/n_2)^2}{n_2 - 1}} \qquad \hat{\sigma}_{\bar{x}_1 - \bar{x}_2} = \sqrt{\frac{s_1^2}{n_1} + \frac{s_2^2}{n_2}}$$

Note: In the case of $n_1 \neq n_2$, the value of ν will not generally be an integer. Round ν down to the nearest integer to use the t table.

Assumptions:

1. Both of the populations from which the samples are selected have relative frequency distributions that are approximately normal.
2. The random samples are selected in an independent manner from the two populations.

NONPARAMETRIC METHODS

Small-sample inferences about $(\mu_1 - \mu_2)$ are also valid if the populations deviate slightly from normality. On the other hand, when the sample populations depart greatly from normality, the t statistic is invalid, and any inferences derived from the procedure are suspect. For the nonnormal case, it is advisable to use a nonparametric statistical method.

---

* A test of hypothesis for comparing two variances is discussed in Chapter 7.

Recall that the mean of a population measures the *location* of the population distribution. Thus, if the data provide sufficient evidence to indicate that μ_1 is larger than μ_2, we envision the distribution for population 1 shifted to the right of population 2. The equivalent nonparametric test is not a test about the difference between population means. Rather, it is a test to detect whether distribution 1 is shifted to the right of distribution 2 or vice versa. The test, based on independent random samples of n_1 and n_2 observations from the respective populations, is known as the **Wilcoxon rank sum test**.

To use the Wilcoxon rank sum test, we first rank all $(n_1 + n_2)$ observations, assigning a rank of 1 to the smallest, 2 to the second smallest, and so on. The **rank sum** is then calculated for each sample. If the two distributions are identical, we would expect the sample rank sums, designated as T_1 and T_2, to be nearly equal. In contrast, if one rank sum, for example T_1, is much larger than the other, T_2, then the data suggest that the distribution for population 1 is shifted to the right of the distribution for population 2. The procedure for conducting a Wilcoxon rank sum test is summarized in the box and illustrated in Example 6.6.

WILCOXON RANK SUM TEST FOR A SHIFT IN POPULATION LOCATIONS: INDEPENDENT RANDOM SAMPLES

Let D_1 and D_2 represent the relative frequency distributions for populations 1 and 2, respectively.

ONE-TAILED TEST	TWO-TAILED TEST
H_0: D_1 and D_2 are identical	H_0: D_1 and D_2 are identical
H_a: D_1 is shifted to the right of D_2 [or H_a: D_1 is shifted to the left of D_2]	H_a: D_1 is shifted either to the left or to the right of D_2

Rank the $n_1 + n_2$ observations in the two samples from the smallest (rank 1) to the largest (rank $n_1 + n_2$). Calculate T_1 and T_2, the rank sums associated with sample 1 and sample 2, respectively. Then calculate the test statistic.

Test statistic:
T_1, if $n_1 < n_2$; T_2, if $n_2 < n_1$
(Either rank sum can be used if $n_1 = n_2$.)

Test statistic:
T_1, if $n_1 < n_2$; T_2, if $n_2 < n_1$
(Either rank sum can be used if $n_1 = n_2$.) We will denote this rank sum as T.

Rejection region:
T_1: $T_1 \geq T_U$ [or $T_1 \leq T_L$]
T_2: $T_2 \leq T_L$ [or $T_2 \geq T_U$]

Rejection region: $T \leq T_L$ or $T \geq T_U$

where T_L and T_U are obtained from Table 4, Appendix A.

Note: Tied observations are assigned ranks equal to the average of the ranks that would have been assigned to the observations had they not been tied.

EXAMPLE 6.6 The data for Example 6.5 are reproduced in Table 6.4. Analyze the data using the Wilcoxon rank sum test. Test using $\alpha = .025$.

TABLE 6.4
Data for Example 6.6

COMPETITIVE BARGAINING (1)	RANK	COORDINATIVE BARGAINING (2)	RANK
$1,857	9	$1,544	2
1,700	6	2,640	15
1,829	8	1,645	4
2,644	16	2,275	13
1,566	3	2,137	11
663	1	2,327	14
1,712	7	2,152	12
1,679	5	2,130	10
	$T_1 = 55$		$T_2 = 81$

Solution In Example 6.5 we wanted to determine whether μ_1, the mean savings for competitive bargaining, is less than μ_2, the mean savings for coordinative bargaining. That is, we wanted to test H_0: $\mu_1 = \mu_2$ versus H_a: $\mu_1 < \mu_2$. The equivalent nonparametric null and alternative hypotheses are:

H_0: The two distributions of buyer savings are identical.

H_a: The distribution of population 1 (buyer savings under competitive bargaining) is shifted to the *left* of the distribution for population 2 (buyer savings under coordinative bargaining).

The ranks of the 16 observations, from lowest to highest, are also shown in Table 6.4. Summing the ranks of each column, we obtain $T_1 = 55$ and $T_2 = 81$. Since $n_1 = n_2 = 8$, the test statistic (from the box) is either T_1 or T_2. Arbitrarily, we choose $T_1 = 55$. This rank sum is shaded in the SAS printout of the analysis shown in Figure 6.10.

FIGURE 6.10
SAS Printout for Example 6.6

```
                    N P A R 1 W A Y   P R O C E D U R E

              Wilcoxon Scores (Rank Sums) for Variable SAVINGS
                      Classified by Variable STRATEGY

                            Sum of      Expected      Std Dev        Mean
          STRATEGY    N     Scores      Under HO      Under HO       Score

          comp        8     55.0        68.0         9.52190457     6.8750000
          coor        8     81.0        68.0         9.52190457     10.1250000

              Wilcoxon 2-Sample Test (Normal Approximation)
              (with Continuity Correction of .5)

              S=  55.0000      Z= -1.31276     Prob > |Z| =    0.1893

              T-Test approx. Significance =     0.2090

              Kruskal-Wallis Test (Chi-Square Approximation)
              CHISQ=  1.8640      DF= 1      Prob > CHISQ=     0.1722
```

Table 4, Appendix A, gives lower- and upper-tailed critical values of the rank sum distribution, denoted T_L and T_U, respectively, for values $n_1 \leq 10$ and $n_2 \leq 10$. The portion of Table 4 for a one-tailed test with $\alpha = .025$ (and for a two-tailed test with $\alpha = .05$) is reproduced in Table 6.5. Values of n_1 are given across the top of the table; values of n_2 are given at the left.

TABLE 6.5

A Portion of the Wilcoxon Rank Sum Table (Table 4, Appendix A); $\alpha = .025$ One-Tailed; $\alpha = .05$ Two-Tailed

n_2 \ n_1	3		4		5		6		7		8		9		10	
	T_L	T_U	T_L	T_U	T_L	T_U	T_L	T_U	T_L	T_U	T_L	T_U	T_L	T_U	T_L	T_U
3	5	16	6	18	6	21	7	23	7	26	8	28	8	31	9	33
4	6	18	11	25	12	28	12	32	13	35	14	38	15	41	16	44
5	6	21	12	28	18	37	19	41	20	45	21	49	22	53	24	56
6	7	23	12	32	19	41	26	52	28	56	29	61	31	65	32	70
7	7	26	13	35	20	45	28	56	37	68	39	73	41	78	43	83
8	8	28	14	38	21	49	29	61	39	73	49	87	51	93	54	98
9	8	31	15	41	22	53	31	65	41	78	51	93	63	108	66	114
10	9	33	16	44	24	5€	32	70	43	83	54	98	66	114	79	131

Examining Table 6.5, you will find that the critical values corresponding to $n_1 = n_2 = 8$ (shaded) are $T_L = 49$ and $T_U = 87$. Therefore, according to the box, for a one-tailed (lower-tailed) test at $\alpha = .025$, we will reject H_0 if $T_1 \leq T_L$, that is, reject H_0 if $T_1 \leq 49$. Since the observed value of the test statistic, $T_1 = 55$, is greater than 49, we fail to reject H_0. There is insufficient evidence (at $\alpha = .025$) that the distribution of buyer savings for competitive bargaining is shifted to the left of the distribution of buyer savings for coordinative bargaining. Note that this is the same conclusion reached by the parametric test in Example 6.5. However, unlike the t test in Example 6.5, no assumptions about the sampled populations are required for the nonparametric test to be valid.

PROBLEMS

6.10 The *American Journal of Small Business* (Winter 1988) reported on a survey designed to compare female managers at large firms with those at small firms (less than 100 employees). Previous studies indicate that female managers in large and small companies are quite similar. In this study, independent random samples of 86 female managers at small firms and 91 female managers at large firms were compared on several job-related variables. One question asked: "How many times have you been promoted in the last three years?" The responses for the two groups of female managers are summarized in the table.

a. Compute a point estimate for the difference between the mean number of promotions awarded to female managers at small firms and at large firms.

b. Compare the mean number of promotions awarded to the two groups of female managers with a 90% confidence interval.

SMALL FIRMS	LARGE FIRMS
$n_1 = 86$	$n_2 = 91$
$\bar{x}_1 = 1.0$	$\bar{x}_2 = .9$
$s_1 = 1.1$	$s_2 = 1.1$

Source: Anderson, R. L., and Anderson, K. P. "A Comparison of Women in Small and Large Companies." *American Journal of Small Business,* Vol. 12, No. 3, Winter 1988, p. 28 (Table 2).

    c. Interpret the interval from part **b**.

    d. How could the researchers reduce the width of the interval in part **b**?

6.11 An industrial plant wants to determine which of two types of fuel—gas or electric—will produce more useful energy at lower cost. One measure of economical energy production, called the *plant investment per delivered quad*, is calculated by taking the amount of money (in dollars) invested by the plant in the particular utility, and dividing by the delivered amount of energy (in quadrillion British thermal units). The smaller this ratio, the less an industrial plant pays for its delivered energy. Random samples of 11 plants using electrical utilities and 16 plants using gas utilities were taken, and the plant investment per quad ratio was calculated for each. The data are listed in the table, followed by a MINITAB printout of the analysis of the data. Do these data provide sufficient evidence at the $\alpha = .05$ level of significance to indicate a difference in the average investment/quad ratio between the plants using gas and those using electrical utilities? What assumptions are required for the procedure you used to be valid?

ELECTRIC				GAS			
204.15	0.57	62.76	89.72	0.78	16.66	74.94	0.01
0.35	85.46	0.78	0.65	0.54	23.59	88.79	0.64
44.38	9.28	78.60		0.82	91.84	7.20	66.64
				0.74	64.67	165.60	0.36

```
TWOSAMPLE T FOR electric VS gas
             N      MEAN     STDEV     SE MEAN
electric    11      52.4      62.4        19
gas         16      37.7      49.0        12

95 PCT CI FOR MU electric - MU gas: (-30, 59)

TTEST MU electric = MU gas (VS NE): T= 0.68  P=0.50  DF=  25

POOLED STDEV =       54.8
```

6.12 Does competition between separate research and development (R&D) teams in the U.S. Department of Defense, working independently on the same project, improve performance? To answer this question, performance ratings were assigned to each of 58 multisource (competitive) and 63 sole-source R&D contracts (*IEEE Transactions on Engineering Management,* Feb. 1990). With respect to quality of reports and products, the competitive contracts had a mean performance rating of 7.62, while the sole-source contracts had a mean of 6.95.

    a. Set up the null and alternative hypotheses for determining whether the mean quality performance rating of competitive R&D contracts exceeds the mean for sole-source contracts.

    b. Find the rejection region for the test using $\alpha = .05$.

    c. The *p*-value for the test was reported to be between .02 and .03. What is the appropriate conclusion?

6.13 As a college student, you may wonder how different variables affect your performance on a test. One such variable studied by *Educational and Psychological Measurement* (Summer 1987) was the format of answer sheets. One hundred college students were asked to complete the DAT Clerical Speed and Accuracy Test on one of two differently formatted answer sheets, a new Westinghouse answer sheet and the test's published answer sheet. Half the students were randomly assigned to the Westinghouse answer sheet and half to the published sheet; then the test scores were recorded. A summary of the results is given in the table.

	WESTINGHOUSE ANSWER SHEET	PUBLISHED ANSWER SHEET
Sample size	50	50
Mean	49.12	52.94
Standard deviation	9.26	11.29

Source: Hodgkinson, G. P. "The Effect of Variations in Answer Sheet Format on Performance on the DAT Clerical Speed and Accuracy Test." *Educational and Psychological Measurement*, Vol. 47, No. 2, Summer 1987, pp. 473–475.

  a. Form a 95% confidence interval for the difference between the mean test scores associated with the two different answer sheets.

  b. The article concludes that the "Westinghouse answer sheet may be used routinely as an alternative to the published answer sheet." Do you agree? Explain.

6.14 The label "Machiavellian" was derived from the 16th century Florentine writer Niccolo Machiavelli, who wrote on ways of manipulating others to accomplish one's objective. Critics often accuse marketers of being manipulative and unethical, or Machiavellian in nature. The question of whether "marketers are more Machiavellian than others" was explored in the *Journal of Marketing* (Summer 1984). The Machiavellian scores (measured by the Mach IV scale) for a sample of marketing professionals were recorded and compared to the Machiavellian scores for other groups of people, including a sample of college students in an earlier study. The results are summarized in the table. (Higher scores are associated with Machiavellian attitudes.) Analyze the data to determine whether, on average, marketers are more Machiavellian than college students.

	MARKETING PROFESSIONALS	COLLEGE STUDENTS
Sample size	1,076	1,782
Mean score	85.7	90.7
Standard deviation	13.2	14.3

Source: Hunt, S. D., and Chanko, L. B. "Marketing Machiavellianism." *Journal of Marketing*, Vol. 48, No. 3, Summer 1984, pp. 30–41. Reprinted with permission from *Journal of Marketing*, published by the American Marketing Association, Chicago, IL.

6.15 Many business decisions are made because of offered incentives that are intended to make the decision-maker "feel good." How does such a positive effect influence the risk preference of decision-makers? This question was the subject of a study conducted at Ohio State University. Before the experiment began, subjects were divided randomly into two groups: the "positive effect" group and the control group. The positive effect group was given a bag of candies as a token of appreciation for participating in the study, while the control group subjects were not given the gift. All subjects were then given 10 gambling chips (worth credit for participation) as a reward for participating in the study, and presented with a choice of (1) betting 5 chips on any one of the bets available in roulette, or (2) not betting. After a short explanation of the probabilities associated with the different roulette bets, the subjects were instructed to indicate on a scale of .00 to 1.00, marked at intervals of .10, the riskiest bet they were willing to make (ie, what the probability of winning would have to be for them to bet). A summary of the results (winning probabilities) is given in the table.

	POSITIVE EFFECT GROUP	CONTROL GROUP
Number of subjects	11	13
Mean probability of winning	.65	.52
Standard deviation	.18	.15

Source: Isen, A. M., and Geva, N. "The Influence of Positive Effect on Acceptable Level of Risk: The Person with the Large Canoe Has a Large Worry." *Organizational Behavior and Human Decision Processes*, Vol. 39, 1987, p. 149.

a. Construct a 95% confidence interval for the difference between the mean probabilities of winning indicated by the two groups of subjects.

b. Interpret the interval obtained in part **a**. Is there evidence of a difference between the mean probabilities selected by subjects in the two groups?

c. What assumptions are required for the inference made in part **b** to be valid?

6.16 As a result of recent advances in educational telecommunications, many colleges and universities are utilizing instruction by interactive television for "distance" education. For example, each semester Ball State University televises six graduate business courses to students at remote off-campus sites (*Journal of Education for Business*, Jan./Feb. 1991). In order to compare the performance of the off-campus MBA students at Ball State (who take the televised classes) to the on-campus MBA students (who attend classes), a test devised by the American Assembly of Collegiate Schools of Business (AACSB) was administered to a sample of both groups of students. (The test included seven exams covering accounting, business strategy, finance, human resources, marketing, management information systems, and production and operations management.) The AACSB test scores (50 points maximum) are summarized in the table. Based on these results, the researchers report that "there was no significant difference between the two groups of students."

	MEAN	STANDARD DEVIATION
On-campus students	41.93	2.86
Off-campus TV students	44.56	1.42

Source: Arndt, T. L., and LaFollette, W. R. "Interactive Television and the Nontraditional Student." *Journal of Education for Business*, Jan./Feb. 1991, p. 184.

a. Note that the sample sizes were not given in the journal article. Assuming 50 students are sampled from each group, perform the desired analysis. Do you agree with the researchers' findings?

b. Repeat part **a**, but assume 15 students are sampled from each group.

6.17 An experiment was conducted to study the effect of reinforced flanges on the torsional capacity of reinforced concrete T-beams (*Journal of the American Concrete Institute*, Jan.–Feb. 1983). Several different types of T-beams were used in the experiment, each type having a different flange width. The beams were tested under combined torsion and bending until failure (ie, cracking). One variable of interest is the cracking torsion moment at the top of the flange of the T-beam. Cracking torsion moments for eight beams with 70 cm slab widths and eight beams with 100 cm slab widths are recorded below:

70 cm slab width: 6.00, 7.20, 10.20, 13.20, 11.40, 13.60, 9.20, 11.20

100 cm slab width: 6.80, 9.20, 8.80, 13.20, 11.20, 14.90, 10.20, 11.80

Is there evidence of a difference in the locations of the cracking torsion moment distributions for the two types of T-beams? Test using $\alpha = .10$.

6.18 Recent research in nursing education has been focused on teaching strategies that link scientific theory and practice. One study compared a traditional approach to teaching basic nursing skills with an innovative approach (*Journal of Nursing Education*, Jan. 1992). The innovative approach utilizes two strategies (Vee heuristics and concept maps) that consciously link theory with practice. Forty-two students enrolled in an upper-division nursing course participated in the study. Half (21) were randomly assigned to labs that utilized the innovative approach. After completing the course, all students were given short-answer questions about scientific principles underlying each of 10 nursing skills. The objective of the research is to compare the mean scores of the two groups of students.

a. What is the appropriate test to use to compare the two groups?

b. Are any assumptions required for the test?

c. One question dealt with the use of clean/sterile gloves. The mean scores for this question were 3.28 (traditional) and 3.40 (innovative). Is there sufficient information to perform the test?

d. Refer to part **c**. The *p*-value for the test was reported as $p = .79$. Interpret this result.

e. Another question concerned the choice of a stethoscope. The mean scores of the two groups were 2.55 (traditional) and 3.60 (innovative) with an associated *p*-value of .02. Interpret these results.

6.19 A state highway department has decided to investigate the increased severity of automobile accidents occurring at a particular urban intersection since the adoption of the "right-turn-on-red law." From police records they chose a random sample of 10 accidents that occurred at the intersection before the law was enacted, and a random sample of 10 accidents that occurred after the law was enacted. They used the total damage estimate for each accident as a measure of the accident's severity. The damage estimates are recorded in the table. Based on the sample data, can you infer that damage estimates after the right-turn law are located (or shifted) to the right of damage estimates before the right-turn law? Test using $\alpha = .05$.

BEFORE RIGHT-TURN LAW		AFTER RIGHT-TURN LAW	
$150	$435	$145	$1,250
500	100	390	290
250	402	680	963
301	716	560	180
242	200	899	550

COMPARING TWO POPULATION MEANS: PAIRED SAMPLES

6.4

The parameteric and nonparametric procedures for making inferences about the difference between two population means presented in Section 6.3 were based on the assumption that the samples were randomly and independently selected from the target populations. Sometimes we can obtain more information about the difference between population means ($\mu_1 - \mu_2$) by selecting **paired observations**.

For example, suppose you want to compare two methods for training managers of a large corporation to be more assertive using samples of 10 managers with each method. One method of sampling would be to randomly select 20 managers from among all available managers and then randomly assign 10 to method 1 and 10 to method 2 (see Figure 6.11). The assertiveness test scores obtained after completion of the experiment would represent independent random samples of scores attained by managers trained by the two different methods. The difference between the mean assertiveness scores, ($\mu_1 - \mu_2$), could be estimated or tested using the procedures described in Section 6.3.

FIGURE 6.11

Independent Random Samples of Managers

	METHOD 1	METHOD 2
	1	2
	5	3
	6	4
MANAGERS	8	7
ASSIGNED TO	11	9
EACH METHOD	14	10
(IDENTIFICATION	15	12
NUMBERS LISTED)	17	13
	19	16
	20	18

The independent sampling plan shown in Figure 6.11, however, has a potential drawback. Suppose method 1 is truly more effective than method 2 in training managers to be assertive. By chance, the sampling plan may assign the 10 least assertive managers to method 1 and the 10 most assertive managers to method 2. This unbalanced assignment may mask the fact that method 1 is more effective than method 2; that is, the confidence interval (or test) on $(\mu_1 - \mu_2)$ may fail to show that μ_1 exceeds μ_2.

A better method of sampling is one that attempts to remove the variation in assertiveness scores that result from extraneous factors such as ability, experience, education, and personality. One way to do this is to match the managers in pairs, where managers in each pair have similar ability, experience, education, personality, etc. Let the managers in each pair be identified by the letters A and B. One member from each pair (say, A) would be randomly selected to be trained by method 1; the other member (say, B) would be assigned to be trained by method 2 (see Figure 6.12). Then the differences between **matched pairs** of assertiveness test scores, d_1, d_2, ..., d_{10}, should provide a clearer picture of the true difference in the effectiveness of the two training methods, because the matching would tend to cancel out the effects of the factors that formed the basis of the matching.

FIGURE 6.12
Matched-Pairs Experiment for Managers

MANAGER PAIR	ASSIGNMENT	
	Method 1	Method 2
1	A	B
2	B	A
.	.	.
.	.	.
.	.	.
10	A	B

PARAMETRIC METHODS

Let $\overline{d}$ represent the mean of the n sample differences d_1, d_2, d_3, ..., d_n. It is easy to show that $\overline{d}$ is also equal to $(\overline{x}_1 - \overline{x}_2)$; thus, $\overline{d}$ is the best estimate of the target parameter, $(\mu_1 - \mu_2)$, in a matched-pairs experiment. Since $\overline{d}$ is a sample mean, its sampling distribution is identical to the sampling distribution of $\overline{x}$ given in Section 6.3. For large n, the sampling distribution of $\overline{d}$ is given in the following box:

SAMPLING DISTRIBUTION OF $\overline{d}$, MATCHED-PAIRS EXPERIMENT, FOR LARGE n

---

Mean: $(\mu_1 - \mu_2)$
Standard error: $\sigma_d/\sqrt{n}$, where σ_d is the standard deviation of the differences d_1, d_2, d_3 ..., d_n
Distribution: Approximately normal

Substituting the value of the standard error of $\overline{d}$ into the general formulas for constructing confidence intervals and tests (Section 6.1), we obtain the following working formulas:

PARAMETRIC METHODS FOR INFERENCES ABOUT $\mu_d = (\mu_1 - \mu_2)$, PAIRED SAMPLES

Let $d_1, d_2, ..., d_n$ represent the differences between the pairwise observations in a random sample of n matched pairs, $\overline{d}$ = the mean of the sample differences, and s_d = the standard deviation.

CONFIDENCE INTERVALS

LARGE SAMPLE

$$\overline{d} \pm z_{\alpha/2}\left(\frac{\sigma_d}{\sqrt{n}}\right)$$

Note: When σ_d, the population standard deviation, is unknown (as will usually be the case), use s_d to approximate σ_d.

SMALL SAMPLE

$$\overline{d} \pm t_{\alpha/2}\left(\frac{s_d}{\sqrt{n}}\right)$$

where $t_{\alpha/2}$ is based on $\nu = (n - 1)$ degrees of freedom

Assumption: The population of paired differences is normally distributed.

TESTS OF HYPOTHESIS

ONE-TAILED TEST

H_0: $\mu_d = D_0$

H_a: $\mu_d < D_0$ [or H_a: $\mu_d > D_0$]

TWO-TAILED TEST

H_0: $\mu_d = D_0$

H_a: $\mu_d \neq D_0$

LARGE SAMPLE

Test statistic: $z_c = \dfrac{\overline{d} - D_0}{\sigma_d/\sqrt{n}}$

Rejection region: $z_c < -z_\alpha$
[or $z_c > z_\alpha$]

p-Value: $p = P(z < z_c)$
[or $p = P(z > z_c)$]

Rejection region: $|z_c| > z_{\alpha/2}$

p-Value: $p = 2P(z > |z_c|)$

Note: When the value of σ_d is unknown (as will usually be the case), use s_d to approximate σ_d.

SMALL SAMPLE

Test statistic: $t_c = \dfrac{\overline{d} - D_0}{s_d/\sqrt{n}}$

Rejection region: $t_c < -t_\alpha$
[or $t_c > t_\alpha$]

p-Value: $p = P(t < t_c)$
[or $p = P(t > t_c)$]

Rejection region: $|t_c| > t_{\alpha/2}$

p-Value: $p = 2P(t > |t_c|)$

where the distribution of t is based on $\nu = (n - 1)$ degrees of freedom.

Assumption: The population of paired differences is normally distributed.

EXAMPLE 6.7 In comparing two methods for training managers to be more assertive (discussed at the beginning of this section), suppose that the $n = 10$ pairs of managerial assertiveness test scores were as shown in Table 6.6. (Higher scores indicate higher levels of assertiveness.) Find a 95% confidence interval for the difference in mean levels of assertiveness, $\mu_d = (\mu_1 - \mu_2)$. Interpret the result.

TABLE 6.6
Managerial Assertiveness Test Scores for Example 6.7

	MANAGER PAIR									
	1	2	3	4	5	6	7	8	9	10
Method 1 Score	78	63	72	89	91	49	68	76	85	55
Method 2 Score	71	44	61	84	74	51	55	60	77	39
Pair Difference	7	19	11	5	17	−2	13	16	8	16

Solution The differences between matched pairs of assertiveness test scores are computed as

$$d = (\text{Method 1 score}) - (\text{Method 2 score})$$

and are shown in the third row of Table 6.6.

To proceed with this small-sample estimation, we must assume that these differences are from an approximately normal population. The mean and standard deviation of the sample differences are shown (shaded) in the SPSS printout, Figure 6.13. From the printout,

$$\bar{d} = 11.0 \qquad s = 6.532$$

The value of $t_{.025}$, based on $(n - 1) = (10 - 1) = 9$ degrees of freedom, is given in Table 3, Appendix A, as

$$t_{.025} = 2.262$$

FIGURE 6.13
SPSS Printout for Example 6.7

```
Paired samples t-test:   SCORE1
                         SCORE2

Variable    Number              Standard   Standard
            of Cases    Mean    Deviation  Error

SCORE1         10      72.6000   14.073     4.450
SCORE2         10      61.6000   14.759     4.667


(Difference) Standard   Standard       2-Tail     t      Degrees of  2-Tail
    Mean     Deviation    Error     Corr. Prob.  Value     Freedom    Prob.

  11.0000      6.532     2.066      .898  .000   5.33         9        .000
```

Substituting these values into the formula for the confidence interval, we obtain

$$\bar{d} \pm t_{.025}\left(\frac{s_d}{\sqrt{n}}\right) = 11.0 \pm 2.262\left(\frac{6.532}{\sqrt{10}}\right)$$
$$= 11.0 \pm 4.67 \quad \text{or} \ (6.33, \ 15.67)$$

We estimate, with 95% confidence, that the interval from 6.33 to 15.67 contains the true difference between mean managerial assertiveness test scores for methods 1 and 2. Since all the values within the interval are positive, we are confident that method 1 yields a mean assertiveness score that is significantly larger than the mean score for method 2.

We can make the same conclusion based on the results of a test of hypothesis. The t statistic and two-tailed p-value for testing the difference between the population mean assertiveness scores using the paired data are shaded at the bottom right of the SPSS printout shown in Figure 6.13. Since the p-value is approximately 0, there is sufficient evidence of a difference in means (at any reasonable α).

NONPARAMETRIC METHODS

The **Wilcoxon signed ranks test** is a nonparametric test to detect shifts in locations of population relative frequency distributions for data collected as paired samples. To perform the test, we assign ranks to the absolute values of the differences and then base the comparison on the rank sums of the negative (T^-) and positive (T^+) differences. Differences equal to 0 are eliminated and the number n of differences is reduced accordingly. Tied absolute differences receive ranks equal to the average of the ranks they would have received had they not been tied. The test is summarized in the box at the top of the next page.

EXAMPLE 6.8 The data of Example 6.7 are reproduced in Table 6.7. Analyze the data using the nonparametric Wilcoxon signed ranks test. Test using $\alpha = .05$.

TABLE 6.7
Managerial Assertiveness Test Scores for Example 6.8

| | MANAGER PAIR | | | | | | | | | |
	1	2	3	4	5	6	7	8	9	10
Method 1 Score	78	63	72	89	91	49	68	76	85	55
Method 2 Score	71	44	61	84	74	51	55	60	77	39
Pair Difference	7	19	11	5	17	−2	13	16	8	16
Absolute Value of Difference	7	19	11	5	17	2	13	16	8	16
Rank of Absolute Value	3	10	5	2	9	1	6	7.5	4	7.5

THE WILCOXON SIGNED RANKS TEST: PAIRED SAMPLES

Let D_1 and D_2 represent the population relative frequency distributions for populations 1 and 2, respectively.

ONE-TAILED TEST	TWO-TAILED TEST
H_0: D_1 and D_2 are identical	H_0: D_1 and D_2 are identical
H_a: D_1 is shifted to the right of D_2 [or H_a: D_1 is shifted to the left of D_2]	H_a: D_1 is shifted either to the left or to the right of D_2

Calculate the difference within each of the n matched pairs of observations. Then rank the absolute values of the n differences from the smallest (rank 1) to the highest (rank n), and calculate the rank sum T^- of the negative differences and the rank sum T^+ of the positive differences.

Test statistic:

T^-, the rank sum of the negative differences [or T^+, the rank sum of the positive differences]

Test statistic:

T, the smaller of T^- or T^+

Rejection region:

$T^- \leq T_0$ [or $T^+ \leq T_0$]

Rejection region: $T \leq T_0$

where T_0 is given in Table 5, Appendix A.

Note: Differences equal to 0 are eliminated and the number n of differences is reduced accordingly. Tied absolute differences receive ranks equal to the average of the ranks they would have received had they not been tied.

Solution   The goal of the study is to determine whether a difference exists in the effectiveness of the two methods in training managers to be assertive. To detect whether such a difference exists using a nonparametric method, we want to conduct the following two-tailed test:

H_0:   The distributions of managerial assertiveness test scores are identical for the two training methods.

H_a: The distribution of managerial assertiveness test scores for training method 1 is shifted either to the right or left of the distribution for training method 2.

The Wilcoxon signed ranks test requires that we calculate the absolute values of the differences between the paired measurements and then rank them. The ranks of the absolute differences are given in the last row of Table 6.7. Based on these ranks, the rank sums of the positive and negative (shaded) differences are T^+ =

54 and $T^- = 1$, respectively. For a two-tailed test, the test statistic is the smaller of these rank sums, namely $T^- = 1$. The rejection region is then

$$\text{Reject } H_0, \text{ if } T^- \leq T_0$$

The critical values of the Wilcoxon signed ranks statistic are provided in Table 5, Appendix A, which gives the value of T_0 for one-tailed tests for values of α equal to .05, .025, .01, and .005, and for two-tailed tests for values of α equal to .10, .05, .02, and .01. A portion of Table 5 is reproduced here in Table 6.8.

TABLE 6.8
A Portion of the Wilcoxon Signed Ranks Table (Table 5, Appendix A)

ONE-TAILED	TWO-TAILED	$n = 5$	$n = 6$	$n = 7$	$n = 8$	$n = 9$	$n = 10$
$\alpha = .05$	$\alpha = .10$	1	2	4	6	8	11
$\alpha = .025$	$\alpha = .05$		1	2	4	6	8
$\alpha = .01$	$\alpha = .02$			0	2	3	5
$\alpha = .005$	$\alpha = .01$				0	2	3
		$n = 11$	$n = 12$	$n = 13$	$n = 14$	$n = 15$	$n = 16$
$\alpha = .05$	$\alpha = .10$	14	17	21	26	30	36
$\alpha = .025$	$\alpha = .05$	11	14	17	21	25	30
$\alpha = .01$	$\alpha = .02$	7	10	13	16	20	24
$\alpha = .005$	$\alpha = .01$	5	7	10	13	16	19

To illustrate the use of Table 5, we will look at the portion of the table corresponding to $n = 10$ differences. Since we want to conduct a two-tailed test, we move down the two-tailed test column to the desired value of $\alpha = .05$. We find the value $T_0 = 8$ (shaded in Table 6.8). Thus, we would reject H_0 if $T^- \leq 8$.

For our example, the computed value of $T^- = 1$ is less than $T_0 = 8$. Therefore, we reject H_0 and conclude that there is sufficient evidence (at $\alpha = .05$) of a difference in locations of the distributions of managerial assertiveness training scores for the two methods. This is exactly the same conclusion we obtained by using the small-sample confidence interval for $(\mu_1 - \mu_2)$.

A MINITAB printout of the identical analysis is shown in Figure 6.14. Note that MINITAB uses $T^+ = 54$ as the test statistic. The two-tailed p-value is $.008/2 = .004$; since this value is less than $\alpha = .05$, we reject H_0.

FIGURE 6.14
MINITAB Printout for Example 6.8

```
TEST OF MEDIAN = 0.000000 VERSUS MEDIAN N.E. 0.000000

                     N FOR    WILCOXON              ESTIMATED
                N    TEST    STATISTIC   P-VALUE     MEDIAN
1minus2        10     10        54.0      0.008      11.50
```

PROBLEMS

6.20 Medical researchers believe that exposure to dust from cotton bract induces respiratory disease in susceptible field workers. An experiment was conducted to determine the effect of air-dried green cotton bract extract (GBE) on the cells of non-dust exposed mill workers (*Environmental Research*, Feb. 1986). Blood samples taken on six workers were incubated with varying concentrations of GBE. After a short period of time, the cyclic AMP level (a measure of cell activity expressed in picomoles per million cells) of each blood sample was measured. The data for two GBE concentrations, 0 mg/ml (salt buffer, control solution) and .2 mg/ml, are reproduced in the table. [Note that one blood sample was taken from each worker, with one aliquot exposed to the salt buffer solution and the other to the GBE.] Use a nonparametric method to analyze the data for the researchers.

	GBE CONCENTRATION	
WORKER	0 mg/ml	.2 mg/ml
A	8.8	4.4
B	13.0	5.7
C	9.2	4.4
D	6.5	4.1
F	9.1	4.4
H	17.0	7.9

Source: Butcher, B. T., Reed, M. A., and O'Neil, C. E. "Biochemical and Immunologic Characterization of Cotton Bract Extract and Its Effect on *in vitro* Cyclic AMP Production." *Environmental Research*, Vol. 39, No. 1, Feb. 1986, p. 119.

6.21 A recent supermarket advertisement states: "Winn-Dixie offers you the lowest total food bill! Here's the proof!" The "proof" (shown here) is a side-by-side listing of the prices of 60 grocery items purchased at Winn-Dixie and at Publix on the same day.

ITEM	WINN-DIXIE	PUBLIX	ITEM	WINN-DIXIE	PUBLIX
Big Thirst Towel	1.21	1.49	Keb Graham Crust	.79	1.29
Camp Crm/Broccoli	.55	.67	Spiffits Glass	1.98	2.19
Royal Oak Charcoal	2.99	3.59	Prog Lentil Soup	.79	1.13
Combo Chdr/Chz Snk	1.29	1.29	Lipton Tea Bags	2.07	2.17
Sure Sak Trash Bag	1.29	1.79	Carnation Hot Coco	1.59	1.89
Dow Handi Wrap	1.59	2.39	Crystal Hot Sauce	.70	.87
White Rain Shampoo	.96	.97	C/F/N/ Coffee Bag	1.17	1.15
Post Golden Crisp	2.78	2.99	Soup Start Bf Veg	1.39	2.03
Surf Detergent	2.29	1.89	Camp Pork & Beans	.44	.49
Sacramento T/Juice	.79	.89	Sunsweet Pit Prune	.98	1.33
SS Prune Juice	1.36	1.61	DM Vgcls Grdn Duet	1.07	1.13
V-8 Cocktail	1.18	1.29	Argo Corn Starch	.69	.89
Rodd Kosher Dill	1.39	1.79	Sno Drop Bowl Clnr	.53	1.15
Bisquick	2.09	2.19	Cadbury Milk Choc	.79	1.29
Kraft Italian Drs	.99	1.19	Andes Crm/De Ment	1.09	1.30
BC Hamburger Helper	1.46	1.75	Combat Ant & Roach	2.33	2.39
Comstock Chrry Pie	1.29	1.69	Joan/Arc Kid Bean	.45	.56
Dawn Liquid King	2.59	2.29	La Vic Salsa Pican	1.22	1.75
DelMonte Ketchup	1.05	1.25	Most N Beef/Chz	2.39	3.19
Silver Floss Kraut	.77	.81	Ortega Taco Shells	1.08	1.33

(continued)

ITEM	WINN-DIXIE	PUBLIX	ITEM	WINN-DIXIE	PUBLIX
Trop Twist Beverag	1.74	2.15	Fresh Step Cat Lit	3.58	3.79
Purina Kitten Chow	1.09	1.05	Field Trial Dg/Fd	3.49	3.79
Niag Spray Starch	.89	.99	Tylenol Tablets	5.98	5.29
Soft Soap Country	.97	1.19	Rolaids Tablets	1.88	2.20
Northwood Syrup	1.13	1.37	Plax Rinse	2.88	3.14
Bumble Bee Tuna	.58	.65	Correctol Laxative	3.44	3.98
Mueller Elbow/Mac	2.09	2.69	Tch Scnt Potpourri	1.50	1.89
Kell Nut Honey Crn	2.95	3.25	Chld Enema 2.250	.98	1.15
Cutter Spray	3.09	3.95	Gillette Atra Plus	5.00	5.24
Lawry Season Salt	2.28	2.97	Colgate Shave	.94	1.10

Source: Advertisement in *Tampa Tribune*, June 2, 1991.

a. Explain why the data should be analyzed as matched pairs.

b. A MINITAB printout showing a 95% confidence interval for $(\mu_{\text{Winn}} - \mu_{\text{Publix}})$, the difference between the mean prices of grocery items purchased at the two supermarkets, is displayed below. Interpret the result.

```
                 N      MEAN    STDEV   SE MEAN    95.0 PERCENT C.I.
       Diff      60    -0.2540  0.2741  0.0354   ( -0.3248, -0.1832)
```

6.22 Refer to the paired comparison of grocery items at Winn-Dixie and Publix supermarkets, Problem 6.21. The SAS printout for testing the hypothesis of no difference between the mean prices of grocery items purchased at the two supermarkets is displayed below.

```
Analysis Variable : DIFF (Winn minus Publix)

N Obs        Mean       Std Dev      Std Error         T   Prob>|T|
-------------------------------------------------------------------
  60     -0.2540000    0.2741223    0.0353890   -7.1773633    0.0001
-------------------------------------------------------------------
```

a. Locate the test statistic in the SAS printout. Interpret its value.

b. Locate the *p*-value of the test statistic in the SAS printout. Interpret its value.

6.23 Refer to the paired comparison of 60 grocery items at Winn-Dixie and Publix supermarkets, Problems 6.21 and 6.22. The data were subjected to a nonparametric analysis in SPSS; the SPSS printout is displayed below. Interpret the results. Is the conclusion consistent with the parametric test conducted in Problem 6.22?

```
- - - - - Wilcoxon Matched-pairs Signed-ranks Test

      WINNDIX
with PUBLIX


    Mean Rank    Cases

       27.90        5   - Ranks  (PUBLIX Lt WINNDIX)
       30.19       54   + Ranks  (PUBLIX Gt WINNDIX)
                    1     Ties   (PUBLIX Eq WINNDIX)
                   --
                   60     Total

     Z =  -5.6270            2-tailed P =  .0000
```

6.24 Refer to the *Chemosphere* study of Vietnam veterans' exposure to Agent Orange, Problem 6.2 (p. 250). In addition to the amount of TCDD (measured in parts per million) in blood plasma, the TCDD in fat tissue drawn from 20 exposed Vietnam veterans was recorded. The data are shown in the table. Construct a confidence interval that will allow you to compare the mean TCDD level in plasma to the mean TCDD level in fat tissue for Vietnam veterans exposed to Agent Orange. Interpret the result.

VETERAN	TCDD LEVELS IN PLASMA	TCDD LEVELS IN FAT TISSUE	VETERAN	TCDD LEVELS IN PLASMA	TCDD LEVELS IN FAT TISSUE
1	2.5	4.9	11	6.9	7.0
2	3.1	5.9	12	3.3	2.9
3	2.1	4.4	13	4.6	4.6
4	3.5	6.9	14	1.6	1.4
5	3.1	7.0	15	7.2	7.7
6	1.8	4.2	16	1.8	1.1
7	6.0	10.0	17	20.0	11.0
8	3.0	5.5	18	2.0	2.5
9	36.0	41.0	19	2.5	2.3
10	4.7	4.4	20	4.1	2.5

Source: Schecter, A., et al. "Partitioning of 2,3,7,8-Chlorinated Dibenzo-p-dioxins and Dibenzofurans Between Adipose Tissue and Plasma Lipid of 20 Massachusetts Vietnam Veterans." *Chemosphere*, Vol. 20, Nos. 7–9, 1990, pp. 954–955 (Tables I, II).

6.25 *USA Today* recently published the results of the *NCAA Graduation Rates Report*. The report makes public, for the first time, the graduation rates of student athletes at individual universities. The data in the table represents a random sample of schools selected from the NCAA report. The percentage of students and the percentage of men's basketball players from the 1983–1984 and 1984–1985 freshmen classes who graduated within 6 years are presented in the table. Use a test of hypothesis to compare the mean graduation rates of students and male basketball players. Is there evidence (at $\alpha = .05$) of a difference between the two groups?

SCHOOL	GRADUATION RATES (%)	
	Students	Men's Basketball Players
Duquesne	70	86
Florida State	52	40
Seton Hall	58	60
Oklahoma	42	13
Michigan	81	50
University of Nevada, Las Vegas	26	25
Virginia Tech	71	33
Drexel	68	70
Arizona	45	36
Georgia	60	13
San Diego State	36	0
Vanderbilt	77	83

Source: *USA Today*, Aug. 13, 1992. Copyright 1992, USA TODAY. Reprinted with permission.

6.26 Merck Research Labs conducted an experiment to evaluate the effect of a new drug using a device called the single-T swim maze. Nineteen impregnated dam rats were captured and allocated a dosage of 12.5 milligrams of the drug. One male and one female pup were randomly selected from each resulting litter to perform in the swim maze. Each rat pup is placed in the water at one end of the maze and allowed to swim until it successfully escapes at the opposite end. If the rat pup fails to escape after a certain period of time, it is placed at the beginning of the maze and given another attempt to escape. The experiment is repeated until three successful escapes are accomplished by each rat pup. The number of swims required by each pup to perform three successful escapes is reported in the table on the next page. Is there sufficient evidence of a difference between the mean number of swims required by male and female rat pups? Test using $\alpha = .10$.

LITTER	MALE	FEMALE	LITTER	MALE	FEMALE
1	8	5	11	6	5
2	8	4	12	6	3
3	6	7	13	12	5
4	6	3	14	3	8
5	6	5	15	3	4
6	6	3	16	8	12
7	3	8	17	3	6
8	5	10	18	6	4
9	4	4	19	9	5
10	4	.4			

Source: Bradstreet, Thomas E. (1993). "Favorite Data Sets from Early Phases of Drug Research—Part 2," Statistical Section Proceedings, Joint Statistical Meetings, Boston, MA, Aug. 9–13, 1993, pp. 219–223.

6.27 The growth of "off-price" retail stores in the 1980's was phenomenal. Off-price stores are speciality stores that claim to sell brand-name and designer clothes, casual wear, and active wear for less than traditional retail stores. A study was conducted to investigate apparel price variations in off-price and department stores. The average prices of 20 women's fall apparel items at both off-price stores and department stores in Montgomery County, Maryland, were recorded for each of 13 weeks. The data are shown in the table. Estimate the mean difference between the average retail prices of the items at the two types of stores. Use a 99% confidence interval.

WEEK	OFF-PRICE STORE AVERAGE PRICE	DEPARTMENT STORE AVERAGE PRICE	WEEK	OFF-PRICE STORE AVERAGE PRICE	DEPARTMENT STORE AVERAGE PRICE
1	$55.63	$81.18	8	$55.16	$74.98
2	55.63	81.80	9	54.11	71.66
3	55.32	79.36	10	54.65	68.64
4	54.11	79.18	11	53.01	68.56
5	54.79	79.55	12	42.61	67.39
6	54.36	78.21	13	50.66	67.01
7	55.33	77.70			

Source: Kirby, G. M., and Dardis, R. "Research Note: A Pricing Study of Women's Apparel in Off-Price and Department Stores," *Journal of Retailing*, Vol. 62, No. 3, Fall 1986, p. 325.

6.28 When long-term resource allocation decisions (eg, building a domed stadium or constructing a major highway system) meet with unexpected major setbacks, the decision-maker must decide whether to abandon the project before irretrievable costs are incurred or to continue in the face of probable losses. Surprisingly, researchers have found that decision-makers all too often persist, or even escalate resources, in these situations. In a study of resource allocation behavior (*Organizational Behavior and Human Decision Processes*, June 1986), 20 undergraduate business school students were asked to allocate resources of an office park and tennis club. For one portion of the study, each student was asked to rate the options of finishing and not finishing the project on a 7 point scale (1 = very negative, 7 = very positive). The differences between the ratings of the two options (rating for finishing option minus rating for not finishing option) were calculated and the mean and standard deviation of the 20 sample differences obtained:

$$\bar{d} = -2.05 \qquad s_d = 1.85$$

a. Conduct a test to determine whether subjects rate the option of finishing more negative, on average, than the option of not finishing the project (ie, test the hypothesis that the mean difference in ratings is less than 0). Use $\alpha = .10$.

b. What assumptions are required for the test of part **a** to be valid?

6.29 Early in 1987, UAL Inc., the parent corporation of United Airlines, changed its name to Allegis Corp. UAL's new name, formed by combining the words *allegiance* and *aegis*, was meant to reflect its recent acquisition of hotel and car-rental units. UAL's new name was just one of the record 1,382 corporate name changes that occurred during that year (*The Wall Street Journal*, Feb. 17, 1987). One reason for the rash of corporate name changes is the belief that a new name is a sign of positive change for investors; this, in turn, leads to a jump in the price of company stock. To investigate this phenomenon, consider the sample of 10 stocks listed in the table, each of which underwent a name change. For each stock, the rate of return from the date of the name change through February 23, 1987, is recorded and compared to the rate of return on the Standard & Poor's 500 Index over the same period. Does it appear that a name change has an effect on stock performance?

NEW NAME	DATE CHANGED	OLD NAME	RATE OF RETURN Stock	S & P 500	Difference
Unisys	11/25/86	Burroughs	32.8%	14.7%	+18.1
Trinova	8/ 1/86	Libbey-Owens-Ford	46.5	22.6	+23.9
USX	7/ 9/86	U.S. Steel	47.2	18.8	+28.4
Varity	6/17/86	Massey-Ferguson	−13.0	18.2	−31.2
Enron	4/10/86	HNG/Internorth	26.3	23.1	+3.2
Navistar Int'l	2/20/86	Int'l Harvester	−10.3	31.5	−41.8
Fidata	2/20/85	Bradford National	−41.9	68.4	−110.3
Figgie Int'l	6/ 1/81	A-T-O	326.9	113.0	+213.9
Citicorp	3/16/74	First Nat'l City Corp.	26.7	189.2	−162.5
Exxon	11/ 1/72	Standard Oil (N.J.)	283.2	153.1	+130.1

Source: The Wall Street Journal, Feb. 27, 1987, p. 17. Reprinted by permission of *The Wall Street Journal*, © 1987 Dow Jones & Company, Inc. All rights reserved worldwide.

DETERMINING THE SAMPLE SIZE

6.5 We have seen that inferences about population means are based on sample means of quantitative data collected from the populations. Ideally, we want to select a random sample from the population (see Section 1.4). An important question that must be faced in the initial stages of the analysis is: "How large a sample must be selected?" Should we sample $n = 10$ observations, $n = 20$, $n = 100$, or $n = 1,000$?

From our discussion of confidence intervals in Section 5.2, we know that the larger the sample size n, the narrower the width of the confidence interval for estimating μ (or any other parameter) and, consequently, the better idea we have of its true value. Therefore, we should select the sample size large enough so that we obtain a confidence interval with the desired (preferably narrow) width. That is, we need to decide how wide a confidence interval (with specified confidence coefficient) we are willing to tolerate. The following example illustrates this procedure.

EXAMPLE 6.9 A mail-order house wants to estimate the mean length of time between shipment of an order and receipt by the customer. The management plans to randomly sample n orders and determine, by telephone, the number of days between shipment and receipt for each order. If the management wants to estimate the mean shipping time correct to within .5 day with confidence coefficient .95, how many orders should be sampled?

Solution We will use $\bar{x}$, the sample mean of the n measurements, to estimate μ, the mean shipping time. For large n, the Central Limit Theorem guarantees that the sampling distribution of $\bar{x}$ will be approximately normal. Then, the probability that $\bar{x}$ will lie within

$$1.96\sigma_{\bar{x}} = 1.96\left(\frac{\sigma}{\sqrt{n}}\right)$$

of the mean shipping time, μ, is the confidence coefficient, .95 (see Figure 6.15). Therefore, we want to choose the sample size n so that $1.96(\sigma/\sqrt{n})$ equals .5 day:

$$1.96\left(\frac{\sigma}{\sqrt{n}}\right) = .5$$

FIGURE 6.15

Sampling Distribution of the Sample Mean, $\bar{x}$

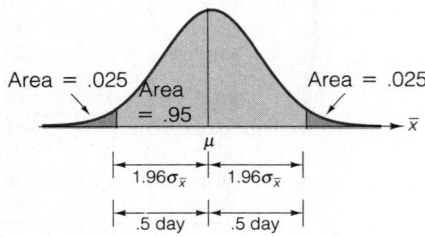

To solve the equation $1.96(\sigma/\sqrt{n}) = .5$, we need to know the value of σ, a measure of variation of the population of all shipping times. Since σ is unknown (as will usually be the case in practical applications), we must approximate its value using the standard deviation of some previous sample data or deduce an approximate value from other knowledge about the population. Suppose, for example, that we know almost all shipments will be delivered within 10 days. Then the population of shipping times might appear as shown in Figure 6.16.

FIGURE 6.16

Hypothetical Relative Frequency Distribution of Population of Shipping Times

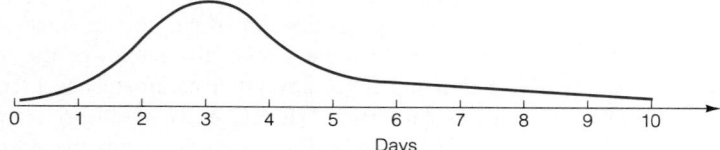

Figure 6.16 provides the information we need to find an approximation for σ. Since the Empirical Rule tells us that almost all the observations in a data set will fall within the interval $\mu \pm 3\sigma$, it follows that the range of a population is approximately 6σ. If the range of the population of shipping times is 10 days, then

$$6\sigma = 10 \text{ days}$$

and σ is approximately equal to $\frac{10}{6}$, or 1.67 days.

The final step in determining the sample size is to substitute this approximate value of σ into the equation obtained previously and solve for n. Thus, we have

$$1.96\left(\frac{1.67}{\sqrt{n}}\right) = .5$$

or

$$\sqrt{n} = \frac{1.96(1.67)}{.5} = 6.55$$

Squaring both sides of this equation yields

$$n = 42.86$$

We will follow the usual convention of rounding the calculated sample size upward. Therefore, the mail-order house needs to sample approximately $n = 43$ shipping times to estimate the mean shipping time correct to within .5 day with 95% confidence.

In Example 6.9, we wanted our sample estimate to lie within .5 day of the true mean shipping time, μ, with confidence coefficient .95. We could calculate the sample size for a confidence coefficient other than .95 by changing the z-value in the equation. In general, if we want $\bar{x}$ to lie within a distance d of μ with confidence coefficient $(1 - \alpha)$, we solve for n in the equation

$$z_{\alpha/2}\left(\frac{\sigma}{\sqrt{n}}\right) = d$$

where the value of $z_{\alpha/2}$ is obtained from Table 2, Appendix A. (Note that d represents the half-width of the confidence interval.) The solution is given by

$$n = \left(\frac{z_{\alpha/2}\sigma}{d}\right)^2$$

For example, for a confidence coefficient of .90, we would require a sample size of

$$n = \left(\frac{1.645\sigma}{d}\right)^2$$

The formula for determining the sample size n for estimating a single population mean μ is given in the box.

CHOOSING THE SAMPLE SIZE FOR ESTIMATING A POPULATION MEAN, μ

$$n = \left(\frac{z_{\alpha/2}\sigma}{d}\right)^2$$

where

d = Half-width of the interval

$z_{\alpha/2}$ = z-Value that corresponds to a confidence coefficient of $(1 - \alpha)$

Note: The population standard deviation σ will usually have to be approximated.

We can also make sample size determinations for tests of hypothesis about μ. In Section 5.3 we noted that for a fixed significance level α, the power of the test increases as the sample size n increases. Recall that the power of the test is the probability of rejecting H_0 when, in fact, H_0 is false. Therefore, increasing the sample size increases the chance that we will detect departures from H_0 when they exist.

The formulas for determining the sample size required to attain the desired power in a test of hypothesis for μ are given (without proof) in the following box:

CHOOSING THE SAMPLE SIZE FOR TESTING A POPULATION MEAN, μ

ONE-TAILED TEST

$$n = \left[\frac{(z_{1-\beta} - z_\alpha)\sigma}{\mu_0 - \mu_a} \right]^2$$

TWO-TAILED TEST

$$n = \left[\frac{(z_{1-\beta} - z_{\alpha/2})\sigma}{\mu_0 - \mu_a} \right]^2$$

where

μ_0 = Value of μ specified in H_0 (ie, H_0: $\mu = \mu_0$)

μ_a = Specific value of μ in H_a

$1 - \beta$ = Power of the test for the specified value of μ_a

α = Fixed significance level of the test

$z_{1-\beta}$ = z-Value such that $P(z > z_{1-\beta}) = 1 - \beta$

z_α = z-Value such that $P(z > z_\alpha) = \alpha$

$z_{\alpha/2}$ = z-Value such that $P(z > z_{\alpha/2}) = \alpha/2$

Note: The population standard deviation σ usually will have to be approximated.

EXAMPLE 6.10 Refer to the problem discussed earlier of determining whether the mean breaking strength of residential sewer pipe produced by a manufacturer meets a city's specifications (Examples 5.9 and 5.10). In Example 5.9, we conducted an $\alpha = .05$ level test of the hypothesis

H_0: $\mu = 2,400$
H_a: $\mu > 2,400$

based on data collected for a sample of $n = 70$ pipe sections. In Example 5.10, we calculated β (the probability of a Type II error) as $\beta = .7764$, for the alternative $\mu_a = 2,420$. Hence, the power of the test for this specific alternative is $(1 - .7764) = .2236$. Determine the sample size required to increase the power of the $\alpha = .05$ test to .60 for the alternative $\mu_a = 2,420$. (Recall that the sample yielded $\bar{x} = 2,430$ and $s = 190$.)

Solution For this one-tailed test, we have $1 - \beta = .60$, $\alpha = .05$, $\mu_0 = 2,400$, and $\mu_a = 2,420$. From Table 2, Appendix A, we find $z_\alpha = z_{.05} = 1.645$ and $z_{1-\beta} =$

FIGURE 6.17

Values of z_α and $z_{1-\beta}$

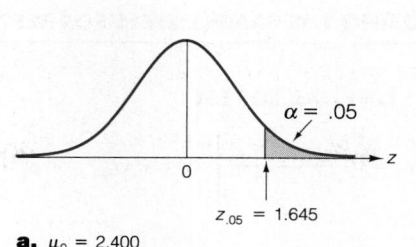

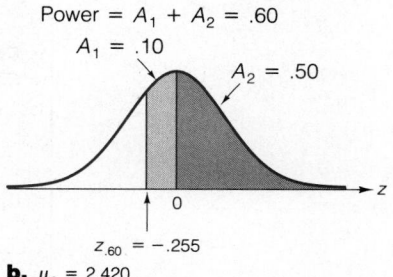

a. $\mu_0 = 2{,}400$ **b.** $\mu_a = 2{,}420$

$z_{.60} = -.255$ (see Figure 6.17). Since σ is unknown, we will use the estimate determined from Example 5.9, namely $s = 190$. Substituting these values into the formula for n given in the box, we find

$$n = \left[\frac{(z_{1-\beta} - z_\alpha)\sigma}{\mu_0 - \mu_a} \right]^2 \approx \left[\frac{(-.255 - 1.645)190}{(2{,}400 - 2{,}420)} \right]^2$$

$$\approx (18.05)^2 = 325.8$$

Rounding up, we obtain $n = 326$. Thus, to attain a power of .60 for detecting the alternative $\mu_a = 2{,}420$ with an $\alpha = .05$ level test, the city must include at least $n = 326$ sections of sewer pipe in the sample.

In this chapter we have also discussed inferences concerning the difference between a pair of population means, $\mu_1 - \mu_2$, with independent samples and the mean difference μ_d of a matched-pairs design. Sample size formulas for estimating and testing μ_d are identical to those for μ. The resulting value of n, however, represents the required number of *pairs* that must be included in the matched-pairs sampling plan.

The procedures for determining the sample sizes for estimating and testing $\mu_1 - \mu_2$ in an independent sampling design are analogous to those for a single mean. The appropriate formulas are summarized in the boxes.

**CHOOSING THE SAMPLE SIZES FOR
ESTIMATING THE DIFFERENCE ($\mu_1 - \mu_2$)**

$$n_1 = n_2 = \left(\frac{z_{\alpha/2}}{d} \right)^2 (\sigma_1^2 + \sigma_2^2)$$

where n_1 and n_2 are the numbers of observations sampled from each of the two populations, σ_1^2 and σ_2^2 are the variances of the two populations, d is the half-width of the interval, and $z_{\alpha/2}$ is the z-value that corresponds to a confidence coefficient of $(1 - \alpha)$.

Note: σ_1^2 and σ_2^2 will usually have to be estimated.

CHOOSING THE SAMPLE SIZES FOR TESTING $(\mu_1 - \mu_2)$

ONE-TAILED TEST	TWO-TAILED TEST
$n_1 = n_2 = \left[\dfrac{(z_{1-\beta} - z_\alpha)}{D_0 - D_a}\right]^2 (\sigma_1^2 + \sigma_2^2)$	$n_1 = n_2 = \left[\dfrac{(z_{1-\beta} - z_{\alpha/2})}{D_0 - D_a}\right]^2 (\sigma_1^2 + \sigma_2^2)$

where

D_0 = Value of $(\mu_1 - \mu_2)$ specified in H_0 (ie, H_0: $\mu_1 - \mu_2 = D_0$)

D_a = Specific value of $(\mu_1 - \mu_2)$ in H_a

$1 - \beta$ = Power of the test for the specified value of D_a

α = Fixed significance level of the test

$z_{1-\beta}$ = z-Value such that $P(z > z_{1-\beta}) = 1 - \beta$

z_α = z-Value such that $P(z > z_\alpha) = \alpha$

$z_{\alpha/2}$ = z-Value such that $P(z > z_{\alpha/2}) = \alpha/2$

Note: σ_1^2 and σ_2^2 will usually have to be estimated.

EXAMPLE 6.11   Refer to Example 6.9. Suppose the mail-order house wanted to estimate the difference in mean shipping times for two different express services. If the company specifies a 99% confidence interval for estimating the difference in means to be no wider than 1 day, how many shipping times would have to be included in each sample?

Solution   To determine the sample sizes, the company needs to know the values of d, the half-width of the interval, $z_{\alpha/2}$, σ_1^2, and σ_2^2. For this problem, the desired width of the entire interval is 1; consequently, the half-width is $d = .5$. Consulting Table 2, Appendix A, we find that for $\alpha = .01$, $z_{\alpha/2} = z_{.005} \approx 2.58$. We will assume that the population standard deviations are approximately equal and will estimate them using the value $\sigma \approx 1.67$ obtained in Example 6.9. Substituting these values into the equation for the required sample sizes, we obtain

$$n_1 = n_2 = \left(\frac{z_{\alpha/2}}{d}\right)^2 (\sigma_1^2 + \sigma_2^2) = \left(\frac{2.58}{.5}\right)^2 [2(1.67)^2] = 148.5$$

Therefore, to estimate the difference in mean shipping times with a 99% confidence interval no wider than 1 day, the mail-order house will have to sample approximately 149 shipments for each express service.

The formulas given in this section are appropriate when the sample size n is small relative to the population size N, which is usually the case in practice. For situations in which n may be large relative to N, adjustments to these formulas must be made. Sample size determination for this special case (called *survey sampling*) is beyond the scope of this text. Consult the references if you want to learn more about this particular application.

PROBLEMS

6.30 Determine the sample size needed to estimate μ for each of the following situations:

    a. $d = 3$, $\sigma = 40$, $(1 - \alpha) = .95$ **b.** $d = 5$, $\sigma = 40$, $(1 - \alpha) = .95$
    c. $d = 5$, $\sigma = 40$, $(1 - \alpha) = .99$

6.31 Find the appropriate value of $n_1 = n_2$ needed to estimate $(\mu_1 - \mu_2)$ to within:

    a. 5 units with confidence coefficient .95 (Assume $\sigma_1 \approx 12$ and $\sigma_2 \approx 15$.)
    b. 5 units with confidence coefficient .99 (Assume $\sigma_1 \approx 12$ and $\sigma_2 \approx 15$.)
    c. 1 unit with confidence coefficient .90 (Assume $\sigma_1^2 \approx 100$ and $\sigma_2^2 \approx 120$.)

6.32 Refer to the U.S. Department of Energy study of brine antiscalants, Example 6.1 (p. 246). How many brine solutions must be treated with antiscalants and tested to estimate the true mean amount of silicon present in an aliquot of brine to within 10 ppm with 90% confidence? Use the sample standard deviation calculated in Example 6.1 as an estimate of σ.

6.33 *Cost Engineering* (Oct. 1988) reports on a study of the percentage difference between the low bid and the engineer's estimate of the cost for building contracts (see Problem 5.6, p. 200). For contracts with four bidders, the mean percentage error is $\mu = -7.02$ and the standard deviation is $\sigma = 24.66$. Suppose you want to estimate the mean percentage error for building contracts with five bidders. How many five-bidder contracts must be sampled to estimate with 90% confidence the mean to within 5 percentage points of its true value? Assume that the standard deviation for five-bidder contracts is approximately equal to the standard deviation for four-bidder contracts.

6.34 Refer to Example 5.12. Based on data collected for a small sample of 21 successful Canadian trade promotions (*Journal of Marketing*, July 1986), we constructed a 95% confidence interval for the mean incremental profit. The interval, ($9,756, $96,244), was too wide to be practical. How many successful trade promotions would have to be sampled to reduce the width of the 95% confidence interval to $30,000? Recall that the sample standard deviation in Example 5.12 was $95,000.

6.35 Some power plants are located near rivers or oceans so that the available water can be used for cooling the condensers. As part of an environmental impact study, suppose a power company wants to estimate the difference in mean water temperature between the discharge of its plant and the offshore waters. How many sample measurements must be taken at each site to estimate the true difference between means to within .2°C with 95% confidence? Assume the range in readings will be about 4°C at each site, and the same number of readings will be taken at each site.

6.36 *The Wall Street Journal* reported on a survey of Kleenex users to determine how many tissues to put in a pack of Kleenex (see Problem 5.20, p. 223). From the diaries of a sample of 250 Kleenex users, researchers at Kimberly-Clark Corporation (the makers of Kleenex) found the following summary statistics on the number of times they blew their noses when they had a cold: $\bar{x} = 57$, $s = 60$. This information was used to test $H_0: \mu = 60$ against $H_a: \mu \neq 60$ using $\alpha = .05$. (According to *The Wall Street Journal*, the researchers have "little doubt that the company should put 60 tissues in each pack.") Determine the number of Kleenex users that must be surveyed if the researchers want to be able to detect the alternative $\mu_a = 55$ with probability of .70.

TESTS AND CONFIDENCE INTERVALS FOR MEANS

In this section we present the computer commands for constructing confidence intervals and tests of hypothesis concerning population means. All three packages, SAS, SPSS, and MINITAB, can perform t tests about μ and $(\mu_1 - \mu_2)$ for independent samples, and μ_d for paired samples. (Remember, for large samples the t and z statistics are nearly equivalent.) Only MINITAB has procedures for constructing confidence intervals. If available, the commands for conducting nonparametric tests are given.

Specifically, the programs below analyze the data from Example 6.1 (parametric and nonparametric tests for μ), Table 6.3 (parametric and nonparametric tests for $\mu_1 - \mu_2$, independent samples), and Table 6.6 (parametric and nonparametric tests for μ_d, matched pairs).

SAS

Command
Line

```
1    DATA EX6_1;              ⎫
2    INPUT SILICON @@;        ⎬  Data entry instructions
3    SIL_300=SILICON-300;     ⎭
4    CARDS;
     229 255 280 203 229   Input data values
5    PROC MEANS T PRT;     ⎫  One-sample t test
6    VAR SIL_300;          ⎬  (H₀:  μ = 300)
```
$$H_0: \mu = 300$$

```
7    DATA TAB6_3;             ⎫
8    INPUT STRATEGY $ SAVINGS; ⎬ Data entry instructions
9    CARDS;
     COMP 1857  ⎫
     COMP 1700  ⎪
       •    •   ⎬  Input data values
       •    •   ⎪  (1 observation per line)
       •    •   ⎪
     COOR 2130  ⎭
10   PROC TTEST;                    ⎫  Independent samples t test
11   CLASS STRATEGY; VAR SAVINGS;   ⎬  (H₀:  μ₁ - μ₂ = 0)
12   PROC NPAR1WAY WILCOXON;        ⎫  Wilcoxon rank sum test
13   CLASS STRATEGY; VAR SAVINGS;   ⎭
```

```
14   DATA TAB6_6;      ⎫
15   INPUT X1 X2;      ⎬  Data entry instructions
16   DIFF=X1-X2;       ⎭
```

(continued)

```
17      CARDS;
        78 71 ⎫
        63 44 ⎪
         ·  · ⎬  Input data values
         ·  · ⎪  (1 observation per line)
         ·  · ⎪
        55 39 ⎭
18      PROC MEANS T PRT; ⎤  Matched-samples t test
19      VAR DIFF;         ⎦  ($H_0$:  $\mu_d = 0$)
```

COMMAND 3 The transformed variable SIL_300 is computed by subtracting the hypothesized mean ($\mu = 300$) from each value of SILICON.

COMMANDS 5–6 The PROC MEANS statement commands SAS to conduct a t test on the variable specified in the VAR statement (eg, SIL_300). SAS will test the null hypothesis H_0: $\mu_{SIL\_300} = 0$, which is equivalent to testing H_0: $\mu_{SILICON} = 300$. [*Note:* The p-value reported in SAS is a *two-tailed* observed significance level. Divide this reported value in half to obtain the p-value for a one-tailed test.]

COMMANDS 10–11 The TTEST procedure conducts a t test on the difference in means of the variable specified in the VAR statement (eg, SAVINGS) for the two groups identified by the variable in the CLASS statement (eg, STRATEGY). [SAS calculates the t-value for both the equal population variances case and the unequal variances case.]

COMMANDS 12–13 The NPAR1WAY procedure with the WILCOXON option conducts a Wilcoxon rank sum test for comparing the distributions of the variable specified in the VAR statement (eg, SAVINGS) for the two groups identified by the variable in the CLASS statement (eg, STRATEGY).

COMMANDS 15–16 The variables X1 and X2 contain the measurements for each member of the matched pair. The difference, DIFF, is computed in line 16.

COMMANDS 18–19 The MEANS procedure with the T option is used to perform the matched-samples t test on the DIFF variable.

GENERAL The nonparametric sign test for a population median and Wilcoxon signed ranks test for matched pairs are not available in SAS.

NOTE The output for this SAS program is displayed in Figure 6.18 (p. 291).

Command Line		
1	`DATA LIST FREE/SILICON.`	} Data entry instructions
2	`BEGIN DATA.`	
	`229 255 280 203 229` Input data values	
3	`END DATA.`	
4	`COMPUTE MU=300.`	
5	`T-TEST PAIRS=SILICON MU.` One-sample t test (H_0: $\mu = 300$)	
6	`NPAR TESTS SIGN=SILICON MU.` Sign test (H_0: $\eta = 300$)	

7	`DATA LIST FREE/STRATEGY SAVINGS.`	} Data entry instructions
8	`BEGIN DATA.`	
	`1 1857`	
	`1 1700`	
	`.    .` Input data values	
	`.    .` (1 observation per line)	
	`.    .`	
	`2 2130`	
9	`END DATA.`	} Independent samples
10	`T-TEST GROUPS=STRATEGY(1,2)/VARIABLES=SAVINGS.`	t test (H_0: $\mu_1 - \mu_2 = 0$)
11	`NPAR TESTS M-W=SAVINGS BY STRATEGY(1,2).` Wilcoxon rank sum test	

12	`DATA LIST FREE/X1 X2.`	} Data entry instructions
13	`BEGIN DATA.`	
	`78 71`	
	`63 44`	
	`.  .` Input data values	
	`.  .` (1 observation per line)	
	`.  .`	
	`55 39`	
14	`END DATA.`	
15	`T-TEST PAIRS=X1 X2.` Matched-pairs t test (H_0: $\mu_d = 0$)	
16	`NPAR TESTS WILCOXON=X1 X2.` Wilcoxon signed ranks test	

COMMAND 4   A constant (MU) is created and given the value of the hypothesized mean or median (eg, 300).

COMMAND 5   The T-TEST procedure tests the difference between the mean of the variable specified (eg, SILICON), and the constant MU. (The t-value and corresponding two-tailed p-value will appear under the heading POOLED VARIANCE ESTIMATE.)

COMMAND 6   The NPAR TESTS procedure with subcommand SIGN conducts a sign test for determining whether the median of the variable specified (eg, SILICON) differs from the constant MU.

COMMAND 7   SAVINGS is the quantitative variable of interest. STRATEGY is a grouping variable name that takes on the value 1 if the observation is from the first sample and the value 2 if the observation is from the second sample.

COMMAND 10   The T-TEST procedure tests the difference in the means of the variable specified (eg, SAVINGS) for the two groups identified by the variable in the GROUPS subcommand (eg, STRATEGY).

COMMAND 11   The NPAR TESTS procedure with subcommand M-W* conducts a Wilcoxon rank sum test for determining whether the distributions of the variable specified (eg, SAVINGS) differ for the two groups identified by STRATEGY. [*Note:* The quantitative variable and grouping variable must be separated by the key word, BY.]

COMMAND 12   The variables X1 and X2 contain the measurements for each member of the matched pair.

COMMAND 15   The T-TEST command performs a *t* test on the difference between the pairs of observations, X1 and X2.

COMMAND 16   The NPAR TESTS procedure with subcommand WILCOXON conducts a Wilcoxon signed ranks test for determining whether the distributions of X1 and X2 differ.

NOTE   The output for the SPSS program is displayed in Figure 6.19 (p. 292).

MINITAB

Command Line	
1	`SET DATA IN C1` Data entry instruction
	`229 255 280 203 229` Input data values
2	`NAME C1='SILICON'`
3	`TINTERVAL 95 C1`
4	`TTEST MU=300 C1;` ⎫ One-sample *t* test (H_0: $\mu = 300$)
5	`ALTERNATIVE=+1.` ⎭
6	`STEST MEDIAN=300 C1;` ⎫ Sign test (H_0: $\eta = 0$)
7	`ALTERNATIVE=+1.` ⎭
8	`SET COMP IN C1` Data entry instruction
	`1857 1700 ••• 1679` Input data values
9	`SET COOR IN C2` Data entry instruction
	`1544 2640 ••• 2130` Input data values
10	`NAME C1='COMP' C2='COOR'`
11	`TWOSAMPLE 95 C1 C2;` ⎫ Independent samples *t* test
12	`POOLED.` ⎭ (H_0: $\mu_1 - \mu_2 = 0$)
13	`MANN-WHITNEY C1 C2` Wilcoxon rank sum test

(continued)

---

* M-W is an abbreviation for Mann–Whitney. The nonparametric Mann–Whitney test is equivalent to the Wilcoxon rank sum test.

```
14      READ TAB6_6 IN C1 C2   Data entry instruction
        78 71 ⎫
        63 44 ⎪
         .  .  ⎬  Input data values
         .  .  ⎪  (1 observation per line)
         .  .  ⎪
        55 39 ⎭
15      SUBTRACT C2 FROM C1, PUT IN C3
16      NAME C3='DIFF'
17      TINTERVAL 95 C3
18      TTEST C3   Matched-pairs t test (H_0:  μ_d = 0)
19      WTEST C3   Wilcoxon signed ranks test
```

COMMAND 3   TINTERVAL produces a confidence interval for the mean of the data stored in C1. The confidence level (eg, 95%) is specified before the variable column. (The default is a 95% confidence interval.)

COMMANDS 4–5   The TTEST procedure performs a t test of the hypothesized mean specified in the MU= subcommand for the variable specified (eg, C1). The subcommand ALTERNATIVE=+1 requests that a one-tailed, upper-tailed test be performed. [Use ALTERNATIVE=−1 for a lower-tailed test. If the subcommand is not used, a two-tailed test is performed.]

COMMANDS 6–7   The STEST procedure tests the hypothesized median specified in the MEDIAN= subcommand for the variable specified (eg, C1). (The ALTERNATIVE subcommand is the same as in TTEST.)

COMMANDS 11–12   TWOSAMPLE performs a t test and confidence interval on the difference between the means of the data in C1 and C2. (The confidence level and confidence interval are specified before the variable columns.) The subcommand POOLED requests that a pooled sample variance be used. (This is appropriate when the population variances are equal.) If you want MINITAB to adjust the t statistic and degrees of freedom for the unequal variances case, omit the POOLED subcommand.

COMMAND 13   MANN–WHITNEY* performs a nonparametric test for comparing the distributions of the data in C1 and C2. (Use the ALTERNATIVE subcommand to obtain a one-tailed test.)

COMMANDS 14–15   The data in columns C1 and C2 contain the measurements for each member of the matched pair. C3 contains the difference between the measurements.

COMMAND 17   TINTERVAL produces a confidence interval (eg, 95) for the difference specified in C3.

---

* The Mann–Whitney test is equivalent to the Wilcoxon rank sum test.

COMMAND 18 TTEST performs a matched-pairs *t* test on the mean of the difference in C3. (Use the ALTERNATIVE subcommand to obtain a one-tailed test.)

COMMAND 19 WTEST performs a Wilcoxon signed ranks test for comparing the distributions of the matched-pairs data in C1 and C2, where the difference is represented by C3. (Use the ALTERNATIVE subcommand to obtain a one-tailed test.)

NOTE The output for the MINITAB program is displayed in Figure 6.20 (p. 294).

FIGURE 6.18

SAS Output for Computer Lab

```
                          Analysis Variable : SIL_300

                          N Obs            T  Prob>|T|
                          -----------------------------
                              5    -4.6408157    0.0097
                          -----------------------------
```

```
                              TTEST PROCEDURE
Variable: SAVINGS

STRATEGY       N              Mean           Std Dev         Std Error
----------------------------------------------------------------------
comp           8      1706.25000000      537.98878108      190.20775765
coor           8      2106.25000000      357.48636338      126.39051586

Variances      T        DF     Prob>|T|
----------------------------------------
Unequal     -1.7515    12.2     0.1050
Equal       -1.7515    14.0     0.1017

For H0: Variances are equal, F' = 2.26    DF = (7,7)    Prob>F' = 0.3029
```

```
                    N P A R 1 W A Y   P R O C E D U R E

            Wilcoxon Scores (Rank Sums) for Variable SAVINGS
                      Classified by Variable STRATEGY

                          Sum of     Expected     Std Dev        Mean
STRATEGY       N          Scores     Under H0     Under H0       Score

comp           8           55.0        68.0      9.52190457    6.8750000
coor           8           81.0        68.0      9.52190457   10.1250000

        Wilcoxon 2-Sample Test (Normal Approximation)
        (with Continuity Correction of .5)

        S= 55.0000     Z= -1.31276    Prob > |Z| =   0.1893

        T-Test approx. Significance =      0.2090

        Kruskal-Wallis Test (Chi-Square Approximation)
        CHISQ=  1.8640     DF= 1     Prob > CHISQ=      0.1722
```

```
                          Analysis Variable : DIFF

                          N Obs            T  Prob>|T|
                          -----------------------------
                             10     5.3253521    0.0005
                          -----------------------------
```

FIGURE 6.19
SPSS Output for Computer Lab

```
Paired samples t-test:   SILICON
                         MU

Variable    Number                 Standard    Standard
            of Cases     Mean      Deviation     Error

SILICON        5       239.2000     29.295      13.101
MU             5       300.0000      .000        .000


(Difference) Standard    Standard  |    2-Tail   |   t    Degrees of   2-Tail
     Mean    Deviation     Error   | Corr. Prob. | Value   Freedom     Prob.

  -60.8000    29.295      13.101   |   .     .   | -4.64     4         .010
```

```
- - - - - Sign Test

     SILICON
with MU


        Cases

        0  - Diffs (MU Lt SILICON)
        5  + Diffs (MU Gt SILICON)        (Binomial)
        0    Ties                         2-tailed P =      .0625
        -
        5    Total
```

```
Independent samples of  STRATEGY

Group 1:  STRATEGY  EQ     1.00          Group 2:  STRATEGY  EQ     2.00

t-test for:  SAVINGS

                    Number                  Standard    Standard
                    of Cases     Mean       Deviation     Error

        Group 1        8       1706.2500    537.989      190.208
        Group 2        8       2106.2500    357.486      126.391

                 | Pooled Variance Estimate | Separate Variance Estimate
   F    2-Tail   |   t    Degrees of 2-Tail |   t    Degrees of  2-Tail
 Value  Prob.    | Value   Freedom   Prob.  | Value   Freedom    Prob.

  2.26   .303    | -1.75     14      .102   | -1.75    12.17     .105
```

(continued)

FIGURE 6.19 (*Continued*)

```
- - - - - Mann-Whitney U - Wilcoxon Rank Sum W Test

      SAVINGS
   by STRATEGY


      Mean Rank     Cases

         6.88          8    STRATEGY = 1.00
        10.13          8    STRATEGY = 2.00
                      --
                      16    Total


                                      EXACT           Corrected for Ties
         U             W            2-tailed P        Z          2-tailed P
        19.0          55.0           .1949         -1.3653         .1722
```

```
Paired samples t-test:  X1
                        X2

Variable    Number              Standard    Standard
            of Cases    Mean    Deviation     Error

X1            10      72.6000    14.073       4.450
X2            10      61.6000    14.759       4.667


(Difference) Standard   Standard        2-Tail       t     Degrees of  2-Tail
    Mean     Deviation    Error     Corr.  Prob.   Value    Freedom    Prob.

  11.0000     6.532      2.066      .898   .000    5.33        9       .000
```

```
- - - - - Wilcoxon Matched-pairs Signed-ranks Test

      X1
with  X2


      Mean Rank     Cases

         6.00          9    - Ranks  (X2 Lt X1)
         1.00          1    + Ranks  (X2 Gt X1)
                       0    Ties     (X2 Eq X1)
                      --
                      10    Total

         Z =  -2.7011              2-tailed P = .0069
```

FIGURE 6.20
MINITAB Output for Computer Lab

```
                 N      MEAN     STDEV   SE MEAN    95.0 PERCENT C.I.
SILICON          5      239.2    29.3    13.1    (   202.8,   275.6)
```

```
TEST OF MU = 300.000 VS MU G.T. 300.000

                 N      MEAN     STDEV   SE MEAN        T     P VALUE
SILICON          5      239.200  29.295  13.101     -4.64      1.00
```

```
SIGN TEST OF MEDIAN = 300.0 VERSUS  G.T.   300.0

                 N   BELOW  EQUAL  ABOVE   P-VALUE     MEDIAN
SILICON          5     5      0      0    1.0000      229.0
```

```
TWOSAMPLE T FOR COMP VS COOR
        N      MEAN     STDEV   SE MEAN
COMP    8      1706     538     190
COOR    8      2106     357     126

95 PCT CI FOR MU COMP - MU COOR: (-890, 90)

TTEST MU COMP = MU COOR (VS NE): T= -1.75  P=0.10  DF=  14

POOLED STDEV =          457
```

```
Mann-Whitney Confidence Interval and Test

COMP       N =   8     Median =      1706.0
COOR       N =   8     Median =      2144.5
Point estimate for ETA1-ETA2 is       -443.0
95.9 pct c.i. for ETA1-ETA2 is (-811.2,156.0)
W = 55.0
Test of ETA1 = ETA2  vs.  ETA1 n.e. ETA2 is significant at 0.1893

Cannot reject at alpha = 0.05
```

```
                 N      MEAN     STDEV   SE MEAN    95.0 PERCENT C.I.
DIFF            10      11.00    6.53    2.07    (   6.33,   15.67)
```

```
TEST OF MU =  0.000 VS MU N.E.  0.000

                 N      MEAN     STDEV   SE MEAN        T     P VALUE
DIFF            10      11.000   6.532   2.066      5.33     0.0005
```

```
TEST OF MEDIAN = 0.000000 VERSUS MEDIAN N.E. 0.000000

                 N FOR    WILCOXON              ESTIMATED
         N       TEST    STATISTIC   P-VALUE     MEDIAN
DIFF    10       10       54.0       0.008       11.50
```

- **Parametric inferences** about the population parameters μ, $\mu_1 - \mu_2$ (independent samples), and μ_d (matched samples) are obtained using the following general formulas:

CONFIDENCE INTERVALS

Large sample: Estimator $\pm$ $(z_{\alpha/2})$Standard error

Small sample: Estimator $\pm$ $(t_{\alpha/2})$Estimated standard error

TEST STATISTICS

Large sample: $z = \dfrac{\text{Estimator} - \text{Hypothesized value in } H_0}{\text{Standard error}}$

Small sample: $t = \dfrac{\text{Estimator} - \text{Hypothesized value in } H_0}{\text{Estimated standard error}}$

- **Estimators** and **standard errors** for each of the parameters μ, $\mu_1 - \mu_2$, and μ_d are provided in the following table:

PARAMETER	ESTIMATOR	STANDARD ERROR	ESTIMATED STANDARD ERROR
μ	$\bar{x}$	$\dfrac{\sigma}{\sqrt{n}}$	$\dfrac{s}{\sqrt{n}}$
$\mu_1 - \mu_2$	$\bar{x}_1 - \bar{x}_2$	$\sqrt{\dfrac{\sigma_1^2}{n_1} + \dfrac{\sigma_2^2}{n_2}}$	$\sqrt{\dfrac{s_1^2}{n_1} + \dfrac{s_2^2}{n_2}}$ (Large samples)
			$\sqrt{\dfrac{s_p^2}{n_1} + \dfrac{s_p^2}{n_2}}$ (Small samples)
			where $s_p^2 = \dfrac{(n_1 - 1)s_1^2 + (n_2 - 1)s_2^2}{n_1 + n_2 - 2}$
μ_d	$\bar{x}_d$	$\dfrac{\sigma_d}{\sqrt{n}}$	$\dfrac{s_d}{\sqrt{n}}$

- The **assumptions** required to make valid parametric inferences for μ, $\mu_1 - \mu_2$, and μ_d with small samples are:

μ: Sampled population has an approximate normal distribution.

$\mu_1 - \mu_2$:
  1. Both sampled populations are approximately normal.
  2. The population variances are equal ($\sigma_1^2 = \sigma_2^2 = \sigma^2$).
     [*Note:* Approximations are available when $\sigma_1^2 \neq \sigma_2^2$.]
  3. The samples are independent.

μ_d: Sampled population of differences is approximately normal.

- Formulas for determining the **sample size** for estimating and testing μ, $\mu_1 - \mu_2$, and μ_d are provided in the table on the next page.

PARAMETER	CONFIDENCE INTERVAL	ONE-TAILED TEST[a]
μ	$n = \left(\dfrac{z_{\alpha/2}\sigma}{d}\right)^2$	$n = \left[\dfrac{(z_{1-\beta} - z_\alpha)\sigma}{\mu_0 - \mu_a}\right]^2$
$\mu_1 - \mu_2$	$n_1 = n_2 = \left(\dfrac{z_{\alpha/2}}{d}\right)^2(\sigma_1^2 + \sigma_2^2)$	$n_1 = n_2 = \left[\dfrac{z_{1-\beta} - z_\alpha}{D_0 - D_a}\right]^2(\sigma_1^2 + \sigma_2^2)$
μ_d	$n = \left(\dfrac{z_{\alpha/2}\sigma_d}{d}\right)^2$	$n = \left[\dfrac{(z_{1-\beta} - z_\alpha)\sigma_d}{D_0 - D_a}\right]^2$

[a] For a two-tailed test, replace z_α with $z_{\alpha/2}$ in the formulas.

- The next table gives the **nonparametric** alternatives to the parametric tests for population means:

NULL HYPOTHESIS	PARAMETRIC METHOD	NONPARAMETRIC METHOD
H_0: $\mu = \mu_0$	One-sample z or t test	Sign test
H_0: $(\mu_1 - \mu_2) = D_0$	Two-sample z or t test (Independent samples)	Wilcoxon rank sum test
H_0: $\mu_d = D_0$	Two-sample z or t test (Matched samples)	Wilcoxon signed ranks test

LOOKING AHEAD

Parametric and nonparametric methods for making inferences about population variances are the topic of Chapter 7.

CASE STUDY

THE SAT PILL

According to *Newsweek* (Nov. 16, 1987), "Some students will do anything to inch closer to a perfect 1600 on the Scholastic Aptitude Tests (SAT). And if you think we're talking lucky shirts or a peek at a neighbor's answers, wake up to the pharmaceutical age. A researcher reports that a prescription drug may help nervous test takers improve their SATs."

The researcher is Dr. Harrison Faigel of Brandeis University. Over a period of 2 years, Faigel experimented with giving propranolol, one of the class of heart drugs called beta blockers, to nervous high school students prior to taking their SATs. Beta blockers, which interfere with adrenaline, have been used for heart conditions and minor stress such as stage fright for over 25 years. Faigel felt that the same calming effect beta blockers provide heart patients could also be used to reduce anxiety in test takers.

To test his theory, he selected 22 high school juniors who had not performed as well on the SAT as they should have based on IQ and other academic evaluations.

Presumably, these students performed poorly because they approached the SAT with a tremendous amount of anxiety and fear. One hour before the students repeated the test in their senior year, Faigel administered each a dosage of a beta blocker.

The (simulated) test scores of these students in both their junior and senior years are provided in Table 6.9.

TABLE 6.9
SAT Scores for the Case

STUDENT	SAT SCORES Junior Year	SAT SCORES Senior Year	STUDENT	SAT SCORES Junior Year	SAT SCORES Senior Year
1	810	984	12	933	945
2	965	1015	13	811	897
3	707	1006	14	774	875
4	652	995	15	780	923
5	983	997	16	913	884
6	822	963	17	655	931
7	874	860	18	906	1136
8	900	915	19	737	854
9	693	847	20	788	927
10	1115	1202	21	878	872
11	749	910	22	912	1054

Note: SAT scores are simulated based on information provided in *Newsweek*.

Nationally, students who retake the test without special preparations will increase their scores by an average of 38 points. Faigel's students, however, improved their scores by an average of 120 points! Nevertheless, Robert Cameron, director of research and development for the College Board (sponsors of the SAT), warns that "the findings have to be taken with a great deal of caution" and that they should not be interpreted to mean "that someone has discovered the magic pill that will unlock the SAT for thousands of teenagers who believe they do not do as well as they should because they're nervous."*

Based on the sample results, what inference would you make about the use of beta blockers to increase SAT scores?

REFERENCES

Conover, W. J. *Practical Nonparametric Statistics*. New York: Wiley, 1971.
Freeman, D., Pisani, R., and Purves, R. *Statistics*. New York: Norton, 1978.
Hollander, M., and Wolfe, D. A. *Nonparametric Statistical Methods*. New York: Wiley, 1973.
McClave, J. T., and Dietrich, F. H. *Statistics*, 6th ed. New York: Macmillan, 1994.
Mendenhall, W. *Introduction to Probability and Statistics*, 7th ed. Boston: Duxbury, 1986.
Mendenhall, W., Wackerly, D., and Scheaffer, R. *Mathematical Statistics with Applications*, 4th ed. Boston: PWS-Kent, 1989.

* *Gainesville Sun*, Oct. 22, 1987.

Sincich, T. *Statistics by Example*, 5th ed. New York: Macmillan, 1993.

Snedecor, G. W., and Cochran, W. G. *Statistical Methods*, 7th ed. Ames: Iowa State University Press, 1980.

SAMPLE EXAM QUESTIONS: CHAPTER 6

(1–3) The methodology for conducting a stress analysis of newly designed timber structures is well-known. However, few data are available on the actual or allowable stress for repairing damaged structures. Consequently, design engineers often propose a repair scheme (eg, gluing) without any knowledge of its structural effectiveness. To partially fill this void, a stress analysis was conducted on epoxy-repaired truss joints (*Journal of Structural Engineering*, Feb. 1986). Tests were conducted on epoxy-bonded truss joints made of various species of wood to determine actual glue-line shear stress (recorded in pounds per square inch, psi). Summary information for independent random samples of southern pine and ponderosa pine truss joints is given in the table.

	SOUTHERN PINE	PONDEROSA PINE
Sample size	100	47
Mean shear stress (psi)	1,312	1,352
Standard deviation	422	271

Source: Avent, R. R. "Design Criteria for Epoxy Repair of Timber Structures." *Journal of Structural Engineering,* Vol. 112, No. 2, Feb. 1986, p. 232.

1. Estimate the difference between the mean shear strengths of epoxy-repaired truss joints for the two species of wood with a 90% confidence interval.
2. Give a practical interpretation of the interval.
3. Give a theoretical interpretation of the phrase "90% confidence."

(4–5) The following experiment was conducted to compare two coatings designed to improve the durability of the soles of jogging shoes. A $\frac{1}{8}$ inch layer of coating 1 was applied to one of a pair of shoes, and a layer of equal thickness of coating 2 was applied to the other shoe. Ten joggers were given pairs of shoes treated in this manner and were instructed to record the number of miles covered in each shoe before the $\frac{1}{8}$ inch coating was worn through in any one place. The results are listed in the table.

JOGGER	COATING 1	COATING 2	JOGGER	COATING 1	COATING 2
1	892	985	6	853	875
2	904	953	7	780	895
3	775	775	8	695	725
4	435	510	9	825	858
5	946	895	10	750	812

4. What type of sampling design is used for this experiment?
5. Analyze the data to determine whether a difference exists between the mean number of miles of wear for the two sole coatings.

(6) The Department of Highway Improvements, responsible for repairing a 25 mile stretch of interstate highway, wants to design a surface that will be structurally efficient. One important consideration is the volume of heavy freight traffic on the interstate. State weigh stations report that the average number of heavy-duty trailers traveling on a 25 mile segment of the interstate is 72 per hour. However, the section of highway to be repaired is located in an urban area and the department engineers believe that the volume of heavy freight traffic for this particular sector is greater than the average reported for the entire interstate. To validate this theory, the department monitors the highway for 50 periods of 1 hour randomly selected throughout a month. Suppose the sample mean and standard deviation of the heavy freight traffic for the 50 sampled hours are

$$\bar{x} = 74.1 \qquad s = 13.3$$

6. Do the data support the department's theory? Use $\alpha = .10$.

(7–9) Gerald Appel, president of Signalert Corporation, an investment advisory firm, has found what he believes to be an indicator of upturns in the stock market. As he explains in *Barron's* (Feb. 27, 1984), "only rarely does the market fall with such velocity that the spread between the weekly [New York Stock Exchange] index and the [10 week] moving average [of that index] stretches to -4.0 or more. Such a dramatic plunge nearly always has indicated a market that is deeply oversold and ready for either recovery or at least a respite from selling pressure." Appel dubs this market signal "the major bottom indicator." Between 1970 and 1984, the major bottom indicator signaled a buy eight times. The performance of these major bottom indicators (measured as percentage gain in NYSE index) 26 weeks after the buy signal is shown in the table. If the major bottom indicator is, in fact, a trustworthy indicator of upward turns in the market in the long run, then the true mean percentage gain for the 26 week period will be greater than 0%.

BUY SIGNAL	PERCENTAGE GAIN IN NYSE INDEX 26 WEEKS AFTER BUY	BUY SIGNAL	PERCENTAGE GAIN IN NYSE INDEX 26 WEEKS AFTER BUY
1	21.1	5	3.6
2	−7.7	6	32.7
3	30.6	7	−2.7
4	7.1	8	33.8

Source: Appel, G. "Have We Hit Bottom? A Trusty Indicator Signals a Possible Turn in the Market." *Barron's*, Feb. 27, 1984, p. 24. Reprinted by permission of *Barron's*, © 1984 Dow Jones & Company, Inc. All rights reserved worldwide.

7. Test this hypothesis at significance level $\alpha = .05$, using a parametric test.
8. Use a nonparametric method to test the hypothesis.
9. Which of the two tests, parametric or nonparametric, do you recommend?

(10–11) Are Japanese managers and their workers more motivated than their American counterparts? Claims in the literature tout the superiority of the Japanese-inspired "Theory Z" management for business productivity. The Theory Z philosophy emphasizes trusting, intimate, and subtle relationships between management and workers; directness and confrontation are avoided. To investigate this phenomenon, researchers surveyed middle-aged Japanese and American business managers (*Personnel Psychology*, Winter 1983). The Japanese sample consisted of 100 managers selected at a 2 day management seminar in Tokyo and Osaka, while the American sample was made up of 211 managers employed in the Bell System. Each manager was administered the Sarnoff Survey of Attitudes Toward Life (SSATL), which measures motivation for upward mobility in three areas: advancement, forward striving, and money. The SSATL scores are summarized in the table. (Higher scores indicate a greater motivation for upward mobility.)

	AMERICAN MANAGERS	JAPANESE MANAGERS
Sample size	211	100
Mean SSATL score	65.75	79.83
Standard deviation	11.07	6.41

10. Set up the null and alternative hypotheses for testing Theory Z.
11. A MINITAB printout of the analysis is shown at the top of the next page. Interpret the results.

```
TWOSAMPLE T FOR USA VS JAPAN
           N      MEAN    STDEV   SE MEAN
USA      211     65.75    11.07     .76
JAPAN    100     79.83     6.41     .64

95 PCT CI FOR MU USA - MU JAPAN: (-16.42, -11.74)

TTEST MU USA = MU JAPAN (VS NE): T= -11.81  P=0.000  DF= 309

POOLED STDEV =      9.82
```

(12–13) In the early 1960's, the air-conditioning systems of a fleet of Boeing 720 jet airplanes came under investigation. The table presents the lifelengths (in hours) of the air-conditioning systems in two different Boeing 720 planes. Assume the data represent random samples from the respective populations.

| PLANE 1 | 23 | 118 | 90 | 29 | 156 | 49 | 10 | 310 | 76 | 62 |
| PLANE 2 | 59 | 32 | 4 | 102 | 66 | 230 | 54 | 152 | 67 | 34 |

Source: Hollander, M., Park, D. H., and Proschan, F. "Testing Whether *F* is "More NBU" Than Is *G.*" *Microelectronics and Reliability*, Vol. 26, No. 1, 1986, p. 43 (Table I). Copyright 1986, Pergamon Press, Ltd. Reprinted with permission.

12. Determine whether a parametric or nonparametric procedure is more appropriate for comparing the lifelength distributions of air-conditioning systems for the two Boeing 720 planes.

13. The SAS printout of the analysis (both parametric and nonparametric) is shown below. Interpret the results.

```
                        TTEST PROCEDURE
Variable: LIFE

PLANE     N       Mean        Std Dev      Std Error      Minimum        Maximum
------------------------------------------------------------------------------------
  1      10   92.30000000   88.66798245   28.03927801   10.00000000   310.0000000
  2      10   80.00000000   66.53820957   21.04122937    4.00000000   230.0000000

Variances        T       DF     Prob>|T|
----------------------------------------
Unequal      0.3509    16.7     0.7301
Equal        0.3509    18.0     0.7298

For H0: Variances are equal, F' = 1.78    DF = (9,9)    Prob>F' = 0.4052


                NPAR1WAY  PROCEDURE

        Wilcoxon Scores (Rank Sums) for Variable LIFE
               Classified by Variable PLANE

                       Sum of     Expected      Std Dev        Mean
    PLANE      N       Scores     Under H0      Under H0       Score

      1       10       107.0       105.0      13.2287566   10.7000000
      2       10       103.0       105.0      13.2287566   10.3000000

        Wilcoxon 2-Sample Test (Normal Approximation)
        (with Continuity Correction of .5)

        S= 107.000      Z= 0.113389    Prob > |Z| =    0.9097

        T-Test approx. Significance =     0.9109

        Kruskal-Wallis Test (Chi-Square Approximation)
        CHISQ= 0.02286    DF= 1    Prob > CHISQ=    0.8798
```

(14–17) Because external audits can be quite expensive, many companies are creating or augmenting internal audit departments to lower auditing costs. A *Harvard Business Review* (Mar.–Apr. 1984) survey of the audit departments of diverse companies was conducted to estimate the mean annual external audit fee paid by the companies.

14. What is the parameter of interest to the researcher?

15. How many companies must be sampled in order to estimate the mean external audit fee to within $50,000 of its true value with 95% confidence? (Assume the standard deviation of audit fees is approximately $250,000.)

16. How can you decrease the width of the 95% confidence interval referred to in the previous question?

17. How can you decrease the sample size of Question 15 and retain the $50,000 bound on the error of estimation?

(18–20) Are learning preferences of college students affected by program instruction or do they remain stable over time? To answer this question, researchers administered the Learning Preference Inventory (LPI) exam to 37 junior students at the University of Illinois during the first week the students were on campus.* (The LPI measures preference for learning in a well-organized, teacher-directed class, with expectations, assignments, and goals clearly defined. The higher the LPI score, the greater the preference.) Following four quarters of academic course work, which included independent study methods and small-group tutorials, as well as the traditional classroom lectures, the students were again administered the LPI. The differences between the LPI scores (score before minus score after) for the sample of 37 students had a mean of 4.11 and a standard deviation of 15.82.

18. Give the null and alternative hypotheses appropriate for testing whether the mean score on the LPI exam given at the beginning of the term differs from the mean score on the LPI exam given after four quarters of academic course work.

19. Note that the data were collected as matched pairs. For this application, what is the advantage of using a matched-pairs experiment rather than independent samples?

20. Conduct the test of Question 18 using $\alpha = .05$. Can you infer that the students' preferences for learning in a teacher-structured atmosphere (as measured by the LPI) changed after four quarters of academic course work? Explain.

* Cahill, R., and Madigan, M. J. "The Influence of Curriculum Format on Learning Preference and Learning Style." *The American Journal of Occupational Therapy*, Vol. 38, No. 10, Oct. 1984, pp. 683–686. Copyright 1984 by the American Occupational Therapy Association, Inc. Reprinted with permission.

CHAPTER 7

ONE-SAMPLE AND TWO-SAMPLE INFERENTIAL METHODS FOR QUANTITATIVE DATA: VARIANCES

CONTENTS

Bid-rigging—that is, fixing the price of goods above the competitive market price—is a problem prevalent within the state of Florida. For example, the pattern of variation in bid prices for white bread sold to the Florida public schools led to discovery of bid-rigging in the bread market. In this chapter we learn how to construct confidence intervals and perform tests of hypothesis about population variances for quantitative data. These methods are applied to the white bread bid price data in the chapter case study.

INFERENCES ABOUT A SINGLE POPULATION VARIANCE

PARAMETRIC METHODS

7.1 Suppose we want to make an inference about the variance, σ^2, of some quantitative population based on a sample of size n. Intuitively, it seems reasonable to use the sample variance, s^2, to estimate σ^2 and to base our inferences on this value. Unlike sample means, the sampling distribution of the sample variance, s^2, does not possess a normal (z) distribution or a t distribution; thus, we cannot use the general formulas for confidence intervals and tests given in Chapters 5 and 6. However, if the sampled population is normally distributed, the sampling distribution of s^2 possesses approximately a **chi-square (χ^2) distribution**. (We use the words "chi-square" and the Greek symbol χ^2 interchangeably.)

SAMPLING DISTRIBUTION OF THE SAMPLE VARIANCE, s^2

Consider a sample of size n from a normal population with variance σ^2. Then the quantity $(n-1)s^2/\sigma^2$ possesses a χ^2 sampling distribution with $(n-1)$ degrees of freedom.

The chi-square probability distribution, like the t distribution, is characterized by a quantity called the **degrees of freedom (df)** associated with the distribution. Several chi-square probability distributions with different degrees of freedom are shown in Figure 7.1. Unlike the z and the t distributions, the chi-square distribution is not symmetric about 0.

FIGURE 7.1
Several Chi-Square Probability Distributions

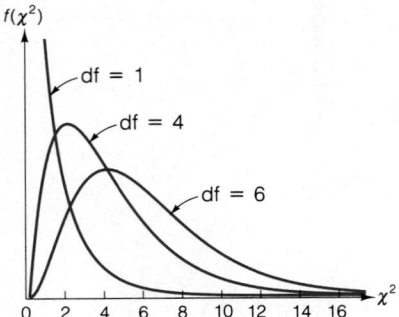

Tabulated values of the χ^2 distribution are given in Table 6, Appendix A. Part of this table is shown in Table 7.1. Entries in the table give an upper-tail value of χ^2 and call it χ^2_α, such that $P(\chi^2 > \chi^2_\alpha) = \alpha$. For example, the tabulated value of χ^2 corresponding to df = 2 and $\alpha = .05$ is $\chi^2_{.05} = 5.99147$. This value is shaded in Table 7.1.

Confidence intervals and tests for the population variance σ^2 based on the χ^2 statistic are carried out as indicated in the box on the next page.

Note that the assumption of a normal population is required regardless of whether the sample size n is large or small.

TABLE 7.1
Reproduction of Part of Table 6, Appendix A: Critical Values for the χ^2 Statistic

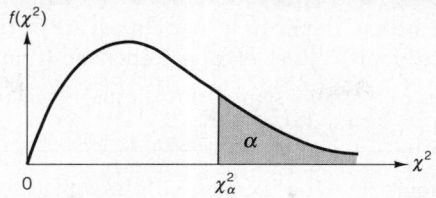

DEGREES OF FREEDOM	$\chi^2_{.100}$	$\chi^2_{.050}$	$\chi^2_{.025}$	$\chi^2_{.010}$	$\chi^2_{.005}$
1	2.70554	3.84146	5.02389	6.63490	7.87944
2	4.60517	5.99147	7.37776	9.21034	10.5966
3	6.25139	7.81473	9.34840	11.3449	12.8381
4	7.77944	9.48773	11.1433	13.2767	14.8602
5	9.23635	11.0705	12.8325	15.0863	16.7496
6	10.6446	12.5916	14.4494	16.8119	18.5476
7	12.0170	14.0671	16.0128	18.4753	20.2777
8	13.3616	15.5073	17.5346	20.0902	21.9550
9	14.6837	16.9190	19.0228	21.6660	23.5893
10	15.9871	18.3070	20.4831	23.2093	25.1882
11	17.2750	19.6751	21.9200	24.7250	26.7569
12	18.5494	21.0261	23.3367	26.2170	28.2995

PARAMETRIC INFERENCES FOR A POPULATION VARIANCE, σ^2

$(1 - \alpha)100\%$ CONFIDENCE INTERVAL

$$\frac{(n - 1)s^2}{\chi^2_{\alpha/2}} \leq \sigma^2 \leq \frac{(n - 1)s^2}{\chi^2_{(1-\alpha/2)}}$$

where $\chi^2_{\alpha/2}$ and $\chi^2_{(1-\alpha/2)}$ are the values of χ^2 that locate an area of $\alpha/2$ to the right and $\alpha/2$ to the left, respectively, of a chi-square distribution based on $(n - 1)$ degrees of freedom. (Values of χ^2 are obtained from Table 6, Appendix A.)

TEST OF HYPOTHESIS

ONE-TAILED TEST

H_0: $\sigma^2 = \sigma_0^2$

H_a: $\sigma^2 > \sigma_0^2$

[or H_a: $\sigma^2 < \sigma_0^2$]

TWO-TAILED TEST

H_0: $\sigma^2 = \sigma_0^2$

H_a: $\sigma^2 \neq \sigma_0^2$

Test statistic: $\dfrac{(n - 1)s^2}{\sigma_0^2}$

(continued)

Rejection region: *Rejection region:*

$$\chi^2 > \chi^2_\alpha \quad [\text{or } \chi^2 < \chi^2_{(1-\alpha)}] \qquad \chi^2 < \chi^2_{(1-\alpha/2)} \text{ or } \chi^2 > \chi^2_{\alpha/2}$$

where χ^2_α and $\chi^2_{(1-\alpha)}$ are values of χ^2 that locate an area of α to the right and α to the left, respectively, of a chi-square distribution based on $(n-1)$ degrees of freedom. (Values of χ^2 are obtained from Table 6, Appendix A.)

Note: σ^2_0 is our symbol for the particular numerical value specified for σ^2 in the null hypothesis.

Assumption: The population from which the random sample is selected has an approximate normal distribution.

EXAMPLE 7.1   A quality control supervisor in a cannery knows that the exact amount each can contains will vary, since there are certain uncontrollable factors that affect the amount of fill. The mean fill per can is important, but equally important is the variation, σ^2, of the amount of fill. If σ^2 is large, some cans will contain too little and others too much. Suppose regulatory agencies specify that the standard deviation of the amount of fill for 8 ounce cans should be less than .1 ounce. The quality control supervisor sampled $n = 10$ of the 8 ounce cans and measured the amount of fill in each. The data (in ounces) are shown below. Do the data provide sufficient evidence to indicate that the standard deviation, σ, of the fill measurements is less than .1 ounce?

    7.96   7.90   7.98   8.01   7.97   7.96   8.03   8.02   8.04   8.02

Solution   Since the null and alternative hypotheses must be stated in terms of σ^2 (rather than σ), we will want to test the null hypothesis that $\sigma^2 = .01$ against the alternative that $\sigma^2 < .01$. Therefore, the elements of the test are

H_0: $\sigma^2 = .01$ That is, $\sigma = .1$

H_a: $\sigma^2 < .01$ That is, $\sigma < .1$

Assumption: The population of amounts of fill in the cans is approximately normal.

Test statistic: $\chi^2 = \dfrac{(n-1)s^2}{\sigma^2_0}$

Rejection region: The smaller the value of s^2 we observe, the stronger the evidence in favor of H_a. Thus, we reject H_0 for "small values" of the test statistic. With $\alpha = .05$ and $(n-1) = 9$ df, the critical χ^2 value is found in Table 6, Appendix A, and pictured in Figure 7.2. We will reject H_0 if $\chi^2 < 3.32511$. (Remember that the area given in Table 6 is the area to the *right* of the numerical value in the table. Thus, to determine the lower-tail value that has $\alpha = .05$ to its *left*, we use the $\chi^2_{.95}$ column in Table 6.)

       To compute the test statistic, we need to find the sample standard deviation, s. Numerical descriptive statistics for the sample data are provided in the SAS printout shown in Figure 7.3. The value of s, shaded in Figure 7.3, is $s = .043$.

FIGURE 7.2
Rejection Region

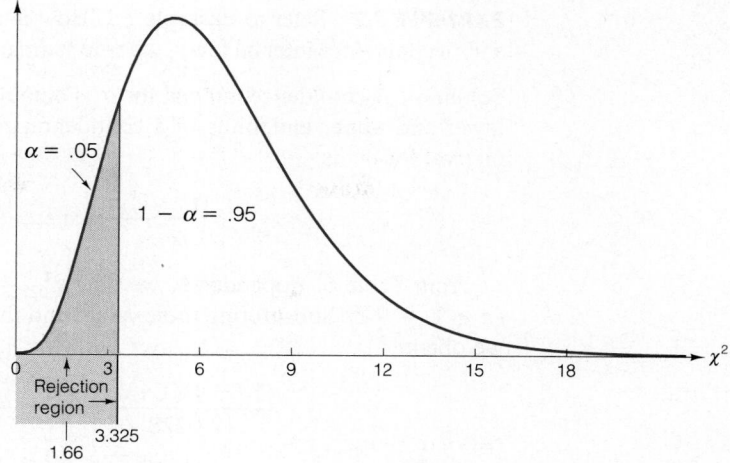

FIGURE 7.3
SAS Printout: Descriptive Statistics

```
Variable=FILL

                       Moments

N                 10    Sum Wgts          10
Mean           7.989    Sum            79.89
Std Dev     0.043063    Variance    0.001854
Skewness     -0.8538    Kurtosis    0.479371
USS         638.2579    CSS          0.01669
CV          0.539032    Std Mean    0.013618
T:Mean=0    586.6587    Prob>|T|      0.0001
Sgn Rank        27.5    Prob>|S|      0.0020
Num ^= 0          10

                  Quantiles(Def=5)

100% Max        8.04         99%         8.04
 75% Q3         8.02         95%         8.04
 50% Med       7.995         90%        8.035
 25% Q1         7.96         10%         7.93
  0% Min         7.9          5%          7.9
                              1%          7.9

Range           0.14
Q3-Q1           0.06
Mode            7.96
```

Substituting $s = .043$, $n = 10$, and $\sigma_0^2 = .01$ into the formula for the test statistic, we obtain

$$\chi^2 = \frac{(10 - 1)(.043)^2}{.01} = 1.66$$

Conclusion: Since the test statistic, $\chi^2 = 1.66$, is less than 3.32511, the supervisor can conclude (at $\alpha = .05$) that the variance of the population of all amounts of fill is less than .01 ($\sigma < .1$). If this procedure (ie, the χ^2 test) is used repeatedly, the significance level, .05, implies that the test will incorrectly reject H_0 only 5% of the time. Thus, the quality control supervisor is confident in the decision that the cannery is operating within the desired limits of variability.

EXAMPLE 7.2   Refer to Example 7.1. How much smaller is σ than .1 ounce? Find a 95% confidence interval for σ, the true standard deviation of the fill measurements.

Solution   A confidence interval for σ is obtained by taking the square roots of the lower and upper endpoints of a confidence interval for σ^2. The 95% confidence interval for σ^2 is

$$\frac{(n-1)s^2}{\chi^2_{.025}} \le \sigma^2 \le \frac{(n-1)s^2}{\chi^2_{.975}}$$

From Table 6, Appendix A, we find $\chi^2_{.025} = 19.0228$ and $\chi^2_{.975} = 2.70039$ for $(n-1) = 9$ df. Substituting these values and the values of s^2 and n into the formula, we obtain

$$\frac{(10-1)(.043)^2}{19.0228} \le \sigma^2 \le \frac{(10-1)(.043)^2}{2.70039}$$

$$.000875 \le \sigma^2 \le .006162$$

Then the 95% confidence interval for σ is

$$\sqrt{.000875} \le \sigma \le \sqrt{.006162}$$

$$.030 \le \sigma \le .079$$

Thus, we are 95% confident that the true standard deviation of the fill measurements is between .030 and .079 ounce.

NONPARAMETRIC METHODS

With nonnormal populations, inferences about σ^2 based on the χ^2 statistic are suspect. In this situation, we can apply a nonparametric procedure that is based on a statistic called the **median absolute deviation, MAD**.

Let $x_1, x_2, ..., x_n$ be a sample of quantitative measurements from some population, and let M represent the sample median. For each x_i, calculate the absolute deviation, $|x_i - M|$. The MAD is the median of these absolute deviations divided by the constant .6745.

DEFINITION 7.1

The **median absolute deviation, MAD**, for a sample of n observations is the median of the absolute deviations $|x_i - M|$ $(i = 1, 2, 3, ..., n)$ divided by .6745.

Just as the median, M, is a robust measure of the center of a distribution, the MAD is a robust measure of spread. For approximately normal data, the population MAD will approximately equal the population standard deviation, σ. However, for skewed distributions, the MAD is less sensitive to extreme observations than σ.

Since the MAD is a median, we can utilize the nonparametric sign test of Section 6.2 to test a hypothesis about spread. The elements of the test are shown in the box.

NONPARAMETRIC TEST FOR POPULATION SPREAD, MAD

ONE-TAILED TEST	TWO-TAILED TEST
H_0: MAD = MAD_0	H_0: MAD = MAD_0
H_a: MAD > MAD_0	H_a: MAD $\neq$ MAD_0
[or H_a: MAD < MAD_0]	

For each measurement in the sample, compute the absolute deviation

$$\frac{|x_i - M|}{.6745}$$

where M is the sample median. Then compare each absolute deviation to MAD_0.

Test statistic:

S = Number of absolute deviations greater than MAD_0.

[or S = Number of absolute deviations less than MAD_0]

Test statistic:

S = Larger of S_1 or S_2

where S_1 is the number of absolute deviations greater than MAD_0, and S_2 is the number of absolute deviations less than MAD_0

Observed significance level:

p-Value = $P(x \geq S)$

Observed significance level:

p-Value = $2P(x \geq S)$

where x has a binomial distribution with parameters n and $\pi = .5$.

Rejection region: Reject H_0 if p-value $< \alpha$.

Note: The median absolute deviation, MAD, is similar to the population standard deviation σ.

EXAMPLE 7.3 Use the nonparametric sign test to analyze the data in Example 7.1. Test using $\alpha = .05$.

Solution Since we want to determine whether the population standard deviation is less than .1 ounce, we will test

H_0: MAD = .1

H_a: MAD < .1

To obtain the test statistic, we first need to compute, for each sample measurement, the absolute deviation

$$\frac{|x_i - M|}{.6745}$$

where the sample median of the 10 fill measurements is $M = 7.995$ (see Figure 7.3). Using the formula, the absolute deviations are

$$\frac{|x_1 - 7.995|}{.6745} = \frac{|7.96 - 7.995|}{.6745} = .0519$$

$$\frac{|x_2 - 7.995|}{.6745} = \frac{|7.90 - 7.995|}{.6745} = .1408$$

$$\vdots \qquad \vdots \qquad \vdots$$

$$\frac{|x_{10} - 7.995|}{.6745} = \frac{|8.02 - 7.995|}{.6745} = .0371$$

All 10 absolute deviations, rearranged in order of magnitude, are shown in Table 7.2.

TABLE 7.2
Absolute Deviation for Data in Example 7.3

ORIGINAL MEASUREMENT x_i	ABSOLUTE DEVIATION $|x_i - 7.995|/.6745$	SIGN OF (ABSOLUTE DEVIATION $-$ MAD$_0$)
8.01	.0222	$-$
7.98	.0222	$-$
8.02	.0371	$-$
8.02	.0371	$-$
7.97	.0371	$-$
8.03	.0519	$-$
7.96	.0519	$-$
7.96	.0519	$-$
8.04	.0667	$-$
7.90	.1408	$+$

You can see that all absolute deviations, except for the one corresponding to the measurement 7.90, are less than the hypothesized value of MAD (ie, MAD$_0$ = .1). Consequently, the test statistic S for this lower-tailed test is

Test statistic: $S = 9$

In Table 1, Appendix A, the binomial table corresponding to $n = 10$ shows that the p-value of the test is

p-Value: $P(x \geq 9) = 1 - P(x \leq 8)$
$$= 1 - .9893 = .0107$$

Since the p-value is smaller than $\alpha = .05$, there is sufficient evidence to reject H_0. Thus, we arrive at the same conclusion as in Example 7.1—the spread of the fill amounts, as measured by MAD, is less than .1 ounce at a significance level of .05.

PROBLEMS

7.1 Snyder and Chrissis (1990) presented a hybrid algorithm for solving a polynomial zero–one mathematical programming problem. The algorithm incorporates a mixture of pseudo-Boolean concepts and time-proven implicit enumeration procedures. Fifty-two random problems were solved using the hybrid algorithm; the times to solution (CPU time in seconds) are listed in the table. The SAS printout giving descriptive statistics for the sample of 52 solution times is provided below. Use this information to compute a 95% confidence interval for the variance of the solution times. Interpret the result.

.045	1.055	.136	1.894	.379	.136	.336	.258
1.070	.506	.088	.242	1.639	.912	.412	.361
8.788	.579	1.267	.567	.182	.036	.394	.209
.445	.179	.118	.333	.554	.258	.182	.070
3.985	.670	3.888	.136	.091	.600	.219	.327
.130	.145	4.170	.227	.064	.194	.209	.258
3.046	.045	.049	.079				

Source: Snyder, W. S., and Chrissis, J. W. "A Hybrid Algorithm for Solving Zero–One Mathematical Programming Problems." *IEEE Transactions*, Vol. 22, No. 2, June 1990, p. 166 (Table 1).

```
Analysis Variable : CPU

N Obs   N      Mean      Variance     Std Dev
-----------------------------------------------
   52   52   0.8121923   2.2643035   1.5047603
-----------------------------------------------
```

7.2 Refer to Problem 7.1. Suppose you want to test whether the true variance of the solution times exceeds $\sigma^2 = 2$.

a. Determine whether a parametric or nonparametric test is more appropriate.
b. Conduct the test from part **a**, and make the proper conclusion.

7.3 A machine used to fill beer cans must operate so that the amount of beer actually dispensed varies very little. If too much beer is released, the cans will overflow, causing waste. If too little beer is released, the cans will not contain enough beer, causing complaints from customers. A random sample of the fills for 20 cans yielded a standard deviation of .07 ounce. Estimate the true standard deviation of the fills using a 95% confidence interval.

7.4 Recording electrical activity of the brain is important in clinical problems as well as neurophysiological research. To improve the signal-to-noise ratio (SNR) in the electrical activity, it is necessary to repeatedly stimulate subjects and average the responses—a procedure that assumes that single responses are homogeneous. A study was conducted to test the homogeneous signal theory (*IEEE Engineering in Medicine and Biology Magazine*, Mar. 1990). The null hypothesis is that the variance of the SNR readings of subjects equals the expected level under the homogeneous signal theory. For this study, the expected level was assumed to be .54. If the SNR variance exceeds this level, the researchers will conclude that the signals are nonhomogeneous.

a. Set up the null and alternative hypotheses for the researchers.
b. SNRs recorded for a sample of 41 normal children ranged from .03 to 3.0. Use this information to obtain an estimate of the sample standard deviation. [*Hint:* Assume that the distribution of SNRs is normal, and that most SNRs in the population will fall within $\mu \pm 2\sigma$, that is, from $\mu - 2\sigma$ to $\mu + 2\sigma$. Note that the range of the interval equals 4σ.]
c. Use the estimate of s in part **b** to conduct the test of part **a**. Test using $\alpha = .10$.

7.5 Refer to Problem 5.16 and the MINITAB printout (repeated below) showing descriptive statistics for the sample of 50 return-to-pay ratios of CEOs. Use the information in the printout to construct a 90% confidence interval for σ, the true standard deviation of the return-to-pay ratios of CEOs. Interpret the interval.

	N	MEAN	STDEV	SE MEAN	95.0 PERCENT C.I.
ratio	50	0.05120	0.04530	0.00641	(0.03832, 0.06408)

7.6 The most common method of disinfecting water for potability is free residual chlorination. Recently, preammoniation (ie, the addition of ammonia to the water prior to applying free chlorine) has received considerable attention as an alternative treatment. In one study, 44 water specimens treated with ammonia had a mean effluent turbidity of 1.8 and a standard deviation of .16 (*American Water Works Journal*, Jan. 1986). Is there sufficient evidence to indicate that the variance of the effluent turbidity in water specimens disinfected by the preammoniation method exceeds .0016? (The value .0016 represents the known effluent turbidity variance of water specimens treated with free chlorine.) Test using $\alpha = .01$.

7.7 Polychlorinated biphenyls (PCBs), used in the manufacture of large electrical transformers and capacitors, are extremely hazardous contaminants when released into the environment. The Environmental Protection Agency (EPA) is experimenting with a new device for measuring PCB concentration in fish. To check the precision of the new instrument, seven PCB readings were taken on the same fish sample. The data are recorded here (in parts per million):

    6.2   5.8   5.7   6.3   5.9   5.8   6.0

Suppose the EPA requires an instrument to yield PCB readings with a variance of less than .1. Does the new instrument meet the EPA's specifications? Use a nonparametric test at $\alpha = .05$.

7.8 A new gun-like apparatus has been devised to replace the needle in administering vaccines. The apparatus, which is connected to a large supply of the vaccine, can be set to inject different amounts of the serum, but the variance in the amount of serum injected in a given person must not be greater than .06 to ensure proper inoculation. A random sample of 25 injections resulted in a variance of .135. Do the data provide sufficient evidence to indicate the gun is not working properly? Use $\alpha = .10$.

7.9 Refer to the *Sleep* (Jan. 1989) study of sleep-deprived college students discussed in Problem 5.25 (p. 227). The overall test scores (lower scores are associated with a decreased ability to think creatively) of 12 sleep-deprived students had a mean of $\bar{x} = 63$ and a standard deviation of $s = 17$. Some sleep experts believe that although most people lose their ability to think creatively when deprived of sleep, others are not nearly as affected. Consequently, they theorize that the variation in test scores for sleep-deprived subjects is larger than 225, the estimated variation in scores of those who receive their usual amount of sleep. Test the hypothesis that σ^2, the variance in test scores of sleep-deprived subjects, is larger than 225. Use $\alpha = .01$.

COMPARING TWO POPULATION VARIANCES

7.2 In this section we present confidence intervals and tests of hypothesis for comparing two population variances, σ_1^2 and σ_2^2. Variance tests have broad applications in business. For example, a production manager may be interested in comparing the variation in the length of eye screws produced on each of two assembly lines. A line with a large variation produces too many individual eye screws that do not meet specifications (either too long or too short), even though the mean length may be satisfactory. Similarly, an investor might want to compare the variation in the monthly rates of return for two different stocks that have the same mean rate of return. In this case, the stock with the smaller variance may be preferred because

---

it is less risky—that is, it is less likely to have many very low and very high monthly return rates.

Variance tests can also be applied before conducting a small-sample t test for $(\mu_1 - \mu_2)$, as discussed in Section 6.3. Recall that the t test requires the variances of the two sampled populations to be equal. If the two population variances are greatly different, any inferences derived from the t test are suspect. Consequently, it is important that we detect a significant difference between the two variances, if it exists, before applying the small-sample t test, so that we can make the necessary modifications.

PARAMETRIC METHODS

The common parametric statistical procedure for comparing two population variances, σ_1^2 and σ_2^2, makes an inference about the ratio σ_1^2/σ_2^2. This is because the sampling distribution of s_1^2/s_2^2, the estimator of σ_1^2/σ_2^2 has an **F distribution** when the samples are randomly and independently selected from two normal populations.

SAMPLING DISTRIBUTION OF s_1^2/s_2^2

For independent random samples selected from normal populations, the ratio s_1^2/s_2^2 has an **F sampling distribution** with $(n_1 - 1)$ **numerator degrees of freedom** and $(n_2 - 1)$ **denominator degrees of freedom**.

FIGURE 7.4

An F Distribution with 7 Numerator Degrees of Freedom and 9 Denominator Degrees of Freedom

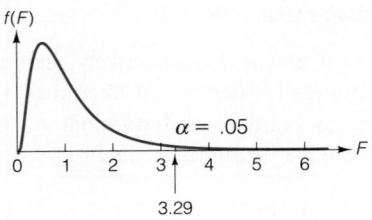

Unlike the z and t distributions, an F distribution can be symmetric about its mean, skewed to the left, or skewed to the right; its exact shape depends on a pair of values called the **numerator and denominator degrees of freedom** (see Figure 7.4).

Upper-tail critical values of F are found in Tables 7–10, Appendix A. Table 8, partially reproduced in Table 7.3 (p. 315), gives F values that correspond to $\alpha = .05$ upper-tail areas for different pairs of degrees of freedom. The columns of the table correspond to various numerator degrees of freedom (ν_1), while the rows correspond to various denominator degrees of freedom (ν_2). Thus, if $\nu_1 = 7$ and $\nu_2 = 9$, we look in the seventh column and ninth row to find the F value:

$F_{.05} = 3.29$ Shaded in Table 7.3

As shown in Figure 7.4, $\alpha = .05$ is the tail area to the right of 3.29 in the F distribution with $\nu_1 = 7$ and $\nu_2 = 9$ degrees of freedom. Thus, the probability that the F statistic will exceed 3.29 is $\alpha = .05$.

The elements of a confidence interval and hypothesis test for the ratio of two population variances, σ_1^2/σ_2^2, based on the F distribution, are given in the box on the next page. Note that assumptions are required regardless of the sizes of the samples selected.

PARAMETRIC INFERENCES FOR THE RATIO OF TWO POPULATION VARIANCES, σ_1^2 / σ_2^2

$(1 - \alpha)100\%$ CONFIDENCE INTERVAL

$$\frac{(s_1^2/s_2^2)}{F_{U,\alpha/2}} \leq \frac{\sigma_1^2}{\sigma_2^2} \leq (s_1^2/s_2^2) \cdot F_{L,\alpha/2}$$

where $F_{U,\alpha/2}$ locates an area $\alpha/2$ in the upper tail of an F distribution with $\nu_1 = (n_1 - 1)$ numerator degrees of freedom and $\nu_2 = (n_2 - 1)$ denominator degrees of freedom, and $F_{L,\alpha/2}$ locates an area $\alpha/2$ in the upper tail of an F distribution with $\nu_1 = (n_2 - 1)$ numerator degrees of freedom and $\nu_2 = (n_1 - 1)$ denominator degrees of freedom.

TEST OF HYPOTHESIS

ONE-TAILED TEST

H_0: $(\sigma_1^2/\sigma_2^2) = 1$

H_a: $(\sigma_1^2/\sigma_2^2) > 1$

  [or H_a: $(\sigma_1^2/\sigma_2^2) < 1$]

Test statistic: $F = \dfrac{s_1^2}{s_2^2}$

$$\left[\text{or } F = \frac{s_2^2}{s_1^2} \right]$$

Rejection region: $F > F_\alpha$

TWO-TAILED TEST

H_0: $(\sigma_1^2/\sigma_2^2) = 1$

H_a: $(\sigma_1^2/\sigma_2^2) \neq 1$

Test statistic:

$$F = \frac{\text{Larger sample variance}}{\text{Smaller sample variance}}$$

$$\text{ie,} \quad F = \begin{cases} \dfrac{s_1^2}{s_2^2} & \text{when } s_1^2 > s_2^2 \\[2ex] \dfrac{s_2^2}{s_1^2} & \text{when } s_2^2 > s_1^2 \end{cases}$$

Rejection region: $F > F_{\alpha/2}$

where F_α and $F_{\alpha/2}$ are values that locate an area α and $\alpha/2$, respectively, in the upper tail of the F distribution with $\nu_1 =$ numerator degrees of freedom (ie, the df for the sample variance in the numerator) and $\nu_2 =$ denominator degrees of freedom (ie, the df for the sample variance in the denominator).

Assumptions:

1. Both of the populations from which the samples are selected have relative frequency distributions that are approximately normal.

2. The random samples are selected in an independent manner from the two populations.

TABLE 7.3
Reproduction of Part of Table 8, Appendix A: Critical Values for the F Statistic: $F_{.05}$

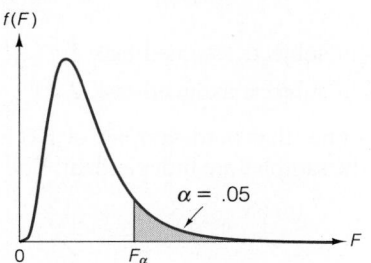

ν_1			NUMERATOR DEGREES OF FREEDOM						
ν_2	1	2	3	4	5	6	7	8	9
1	161.4	199.5	215.7	224.6	230.2	234.0	236.8	238.9	240.5
2	18.51	19.00	19.16	19.25	19.30	19.33	19.35	19.37	19.38
3	10.13	9.55	9.28	9.12	9.01	8.94	8.89	8.85	8.81
4	7.71	6.94	6.59	6.39	6.26	6.16	6.09	6.04	6.00
5	6.61	5.79	5.41	5.19	5.05	4.95	4.88	4.82	4.77
6	5.99	5.14	4.76	4.53	4.39	4.28	4.21	4.15	4.10
7	5.59	4.74	4.35	4.12	3.97	3.87	3.79	3.73	3.68
8	5.32	4.46	4.07	3.84	3.69	3.58	3.50	3.44	3.39
9	5.12	4.26	3.86	3.63	3.48	3.37	3.29	3.23	3.18
10	4.96	4.10	3.71	3.48	3.33	3.22	3.14	3.07	3.02
11	4.84	3.98	3.59	3.36	3.20	3.09	3.01	2.95	2.90
12	4.75	3.89	3.49	3.26	3.11	3.00	2.91	2.85	2.80
13	4.67	3.81	3.41	3.18	3.03	2.92	2.83	2.77	2.71
14	4.60	3.74	3.34	3.11	2.96	2.85	2.76	2.70	2.65
15	4.54	3.68	3.29	3.06	2.90	2.79	2.71	2.64	2.59
16	4.49	3.63	3.24	3.01	2.85	2.74	2.66	2.59	2.54
17	4.45	3.59	3.20	2.96	2.81	2.70	2.61	2.55	2.49
18	4.41	3.55	3.16	2.93	2.77	2.66	2.58	2.51	2.46

DENOMINATOR DEGREES OF FREEDOM

TABLE 7.4
Data on ETO Levels

	TASK 1	TASK 2
Sample size	21	13
Mean	5.90	5.60
Standard deviation	1.93	3.10

EXAMPLE 7.4 Heavy doses of ethylene oxide (ETO) in rabbits have been shown to alter significantly the DNA structure of cells. Although it is a known mutagen and suspected carcinogen, ETO is used quite frequently in sterilizing hospital supplies. A study was conducted to investigate the effect of ETO on hospital personnel involved with the sterilization process. Thirty-four subjects were randomly selected and assigned to one of two tasks: 21 subjects were assigned the task of opening the sterilization package that contains ETO (task 1); the remaining 13 subjects were assigned the task of opening and unloading the sterilizer gun filled with ETO (task 2). After the tasks were performed, researchers measured the amount of ETO (in milligrams) present in the bloodstream of each subject. A summary of the results appears in Table 7.4.

a. Do the data provide sufficient evidence to indicate a difference in the variability of the ETO levels in subjects assigned to the two tasks? Test using $\alpha = .10$.

b. Construct a 90% confidence interval for the ratio of the task 1 ETO variance to the task 2 variance. Does the result agree with part **a**?

Solution

a. Let

$$\sigma_1^2 = \text{Population variance of ETO levels in subjects assigned task 1}$$
$$\sigma_2^2 = \text{Population variance of ETO levels in subjects assigned task 2}$$

For this test to yield valid results, we must assume that both samples of ETO levels come from normal populations and that the samples are independent. The hypotheses of interest are

$$H_0: \quad \frac{\sigma_1^2}{\sigma_2^2} = 1 \quad \text{That is, } \sigma_1^2 = \sigma_2^2$$

$$H_a: \quad \frac{\sigma_1^2}{\sigma_2^2} \neq 1 \quad \text{That is, } \sigma_1^2 \neq \sigma_2^2$$

According to the box on p. 314, the test statistic for this two-tailed test is

$$F = \frac{\text{Larger } s^2}{\text{Smaller } s^2} = \frac{s_2^2}{s_1^2} = \frac{(3.10)^2}{(1.93)^2} = 2.58$$

To find the appropriate rejection region, we need to know the sampling distribution of the test statistic. Under the assumption that both samples of ETO measurements come from normal populations, the F statistic, $F = s_2^2/s_1^2$, possesses an F distribution with $\nu_1 = (n_2 - 1) = 12$ numerator degrees of freedom and $\nu_2 = (n_1 - 1) = 20$ denominator degrees of freedom.

Given this information on the F distribution, we are able to find the rejection region for this test. Since the test is two-tailed, we will reject H_0 if $F > F_{\alpha/2}$ (see the box). For $\alpha = .10$, we have $\alpha/2 = .05$, and from Table 8, Appendix A, $F_{.05} = 2.28$ (based on $\nu_1 = 12$ and $\nu_2 = 20$ df). Thus, the rejection region is

Rejection region: Reject H_0 if $F > 2.28$.

Since the test statistic, $F = 2.58$, falls in the rejection region (see Figure 7.5), we reject H_0. Therefore, at $\alpha = .10$, the data provide sufficient evidence to indicate that the population variances differ. It appears that hospital personnel involved with opening the sterilization package (task 1) have less variable ETO levels than those involved with opening and unloading the sterilizer gun (task 2).

FIGURE 7.5
Rejection Region

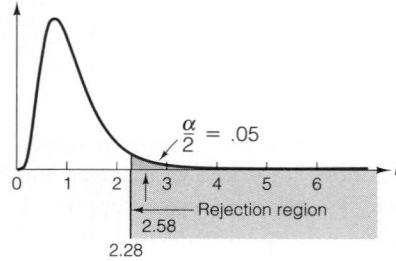

b. A 90% confidence interval for σ_1^2/σ_2^2 is (from the box)

$$\frac{(s_1^2/s_2^2)}{F_{U,\alpha/2}} < \frac{\sigma_1^2}{\sigma_2^2} < (s_1^2/s_2^2) \cdot F_{L,\alpha/2}$$

where $F_{U,\alpha/2} = F_{U,.05}$ is based on $(n_1 - 1) = 20$ numerator df and $(n_2 - 1) = 12$ denominator df, and $F_{L,.05}$ is based on $(n_2 - 1) = 12$ numerator df and $(n_1 - 1) = 20$ denominator df. From Table 8, Appendix A, we find $F_{U,.05} =$

2.54 and $F_{L,.05} = 2.28$. Substituting these values into the formula, we obtain

$$\frac{[(1.93)^2/(3.10)^2]}{2.54} \le \frac{\sigma_1^2}{\sigma_2^2} \le [(1.93)^2/(3.10)^2] \cdot (2.28)$$

$$.153 \le \frac{\sigma_1^2}{\sigma_2^2} \le .884$$

We estimate with 90% confidence that the ratio σ_1^2/σ_2^2 of the true population variances will fall between .153 and .884. Since all the values within the interval (.153, .884) are less than 1.0, we can be 90% confident that the variation in ETO levels of task 1 (measured by σ_1^2) is less than the variation with task 2 (measured by σ_2^2). This is the same conclusion that we reached using the test in part **a**.

Example 7.4 illustrates the technique for calculating the test statistic and rejection region for a two-tailed F test. The reason we place the larger sample variance in the numerator of the test statistic is that only upper-tail values of F are shown in the F tables in Appendix A—no lower-tail values are given. By placing the larger sample variance in the numerator, we make certain that only the upper tail of the rejection region is used. The fact that the upper-tail area is $\alpha/2$ reminds us that the test is two-tailed.

The problem of not being able to locate an F value in the lower tail of the F distribution is easily avoided in a one-tailed test, because we can control how we specify the ratio of the population variances in H_0 and H_a. That is, we can always make a one-tailed test an *upper-tailed* test. For example, if we want to test whether σ_1^2 is greater than σ_2^2, then we write the alternative hypothesis as

$$H_a: \quad \frac{\sigma_1^2}{\sigma_2^2} > 1 \quad \text{That is, } \sigma_1^2 > \sigma_2^2$$

and the appropriate test statistic is $F = s_1^2/s_2^2$. Conversely, if we want to test whether σ_1^2 is less than σ_2^2 (ie, whether σ_2^2 is greater than σ_1^2), we write

$$H_a: \quad \frac{\sigma_2^2}{\sigma_1^2} > 1 \quad \text{That is, } \sigma_2^2 > \sigma_1^2$$

and the corresponding test statistic is $F = s_2^2/s_1^2$.

NONPARAMETRIC METHODS

When the distribution of at least one of the two populations deviates greatly from normality, the inference derived from the parametric F test for σ_1^2/σ_2^2 is suspect. In this situation, we apply a nonparametric test.

The **Ansari–Bradley test** is appropriate if we can assume that the medians of the two populations are equal. In the case of unequal medians, which is more likely to occur in practice, we can apply the **Moses test**. Both of these tests are rank tests and are illustrated in the following examples.

ANSARI–BRADLEY RANK TEST FOR THE RATIO OF TWO POPULATION VARIANCES, σ_1^2/σ_2^2: EQUAL MEDIANS

ONE-TAILED TEST

$H_0:\quad \dfrac{\sigma_1^2}{\sigma_2^2} = 1$

$H_a:\quad \dfrac{\sigma_1^2}{\sigma_2^2} > 1$

$$\left[\text{or } H_a:\quad \frac{\sigma_1^2}{\sigma_2^2} < 1\right]$$

TWO-TAILED TEST

$H_0:\quad \dfrac{\sigma_1^2}{\sigma_2^2} = 1$

$H_a:\quad \dfrac{\sigma_1^2}{\sigma_2^2} \neq 1$

Rank the $n_1 + n_2$ observations in the two samples as follows: Assign rank 1 to both the smallest and largest values, rank 2 to both the second smallest and second largest values, etc. [If $n_1 + n_2$ is even, the largest rank assigned is $(n_1 + n_2)/2$. If $n_1 + n_2$ is odd, the largest rank assigned is $(n_1 + n_2 + 1)/2$.]

Calculate W_1 and W_2, the rank sums associated with sample 1 and sample 2, respectively. Then find the test statistic:

Test statistic: $\quad W_1$ if $n_1 < n_2$
$\qquad\qquad\qquad W_2$ if $n_2 < n_1$

(Either rank sum can be used if $n_1 = n_2$.) Denote this calculated rank sum as W_c.

Observed significance level:

$W_1:\quad$ *p*-Value $= 1 - P(W \geq W_c + 1)$
$\qquad$ [or *p*-Value $= P(W \geq W_c)$]

$W_2:\quad$ *p*-Value $= P(W \geq W_c)$
$\qquad$ [or *p*-Value $= 1 - P(W \geq W_c + 1)$]

Observed significance level:

Find $p_1 = P(W \geq W_c)$ and
$p_2 = [1 - P(W \geq W_c + 1)]$.
Then *p*-value $= 2\min(p_1, p_2)$.

where $P(W \geq x)$ is obtained from Table 11, Appendix A.

Assumptions:

1. Independent random samples are selected from the populations.
2. The medians of the two populations are equal.

TABLE 7.5

Reflectance Measurements

INSTRUMENT 1	INSTRUMENT 2
29	26
28	34
30	30
28	32
30	28

EXAMPLE 7.5 The quality control department of a paper company measures the brightness (a measure of reflectance) of finished paper periodically throughout the day. Two instruments used to measure the paper specimens are subject to error, but they can be adjusted so that the mean readings for a control paper specimen are the same for both instruments. Suppose you are concerned about the precision of the two instruments—namely, that the variation in readings from instrument 2 exceeds that for instrument 1. To check this theory, 5 measurements of a single paper sample are made on both instruments. The data are shown in Table 7.5. Use

the Ansari–Bradley test to determine whether instrument 2 readings are less precise (ie, more variable) than those taken with instrument 1. Test using $\alpha = .05$.

Solution Let σ_1^2 and σ_2^2 be the population variances in readings from instruments 1 and 2, respectively. We want to test

$$H_0: \quad \frac{\sigma_1^2}{\sigma_2^2} = 1 \quad \text{That is, } \sigma_1^2 = \sigma_2^2$$

$$H_a: \quad \frac{\sigma_1^2}{\sigma_2^2} < 1 \quad \text{That is, } \sigma_1^2 < \sigma_2^2$$

As shown in the box, the Ansari–Bradley test requires that we rank the observations in the combined samples, assigning rank 1 to both the largest and the smallest measurements, rank 2 to both the second largest and second smallest measurements, etc. (Ties are assigned ranks in the usual manner.) Thus, the 5 smallest readings, 26, 28, 28, 28, and 29, are assigned the ranks 1, 3, 3, 3, and 5, respectively. Likewise, the 5 largest readings, 34, 32, 30, 30, and 30, are assigned the ranks 1, 2, 4, 4, and 4, respectively. These ranks are shown in Table 7.6.

TABLE 7.6
Ranks of Instrument Readings

INSTRUMENT 1	RANK	INSTRUMENT 2	RANK
29	5	26	1
28	3	34	1
30	4	30	4
28	3	32	2
30	4	28	3
	$W_1 = 19$		$W_2 = 11$

The rank sums for the two samples are $W_1 = 19$ and $W_2 = 11$. Since the sample sizes are equal, either rank sum may be used as the test statistic. Arbitrarily, we choose $W_1 = 19$.

From the box, if W_1 is the test statistic and the test is lower-tailed, the observed significance level of the test is

$$p\text{-Value} = P(W \geq W_1) = P(W \geq 19)$$

where $P(W \geq 19)$ is obtained from Table 11, Appendix A, a portion of which, for the case when $n_2 = 5$, is shown in Table 7.7. The entries of the table give the probability that the test statistic W exceeds some constant x (given in the first column) for different values of α. Since we want $P(W \geq 19)$, we look in the row corresponding to $x = 19$ and the column corresponding to $n_1 = 5$, and find the entry .0714. This value, .0714 (shaded in Table 7.7), represents the p-value of the test.

Our choice of $\alpha = .05$ is less than .0714; hence, there is insufficient evidence to reject H_0. We cannot conclude that instrument 2 is less precise than instrument 1.

TABLE 7.7

Partial Reproduction of Table 11, Appendix A:
Critical Values for the Ansari–Bradley Test ($n_2 = 5$)

x	$n_1 = 5$	$n_1 = 6$	$n_1 = 7$	$n_1 = 8$	$n_1 = 9$	$n_1 = 10$	$n_1 = 11$
9	1.0000	1.0000	1.0000	1.0000	1.0000	1.0000	1.0000
10	.9921	.9957	.9975	.9984	.9990	.9993	.9995
11	.9762	.9870	.9924	.9953	.9970	.9980	.9986
12	.9286	.9610	.9773	.9860	.9910	.9940	.9959
13	.8492	.9156	.9495	.9689	.9800	.9867	.9908
14	.7302	.8420	.9015	.9386	.9600	.9734	.9817
15	.5873	.7446	.8333	.8936	.9291	.9524	.9670
16	.4127	.6147	.7374	.8275	.8821	.9197	.9437
17	.2698	.4805	.6237	.7451	.8212	.8761	.9116
18	.1508	.3463	.5000	.6457	.7423	.8182	.8681
19	.0714	.2294	.3763	.5385	.6523	.7483	.8132
20	.0238	.1342	.2626	.4266	.5514	.6663	.7468

The requirement that the medians of the two populations be equivalent is essential for the proper application of the Ansari–Bradley rank test. This assumption appears to be satisfied in Example 7.5. (The sample medians for the two instruments are 29 and 30, respectively.) For cases in which the medians are unequal, use the Moses rank test described in the box on the next page.

EXAMPLE 7.6 Suppose an investor wants to compare the risks associated with two different stocks, where the risk of a given stock is measured by the variation in daily price changes. Independent random samples of 25 daily price changes for stock 1 and for stock 2 are obtained and the data are shown in Table 7.8. Compare the risks associated with the two stocks by testing the null hypothesis that the variances of the price changes for the stocks are equal. Use $\alpha = .10$.

TABLE 7.8

Daily Price Changes for Two Stocks

STOCK 1			STOCK 2		
−.42	.47	.52	.17	−.42	.11
.36	.31	.28	.06	.28	−.16
.20	.39	−.14	−.33	.01	.37
.45	−.34	−.63	−.25	−.19	−.26
.57	.56	.40	.38	−.30	−.39
−.22	.32	−.13	.21	.14	−.12
.05	.46	.19	−.15	.35	.24
.23	.11	.42	−.22	−.02	−.28
.44			−.37		

MOSES RANK TEST FOR THE RATIO OF TWO POPULATION VARIANCES, σ_1^2/σ_2^2: UNEQUAL MEDIANS

ONE-TAILED TEST	TWO-TAILED TEST
H_0: $\dfrac{\sigma_1^2}{\sigma_2^2} = 1$	H_0: $\dfrac{\sigma_1^2}{\sigma_2^2} = 1$
H_a: $\dfrac{\sigma_1^2}{\sigma_2^2} > 1$	H_a: $\dfrac{\sigma_1^2}{\sigma_2^2} \neq 1$
$\left[\text{or } H_a: \ \dfrac{\sigma_1^2}{\sigma_2^2} < 1 \right]$	

STEP 1   Select a positive integer $k \geq 2$.

STEP 2   Randomly divide the observations in the first sample into m_1 subgroups of size k, discarding any extra observations.

STEP 3   Randomly divide the observations in the second sample into m_2 subgroups of size k, discarding any extra observations.

STEP 4   Compute the sum of squared errors, SSE, for each subgroup, where

$$\textit{Sample 1:} \quad \text{SSE}_i = \sum_{s=1}^{k} (x_{is} - \bar{x}_i)^2 \qquad i = 1, 2, ..., m_1$$

$$\textit{Sample 2:} \quad \text{SSE}_j = \sum_{s=1}^{k} (x_{js} - \bar{x}_j)^2 \qquad j = 1, 2, ..., m_2$$

STEP 5   Rank the $m_1 + m_2$ SSEs in the two samples as follows: Assign rank 1 to both the smallest and largest values, rank 2 to both the second smallest and second largest values, etc.

STEP 6   Calculate W_1 and W_2, the rank sums associated with sample 1 and sample 2, respectively.

Test statistic: W_1, if $m_1 < m_2$; W_2, if $m_2 < m_1$

(Either rank sum can be used if $m_1 = m_2$.) We will denote the calculated rank sum as W_c.

Observed significance level:

W_1: p-Value = $1 - P(W \geq W_c + 1)$
           [or p-Value = $P(W \geq W_c)$]

W_2: p-Value = $P(W \geq W_c)$
           [or p-Value = $1 - P(W \geq W_c + 1)$]

Observed significance level:

Find $p_1 = P(W \geq W_c)$ and
$p_2 = [1 - P(W \geq W_c + 1)]$.
Then p-value = $2 \min(p_1, p_2)$.

where $P(W \geq x)$ is obtained from Table 11, Appendix A.

Assumption: Independent random samples are selected from the populations.

Solution   Let σ_1^2 and σ_2^2 represent the true variances of daily price changes for stock 1 and stock 2, respectively. We want to test

$$H_0: \quad \frac{\sigma_1^2}{\sigma_2^2} = 1$$

$$H_a: \quad \frac{\sigma_1^2}{\sigma_2^2} \neq 1$$

To conduct the parametric F test, we must first check to see that the samples of daily price changes are from normal populations. Figure 7.6 shows the MINITAB stem-and-leaf displays for the two samples. Note that the graph for stock 1 (Figure 7.6a) is mound-shaped but highly skewed, while the graph for stock 2 (Figure 7.6b) is flat. Consequently, the assumption upon which the F test is based, namely, normal populations, does not appear to be satisfied, and we must resort to a nonparametric test.

FIGURE 7.6

MINITAB Stem-and-Leaf Displays

a. Stem-and-leaf display of daily price changes for stock 1

b. Stem-and-leaf display of daily price changes for stock 2

```
Stem-and-leaf of Stock1    N = 25
Leaf Unit = 0.010

   1    -6  3
   1    -5
   2    -4  2
   3    -3  4
   4    -2  2
   6    -1  43
   6    -0
   7     0  5
   9     1  19
  12     2  038
  (4)    3  1269
   9     4  024567
   3     5  267
```

```
Stem-and-leaf of Stock2    N = 25
Leaf Unit = 0.010

   1    -4  2
   5    -3  9730
   9    -2  8652
  (4)   -1  9652
  12    -0  2
  11     0  16
   9     1  147
   6     2  148
   3     3  578
```

The Ansari–Bradley rank test requires that the medians of the two populations be equal. This assumption also appears to be violated. From the MINITAB printout of descriptive statistics (Figure 7.7), the medians of the two samples are .31 and −.12. Thus, the appropriate test to conduct is the Moses rank test.

STEP 1   As shown in the box, the first step in the Moses rank test is to select a positive integer $k \geq 2$. Arbitrarily, we'll choose $k = 5$. This will be the number of sample observations in each subgroup.

STEP 2   We randomly divide the daily price changes for stock 1 into $m_1 = 5$ subgroups of size 5. (Since there are no extra observations, none need to be discarded.) These subgroups are shown in Table 7.9.

FIGURE 7.7

MINITAB Printout: Descriptive
Statistics

	N	MEAN	MEDIAN	TRMEAN	STDEV	SEMEAN
Stock1	25	0.1940	0.3100	0.2135	0.3297	0.0659
Stock2	25	-0.0456	-0.1200	-0.0478	0.2595	0.0519

	MIN	MAX	Q1	Q3
Stock1	-0.6300	0.5700	-0.0400	0.4450
Stock2	-0.4200	0.3800	-0.2700	0.1900

TABLE 7.9

The Data of Table 7.8 Randomly Divided into Subgroups of Size $k = 5$

	STOCK 1					STOCK 2				
Subgroup 1	.42	.19	-.13	.40	-.63	-.30	-.19	.01	.28	-.42
Subgroup 2	.05	-.22	.23	.57	.45	-.26	-.39	.37	-.16	.11
Subgroup 3	.56	.32	.46	-.34	.39	.38	-.25	-.33	.06	.17
Subgroup 4	-.14	.39	.20	.36	.31	-.28	-.02	-.22	-.37	.24
Subgroup 5	.44	.28	.52	-.42	.47	.35	-.15	.21	.14	-.12

STEP 3　Similarly, we randomly divide the daily price changes for stock 2 into $m_2 = 5$ subgroups of size 5. (See Table 7.9.)

STEP 4　Next, we compute the SSE for each subgroup. For example, the SSE for the first subgroup of stock 1 daily price changes is

$$SSE = \sum_{s=1}^{5}(x_{1s} - \bar{x}_1)^2 = \sum_{s=1}^{5}x_{1s}^2 - \frac{\left(\sum_{s=1}^{5}x_{1s}\right)^2}{5}$$

$$= (.42)^2 + (.19)^2 + (-.13)^2 + (.40)^2 + (-.63)^2$$

$$- \frac{(.42 + .19 - .13 + .40 - .63)^2}{5}$$

$$= .7863 - \frac{(.25)^2}{5}$$

$$= .7863 - .0125 = .7738$$

The SSEs for all $m_1 + m_2 = 10$ subgroups are shown in Table 7.10.

STEP 5　The ranks of the SSEs for the combined samples are also shown in Table 7.10. Remember, we assign rank 1 to both the smallest and largest SSEs, rank 2 to the next smallest and next largest SSEs, etc.

STEP 6　The rank sums for stock 1 and stock 2 are $W_1 = 13$ and $W_2 = 17$, respectively (see Table 7.10). Since $m_1 = m_2 = 5$, either W_1 or W_2 can be used as a test statistic. Arbitrarily, we select $W_1 = 13$ as the computed value of the test statistic, W_c.

TABLE 7.10

SSEs and Ranks for Subgroups of Table 7.9

	STOCK 1			STOCK 2	
Subgroup	SSE	Rank	Subgroup	SSE	Rank
1	.7738	1	1	.3041	4
2	.3979	5	2	.3725	5
3	.5089	3	3	.3481	4
4	.1865	2	4	.2372	3
5	.6069	2	5	.1861	1
		$W_1 = 13$			$W_2 = 17$

According to the box, the p-value of the two-tailed test with $W_c = 13$ is the smaller of the two probabilities

$$p_1 = P(W \geq 13)$$
$$p_2 = 1 - P(W \geq 14)$$

From Table 11, Appendix A, for $n_1 = n_2 = 5$, $p_1 = P(W \geq 13) = .8492$ and $p_2 = 1 - P(W \geq 14) = 1 - .7302 = .2698$; thus, the p-value of the test is .2698. Since the p-value exceeds $\alpha = .10$, there is insufficient evidence to reject H_0. According to this nonparametric test, there is no evidence (at $\alpha = .10$) to indicate a difference between the daily price change variances for the two stocks.

PROBLEMS

7.10 A study was conducted to compare the variation in the price of wholesale residual petroleum sold in rural (low-density) and urban (high-density) counties. In particular, the variable of interest was the natural logarithm of the ratio of county price to state price, that is, ln(County price/State price). Based on independent random samples of 10 rural counties and 23 urban counties, the descriptive statistics shown in the table were obtained. Is there evidence of a difference between the variances in the log–price ratios of rural and urban counties?

	n	$\bar{x}$	s
Rural	10	.239	.310
Urban	23	.117	.199

Source: Saavedra, P., et al. "Geographical Stratification of Petroleum Retailers and Resellers." Paper presented at Joint Statistical Meetings, Anaheim, CA, Aug. 1990.

7.11 Wet samplers are standard devices used to measure the chemical composition of precipitation. The accuracy of the wet deposition readings, however, may depend on the number of samplers stationed in the field. Experimenters in The Netherlands collected wet deposition measurements using anywhere from one to eight identical wet samplers (*Atmospheric Environment*, Vol. 24A, 1990). For each sampler (or sampler combination) data were collected every 24 hours for an entire year; thus, 365 readings were collected per sampler (or sampler combination). When one wet sampler was used, the standard deviation of the hydrogen readings (measured as percentage relative to the average reading from all eight samplers) was 6.3%. When three wet samplers were used, the standard deviation of the hydrogen readings (measured as percentage relative to the average reading from all eight samplers) was 2.6%. Compare the variation in hydrogen readings for the two sampling schemes (ie, one wet sampler versus three wet samplers) using a 95% confidence interval.

7.12 General trace organic monitoring describes the process in which water engineers analyze water samples for various types of organic material (eg, contaminants). The total organic carbon (TOC) level was measured in water samples collected at two sewage treatment sites in England. The table gives the summary information on the TOC levels (measured in milligrams per liter) found in the rivers adjacent to the two sewage facilities. Since the river at the Foxcote sewage treatment works was subject to periodic spillovers, not far upstream of the plant's intake, it is believed that the TOC levels found at Foxcote will have greater variation than the levels at Bedford. Does the sample information support this hypothesis? Test using $\alpha = .05$.

BEDFORD	FOXCOTE
$n_1 = 61$	$n_2 = 52$
$\bar{x}_1 = 5.35$	$\bar{x}_2 = 4.27$
$s_1 = .96$	$s_2 = 1.27$

Source: Pinchin, M. J. "A Study of the Trace Organics Profiles of Raw and Potable Water Systems." *Journal of the Institute of Water Engineers & Scientists*, Vol. 40, No. 1, Feb. 1986, p. 87.

7.13 An experiment was conducted in England to examine the metabolizable energy (ME) content of commercial cat foods. The researchers monitored the diets of 57 adult domestic short-haired cats; 28 cats were fed a diet of commercial canned cat food, while 29 cats were fed a diet of dry cat food over a 3 week period. At the end of the trial, the ME content was determined for each cat, with the results shown in the table. Compare the variances in ME contents for the two cat food diets using a 90% confidence interval. Interpret the results.

	CANNED FOOD	DRY FOOD
Sample size	28	29
Mean ME content	.96	3.70
Standard deviation	.26	.48

Source: Kendall, P. T., Burger, I. N., and Smith, P. M. "Methods of Estimation of the Metabolizable Energy Content of Cat Foods." *Feline Practice*, Vol. 15, No. 2, Feb. 1985, pp. 38–44.

7.14 An experiment was conducted to study the effect of reinforced flanges on the torsional capacity of reinforced concrete T-beams (*Journal of the American Concrete Institute*, Jan.–Feb. 1986). Several different types of T-beams were used in the experiment, each type having a different flange width. The beams were tested under combined torsion and bending until failure (cracking). One variable of interest is the cracking torsion moment at the top of the flange of the T-beam. Cracking torsion moments for 8 beams with 70 cm slab widths and 8 beams with 100 cm slab widths are recorded below:

70 cm slab width:	6.00	7.20	10.20	13.20	11.40	13.60	9.20	11.20
100 cm slab width:	6.80	9.20	8.80	13.20	11.20	14.90	10.20	11.80

a. Is there evidence of a difference in the variation in the cracking torsion moments of the two types of T-beams? Use $\alpha = .10$.

b. What assumptions are required for the test to be valid?

7.15 Analyze the data of Problem 7.14 using a nonparametric method. Compare the results to those of the parametric test.

7.16 A computer programmer wants to compare the variability in the cost of running jobs using Time-Sharing Options (TSO) and Terminal Control Programming (TCP) from a computer terminal. Independent random samples of 20 TSO jobs and 15 TCP jobs programmed to perform similar tasks were selected and their costs (in dollars) recorded in the table. Is there evidence of a difference in the variability of costs of TSO and TCP jobs? Use a nonparametric test ($\alpha = .05$).

	TSO				TCP		
1.32	.73	3.05	1.15	2.49	2.02	1.84	1.76
.86	2.59	1.73	1.60	1.57	2.13	2.83	2.05
.11	.57	1.32	1.85	1.19	3.45	1.85	2.22
2.81	2.04	.39	1.70	2.74	2.10	1.66	
1.49	1.25	1.21	.84				

COMPUTER LAB

TESTING VARIANCES

Automated procedures for testing population variances are, in general, unavailable in the current versions of SAS, SPSS, and MINITAB. Several of the test statistics presented in this chapter can be obtained by using the programming features of the software packages, but this is recommended only for the experienced user. It is usually much easier to compute the test statistic by hand (or hand calculator).

For those who are interested, we provide program segments that compute the parametric test statistics (and p-values) for the data of Example 7.1 (H_0: $\sigma^2 = .01$) and Table 7.5 (H_0: $\sigma_1^2/\sigma_2^2 = 1$).

SAS

Command Line		
1	`DATA EX7_1;`	Data entry instruction
2	`FILLVAR=VAR(7.96,7.90,7.98,8.01,7.97,7.96,8.03,8.02,8.04,8.02);`	
3	`CHISQ=9*FILLVAR/.01;`	
4	`PVALUE=PROBCHI(CHISQ,9);`	χ^2-test (H_0: $\sigma^2 = .01$)
5	`PROC PRINT;`	
6	`DATA TAB7_5;`	
7	`VAR1=VAR(29,28,30,28,30);`	Data entry instructions
8	`VAR2=VAR(26,34,30,32,28);`	
9	`F=VAR2/VAR1;`	
10	`PVALUE=1-PROBF(F,4,4);`	F test (H_0: $\sigma_1^2/\sigma_2^2 = 1$)
11	`PROC PRINT;`	

COMMAND 2   The VAR function computes the variance of the sample observations specified in parentheses. [*Note:* The sample observations must be separated by commas.]

COMMAND 4   The PROBCHI function computes the probability of observing a value of χ^2 less than the first value specified in parentheses (CHISQ). The second value within the parentheses (9) represents the degrees of freedom for the test. [*Note:*   The p-value computed here is for a lower-tailed test. The upper-tailed p-value is $1 - \text{PROBCHI(CHISQ,9)}$.]

COMMAND 10   The PROBF function computes the probability of observing a value of F less than the first value (F) specified within the parentheses. The last two values in the parentheses (4,4) represent the numerator degrees of freedom and denominator degrees of freedom, respectively, for the test. [*Note:*   The p-value computed here is for a one-tailed test. The two-tailed p-value is twice this value.]

NOTE   The output for the SAS program is displayed in Figure 7.8a (p. 328).

SPSS

```
Command
   Line
     1      DATA LIST FREE/INST READING.⎫  Data entry instructions
     2      BEGIN DATA.                    ⎭
            1 29 1 28 1 30 1 28 1 30⎫  Input data values
            2 26 2 34 2 30 2 32 2 28⎭  (5 observations per line)
     3      END DATA.
     4      T-TEST GROUPS=INST(1,2)/      ⎫  F test (H0:  σ1²/σ2² = 1)
     5             VARIABLES=READING.     ⎭
```

F test (H_0: $\sigma_1^2/\sigma_2^2 = 1$)

COMANDS 4–5   The T-TEST command, designed primarily for testing two means, also conducts a test of the equality of two variances. The two different populations are specified in the GROUPS subcommand and the variable of interest in the VARIABLES subcommand.

NOTE   The output for the SPSS program is displayed in Figure 7.8b (p. 329).

MINITAB

```
Command
   Line
     1      SET EX7_1 IN C1   Data entry instruction
            7.96   7.90   7.98   8.01   7.97⎫  Input data values
            7.96   8.03   8.02   8.04   8.02⎭  (5 observations per line)
     2      STDEV C1 C2
     3      LET C3=9*C2*C2/.01⎫
     4      CDF C3 C4;          ⎬  χ²-test (H0:  σ² = .01)
     5         CHISQUARE 9.   ⎭
     6      NAME C1='FILL' C2='STDEV' C3='CHISQUARE' C4='PVALUE'
     7      PRINT C1-C4
```

χ^2-test (H_0: $\sigma^2 = .01$)

(continued)

```
8      SET SAMPLE1 IN C1    Data entry instruction
       29   28   30   28   30   Input data values
9      SET SAMPLE2 IN C2    Data entry instruction
       26   34   30   32   28   Input data values
10     STDEV C1 C3       ⎫
11     STDEV C2 C4       ⎬
12     LET C5=C4*C4/(C3*C3) ⎬  F test (H_0:  σ_1^2/σ_2^2 = 1)
13     CDF C5 C6;         ⎬
14        F 4 4.          ⎭
15     LET C7=1-C6
16     NAME C1='SAMP1' C2='SAMP2' C3='STDEV1'
17     NAME C4='STDEV2' C5='FVALUE' C7='PVALUE'
18     PRINT C1-C5 C7
```

COMMAND 2   The STDEV function computes the standard deviation of the sample observations stored in the first specified column (C1). This standard deviation is stored in the second column specified (C2).

COMMANDS 4–5   The CDF function with the CHISQUARE option computes the probability of observing a value of χ^2 less than the value stored in the first specified column (C3); the degrees of freedom for the χ^2 distribution are specified after the CHISQUARE subcommand. This probability is stored in the second specified column (C4). [*Note:*   The p-value computed here is for a lower-tailed test. The upper-tailed p-value is 1 minus this value.]

COMMANDS 13–14   The CDF with the F option computes the probability of observing a value of F less than the value stored in the first specified column (C5); the numerator and denominator degrees of freedom for the F distribution are specified after the F subcommand. This probability is stored in the second specified column (C6).

COMMAND 15   The p-value computed here is for a one-tailed test. The two-tailed p-value is twice this value.

NOTE   The output for the MINITAB program is displayed in Figure 7.8c (p. 329).

FIGURE 7.8

Output for Computer Lab

a. SAS

```
        Chi-Square Test of Ho: Var=.01

    OBS      FILLVAR      CHISQ      PVALUE

     1       .0018544     1.669      0.004320



        F Test of Ho: Var1=Var2

    OBS    VAR1    VAR2     F      PVALUE

     1      1      10      10     0.023291
```

b. SPSS

```
Independent samples of  INST

Group 1:  INST EQ     1.00         Group 2:  INST EQ     2.00

t-test for:  READING
```

	Number of Cases	Mean	Standard Deviation	Standard Error
Group 1	5	29.0000	1.000	.447
Group 2	5	30.0000	3.162	1.414

F Value	2-Tail Prob.	Pooled Variance Estimate			Separate Variance Estimate		
		t Value	Degrees of Freedom	2-Tail Prob.	t Value	Degrees of Freedom	2-Tail Prob.
10.00	.047	-.67	8	.519	-.67	4.79	.531

c. MINITAB

ROW	FILL	STDEV	CHISQ	PVALUE
1	7.96	0.0430633	1.66900	0.0043198
2	7.90			
3	7.98			
4	8.01			
5	7.97			
6	7.96			
7	8.03			
8	8.02			
9	8.04			
10	8.02			

ROW	SAMP1	SAMP2	STDEV1	STDEV2	FVALUE	PVALUE
1	29	26	1	3.16228	10	0.0232908
2	28	34				
3	30	30				
4	28	32				
5	30	28				

CHAPTER NOTES

- **Parametric inferences** for a single population variance, σ^2, and for the ratio between two population variances, σ_1^2/σ_2^2, are obtained using the following formulas:

CONFIDENCE INTERVALS

$$\frac{(n-1)s^2}{\chi_{\alpha/2}^2} \leq \sigma^2 \leq \frac{(n-1)s^2}{\chi_{(1-\alpha/2)}^2}$$

$$\frac{(s_1^2/s_2^2)}{F_{U,\alpha/2}} \leq \frac{\sigma_1^2}{\sigma_2^2} \leq (s_1^2/s_2^2) \cdot F_{L,\alpha/2}$$

HYPOTHESIS TEST	TEST STATISTIC	REJECTION REGION
$H_0: \quad \sigma^2 = \sigma_0^2$	$\chi^2 = \dfrac{(n-1)s^2}{\sigma_0^2}$	$\chi^2 > \chi_\alpha^2 \ (\text{df} = n - 1)$
$H_0: \quad \dfrac{\sigma_1^2}{\sigma_2^2} = 1$	$F = \dfrac{s_1^2}{s_2^2}$	$F > F_\alpha \ (\text{numerator df} = n_1 - 1,$ denominator df $= n_2 - 1)$

- The **assumptions** required to make valid parametric inferences for population variances are:

σ^2:   The sampled population has an approximately normal distribution.

σ_1^2/σ_2^2:   **1.** Both sampled populations are approximately normal.
            2. The samples are independent.

- The **nonparametric** alternatives to the parametric tests for population variances are listed below:

NULL HYPOTHESIS	PARAMETRIC METHOD	NONPARAMETRIC METHOD
$H_0: \quad \sigma^2 = \sigma_0^2$	χ^2 test	Sign test using MAD
$H_0: \quad \dfrac{\sigma_1^2}{\sigma_2^2} = 1$	F test	Ansari–Bradley test (equal medians); Moses test (unequal medians)

LOOKING AHEAD

In Chapter 8 we present several methods for making inferences about populations of qualitative data. The inferential techniques focus on the proportion of observations in the population that have a certain qualitative characteristic.

CASE STUDY

BID-RIGGING IN THE FLORIDA BREAD MARKET

Many products and services are purchased by governments and businesses on the basis of competitive bids, and frequently, contracts are awarded to the lowest bidders. This process works extremely well in competitive markets, but it has the potential to increase the cost of purchasing if the markets are noncompetitive or if collusive practices are present.

Numerous methods exist for detecting the possibility of collusive practices among bidders. In general, these procedures involve the detection of significant departures from normal market conditions, such as (1) systematic rotation of the winning bid, (2) stable market shares over time, (3) geographic market divisions, (4) lack of relationship between delivery costs and bid levels, (5) high degree of uniformity and stability in bid levels over time, and (6) presence of a baseline point pricing scheme (see Rothrock and McClave, 1979). For example, consider condition (5). An investigation of the supplier of a product associated with the low (winning) bids might show that most of the low bids were submitted by the same supplier, or it might indicate a very small variation in the low bids among a group of different suppliers. Unusual regularities or patterns of this type indicate unusual market conditions, which may warrant further investigation.

This case focuses on the bidding competition (or lack thereof) in the Florida bread market. Each county in the state of Florida negotiates an annual contract for bread to supply the county's public schools. Sealed bids are submitted by the vendors and the lowest bid (price per pound of bread) is selected as the bid winner. The data of interest in this case are the low-bid prices for white bread for most of the 67 county school boards in a selected year. For the analysis, the state was divided into eight geographic market areas. Each region contained counties that were adjacent to one another, possessed similar economic characteristics, and were served by the same group of vendors. The data for the two largest Florida markets are listed in Table 7.11.

TABLE 7.11
Low-Bid Prices (Cents per Pound) of White Bread

MARKET 1	36.400	34.000	32.889	32.667	34.000
	31.111	32.889	32.889	37.500	
MARKET 2	28.000	28.000	28.000	26.667	26.000
	27.600	26.600	25.333	29.100	27.600
	29.440	27.000	27.450	27.000	27.000

Source: Florida Attorney General's Office, Tallahassee.

The Florida Attorney General's Office (FLAG) is investigating the possibility of bid-rigging in the Florida bread market. It is expected that the mean cost per pound of bread (and hence, the mean low-bid price) will vary depending on region. This is due to the market-to-market variation in distances required to transport the bread and the costs of labor, rent, and other forms of overhead. In a stable market, however, FLAG expects the variances of the low-bid prices to be the same across the two markets.

Analyze the data for FLAG and make the appropriate conclusions.

REFERENCES

Hollander, M., and Wolfe, D. A. *Nonparametric Statistical Methods.* New York: Wiley, 1973.

Mason, R. L., Gunst, R. F., and Hess, J. L. *Statistical Design and Analysis of Experiments.* New York: Wiley, 1989.

Mendenhall, W., Wackerly, D., and Scheaffer, R. *Mathematical Statistics with Applications,* 4th ed. Boston: PWS-Kent, 1989.

Rothrock, T. P., and McClave, J. T. "An Analysis of Bidding Competition in the Florida School Bread Market Using a Statistical Model." Paper presented at the ORSA/TIMS National Meeting, Chicago, 1979.

Snedecor, G. W., and Cochran, W. G. *Statistical Methods,* 7th ed. Ames: Iowa State University Press, 1980.

(1–2) Specifications require the percentage nickel content of manufactured stainless steel hydraulic valves to have a process standard deviation of less than .5%. To monitor the production process, 32 valves were selected from the production line and the percentage nickel content was measured for each, with the results recorded in the table. A summary of the results is shown in the MINITAB printout.

NICKEL CONTENT

13.1	12.8	12.7	12.9	12.8	13.3	13.0	13.6
12.5	13.0	13.6	13.1	12.6	13.9	12.8	11.9
12.9	12.9	13.2	13.3	13.5	13.5	12.7	12.4
12.4	13.0	12.1	12.6	13.1	12.7	12.9	13.2

	N	MEAN	MEDIAN	TRMEAN	STDEV	SEMEAN
Nickel	32	12.938	12.900	12.946	0.438	0.077

	MIN	MAX	Q1	Q3
Nickel	11.900	13.900	12.700	13.200

1. Construct a 95% confidence interval for the process variance.
2. Based on the interval, are specifications being met?

(3–5) The testing department of a tire and rubber company schedules truck and passenger tires for durability tests. Currently, tires are scheduled twice weekly on flexible processors (machines that can handle either truck or passenger tires) using the shortest processing time (SPT) approach. Under SPT, the tire with the shortest processing time is scheduled first. Company researchers have developed a new scheduling rule that they believe will reduce the variation in flow time (ie, the variation in the completion time of a test) and lead to a reduction in the variation in tardiness of a scheduled test. To compare the two scheduling rules, 20 tires were randomly selected and divided into two groups of equal size. One set of tires was scheduled using SPT, the other using the proposed rule. The flow times (in hours) of the 20 tire tests are provided in the table.

SPT		PROPOSED RULE	
251	430	320	224
317	276	219	98
188	149	267	183
222	511	145	255
75	236	170	401

3. Use a parametric test to compare the variation in flow times under the two schedules. Test at $\alpha = .05$.
4. Use a nonparametric test to compare the variation in flow times under the two schedules. Test at $\alpha = .05$.
5. Which method, parametric or nonparametric, would you recommend for analyzing the data? Explain.

(6–7) In the manufacture of machinery it is essential to utilize parts that conform to specifications. In the past, diameters of the ball bearings produced by a certain manufacturer had a variance of .00156. To cut costs, the manufacturer instituted a less expensive production method. The variance of the diameters of 100 randomly sampled bearings produced by the new process was .00181.

6. Do the data provide evidence to indicate that diameters of ball bearings produced by the new process are more variable than those produced by the old process? Test at $\alpha = .05$.
7. A stem-and-leaf display and normal probability plot for the 100 bearing diameters are shown at the top of the next page. Comment on the validity of the inference in Question 6. How should you proceed?

Stem-and-Leaf Display

```
Stem Leaf                        #
112  5                           1
110
108  34                          2
106  009                         3
104  183                         3
102  144568991367               12
100  0022556788001223599        19
 98  12344568223356789          17
 96  06689033335566678889       19
 94  2489114468                 10
 92  40135788                    8
 90  368                         3
 88  679                         3
     ----+----+----+----+
Multiply Stem.Leaf by 10**-2
```

Normal Probability Plot

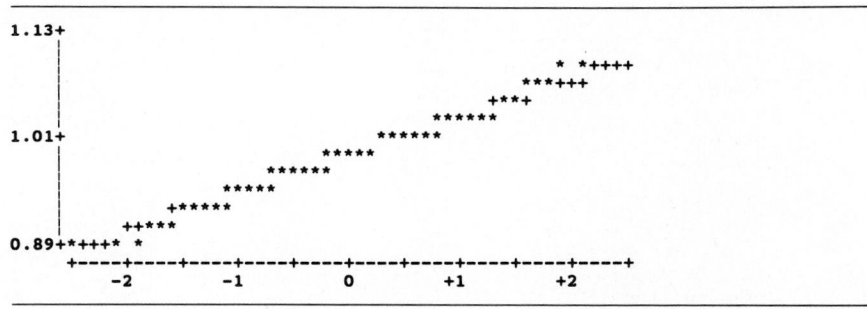

(8–10)   A drug company synthesized two new drugs that should alleviate pain due to ulcers. To determine whether the drugs will be absorbed by the stomach (and hence, have a possibility of being effective), 16 pigs were randomly assigned to two groups of 8, with each group receiving oral doses of one drug. After a given amount of time, the concentration of the drug in the stomach lining of each pig was determined. The data (in cubic centimeters) and summary statistics are shown in the table. The ultimate goal of the analysis is to determine whether there is a difference between the mean concentrations for the two drugs.

	DRUG	
	1	2
	1.73	1.67
	1.79	1.63
	1.76	1.60
	1.75	1.55
	1.70	1.63
	1.80	1.61
	1.81	1.67
	1.73	1.59
Mean:	1.75875	1.61875
Median:	1.755	1.62
Variance:	.001489	.001641

8. Explain why it is important to determine whether the variances of the drug concentrations differ before conducting the analysis of means.
9. Should you conduct a parametric or nonparametric test of equality of variances? Explain.
10. Conduct the appropriate test and interpret the results.

CHAPTER 8   INFERENCE FOR QUALITATIVE DATA: PROPORTIONS

CONTENTS

The *New England Journal of Medicine* (NEJM) reported on a study designed to determine whether aspirin reduces the risk of fatal heart attacks. The researchers collected heart attack data on physicians, half of whom took an aspirin tablet every other day, and half who took a placebo. In this chapter we learn how to make inferences about populations of qualitative data. The parameter of interest is the proportion π of the population that exhibits a certain qualitative characteristic (eg, die of a heart attack). The results of the NEJM study are reported and analyzed in the chapter case study.

INFERENCES ABOUT A SINGLE POPULATION PROPORTION

8.1 Consider the problem of estimating the binomial proportion of successes—that is, the proportion π of elements in a population that have a certain characteristic. For example, a quality control inspector may be interested in the proportion of defective items produced on an assembly line; a pollster may be interested in the proportion of Americans who favor the president's policy of limited government spending; or a supplier of heating oil may be interested in the proportion of homes in its service area that are heated by natural gas.

A logical candidate for a point estimate of the population proportion π is the proportion of observations in the sample that have the characteristic of interest (called a success). If x is the number of successes in a random sample of n observations, then the sample proportion p is

$$p = \frac{x}{n}$$

To assess the reliability of the point estimate p, we need to know its sampling distribution. This information may be derived by an application of the Central Limit Theorem. Properties of the sampling distribution of p (illustrated in Figure 8.1) are given in the next box.

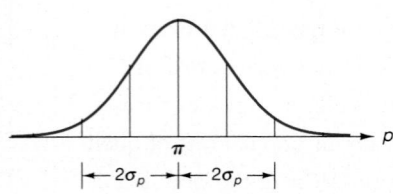

FIGURE 8.1
Sampling Distribution of p

SAMPLING DISTRIBUTION OF THE SAMPLE PROPORTION, p

For sufficiently large samples, the sampling distribution of $p = x/n$ is approximately normal, with

Mean: $\mu_p = \pi$

Standard error: $\sigma_p = \sqrt{\dfrac{\pi(1-\pi)}{n}}$

where

π = The true population proportion of successes

x = Number of successes in the sample

n = Sample size

Large-sample confidence intervals and tests of hypothesis for π are constructed by substituting the estimator, p, and the standard error, $\sqrt{\pi(1-\pi)/n}$, into the general formulas given in Chapter 5. The details are given in the box on p. 337.

Note that we must substitute p and $q = 1 - p$ into the formula for $\sigma_p = \sqrt{\pi(1-\pi)/n}$ in order to construct the confidence interval. This approximation will be valid as long as the sample size n is sufficiently large. Many researchers adopt the rule of thumb that n is sufficiently large if the interval $p \pm 2\sqrt{pq/n}$ does not contain 0 or 1.

EXAMPLE 8.1 Potential advertisers value television's well-known Nielsen ratings as a barometer of a TV show's popularity among viewers. The Nielsen rating of a certain TV program is an estimate of the proportion of viewers, expressed as a percentage, who tune their sets to the program on a given night. In a random sample of 165 families who regularly watch television, a Nielsen survey indicated that 101 of the families were tuned to the last episode of NBC's *Cheers*. Estimate π, the true proportion of all TV-viewing families who watched the final episode of *Cheers*, using a 90% confidence interval.

Solution   In this problem, the variable of interest is the response (yes or no) to the question, "Did you watch the last episode of *Cheers*?" The sample proportion of families that watched the last episode is

$$p = \frac{\text{Number of families in sample who watched the final episode}}{\text{Number of families in sample}}$$

$$= \frac{101}{165} = .612$$

Thus, $q = 1 - .612 = .388$. Using the formula in the box, the approximate 90% confidence interval is

$$p \pm z_{.05}\sqrt{\frac{pq}{n}} = .612 \pm 1.645\sqrt{\frac{(.612)(.388)}{165}}$$

$$= .612 \pm .062 \quad \text{or } (.550, .674)$$

We are 90% confident that the interval from .550 to .674 encloses the true proportion of TV-viewing families who watched the last episode of *Cheers*. If we repeatedly selected random samples of $n = 165$ families and constructed a 90% confidence interval based on each sample, then we would expect 90% of the confidence intervals constructed to contain π.

EXAMPLE 8.2   An *American Demographics* study conducted in 1980 found that 40% of new car buyers were women. Suppose that in a random sample of $n = 120$ new car buyers in 1994, 57 are women. Does this evidence indicate that the true proportion of new car buyers in 1994 who are women is significantly larger than .40, the 1980 proportion? Use the rejection region approach, testing at significance level $\alpha = .10$.

Solution   We wish to perform a large-sample test about a population proportion, π:

H_0: $\pi = .40$ No change from 1980 to 1994

H_a: $\pi > .40$ Proportion of new car buyers who are women is greater in 1994

where π represents the true proportion of all new car buyers in 1994 who are women.

At significance level $\alpha = .10$, the rejection region for this one-tailed test consists of all values of z for which

$$z > z_{.10} = 1.28 \quad \text{See Figure 8.2}$$

The test statistic requires the calculation of the sample proportion, p, of new car buyers who are women:

$$p = \frac{\text{Number of sampled new car buyers who are women}}{\text{Number of new car buyers sampled}}$$

$$= \frac{57}{120} = .475$$

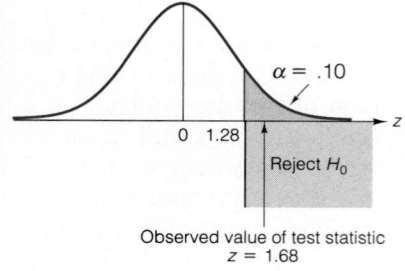

FIGURE 8.2

Rejection Region for Example 8.2

Substituting, we obtain the following value of the test statistic:

$$z = \frac{p - \pi_0}{\sqrt{\pi_0(1 - \pi_0)}} = \frac{.475 - .40}{\sqrt{(.40)(.60)/120}} = 1.68$$

This value of z lies within the rejection region; we thus conclude that the proportion of new car buyers in 1994 who are women increased significantly from .40. The probability of our having made a Type I error (rejecting H_0 when, in fact, it is true) is $\alpha = .10$. [Note that the interval

$$p \pm 2\sqrt{\frac{p(1-p)}{n}} = .475 \pm 2\sqrt{\frac{(.475)(.525)}{120}}$$

$$= .475 \pm .091$$

does not contain 0 or 1. Thus, the sample size is large enough to guarantee the validity of the hypothesis test.]

EXAMPLE 8.3 Refer to Example 8.2. Calculate the observed significance level (p-value) of the test and interpret its value.

Solution   For this large-sample, upper-tailed test, the computed value of the test statistic is $z_c = 1.68$. Thus, the p-value is

$$P(z > z_c) = P(z > 1.68)$$

From Table 2, Appendix A, this probability is $.5 - .4535 = .0465$.

Remember, p-value $= .0465$ is the minimum value of α that leads to a rejection of the null hypothesis. Consequently, we will reject H_0 for any value of α exceeding .0465 (as in Example 8.2), but we will fail to reject H_0 for values of α below .0465. Therefore, a researcher who desires a Type I error rate of only $\alpha = .01$ or $\alpha = .02$ will have insufficient evidence to say that the proportion of new car buyers who are women in 1994 exceeds .40.

Although small-sample procedures are available for confidence intervals and testing hypotheses about a population proportion, the details are omitted from our discussion. It is our experience that they are of limited use, since most surveys of binomial populations (eg, opinion polls) performed in the real world use samples that are large enough to employ the techniques of this section. (See Section 8.3.)

PROBLEMS

8.1   A University of Minnesota survey of brand names (eg, Levi's, Lee, Calvin Klein) and private labels manufactured for retail chains found a high percentage of jeans with incorrect waist and/or inseam measurements on the label. The study found that only 18 of 240 pairs of men's five-pocket, prewashed jeans sold in Minneapolis stores came within a half inch of their label measurements (*Tampa Tribune*, May 20, 1991). Let π represent the true proportion of men's five-pocket, prewashed jeans sold in Minneapolis that have inseam and waist measurements that fall within .5 inch of the labeled measurements.

   a. Find a point estimate of π.
   b. Find an interval estimate of π. Use a confidence coefficient of .90.
   c. Interpret the interval found in part **b**.

8.2 Hospital patients over the age of 65 apparently face a high risk of serious treatment errors, according to a study in the *Journal of the American Geriatric Society* (Dec. 1990). The records of 122 randomly selected elderly patients were checked for errors in their prescribed medications. Of these, 73 patients were found to have at least one erroneously prescribed medication (ie, they received an unneeded drug that might cause harmful side effects, or they failed to receive a necessary drug). Prior to the study, the researcher did not expect such a high error rate. Suppose the researcher wants to test whether the true proportion of elderly (over age 65) patients who have at least one erroneously prescribed drug exceeds .20.

    a. Set up the null and alternative hypotheses of interest to the researcher.
    b. Conduct the test from part **a**. Use $\alpha = .05$.
    c. Compute the *p*-value of the test. Interpret the result.

8.3 "Are today's undergraduates more willing to cheat in order to get good grades?" This was the question posed to a national sample of 5,000 college professors by the Carnegie Foundation for the Advancement of Teaching. Given the "make it at all costs" mentality of the past decade, it is not surprising that 43% of the professors responded "yes" (*Tampa Tribune*, Mar. 7, 1990). Based on this survey, estimate the proportion of all college professors who feel their undergraduate students are more willing to cheat in order to get good grades. Use a confidence coefficient of .90.

8.4 In order to significantly reduce soil erosion in our country, the Conservation Title of the 1985 farm bill requires that conservation compliance be implemented by 1995. Despite controversy over the bill, the U.S. Soil Conservation Service (SCS) claims that 80% of farmers who already have a soil conservation plan feel their plan is reasonable and practical (*Prairie Farmer*, Mar. 20, 1990). An independent survey conducted by *Prairie Farmer* magazine found that of 144 Indiana farmers who have a conservation plan, only 78 believe their plan is realistic.

    a. Does this survey refute or support the SCS claim? Test using $\alpha = .01$.
    b. Compute the *p*-value of the test. Interpret the result.

8.5 According to an Internal Revenue Service (IRS) study, most IRS officials believe that taxpayers are unethical when filing their tax returns. Of a sample of 800 IRS executives and managers from across the country, only 144 rated the ethics of the average taxpayer as good or excellent (*Arizona Republic*, Mar. 23, 1991). Estimate the true proportion of IRS officials who rate the ethics of the average taxpayer as good or excellent with a 99% confidence interval. Interpret the result.

8.6 The "Black Hole" survey, sponsored by the Professional Employment Research Council, reports on the toughest jobs to fill on recruiters' lists. In the most recent survey, 95 of 285 recruiters listed engineering positions as the toughest to fill (*Industrial Engineering*, Aug. 1990). Estimate the true percentage of recruiters who find it toughest to fill engineering positions. Use a 99% confidence interval.

8.7 Researchers at the University of South Florida College of Medicine conducted a study of the drug usage of U.S. physicians (*Journal of the American Medical Association*, May 6, 1992). The anonymous survey of 5,426 randomly selected physicians revealed that 7.9% (or 429) experienced substance abuse or drug dependency in their lifetime. Test the hypothesis that more than 5% of U.S. physicians have abused or depended on drugs in their lifetime. Use $\alpha = .10$.

8.8 Do colleges provide good value for the dollar? A majority of Americans do not think so, according to a Media General–Associated Press telephone poll. Of the 1,348 adult Americans who participated in the nationwide poll, 805 believe tuition at most private colleges and universities is too high for the quality of education provided (*Gainesville Sun*, Sept. 1, 1987).

    a. Construct a 95% confidence interval for π, the true proportion of adult Americans who think colleges are too expensive, given the quality of education provided.
    b. How would the width of the confidence interval in part **a** change if the confidence coefficient were increased from .95 to .99?

8.9 Do most state lottery winners who win big payoffs quit their jobs? Not according to a study conducted by sociologist and professor, H. Roy Kaplan (*Journal of the Institute for Socioeconomic Studies*, Sept. 1985). Kaplan mailed questionnaires to over 2,000 lottery winners who won at least $50,000 in the past 10 years. Of the 576 who responded, only 11% had quit their jobs during the first year after striking it rich.

a. Use a 95% confidence interval to estimate the true proportion of all state lottery winners (at least $50,000) who quit their jobs during the first year after striking it rich.

b. Do you think the 576 lottery winners who returned the questionnaire represent a random sample of all state lottery winners? Explain how a nonrandom sample could bias the results.

8.10 The U.S. Food and Drug Administration (FDA) approved the marketing of a new chemical solution, Caridex, which dissolves cavities. In a study conducted by dental researchers at Northwestern University, 21 of 35 patients with cavities preferred treatment with Caridex to drilling (*Gainesville Sun*, Feb. 11, 1988). Test whether the true proportion of dental patients who prefer having their cavities dissolved with Caridex rather than drilled is larger than .50. Use $\alpha = .01$.

COMPARING TWO POPULATION PROPORTIONS

8.2

This section extends the method of Section 8.1 to the case in which we want to estimate the difference between two population proportions. For example, we may be interested in comparing the proportions of defective items produced by two machines, or the proportions of homes in two states that are heated by natural gas, or the proportions of U.S. and Japanese firms that employ industrial robots.

Let π_1 and π_2 represent the true proportions of successes in populations 1 and 2, respectively. Now consider a random sample of size n_1 from population 1 and an independent random sample of size n_2 from population 2, and let x_1 and x_2 be the number of successes observed in each sample, respectively. As a point estimate of $(\pi_1 - \pi_2)$, we will use the difference between the corresponding sample proportions, $(p_1 - p_2)$, where

$$p_1 = \frac{x_1}{n_1} \quad \text{and} \quad p_2 = \frac{x_2}{n_2}$$

To judge the reliability of the point estimate $(p_1 - p_2)$, we need to know the characteristics of its performance in repeated independent sampling from two populations. This information is provided by the sampling distribution of $(p_1 - p_2)$ illustrated in Figure 8.3 and shown in the next box.

SAMPLING DISTRIBUTION OF $(p_1 - p_2)$

For sufficiently large sample sizes, n_1 and n_2, the sampling distribution of $(p_1 - p_2)$, based on independent random samples from two binomial populations, is approximately normal with

Mean: $\mu_{(p_1-p_2)} = (\pi_1 - \pi_2)$

Standard error: $\sigma_{(p_1-p_2)} = \sqrt{\dfrac{\pi_1(1 - \pi_1)}{n_1} + \dfrac{\pi_2(1 - \pi_2)}{n_2}}$

FIGURE 8.3

Sampling Distribution of $(p_1 - p_2)$

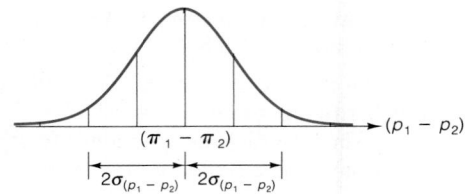

Large-sample confidence intervals and tests for $(\pi_1 - \pi_2)$ are obtained by substituting the estimator, $(p_1 - p_2)$, and standard error, $\sigma_{(p_1-p_2)}$, into the general formulas provided in Chapter 5. The complete formulas are shown in the following box:

PARAMETRIC INFERENCES FOR THE DIFFERENCE IN POPULATION PROPORTIONS, $(\pi_1 - \pi_2)$

$(1 - \alpha)100\%$ CONFIDENCE INTERVAL

$$(p_1 - p_2) \pm z_{\alpha/2}\sigma_{(p_1-p_2)} \approx (p_1 - p_2) \pm z_{\alpha/2}\sqrt{\frac{p_1q_1}{n_1} + \frac{p_2q_2}{n_2}}$$

where p_1 and p_2 are the sample proportions of observations with the characteristic of interest, $q_1 = 1 - p_1$, and $q_2 = 1 - p_2$.

Note: We have followed the usual procedure of substituting the sample values p_1, q_1, p_2, and q_2 for the corresponding population values required for $\sigma_{(p_1-p_2)}$.

TEST OF HYPOTHESIS

ONE-TAILED TEST   **TWO-TAILED TEST**

H_0: $(\pi_1 - \pi_2) = D_0$ H_0: $\pi_1 - \pi_2 = D_0$

H_a: $(\pi_1 - \pi_2) > D_0$ H_a: $(\pi_1 - \pi_2) \neq D_0$

[or H_a: $(\pi_1 - \pi_2) < D_0$]

Test statistic: $z = \dfrac{(p_1 - p_2) - D_0}{\sigma_{(p_1-p_2)}} \approx \dfrac{(p_1 - p_2) - D_0}{\sqrt{\dfrac{p_1q_1}{n_1} + \dfrac{p_2q_2}{n_2}}}$

Rejection region: $z > z_\alpha$ [or $z < -z_\alpha$]   Rejection region: $|z| > z_{\alpha/2}$

Assumptions:

1. Independent random samples are selected from the two populations.
2. The sample sizes n_1 and n_2 are large; this will usually be satisfied if the intervals

$$p_1 \pm 2\sqrt{\frac{p_1q_1}{n_1}} \quad \text{and} \quad p_2 \pm 2\sqrt{\frac{p_2q_2}{n_2}}$$

do not contain 0 or 1.

To obtain the confidence interval or test statistic,* we must substitute the values of p_1 and p_2 for π_1 and π_2, respectively, to obtain an estimate of $\sigma_{(p_1-p_2)}$. Also, the sample sizes n_1 and n_2 must be sufficiently large to ensure that the sampling distributions of p_1 and p_2, and hence, of the difference $(p_1 - p_2)$, are approximately normal. The rule of thumb given in the box may be used to determine whether the sample sizes are sufficiently large.

EXAMPLE 8.4 Over the years, one of the issues studied in depth by organizational behavior theorists involves the area of ethical management decision-making. Prior to 1980, these studies focused on the male manager because the management field was male-dominated. Today, with women entering management careers in record numbers, researchers are studying the differences in ethical perceptions between male and female managers. In one study, 48 of 50 female managers responded that concealing one's on-the-job errors was very unethical, while only 30 of 50 male managers responded in like manner (*Journal of Business Ethics*, Aug. 1987). Use this information to construct a 95% confidence interval for the difference between the proportions of female and male managers who believe that concealing one's errors is very unethical. Interpret your results.

Solution For this example, define

π_1 = Proportion of female managers who believe that concealing on-the-job errors is unethical

π_2 = Proportion of male managers who believe that concealing on-the-job errors is unethical

Using the sample results, $x_1 = 48$, $n_1 = 50$, $x_2 = 30$, and $n_2 = 50$, we have

$$p_1 = \frac{x_1}{n_1} = \frac{48}{50} = .96 \qquad p_2 = \frac{x_2}{n_2} = \frac{30}{50} = .60$$

Thus, $q_1 = 1 - .96 = .04$ and $q_2 = 1 - .60 = .40$. Substituting these values into the formula for a 95% confidence interval for $(\pi_1 - \pi_2)$, we obtain

$$(p_1 - p_2) \pm z_{.025} \sqrt{\frac{p_1 q_1}{n_1} + \frac{p_2 q_2}{n_2}} = (.96 - .60) \pm 1.96 \sqrt{\frac{(.96)(.04)}{50} + \frac{(.60)(.40)}{50}}$$

$$= .36 \pm .146$$

or $(.214, .506)$. Thus, we estimate that the interval $(.214, .506)$ encloses the difference $(\pi_1 - \pi_2)$ with 95% confidence. It appears that there are between 21.4% and

---

* For the special case $D_0 = 0$, some researchers use the proportion of successes in the combined samples,

$$p = \frac{x_1 + x_2}{n_1 + n_2}$$

to estimate the standard error, $\sigma_{(p_1-p_2)}$. The estimate of $\sigma_{(p_1-p_2)}$ is then

$$\sqrt{pq\left(\frac{1}{n_1} + \frac{1}{n_2}\right)}$$

50.6% more female managers than male managers who believe that concealing on-the-job errors is very unethical.

EXAMPLE 8.5 Several U.S. cities have created an incentive for car-pooling by designating certain highway traffic lanes as "car-pool only" (ie, only cars with two or more passengers can use these lanes). To evaluate the effectiveness of this plan, toll booth personnel in Washington, DC, monitored 2,000 randomly selected cars 6 months before the car-pool only lanes were established and 1,500 cars 6 months after the car-pool only lanes were established. The results of the study are shown in Table 8.1, where x_1 and x_2 represent the numbers of cars with two or more passengers (ie, car-pool riders) in the after and before samples, respectively. Do the data indicate that the fraction of cars with car-pool riders has increased over this 6 month period? Use $\alpha = .05$.

TABLE 8.1
Results of Car-Pool Survey

AFTER CAR-POOL LANES	BEFORE CAR-POOL LANES
$n_1 = 1,500$	$n_2 = 2,000$
$x_1 = 576$	$x_2 = 652$

Solution If we define π_1 and π_2 as the true proportions of cars with car-pool riders after and before installing car-pool only lanes, respectively, the elements of our test are

$$H_0: \quad (\pi_1 - \pi_2) = 0$$
$$H_a: \quad (\pi_1 - \pi_2) > 0$$

(The test is one-tailed, since we are interested only in determining whether the proportion of cars with car-pool riders has increased.)

Test statistic: $\quad z = \dfrac{(p_1 - p_2) - 0}{\sigma_{(p_1 - p_2)}}$

Rejection region: $\quad z > z_{.05} = z > 1.645$ $\quad$ See Figure 8.4

We now calculate the sample proportions of cars with car-pool riders:

$$p_1 = \frac{576}{1,500} = .384 \qquad p_2 = \frac{652}{2,000} = .326$$

The test statistic is

$$z = \frac{(p_1 - p_2)}{\sigma_{(p_1 - p_2)}} \approx \frac{(p_1 - p_2)}{\sqrt{\dfrac{p_1 q_1}{n_1} + \dfrac{p_2 q_2}{n_2}}}$$

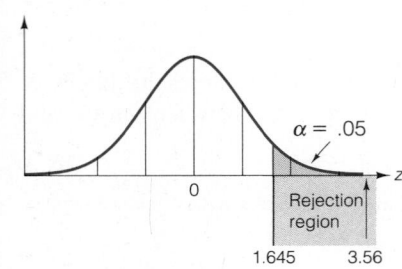

$\alpha = .05$

Rejection region

1.645 $\quad$ 3.56

FIGURE 8.4
Rejection Region

where $q_1 = 1 - p_1 = .616$ and $q_2 = 1 - p_2 = .674$. Thus,

$$z \approx \frac{.384 - .326}{\sqrt{\dfrac{(.384)(.616)}{1,500} + \dfrac{(.326)(.674)}{2,000}}} = \frac{.058}{.0163} = 3.56$$

There is sufficient evidence at $\alpha = .05$ to conclude that the proportion of all cars with car-pool riders has increased over the 6 month period. We could place a confidence interval on $(\pi_1 - \pi_2)$ if we were interested in estimating the extent of the increase.

In Example 8.5 note that neither of the intervals

$$p_1 \pm 2\sqrt{\frac{p_1 q_1}{n_1}} = .384 \pm 2\sqrt{\frac{(.384)(.616)}{1,500}} = .384 \pm .025$$

$$p_2 \pm 2\sqrt{\frac{p_2 q_2}{n_2}} = .326 \pm 2\sqrt{\frac{(.326)(.674)}{2,000}} = .326 \pm .021$$

includes 0 or 1. Therefore, the samples are sufficiently large to guarantee the validity of the test. When the samples are not sufficiently large, we must resort to an alternative technique for comparing π_1 and π_2 discussed in Section 8.5.

PROBLEMS

8.11 A research team at the University of South Florida conducted a study of former cigarette smokers. One phase of the study compared the percentage of black former smokers who quit smoking on their own to the corresponding percentage of white former smokers (*USF Magazine*, Summer 1992). Of the 153 black former smokers sampled, 150 quit on their own; of the 381 white former smokers sampled, 324 quit without assistance.

   a. Compare the percentages of the two groups of former smokers with a 90% confidence interval.

   b. Based on the interval found in part **a**, can you infer that one group of former smokers had more difficulty quitting on their own than the other group? Explain.

8.12 According to new research, inositol (a sugar alcohol nutrient found in breast milk) has been found to reduce the risk of lung and eye damage in premature infants. The study, published in the *New England Journal of Medicine* (May 7, 1992), involved 220 infants born prematurely. The infants were randomly divided into two groups; half (110) of the infants received an intravenous feeding of inositol, while the other half received standard nutrition. The researchers found that 14 of the inositol-fed infants suffered retinopathy of prematurity, an eye injury that results from high oxygen levels needed to compensate for poorly developed lungs. In contrast, 29 of the infants on the standard diet developed this disease. Analyze the results with a test of hypothesis. Use $\alpha = .01$.

8.13 Are black teachers in Florida's public universities earning tenure at the same rate as their white colleagues? A Florida university system study found that of the 20 black professors hired in 1983, only one had received tenure by their seventh year. Comparatively, 60 of the 150 white professors hired in 1983 earned tenure by their seventh year (*Tampa Tribune*, Sept. 16, 1990).

   a. Is there sufficient evidence to indicate that black professors in Florida have a lower tenure rate than white professors? Test using $\alpha = .05$.

   b. Find the p-value of the test in part **a**. Interpret the result.

8.14   Refer to Problem 6.10 (p. 264), the *American Journal of Small Business* study of female managers. The two groups of managers surveyed were also asked if they would change jobs if given the opportunity. Of the 86 small-firm managers, 65 responded negatively, while 51 of the 91 large-firm managers answered negatively.

   a. Construct a 95% confidence interval for the difference between the percentages who would not change jobs if given the opportunity for the two groups of female managers.
   b. Interpret the interval from part **a**.

8.15   According to the *Harvard Business Review* (July–Aug. 1986), approximately two-thirds of the 500 largest U.S. corporations have, in varying degrees, committed some form of unethical behavior. The lack of ethics in business has led many to question higher education's role in the ethics process. A more recent study found that the presence of ethics in the business school curriculum is sorely lacking. In a sample of 94 MBA programs, only 7 required a course on ethics, while 18 of 86 sampled undergraduate business programs required an ethics course (*Journal of Education for Business*, Nov.–Dec. 1990).

   a. Conduct a test to determine whether the percentages of business school programs that require an ethics course differ at the undergraduate and MBA level. Use $\alpha = .10$.
   b. Find the *p*-value of the test from part **a**. Interpret the result.

8.16   According to an American Heart Association (AHA) researcher, "people who are hostile and mistrustful are more likely to die young or develop life-threatening heart disease than those with more 'trusting hearts' " (*Tampa Tribune*, Jan. 17, 1989). A sample of 118 male doctors, lawyers, and workers in a large industrial firm in Chicago were divided into two groups based on a standard psychological test designed to measure hostility. Of the 35 men who scored high in hostility, 7 died at a relatively early age (ie, between the ages of 25 and 50). In contrast, only 4 of the 83 men whose hostility rating was low died at an early age.

   a. Estimate the true difference between the proportion of men with high hostility scores who die at an early age and the corresponding proportion of men with low hostility scores. Use a 95% confidence interval.
   b. Are the sample sizes large enough for the interval in part **a** to be valid?
   c. Interpret the interval in part **a**. Do you agree with the AHA researcher?

8.17   According to a Gallup study for the American Society of Quality Control, "men focus on product performance and durability when assessing quality [of American-made goods] while women also consider the availability of service, whether a product can be repaired, and type of warranty" (*American Demographics*, June 1986). Overall, 58% of the women surveyed rated American products high in quality, compared to 43% of the men. Assuming that the sample survey included 500 men and 500 women, conduct a test to determine whether the true percentage of women who rate American products high in quality exceeds the true percentage of men. Use $\alpha = .01$.

8.18   In the travel industry, "destination-specific travel literature (DSTL)" refers to booklets, brochures, and pamphlets that describe a destination in detail (eg, information on activities, facilities, and prices). DSTL is available to travelers free of charge upon request. A study was undertaken to investigate the differences between information seekers (ie, those who request DSTL) and nonseekers on a variety of consumer travel dimensions. Independent random samples of 288 seekers and 367 nonseekers were asked several questions about their "most recent pleasure trip or vacation of two or more days away from home." One interesting question asked whether the vacation was "active" (ie, involved mainly challenging events or educational activities) or "passive" (ie, involved mainly rest and relaxation). The number of passive vacations in each group is given in the table. Do the data provide sufficient evidence to indicate that information seekers are less likely to have a passive vacation than nonseekers? Test using $\alpha = .10$.

	SEEKERS	NONSEEKERS
Number surveyed	288	367
Number who experienced a passive vacation	197	301

Source: Etzel, M. J., and Wahlers, R. G. "The Use of Requested Promotional Material by Pleasure Travelers." *Journal of Travel Research*, Vol. 23, No. 4, Spring 1985, pp. 2–6. The *Journal of Travel Research* is published by the Travel and Tourism Research Association (TTRA) and the Business Research Division, University of Colorado at Boulder.

8.19 The city of Niagara Falls, New York, and the surrounding Niagara County are known to contain a large number of toxic-waste disposal sites (dump sites). Following the negative publicity of the "Love Canal" in Niagara Falls, the New York State Department of Health funded a study of death certificates to determine whether lung cancer in Niagara County might be associated with exposure to pollution from the dump sites (*Environmental Research*, Feb. 1989). The study involved a comparison of two samples. The first sample (called "cases") was comprised of the $n_1 = 327$ residents of Niagara County who died of cancer of the trachea, bronchus, or lung. The second sample (called "controls") consisted of $n_2 = 667$ residents of Niagara County who died from causes other than respiratory cancers. Of the 327 cases, 50 resided near dump sites containing lung carcinogens; of the 667 controls, 102 resided near dump sites containing lung carcinogens.

  a. Compare the percentages of cases and controls with residence near a dump site with a 90% confidence interval.

  b. If the confidence coefficient were decreased to .80, would you expect the width of the interval to increase, decrease, or stay the same? Would you recommend decreasing the confidence coefficient to .80? Explain.

8.20 A study was conducted to determine the impact of a multifunction workstation (MFWS) on the way managers work (*Datamation*, Feb. 15, 1986). Two groups of managers at a St. Louis-based defense agency took part in the survey: a test group consisting of 12 managers who currently use MFWS software and a control group of 25 non-MFWS users. One question on the survey concerned the information sources of the managers. In the test group (MFWS users), 4 of the 12 managers reported that their major source of information is the computer, while 2 of the 25 managers in the control group (non-MFWS users) rely on the computer as their major source of information.

  a. Is there evidence of a difference between the proportions of MFWS users and non-MFWS users who rely on the computer as their major information source? Test using $\alpha = .10$.

  b. Refer to the test in part **a**. Are the samples sufficiently large to properly apply the test? How does this affect the validity of the inference derived in part **a**?

DETERMINING THE SAMPLE SIZE

8.3

The procedures for determining the sample sizes needed to estimate and test a population proportion or the difference between two population proportions are analogous to the sample size procedures for means given in Section 6.5. The appropriate formulas are shown in the following boxes.

CHOOSING THE SAMPLE SIZE FOR ESTIMATING A POPULATION PROPORTION, π

$$n = \left(\frac{z_{\alpha/2}}{d}\right)^2 \pi(1 - \pi)$$

where

  d = Half-width of interval

  $z_{\alpha/2}$ = z-Value that corresponds to a confidence coefficient of $(1 - \alpha)$

Note: This technique requires a previous estimate of π. If none is available, use $\pi = .5$ for a conservative choice of n.

**CHOOSING THE SAMPLE SIZE FOR
TESTING A POPULATION PROPORTION, π**

ONE-TAILED TEST

$$n = \left[\frac{z_{1-\beta} - z_\alpha}{\pi_0 - \pi_a} \right]^2 \pi(1 - \pi)$$

TWO-TAILED TEST

$$n = \left[\frac{z_{1-\beta} - z_{\alpha/2}}{\pi_0 - \pi_a} \right]^2 \pi(1 - \pi)$$

where

$\pi_0 =$ Value of π specified in H_0 (ie, H_0: $\pi = \pi_0$)

$\pi_a =$ Specific value of π in H_a

$1 - \beta =$ Power of the test for the specified value of π_a

$\alpha =$ Fixed significance level of the test

$z_{1-\beta} = z$-Value such that $P(z > z_{1-\beta}) = 1 - \beta$

$z_\alpha = z$-Value such that $P(z > z_\alpha) = \alpha$

$z_{\alpha/2} = z$-Value such that $P(z > z_{\alpha/2}) = \alpha/2$

Note: The technique requires a previous estimate of π. If none is available, use $\pi = .5$ for a conservative choice of n.

**CHOOSING THE SAMPLE SIZES FOR TESTING THE DIFFERENCE
BETWEEN PROPORTIONS $(\pi_1 - \pi_2)$: $n = n_1 = n_2$**

ONE-TAILED TEST

$$n = \left[\frac{z_{1-\beta} - z_\alpha}{D_0 - D_a} \right]^2 [\pi_1(1 - \pi_1) + \pi_2(1 - \pi_2)]$$

TWO-TAILED TEST

$$n = \left[\frac{z_{1-\beta} - z_{\alpha/2}}{D_0 - D_a} \right]^2 [\pi_1(1 - \pi_1) + \pi_2(1 - \pi_2)]$$

where

$D_0 =$ Value of $(\pi_1 - \pi_2)$ specified in H_0 (ie, H_0: $\pi_1 - \pi_2 = D_0$)

$D_a =$ Specific value of $(\pi_1 - \pi_2)$ in H_a

$1 - \beta =$ Power of the test for the specified value of D_a

$\alpha =$ Fixed significance level of the test

$z_{1-\beta} = z$-Value such that $P(z > z_{1-\beta}) = 1 - \beta$

$z_\alpha = z$-Value such that $P(z > z_\alpha) = \alpha$

$z_{\alpha/2} = z$-Value such that $P(z > z_{\alpha/2}) = \alpha/2$

Note: This technique requires previous estimates of π_1 and π_2. If none are available, use $\pi_1 = \pi_2 = .5$ for a conservative choice of n.

CHOOSING THE SAMPLE SIZES FOR ESTIMATING THE DIFFERENCE
$(\pi_1 - \pi_2)$ BETWEEN TWO POPULATION PROPORTIONS: $n = n_1 = n_2$

$$n = \left(\frac{z_{\alpha/2}}{d}\right)^2 [\pi_1(1 - \pi_1) + \pi_2(1 - \pi_2)]$$

where π_1 and π_2 are the proportions for populations 1 and 2, respectively, n_1 and n_2 are the numbers of observations to be sampled from each population,

d = Half-width of the interval

$z_{\alpha/2}$ = z-Value that corresponds to a confidence coefficient of $(1 - \alpha)$

Note: This technique requires previous estimates of π_1 and π_2. If none are available, use $\pi_1 = \pi_2 = .5$ for a conservative choice of n.

EXAMPLE 8.6   According to a magazine advertisement, the twin-blade Daisy shaver made by Gillette shaves legs smoother, closer, and safer than any single-blade shaver. In order to substantiate the advertisement's claim, a consumer reporter for a daily newspaper wants to conduct her own survey. Using a test similar to Gillette's, she will ask a sample of women ranging in age from 19 to 50 to shave one leg with a Daisy and the other leg with a Lady Bic (a single-blade disposable razor for women). After shaving according to their own routine, each participant will give her opinion as to which of the two shavers gave a "smoother, closer, and safer" shave. How large a survey would be required in order to estimate π to within .03 with 90% confidence?

Solution   To calculate n using the equation given in the box, we must find the value of $z_{\alpha/2}$, the half-width of the interval d, and an approximation for the unknown population proportion π.

For a confidence coefficient of $(1 - \alpha) = .90$, we have $\alpha = .10$. Thus, from Table 2, Appendix A, the z-value corresponding to an area of $\alpha/2 = .05$ in the upper tail of the standard normal distribution is $z_{.05} = z_{\alpha/2} = 1.645$.

Since the consumer reporter wants to estimate π to within .03 of its true value, she wants the half-width of the interval to be $d = .03$. Also, no previous estimate of π is available; therefore, we'll use the conservative estimate, $\pi = .5$.

Substituting the values of $\pi = .5$, $z_{.05} = 1.645$, and $d = .03$ into the equation for n, we have

$$n = \left(\frac{z_{\alpha/2}}{d}\right)^2 \pi(1 - \pi) = \left(\frac{1.645}{.03}\right)^2 (.5)(.5) = 751.7$$

Thus, a random sample of 752 women will provide an estimate of π that will, with 90% confidence, lie within .03 of the proportion of all women shavers who prefer the Daisy razor over the Lady Bic.

EXAMPLE 8.7 A soft-drink bottler wants to assess the effect of an advertising campaign designed to increase customer recognition of a new cola drink. Random samples of consumers are to be selected from the marketing area both before and after the advertising campaign, and consumers will be asked whether they have heard of the new cola drink. Suppose the bottler wants to test for a difference in the proportions of consumers who recognize the brand name of the cola drink using $\alpha = .05$. How many people should be included in each sample if the bottler wants the test to detect a difference of .10 with probability .75?

Solution The bottler wants to conduct the two-tailed test $H_0: (\pi_1 - \pi_2) = 0$ against $H_a: (\pi_1 - \pi_2) \neq 0$ using $\alpha = .05$. Thus, $D_0 = 0$ and $z_{\alpha/2} = z_{.025} = 1.96$. Also, the bottler desires a power of $1 - \beta = .75$ for the alternative $D_a = .10$.

The value $z_{1-\beta} = z_{.75}$, obtained from Table 2, Appendix A, is $z_{.75} = -.675$ (see Figure 8.5).

FIGURE 8.5

Values of $z_{\alpha/2}$ and $z_{1-\beta}$

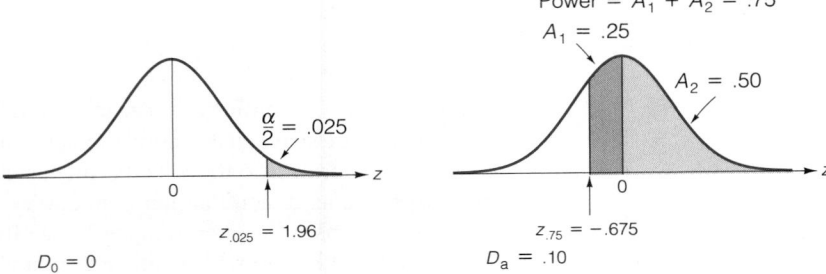

Since no previous estimates of π_1 and π_2 are provided, we use the conservative estimates $\pi_1 = .5$ and $\pi_2 = .5$. Substituting these values into the formula for n_1 and n_2, we obtain

$$n_1 = n_2 = \left[\frac{z_{1-\beta} - z_{\alpha/2}}{D_0 - D_a} \right]^2 [\pi_1(1 - \pi_1) + \pi_2(1 - \pi_2)]$$

$$= \left[\frac{-.675 - 1.96}{0 - .10} \right]^2 [(.5)(.5) + (.5)(.5)] = 347.2$$

Therefore, the bottler should include approximately 348 consumers in each of the two samples to detect a difference in proportions of .10 with probability .75 using an $\alpha = .05$ test.

Examples 8.6 and 8.7 both deal with finding the number of persons to be included in a consumer survey or preference poll. It is important to mention two critical problems associated with sampling of this type. The first is the problem of **nonresponse**, that is, the inability of the researcher to contact one or more of the persons (or elements) listed in the sample or the refusal of a sampled person to respond. Nonresponse is an important problem to address because the exclusion of the nonrespondents may produce a serious bias in the resulting sample. For example, it is quite common for television stations to request viewers to call in their opinion regarding some political candidate or issue. This type of "self-selected" sample is likely to include people who want to produce a strong showing for one side or the other and exclude people who are less ardent in expressing their political opinions. Nonresponse often occurs in mailed surveys because busy people, a particular and unique social class, do not want to take the time to complete the survey's questionnaire. The survey of state lottery winners mentioned in Problem 8.9 is a case in point. Of the approximately 2,000 questionnaires sent out to state lottery winners, only 576 (about 29%) were returned. It is impossible to know how much bias seeped into the results because of this low response rate.

Another problem encountered in some business surveys is the difficulty in eliciting **valid responses** from persons included in the sample. For example, suppose that one question in a survey of employees asks whether the employee wrongly took sick leave during the year and used it for vacation. An employee who was habitual in misusing sick leave might want to conceal the fact by falsifying his or her response to the question. This, again, would introduce bias into the survey results.

To deal with the numerous problems encountered in conducting business surveys, consumer preference polls, and so forth, a particular area of statistics known as **survey sampling** has been developed. Consult the references at the end of this chapter for details on this methodology.

PROBLEMS

8.21 Astronauts often report episodes of disorientation as they move around the zero-gravity spacecraft. To compensate, crew members rely heavily on visual information to establish a top-down orientation. An empirical study was conducted to assess the potential of using color brightness as a body orientation clue (*Human Factors*, Dec. 1988). Ninety college students, reclining on their backs in the dark, were disoriented when positioned on a rotating platform under a slowly rotating disk that filled their entire field of vision. Half the disk was painted with a brighter level of color than the other half. The students were asked to say "stop" when they believed they were right-side up, and the brightness level of the disk was recorded. Of the 90 students, 58 selected the brighter color level. How many subjects are required for a similar experiment to estimate the true proportion who use a bright color level as a cue to being right-side up to within .05 with 95% confidence? Use the sample proportion in the *Human Factors* study as an estimate of π.

8.22 Refer to Problem 8.2 (p. 340), the *Journal of the American Geriatric Society* study of errors in prescribed medications. Recall that the researcher wants to test H_0: $\pi = .20$ against H_a: $\pi > .20$, where π = proportion of elderly patients who have erroneously prescribed drugs, using $\alpha = .05$. How many elderly patients must be sampled for the test to attain a power of .6 if the true π is .30?

8.23 Rat damage creates a large financial loss in the production of sugar cane. One aspect of the problem that has been investigated by the U.S. Department of Agriculture concerns the optimal place to locate rat poison. To be more effective in reducing rat damage, should the poison be located in the middle of the field or on the outer perimeter? One way to answer this question is to determine where the greater amount of damage occurs. If damage is measured by the proportion of cane stalks that have been damaged by rats, how many stalks from each section of the field should be sampled to estimate the true difference between the proportions of stalks damaged in the two sections to within .02 with probability .95? (Assume that samples of equal size are to be selected from each section.)

8.24 Refer to Problem 8.10 (p. 341), the Northwestern University study on the use of Caridex by dental patients. How many patients would the dental researchers need to include in their study to estimate the true proportion of dental patients who prefer Caridex to drilling with a 99% confidence interval no wider than .20?

8.25   Refer to Problem 8.20 (p. 347), the *Datamation* study on the impact of a multifunction workstation (MFWS) on managers. Suppose the researchers want to detect a difference between the proportions of MFWS users and nonusers of .10 with probability .75 using an $\alpha = .10$ level test. How many managers in each group would need to be sampled to attain the desired power?

8.4   COMPARING MULTINOMIAL PROPORTIONS: ONE-WAY TABLE

In the preceding sections, the parameter of interest was the proportion π of successes associated with a binomial experiment, that is, an experiment that results in one of two possible outcomes. Many types of experiments result in observations on a qualitative variable with three or more possible outcomes. For example, suppose that a particular personal computer (PC) is manufactured on one of five different production lines, A, B, C, D, or E. In order to compare the proportions of defective PCs that can be attributed to the five production lines, all defective computers located by an inspection program are classified each day according to the production line. Each PC is an experimental unit and the observation is a letter that identifies the production line on which it was produced. Production line is clearly a qualitative variable.

Suppose that $n = 103$ computers are found to be defective in a given week. The $n = 103$ qualitative observations, each resulting in an A, B, C, D, or E, produce counts giving the numbers of defectives emerging from the five production lines. For example, if there were $n_1 = 15$ A's, $n_2 = 27$ B's, $n_3 = 31$ C's, $n_4 = 19$ D's, and $n_5 = 11$ E's, the classified data would appear as shown in Table 8.2, which shows the counts in each category of the classification. Table 8.2 is called a **one-way table**, since it summarizes the responses in the categories of a *single* qualitative variable. Note that the sum of the numbers of defective PCs produced by the five lines must equal the total number of defective PCs:

$$n = n_1 + n_2 + n_3 + n_4 + n_5 = 15 + 27 + 31 + 19 + 11 = 103$$

The classification experiment we have just described is called a **multinomial experiment** and represents an extension of the binomial experiment discussed in Chapter 4. Such an experiment consists of n identical trials—that is, observations on n experimental units. Each trial must result in one and only one of k outcomes, the k classification categories (for the binomial experiment, $k = 2$). The probability that the outcome of a single trial will fall in category i is π_i ($i = 1, 2, ..., k$). Finally, the trials are independent, and we are interested in the numbers of observations, $n_1, n_2, ..., n_k$, falling in the k classification categories.

The ultimate objective of a multinomial experiment is to make inferences about the unknown category probabilities, $\pi_1, \pi_2, ..., \pi_k$. The practical question to be answered in the study of the defective personal computers is whether the proportions of defective PCs differ among the five production lines. That is, do the data provide evidence to contradict the following null hypothesis?

$$H_0: \quad \pi_1 = \pi_2 = \cdots = \pi_5 = .2$$

(Note that the sum of the hypothesized probabilities must equal 1.) If the data contradict this hypothesis, the manufacturer would want to know why the rate of production of defective PCs is greater on some production lines than others, and would take countermeasures to reduce the production of defective PCs.

TABLE 8.2

Classification of the $n = 103$ Defective Personal Computers According to Production Line

PRODUCTION LINE				
A	B	C	D	E
15	27	31	19	11

1. The experiment consists of n identical trials.
2. There are k possible outcomes to each trial.
3. The probabilities of the k outcomes, denoted by $\pi_1, \pi_2, ..., \pi_k$, remain the same from trial to trial, where $\pi_1 + \pi_2 + \cdots + \pi_k = 1$.
4. The trials are independent.
5. The random variables of interest are the counts $n_1, n_2, ..., n_k$ in each of the k classification categories.

The appropriate test is based on the deviations of the observed category counts, $n_1, n_2, ..., n_5$, from their expected (or mean) values, where the formula for the **expected cell count**, E_i, is given in the box. Large deviations between the observed and expected category counts would provide evidence to indicate that the hypothesized category probabilities are incorrect. This test, often called a **goodness of fit test**, is based on the χ^2 distribution.

FORMULA FOR CALCULATING EXPECTED CELL COUNTS IN A
MULTINOMIAL EXPERIMENT

$E_i = n\pi_i$

where

E_i = Expected cell count for cell i

n = Sample size

π_i = Hypothesized probability that an observation will fall in cell i

The elements of the χ^2 goodness of fit test for a one-way table are given in the next box. Note that the test requires that the number n of trials is large enough so that $E_i \geq 5$ for all categories.*

---

* For some applications, the expected cell counts can be less than 5. Consult the references at the end of this chapter.

A TEST OF HYPOTHESIS ABOUT MULTINOMIAL PROBABILITIES: ONE-WAY TABLE

H_0: The k cell probabilities are π_1, π_2, ..., π_k.

H_a: At least two of the cell probabilities differ from the values specified in H_0.

Test statistic: $\sum_{i=1}^{k} \frac{(O_i - E_i)^2}{E_i}$

where

k = Number of cells in the categorization table

O_i = Observed count for cell i

E_i = Expected count for cell i

n = Sample size

$= O_1 + O_2 + \cdots + O_k$

Rejection region: $\chi^2 > \chi^2_\alpha$, where χ^2 depends on $(k - 1)$ df.

Assumptions:

1. The properties of a multinomial experiment are satisfied.
2. The expected count for each of the k cells is at least 5.

EXAMPLE 8.8 Refer to the data provided in the one-way table, Table 8.2. Test the hypothesis that the proportions of all defective computers attributable to the five production lines are equal. Test using $\alpha = .05$.

Solution   We want to test

H_0: $\pi_1 = \pi_2 = \cdots = \pi_5 = .2$

H_a: At least two of the category probabilities are unequal.

For this example, the expected cell counts are

$$E_i = n\pi_i = (103)(.2) = 20.6 \qquad (i = 1, 2, ..., 5)$$

The observed and expected (in parentheses) category counts are shown in Table 8.3.

TABLE 8.3
Observed and Expected Category Counts for the Data of Table 8.2

Observed	15	27	31	19	11
Expected	(20.6)	(20.6)	(20.6)	(20.6)	(20.6)

FIGURE 8.6

Rejection Region for Example 8.8

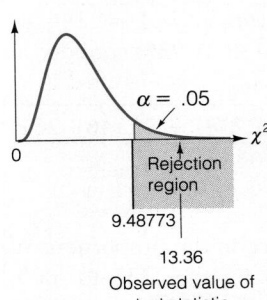

$\alpha = .05$

Rejection region

9.48773

13.36

Observed value of test statistic

Substituting the observed and expected values of the category counts into the formula for χ^2, we obtain

$$\chi^2 = \sum_{i=1}^{5} \frac{(O_i - E_i)^2}{E_i} = \frac{(15 - 20.6)^2}{20.6} + \frac{(27 - 20.6)^2}{20.6} + \cdots + \frac{(11 - 20.6)^2}{20.6}$$

$$= 13.36$$

The rejection region for the test is $\chi^2 > \chi^2_{.05}$, where $\chi^2_{.05}$ is based on $k - 1 = 5 - 1 = 4$ degrees of freedom. This value, found in Table 6, Appendix A, is $\chi^2_{.05} = 9.48773$ (see Figure 8.6). Since the observed value of χ^2 exceeds this value, there is sufficient evidence to reject H_0. It appears that at least one production line is responsible for a higher proportion of defective computers than the other lines.

The same information can be obtained from a computer printout. The SPSS printout of the analysis is shown in Figure 8.7. The value of χ^2 and the p-value of the test are shaded in Figure 8.7. Since p-value $= .010$ is less than $\alpha = .05$, we reject H_0 and conclude that at least one of the proportions differs from .2.

FIGURE 8.7

SPSS Printout for Example 8.8

```
- - - - - Chi-square Test
    LINE

                    Cases
    Category  Observed  Expected  Residual

        1.00      15      20.60     -5.60
        2.00      27      20.60      6.40
        3.00      31      20.60     10.40
        4.00      19      20.60     -1.60
        5.00      11      20.60     -9.60
                 ---
    Total        103
```

Chi-Square 13.359	D.F. 4	Significance .010

Once we have determined that the cell probabilities differ from their hypothesized values, we may want to follow up the analysis with confidence intervals on those proportions. Large-sample confidence intervals for a single multinomial proportion and the difference between two multinomial proportions are given in the box.

LARGE-SAMPLE $(1 - \alpha)100\%$ CONFIDENCE INTERVALS FOR π_i's OF A MULTINOMIAL EXPERIMENT

$$\pi_i: \quad p_i \pm z_{\alpha/2} \sqrt{\frac{p_i q_i}{n}}$$

$$(\pi_i - \pi_j): \quad (p_i - p_j) \pm z_{\alpha/2} \sqrt{\frac{p_i q_i + p_j q_j + 2p_i p_j}{n}}$$

where $p_i = n_i/n$, $q_i = 1 - p_i$, and $z_{\alpha/2}$ is found in Table 2, Appendix A.

EXAMPLE 8.9 Refer to Example 8.8 and find a 95% confidence interval for $(\pi_1 - \pi_2)$, the difference between the proportions of defective PCs attributable to production lines A and B, respectively.

Solution From Table 8.2, we have $n_1 = 15$, $p_1 = \frac{15}{103} = .146$, $q_1 = 1 = .146 = .854$, $n_2 = 27$, $p_2 = \frac{27}{103} = .262$, and $q_2 = 1 - .262 = .738$. A 95% confidence interval for $(\pi_1 - \pi_2)$ is

$$(p_1 - p_2) \pm z_{\alpha/2}\sqrt{\frac{p_1q_1 + p_2q_2 + 2p_1p_2}{n}} = (.146 - .262) \pm 1.96\sqrt{\frac{(.146)(.854) + (.262)(.738) + 2(.146)(.262)}{103}}$$

$$= -.116 \pm .121$$

Therefore, our interval estimate of $(\pi_1 - \pi_2)$, the difference in the proportions of the defective PCs attributable to production lines A and B, is $-.237$ to $.005$, with 95% confidence. Since the 95% confidence interval includes 0, the two lines apparently are producing the same proportion of defective computers.

PROBLEMS

8.26 Piracy of popular computer software such as Lotus and WordStar is growing at a phenomenal rate. Recent court rulings have made companies liable for employees who make unauthorized copies of software purchased by the company, even if the employer is unaware of the copying. Are companies adopting tougher software copying policies and do they enforce them? To answer this question, a researcher surveyed 121 industrial *Fortune 500* companies that use personal computers (PCs) in the workplace (*Journal of Systems Management*, July 1989). Of particular interest were the policy enforcement methods of the companies. The responses for the 121 companies are summarized in the table. Do the data disagree with the hypothesis that the companies' responses are equally divided among the five policy enforcement methods?

POLICY ENFORCEMENT METHOD	NUMBER OF COMPANIES
1. Do not take any action	10
2. Internal audits	49
3. Honor system	28
4. Manager audits/random checks	12
5. Others	22
Total	121

Source: Athey, S. A. "Software Copying Policies of the Fortune 500." *Journal of Systems Management*, July 1989, p. 33 (Table 6).

8.27 A *New England Journal of Medicine* (Nov. 13, 1986) study found that a substantial portion of acute hospital care is reported to be unnecessary. The physicians who conducted the study reviewed the medical records of 1,132 patients hospitalized at six different locations across the country. Overall, 60% of the admissions in the sample were judged to be appropriate and 23% were deemed inappropriate, while the remaining 17% could have been avoided by the use of ambulatory surgery. Let π_1, π_2, and π_3 represent the true percentages of hospital admissions in the three categories: appropriate, inappropriate, and avoidable by ambulatory surgery, respectively. Test the null hypothesis H_0: $\pi_1 = .8$, $\pi_2 = .1$, $\pi_3 = .1$. Use $\alpha = .10$.

8.28 In a survey of personality profiles of marketing and research and development (R&D) managers, questionnaires were mailed to the top managers of the 1,000 largest U.S. companies (*Psychology & Marketing*, Spring 1988). Since only

234 questionnaires were returned, the researchers were concerned about nonresponse bias. To determine the degree of bias, the researchers classified each company in the sample according to annual sales revenue. The percentages of the 234 sampled firms in each sales revenue category are shown in the table. The table also gives the true population percentages for the 1,000 largest U.S. firms. Conduct a test to determine whether any of the sample percentages differ from the true population percentages. Use $\alpha = .10$.

| | PERCENTAGE | |
SALES REVENUE	Sample Firms ($n = 234$)	1,000 Largest Firms
< $250 million	13	10
$250 million–$750 million	28	28
$750 million–$1.5 billion	17	20
$1.5 billion–$2.0 billion	7	8
$2.0 billion–$4.0 billion	15	16
$4.0 billion–$7.0 billion	10	9
$7.0 billion–$9.0 billion	3	3
> $9.0 billion	7	6

Source: Bush, A. J., and Lucas, G. H. "Personality Profiles of Marketing vs. R&D Managers." *Psychology & Marketing*, Vol. 5, No. 1, Spring 1988, p. 22 (Table 1).

8.29   A lastborn child typically possesses the following personality traits: manipulative, charming, blames others, shows off, people person, engaging. Since these personality traits are thought by many to be those characteristics required of a good salesperson, lastborn children have traditionally been viewed as most likely to be successful sales professionals. Is this stereotype based on fact or fantasy? *Personal Selling & Sales Management* (Aug. 1988) reported on a study designed to answer this question. A systematic sample of 138 automobile dealerships was selected from the telephone directory listings of three cities in Alabama, Florida, and Washington. A personal interview was conducted with one salesperson from each of the dealerships to determine the salesperson's birth order. Thus, the data consisted of the birth orders of the 138 salespeople. The table gives the number of salespeople in the sample in each of three birth order categories. One approach to analyzing the data is to compare the sample percentages of automobile salespeople in the birth order categories to the percentages for the general population. U.S. census data reveal that 66% of the general public are firstborn or only children, 21% are middle children, and 13% are lastborn children.

| | BIRTH ORDER CATEGORY | | |
	Firstborn/ Only Child	Middle Child	Lastborn
Number of Salespersons	56	50	32

Source: Boone, L. E., and Kurtz, D. L. "Birth Order and the Sales Professional." *Personal Selling & Sales Management*, Vol. 8, Aug. 1988, pp. 53–55.

a. Conduct a test to determine whether the distribution of the percentages of automobile salespeople in the three birth order categories differs from that of the general population. Use $\alpha = .01$.

b. Does the result in part a confirm the lastborn sales stereotype?

c. If the lastborn sales stereotype is true, then the percentage of salespeople who are lastborn children will exceed 13%. Conduct a test of this hypothesis.

8.30   A recent survey of deans at business schools accredited by the American Assembly of Collegiate Schools of Business found that statistical analysis is the microcomputer software application with the highest level of exposure for both undergraduate and graduate marketing majors (*Journal of Marketing Education*, Fall 1988). The same survey reported on the degree of usage of microcomputer statistical software packages for marketing undergraduates. The responses for the 51 deans in the survey are summarized in the table at the top of the next page. Test to determine whether the percentages in the five response categories are equal. Use $\alpha = .05$.

Data for Problem 8.30

DEGREE OF USAGE OF MICROCOMPUTER STATISTICAL SOFTWARE				
High	Moderate	Low	Trial	Not Using
21	10	10	5	5

8.31 In March 1981, a waterborne nonbacterial gastroenteritis outbreak occurred in Colorado as the result of a long-standing filter deficiency and malfunction of a sewage treatment plant. A study was conducted to determine whether the incidence of gastrointestinal disease during the epidemic was related to water consumption (*American Water Works Journal*, Jan. 1986). A telephone survey of households yielded the information in the table on daily consumption of 8 ounce glasses of water for a sample of 40 residents who exhibited gastroenteritis symptoms during the epidemic. Conduct a test to determine whether the incidence of gastrointestinal disease during the epidemic is related to water consumption. Use $\alpha = .01$.

	DAILY CONSUMPTION OF 8 OUNCE GLASSES OF WATER				
	0	1–2	3–4	5 or more	Total
Number of Respondents with Symptoms	6	11	13	10	40

Source: Hopkins, R. S., et al. "Gastroenteritis: Case Study of a Colorado Outbreak." *American Water Works Journal*, Vol. 78, No. 1, Jan. 1986, p. 42, Table 1, Copyright © 1986, American Water Works Association. Reprinted by permission.

8.32 J. A. Breaugh investigated employees' reactions to compressed work weeks (*Personnel Psychology*, Summer 1983). *Compressed work weeks* are defined as "alternative work schedules in which a trade is made between the number of hours worked per day, and the number of days worked per week, in order to work the standard number of weekly hours in less than 5 days." A field study was conducted at a large midwestern continuous-processing (7 days/24 hours) chemical plant that had experimented with four different work schedules, two of which were compressed:

Three 8 hour fixed shifts (day, evening, midnight)

Three 8 hour rotating shifts

Two 12 hour fixed shifts (12 A.M.–12 P.M., 12 P.M.–12 A.M.)

Two 12 hour rotating shifts

Six hundred seventy-one hourly employees were asked to rank the four work schedules in order of preference. The table gives the number of first-place rankings for each schedule. Is there sufficient evidence to indicate that the hourly employees have a preference for one of the work schedules? Test using $\alpha = .01$.

8 HOUR FIXED	8 HOUR ROTATING	12 HOUR FIXED	12 HOUR ROTATING
389	54	208	20

8.5 COMPARING MULTINOMIAL PROPORTIONS: TWO-WAY TABLE

Qualitative data are often categorized according to two qualitative variables. As a practical example of a two-variable classification of data, we will consider an R. H. Bruskin survey of shoppers at four of America's largest department store chains.

One thousand shoppers were surveyed at Kmart, Sears, J.C. Penney, and Montgomery Ward's, and asked to rate the store as excellent, good, or fair/poor. Therefore, the study involved the classification of shoppers according to each of two qualitative

TABLE 8.4
Contingency Table for the Department Store Chain Survey

	EXCELLENT	GOOD	FAIR/POOR	Totals
Kmart	272	477	251	1,000
Sears	315	457	228	1,000
J.C. Penney	323	470	207	1,000
Ward's	391	404	205	1,000
Totals	1,301	1,808	891	4,000

Source: Journal of Advertising Research, Sept. 1984.

variables, store chain (4 categories) and store rating (3 categories). The numbers of shoppers falling into the $3 \times 4 = 12$ chain-rating categories are shown in Table 8.4.

The two-variable classification of data presented in Table 8.4 is called a **two-way contingency table**, because the objective of the study was to investigate whether the proportions of shoppers that rate the store excellent, good, or fair/poor *depend* (or are *contingent*) on the store chain. Thus, the purpose of a contingency table analysis is to determine whether a dependence exists between the two qualitative variables, "store chain" and "store rating." In other words, it is analogous to the correlation analysis conducted for quantitative random variables in Section 3.8.

From our discussion of independent events in Section 4.1, we know that the probability of one event occurring (eg, a shopper shops at Kmart) does not depend on the other event (eg, a shopper rates the store excellent). Consequently, if the two variables "store chain" and "store rating" are independent, then the percentages of shoppers who rate the store excellent will be the same for all four store chains. Similar statements can be made about the other two rating categories, good and fair/poor. Independence implies that, when all three rating categories are considered simultaneously, the distributions of percentages of shoppers in the categories corresponding to store rating are identical for the four store chains.

A test of the null hypothesis that "store chain" is independent of "store rating" uses the chi-square goodness of fit statistic of Section 8.4 as a test statistic. The details of the test are given in the box.

A TEST OF HYPOTHESIS ABOUT CATEGORY PROBABILITIES: TWO-WAY TABLE

H_0: The two directions of classification in the contingency table are independent.

H_a: The two directions of classification in the contingency table are dependent.

Test statistic: $\chi^2 = \sum\limits_{i=1}^{r} \sum\limits_{j=1}^{c} \dfrac{(O_{ij} - E_{ij})^2}{E_{ij}}$

(continued)

---

where

r = Number of rows in the table

c = Number of columns in the table

O_{ij} = Observed number of responses in the cell row i and column j

E_{ij} = Estimated expected number of responses in cell (ij)

$$= \frac{(R_i)(C_j)}{n}$$

R_i = Row total corresponding to row i

C_j = Column total corresponding to column j

n = Sample size

Rejection region: $\chi^2 > \chi_\alpha^2$

where χ_α^2 is the tabulated value of the chi-square distribution based on $(r-1)(c-1)$ degrees of freedom, such that $P(\chi^2 > \chi_\alpha^2) = \alpha$.

Assumptions:

1. The properties of a multinomial experiment are satisfied.
2. The expected count for each of the $r \times c$ cells is at least 5.

EXAMPLE 8.10 Refer to the data in Table 8.4. Test the null hypothesis that the two directions of classification, "store chain" and "store rating," are independent against the alternative hypothesis that the two directions of classification are dependent.

Solution The first step is to find the expected cell counts of Table 8.4. Since the cell probabilities are not specified in the null hypothesis, we must eliminate the expected cell counts. For example, if "store chain" is independent of "store rating," we would expect $\frac{1,000}{4,000} = \frac{1}{4}$ of the shoppers who rated the store excellent to fall in the first row of Table 8.4—that is, in the Kmart row. Therefore, the estimated expected number of shoppers falling in row 1, column 1, is

$$E_{11} = \frac{1,000}{4,000}(1,301) = \frac{\text{Row 1 total}}{n}(\text{Column 1 total}) = 325.25$$

The formula for calculating any estimated expected value can be deduced from the value calculated above. Each estimated expected cell count is equal to the product of its respective row and column totals divided by the total sample size n. The general formula for calculating the estimated expected cell count for a cell in any row and column of a contingency table is given in the preceding box. The observed and estimated expected cell counts for all $4 \times 3 = 12$ cells of the contingency table are shown in the SAS printout, Figure 8.8.

FIGURE 8.8

SAS Printout for Example 8.10

TABLE OF STORE BY RATING

STORE   RATING

Frequency Expected	Excl	Good	Poor	Total
1KMart	272	477	251	1000
	325.25	452	222.75	
2Sears	315	457	228	1000
	325.25	452	222.75	
3JCPen	323	470	207	1000
	325.25	452	222.75	
4Wards	391	404	205	1000
	325.25	452	222.75	
Total	1301	1808	891	4000

STATISTICS FOR TABLE OF STORE BY RATING

Statistic	DF	Value	Prob
Chi-Square	6	35.835	0.000
Likelihood Ratio Chi-Square	6	35.622	0.000
Mantel-Haenszel Chi-Square	1	25.536	0.000
Phi Coefficient		0.095	
Contingency Coefficient		0.094	
Cramer's V		0.067	

Sample Size = 4000

Next, the differences between the observed cell counts O_{ij} and (estimated) expected cell counts E_{ij} are computed, and the chi-square test statistic is calculated:

$$\chi^2 = \frac{(O_{11} - E_{11})^2}{E_{11}} + \frac{(O_{12} - E_{12})^2}{E_{12}} + \cdots + \frac{(O_{43} - E_{43})^2}{E_{43}}$$

$$= \frac{(272 - 325.25)^2}{325.25} + \frac{(477 - 452)^2}{452} + \cdots + \frac{(205 - 222.75)^2}{222.75}$$

$$= 35.835$$

Note that this value of χ^2 is also given at the bottom of the SAS printout in Figure 8.8.

The rejection region for the test is $\chi^2 > \chi^2_{.05}$. The approximate degrees of freedom for a contingency table analysis will always be $(r - 1)(c - 1)$, where r is the number of rows and c is the number of columns in the table. For the department store data, we have $r = 4$ and $c = 3$; hence, the appropriate number of degrees of freedom for χ^2 is

$$\text{df} = (r - 1)(c - 1) = (4 - 1)(3 - 1) = 6$$

The tabulated value of $\chi^2_{.05}$ corresponding to 6 df is 12.5916; therefore, the rejection region (shaded in Figure 8.9) is

$$\chi^2 > 12.5916$$

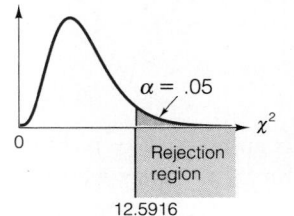

$\alpha = .05$

Rejection region

12.5916

FIGURE 8.9

Rejection Region for the Department Store Data in Example 8.10

Since the computed value, $\chi^2 = 35.835$, exceeds the critical value, 12.5916, we reject the null hypothesis in favor of the alternative. At significance level $\alpha = .05$, the data of Table 8.4 indicate that "store chain" and "store rating" are dependent; that is, the distributions of the percentages of responses in the categories corresponding to store rating differ among the four department store chains.

This same conclusion can be obtained from the *p*-value of the test. The approximate *p*-value, shaded in Figure 8.8, is 0. Since this value is less than .05, we reject H_0.

<hr>

The data of Table 8.4 could also be used to obtain an estimate of the percentage of responses in a specific category of the population or to test a hypothesis about the value of a particular percentage. The techniques are identical to those presented in Sections 8.1 and 8.2.

EXAMPLE 8.11   Use the data of Table 8.4 to estimate the proportion of Kmart shoppers who rate the store as excellent. Use a 95% confidence interval.

Solution   Note that the data in Table 8.4 represent four independent random samples of shoppers—one from Kmart, one from Sears, one from J.C. Penney, and one from Montgomery Ward's. We will restrict our attention to the sample of 1,000 shoppers surveyed at Kmart.

Let the true proportion of Kmart shoppers who rate the store excellent be denoted by π. Since we are now interested in only one population proportion, we may treat the data of Table 8.4 as binomial data. We can classify Kmart shoppers in one of two categories: (1) rated the store excellent or (2) did not rate the store excellent. The proportion π then represents the probability of success in a binomial experiment consisting of $n = 1,000$ trials (ie, 1,000 Kmart shoppers surveyed), where a success is defined as observing a shopper who gives the store an excellent rating.

Following the procedure of Section 8.1, we construct a 95% confidence interval for π as

$$p \pm 1.96 \sqrt{\frac{pq}{n}}$$

where p is the sample proportion of successes in n trials and $q = 1 - p$. From Table 8.4, the number of successes (ie, the number of Kmart shoppers who rate the store as excellent) is 272. Thus, our estimate is

$$p = \frac{\text{Number of successes in the sample}}{n}$$

$$= \frac{272}{1,000} = .272$$

Substituting $p = .272$, $q = 1 - p = 1 - .272 = .728$, and $n = 1,000$ into the confidence interval for π, we obtain

$$p \pm 1.96\sqrt{\frac{pq}{n}} = .272 \pm 1.96\sqrt{\frac{(.272)(.728)}{1,000}}$$

$$= .272 \pm 1.96(.01407)$$

$$= .272 \pm .028$$

or (.244, .300). We estimate, with 95% confidence, that the percentage of Kmart shoppers who rate the store excellent falls between 24.4% and 30.0%.

PROBLEMS

8.33 According to research reported in the *Journal of the National Cancer Institute* (Apr. 1991), eating foods high in fiber may help protect against breast cancer. The researchers randomly divided 120 laboratory rats into four groups of 30 each. All rats were injected with a drug that causes breast cancer; then each rat was fed a diet of fat and fiber for 15 weeks. However, the levels of fat and fiber varied from group to group. At the end of the feeding period, the number of rats with cancer tumors was determined for each group. The data are summarized in the contingency table.

CANCER TUMORS	DIET				Totals
	High Fat/ No Fiber	High Fat/ Fiber	Low Fat/ No Fiber	Low Fat/ Fiber	
Yes	27	20	19	14	80
No	3	10	11	16	40
Totals	30	30	30	30	120

Source: The *Journal of the National Cancer Institute* (Apr. 1991) as reported in the *Tampa Tribune*, Apr. 3, 1991.

a. Does the sampling appear to satisfy the assumptions for a multinomial experiment? Explain.
b. Calculate the expected cell counts for the contingency table.
c. Calculate the χ^2 statistic.
d. Is there evidence to indicate that diet and presence/absence of cancer are independent? Test using $\alpha = .05$.
e. Compare the percentage of rats on a high fat/no fiber diet with cancer to the percentage of rats on a high fat/fiber diet with cancer using a 95% confidence interval. Interpret the result.

8.34 An Ernst and Young survey of 126 warehouses operated by retail stores was conducted for *Stores* magazine (Feb. 1991). The data in the table are the numbers of responses in the categories for two variables: frequency of warehouse deliveries to stores (per week) and size of warehouse. A MINITAB printout of a contingency table analysis of the data is shown at the top of the next page. Is there evidence that frequency of deliveries and size of warehouse are dependent? Test using $\alpha = .01$.

FREQUENCY OF DELIVERIES	WAREHOUSE SIZE (THOUSAND SQUARE FEET)			
	<100	100–249.9	250–400	>400
≤1 Time per Week	5	13	9	5
2–3 Times per Week	12	11	13	6
4–5 Times per Week	9	14	13	16

```
Expected counts are printed below observed counts

          <100   100-249  250-400    >400    Total
   1        5       13        9         5       32
          6.60     9.65     8.89      6.86

   2       12       11       13         6       42
          8.67    12.67    11.67      9.00

   3        9       14       13        16       52
         10.73    15.68    14.44     11.14

Total      26       38       35        27      126

ChiSq =   0.389 +  1.162 +  0.001 +  0.503 +
          1.282 +  0.219 +  0.152 +  1.000 +
          0.279 +  0.181 +  0.144 +  2.117 = 7.431

df = 6
```

8.35 One of the biggest problems with conducting mail surveys is poor response rates. In an effort to reduce nonresponse, several different techniques for formatting questionnaires have been proposed. An experiment was conducted to study the effect of questionnaire layout and page size on response rates in a mail survey. Approximately 850 students enrolled at the University of Leiden (The Netherlands) were questioned about their attitudes toward suicide. Four different questionnaire formats were used: (1) typewriting on small (15 × 21 cm) page; (2) typewriting on large (18.5 × 25.5 cm) page; (3) typeset on small page; and (4) typeset on large page. The numbers of students who received each type of questionnaire and the numbers who responded are given in the table. Do the response rates appear to differ among the four questionnaire formats?

QUESTIONNAIRE FORMAT	NUMBER OF RESPONSES	NUMBER OF NONRESPONSES	Total Number Mailed
Typewritten, Small Page	86	57	143
Typewritten, Large Page	191	97	288
Typeset, Small Page	72	69	141
Typeset, Large Page	192	92	284
Totals	541	315	856

Source: Reproduced with permission of author and publisher from Jansen, J. H. "Effect of Questionnaire Layout and Size and Issue-Involvement on Response Rates in Mail Surveys." *Perceptual and Motor Skills*, Vol. 61, 1985, pp. 139–142.

8.36 As a business major, did you study foreign languages? If so, will your foreign language skills make you more marketable in the business community? To answer these (and other) questions, researchers mailed questionnaires to personnel directors of both foreign-based and domestic businesses (*Journal of Education for Business*, Jan./Feb. 1991). The 215 responses to the question of whether a firm would give hiring preference to business majors knowledgeable in foreign languages are summarized in the table.

Would You Give Hiring Preference to Business Majors Knowledgeable in Foreign Languages?

	YES	NEUTRAL	NO
U.S. Firms	50	57	19
Foreign Firms	60	22	7

Source: Cornick, M. F., et al. "The Value of Foreign Language Skills for Accounting and Business Majors." *Journal of Education for Business*, Jan./Feb. 1991, p. 162 (Table 2).

a. Conduct an analysis to determine whether the percentages in the response categories for the question depend on type of firm. Test using $\alpha = .10$.

b. Construct a 90% confidence interval for the difference between the percentages of U.S. and foreign firms that give hiring preference to business majors with foreign language skills. Interpret the interval.

8.37 One of the keys to developing successful information systems is to implement structured design and programming techniques. Computer-aided software engineering (CASE) technology provides several automated tools (eg, data flow diagrams) that can facilitate structured techniques. A *Journal of Systems Management* (July 1989) survey asked each user in a sample of CASE users how often they use data flow diagrams on the job and how satisfied they are with the design charting techniques they are using. The percentages responding in each of the cells of the contingency table are given below. Analyze the survey data assuming 1,000 CASE users participated in the study.

USE OF DATA FLOW DIAGRAMS	USER SATISFACTION OF DESIGN CHARTING TECHNIQUES		Totals
	Satisfied	Unsatisfied	
Always	27.5	0.0	27.5
Most of the time	31.3	2.5	33.8
Occasionally	31.2	3.8	35.0
Never	2.5	1.2	3.7
Totals	92.5	7.5	100.0

Source: Kievit, K., and Martin, M. "Systems Analysis Tools—Who's Using Them?" *Journal of Systems Management*, July 1989, p. 29 (Table 6).

8.38 "Toehold acquisition" is a term used by financial analysts to describe the purchase of a relatively small proportion (often less than 10%) of the shares of a corporation by a corporate raider whose ultimate objective is to take over control of the firm. For each toehold acquisition, the potential raider of the firm must report the transaction to the Securities and Exchange Commission by filing form 13D. Experts hypothesize that the filing of form 13D provides a clear signal to investors of the corporate raider's intention. To test this theory, a sample of 461 transactions was drawn from a list of firms in which corporate raiders acquired at least 5% of the outstanding shares (*Akron Business and Economic Review*, Spring 1990). A contingency table relating transaction type and transaction timing for the 461 transactions is shown below.

TRANSACTION TYPE	TIME RELATIVE TO FORM 13D FILING	
	Before	After
Purchase	184	83
Sale	105	89

a. If, in fact, the experts' theory is true, describe the relationship between transaction type and transaction timing.
b. The value of the χ^2 statistic for testing whether transaction type and transaction timing are independent was reported in the article to be $\chi^2 = 13.28$. Also, the *p*-value of the test was reported to be less than .01. Interpret the results.

8.39 Marketing strategists recognize that the success or failure of new and established products often varies regionally. Consequently, understanding the values of consumers residing in the various regions of the United States is essential for designing an effective, regionalized marketing strategy. Typically, marketers segment the United States into four geographic regions: East, Midwest, South, and West. An alternative conceptualization of regions within the United States, based on cultural rather than political boundaries, has been proposed. The "nine nations of North America" are New England (capital city, Boston); Quebec (Quebec City); The Foundry (Detroit); Dixie (Atlanta); The Islands (Miami); Empty Quarter (Denver); Breadbasket (Kansas City); MexAmerica (Los Angeles); and Ecotopia (San Francisco). A study was conducted to compare attitudes of consumers in the eight U.S. "nations" (*Journal of Marketing*, Apr. 1986). In a random sample of 2,235 Americans, each person was classified according to "nation" and his or her response to the following question: "What is your most important value?" The results (numbers in each of the response categories) are given in the table.

MOST IMPORTANT VALUE	NEW ENGLAND	THE FOUNDRY	DIXIE	THE ISLANDS	BREADBASKET	MEXAMERICA	EMPTY QUARTER	ECOTOPIA
Self-Respect	27	154	147	8	55	34	12	34
Security	26	147	152	5	62	26	6	37
Warm Relationships	17	125	90	3	63	27	2	35
Sense of Accomplishment	17	88	65	3	38	17	3	23
Self-Fulfillment	11	74	55	1	23	24	2	24
Being Well-Respected	10	65	72	5	31	4	1	8
Sense of Belonging	6	63	49	4	24	10	6	15
Fun–Enjoyment	6	34	23	3	11	8	2	13

Source: Kahle, L. R. "The Nine Nations of North America and the Value Basis of Geographic Segmentation." *Journal of Marketing*, Vol. 50, No. 2, Apr. 1986, pp. 37–46. Reprinted with permission from *Journal of Marketing*, published by the American Marketing Association, Chicago, IL.

a. What hypothesis would you test to determine whether the distributions of percentages in the "most important value" categories differ for the eight U.S. "nations"?

b. A computer printout of the analysis is reproduced below. Interpret the results.

TABLE OF VALUE BY NATION

VALUE   NATION

Frequency Expected	1NewEngl	2Foundry	3Dixie	4Islands	5Breadbk	6MexAmer	7EmptyQt	8Ecotopi	Total
1SelfRespect	27 / 25.323	154 / 157.63	147 / 137.8	8 / 6.7527	55 / 64.784	34 / 31.653	12 / 7.1747	34 / 39.883	471
2Security	26 / 24.785	147 / 154.29	152 / 134.87	5 / 6.6093	62 / 63.408	26 / 30.981	6 / 7.0224	37 / 39.036	461
3WarmRelation	17 / 19.462	125 / 121.15	90 / 105.91	3 / 5.19	63 / 49.791	27 / 24.328	2 / 5.5143	35 / 30.653	362
4Accomplish	17 / 13.656	88 / 85.008	65 / 74.311	3 / 3.6416	38 / 34.936	17 / 17.07	3 / 3.8692	23 / 21.508	254
5SelfFullfil	11 / 11.505	74 / 71.621	55 / 62.608	1 / 3.0681	23 / 29.435	24 / 14.382	2 / 3.2599	24 / 18.121	214
6WellRespect	10 / 10.376	62 / 64.593	72 / 56.465	5 / 2.767	31 / 26.546	4 / 12.97	1 / 2.94	8 / 16.343	193
7Belonging	6 / 9.5161	63 / 59.238	49 / 51.784	4 / 2.5376	24 / 24.345	10 / 11.895	6 / 2.6962	15 / 14.988	177
8Fun	6 / 5.3763	34 / 33.468	23 / 29.256	3 / 1.4337	11 / 13.754	8 / 6.7204	2 / 1.5233	13 / 8.4677	100
Total	120	747	653	32	307	150	34	189	2232

Statistic	DF	Value	Prob
Chi-Square	49	68.758	0.033
Likelihood Ratio Chi-Square	49	69.935	0.026
Mantel-Haenszel Chi-Square	1	0.370	0.543
Phi Coefficient		0.176	
Contingency Coefficient		0.173	
Cramer's V		0.066	

Sample Size = 2232

c. Compare the proportions of Americans in New England and Dixie whose most important value is self-respect. Use a 95% confidence interval.

TESTING MULTINOMIAL PROPORTIONS

In this computer lab section we give the SAS, SPSS, and MINITAB commands for testing multinomial probabilities from one-way tables (if available) and two-way tables. The following programs analyze the data in the one-way table of Table 8.2 and the two-way table of Table 8.4.

SAS

Command Line		
1	`DATA CT;`	
2	`INPUT STORE $ RATING $ NUMBER @@;`	} Data entry instructions
3	`CARDS;`	

```
KMART    EXC    272    KMART    GOOD    477    KMART    FAIR    251
  .       .      .       .        .       .       .        .       .
  .       .      .       .        .       .       .        .       .
  .       .      .       .        .       .       .        .       .
WARDS    EXC    391    WARDS    GOOD    404    WARDS    FAIR    205
```
Input data values (3 observations per line)

4	`PROC FREQ;`	
5	`TABLES STORE*RATING/EXPECTED CHISQ;`	} Contingency table analysis
6	`WEIGHT NUMBER;`	

COMMAND 4 The FREQ procedure generates a frequency (or contingency) table for the data.

COMMAND 5 The TABLES statement defines the two classification variables for the contingency table. Variable names are separated by an asterisk (*). The options EXPECTED and CHISQ (following the slash) request that expected cell frequencies and the χ^2 statistic for the contingency table be printed.

COMMAND 6 The WEIGHT statement defines the weighting variable of the contingency table (eg, NUMBER). This statement is necessary when the cell counts have already been tabulated, as in Table 8.4. If the cell counts have not been tabulated (ie, if the data are raw), omit the WEIGHT statement.

GENERAL A chi-square analysis of a one-way table is not available in SAS.

NOTE The printout for this SAS program is displayed in Figure 8.10 (p. 370).

SPSS

```
   1    DATA LIST FREE/NUMBER LINE,  ⎤
   2    WEIGHT BY NUMBER,            ⎬  Data entry instructions
   3    BEGIN DATA,                  ⎦
        15 1  27 2  31 3  19 4  11 5    Input data values
   4    END DATA,
   5    NPAR TESTS CHISQUARE=LINE/       ⎤  One-way χ² analysis
   6           EXPECTED=1,1,1,1,1,       ⎦
```

```
   7    DATA LIST FREE/STORE (A5) RATING (A4) NUMBER,}  Data entry instructions
   8    WEIGHT BY NUMBER,
   9    BEGIN DATA,
        KMART    EXC    272    KMART    GOOD    477    KMART    FAIR    251⎤
          ·       ·      ·       ·       ·       ·       ·       ·      ·  ⎬  Input data values
          ·       ·      ·       ·       ·       ·       ·       ·      ·  ⎠  (3 observations per line)
          ·       ·      ·       ·       ·       ·       ·       ·      ·  ⎦
        WARDS    EXC    391    WARDS    GOOD    404    WARDS    FAIR    205⎦
  10    END DATA,
  11    CROSSTABS TABLES=STORE BY RATING/  ⎤
  12           CELLS=COUNT EXPECTED/       ⎬  Contingency table analysis
  13           STATISTICS=CHISQ,           ⎦
```

COMMAND 2 The WEIGHT statement defines the weighting variable of the one- or two-way contingency table (eg, NUMBER). This statement is necessary when the cell counts have already been tabulated (as in Tables 8.2 and 8.4). If the cell counts have not been tabulated (if the data are raw), omit the WEIGHT statement.

COMMAND 5 The NPAR TESTS procedure with subcommand CHISQUARE produces a one-way chi-square analysis of the categorical variable specified (eg, LINE). [*Note:* The categories of the specified variable must be numeric on the input data lines.]

COMMAND 6 The EXPECTED subcommand gives the hypothesized proportions for each cell of the table. The proportions are obtained by dividing each value specified by the sum of the values. Thus, for equal proportions, specify all 1's in the EXPECTED subcommand.

COMMAND 11 The CROSSTABS procedure generates a contingency (or cross-classification) table for the data. The classification variables are specified following TABLES=, and separated by the keyword BY.

COMMAND 12 The CELLS command with COUNT and EXPECTED options generates expected cell frequencies, as well as cell counts for the contingency table.

COMMAND 13   STATISTICS=CHISQ generates the χ^2 statistic (and p-value) for the contingency table analysis.

NOTE   The printout for this SPSS program is displayed in Figure 8.11 (p. 371).

MINITAB

Command
Line

```
1      READ TABLE IN C1 C2 C3    Data entry instruction
       272  477  251⎤
       315  457  228⎟    Input data values
       303  470  207⎟    (each row represents one row of the contingency table)
       391  404  205⎦
2      CHISQUARE TEST ON TABLE IN C1-C3    Contingency table analysis
```

COMMAND 2   The CHISQUARE command generates expected cell frequencies and the χ^2 statistic for the contingency table stored in the columns specified.

GENERAL   The pretabulated cell counts of the contingency table are read into the columns of the MINITAB worksheet. Each row represents one row and each column represents one column of the contingency table.

GENERAL   A chi-square analysis of a one-way table is not available in MINITAB.

NOTE   The printout for this MINITAB program is displayed in Figure 8.12 (p. 372).

FIGURE 8.10

SAS Output for Computer Lab

```
                        TABLE OF STORE BY RATING

STORE       RATING

Frequency|
Expected |
Percent  |
Row Pct  |
Col Pct  | exc     | fair    | good    |  Total
---------+---------+---------+---------+
jcpen    |    323  |    207  |    470  |   1000
         | 325.25  | 222.75  |    452  |
         |   8.08  |   5.17  |  11.75  |  25.00
         |  32.30  |  20.70  |  47.00  |
         |  24.83  |  23.23  |  26.00  |
---------+---------+---------+---------+
kmart    |    272  |    251  |    477  |   1000
         | 325.25  | 222.75  |    452  |
         |   6.80  |   6.28  |  11.93  |  25.00
         |  27.20  |  25.10  |  47.70  |
         |  20.91  |  28.17  |  26.38  |
---------+---------+---------+---------+
sears    |    315  |    228  |    457  |   1000
         | 325.25  | 222.75  |    452  |
         |   7.87  |   5.70  |  11.43  |  25.00
         |  31.50  |  22.80  |  45.70  |
         |  24.21  |  25.59  |  25.28  |
---------+---------+---------+---------+
wards    |    391  |    205  |    404  |   1000
         | 325.25  | 222.75  |    452  |
         |   9.78  |   5.12  |  10.10  |  25.00
         |  39.10  |  20.50  |  40.40  |
         |  30.05  |  23.01  |  22.35  |
---------+---------+---------+---------+
Total         1301      891     1808      4000
             32.53    22.27    45.20    100.00
```

STATISTICS FOR TABLE OF STORE BY RATING

Statistic	DF	Value	Prob
Chi-Square	6	35.835	0.000
Likelihood Ratio Chi-Square	6	35.622	0.000
Mantel-Haenszel Chi-Square	1	14.200	0.000
Phi Coefficient		0.095	
Contingency Coefficient		0.094	
Cramer's V		0.067	

Sample Size = 4000

FIGURE 8.11
SPSS Output for Computer Lab

```
- - - - - Chi-square Test
    LINE

                    Cases
        Category  Observed   Expected   Residual

          1.00        15      20.60      -5.60
          2.00        27      20.60       6.40
          3.00        31      20.60      10.40
          4.00        19      20.60      -1.60
          5.00        11      20.60      -9.60
                     ---
        Total       103

        Chi-Square              D.F.         Significance
          13.359                  4               .010
```

STORE by RATING

| STORE | Count
Exp Val | RATING | | | |
		exc	fair	good	Row Total
	jcpen	323 325.3	207 222.8	470 452.0	1000 25.0%
	kmart	272 325.3	251 222.8	477 452.0	1000 25.0%
	sears	315 325.3	228 222.8	457 452.0	1000 25.0%
	wards	391 325.3	205 222.8	404 452.0	1000 25.0%
	Column Total	1301 32.5%	891 22.3%	1808 45.2%	4000 100.0%

```
       Chi-Square              Value         DF        Significance
--------------------         ----------     ----       ------------

Pearson                       35.83497        6           .00000
Likelihood Ratio              35.62187        6           .00000

Minimum Expected Frequency -   222.750

Number of Missing Observations:  0
```

FIGURE 8.12

MINITAB Output for Computer Lab

```
Expected counts are printed below observed counts

              C1       C2       C3     Total
    1        272      477      251     1000
          325.25   452.00   222.75

    2        315      457      228     1000
          325.25   452.00   222.75

    3        323      470      207     1000
          325.25   452.00   222.75

    4        391      404      205     1000
          325.25   452.00   222.75

Total       1301     1808      891     4000

ChiSq =   8.718 +   1.383 +   3.583 +
          0.323 +   0.055 +   0.124 +
          0.016 +   0.717 +   1.114 +
         13.292 +   5.097 +   1.414 = 35.835
df = 6
```

CHAPTER NOTES

- Large-sample **parametric inferences** about the population parameters π and $\pi_1 - \pi_2$ (independent samples) are obtained using the following formulas:

Confidence interval: Estimator $\pm$ $(z_{\alpha/2})$ Standard error

Test statistic: $z = \dfrac{\text{Estimator} - \text{Hypothesized value in } H_0}{\text{Standard error}}$

- **Estimators** and **standard errors** for the parameters π and $\pi_1 - \pi_2$ are provided in the following table:

PARAMETER	ESTIMATOR	STANDARD ERROR	ESTIMATED STANDARD ERROR
π	p	$\sqrt{\dfrac{\pi(1-\pi)}{n}}$	$\sqrt{\dfrac{pq}{n}}$
$\pi_1 - \pi_2$	$p_1 - p_2$	$\sqrt{\dfrac{\pi_1(1-\pi_1)}{n_1} + \dfrac{\pi_2(1-\pi_2)}{n_2}}$	$\sqrt{\dfrac{p_1 q_1}{n_1} + \dfrac{p_2 q_2}{n_2}}$

- To make valid parametric inferences for π and $\pi_1 - \pi_2$, the **sample size must be sufficiently large**. This requirement usually will be satisfied if, for each proportion π estimated, the interval $p \pm 2\sigma_p$ does not contain 0 or 1.
- Formulas for determining the sample size for estimating and testing π and $\pi_1 - \pi_2$ are provided in the table.

PARAMETER	CONFIDENCE INTERVAL	ONE-TAILED TEST[a]
π	$n = \left(\dfrac{z_{\alpha/2}}{d}\right)^2 \pi(1 - \pi)$	$n = \left[\dfrac{(z_{1-\beta} - z_\alpha)}{(\pi_0 - \pi_a)}\right]^2 \pi(1 - \pi)$
$\pi_1 - \pi_2$	$n_1 = n_2 = \left(\dfrac{z_{\alpha/2}}{d}\right)^2 [\pi_1(1 - \pi_1) + \pi_2(1 - \pi_2)]$	$n_1 = n_2 = \left[\dfrac{(z_{1-\beta} - z_\alpha)}{D_0 - D_a}\right]^2 [\pi_1(1 - \pi_1) + \pi_2(1 - \pi_2)]$

[a] For a two-tailed test, replace z_α with $z_{\alpha/2}$ in the formula.

- The properties of a **multinomial experiment** are:

  1. Experiment consists of n identical trials.
  2. Each trial results in one of k outcomes (categories).
  3. The probabilities of the k outcomes sum to 1, that is,

  $$\pi_1 + \pi_2 + \cdots + \pi_k = 1$$

  4. The trials are independent.
  5. $n_1, n_2, \ldots, n_k$ are the numbers of observations falling into the k classification categories.

- The **chi-square test statistic** for testing hypotheses about multinomial probabilities is

$$\chi^2 = \sum_{i=1}^{k} \frac{(O_i - E_i)^2}{E_i}$$

where

$$O_i = \text{Observed number in cell } i$$
$$E_i = \text{Expected number in cell } i$$

- **Expected cell counts** and **degrees of freedom (df)** for the χ^2-tests are tabulated as follows:

One-way table: $E_i = n\pi_i$;   df = Number of cells $-$ 1;

where

$$n = \text{Total sample size}$$
$$\pi_i = \text{Hypothesized probability of cell } i$$

Two-way table: $E_{ij} = \dfrac{R_i C_j}{n}$;   df = $(r - 1)(c - 1)$;

where

$$R_i = \text{Row } i \text{ total}$$
$$C_j = \text{Column } j \text{ total}$$
$$n = rc$$
$$r = \text{Number of rows}$$
$$c = \text{Number of columns}$$

■ **Confidence intervals** for multinomial probabilities are constructed as follows:

ONE-WAY TABLE

Cell proportion: $p_i \pm z_{\alpha/2} \sqrt{\dfrac{p_i q_i}{n}}$

where

$$p_i = \frac{x_i}{n} \qquad (i = 1, 2, ..., k)$$

Difference between cell proportions: $(p_i - p_j) \pm z_{\alpha/2} \sqrt{\dfrac{p_i q_i + p_j q_j + 2 p_i p_j}{n}}$

where

$$p_i = \frac{x_i}{n} \qquad (i = 1, 2, ..., k)$$

TWO-WAY TABLE

Single proportion: Apply the formula above.

Difference between proportions: If independent samples, apply the formula for $(\pi_1 - \pi_2)$ for independent samples; otherwise, apply the formula for a one-way table above.

LOOKING AHEAD

Methods for inferring the nature of process data are the focus of the next several chapters. Chapter 9 deals with process and quality control, while Chapters 10 and 11 present methods for modeling the relationship between variables.

CASE STUDY

DOES AN ASPIRIN A DAY REALLY KEEP THE HEART DOCTOR AWAY?

According to the National Center for Health Statistics, heart disease is the leading cause of death in the United States; heart attacks and strokes account for about 40% of all deaths.* With this statistic in mind, it is no surprise that the following headline appeared across the front page of nearly every U.S. daily newspaper in late January 1988: "Aspirin cuts the risk of heart attack."

The exciting news was based on a nationwide study of 22,071 U.S. physicians, the results of which were reported in the *New England Journal of Medicine* (Jan. 27, 1988). The U.S. Physicians' Health Study, as it is known, involved a randomized

* Greenhouse, J. B., and Greenhouse, S. W. "An Aspirin a Day ...?" *Chance: New Directions for Statistics and Computing*, Vol. 1, No. 4, Fall 1988, pp. 24–31. New York: Springer-Verlag.

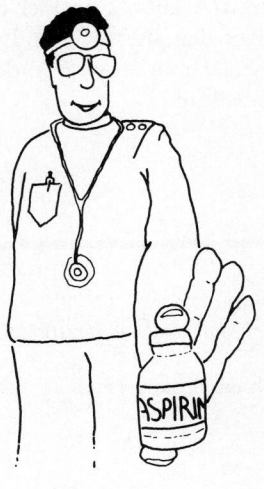

clinical trial in which about half (11,037) of the physicians were assigned at random to receive one Bufferin brand aspirin tablet every other day. The other half (11,034) received a placebo, a harmless and ineffective substitute. The study was "double-blind" so that neither the participants (ie, the physicians) nor the medical scientists who were conducting the research knew which tablet, the Bufferin or the placebo, was being administered. After 5 years, the researchers found that the incidence of fatal heart attacks among the placebo group was over three times greater than that for the aspirin group. (See Table 8.5.) Based on these findings, the study was halted so that those physicians who were taking the placebo could immediately switch to aspirin and receive its "extreme beneficial effects on fatal heart attacks."

TABLE 8.5

Results of Two Studies on the Use of Aspirin in the Prevention of Heart Attacks

a. U.S. PHYSICIANS' HEALTH STUDY	ASPIRIN GROUP	PLACEBO GROUP
Sample size	11,037	11,034
Number of fatal heart attacks	5	18
b. BRITISH STUDY	ASPIRIN GROUP	NO ASPIRIN GROUP
Sample size	3,429	1,710
Number of fatal heart attacks	89	47

The good news of the U.S. Physicians' Health Study was followed by an avalanche of television commercials for aspirin, promoting its newfound status as the "heart attack prevention drug." Unfortunately, the excitement over the "cure" for heart disease was short-lived "and turned to confusion, when," according to *Chance* (Fall 1988), "three days later a headline in the *New York Times* read, 'Value of Daily Aspirin Disputed in British Study of Heart Attacks.' It seemed that a similar study conducted in England did not show that aspirin had any beneficial effect in reducing the risk of heart attack."

The 6 year British study involved 5,139 doctors in which two-thirds (3,429) were randomly chosen to take daily aspirin. The remaining physicians (1,710) were not given a placebo, but instead were instructed "to avoid aspirin and products containing aspirin unless some specific indication for aspirin was thought to have developed." The results reported in the *British Medical Journal* (Jan. 1988) showed that the fatal heart attack rate was essentially the same in both groups. (See Table 8.5.)

a. Based on the results of the U.S. Physicians' Health Study, make an inference about the true difference between the fatal heart attack rates of the aspirin group and the placebo group.

b. Based on the British study, make an inference about the true difference between the heart attack rates of the aspirin group and the control group.

c. Refer to parts **a** and **b**. Does your inference about the beneficial effect of aspirin in the prevention of heart attacks depend on which study you consider?

d. Why might the two studies yield contrasting results? [*Hint:* Consider one or more of the following issues: sample size; the fact that the U.S. study used physicians who had extraordinarily low cardiovascular mortality rates; double-blind versus unblinded study; placebo versus "no aspirin."]

REFERENCES

Agresti, A. *Categorical Data Analysis*. New York: Wiley, 1990.

Cochran, W. G. "The χ^2 Test of Goodness of Fit." *Annals of Mathematical Statistics*, Vol. 23, 1952, pp. 315–345.

Mendenhall, W. *Introduction to Probability and Statistics*, 8th ed. Boston: Duxbury, 1989.

SAMPLE EXAM QUESTIONS: CHAPTER 8

(1–4) Marketing executives are continually searching for quantitative decision-making techniques that can be applied in practice. J. C. Higgins and E. J. Opdebeeck conducted a survey on the use of microcomputers as a marketing decision aid in the United Kingdom (*Journal of the Market Research Society*, July 1984). A random sample of 36 senior marketing executives of companies that use microcomputers was asked how frequently they make a decision based on a computer printout. The results are summarized below:

	NUMBER OF MARKETING EXECUTIVES
Frequently (more than once per week)	8
Moderately frequently (between once per week and once per month)	18
Infrequently (less than once per month)	8
Never	2

1. Assuming there are no differences in the percentages of marketing executives in the four response categories, what would you expect the values of the cell probabilities (π_1, π_2, π_3, and π_4) to be?

2. Assuming no differences in the percentages in the four categories, calculate the expected cell counts.

3. Find the value of the chi-square statistic.

4. Do the data provide sufficient evidence to indicate that the percentages of marketing executives in the response categories differ? Test using $\alpha = .05$.

(5–6) In recent years there has been a trend toward both parents working outside the home. Do working mothers experience the same burdens and family pressures as their spouses? A popular belief is that the proportion of working mothers who feel they have enough spare time for themselves is significantly less than the corresponding proportion of working fathers. To test this claim, independent random samples of 100 working mothers and 100 working fathers were selected and their views on spare time for themselves were recorded. A summary of the data is given below. (Assume that the spouses of all individuals sampled were also working outside the home.)

	WORKING MOTHERS	WORKING FATHERS
Number sampled	100	100
Number in sample who feel they have enough time for themselves	37	56

5. Does the sample information support the belief that the proportion of working mothers who feel they have enough spare time for themselves is less than the corresponding proportion of working fathers? Test at significance level $\alpha = .01$.
6. How many working parents must be sampled to estimate the true difference between the proportions of mothers and fathers who feel they have enough spare time to within .02 with 99% confidence?

(7–9)   The U.S. Social Security system, which now collects taxes from approximately 115 million workers and pays benefits to 36 million people, faces serious financial problems because of high inflation, high unemployment, and low worker productivity. Consequently, many Americans are worried that the system will go broke before they can receive their retirement benefits. A recent Associated Press–NBC News poll found that 1,184 of the 1,600 American adults interviewed have little or no confidence that the Social Security system will have the funds available to pay their retirement benefits.

7. Construct a 97% confidence interval for π, the true proportion of all American adults who have little or no confidence that the Social Security system will have the funds available to pay their retirement benefits.
8. Give a precise interpretation of the phrase, "We are 97% confident that the interval encloses the true value of π."
9. A government official claims that less than half of all Americans have little or no confidence in the Social Security system. Use the confidence interval to make an inference about this claim.

(10–12)   As discussed in Problem 8.18, in the travel industry, "destination-specific travel literature (DSTL)" refers to booklets, brochures, and pamphlets that describe a destination in detail (eg, information on activities, facilities, and prices). DSTL is made available to travelers free of charge upon request. A study was undertaken to investigate the differences between information seekers (ie, those who request DSTL) and nonseekers on a variety of consumer travel dimensions, including education. The table gives the breakdown of the number of seekers/nonseekers at each level of education.

EDUCATION LEVEL	TOURIST TYPE	
	Information Seeker	Nonseeker
Some High School	13	27
High School Degree	64	118
Some College	100	123
College Degree	59	69
Graduate Degree	67	46
Totals	303	383

Source: Etzel, M. J., and Wahlers, R. G. "The Use of Requested Promotional Material by Pleasure Travelers." *Journal of Travel Research*, Vol. 23, No. 4, Spring 1985, pp. 2–6. The *Journal of Travel Research* is published by the Travel and Tourism Research Association (TTRA) and the Business Research Division, University of Colorado at Boulder.

10. Compute the expected number of tourists in the nonseeker/graduate degree cell, assuming the two qualitative variables, tourist type and education level, are independent.
11. Conduct a test to determine whether the two qualitative variables, tourist type and education level, are independent. Test using $\alpha = .01$.
12. Construct and interpret a 95% confidence interval for the proportion of information seekers who have a college degree.

(13–15)   Concerned about airport and airline security, the Federal Aviation Administration (FAA) has begun imposing sanctions against airlines that fail security tests. One series of tests conducted at Los Angeles International Airport (LAX) showed that security guards detected only 72 of the 100 mock weapons carried on by FAA inspectors or included in their carry-on luggage (*Gainesville Sun*, Dec. 11, 1987). According to the FAA, the "detection rate was well below the national rate of .80."

13. Set up the null and alternative hypotheses for testing whether the true mock weapon detection rate at LAX is less than the national rate of .80.
14. Find the rejection region for the test if $\alpha = .10$.
15. Compute the test statistic and make the appropriate conclusion.

(16–18)   According to University of Florida sociologist Michael Radelet, "If you kill a white person (in Florida), the chances of getting the death penalty are three times greater than if you kill a black person" (*Gainesville Sun*, Oct. 20, 1986). Radelet formed his opinion by studying over 1,000 murder cases in Florida—a study that was eventually reviewed by the U.S. Supreme Court and used to overturn a Florida murder conviction. Concentrating only on crimes against strangers, Radelet classified the data of 326 murders according to race of the victim and death sentence, as shown in the two-way table.

RACE OF VICTIM	DEATH SENTENCE		Totals
	Yes	No	
White	30	184	214
Black	6	106	112
Totals	36	290	326

16. An analysis of the data is shown in the MINITAB printout. Interpret the results.

```
Expected counts are printed below observed counts

        Death=Y  Death=N   Total
   1         30      184      214
         23.63   190.37

   2          6      106      112
         12.37    99.63

Total       36      290      326

ChiSq =  1.716 +  0.213 +
         3.279 +  0.407 = 5.615
df = 1
```

17. Construct a 95% confidence interval for $(\pi_1 - \pi_2)$, where π_1 is the percentage of murderers of whites who received the death penalty, and π_2 is the percentage of murderers of blacks who received the death penalty.
18. Interpret the 95% confidence interval.

CHAPTER 9

STATISTICAL PROCESS AND QUALITY CONTROL

Consider a manufacturing process in which steel rods are mass produced on an assembly line. How can the manufacturer be certain of the quality of the rods before they are shipped to retailers? In this chapter we present some simple but powerful statistical procedures, called *control charts*, for monitoring the quality of process data. Monitoring the diameters of steel rods is the subject of the chapter case study.

TOTAL QUALITY MANAGEMENT

9.1 When we think of product quality, we think of a set of characteristics that we expect a product to possess. We want light bulbs to have a long life, paper towels to be strong and absorbent, and a quarter-pound hamburger to weigh at least one-quarter pound. But producing a quality product is not an easy job. Variations in the characteristics of raw materials and workmanship tend to produce variations in product quality. The length of life of a light bulb produced in an automated production line may differ markedly from the length of life of a bulb produced seconds later. Similarly, the strength of paper produced by a paper machine may vary from one point in time to another due to variations in the characteristics of the pulp fed into the machine. Consequently, it is vital that manufacturers monitor the quality of the product they produce.

Today, U.S. business leaders are promoting the concept of **total quality management (TQM)**. As shown in Figure 9.1, TQM has three key components: (1) concepts, (2) systems, and (3) tools. The "concepts" component of TQM includes a number of ideas that surround the total quality movement. These include *customer satisfaction*, *all work is a process*, *speak with data*, and *upstream mangement*. (Speaking with data is a particularly relevant concept for this text, since it involves measuring and monitoring process variables.)

FIGURE 9.1
TQM Components

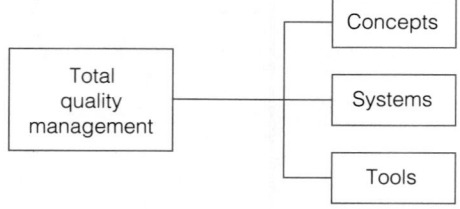

The second component, "systems," involves the notion of systems management. Systems such as *general management*, *market creation*, *product creation*, and *product supply* must be responsibly managed by the company's owners.

Finally, several "tools" are available to implement a TQM program. These include *flowcharts*, *cause-and-effect diagrams*, and *statistical process control charts*.

All three components of Figure 9.1 are necessary to successfully implement a TQM philosophy at a company. In this chapter, we focus on the statistical process control element of TQM. **Statistical process control (SPC)** allows managers to understand and monitor process variation through **control charts**.

VARIABLE CONTROL CHARTS

9.2 Although TQM in U.S. business is a recent trend, the idea of a control chart to monitor process data was developed in 1924 by W. A. Shewhart.

Control charts are constructed by plotting a product's quality variable over time in a sequence plot, as shown in Figure 9.2. The variable plotted can be either a quantitative characteristic (eg, weight of a quarter-pound hamburger) or a qualitative attribute (eg, defective or nondefective light bulb) of a manufactured product. The power of this simple chart lies in its ability to separate two types of variation in a product quality characteristic: (1) variation due to **assignable causes** and (2) **random variation**.

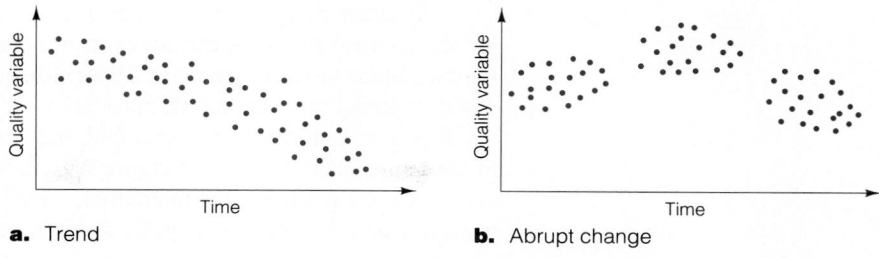

a. Trend **b.** Abrupt change

DEFINITION 9.1

A **control chart for a quality variable** is obtained by plotting the measurements of the variable periodically over time.

Variations due to assignable causes are produced by such things as the wear in a metallic cutting machine, the wear in an abrasive wheel, changes in the humidity and temperature in the production area, worker fatigue, and so on. The effects of wear in cutting edges, abrasive surfaces, or changes in the environment are usually evidenced by gradual trends in a characteristic over time (see Figure 9.2a). In contrast, the raw material will often produce an abrupt change in the level of a quality characteristic (see Figure 9.2b). Quality control and production engineers attempt to identify trends or abrupt changes in a quality characteristic when they occur and to modify the process to reduce or eliminate this type of variation.

Even when variation due to assignable causes is accounted for, measurements taken on a product quality characteristic tend to vary in a random manner from one point in time to another. This second category of variation—random (or chance) variation—is caused by minute and random changes in raw materials, worker behavior, and so on. Since some stable system of chance causes is inherent in any production process, this type of variation is accepted as the normal variation of the process. When the quality characteristics of a product are subject only to random variation, the process is said to be **in control**.

DEFINITION 9.2

The variation in a variable that measures a product quality characteristic is due to either an **assignable cause** or **random (chance) variation**.

DEFINITION 9.3

A production process is said to be **in control** when the quality characteristics of a product are subject only to random variation.

To illustrate these ideas, consider a manufacturing process that produces shafts for an electrical motor. A quality control inspector might select one shaft every 10 minutes and measure its diameter. These measurements, plotted against time, provide visual evidence of whether the process is subject to only random variation (ie, whether it is in control). For example, the diameters of 10 shafts might appear as in the sequence plot shown in Figure 9.3. Although the diameters of these 10 shafts vary from one point in time to another, all fall within the **control limits** set by the manufacturer. The process appears to be in control.

FIGURE 9.3

Sequence Plot of the Diameters of 10 Motor Shafts

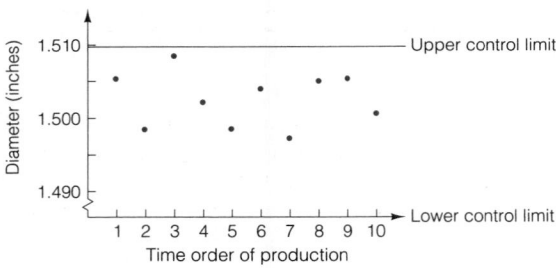

How are these control limits established? A widely used (and successful) technique is to monitor the process during a period when it is known to be in control and calculate the mean and standard deviation of the sample quality measurements. Then, for future measurements, apply the z-score rule for detecting outliers (Section 3.8). We know that it is highly unlikely that a sample measurement will fall more than 3 standard deviations away from the mean. Consequently, if a quality measurement falls below $\bar{x} - 3s$ or above $\bar{x} + 3s$, we say the process is "out of control," and modifications in the production may be necessary.

EXAMPLE 9.1 A corporation that manufactures field rifles for the Department of Defense operates a production line that turns out finished firing pins. To monitor the process, an inspector randomly selects a firing pin from the production line every 30 minutes and measures its length (in inches). The lengths for a sample of 20 firing pins obtained in this manner are provided in Table 9.1. Construct a control chart for the quality variable, "length of firing pins." Is the process out of control?

TABLE 9.1

Lengths of Firing Pins

PIN	LENGTH	PIN	LENGTH	PIN	LENGTH	PIN	LENGTH
1	1.00	6	0.99	11	1.01	16	1.01
2	0.99	7	1.06	12	0.99	17	0.99
3	0.98	8	0.99	13	0.98	18	0.99
4	1.01	9	0.99	14	0.99	19	0.97
5	1.01	10	1.03	15	0.87	20	0.99

Solution The first step in constructing the control chart is to calculate the mean and standard deviation of the sample firing pin lengths. These values, obtained using a computer, are shown in the SAS printout, Figure 9.4. You can see that the sample mean is $\bar{x} = .992$ and the sample standard deviation is $s = .035$.

FIGURE 9.4

SAS Printout Showing Descriptive Statistics for Firing Pin Lengths

```
Analysis Variable:    LENGTH

N Obs   N     Minimum       Maximum        Mean         Std Dev
-------------------------------------------------------------------
  20    20   0.8700000     1.0600000     0.9920000     0.0348833
-------------------------------------------------------------------
```

Next, we plot the 20 sample measurements in a sequence plot (in time order), as shown in Figure 9.5. Typically, three horizontal lines are drawn on the control chart. For variable control charts, the **center line** is the sample mean, $\bar{x}$. The center line estimates the mean value μ of the process. For this example, we estimate that the mean length of firing pins is .992 inch.

FIGURE 9.5

Control Chart for Firing Pin Lengths

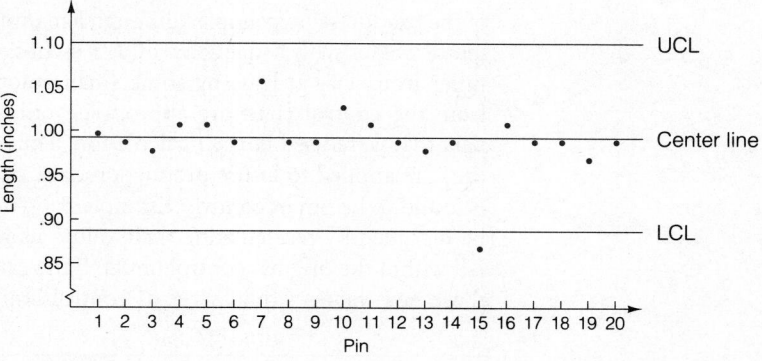

The two lines located above and below the center line in Figure 9.5 establish the **upper control limit (UCL)** and **lower control limit (LCL)** between which we expect the measurements to fall if the process is in control. For variable control charts, LCL = $\bar{x} - 3s$ and UCL = $\bar{x} + 3s$. Consequently, we have

$$LCL = .992 - 3(.035) = .887$$
$$UCL = .992 + 3(.035) = 1.097$$

Note that the length measurement of firing pin 15 falls below the LCL. Thus, the process is out of control, indicating possible trouble in the production line. In this situation, process engineers are usually assigned to determine the cause of the unusually small (or large) measurement.

In concluding our discussion of an individual variable control chart (or, as it is often called, an **individuals control chart**), it is important to note that the chart describes the process as it is, not the way we want it to be. The process mean and control limits may differ markedly from the specifications set by the manufacturer of the product. For example, although a manufacturer may want to produce electrical motor shafts with a diameter of 1.5 inches, the actual process mean will usually differ from 1.5, at least by some small amount. Also, the control limits obtained from the control chart are appropriate only for analyzing past data—that is, the data that were used in their calculation. Thus, they may require modification before they are applied to future production data. For example, in cases where the process is found to be out of control (Example 9.1), the control limits and center line would be modified by recalculating their values using only the sample measurements that fall within the original control limits. If the cause of the problem has been corrected, these new values would serve as control limits for future data.

In this section we presented control charts for a single quality variable (eg, firing pin length). Control charts also can be constructed for process means, process variation, percent defectives, and number of defects per item. We present these types of control charts in the sections that follow.

PROBLEMS

9.1 Suppose the process for manufacturing electrical motor shafts is in control. At the end of each hour, for a period of 20 hours, the manufacturer randomly selects one shaft and measures the diameter of each. The measurements (in inches) for the 20 samples are recorded below. Construct and interpret a control chart for shaft diameter.

SAMPLE	DIAMETER (INCHES)	SAMPLE	DIAMETER (INCHES)
1	1.505	11	1.491
2	1.496	12	1.486
3	1.516	13	1.510
4	1.507	14	1.495
5	1.502	15	1.504
6	1.502	16	1.499
7	1.489	17	1.501
8	1.485	18	1.497
9	1.503	19	1.503
10	1.485	20	1.494

9.2 A rheostat knob, produced by plastic molding, contains a metal insert. The fit of this knob into its assembly is determined by the distance from the back of the knob to the far side of a pin hole. To monitor the molding operation, one knob from each hour's production was randomly sampled and the dimension measured on each. The table gives the distance measurements (in inches) for the first 27 hours the process was in operation.

HOUR	DISTANCE MEASUREMENT	HOUR	DISTANCE MEASUREMENT
1	.140	15	.144
2	.138	16	.140
3	.139	17	.137
4	.143	18	.137
5	.142	19	.142
6	.136	20	.136
7	.142	21	.142
8	.143	22	.139
9	.141	23	.140
10	.142	24	.134
11	.137	25	.138
12	.137	26	.140
13	.142	27	.145
14	.137		

Source: Grant, E. L., and Leavenworth, R. S. *Statistical Quality Control,* 5th ed. New York: McGraw-Hill, 1980 (Table 1-2). Reprinted with permission.

a. Construct a variable control chart for the process.
b. Locate the center line, upper control limit, and lower control limit on the chart.
c. Does the process appear to be in control?

9.3 Molded-rubber expansion joints, used in heating and air-conditioning systems, are designed to have internal diameters of 5 inches. To monitor the manufacturing process, one joint was randomly selected from the production line and its diameter (in inches) measured each hour, for a period of 12 hours, as shown in the table at the top of the next page. The data will be used to construct a variable control chart.

HOUR	DIAMETER	HOUR	DIAMETER
1	5.08	7	5.02
2	4.88	8	4.91
3	4.99	9	5.06
4	5.04	10	4.92
5	5.00	11	5.01
6	4.83	12	4.92

a. Locate the center line for the variable control chart.

b. Locate upper and lower control limits.

c. Does the process appear to be in control?

9.4 Each month the quality control engineer at a bottle manufacturing company randomly samples one finished bottle from the production process at 20 points in time (days) and records the weight of each bottle (in ounces). The data for last month's inspection are provided in the table.

DAY	BOTTLE WEIGHT	DAY	BOTTLE WEIGHT
1	5.6	11	6.2
2	5.7	12	5.9
3	6.1	13	5.2
4	6.3	14	6.0
5	5.2	15	6.3
6	6.0	16	5.8
7	5.8	17	6.1
8	5.8	18	6.2
9	6.4	19	5.3
10	6.0	20	6.0

a. Construct a variable control chart for the weights of the finished bottles.

b. Does the process appear to be in control for this particular month?

CONTROL CHART FOR MEANS

9.3 A control chart constructed to monitor a quantitative product quality characteristic is usually based on random samples of several units of the product rather than on the characteristics of individual industrial units (as shown in Figure 9.3). For example, the manufacturer of electrical motor shafts in Section 9.2 might select a sample of five shafts at the end of each hour. A plot showing the mean diameters of the samples, with one mean corresponding to each point in time, is called a **control chart for means**, or an **$\bar{x}$-chart**.

In practice, control charts are constructed after a process has been adjusted to correct for assignable causes of variation and the process is deemed to be in control. When the process is in control, an $\bar{x}$-chart would show only random variation in the sample mean over time. Theoretically, $\bar{x}$ should vary about the process mean, μ, and fall within the limits $\mu \pm 3\sigma_{\bar{x}}$ with a high probability. A control chart constructed for the means of samples of $n = 5$ motor shafts taken each hour might appear as shown in Figure 9.6.

An $\bar{x}$-chart such as that shown in Figure 9.6 contains three horizontal lines. The **center line** establishes the mean value μ of the process. Although this value is

FIGURE 9.6

$\bar{x}$-Chart for Samples of $n = 5$ Shaft Diameters

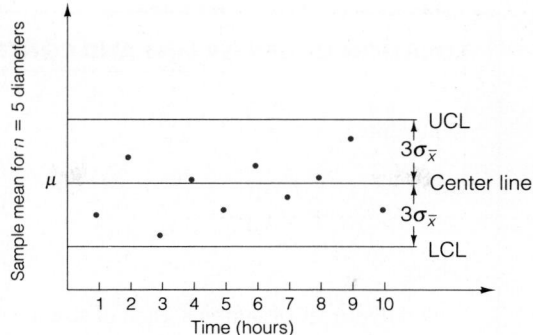

usually unknown, it can be estimated by averaging a large number (eg, 20) of sample means obtained when the process is in control. For example, if we average the values of k sample means, then

$$\text{Center line} = \bar{\bar{x}} = \frac{\sum_{i=1}^{k} \bar{x}_i}{k}$$

The two lines located above and below the center line establish the **upper control limit (UCL)** and the **lower control limit (LCL)**, between which we would expect the sample means to fall if the process is in control. They are located a distance of $3\sigma_{\bar{x}} = 3\sigma/\sqrt{n}$ above and below the center line.

The process standard deviation σ is usually unknown, but it can be estimated from a large sample of data collected while the process is in control. Prior to the advent of computers, it was common to estimate σ by first computing the sample range R, the difference between the largest and smallest sample measurements. The process standard deviation σ was estimated by dividing the average $\bar{R}$ of k sample ranges by a constant d_2, the value of which depended on the sample size n:

$$\hat{\sigma} = \frac{\bar{R}}{d_2} = \frac{\sum_{i=1}^{k} R_i/k}{d_2}$$

Since the control limits are located a distance of $3\sigma_{\bar{x}} = 3\sigma/\sqrt{n}$ above and below the center line, this distance was estimated to be

$$3\hat{\sigma}_{\bar{x}} = \frac{3(\bar{R}/d_2)}{\sqrt{n}} = \left(\frac{3}{d_2\sqrt{n}}\right)\bar{R} = A_2\bar{R}$$

where

$$A_2 = \frac{3}{d_2\sqrt{n}}$$

Values of A_2 and d_2 for sample sizes $n = 2$ to $n = 25$ are given in Table 12, Appendix A.

LOCATION OF CENTER LINE AND CONTROL LIMITS FOR AN $\bar{x}$-CHART

Center line: $\quad \bar{\bar{x}} = \dfrac{\Sigma \bar{x}_i}{k}$

UCL: $\qquad \bar{\bar{x}} + A_2 \bar{R}$

LCL: $\qquad \bar{\bar{x}} - A_2 \bar{R}$

where

$\quad k$ = Number of samples, each of size n

$\quad \bar{x}_i$ = Sample mean for the ith sample

$\quad R_i$ = Range of the ith sample

$\quad \bar{R} = \dfrac{\Sigma R_i}{k}$

and A_2 is given in Table 12, Appendix A.

Note: For a stable process with large samples (say, $n > 15$), the upper and lower control limits may be computed as follows:

UCL: $\quad \bar{\bar{x}} + \dfrac{3s}{\sqrt{n}}$

LCL: $\quad \bar{\bar{x}} - \dfrac{3s}{\sqrt{n}}$

where s is the standard deviation of all nk sample measurements.

Today, the sample measurements for quality control processes can be entered into an on-site computer that is programmed to compute the means and standard deviations of the individual samples, as well as the means and standard deviations of the data contained in any set of k samples. For large samples from a process with no time trend and a stable variance, the best estimate of σ is then the standard deviation s of the data contained in the k sets of data.* The computer calculates $\bar{\bar{x}}$ and s and provides a printout of the control chart. However, the simplicity of calculating a sample range is not to be overlooked. Time, energy, and money often can be saved by reporting the sample ranges rather than s. Thus, in practice, $\bar{x}$-charts based on $\bar{R}$ remain the standard.

EXAMPLE 9.2 Suppose the process for manufacturing electrical motor shafts is in control. At the end of each hour, for a period of 20 hours, the manufacturer selected a random sample of four shafts and measured the diameter of each. The measurements

---

* Grant and Leavenworth (1980) suggest using s to estimate σ when the sample size n is greater than 15. For smaller samples, $\bar{R}/d_2$ will usually provide a better estimate.

(in inches) for the 20 samples are recorded in Table 9.2. Construct a control chart for the sample means and interpret the results.

Solution   The first step in constructing an $\bar{x}$-chart is to compute the sample mean, $\bar{x}$, and range, R, for each of the 20 samples. These values are shown in the last two columns of Table 9.2.

Next, we calculate $\bar{\bar{x}}$, the average of the 20 sample means, and $\bar{R}$, the average of the 20 sample ranges:

$$\bar{\bar{x}} = \frac{\Sigma\, \bar{x}_i}{20} = \frac{1.4983 + 1.5055 + 1.4990 + \cdots + 1.5055}{20} = 1.50045$$

$$\bar{R} = \frac{\Sigma\, R_i}{20} = \frac{.017 + .017 + .031 + \cdots + .025}{20} = .01985$$

The value of $\bar{\bar{x}} = 1.50045$ locates the center line on the control chart. To find upper and lower control limits, we need the value of the control limit factor A_2, found in Table 12, Appendix A. For $n = 4$ measurements in each sample, $A_2 = .729$. Then

$$\text{UCL} = \bar{\bar{x}} + A_2\bar{R} = 1.50045 + (.729)(.01985) = 1.51492$$
$$\text{LCL} = \bar{\bar{x}} - A_2\bar{R} = 1.50045 - (.729)(.01985) = 1.48598$$

Using these limits, we construct the control chart for the sample means shown in Figure 9.7. Note that all 20 sample means fall within the control limits.

TABLE 9.2
Samples of $n = 4$ Shaft Diameters, Example 9.2

SAMPLE NUMBER	SAMPLE MEASUREMENTS Inches				SAMPLE MEAN $\bar{x}$	RANGE R
1	1.505	1.499	1.501	1.488	1.4983	.017
2	1.496	1.513	1.512	1.501	1.5055	.017
3	1.516	1.485	1.492	1.503	1.4990	.031
4	1.507	1.492	1.511	1.491	1.5003	.020
5	1.502	1.491	1.501	1.502	1.4990	.011
6	1.502	1.488	1.506	1.483	1.4948	.023
7	1.489	1.512	1.496	1.501	1.4995	.023
8	1.485	1.518	1.494	1.513	1.5025	.033
9	1.503	1.495	1.503	1.496	1.4993	.008
10	1.485	1.519	1.503	1.507	1.5035	.034
11	1.491	1.516	1.497	1.493	1.4993	.025
12	1.486	1.505	1.487	1.492	1.4925	.019
13	1.510	1.502	1.515	1.499	1.5065	.016
14	1.495	1.485	1.493	1.503	1.4940	.018
15	1.504	1.499	1.504	1.500	1.5018	.005
16	1.499	1.503	1.508	1.497	1.5018	.011
17	1.501	1.493	1.509	1.491	1.4985	.018
18	1.497	1.510	1.496	1.500	1.5008	.014
19	1.503	1.526	1.497	1.500	1.5065	.029
20	1.494	1.501	1.508	1.519	1.5055	.025

FIGURE 9.7
$\bar{x}$-Chart for Shaft Diameters, Example 9.2

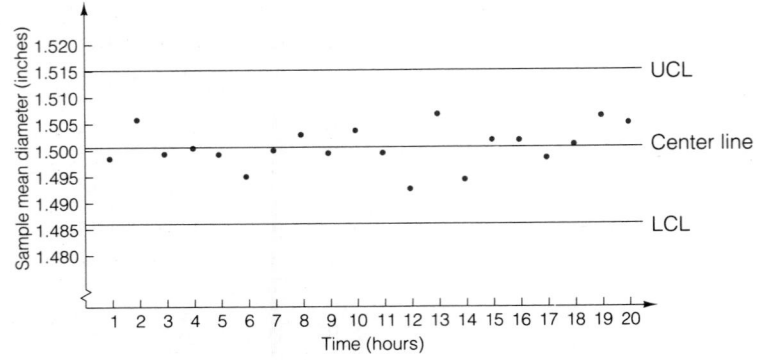

FIGURE 9.8
Computer-Generated $\bar{x}$-Chart for Example 9.2

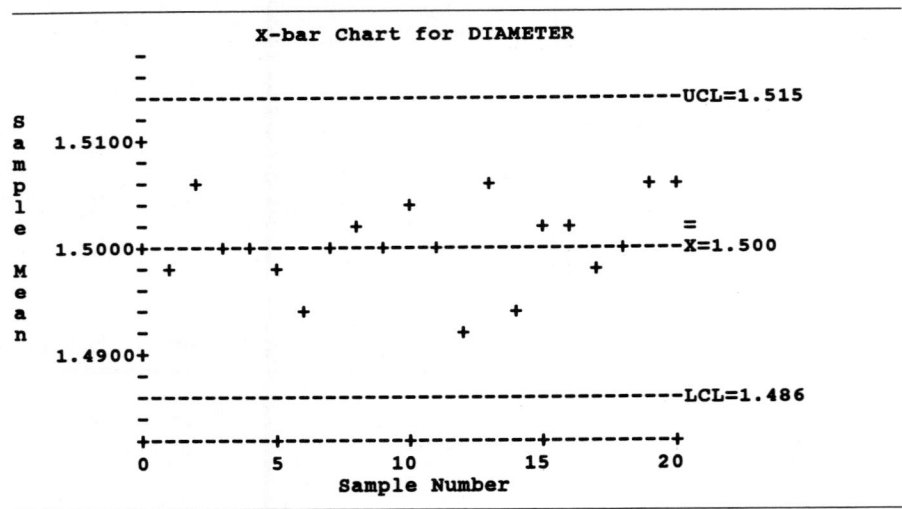

A computer-generated (MINITAB) control chart for the sample means is shown in Figure 9.8. The upper and lower control limits in the MINITAB printout differ slightly from those in Figure 9.7, because the computer uses the standard deviation s of all 80 measurements to establish these limits.

The purpose of the $\bar{x}$-chart is to detect departures from process control. If the process is in control, the probability that a sample mean will fall within the control limits is very high. This result is due to the Central Limit Theorem (Section 5.1), which guarantees that the sampling distribution of $\bar{x}$ will be approximately normal for large samples. Consequently, the probability that $\bar{x}$ will fall within the control limits (ie, within $\pm 3\sigma_{\bar{x}}$) is approximately .997. Therefore, a sample mean falling outside the control limits is taken as an indication of possible trouble in the production process. When this occurs, we say the process is out of control with a high degree of confidence, and process engineers are usually assigned to determine the cause of the unusually large (or small) value of $\bar{x}$.

On the other hand, when all the sample means fall within the control limits (as in Figure 9.7), we say that the process is in control. However, we do not have the same degree of confidence in this statement as with the out of control conclusion above. In one sense, we are using the control chart to test the null hypothesis H_0: Process in control (ie, no assignable causes of variation are present). Recall from Section 5.3 that we must be careful not to accept H_0, because the probability of a Type II error is unknown. In practice, when quality control engineers say "the process is in control," they really mean that "it pays to act as if no assignable causes of variation are present." In this situation it is better to leave the process alone than to spend a great deal of time and money looking for trouble that may not exist.

INTERPRETING AN $\bar{x}$-CHART

Process out of control: One or more of the sample means fall outside the control limits.* This indicates possible trouble in the production process, and efforts should be made to determine the cause of the unusually large (or small) values of $\bar{x}$.

Process in control: All sample means fall within the control limits. Although assignable causes of variation may be present, it is better to leave the process alone than to look for trouble that may not exist.

Before concluding our discussion of the $\bar{x}$-chart, two important points must be made. First, in practice, the $\bar{x}$-chart is typically used in conjunction with a chart that monitors the variation of the process, called an R-chart. In fact, since the sample range (or standard deviation) is used to construct the $\bar{x}$-chart, it is essential to examine an R-chart first to be sure that the process variation is stable. The R-chart is the topic of the next section.

The second point to be made about $\bar{x}$-charts, and control charts in general, is the importance of the sampling plan. Ideally, we want to choose samples of items

---

* In addition to the "one point beyond the control limits" rule, there are several other "pattern analysis" rules that help the analyst determine whether the process is out of control. For example, the process is also out of control if four of five consecutive points are beyond $\mu + 2\sigma_{\bar{x}}$ or $\mu - 2\sigma_{\bar{x}}$. Consult the references for a detailed discussion of these other rules of thumb.

over time so that we maximize the chance of detecting process change, if it exists. To do this, we choose **rational subgroups** (samples) of items so that the change in the process mean (if it exists) occurs *between* samples, *not within* samples (ie, not during the period that the sample is drawn). The next example illustrates this point.

DEFINITION 9.6

Rational subgroups are samples of items collected that maximize the chance that (1) quality measurements within each sample are similar and (2) quality measurements between samples differ.

EXAMPLE 9.3   Refer to the discussion of the process for manufacturing electrical motor shafts in Example 9.2. Suppose that the operations manager suspects that workers on the night shift are producing shafts with larger mean diameters than workers on the morning and afternoon shifts. The manager wants to use an $\bar{x}$-chart to determine whether the process mean has changed. Suggest a sampling plan for the manager that follows rational subgrouping strategy. That is, how should the samples of four shafts be selected so that the chance of detecting the shift in means is maximized?

Solution   Obviously, the control chart should be constructed using samples of shafts that are drawn within each shift. For example, the manager could sample four shafts each hour for 24 consecutive hours. Then the first eight samples will come from the morning shift, the next eight from the afternoon shift, and the last eight from the night shift. In this way, none of the samples would span shifts. (This is in contrast to a sample of, say, two shafts from the afternoon shift, and two from the night shift.) These 24 samples represent rational subgroups of shafts designed to maximize the chance of detecting the change in mean shaft diameters attributable to the night shift workers.

PROBLEMS

9.5   As described in Problem 9.2, a rheostat knob, produced by plastic molding, contains a metal insert. The fit of this knob into its assembly is determined by the distance from the back of the knob to the far side of a pin hole. To monitor the molding operation, five knobs from each hour's production were randomly sampled and the dimension measured on each. The table gives the distance measurements (in inches) for the first 27 hours the process was in operation. Does the process appear to be in control?

HOUR	DISTANCE MEASUREMENTS					HOUR	DISTANCE MEASUREMENTS				
1	.140	.143	.137	.134	.135	5	.142	.142	.145	.135	.136
2	.138	.143	.143	.145	.146	6	.136	.144	.143	.136	.137
3	.139	.133	.147	.148	.139	7	.142	.147	.137	.142	.138
4	.143	.141	.137	.138	.140	8	.143	.137	.145	.137	.138

(continued)

HOUR	DISTANCE MEASUREMENTS					HOUR	DISTANCE MEASUREMENTS				
9	.141	.142	.147	.140	.140	19	.142	.142	.143	.140	.135
10	.142	.137	.145	.140	.132	20	.136	.142	.140	.139	.137
11	.137	.147	.142	.137	.135	21	.142	.144	.140	.138	.143
12	.137	.146	.142	.142	.140	22	.139	.146	.143	.140	.139
13	.142	.142	.139	.141	.142	23	.140	.145	.142	.139	.137
14	.137	.145	.144	.137	.140	24	.134	.147	.143	.141	.142
15	.144	.142	.143	.135	.145	25	.138	.145	.141	.137	.141
16	.140	.132	.144	.145	.141	26	.140	.145	.143	.144	.138
17	.137	.137	.142	.143	.141	27	.145	.145	.137	.138	.140
18	.137	.142	.142	.145	.143						

Source: Grant, E. L., and Leavenworth, R. S. *Statistical Quality Control,* 5th ed. New York: McGraw-Hill, 1980 (Table 1-2). Reprinted with permission.

9.6 As described in Problem 9.3, molded-rubber expansion joints, used in heating and air-conditioning systems, are designed to have internal diameters of 5 inches. To monitor the manufacturing process, eight joints were randomly selected from the production line and their diameters (in inches) measured each hour, for a period of 12 hours, as shown in the table. The data for the 12 samples will be used to construct an $\bar{x}$-chart. Calculate and plot the 12 sample means to produce an $\bar{x}$-chart for the joint diameters. Does the process appear to be in control?

HOUR	MOLDED-RUBBER EXPANSION JOINT DIAMETERS							
1	5.08	5.01	4.99	4.93	4.98	5.00	5.04	4.97
2	4.88	5.10	4.93	5.02	5.06	4.99	4.92	4.91
3	4.99	5.00	5.02	5.01	5.03	4.92	4.97	5.01
4	5.04	4.96	5.01	5.00	5.00	4.98	4.91	4.96
5	5.00	4.93	4.94	5.02	5.01	4.97	5.08	5.11
6	4.83	4.92	4.96	4.91	5.01	5.03	4.93	5.00
7	5.02	5.01	4.96	4.98	5.00	5.07	4.94	5.01
8	4.91	5.00	4.97	5.03	5.02	4.99	4.98	4.99
9	5.06	5.04	4.99	5.02	4.97	5.00	5.01	5.01
10	4.92	4.98	5.01	5.01	4.97	5.00	5.02	4.93
11	5.01	5.00	5.02	4.98	4.99	5.00	5.01	5.01
12	4.92	5.12	5.06	4.93	4.98	5.02	5.04	4.97

9.7 As described in Example 9.1, a corporation that manufactures field rifles for the Department of Defense operates a production line that turns out finished firing pins. To monitor the process, an inspector randomly selects five firing pins from the production line, measures their lengths (in inches), and repeats this process at 30 minute intervals over a 5 hour period. Suppose the specification for the firing pins is that they be 1.00 inch plus or minus .08 inch in length. Does the manufacturing process appear to be in control?

30 MINUTE INTERVAL	FIRING PIN LENGTHS				
1	1.05	1.03	.99	1.00	1.03
2	.93	.96	1.01	.98	.97
3	1.02	.99	.99	1.00	.98
4	.98	1.01	1.02	.99	.97
5	1.02	.99	1.04	1.07	.98
6	1.05	.98	.96	.91	1.02
7	.92	.95	1.00	.99	1.01
8	1.06	.98	.98	1.04	1.00
9	.97	.99	.99	.98	1.01
10	1.00	.96	1.02	1.03	.99

9.8 One of the operations in a plant consists of thread grinding a fitting for an aircraft hydraulic system. To monitor the process, a production supervisor randomly sampled five fittings each hour, for a period of 20 hours, and measured the pitch diameters of the threads. The measurements, expressed in units of .0001 inch in excess of .4000 inch, are shown in the table. (For example, the value 36 represents .4036 inch.) Does the process appear to be in control? Eliminate the points that fall outside the control limits and recalculate the values of the control limits. Would you recommend using these modified control limits for future data?

HOUR	PITCH DIAMETERS OF THREADS					HOUR	PITCH DIAMETERS OF THREADS				
1	36	35	34	33	32	11	34	38	35	34	38
2	31	31	34	32	30	12	36	38	39	39	40
3	30	30	32	30	32	13	36	40	35	26	33
4	32	33	33	32	35	14	36	35	37	34	33
5	32	34	37	37	35	15	30	37	33	34	35
6	32	32	31	33	33	16	28	31	33	33	33
7	33	33	36	32	31	17	33	30	34	33	35
8	23	33	36	35	36	18	27	28	29	27	30
9	43	36	35	24	31	19	35	36	29	27	32
10	36	35	36	41	41	20	33	35	35	39	36

Source: Grant, E. L., and Leavenworth, R. S. *Statistical Quality Control*, 5th ed. New York: McGraw-Hill, 1980 (Table 1-1). Reprinted with permission.

CONTROL CHART FOR PROCESS VARIATION

9.4

In quality control we want to control not only the mean value of some quality characteristic, but also its variability. An increase in the process standard deviation, σ, means that the quality characteristic variable will vary over a wider range, thereby increasing the probability of producing an inferior product. Consequently, a process that is in control generates data with a relatively constant process mean μ and standard deviation σ.

The variation in a quality characteristic is monitored using a **range chart**, or **R-chart**. Thus, in addition to calculating the mean, $\bar{x}$, for each sample, we also calculate and plot the sample range, R. As with an $\bar{x}$-chart, an R-chart also contains a center line and lines corresponding to the upper and lower control limits.

It can be shown (proof omitted) that the mean and standard deviation of the sample range are

$$\mu_R = d_2\sigma \quad \text{and} \quad \sigma_R = d_3\sigma$$

where d_2 and d_3 are constants (see Table 12, Appendix A) that depend on the sample size n. Therefore, we locate the center line of the R-chart at $d_2\sigma$ where, if σ is unknown, μ_R is estimated by the mean $\bar{R}$ of the ranges of k samples.*

The upper and lower control limits are located a distance $3\sigma_R = 3d_3\sigma$ above and below the center line. Using $\bar{R}/d_2$ to estimate σ, we locate the upper and lower control limits as follows:

$$\text{UCL:} \quad \bar{R} + 3\left(\frac{d_3}{d_2}\right)\bar{R} = \left[1 + 3\left(\frac{d_3}{d_2}\right)\right]\bar{R} = D_4\bar{R}$$

---

* As an alternative procedure, we could estimate σ using the standard deviation of all the data contained in the k samples.

$$\text{LCL:} \quad \overline{R} - 3\left(\frac{d_3}{d_2}\right)\overline{R} = \left[1 - 3\left(\frac{d_3}{d_2}\right)\right]\overline{R} = D_3\overline{R}$$

where

$$D_4 = 1 + 3\left(\frac{d_3}{d_2}\right) \quad \text{and} \quad D_3 = 1 - 3\left(\frac{d_3}{d_2}\right)$$

Values of D_3 and D_4 have been computed for sample sizes of $n = 2$ to $n = 25$, and appear in Table 12, Appendix A. The formulas for the center line, UCL, and LCL are summarized in the box.

LOCATION OF CENTER LINE AND CONTROL LIMITS FOR AN *R*-CHART

Center line: $\overline{R}$

UCL: $D_4\overline{R}$

LCL: $D_3\overline{R}$

where

$k = $ Number of samples, each size n

$R_i = $ Range of the ith sample

$$\overline{R} = \frac{\sum_{i=1}^{k} R_i}{k}$$

and D_3 and D_4 are given in Table 12, Appendix A, for $n = 2$ to $n = 25$.

EXAMPLE 9.4 Refer to the problem of monitoring the manufacturing of electrical motor shafts, discussed in Example 9.2. Recall that the manufacturer selected a sample of four shafts each hour, for a period of 20 hours, and measured the diameter of each shaft. The data are reproduced in Table 9.3 (p. 396). Assuming the process is in control, construct and interpret an *R*-chart for process variation.

Solution The 20 sample ranges listed in Table 9.3 are plotted in the sequence plot shown in Figure 9.9.

In Example 9.2, we calculated the mean of the 20 sample ranges to be $\overline{R} = .01985$. This value represents the center line and is shown in the control chart in Figure 9.9. For $n = 4$, the values of D_3 and D_4 given in Table 12, Appendix A, are 0 and 2.282, respectively. Then the upper and lower control limits for the *R*-chart are

$$\text{UCL} = D_4\overline{R} = (2.282)(.01985) = .045298$$
$$\text{LCL} = D_3\overline{R} = (0)(.01985) = 0$$

TABLE 9.3
Samples of $n = 4$ Shaft Diameters, Example 9.4

SAMPLE NUMBER	SAMPLE MEASUREMENTS Inches				SAMPLE MEAN $\bar{x}$	RANGE R
1	1.505	1.499	1.501	1.488	1.4983	.017
2	1.496	1.513	1.512	1.501	1.5055	.017
3	1.516	1.485	1.492	1.503	1.4990	.031
4	1.507	1.492	1.511	1.491	1.5003	.020
5	1.502	1.491	1.501	1.502	1.4990	.011
6	1.502	1.488	1.506	1.483	1.4948	.023
7	1.489	1.512	1.496	1.501	1.4995	.023
8	1.485	1.518	1.494	1.513	1.5025	.033
9	1.503	1.495	1.503	1.496	1.4993	.008
10	1.485	1.519	1.503	1.507	1.5035	.034
11	1.491	1.516	1.497	1.493	1.4993	.025
12	1.486	1.505	1.487	1.492	1.4925	.019
13	1.510	1.502	1.515	1.499	1.5065	.016
14	1.495	1.485	1.493	1.503	1.4940	.018
15	1.504	1.499	1.504	1.500	1.5018	.005
16	1.499	1.503	1.508	1.497	1.5018	.011
17	1.501	1.493	1.509	1.491	1.4985	.018
18	1.497	1.510	1.496	1.500	1.5008	.014
19	1.503	1.526	1.497	1.500	1.5065	.029
20	1.494	1.501	1.508	1.519	1.5055	.025

FIGURE 9.9
R-Chart for the $k = 20$ Sample Ranges of Table 9.3

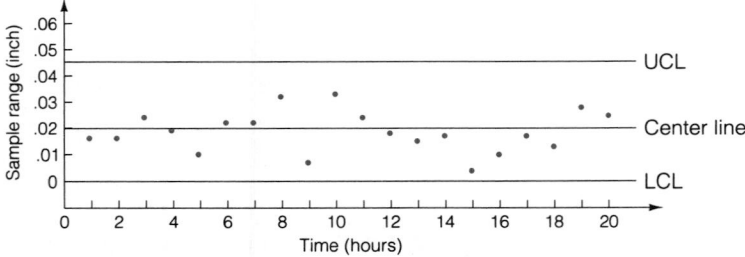

These lines are also shown in the control chart. To monitor the variation in shaft diameters produced by the manufacturing process, a quality control engineer would check to determine that the sample range does not exceed the UCL of .045298 inch. (Since the LCL is 0, no diameter can fall below this value.)

The practical implications to be derived from an R-chart are similar to those associated with an $\bar{x}$-chart. Values of R that fall outside the control limits are suspect and suggest a possible change in the process. Trends in the sample range may also indicate problems, such as wear within a machine. (We investigate this type of problem in the next section.) As in the case of the $\bar{x}$-chart, the R-chart can provide an indication of possible trouble in the process. A process engineer then attempts to locate the difficulty, if in fact it exists.

Process out of control: One or more of the sample ranges fall outside the control limits. As with the x̄-chart, this indicates a possible change in the production process and efforts should be made to locate the trouble.

Process in control: All sample ranges fall within the control limits. In this case it is better to leave the process alone than to look for trouble that may not exist.

Remember, it is important to construct and interpret an *R*-chart before the x̄-chart. When the *R*-chart indicates that process variation is in control, only then does it make sense to analyze the x̄-chart.

PROBLEMS

9.9 The data of Problem 9.5 are reproduced below. Construct an *R*-chart for the variation of the process.

HOUR	DISTANCE MEASUREMENTS					HOUR	DISTANCE MEASUREMENTS				
1	.140	.143	.137	.134	.135	15	.144	.142	.143	.135	.145
2	.138	.143	.143	.145	.146	16	.140	.132	.144	.145	.141
3	.139	.133	.147	.148	.139	17	.137	.137	.142	.143	.141
4	.143	.141	.137	.138	.140	18	.137	.142	.142	.145	.143
5	.142	.142	.145	.135	.136	19	.142	.142	.143	.140	.135
6	.136	.144	.143	.136	.137	20	.136	.142	.140	.139	.137
7	.142	.147	.137	.142	.138	21	.142	.144	.140	.138	.143
8	.143	.137	.145	.137	.138	22	.139	.146	.143	.140	.139
9	.141	.142	.147	.140	.140	23	.140	.145	.142	.139	.137
10	.142	.137	.145	.140	.132	24	.134	.147	.143	.141	.142
11	.137	.147	.142	.137	.135	25	.138	.145	.141	.137	.141
12	.137	.146	.142	.142	.140	26	.140	.145	.143	.144	.138
13	.142	.142	.139	.141	.142	27	.145	.145	.137	.138	.140
14	.137	.145	.144	.137	.140						

Source: Grant, E. L., and Leavenworth, R. S. *Statistical Quality Control*, 5th ed. New York: McGraw-Hill, 1980 (Table 1-2). Reprinted with permission.

9.10 The data of Problem 9.6 are reproduced in the table. Construct an *R*-chart to monitor the variation in the diameters of the molded-rubber expansion joints produced by the manufacturing process. Does the process appear to be in control?

HOUR	MOLDED-RUBBER EXPANSION JOINT DIAMETERS							
1	5.08	5.01	4.99	4.93	4.98	5.00	5.04	4.97
2	4.88	5.10	4.93	5.02	5.06	4.99	4.92	4.91
3	4.99	5.00	5.02	5.01	5.03	4.92	4.97	5.01
4	5.04	4.96	5.01	5.00	5.00	4.98	4.91	4.96
5	5.00	4.93	4.94	5.02	5.01	4.97	5.08	5.11
6	4.83	4.92	4.96	4.91	5.01	5.03	4.93	5.00
7	5.02	5.01	4.96	4.98	5.00	5.07	4.94	5.01

(continued)

HOUR	MOLDED-RUBBER EXPANSION JOINT DIAMETERS							
8	4.91	5.00	4.97	5.03	5.02	4.99	4.98	4.99
9	5.06	5.04	4.99	5.02	4.97	5.00	5.01	5.01
10	4.92	4.98	5.01	5.01	4.97	5.00	5.02	4.93
11	5.01	5.00	5.02	4.98	4.99	5.00	5.01	5.01
12	4.92	5.12	5.06	4.93	4.98	5.02	5.04	4.97

9.11 The data of Problem 9.7 are reproduced below. Construct an R-chart to monitor the variation in firing pin lengths. Does the process appear to be in control?

30 MINUTE INTERVAL	FIRING PIN LENGTHS				
1	1.05	1.03	.99	1.00	1.03
2	.93	.96	1.01	.98	.97
3	1.02	.99	.99	1.00	.98
4	.98	1.01	1.02	.99	.97
5	1.02	.99	1.04	1.07	.98
6	1.05	.98	.96	.91	1.02
7	.92	.95	1.00	.99	1.01
8	1.06	.98	.98	1.04	1.00
9	.97	.99	.99	.98	1.01
10	1.00	.96	1.02	1.03	.99

9.12 The data of Problem 9.8 are reproduced below. Construct an R-chart to monitor the variation in pitch diameters of the threaded fittings. If the process is out of control, modify the control limits on the R-chart so it can be applied to future data.

HOUR	PITCH DIAMETERS OF THREADS					HOUR	PITCH DIAMETERS OF THREADS				
1	36	35	34	33	32	11	34	38	35	34	38
2	31	31	34	32	30	12	36	38	39	39	40
3	30	30	32	30	32	13	36	40	35	26	33
4	32	33	33	32	35	14	36	35	37	34	33
5	32	34	37	37	35	15	30	37	33	34	35
6	32	32	31	33	33	16	28	31	33	33	33
7	33	33	36	32	31	17	33	30	34	33	35
8	23	33	36	35	36	18	27	28	29	27	30
9	43	36	35	24	31	19	35	36	29	27	32
10	36	35	36	41	41	20	33	35	35	39	36

Source: Grant, E. L., and Leavenworth, R. S. *Statistical Quality Control*, 5th ed. New York: McGraw-Hill, 1980 (Table 1-1). Reprinted with permission.

DETECTING TRENDS IN A CONTROL CHART: RUNS ANALYSIS

9.5 Control charts are also examined for trends or cyclical behavior in the values of $\bar{x}$ and R collected over time. Even when the sample values fall within the control limits, such a trend may indicate the presence of one or more assignable causes of variation that can be determined and controlled. For example, the true process mean may have shifted slightly due to wear in the machine.

Trends in the process can be detected by observing runs of points above or below the center line of a control chart. In quality control, a **run** is defined as a sequence of one or more consecutive points, all of which fall above (or below) the center line. For example, the runs (indicated by braces) for the R-chart of Figure 9.9 are shown in Figure 9.10. Sample ranges that fall above the center line are denoted by a " + " symbol, and ranges that fall below the center line by a " − " symbol. Note that the sequence of 20 points consists of a total of 8 runs, starting with a run of 2 " − ," followed by a run of 2 " + ," and so forth.

FIGURE 9.10

Runs for the k = 20 Sample Ranges in the R-Chart of Figure 9.9

$$
\underbrace{- \; -}_{1} \quad \underbrace{+ \; +}_{2} \quad \underbrace{-}_{3} \quad \underbrace{+ \; + \; +}_{4} \quad \underbrace{-}_{5} \quad \underbrace{+ \; +}_{6} \quad \underbrace{- \; - \; - \; - \; - \; - \; -}_{7} \quad \underbrace{+ \; +}_{8}
$$

Run:

DEFINITION 9.7

A **run** is a sequence of one or more consecutive points that fall on the same side of the center line in a control chart.

Considerable work has been done by researchers on the development of statistical tests based on the **theory of runs**. Many of these techniques are useful for testing whether the sample observations have been drawn at random from the target population. These tests require that the total number of runs, long and short alike, be determined. In quality control, however, a few simple rules have been developed for detecting trends based on only the **extreme** (or **longest**) **runs** in the control chart, as the following example illustrates.

EXAMPLE 9.5   Consider the sequence of runs in Figure 9.10. The extreme (longest) run in the sequence is composed of 7 " − " symbols. These represent the 7 consecutive sample ranges of Example 9.4 that fell below the center line during hours 12, 13, ..., 18. How likely is it to observe 7 consecutive points on the control chart, all on the same side of the center line, if in fact no assignable causes of variation are present?

Solution   To answer this question, we use the laws of probability presented in Chapter 4. First, note that the probability of any one point falling above (or below) the center line is $\frac{1}{2}$ when the process is in control. Then, from Probability Rule 3 for independent events (see Section 4.1), the probability of 7 consecutive points falling, say, *above* the center line is

$$\left(\tfrac{1}{2}\right)\left(\tfrac{1}{2}\right)\left(\tfrac{1}{2}\right)\left(\tfrac{1}{2}\right)\left(\tfrac{1}{2}\right)\left(\tfrac{1}{2}\right)\left(\tfrac{1}{2}\right) = \left(\tfrac{1}{2}\right)^7 = \tfrac{1}{128}$$

Likewise, the probability of 7 consecutive points falling *below* the center line is

$(\frac{1}{2})^7 = \frac{1}{128}$. Therefore, the probability of 7 consecutive points falling on the same side of the center line is, by the additive law of probability (Probability Rule 1),

$$P(7 \text{ consecutive points on the same side of the center line})$$
$$= P(7 \text{ consecutive points above the center line})$$
$$+ P(7 \text{ consecutive points below the center line})$$
$$= \tfrac{1}{128} + \tfrac{1}{128} = \tfrac{2}{128} = \tfrac{1}{64}$$
$$= .0156$$

Since it is very unlikely (probability of .0156) to observe such a pattern if the process is in control, the trend in the control chart is taken as a signal of possible trouble in the production press.

A probability such as the one found in Example 9.5 can be calculated for any run in the control chart, and, based on its value, a decision can be made about whether to look for trouble in the process. Grant and Leavenworth (1980) recommend looking for assignable causes of variation if any one of the sequences of points given in the following box occurs in the control chart.

DETECTING TREND IN A CONTROL CHART: RUNS ANALYSIS

If any one of the following sequences of runs occurs in a control chart, assignable causes of variation (eg, a trend) are likely to be present:

- 7 or more consecutive points on the same side of the center line
- At least 10 out of 11 consecutive points on the same side of the center line
- At least 12 out of 14 consecutive points on the same side of the center line
- At least 14 out of 17 consecutive points on the same side of the center line

---

The rules in the box are easy to apply in practice, because they simply require that we count consecutive points in the control chart. In each case, it can be shown (proof omitted) that the probability of observing that particular sequence of points when the process is in control is approximately .01. Consequently, if one of these sequences occurs, we are highly confident that some problem in the production process, possibly a shift in the process mean, exists.

More formal statistical tests of runs are available. Consult the references at the end of this chapter if you want to learn more about these techniques.

PROBLEMS

9.13   Examine the sequences of points in parts **a–f** for any trends.

    a. + + − − − − − + + + +   **b.** − + − − − + + − + + + +   **c.** − − − − − + + + + + − −

    d. − + + + + + − + + + + + + + +   **e.** + − + + + − − + + −   **f.** − + + + + + + + + + + −

9.14 Refer to the $\bar{x}$- and R-charts of Problems 9.5 and 9.9. Conduct a runs analysis to detect any trend in the process.

9.15 Refer to the $\bar{x}$- and R-charts of Problems 9.6 and 9.10. Conduct a runs analysis to detect any trend in the process.

9.16 Refer to the $\bar{x}$- and R-charts of Problems 9.7 and 9.11. Conduct a runs analysis to detect any trend in the process.

9.17 Refer to the $\bar{x}$- and R-charts of Problems 9.8 and 9.12. Conduct a runs analysis to detect any trend in the process.

CONTROL CHART FOR PERCENT DEFECTIVES

9.6 In addition to measuring quantitative product characteristics, we are also interested in monitoring the binomial proportion, π, of the items produced that are defective. As in the case of the $\bar{x}$-chart and R-chart, rational subgroups (samples) of n items are selected from the production line at the end of some specified interval of time. For each sample, we compute the sample proportion,

$$p = \frac{x}{n}$$

where x is the number of defective items in the sample. The sample proportions are then plotted against time and displayed in a **p-chart**.

The center line for a p-chart is the average proportion of defectives in a large number, k, of samples. It also can be determined by combining the data contained in the k samples and finding the overall proportion of defectives. That is, the estimate of the process proportion defective, π, is

$$\bar{p} = \frac{\text{Total number of defectives}}{\text{Total number inspected}} = \frac{n \sum_{i=1}^{k} p_i}{nk} = \frac{\sum_{i=1}^{k} p_i}{k}$$

The upper and lower control limits are located a distance of

$$3\sigma_p = 3\sqrt{\frac{\pi(1-\pi)}{n}}$$

above and below the center line. Using $\bar{p}$ to estimate the process proportion defective, π, we find

$$\text{UCL:} \quad \bar{p} + 3\sqrt{\frac{\bar{p}(1-\bar{p})}{n}}$$

$$\text{LCL:} \quad \bar{p} - 3\sqrt{\frac{\bar{p}(1-\bar{p})}{n}}$$

The interpretation of a p-chart is similar to the interpretations of $\bar{x}$- and R-charts. When the process is in control, we expect the sample proportions defective to fall within the control limits. Failure to do so suggests difficulties with the production process and should be investigated.

LOCATION OF CENTER LINE AND CONTROL LIMITS FOR *p*-CHART

Center line: $\quad \bar{p} = \dfrac{\text{Total number of defectives in } k \text{ samples}}{\text{Total number of items inspected}}$

$$= \dfrac{\sum\limits_{i=1}^{k} p_i}{k}$$

UCL: $\quad \bar{p} + 3\sqrt{\dfrac{\bar{p}(1-\bar{p})}{n}}$

LCL: $\quad \bar{p} - 3\sqrt{\dfrac{\bar{p}(1-\bar{p})}{n}}$

where

k = Number of samples, each of size n

x_i = Number of defective items in the ith sample

p_i = x_i/n is the proportion of defectives in the ith sample

EXAMPLE 9.6   To monitor the manufacturing process of rubber support bearings used between the superstructure and foundation pads of nuclear power plants, a quality control engineer randomly samples 100 bearings from the production line each day over a 15 day period. The bearings are inspected for defects, and the number of defective bearings found each day is recorded in Table 9.4. Construct a *p*-chart for the fraction of defective bearings and interpret the results.

TABLE 9.4
Defective Bearings in 15 Samples of *n* = 100, Example 9.6

	DAY															
	1	2	3	4	5	6	7	8	9	10	11	12	13	14	15	Totals
Number of Defectives	2	12	3	4	4	1	3	5	3	2	10	3	3	2	3	60
Proportion of Defectives	.02	.12	.03	.04	.04	.01	.03	.05	.03	.02	.10	.03	.03	.02	.03	.04

Solution   The center line for the *p*-chart is the proportion of defective bearings in the combined sample of $nk = 1{,}500$ bearings:

$$\bar{p} = \frac{\text{Total number of defective bearings}}{\text{Total number inspected}} = \frac{60}{1{,}500} = .04$$

Upper and lower control limits are then computed as follows:

$$\text{UCL} = \bar{p} + 3\sqrt{\frac{\bar{p}(1 - \bar{p})}{n}} = .04 + 3\sqrt{\frac{(.04)(.96)}{100}}$$

$$= .04 + .059 = .099$$

$$\text{LCL} = \bar{p} - 3\sqrt{\frac{\bar{p}(1 - \bar{p})}{n}} = .04 - 3\sqrt{\frac{(.04)(.96)}{100}}$$

$$= .04 - .059 = -.019$$

Thus, if the process is in control, we expect the sample proportion of defective rubber bearings to fall between 0 (since no sample proportion can be negative) and .099 with a high probability.

A control chart for the percentage of defective bearings is shown in Figure 9.11. Note that on days 2 and 11, the sample proportion fell outside the control limits. This suggests possible problems with the manufacturing process and warrants further investigation.

FIGURE 9.11

p-Chart for the Percentage of Defective Bearings, Example 9.6

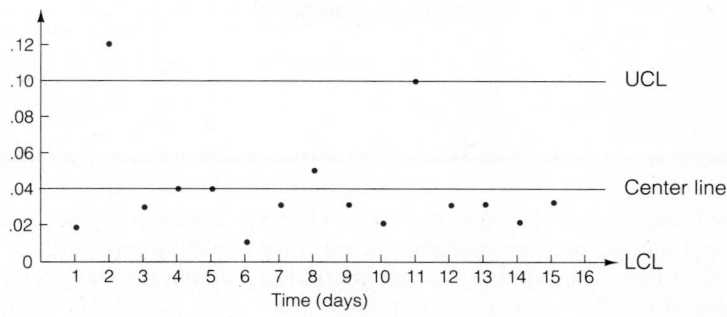

INTERPRETING A p-CHART

Process out of control: One or more of the sample proportions fall outside the control limits. This indicates possible trouble in the production process and warrants further investigation.

Process in control: All sample proportions fall within the control limits. In this case it is better to leave the process alone than to look for trouble that may not exist.

Once the problem that caused the two unusually large sample proportions defective in Example 9.6 has been identified and corrected, the control limits should be modified so that they can be applied to future data. As mentioned in Section 9.3, one method of adjusting is to recalculate their values based only on the sample points that fall within the control limits of Figure 9.11.

For example, by omitting the data for days 2 and 11 (the sample proportions that fall outside the control limits in Example 9.6), we obtain the modified values

$$\bar{p} = \frac{\text{Total number of defective bearings (excluding days 2 and 11)}}{\text{Total number inspected (excluding days 2 and 11)}}$$

$$= \frac{38}{1,300} = .029$$

$$\text{UCL} = \bar{p} + 3\sqrt{\frac{\bar{p}(1 - \bar{p})}{n}} = .029 + 3\sqrt{\frac{(.029)(.971)}{100}}$$

$$= .029 + .050 = .079$$

$$\text{LCL} = \bar{p} - 3\sqrt{\frac{\bar{p}(1 - \bar{p})}{n}} = .029 - 3\sqrt{\frac{(.029)(.971)}{100}}$$

$$= .029 - .050 = -.021$$

Now a control chart with center line $\bar{p} = .029$, UCL $= .079$ and LCL $= 0$ can be used to monitor the percent defectives produced in future days of the process described in Example 9.6.

PROBLEMS

9.18 Prestressed concrete cylinder pipe (PCCP) is a rigid pipe designed to take optimum advantage of the tensile strength of steel and the compressive strength and corrosive-inhibiting properties of concrete. PCCP, produced in laying lengths of 24 feet, is susceptible to major stress cracks during the manufacturing process. To monitor the process, 20 sections of PCCP were sampled each week for a 6 week period. The numbers of defective sections (ie, sections with major stress cracks) in each sample are recorded in the table.

SAMPLE	NUMBER DEFECTIVE	SAMPLE	NUMBER DEFECTIVE	SAMPLE	NUMBER DEFECTIVE	SAMPLE	NUMBER DEFECTIVE
1	2	6	0	11	0	16	3
2	0	7	1	12	1	17	2
3	5	8	3	13	15	18	0
4	6	9	10	14	2	19	1
5	1	10	4	15	2	20	2

a. Calculate the proportion of defective sections of cylinder pipe found in each sample.
b. Calculate upper and lower control limits for a p-chart.
c. Plot the 20 sample proportions to form a p-chart. Is the manufacturing process in control?

9.19 A manufacturer of computer terminal fuses wants to establish a control chart to monitor the production process. Each hour, for a period of 25 hours, during a time when the process is known to be in control, a quality control engineer randomly selected and tested 100 fuses from the production line. The number of defective fuses found each hour is recorded in the table.

HOUR	NUMBER DEFECTIVE	HOUR	NUMBER DEFECTIVE	HOUR	NUMBER DEFECTIVE
1	6	10	2	18	1
2	4	11	1	19	0
3	9	12	3	20	3
4	3	13	4	21	7
5	0	14	5	22	9
6	6	15	5	23	2
7	4	16	2	24	10
8	2	17	1	25	3
9	1				

a. Construct a *p*-chart for the sample percentage of defective computer terminal fuses.
b. Locate the center line on the *p*-chart.
c. Locate the upper and lower control limits on the *p*-chart. Does the process appear to be in control?
d. Conduct a runs analysis on the points of the *p*-chart constructed in part **a**. What does this imply?

9.20 Refer to Problem 9.19. Suppose the next sample of 100 terminal fuses selected from the production line contains 11 defective fuses. Is the process now out of control? Explain.

9.21 An electronics company mass produces several types of cathode ray tubes. To monitor the process, 50 tubes of a certain type were randomly sampled from the production line and inspected each day over a 21 day period. The numbers of defectives found each day are listed in the table.

DAY	NUMBER DEFECTIVE	DAY	NUMBER DEFECTIVE	DAY	NUMBER DEFECTIVE
1	11	8	14	15	11
2	15	9	9	16	11
3	12	10	13	17	16
4	10	11	15	18	15
5	9	12	23	19	10
6	12	13	15	20	13
7	12	14	12	21	12

a. Construct a *p*-chart for the sample fraction of defective cathode ray tubes.
b. Locate the center line on the *p*-chart.
c. Locate the upper and lower control limits on the *p*-chart.
d. Does the process appear to be in control? If not, modify the control limits for future data.
e. Conduct a runs analysis to detect a trend in the production process.

TOLERANCE LIMITS

9.7

The Shewhart control charts described in the previous sections provide valuable information on the quality of the production process as a whole. Even if the process is deemed to be in control, however, an individual manufactured item may not always meet the manufacturer's specifications. Therefore, in addition to process control, it is often important to know that a large proportion of the individual quality measurements fall within certain limits with a high degree of confidence. An interval that includes a certain percentage of measurements with a known probability is called a **tolerance interval**, and the endpoints of the interval are called **tolerance limits**.

Tolerance intervals are identical to confidence intervals, except that we are attempting to capture a proportion, γ, of measurements in a population rather than a population parameter (eg, the population mean μ). For example, a production supervisor may want to establish tolerance limits for 99% of the length measurements of eye screws manufactured on the production line, using a 95% tolerance interval. Here, the confidence coefficient is $1 - \alpha = .95$ and the proportion of measurements the supervisor wants to capture is $\gamma = .99$. The confidence coefficient, .95, has the same meaning as in Chapter 5. That is, approximately 95 out of every 100 similarly constructed tolerance intervals will contain 99% of the length measurements in the population.

DEFINITION 9.8

A $(1 - \alpha)100\%$ **tolerance interval** for $100(\gamma)\%$ of the quality measurements of a product is an interval that includes $100(\gamma)\%$ of the measurements with confidence coefficient $(1 - \alpha)$.

DEFINITION 9.9

The endpoints of a tolerance interval are called **tolerance limits**.

When the population of measurements that characterize the product is normally distributed with known mean μ and known standard deviation σ, tolerance limits are easily constructed. In fact, such an interval is a 100% tolerance interval; that is, the confidence coefficient is 1.0. We illustrate with an example.

EXAMPLE 9.7 Suppose the lengths of eye screws manufactured on a production line have a normal distribution with $\mu = .50$ inch and $\sigma = .01$ inch. Construct a 100% tolerance interval for 99% of the eye screw length measurements. Interpret the interval.

Solution   From our knowledge of the standard normal (z) distribution, we know with certainty (ie, with probability $1 - \alpha = 1.0$) that 99% of the measurements will fall within $z = 2.58$ standard deviations of the mean (see Figure 9.12). Thus, a 100% tolerance interval for 99% of the length measurements is

$$\mu \pm 2.58\sigma = .50 \pm 2.58(.01)$$
$$= .50 \pm .0258$$

or (.4742, .5258). Our interpretation (with 100% confidence) is that 99% of the eye screw lengths produced will fall between .4742 and .5258 inch.

FIGURE 9.12

Normal Distribution of Eye Screw
Lengths, Example 9.7

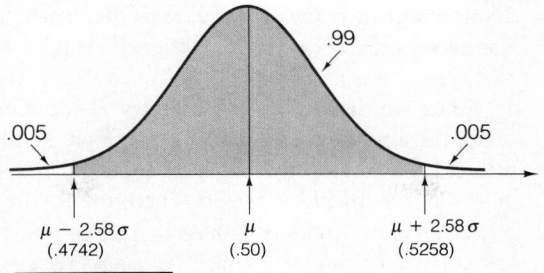

In practice, quality control engineers will rarely know the true values of μ and σ. Fortunately, tolerance intervals can be constructed by substituting the sample estimates $\bar{x}$ and s for μ and σ, respectively. Due to the errors introduced by the sample estimators, however, the confidence coefficient for the tolerance interval will no longer equal 1.0. The procedure for constructing tolerance limits for a normal population of measurements is described in the box.

A TOLERANCE INTERVAL FOR THE MEASUREMENTS IN A NORMAL POPULATION

A $(1 - \alpha)100\%$ tolerance interval for $100(\gamma)\%$ of the measurements in a population is given by

$$\bar{x} \pm Ks$$

where

$\bar{x}$ = Mean of a sample of n measurements

s = Sample standard deviation

and K is found from Table 13, Appendix A, based on the values of the confidence coefficient $(1 - \alpha)$, γ, and the sample size n.

Assumption: The population of measurements is approximately normal.

EXAMPLE 9.8 Refer to Example 9.2 (p. 388). Use the sample information provided in Table 9.2 to find a 95% tolerance interval for 99% of the shaft diameters produced by the manufacturing process. Assume that the distribution of shaft diameters is approximately normal.

Solution Table 9.2 contains diameters for 20 samples of four shafts each, or a total of $n = 80$ shaft diameters. The mean diameter of the entire sample is

$$\bar{x} = \frac{\sum_{i=1}^{k} x_i}{80} = \frac{1.505 + 1.499 + 1.501 + 1.488 + \cdots + 1.519}{80} = 1.50045$$

(Note that this is the same value as the center line computed in Example 9.2.) The sample standard deviation (obtained using a statistical software package) is $s = .009244$.

Since we desire a tolerance interval for 99% of the shaft diameters, $\gamma = .99$. Also, the confidence coefficient is $1 - \alpha = .95$. Table 13, Appendix A, gives the values of K for several values of γ and $1 - \alpha$. For $\gamma = .99$, $1 - \alpha = .95$, and $n = 80$, we find $K = 2.986$. Then, the 95% tolerance interval is

$$\bar{x} \pm 2.986s = 1.50045 \pm (2.986)(.009244)$$

$$= 1.50045 \pm 0.2760$$

or (1.47285, 1.52805). Thus, the lower and upper 95% tolerance limits for 99% of the shaft diameters are 1.47285 and 1.52805 inches, respectively. Our confidence in the procedure is based on the premise that approximately 95 out of every 100 similarly constructed tolerance intervals will contain 99% of the shaft diameters in the population.

The technique applied in Example 9.8 gives tolerance limits for a normal distribution of measurements. If we are unwilling or unable to make the normality assumption, we must resort to a "distribution-free," or nonparametric method. Nonparametric tolerance limits are based on only the smallest and largest measurements in the sample data, as shown in the box. Unlike the procedures used in previous examples, these tolerance intervals can be applied to any set of quality measurements, regardless of the shape of the probability distribution.

A NONPARAMETRIC TOLERANCE INTERVAL

Let x_{min} and x_{max} be the smallest and largest observations, respectively, in a sample of size n from any distribution of measurements. Then, we can select n so that

$$(x_{min}, x_{max})$$

forms a $(1 - \alpha)100\%$ tolerance interval for at least $100(\gamma)\%$ of the population. Values of n for several values of the confidence coefficient $(1 - \alpha)$ and γ are given in Table 14, Appendix A.

EXAMPLE 9.9 Refer to Example 9.8. Determine the sample size required so that the interval (x_{min}, x_{max}) forms a 95% tolerance interval for at least 90% of the shaft diameters produced by the manufacturing process.

Solution Here, the confidence coefficient is $1 - \alpha = .95$ and the proportion of measurements we want to capture is $\gamma = .90$. From Table 14, Appendix A, the sample size corresponding to $1 - \alpha = .95$ and $\gamma = .90$ is $n = 46$. Therefore, if we randomly sample $n = 46$ shafts, the smallest and largest diameters in the sample will represent the lower and upper tolerance limits, respectively, for at least 90% of the shaft diameters with confidence coefficient .95.

The information provided by tolerance intervals is often used to determine whether product specifications are being satisfied. **Specification limits**, unlike tolerance or control limits, are not determined by sampling the process. Rather, they define acceptable values of the quality variable that are set by customers, management, and/or product designers. To determine whether the specifications are realistic, the specification limits are compared to the "natural" tolerance limits of the process, that is, the tolerance limits obtained from sampling. If the tolerance limits do not fall within the specification limits, a review of the production process is strongly recommended. An investigation may reveal that the specifications are tighter than necessary for the functioning of the production, and, consequently, should be widened. Or, if the specifications cannot be changed, a fundamental change in the production process may be necessary to reduce product variability.

PROBLEMS

9.22 Refer to Problem 9.5 (p. 392). Find a 99% tolerance interval for at least 95% of the distance measurements, assuming:
  a. A normal distribution   **b.** A nonnormal distribution

9.23 Refer to Problem 9.7 (p. 393). Use all the sample information to find a 95% tolerance interval for 90% of the firing pin lengths. Assume that the distribution of firing pin lengths is approximately normal.

9.24 Refer to Problem 9.8 (p. 394).

  a. Use all the sample information to find a 95% tolerance interval for 99% of all the pitch diameters. Assume that the distribution of pitch diameters is approximately normal.
  b. Specifications require the pitch diameter of the thread to fall within .4037 ± .0013 inch. Based on the "natural" tolerance limits of the process (ie, the tolerance limits of part **a**), does it appear that the specifications are being met?
  c. How large a sample is required to construct a nonparametric 95% tolerance interval for at least 95% of the pitch diameters? If n is large enough for this case, give the nonparametric tolerance limits.

9.25 J. Namias used the techniques of statistical quality control to determine when to conduct a search for specific causes of consumer complaints at a beverage company (*Journal of Marketing Research*, Aug. 1964). Namias discovered that when the process was in control, the biweekly complaint rate of a bottled product (ie, the number of customer complaints per 10,000 bottles sold in a 2 week period) had an approximately normal distribution with $\mu = 26$ and $\sigma = 11.3$. Customer complaints primarily concerned chipped bottles that looked dangerous.

  a. Find a tolerance interval for 99% of the complaint rates when the bottling process is assumed to be in control. What is the confidence coefficient for the interval? Explain.
  b. In one 2 week period, the observed complaint rate was 93.12 complaints per 10,000 bottles sold. Based on your knowledge of statistical quality control, do you think the observed rate is due to chance or some specific cause? (In actuality, a search for a possible problem in the bottling process led to a discovery of rough handling of the bottled beverage in the warehouse by newly hired workers. As a result, a training program for new workers was instituted.)

9.26 Many hand tools used by mechanics involve attachments that fit into sockets (eg, a socket wrench). In manufacturing the tools, specifications require the inside diameter of the socket to be larger than the outside diameter of the extension. That is, there must be enough clearance so that the extensions actually fit in the sockets. To establish tolerances for the tools, independent random samples of 50 sockets and 50 attachments were selected from the production process and the diameters (inside for sockets and outside for extensions) were measured. An analysis revealed that the distributions for both dimensions were approximately normal. The means and standard deviations (in inches) for the two samples are given in the table.

	SOCKETS	ATTACHMENTS
Sample Mean	.5120	.5005
Standard Deviation	.0010	.0015

a. Find a 95% tolerance interval for 99% of the socket diameters.

b. Find a 95% tolerance interval for 99% of the attachment diameters.

c. Specifications require that the clearance between attachment and socket (ie, the difference between the inside socket diameter and outside attachment diameter) be at least .004 inch. Based on the tolerance limits obtained in parts **a** and **b**, is it likely to find an extension and socket with less than the desired minimum clearance of .004 inch?

d. Specifications also require a maximum of .015 inch clearance between attachment and socket. (This is to prevent fits that are too loose.) Based on the tolerance intervals obtained in parts **a** and **b**, would you expect to find some attachment and socket pairs that fit too loosely?

COMPUTER LAB

CONTROL CHARTS

In this lab section, we provide instructions on how to use the control charts available in MINITAB. MINITAB will automatically compute control limits and plot the points on a control chart. Specifically, the program statements generate a variable chart for the data of Table 9.1, an $\bar{x}$-chart and R-chart for the data of Table 9.2, and a p-chart for the data of Table 9.4. [*Note:* Although control chart routines are not available in SAS and SPSS, you can generate these charts by using the plotting commands of these packages.]

MINITAB

Command Line						
1	SET C1	Data entry instruction				
2	1.00	.99	.98	1.01	1.01	Input data values (5 observations per line)
	1.01	.99	.99	.97	.97	
3	NAME C1='LENGTH'					
4	ICHART C1	Individuals chart				
5	SET C2	Data entry instruction				
	1.505	1.499	1.501	1.488		Input data values (4 observations per line)
6	1.494	1.501	1.508	1.519		

```
7      NAME C2='DIAMETER'
8      XBARCHART C2 4   x̄-Chart
9      RCHART C2 4   Range chart
```
```
10     SET C3   Data entry instruction
       2 12 3 4 ...   Input data values
11     NAME C3='DEFECTS'
12     PCHART C3 100   p-Chart
```

COMMAND 4   ICHART generates an individuals chart for the variable in the specified column.

COMMAND 8   XBARCHART generates an x̄-chart for the variable in the specified column. The number of observations in each subgroup (sample) is specified after the column. (In this program, MINITAB reads the first four numbers as the first sample, the second four numbers as the second sample, etc.)

COMMAND 9   RCHART generates an R-chart for the variable in the specified column. The number of observations in each subgroup (sample) is specified after the column.

COMMAND 10   One observation is read for each sample (usually the observation represents the number of nonconformities).

COMMAND 12   PCHART produces a p-chart for the variable (number of nonconformities) in the column specified. The sample size is specified after the column.

NOTE   The output for this MINITAB program is displayed in Figure 9.13.

FIGURE 9.13
MINITAB Output for Computer Lab

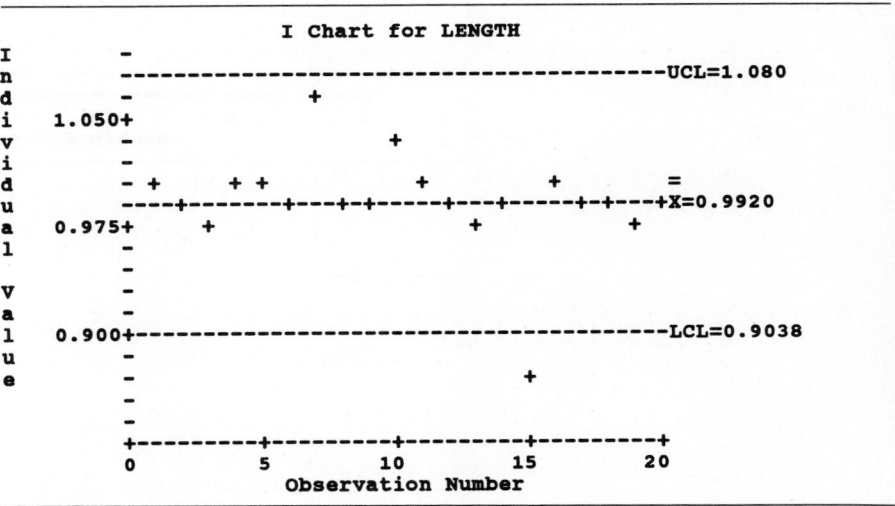

(continued)

FIGURE 9.13 (Continued)
Output for Computer Lab

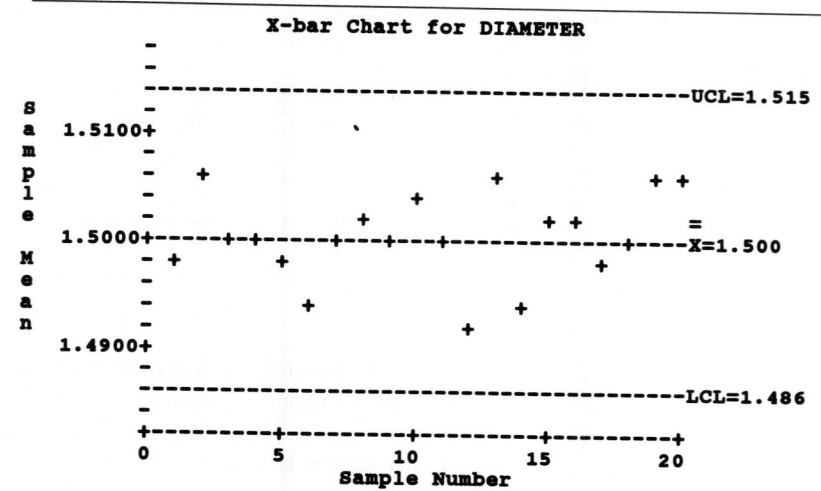

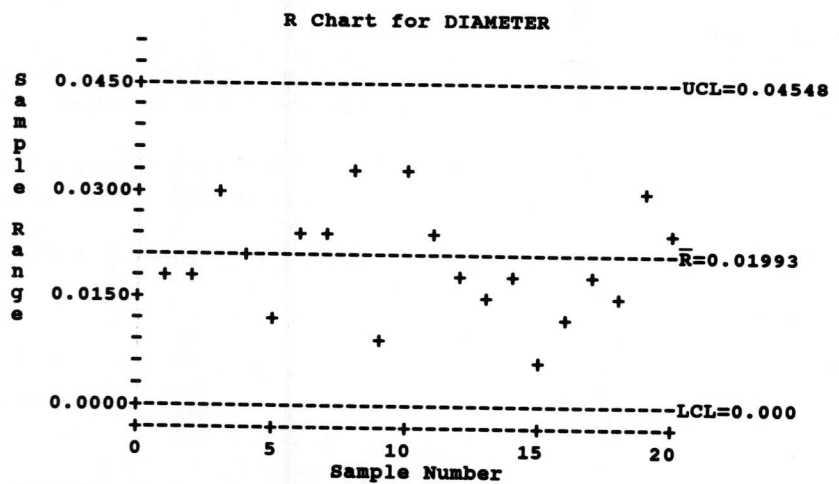

(continued)

FIGURE 9.13 (Continued)
Output for Computer Lab

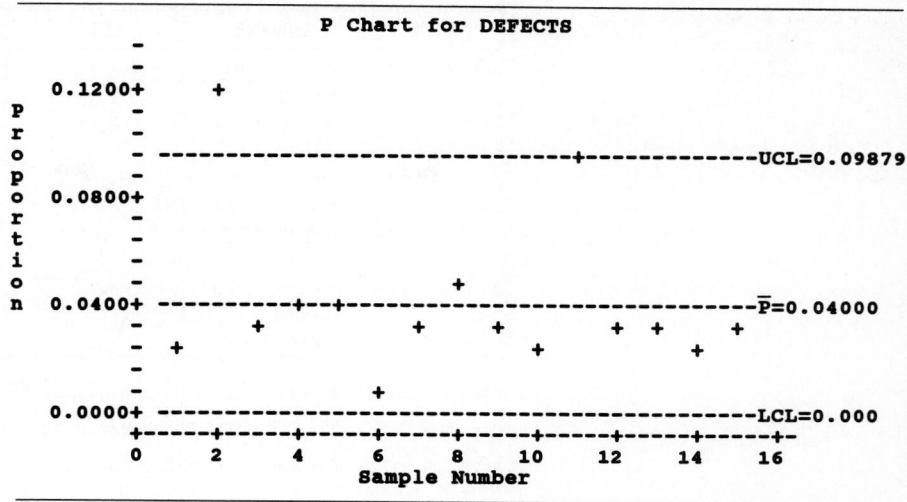

CHAPTER NOTES

- **Total quality management (TQM)** is a company-wide program designed ultimately to improve the quality of a manufactured product. Three key TQM components are: (1) quality concepts, (2) systems management, and (3) tools used to implement total quality.
- **Statistical process control (SPC)** is one of the tools used to improve total quality by allowing managers to understand and monitor process variation.
- **Control charts**, developed by W. A. Shewhart, are sequence (ie, time-order) plots, which are the foundation of SPC. Each control chart has a **center line, upper control limit (UCL)**, and **lower control limit (LCL)**.
- A **variable control chart** (or **individuals chart**) for a product quality characteristic is a plot of the measurements of the variable over time.
- Variation in a product quality characteristic is due to either an **assignable cause** or **random (chance) variation**.
- A production process is **in control** when the quality characteristic is subject only to random variation.
- A production process is **out of control** when the quality characteristic's values fall outside the control limits on a control chart.
- A **control chart for means**, or $\bar{x}$**-chart**, is a plot of the means of random samples of quantitative product measurements over time.
- A **control chart for process variation**, or **R-chart**, is a plot of the ranges of random samples of quantitative product measurements over time.
- A **control chart for percent defectives**, or **p-chart**, is a plot of the proportions defective in random samples of qualitative product measurements over time.
- The center line, LCL, and UCL of the different types of control charts are calculated as shown in the table on the top of the next page.

TYPE	SAMPLE	LCL	CENTER LINE	UCL
Individuals chart	n quantitative measurements	$\bar{x} - 3s$	$\bar{x}$	$\bar{x} + 3s$
$\bar{x}$-Chart	k samples of n quantitative measurements	$\bar{\bar{x}} - A_2\bar{R}$	$\bar{\bar{x}}$	$\bar{\bar{x}} + A_2\bar{R}$
R-Chart	k samples of n quantitative measurements	$D_3\bar{R}$	$\bar{R}$	$D_4\bar{R}$
p-Chart	k samples of n qualitative measurements	$\bar{p} - 3\sqrt{\dfrac{\bar{p}(1-\bar{p})}{n}}$	$\bar{p}$	$\bar{p} + 3\sqrt{\dfrac{\bar{p}(1-\bar{p})}{n}}$

where $\bar{x}_i$ = mean of the ith sample, s = standard deviation of the sample, $\bar{\bar{x}} = \sum\limits_{i=1}^{k} \bar{x}_i/k$,
R_i = range of ith sample, $\bar{R} = \sum\limits_{i=1}^{k} R_i/k$, p_i = proportion defective in ith sample, $\bar{p} = \sum\limits_{i=1}^{k} p_i/k$,
and A_2, D_3, and D_4 are constants from Table 12, Appendix A.

- **Rational subgroups** are samples of items collected that maximize the chance that (1) the quality measurements within each sample are similar and (2) the quality measurements between samples differ.
- A **run** is a sequence of one or more points that fall on the same side of the center line in a control chart.
- If any one of the following runs occur in a control chart, a **trend** is likely to be present:

  1. A run of 7 or more.
  2. At least 10 out of 11 consecutive points on the same side of the center line.
  3. At least 12 out of 14 consecutive points on the same side of the center line.
  4. At least 14 out of 17 consecutive points on the same side of the center line.

- A $(1 - \alpha)100\%$ **tolerance interval** for $100(\gamma)\%$ of the quantitative measurements in a *normal population* is

$$\bar{x} \pm Ks$$

  where $\bar{x}$ = mean of a sample of n measurements, s = sample standard deviation, and K is found in Table 13, Appendix A (based on $(1 - \alpha)$, γ, and n.
- The endpoints of a tolerance interval are called **tolerance limits**.
- A **nonparametric tolerance interval** is (x_{min}, x_{max}), where x_{min} and x_{max} are the smallest and largest measurements, respectively, in the sample. Consult Table 14, Appendix A, for the sample size n required to obtain a $100(\gamma)\%$ tolerance interval with confidence coefficient $1 - \alpha$.
- **Specification limits** define acceptable values of a product quality variable that are set by customers, management, and/or product designers.

Methods for inferring the nature of the relationship between a quantitative dependent variable (y) and one or more independent variables (x_1, x_2, ...) are the subject of Chapters 10 and 11. Using a technique called **regression**, we will learn how to build a useful model for predicting y.

CASE STUDY

MONITORING THE MANUFACTURE OF STEEL RODS

In the case study of Chapter 3, we considered the problem of monitoring the production of steel rods. The diameters (in centimeters) of 500 steel rods selected from a single day's production are reproduced in Table 9.5. The large data set in Table 9.5 provides us with an opportunity to apply the key concepts of quality control discussed in this chapter.

Suppose that quality control inspectors randomly select 10 rods from the production process each half-hour for 40 consecutive half-hour periods, and measure the diameter of each. Note that the data in Table 9.5 are divided into 50 subgroups of 10 diameters each. The first 10 subgroups appear in time order in the first row of the table, the second 10 subgroups in the second row, the third 10 subgroups in the third row, and the final 10 subgroups in the fourth row. (The last row will be used later in this case study.)

a. Calculate $\bar{x}$ and R for each of the 40 subgroups.

b. Construct an R-chart for the data.

c. Construct an $\bar{x}$-chart for the data.

d. Refer to the charts constructed in parts **b** and **c**. Does the process appear to be in control? If not, modify the control limits so they can be applied to future data.

e. Check the control charts from parts **b** and **c** for trends.

f. Assume that observations in the last row of Table 9.5 represent 10 future samples of 10 diameters each. Calculate $\bar{x}$ and R for each of these 10 subgroups.

g. Plot the 10 values of R from part **f** on the R-chart. Interpret the result.

h. Plot the 10 values of $\bar{x}$ from part **f** on the $\bar{x}$-chart. Interpret the result.

i. Use the entire data set in Table 9.5 to compute a 99% tolerance interval for 99% of the rod diameters. Interpret the interval.

j. Recall, from the case study in Chapter 3, that the manufacturer set a lower specification limit (LSL) of 1 centimeter for the steel rod diameters. Do the rods conform to specifications?

TABLE 9.5
Diameters of 500 Steel Rods from One Day's Production

1.000	1.005	1.002	1.003	1.001	1.002	1.000	1.005	1.001	1.001
1.003	1.000	1.000	1.001	1.004	1.000	1.002	1.005	1.004	1.000
1.003	1.001	1.001	1.002	1.004	1.006	1.003	1.002	1.006	1.000
.997	1.003	1.000	1.004	1.000	1.002	.998	1.007	.998	1.004
1.000	1.004	1.002	1.002	1.002	1.005	.997	1.005	1.003	1.003
1.004	1.000	1.000	1.003	1.002	1.000	1.006	1.002	1.004	1.006
1.001	1.004	1.002	1.007	1.001	1.004	1.004	1.003	1.000	1.005
1.005	.997	1.001	1.005	1.002	1.003	1.000	1.003	1.003	1.003
1.000	.998	1.001	1.004	.997	1.003	1.005	.998	1.000	1.000
1.002	1.004	1.004	1.004	1.005	1.000	1.001	1.002	1.004	1.003
1.002	1.005	1.004	1.003	1.001	1.005	1.000	1.004	1.000	1.003
1.001	1.005	1.001	1.002	1.006	1.004	1.005	1.002	1.002	1.004
1.003	1.005	1.001	1.004	1.003	1.003	1.002	1.004	1.007	1.002
.997	1.007	1.002	1.003	1.000	1.001	.998	1.000	1.001	1.003
1.003	1.002	1.000	1.001	1.002	1.004	1.003	1.006	1.005	1.006
1.003	1.003	1.007	1.006	1.000	1.002	1.002	1.002	1.003	.997
1.002	1.005	1.002	1.002	1.005	1.002	1.002	1.002	1.002	1.000
1.003	1.004	1.001	.998	1.002	1.001	.998	1.001	1.003	1.000
1.001	1.002	.998	1.002	1.003	1.004	1.001	1.000	1.003	1.002
1.004	1.002	.998	1.005	1.005	1.004	1.004	1.005	1.003	1.002
1.001	1.002	1.004	1.004	1.003	1.004	1.002	1.003	1.004	1.002
1.005	1.004	1.000	.998	1.003	1.003	1.000	1.002	1.001	1.001
1.006	1.006	1.006	1.000	1.004	1.002	1.004	1.001	1.000	1.000
1.001	1.001	1.002	1.001	1.001	1.003	1.005	1.002	1.002	1.006
1.001	1.007	.998	1.000	1.003	1.003	1.001	1.001	1.001	1.003
1.003	1.002	1.000	1.004	1.000	1.003	1.003	1.002	1.003	.998
1.004	1.001	1.002	1.002	1.002	1.001	1.000	1.003	.997	1.004
1.005	1.006	1.002	1.000	1.002	1.002	1.002	1.001	.998	1.002
.998	1.001	1.003	1.005	1.004	1.003	1.006	1.000	1.003	.998
1.004	1.003	1.003	1.000	1.001	1.002	1.004	1.004	1.002	1.001
1.000	1.001	1.002	1.004	.997	1.001	1.000	1.001	1.005	.998
1.003	1.001	1.001	1.005	1.004	1.004	1.003	1.006	1.000	1.000
1.001	1.003	1.000	1.000	1.002	.998	1.006	1.004	1.000	1.005
1.002	1.004	1.001	1.003	1.002	1.002	1.001	1.001	1.002	1.002
1.002	1.002	1.000	.998	1.005	1.007	1.002	1.002	1.003	1.001
1.000	1.002	1.005	.998	1.002	1.002	1.000	.997	1.003	1.001
.998	1.007	1.003	1.002	1.001	1.003	1.001	1.004	1.002	1.006
1.004	1.000	1.000	1.000	1.005	1.000	1.007	1.004	1.007	1.001
.997	1.001	1.005	1.000	1.002	.998	1.004	1.003	1.004	1.002
1.004	1.004	1.000	1.004	1.000	1.003	1.005	1.000	1.004	1.003
1.000	1.007	1.004	1.004	1.003	1.003	1.002	1.002	1.002	1.000
1.003	1.001	1.002	1.002	1.003	1.003	1.001	.998	1.006	1.004
1.002	1.001	1.000	1.001	1.004	.998	1.000	1.000	1.002	1.003
1.006	1.002	1.005	1.000	1.003	1.003	1.002	1.003	.998	1.002
.998	1.000	1.000	1.002	1.000	1.000	1.005	1.006	1.003	1.003
1.000	1.002	1.000	1.002	1.001	1.003	1.001	1.005	1.001	1.003
1.002	.998	1.003	1.001	1.004	1.003	1.001	1.005	1.001	1.003
1.004	1.004	.998	1.000	.998	1.003	1.003	1.005	1.004	1.006
1.000	1.003	1.000	1.004	1.001	1.003	1.001	1.000	1.005	1.002
1.005	1.004	1.002	1.002	1.003	1.000	1.004	.998	1.000	.998

Note. The data were simulated based on information provided in the essay.

Deming, W. E. *Quality, Productivity, and Competitive Position.* Cambridge, MA: MIT, 1982.

Grant, E. L., and Leavenworth, R. S. *Statistical Quality Control,* 5th ed. New York: McGraw-Hill, 1980.

Juran, J. M., and Gryna, F. M. *Quality Planning and Analysis.* New York: McGraw-Hill, 1970.

McClave, J. T., and Benson, P. G. *Statistics for Business and Economics,* 6th ed. New York: Macmillan, 1994.

Mendenhall, W. *The Design and Analysis of Experiments.* Belmont, CA: Wadsworth, 1968.

Ott, E. R. *Process Quality Control: Trouble-Shooting and Interpretation of Data.* New York: McGraw-Hill, 1975.

Ryan, T. P. *Statistical Methods for Quality Improvement.* New York: Wiley, 1989.

Shewhart, W. A. *Economic Control of Quality of Manufactured Product.* Princeton, NJ: Van Nostrand Reinhold, 1931.

SAMPLE EXAM QUESTIONS: CHAPTER 9

(1–2) One of the operations in a plant consists of thread grinding a fitting for an aircraft hydraulic system. In order to monitor the process, a production supervisor randomly selects one fitting each hour, for a period of 20 hours, and measures the pitch diameter of the thread. The 20 time-ordered measurements, expressed in units of .0001 inch in excess of .4000 inch, are given below. (For example, the value 36 represents .4036 inch.)

| 36 | 31 | 30 | 32 | 32 | 32 | 33 | 23 | 43 | 36 |
| 34 | 36 | 36 | 36 | 30 | 28 | 33 | 27 | 35 | 33 |

1. Construct a control chart for the pitch diameter of the threads.
2. Does the process appear to be in control? If not, what recommendations would you give to the production supervisor?

(3–5) High-level computer technology has developed bit-sized microprocessors for use in operating industrial robots. To monitor the fraction of defective microprocessors produced by a manufacturing process, 50 microprocessors are sampled each hour. The results for 20 hours of sampling are provided in the table.

Sample	1	2	3	4	5	6	7	8	9	10
Number of Defectives	5	6	4	7	1	3	6	5	4	5
Sample	11	12	13	14	15	16	17	18	19	20
Number of Defectives	8	3	2	1	0	1	1	2	3	3

3. Construct a control chart for the proportion of defective microprocessors.
4. Locate the center line and upper and lower control limits on the chart. Does the process appear to be in control?
5. Conduct a runs analysis for the control chart. Interpret the result.

(6–9) Consider a problem of deciding whether to investigate the prescription-filling process in a hospital pharmacy. Assume that the time required to fill a certain type of prescription has an expected probability distribution with $\mu = 24$ minutes and $\sigma = 2.7$ minutes when the process is in control.

6. Assuming the distribution is approximately normal, find a tolerance interval for 90% of the fill times. What is the confidence coefficient of the interval?

7. Unfortunately, the true values of μ and σ are unknown. To estimate their values, the manager of the pharmacy sampled $n = 30$ prescriptions of this type and recorded the time to fill each. The results are summarized below:

$$\bar{x} = 25.6 \text{ minutes} \qquad s = 4.1 \text{ minutes}$$

Use this information to establish a 95% tolerance interval for 90% of the fill times. (Assume again that the distribution of fill times is approximately normal.) Interpret the result.

8. Suppose the manager is unwilling (or unable) to make the normality assumption. How large a sample of fill times must be collected to construct a nonparametric interval?

9. Explain why the manager must be sure to establish the tolerance interval for data collected during a period when the process is in control.

(10–16) Specifications require the nickel content of manufactured stainless steel hydraulic valves to be 13% by weight. To monitor the production process, four valves were selected from the production line each hour over an 8 hour period, and the percentage nickel content was measured for each, with the results recorded in the table. Summary statistics for the data are shown in the SAS printout.

HOUR	NICKEL CONTENT			
1	13.1	12.8	12.7	12.9
2	12.5	13.0	13.6	13.1
3	12.9	12.9	13.2	13.3
4	12.4	13.0	12.1	12.6
5	12.8	11.9	12.7	12.4
6	13.0	13.6	13.2	12.9
7	13.5	13.5	13.1	12.7
8	12.6	13.9	13.3	12.8

```
                        Summary Statistics by Hour

        Analysis Variable : NICKEL

    ------------------------------------ HOUR=1 ------------------------------------

        N Obs   N      Minimum       Maximum          Mean        Std Dev
        ------------------------------------------------------------------
          4     4    12.7000000    13.1000000    12.8750000     0.1707825
        ------------------------------------------------------------------

    ------------------------------------ HOUR=2 ------------------------------------

        N Obs   N      Minimum       Maximum          Mean        Std Dev
        ------------------------------------------------------------------
          4     4    12.5000000    13.6000000    13.0500000     0.4509250
        ------------------------------------------------------------------

    ------------------------------------ HOUR=3 ------------------------------------

        N Obs   N      Minimum       Maximum          Mean        Std Dev
        ------------------------------------------------------------------
          4     4    12.9000000    13.3000000    13.0750000     0.2061553
        ------------------------------------------------------------------

    ------------------------------------ HOUR=4 ------------------------------------

        N Obs   N      Minimum       Maximum          Mean        Std Dev
        ------------------------------------------------------------------
          4     4    12.1000000    13.0000000    12.5250000     0.3774917
        ------------------------------------------------------------------
```

(continued)

```
-------------------------------------- HOUR=5 --------------------------------------

    N Obs    N      Minimum        Maximum          Mean        Std Dev
    -----------------------------------------------------------------------
        4    4    11.9000000     12.8000000     12.4500000     0.4041452
    -----------------------------------------------------------------------


-------------------------------------- HOUR=6 --------------------------------------

    N Obs    N      Minimum        Maximum          Mean        Std Dev
    -----------------------------------------------------------------------
        4    4    12.9000000     13.6000000     13.1750000     0.3095696
    -----------------------------------------------------------------------


-------------------------------------- HOUR=7 --------------------------------------

    N Obs    N      Minimum        Maximum          Mean        Std Dev
    -----------------------------------------------------------------------
        4    4    12.7000000     13.5000000     13.2000000     0.3829708
    -----------------------------------------------------------------------


-------------------------------------- HOUR=8 --------------------------------------

    N Obs    N      Minimum        Maximum          Mean        Std Dev
    -----------------------------------------------------------------------
        4    4    12.6000000     13.9000000     13.1500000     0.5802298
    -----------------------------------------------------------------------

                        Overall Summary Statistics

    Analysis Variable : NICKEL

    N Obs    N      Minimum        Maximum          Mean        Std Dev
    -----------------------------------------------------------------------
       32   32    11.9000000     13.9000000     12.9375000     0.4375518
    -----------------------------------------------------------------------
```

10. Construct a control chart for the mean nickel content of the hydraulic valves.
11. Establish control limits for the mean using Table 12, Appendix A.
12. Establish control limits for the mean using the standard deviation of the overall sample. Compare to the limits obtained in part **b**.
13. Do all observed sample means lie within the control limits? What are the consequences of this?
14. Construct a control chart with control limits for the variability in the nickel contents of the hydraulic valves.
15. Interpret the control chart. Is the process out of control?
16. If the process is out of control, explain how to obtain revised control limits.

CHAPTER 10

MODELING RELATIONSHIPS BETWEEN VARIABLES: REGRESSION (PART I)

U pon accepting employment, you expect your salary to be dependent on your qualifications (eg, experience, education) and the location and nature of the job. But will your salary depend on your gender? In this chapter we learn how to use sample data to investigate the relationships among a group of variables, and ultimately to create a model for a variable that can be used to predict its value in the future. The statistical technique used to accomplish this, called **regression analysis**, is applied to the salary–gender problem in the chapter case study.

THE CONCEPT OF A STATISTICAL MODEL

10.1

Suppose a tax assessor in a metropolitan area wants to **model** the percentage increase in residential property values over the past year. That is, the assessor wants to build a mathematical equation to predict the percentage increase in value for any particular property. The process of finding a mathematical model, or equation, to predict the value of a variable is part of a statistical method known as **regression analysis**.

In regression analysis, the variable y to be predicted is called the **dependent** (or **response**) **variable**, and its true mean (or **expected value**) is denoted $E(y)$.* In this example,

$$y = \text{Percentage increase in residential property value}$$

$$E(y) = \text{Mean percentage increase of all residential properties}$$

DEFINITION 10.1

The variable to be predicted (or modeled), y, is called the **dependent** (or **response**) **variable**.

The assessor knows that the actual value of y will vary from property to property depending on location, square footage of heated space, size of lot, and numerous other factors. Consequently, the real percentage increases in value for all residential properties may have the distribution shown in Figure 10.1.

FIGURE 10.1

Distribution of Percentage Increases in Residential Property Values, y

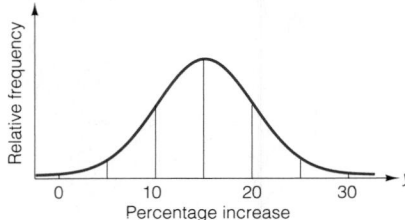

Thus, the assessor is modeling the percentage increase in value y for a particular property by stating that y is equal to the mean increase, $E(y)$, plus or minus some random amount (which is unknown to the assessor). That is,

$$y = E(y) + \text{Random error}$$

This model is called a **probabilistic model** for y. The adjective "probabilistic" is used, because when certain assumptions about the model are satisfied, we can make a probability statement about the magnitude of the deviation between y and $E(y)$. For example, if y is normally distributed with mean 15% and standard deviation 5% (as shown in Figure 10.1), then the probability that y will fall within 2 standard

---

* In regression analysis, the symbol $E(y)$ is used in place of μ to represent the true mean of y.

deviations (ie, 10%) of its mean is .95. The probabilistic model given in the box is the foundation of all models considered in this chapter.

GENERAL FORM OF A PROBABILISTIC MODEL IN REGRESSION ANALYSIS

$$y = E(y) + \epsilon$$

where

y = Dependent variable

$E(y)$ = Mean (or expected) value of y

ϵ = Unexplainable, or random, error

In practice, we will need to use sample data to estimate the parameters of the probabilistic model—namely, the mean $E(y)$ and the random error ϵ. In Section 10.3 we will see that a standard assumption in regression analysis is that the mean error is 0. Based on this assumption, our best *estimate* of ϵ is 0. Thus, we only need to estimate $E(y)$.

A logical estimator of $E(y)$ is the sample mean, $\bar{y}$. For example, the tax assessor could select a random sample of residential sales during the past year and note the percentage increase, y, in each sale over the current assessed value. The sample mean $\bar{y}$ could then be used as an estimate of the true mean percentage increase, $E(y)$. Denoting the predicted value of y as $\hat{y}$, a prediction equation for the simple model is

$$\hat{y} = \bar{y}$$

Therefore, this simple model uses the sample mean percentage increase $\bar{y}$ to predict the percentage increase y for any property. Unfortunately, this simple model does not take into consideration a number of variables, called **independent variables**,* that are related to the assessed value of a property. Logically, a more accurate model can be obtained by using the independent variables (eg, location, square footage, size of lot, etc.) to estimate $E(y)$.

DEFINITION 10.2

The variables used to predict (or model) y are called **independent variables** and are denoted by the symbols x_1, x_2, x_3, etc.

---

* The word *independent* should not be interpreted in a probabilistic sense. The phrase *independent variable* is used in regression analysis to refer to a predictor variable for the response y.

One way to incorporate these independent variables into the model for y is to form a **deterministic model** for $E(y)$. For example, we might propose that $E(y)$ is a function of square footage, x_1, and lot size, x_2, using the expression

$$E(y) = \beta_0 + \beta_1 x_1 + \beta_2 x_2$$

where β_0, β_1, and β_2 are constants (or weights) that would have to be estimated from the sample data. Note that the model for $E(y)$ is *deterministic*, because when the constants β_0, β_1, and β_2 are known, the values of x_1 and x_2 determine *exactly* the value of $E(y)$.

Replacing $E(y)$ with $\beta_0 + \beta_1 x_1 + \beta_2 x_2$ in the probabilistic model for y, we obtain the full equation for y:

$$y = \beta_0 + \beta_1 x_1 + \beta_2 x_2 + \epsilon$$

Now the tax assessor would obtain a sample of residential properties and record square footage, x_1, and lot size, x_2, in addition to percentage increase y in assessed value. Subjecting the sample data to a regression analysis will yield estimates of the model parameters and enable the assessor to predict percentage increase y for a particular property. The prediction equation takes the form

$$\hat{y} = \hat{\beta}_0 + \hat{\beta}_1 x_1 + \hat{\beta}_2 x_2$$

where $\hat{y}$ is the predicted value of y, and $\hat{\beta}_0$, $\hat{\beta}_1$, and $\hat{\beta}_2$ are estimates of the model parameters. Since the regression model takes into account square footage and lot size, the error of prediction for the model should be smaller than the error of prediction obtained using the simple model $\hat{y} = \bar{y}$. Consequently, we say that the regression model utilizing x_1 and x_2 is superior to the simple model represented in Figure 10.1.

It is helpful to think of regression modeling as a six-step procedure:

STEP 1 Hypothesize the form of the model for $E(y)$.

STEP 2 Collect the sample data.

STEP 3 Use the sample data to estimate unknown parameters in the model.

STEP 4 Specify the probability distribution of the random error term, and estimate any unknown parameters of this distribution.

STEP 5 Statistically check the usefulness of the model.

STEP 6 When satisfied that the model is useful, use it for prediction, estimation, and so on.

In Section 10.2 we discuss some important issues of step 2, collecting the sample data. We present the simplest of all regression models, the straight-line model, in Section 10.3. More complex models are discussed in Sections 10.4–10.8.

10.2 COLLECTING THE DATA FOR REGRESSION ANALYSIS

COLLECTING THE DATA FOR REGRESSION ANALYSIS

10.2

Once the model for $E(y)$ has been hypothesized, the next step is to collect the sample data that will be used to estimate the model parameters (β's). This entails collecting observations on both the dependent variable, y, and the independent variables, $x_1, x_2, ..., x_k$, for each experimental unit in the sample. Thus, a sample to be analyzed by regression includes observations on several variables ($y, x_1, ..., x_k$), not just a single variable.

The data for regression can be of two types: **observational** or **experimental**. Observational data are obtained if no attempt is made to control the values of the independent variables, as illustrated in the next example.

DEFINITION 10.3

If the values of the independent variables (x's) in regression are uncontrolled (ie, not set in advance before the value of y is observed) but are measured without error, the data are **observational**.

EXAMPLE 10.1 To reward their executives appropriately, many large corporations obtain advice from a consulting firm as to the amount of compensation each executive should receive. To provide this advice, the consulting firm uses regression analysis to build a good prediction equation for a corporate executive's annual compensation, as a function of the following variables:

1. Experience (years)
2. College education (years)
3. Number of employees supervised
4. Corporate division assets (dollars)
5. Age of the executive (years)

If the consulting company is successful in building the model, it can sell its services to both participating and nonparticipating corporations, providing them with reasonable compensation projections for their executives.

a. Identify the experimental unit, dependent variable, and independent variables for the analysis.

b. Explain why the data collected are observational.

Solution

a. Recall from Chapter 1 that an experimental unit is the object (person, place, thing, etc.) upon which the measurements are collected. Since the consulting firm is interested in predicting the annual compensation of a corporate executive, the experimental unit is a corporate executive and the dependent variable is annual compensation, y. For each executive in the sample, the firm records compensation, y, and the values of the following independent (ie, predictor) variables:

$$x_1 = \text{Years of experience}$$
$$x_2 = \text{Years of college education}$$
$$x_3 = \text{Number of employees supervised}$$
$$x_4 = \text{Assets of corporate division (million dollars)}$$
$$x_5 = \text{Age (years)}$$

Note that all five independent variables are quantitative variables. (We consider qualitative independent variables in Section 10.8.) The data for the first five executives in the sample might look like the data in Table 10.1.

TABLE 10.1
Sample Data for Example 10.1

EXECUTIVE	ANNUAL COMPENSATION y, Dollars	EXPERIENCE x_1	EDUCATION x_2	EMPLOYEES x_3	ASSETS x_4	AGE x_5
1	85,420	8	4	13	1.60	42
2	61,333	2	8	6	.25	30
3	107,500	7	6	24	3.14	53
4	59,225	3	7	9	.10	36
5	98,400	11	2	4	2.22	51

b. Note that $x_1, ..., x_5$ for each executive were not specified in advance of observing salary y; that is, the x-values were uncontrolled. Therefore, by Definition 10.3, the sample data are observational.

How large should the sample be in a regression analysis? In Section 6.3 we learned that when estimating a population mean, the sample size n will depend on (1) the (estimated) population standard deviation, (2) the confidence level, and (3) the desired half-width of the confidence interval used to estimate the mean. Because regression involves estimation of the mean response $E(y)$, the sample size will depend on these three factors. The problem, however, is not as straightforward as in Section 6.3, since $E(y)$ is modeled as a function of a set of independent variables, and the additional parameters in the model (ie, the β's) also must be estimated. In a regression analysis, the sample size should be large enough so that the β's are both estimable and testable. This is not possible unless n is at least as large as the number of β parameters included in the model for $E(y)$.

To ensure a sufficiently large sample, a good rule of thumb is to select n greater than or equal to 10 times the number of β parameters in the model.

For example, suppose the consulting firm of Example 10.1 wants to use the following model for annual compensation, y, of a corporate executive:

$$E(y) = \beta_0 + \beta_1 x_1 + \beta_2 x_2 + \cdots + \beta_5 x_5$$

where x_1, x_2, ..., x_5 are defined in Example 10.1. Excluding β_0, there are five β parameters in the model; thus, the firm should include *at least* $10 \times 5 = 50$ corporate executives in its sample.

The second type of data in regression, **experimental data**, are generated by designed experiments where the values of the independent variables are set in advance (ie, controlled) before the value of y is observed. For example, suppose a production supervisor wants to investigate the effect of two quantitative independent variables, say, temperature x_1 and pressure x_2, on the purity of batches of a certain chemical substance. The supervisor might decide to produce batches at three values of temperature (100°C, 125°C, and 150°C) and three values of pressure (50, 60, and 70 pounds per square inch), and to measure the impurity y in one batch of the substance for each of the $3 \times 3 = 9$ temperature–pressure combinations (see Table 10.2). For this experiment, the settings of the independent variables are controlled, in contrast to the uncontrolled nature of observational data in Example 10.1.

TABLE 10.2
Experimental Data

TEMPERATURE x_1	PRESSURE x_2	IMPURITY y
100	50	2.7
	60	2.4
	70	2.9
125	50	2.6
	60	3.1
	70	3.0
150	50	1.5
	60	1.9
	70	2.2

DEFINITION 10.4

If the values of the independent variables (x's) in regression are controlled using a designed experiment (ie, set in advance before the value of y is observed), the data are **experimental**.

In business studies, it is usually not possible to control the values of the x's; consequently, most data collected for regression applications are observational. (Consider the executive compensation data in Example 10.1. Clearly, it is impossible or impractical to control the values of the independent variables.) Therefore, you may want to know why we distinguish between the two types of data. We will see in Chapter 13 that inferences made from regression studies based on observational data have more limitations than those based on experimental data. In particular, we will learn that establishing a cause-and-effect relationship between variables is much more difficult with observational data than with experimental data. The majority of the examples and exercises in this chapter and Chapter 11 are based on observational data. In Chapter 13, we describe regression analyses based on data collected from a designed experiment.

SIMPLE LINEAR REGRESSION

10.3 In this section we present the simplest of probabilistic models—a first-order (linear) model* that relates one quantitative variable to another and graphs as a straight line. Each step in a regression analysis of this model will be discussed in detail to build the foundation for the more complex models of Sections 10.4–10.8.

The elements of the straight-line model are summarized in the box.

A FIRST-ORDER (STRAIGHT-LINE) MODEL

$$y = \beta_0 + \beta_1 x + \epsilon$$

where

y = Quantitative dependent variable

x = Quantitative independent variable

$E(y) = \beta_0 + \beta_1 x$ = Deterministic component

ϵ = Random error component

β_0 = y-Intercept of the line   Point at which the line intercepts, or cuts through, the y-axis (see Figure 10.2)

β_1 = Slope of the line   Amount of increase (or decrease) in the mean of y for every 1 unit increase in x (see Figure 10.2)

FIGURE 10.2

The Straight-Line Model

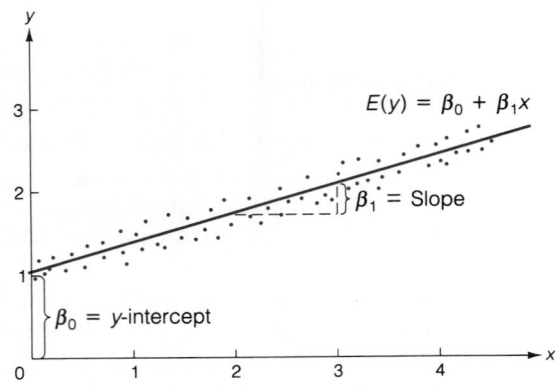

* A general definition of the expression *first-order* is given in Section 10.5.

Note that the deterministic component of the straight-line probabilistic model represents a line of means $E(y) = \beta_0 + \beta_1 x$; if the model fits the data well, the individual y-values will fluctuate closely around the line of means, as shown in Figure 10.2. The parameters β_0 and β_1 represent the y-intercept and slope of the line, respectively. They are population parameters with numerical values that will be known only if we have access to the entire population of (x, y) measurements.

FITTING THE MODEL: THE METHOD OF LEAST SQUARES

Suppose an appliance store conducts a 5 month experiment to determine the effect of advertising on sales revenue. The results are shown in Table 10.3. (The number of measurements is small, and the measurements themselves are unrealistically simple to avoid arithmetic confusion in this initial example.) The straight-line model is hypothesized to relate sales revenue, y, to advertising expenditure, x. That is,

$$y = \beta_0 + \beta_1 x + \epsilon$$

The question is this: How do we perform step 3 of a regression analysis? That is, how can we best use the information in the sample of five observations in Table 10.3 to estimate the unknown y-intercept β_0 and slope β_1?

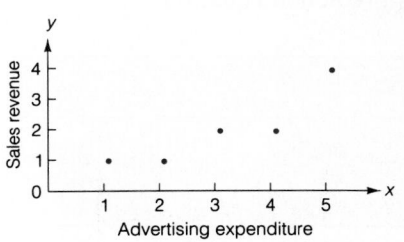

FIGURE 10.3

Scattergram for Data in Table 10.3

TABLE 10.3

MONTH	ADVERTISING EXPENDITURE x, Hundred Dollars	SALES REVENUE y, Thousand Dollars
1	1	1
2	2	1
3	3	2
4	4	2
5	5	4

To gain some information on the approximate values of these parameters, it is helpful to plot the sample data in a scattergram, as in Figure 10.3. Note that the scattergram suggests a general tendency for y to increase as x increases. If you place a ruler on the scattergram, you will see that a line may be drawn through three of the five points, as shown in Figure 10.4. To obtain the equation of this visually fitted line, notice that the line intersects the y-axis at $y = -1$, so the y-intercept is -1. Also, y increases exactly 1 unit for every 1 unit increase in x, indicating that the slope is $+1$. Therefore, the equation is

$$\tilde{y} = -1 + 1(x) = -1 + x$$

where $\tilde{y}$ denotes the predictor of y based on the visually fitted model.

One quantitative way to decide how well a straight line fits a set of data is to determine how much the data points deviate from the line. For example, to evaluate the visually fitted model in Figure 10.4, we calculate the magnitude of the **deviations**—that is, the differences between the observed and the predicted values of y. These deviations, or **errors**, are the vertical distances between observed and predicted values of y (see Figure 10.4). The observed and predicted values of y, their differences,

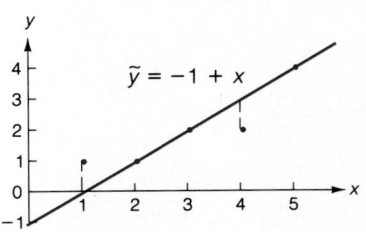

FIGURE 10.4

Visual Straight-Line Fit to the Data in Table 10.3

and their squared differences are shown in Table 10.4. Note that the **sum of the errors (SE)** equals 0. Also, the **sum of squares of the errors (SSE)**, which gives greater emphasis to large deviations of the points from the line, equals 2.

TABLE 10.4

Comparing Observed and Predicted Values for the Visual Model

x	y	$\hat{y} = -1 + x$	$(y - \bar{y})$	$(y - \bar{y})^2$
1	1	0	$(1 - 0) =$ 1	1
2	1	1	$(1 - 1) =$ 0	0
3	2	2	$(2 - 2) =$ 0	0
4	2	3	$(2 - 3) = -1$	1
5	4	4	$(4 - 4) =$ 0	0
			Sum of errors (SE) = 0	Sum of squared errors (SSE) = 2

You can see by shifting the ruler around the graph that it is possible to find many lines for which the SE is equal to 0, but it can be shown that there is one (and only one) line for which the SSE *is a minimum*. The estimates $\hat{\beta}_0$ and $\hat{\beta}_1$ that make the SSE a minimum are called the **least squares estimates** of the population parameters β_0 and β_1, and the equation $\hat{y} = \hat{\beta}_0 + \hat{\beta}_1 x$ is called the **least squares line**, the **regression line**, or the **least squares prediction equation**.

DEFINITION 10.5

The **least squares line**, $\hat{y} = \hat{\beta}_0 + \hat{\beta}_1 x$, is one that has a smaller SSE than any other straight-line model with SE = 0.

The values of $\hat{\beta}_0$ and $\hat{\beta}_1$ that minimize the SSE are given (proof omitted) by the formulas in the box at the top of the next page.*

Preliminary computations for finding the least squares line for the advertising–sales example are contained in Table 10.5. We can now calculate†

$$SS_{xy} = \Sigma x_i y_i - \frac{(\Sigma x_i)(\Sigma y_i)}{n} = 37 - \frac{(15)(10)}{5}$$

$$= 37 - 30 = 7$$

$$SS_{xx} = \Sigma x_i^2 - \frac{(\Sigma x_i)^2}{n} = 55 - \frac{(15)^2}{5}$$

$$= 55 - 45 = 10$$

---

* Students who are familiar with calculus should note that the values of β_0 and β_1 that minimize SSE $= \Sigma_{i=1}^{n}(y_i - \hat{y}_i)^2$ are obtained by setting the two partial derivatives $\partial SSE/\partial\beta_0$ and $\partial SSE/\partial\beta_1$ equal to 0. The solutions to these two equations yield the formulas shown in the box.

† Since summations will be used extensively from this point on, we will simplify the notation by omitting the limits on Σ when the summation includes all the measurements in the sample. That is, when the summation is $\Sigma_{i=1}^{n}$, we will simply write Σ.

FORMULAS FOR THE LEAST SQUARES ESTIMATES

Slope: $\hat{\beta}_1 = \dfrac{SS_{xy}}{SS_{xx}}$

y-Intercept: $\hat{\beta}_0 = \bar{y} - \hat{\beta}_1 \bar{x}$

where

$$SS_{xy} = \sum_{i=1}^{n} x_i y_i - \frac{\left(\sum\limits_{i=1}^{n} x_i\right)\left(\sum\limits_{i=1}^{n} y_i\right)}{n}$$

$$SS_{xx} = \sum_{i=1}^{n} x_i^2 - \frac{\left(\sum\limits_{i=1}^{n} x_i\right)^2}{n}$$

$n = $ Sample size

TABLE 10.5
Preliminary Computations for the Advertising–Sales Example

x_i	y_i	x_i^2	$x_i y_i$
1	1	1	1
2	1	4	2
3	2	9	6
4	2	16	8
5	4	25	20
Totals $\Sigma x_i = 15$	$\Sigma y_i = 10$	$\Sigma x_i^2 = 55$	$\Sigma x_i y_i = 37$

Then, the slope of the least squares line is

$$\hat{\beta}_1 = \frac{SS_{xy}}{SS_{xx}}$$

$$= \frac{7}{10} = .7$$

and the y-intercept is

$$\hat{\beta}_0 = \bar{y} - \hat{\beta}_1 \bar{x} = \frac{\Sigma y_i}{5} - \hat{\beta}_1\left(\frac{\Sigma x_i}{5}\right)$$

$$= \frac{10}{5} - (.7)\left(\frac{15}{5}\right)$$

$$= 2 - (.7)(3) = 2 - 2.1 = -.1$$

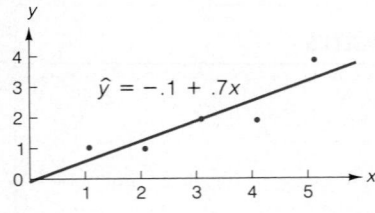

FIGURE 10.5

The Line $\hat{y} = -.1 + .7x$ Fit to the Data

The least squares line is then

$$\hat{y} = \hat{\beta}_0 + \hat{\beta}_1 x = -.1 + .7x$$

The graph of this line is shown in Figure 10.5.

The observed and predicted values of y, the deviations of the y-values about their predicted values, and the squares of these deviations are shown in Table 10.6. Note that the sum of squares of the deviations, SSE, is 1.10, and (as we would expect) this is less than the SSE = 2.0 obtained in Table 10.4 for the visually fitted line.

TABLE 10.6

Comparing Observed and Predicted Values for the Least Squares Model

x	y	$\hat{y} = -.1 + .7x$	$(y - \hat{y})$	$(y - \hat{y})^2$
1	1	.6	$(1 - .6) = .4$	.16
2	1	1.3	$(1 - 1.3) = -.3$	.09
3	2	2.0	$(2 - 2.0) = 0$	.00
4	2	2.7	$(2 - 2.7) = -.7$	.49
5	4	3.4	$(4 - 3.4) = .6$	.36
			Sum of errors = 0	SSE = 1.10

To summarize, we have defined the best-fitting straight line to be the one that satisfies the least squares criterion; that is, the sum of the squared errors will be smaller than for any other straight-line model. This line is called the *least squares line*, and its equation is called the *least squares prediction equation*. In practice, the least squares line is rarely computed by hand using the formulas in the box. Most analysts have access to a statistical computer software package that automatically performs the regression analysis, as the next example illustrates.

EXAMPLE 10.2 For a company to maintain a competitive edge in the marketplace, spending on research and development (R&D) is essential. To determine the optimum level for R&D spending and its effect on a company's value, a simple linear regression analysis was performed. Data collected for the largest R&D spenders were used to fit the straight-line model

$$y = \beta_0 + \beta_1 x + \epsilon$$

where

$$y = \text{Price/Earnings (P/E) ratio}$$
$$x = \text{R\&D expenditures/Sales (R/S) ratio}$$

The data for 20 of the companies used in the study are provided in Table 10.7. Use a computer to perform the regression analysis.

a. Plot the data in a scattergram.
b. Find the least squares prediction equation from the printout.
c. Interpret the values of $\hat{\beta}_0$ and $\hat{\beta}_1$.

TABLE 10.7
Data for Example 10.2

COMPANY	P/E RATIO y	R/S RATIO x	COMPANY	P/E RATIO y	R/S RATIO x
1	5.6	.003	11	8.4	.058
2	7.2	.004	12	11.1	.058
3	8.1	.009	13	11.1	.067
4	9.9	.021	14	13.2	.080
5	6.0	.023	15	13.4	.080
6	8.2	.030	16	11.5	.083
7	6.3	.035	17	9.8	.091
8	10.0	.037	18	16.1	.092
9	8.5	.044	19	7.0	.064
10	13.2	.051	20	5.9	.028

Source: Wallin, C. C., and Gilman, J. J. "Determining the Optimum Level for R&D Spending." *Research Management,* Vol. 14, No. 5, Sept./Oct. 1986, pp. 19–24 (adapted from Fig. 1, p. 20).

Solution

a. Before performing a regression analysis, it is always advisable to plot the data in a scattergram. A computer-generated (SPSS) scattergram for the data of Table 10.7 is shown in Figure 10.6. Note that an increasing relationship appears to exist between y and x.

FIGURE 10.6

SPSS Scattergram of the Data in Table 10.7

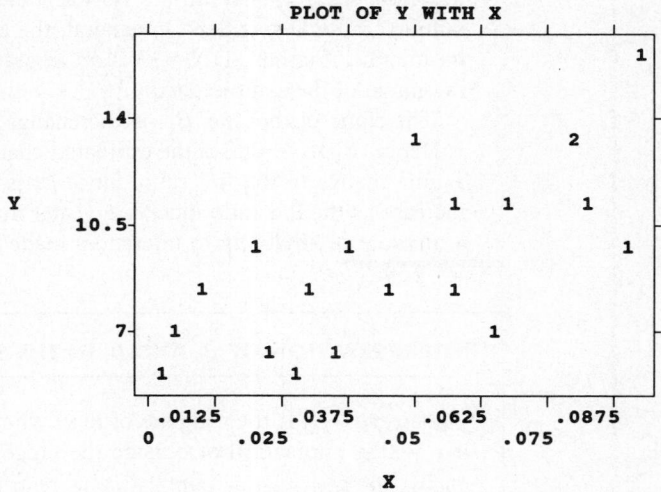

b. The SAS printout of the simple linear regression analysis is displayed in Figure 10.7. The least squares estimates of the y-intercept and slope are found (shaded) under the column labeled Parameter Estimate (in the bottom portion of the printout) in the rows labeled INTERCEP and X, respectively. The estimate of the y-intercept is $\hat{\beta}_0 = 5.977$, and the estimate of the slope is $\hat{\beta}_1 = 74.068$.

FIGURE 10.7

SAS Printout for Example 10.2

Model: MODEL1
Dependent Variable: Y

Analysis of Variance

Source	DF	Sum of Squares	Mean Square	F Value	Prob>F
Model	1	86.40357	86.40357	20.090	0.0003
Error	18	77.41393	4.30077		
C Total	19	163.81750			

Root MSE	2.07383	R-square	0.5274
Dep Mean	9.52500	Adj R-sq	0.5012
C.V.	21.77250		

Parameter Estimates

Variable	DF	Parameter Estimate	Standard Error	T for H0: Parameter=0	Prob > |T|
INTERCEP	1	5.977162	0.91737112	6.516	0.0001
X	1	74.067607	16.52478400	4.482	0.0003

Consequently, the least squares prediction equation is

$$\hat{y} = 5.977 + 74.068x$$

c. Recall that β_0 is the y-intercept of the line of means; that is, it is the value of $E(y)$ when the R/S ratio (x) is 0. Then, $\hat{\beta}_0 = 5.977$ is the estimated mean P/E ratio when the R/S ratio is 0. This number has no practical interpretation, however, since $x = 0$ implies no R&D expenditures, and all the firms in the sample are R&D spenders. In general, the estimated y-intercept, $\hat{\beta}_0$, will not be meaningful if either (1) $x = 0$ is an impractical value, or (2) $x = 0$ is outside the range of the sample data.

The slope of the line, β_1, is the change in $E(y)$ for every 1 unit increase in x. Hence, $\hat{\beta}_1 = 74.068$ is the estimated change in the average P/E ratio for every 1 unit change in the R/S ratio. Since $\hat{\beta}_1$ is positive, we expect the P/E ratio to increase as the R/S ratio increases. (Later in this section, we show how to attach a measure of reliability to inferences made about β_1.)

INTERPRETATION OF $\hat{\beta}_0$ AND $\hat{\beta}_1$ IN THE STRAIGHT-LINE MODEL

y-Intercept: $\hat{\beta}_0$ is the estimate of $E(y)$ when $x = 0$ (value is not meaningful if $x = 0$ is impractical or outside the range of sample data).

Slope: $\hat{\beta}_1$ is the estimated change in $E(y)$ for every 1 unit increase in x.

MODEL ASSUMPTIONS   Now we turn our attention to step 4 of a regression analysis: specifying the probability distribution of the random component ϵ of the probabilistic model. In particular, we will see how the probability distribution of ϵ determines how well the model describes the true relationship between the dependent variable, y, and the independent variable, x.

We will make four basic assumptions about the general form of the probability distribution of ϵ:

Assumption 1: The mean of the probability distribution of ϵ is 0. That is, the average of the errors over an infinitely long series of experiments is 0 for each setting of the independent variable, x. This assumption implies that the mean value of y, $E(y)$, for a given value of x is $E(y) = \beta_0 + \beta_1 x$.

Assumption 2: The variance of the probability distribution of ϵ is constant for all settings of the independent variable, x. For our straight-line model, this assumption means that the variance of ϵ is equal to a constant, say σ^2, for all values of x.

Assumption 3: The probability distribution of ϵ is normal.

Assumption 4: The errors associated with any two different observations are independent. That is, the error associated with one value of y has no effect on the errors associated with other y-values.

The implications of the first three assumptions are shown in Figure 10.8, which shows distributions of errors for three particular values of x, namely x_1, x_2, and x_3. Note that the relative frequency distributions of the errors are normal, with a mean of 0, and a constant variance σ^2 (all the distributions shown have the same amount of spread or variability).

FIGURE 10.8
The Probability Distribution of ϵ

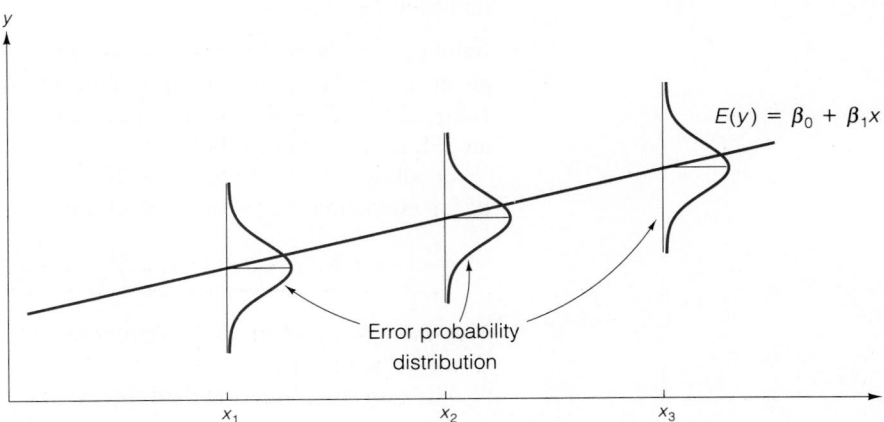

In most practical situations, σ^2 will be unknown, and we must use the data to estimate its value. The best (proof omitted) estimate of σ^2 is s^2, which is obtained by dividing the sum of squares of errors,

$$\text{SSE} = \Sigma(y_i - \hat{y}_i)^2$$

by the number of degrees of freedom associated with this quantity. We use 2 df to estimate the y-intercept and slope in the straight-line model, leaving $(n - 2)$ df for the error variance estimation (see the formulas in the box).

ESTIMATION OF σ^2 FOR THE STRAIGHT-LINE MODEL

$$s^2 = \frac{\text{SSE}}{\text{Degrees of freedom for error}} = \frac{\text{SSE}}{n - 2}$$

where

$$\text{SSE} = \Sigma(y_i - \hat{y}_i)^2$$
$$= \text{SS}_{yy} - \hat{\beta}_1 \text{SS}_{xy} \quad \text{Calculation formula}$$
$$\text{SS}_{yy} = \Sigma(y_i - \bar{y})^2 = \Sigma y_i^2 - \frac{(\Sigma y_i)^2}{n}$$

Warning: When performing these calculations, you may be tempted to round the calculated values of SS_{yy}, $\hat{\beta}_1$, and SS_{xy}. Be certain to carry at least six significant figures for each of these quantities to avoid substantial errors in the calculation of SSE.

EXAMPLE 10.3   Refer to the SAS printout of the straight-line model relating the P/E ratio to the R/S ratio in Example 10.2. Find SSE, s^2, and s in the printout, and interpret their values.

Solution   In the SAS printout shown in Figure 10.7, the value of SSE (shaded) is given under the column heading Sum of Squares in the row labeled Error. This value, SSE = 77.414, is a minimum. That is, there are no other straight lines with an SSE smaller than 77.414.

Recalling that there were $n = 20$ data points, we have $n - 2 = 20 - 2 = 18$ df for estimating the variance σ^2 of the random error ϵ. Thus,

$$s^2 = \frac{\text{SSE}}{n - 2} = \frac{77.414}{18} = 4.301$$

This value is shown in the SAS printout as Mean Square for Error and is given next to the value of SSE.

The estimate of the standard deviation σ of the random error ϵ is

$$s = \sqrt{4.301} = 2.074$$

The value of s is given in the printout next to the heading Root MSE.

Since s measures the spread of the distribution of y-values about the least squares line, and the distribution is assumed to be normal, we should not be surprised to find that most of the observations lie within $2s$ or $2(2.074) = 4.148$ of the least squares line. For this example, all 20 data points fall within $2s$ of the least squares line. Later in this section, we will use s to evaluate the error of prediction when the least squares line is used to predict a value of y to be observed for a given value of x.

INTERPRETATION OF s, THE ESTIMATED STANDARD DEVIATION OF ϵ

When the standard regression assumptions about the random error ϵ are satisfied, we expect most of the observed y-values to lie within $2s$ of their respective least squares predicted values, $\hat{y}$.

Various techniques exist for checking the validity of the four assumptions about ϵ, and there are remedies to be applied when the assumptions appear to be invalid. (See Chapter 11.) In actual practice, the assumptions will be satisfied adequately for many applications encountered in business, although they may not hold exactly.

ASSESSING MODEL UTILITY: TESTS AND CONFIDENCE INTERVALS

In step 5 of a regression analysis, we want to make an inference about the utility of the model. For the straight-line model, $E(y) = \beta_0 + \beta_1 x$, the key question is: Is x a useful linear predictor of y?

One way to answer this question is to conduct a test of hypothesis about the β parameters in the model. If x contributes no information for the prediction of y, then the mean of y does not change as x changes. In the straight-line model, this indicates that the true slope, β_1, is equal to 0. Therefore, to test the null hypothesis that x contributes no information for the prediction of y against the alternative hypothesis that these variables are linearly related with a slope differing from 0, we test

$$H_0: \quad \beta_1 = 0$$
$$H_a: \quad \beta_1 \neq 0$$

If the data support the alternative hypothesis, we will conclude that x does contribute information for the prediction of y using the straight-line model [although the true relationship between $E(y)$ and x could be more complex than a straight line]. Thus, to some extent, this is a test of the utility of the hypothesized model.

The appropriate test statistic is found by considering the sampling distribution of $\hat{\beta}_1$, the least squares estimator of the slope β_1.

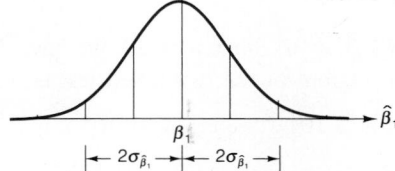

FIGURE 10.9
Sampling Distribution of $\hat{\beta}_1$

SAMPLING DISTRIBUTION OF $\hat{\beta}_1$

If we make the four assumptions about ϵ, then the sampling distribution of $\hat{\beta}_1$, the least squares estimator of the slope, will be a normal distribution with mean β_1 (the true slope) and standard error

$$\sigma_{\hat{\beta}_1} = \frac{\sigma}{\sqrt{SS_{xx}}} \quad \text{See Figure 10.9}$$

Since σ usually will be unknown, the appropriate test statistic generally will be a Student's t statistic formed as follows:

$$t = \frac{\hat{\beta}_1 - \text{Hypothesized value of } \beta_1}{s_{\hat{\beta}_1}} \qquad \text{where } s_{\hat{\beta}_1} = \frac{s}{\sqrt{SS_{xx}}}$$

$$= \frac{\hat{\beta}_1 - 0}{s/\sqrt{SS_{xx}}}$$

Note that we have substituted the estimator s for σ, and then formed $s_{\hat{\beta}_1}$ by dividing s by $\sqrt{SS_{xx}}$. The number of degrees of freedom associated with this t statistic is the same as the number of degrees of freedom associated with s. Recall that this will be $(n - 2)$ df when the hypothesized model is a straight line.

The test of the utility of the model is summarized in the box.

A TEST OF UTILITY FOR THE STRAIGHT-LINE MODEL

ONE-TAILED TEST	**TWO-TAILED TEST**

H_0: $\beta_1 = 0$ H_0: $\beta_1 = 0$

H_a: $\beta_1 < 0$ H_a: $\beta_1 \neq 0$

    [or H_a: $\beta_1 > 0$]

Test statistic: $t = \dfrac{\hat{\beta}_1}{s_{\hat{\beta}_1}} = \dfrac{\hat{\beta}_1}{s/\sqrt{SS_{xx}}}$

Rejection region: $t < -t_\alpha$ *Rejection region:* $|t| > t_{\alpha/2}$

    [or $t > t_\alpha$]

where t_α and $t_{\alpha/2}$ are based on $(n - 2)$ df.

Assumptions: The four assumptions about ϵ (listed earlier)

Note: The test statistic is derived from the sampling distribution of the least squares estimator of the slope, $\hat{\beta}_1$.

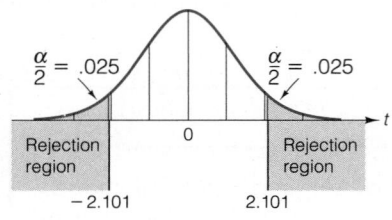

$\dfrac{\alpha}{2} = .025$ $\dfrac{\alpha}{2} = .025$

Rejection region   Rejection region

-2.101 2.101

FIGURE 10.10

Rejection Region and Calculated *t*-Value for Testing Whether the Slope $\beta_1 = 0$

EXAMPLE 10.4 Refer to the simple linear regression analysis in Examples 10.2 and 10.3, relating the P/E ratio (y) to the R/S ratio (x). Conduct a test of model utility. Use $\alpha = .05$.

Solution We want to test H_0: $\beta_1 = 0$ versus H_a: $\beta_1 \neq 0$. Since $n = 20$, we have df $= (n - 2) = 20 - 2 = 18$, and the rejection region for the two-tailed test is

$$t < -t_{.025} = -2.101 \qquad \text{or} \qquad t > t_{.025} = 2.101 \quad \text{See Figure 10.10}$$

where $t_{.025}$ is obtained from Table 3, Appendix A.

In Example 10.2, we found $\hat{\beta}_1 = 74.068$ from the SAS printout, Figure 10.7. The estimated standard deviation of $\hat{\beta}_1$, $s_{\hat{\beta}_1}$, is also given in Figure 10.7, next to the estimate of β_1 under the Standard Error column and in the row corresponding

---

to X. The value is $s_{\hat{\beta}_1} = 16.525$. Therefore, the test statistic is

$$t = \frac{\hat{\beta}_1}{s_{\hat{\beta}_1}} = \frac{74.068}{16.525} = 4.482$$

Note that the t statistic is also given in the SAS printout under the column T for H0: Parameter=0 in the X row.

Since this calculated t-value falls in the upper-tail rejection region (see Figure 10.10), we reject the null hypothesis and conclude that the slope β_1 is not 0. At $\alpha = .05$, the sample evidence indicates that the R/S ratio (x) contributes information for the prediction of the P/E ratio (y) using a linear model.

The same conclusion can be obtained using the p-value approach. The p-value for the two-tailed test is given in the printout shown in Figure 10.7 under the column Prob $> |T|$. Since p-value $= .0003$ is less than .05, we reject H_0.

What conclusion can be drawn if the calculated t-value does not fall in the rejection region (or if the p-value exceeds the selected value of α)? We know from previous discussions of the philosophy of hypothesis testing that such a t-value does *not* lead us to accept the null hypothesis. That is, we do not conclude that $\beta_1 = 0$. Additional data might indicate that β_1 differs from 0, or a more complex relationship may exist between x and y, requiring the fitting of a model other than the straight-line model. We will discuss several such models in Sections 10.4–10.8.

Another way to make inferences about the slope β_1 is to estimate it using a confidence interval. This interval is formed as shown in the box.

A 100(1 − α)% CONFIDENCE INTERVAL FOR THE SLOPE β_1 OF THE STRAIGHT-LINE MODEL

$$\hat{\beta}_1 \pm t_{\alpha/2} s_{\hat{\beta}_1} \qquad \text{where } s_{\hat{\beta}_1} = \frac{s}{\sqrt{SS_{xx}}}$$

and $t_{\alpha/2}$ is based on $(n - 2)$ df.

EXAMPLE 10.5 Refer to Examples 10.2–10.4. Calculate and interpret a 95% confidence interval for the slope of the P/E ratio–R/S ratio line.

Solution From the earlier examples, we have $\hat{\beta}_1 = 74.068$, $s_{\hat{\beta}_1} = 16.525$, and $t_{.025} = 2.101$. Then, a 95% confidence interval for the slope β_1 is

$$\hat{\beta}_1 \pm t_{.025} s_{\hat{\beta}_1} = 74.068 \pm 2.101(16.525)$$

$$= 74.068 \pm 34.719$$

Thus, we estimate that the interval from 39.349 to 108.787 includes the slope parameter β_1, with 95% confidence.

Since all the values in this interval are positive, we are 95% confident that β_1 is positive. That is, we are 95% confident that the mean P/E ratio, $E(y)$, increases as the R/S ratio increases. Furthermore, we can say that for every 1 unit increase in the R/S ratio, the increase in the mean P/E ratio could be as small as 39.349 or as large as 108.787. However, the rather large width of the confidence interval reflects the relatively small number of data points (and, consequently, a lack of information) in the experiment. We would expect a narrower interval if the sample size were increased.

ASSESSING MODEL UTILITY: NUMERICAL DESCRIPTIVE MEASURES

In addition to a test and confidence interval for β_1, two numerical descriptive measures of model adequacy are available: (1) the **coefficient of determination**, which measures how much the errors of prediction of y were reduced by using the information provided by x, and (2) the **correlation coefficient** described in Section 3.10.

To illustrate the first, suppose a sample of data produces the scattergram shown in Figure 10.11a. If we assume that x contributes no information for the prediction of y, the best prediction for a value of y is the sample mean, $\bar{y}$, which graphs as the horizontal line shown in Figure 10.11b. The vertical line segments in Figure 10.11b are the deviations of the points about the mean, $\bar{y}$. Note that the sum of squares of deviations for the model $\hat{y} = \bar{y}$ is

$$SS_{yy} = \Sigma(y_i - \bar{y})^2$$

Now suppose you fit a least squares line to the same set of data and locate the deviations of the points about the line as shown in Figure 10.11c. Compare the deviations about the prediction lines in parts b and c of Figure 10.11. You can see that:

1. If x contributes little or no information for the prediction of y, the sums of squares of deviations for the two lines,

$$SS_{yy} = \Sigma(y_i - \bar{y})^2 \quad \text{and} \quad SSE = \Sigma(y_i - \hat{y}_i)^2$$

will be nearly equal.
2. If x does contribute information for the prediction of y, then SSE will be smaller than SS_{yy}. In fact, if all the points fall on the least squares line, then SSE = 0.

A convenient way of measuring how well the least squares equation $\hat{y} = \hat{\beta}_0 + \hat{\beta}_1 x$ performs as a predictor of y is to compute the reduction in the sum of squares of deviations that can be attributed to x, expressed as a proportion of SS_{yy}. This quantity, called the **coefficient of determination**, is

$$R^2 = \frac{SS_{yy} - SSE}{SS_{yy}}$$

Note that R^2 is always between 0 and 1, because SSE will always be less than or equal to SS_{yy}. Thus, a coefficient R^2 of .60 means that the sum of squares of deviations of the y-values about their predicted values has been reduced 60% by the use of $\hat{y}$, instead of $\bar{y}$, to predict y.

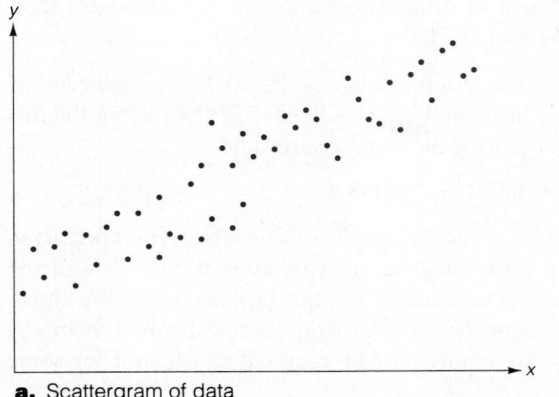

a. Scattergram of data

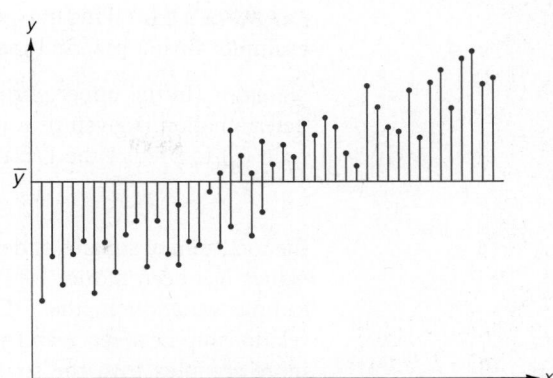

b. Assumption: x contributes no information for predicting y; $\hat{y} = \bar{y}$

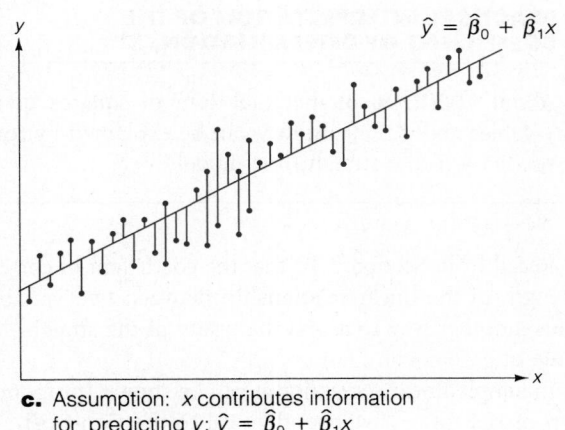

$\hat{y} = \hat{\beta}_0 + \hat{\beta}_1 x$

c. Assumption: x contributes information for predicting y; $\hat{y} = \hat{\beta}_0 + \hat{\beta}_1 x$

FIGURE 10.11

Comparison of the Sum of Squares of Deviations for Two Models

---

DEFINITION 10.6

The **coefficient of determination** is

$$R^2 = \frac{SS_{yy} - SSE}{SS_{yy}} = 1 - \frac{SSE}{SS_{yy}} \qquad \text{where } 0 \le R^2 \le 1$$

This represents the proportion of the sum of squares of deviations of the y-values about their mean that can be attributed to a linear relationship between y and x.

EXAMPLE 10.6 Find the coefficient of determination for the P/E ratio–R/S ratio example. Give a practical interpretation of R^2.

Solution   In the upper portion of the SAS printout, Figure 10.7, the coefficient of determination is given next to the heading R-square: $R^2 = .5274$. By using the R/S ratio (x) to predict the P/E ratio (y) with the least squares line

$$\hat{y} = 5.977 + 74.068x$$

the total sum of squares of deviations of the 20 sample y-values about their predicted values has been reduced 53%. A more practical interpretation is that 53% of the sample variation in the P/E ratio is accounted for (or explained by) the linear relationship between x and y. Thus, 47% of the variation is unexplained. A model more complex than the straight-line model may be required to account for some of this unexplained variation.

> ### PRACTICAL INTERPRETATION OF THE COEFFICIENT OF DETERMINATION, R^2
>
> ---
>
> About $100(R^2)\%$ of the total sum of squares of deviations of the sample y-values about their mean $\bar{y}$ can be explained by (or attributed to) using x to predict y in the straight-line model.

Recall from Section 3.10 that the coefficient of correlation, r, is a measure of the strength of the linear relationship between two variables, y and x, in the sample. Thus, another way to assess the utility of the straight-line model is to interpret the value of r.

In simple linear regression it can be shown (proof omitted) that $r = \pm\sqrt{R^2}$. The sign of r ($+$ or $-$) will be identical to the sign of $\hat{\beta}_1$. For the P/E ratio–R/S ratio example, $R^2 = .5274$ and the sign of $\hat{\beta}_1$ is positive; hence,

$$r = +\sqrt{.5274} = .726$$

measures the strength of the linear relationship between the P/E ratio and the R/S ratio.

Inferences about the **population correlation coefficient** can be obtained by conducting the test

H_0: $\rho = 0$

H_a: $\rho \neq 0$

That is, we might want to test the hypothesis that x contributes no information for the prediction of y, using the straight-line model against the alternative that the two variables are at least linearly related. However, we have already performed this identical test when we tested H_0: $\beta_1 = 0$ against H_a: $\beta_1 \neq 0$. It can be shown that the null hypothesis H_0: $\rho = 0$ is equivalent to the hypothesis H_0: $\beta_1 = 0$. When we tested the null hypothesis H_0: $\beta_1 = 0$ in connnection with the P/E ratio–R/S ratio example, the data led to a rejection of the null hypothesis for $\alpha = .05$. This implies that the null hypothesis of a zero linear correlation between the two variables (P/E ratio and R/S ratio) also can be rejected at $\alpha = .05$. The only real difference between the least squares slope, $\hat{\beta}_1$, and the coefficient of correlation, r, is the measurement scale. Therefore, the information they provide about the utility of the least squares model is to some extent redundant. Furthermore, the slope β_1 gives us additional information on the amount of increase (or decrease) in y for every 1 unit increase in x. For this reason, we recommend using the slope to make inferences about the existence of a positive or negative linear relationship between two variables.

For those who prefer to test for a linear relationship between two variables using the coefficient of correlation r, we outline the procedure in the next box.

TEST OF HYPOTHESIS FOR LINEAR CORRELATION

ONE-TAILED TEST	TWO-TAILED TEST
H_0: $\rho = 0$	H_0: $\rho = 0$
H_a: $\rho > 0$	H_a: $\rho \neq 0$
[or H_a: $\rho < 0$]	

$$\text{Test statistic:} \quad t = \frac{r\sqrt{n-2}}{\sqrt{1-r^2}}$$

| Rejection region: $t > t_\alpha$ [or $t < -t_\alpha$] | Rejection region: $|t| > t_{\alpha/2}$ |

where the distribution of t depends on $(n - 2)$ df, and t_α and $t_{\alpha/2}$ are the critical values obtained from Table 3, Appendix A.

Assumptions: The sample of (x, y) values is randomly selected from a (bivariate) normal population.*

USING THE MODEL FOR ESTIMATION AND PREDICTION

If we are satisfied that a useful model has been found to describe the relationship between y and x, we are ready to perform step 6: Use the model for estimation and prediction.

The most common uses of a probabilistic model can be divided into two categories: (1) use the model to estimate the mean value of y, $E(y)$, for a specific value of x, and (2) use the model to predict a particular y-value for a given x.

In the case of estimating a mean value of y, we are attempting to estimate the mean result of a very large number of experiments at the given x-value. For example, we may want to estimate the mean P/E ratio for all firms with an R/S ratio of $x = .07$. In the second case, we are trying to predict the outcome of a single experiment at the given x-value. For example, we might want to predict the P/E ratio for a particular firm with an R/S ratio of $x = .07$.

---

* A bivariate normal population will result if the probability distributions of both x and y are normal.

The least squares model

$$\hat{y} = \hat{\beta}_0 + \hat{\beta}_1 x$$

is used both to estimate $E(y)$ and to predict a particular value for y for a given value of x. In Example 10.2, we found

$$\hat{y} = 5.977 + 74.068x$$

so that the estimated mean P/E ratio for all firms with an R/S ratio of $x = .07$ is

$$\hat{y} = 5.977 + 74.068(.07)$$
$$= 11.162$$

The identical value is used to predict the y-value when $x = .07$. That is, both the estimated mean value and the predicted value of y equal $\hat{y} = 11.162$ when $x = .07$, as shown in Figure 10.12.

FIGURE 10.12

Estimated Mean Value and Predicted Individual Value of P/E Ratio y for $x = .07$

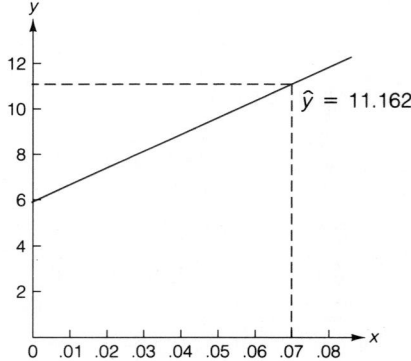

The difference in the uses of these two models lies in the relative accuracy of the estimate and the prediction. These accuracies are best measured by the standard errors of the least squares line when it is used as an estimator and as a predictor, respectively. These errors are given in the box.

STANDARD ERRORS FOR THE ESTIMATOR OF THE MEAN OF y AND THE PREDICTOR OF AN INDIVIDUAL y FOR $x = x_p$: STRAIGHT-LINE MODEL

1. The standard deviation of the sampling distribution of the estimator $\hat{y}$ of the mean value of y at a particular value of x, say x_p, is

$$\sigma_{\hat{y}} = \sigma \sqrt{\frac{1}{n} + \frac{(x_p - \bar{x})^2}{SS_{xx}}}$$

where σ is the standard deviation of the random error ϵ.

(continued)

---

2. The standard deviation of the prediction error for the predictor $\hat{y}$ of an individual y-value for $x = x_p$ is

$$\sigma_{(y-\hat{y})} = \sigma \sqrt{1 + \frac{1}{n} + \frac{(x_p - \bar{x})^2}{SS_{xx}}}$$

where σ is the standard deviation of the random error ϵ.

The true value of σ will rarely be known. Thus, we estimate σ by s and calculate the estimation and prediction intervals as shown in the next two boxes.

A 100(1 − α)% CONFIDENCE INTERVAL FOR THE MEAN VALUE OF y FOR $x = x_p$: STRAIGHT-LINE MODEL

$\hat{y} \pm t_{\alpha/2} \cdot$ (Estimated standard error of $\hat{y}$)

or

$$\hat{y} \pm t_{\alpha/2} s \sqrt{\frac{1}{n} + \frac{(x_p - \bar{x})^2}{SS_{xx}}}$$

where $t_{\alpha/2}$ is based on $(n - 2)$ df.

A 100(1 − α)% PREDICTION INTERVAL FOR AN INDIVIDUAL y FOR $x = x_p$: STRAIGHT-LINE MODEL

$\hat{y} \pm t_{\alpha/2} \cdot$ [Estimated standard error of $(y - \hat{y})$]

or

$$\hat{y} \pm t_{\alpha/2} s \sqrt{1 + \frac{1}{n} + \frac{(x_p - \bar{x})^2}{SS_{xx}}}$$

where $t_{\alpha/2}$ is based on $(n - 2)$ df.

EXAMPLE 10.7 Refer to Examples 10.2–10.6. Find a 95% confidence interval for the mean P/E ratio of all firms with an R/S ratio of .07. Interpret the interval.

Solution From our previous work, $\hat{y} = 11.162$, $x_p = .07$, $n = 20$, df $= n - 2 = 18$, $t_{.025} = 2.101$, and $s = 2.074$. Use the data in Table 10.7 to verify that $\bar{x} = .0479$ and $SS_{xx} = .01575$. Then the confidence interval for the mean value of y is

$$\hat{y} \pm t_{\alpha/2} s \sqrt{\frac{1}{n} + \frac{(x_p - \bar{x})^2}{SS_{xx}}} = 11.162 \pm (2.101)(2.074) \sqrt{\frac{1}{20} + \frac{(.07 - .0479)^2}{.01575}}$$

$$= 11.162 \pm (2.101)(2.074)(.285)$$

$$= 11.162 \pm 1.240 \quad \text{or} \quad (9.922, 12.402)$$

We estimate (with 95% confidence) that the interval from 9.922 to 12.402 encloses the mean P/E ratio of all firms with an R/S ratio of .07.

Confidence intervals for $E(y)$ and prediction intervals for y also can be obtained using a computer.

EXAMPLE 10.8   Refer to Example 10.7. Predict the P/E ratio of a particular firm with an R/S ratio of .07. Use a 95% prediction interval and interpret the result.

Solution   The SAS printout for the P/E ratio–R/S ratio simple linear regression is reproduced in Figure 10.13. The 95% prediction intervals for y are reported in the lower portion of the printout. The lower and upper endpoints of the 95% prediction interval for y when $x_p = .07$ are shaded in Figure 10.13. The interval is (6.632, 15.692).

FIGURE 10.13
SAS Printout for Example 10.8

Model: MODEL1
Dependent Variable: Y

Analysis of Variance

Source	DF	Sum of Squares	Mean Square	F Value	Prob>F
Model	1	86.40357	86.40357	20.090	0.0003
Error	18	77.41393	4.30077		
C Total	19	163.81750			

Root MSE	2.07383	R-square	0.5274	
Dep Mean	9.52500	Adj R-sq	0.5012	
C.V.	21.77250			

Parameter Estimates

Variable	DF	Parameter Estimate	Standard Error	T for H0: Parameter=0	Prob > |T|
INTERCEP	1	5.977162	0.91737112	6.516	0.0001
X	1	74.067607	16.52478400	4.482	0.0003

Obs	X	Dep Var Y	Predict Value	Std Err Predict	Lower95% Predict	Upper95% Predict	Residual
1	0.003	5.6000	6.1994	0.875	1.4705	10.9282	-0.5994
2	0.004	7.2000	6.2734	0.861	1.5559	10.9909	0.9266
3	0.009	8.1000	6.6438	0.793	1.9795	11.3081	1.4562
4	0.021	9.9000	7.5326	0.642	2.9714	12.0937	2.3674
5	0.023	6.0000	7.6807	0.620	3.1333	12.2282	-1.6807
6	0.03	8.2000	8.1992	0.550	3.6916	12.7068	0.00081
7	0.035	6.3000	8.5695	0.510	4.0826	13.0565	-2.2695
8	0.037	10.0000	8.7177	0.497	4.2371	13.1982	1.2823
9	0.044	8.5000	9.2361	0.468	4.7696	13.7027	-0.7361
10	0.051	13.2000	9.7546	0.467	5.2888	14.2204	3.4454
11	0.058	8.4000	10.2731	0.493	5.7948	14.7514	-1.8731
12	0.058	11.1000	10.2731	0.493	5.7948	14.7514	0.8269
13	0.067	11.1000	10.9397	0.561	6.4262	15.4532	0.1603
14	0.08	13.2000	11.9026	0.705	7.3011	16.5041	1.2974
15	0.08	13.4000	11.9026	0.705	7.3011	16.5041	1.4974
16	0.083	11.5000	12.1248	0.743	7.4969	16.7526	-0.6248
17	0.091	9.8000	12.7173	0.850	8.0087	17.4259	-2.9173
18	0.092	16.1000	12.7914	0.864	8.0716	17.5111	3.3086
19	0.064	7.0000	10.7175	0.535	6.2181	15.2169	-3.7175
20	0.028	5.9000	8.0511	0.568	3.5334	12.5687	-2.1511
21	0.07	.	11.1619	0.590	6.6319	15.6919	.

Therefore, we predict that the P/E ratio for this firm will fall in the interval from 6.632 to 15.692, with 95% confidence.

A comparison of the confidence interval for the mean value of *y* and the prediction interval for some future value of *y* in Examples 10.7 and 10.8 is illustrated in Figure 10.14. It is important to note that the prediction interval for an individual value of *y* will always be wider than the confidence interval for a mean value of *y*. You can see this by examining the formulas for the two intervals, and you can see it in Figure 10.14.

FIGURE 10.14

Comparison of Widths of 95% Confidence and Prediction Intervals

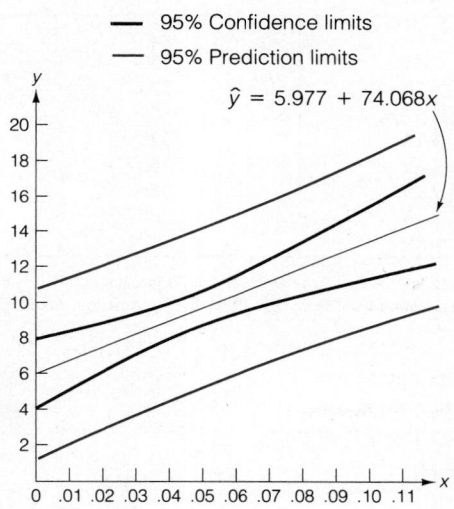

Additionally, over the range of the sample data, the widths of both intervals increase as the value of *x* gets further from $\bar{x}$ (see Figure 10.14). Thus, the more the value of *x* deviates from the sample mean $\bar{x}$, the less useful the interval will be in practice. In fact, when *x* is selected far enough away from $\bar{x}$ so that it falls outside the range of the sample data, it is dangerous to make any inference about $E(y)$ or *y*.

WARNING

Using the least squares prediction equation to estimate the mean value of *y* or to predict a particular value of *y* for values of *x* that fall *outside the range* of the values of *x* contained in your sample data may lead to errors of estimation or prediction that are much larger than expected. Although the least squares model may provide a very good fit to the data over the range of *x*-values contained in the sample, *it could give a poor representation of the true model for values of x outside this region.*

10.1   Two processes for hydraulic drilling of rock are dry drilling and wet drilling. In a dry hole, compressed air is forced down the drill rods in order to flush the cuttings and drive the hammer; in a wet hole, water is forced down. An experiment was conducted to determine whether the time y it takes to dry drill a distance of 5 feet in rock increases with depth x (*The American Statistician*, Feb. 1991). The results for one portion of the experiment are shown in the table.

DEPTH AT WHICH DRILLING BEGINS x, Feet	TIME TO DRY DRILL 5 FEET y, Minutes	DEPTH AT WHICH DRILLING BEGINS x, Feet	TIME TO DRY DRILL 5 FEET y, Minutes
0	4.90	225	8.28
25	7.41	250	4.84
50	6.19	275	8.29
75	5.57	300	8.91
100	5.17	325	8.54
125	6.89	350	11.79
150	7.05	375	12.12
175	7.11	395	11.02
200	6.19		

Source: Penner, R., and Watts, D. G. "Mining Information." *The American Statistician*, Vol. 45, No. 1, Feb. 1991, p. 6 (Table 1). Reprinted with permission from *The American Statistician*. Copyright 1991 by the American Statistical Association. All rights reserved.

a. Construct a scattergram for the data.
b. Find the least squares prediction equation.
c. Graph the least squares line on the scattergram.
d. Interpret the values of $\hat{\beta}_0$ and $\hat{\beta}_1$.
e. Find SSE and s^2 for the data.
f. Calculate s, the estimate of σ.
g. Interpret the value of s obtained in part **b**.
h. Is there evidence to indicate that dry drilling time y increases with depth x? Test using $\alpha = .10$.
i. Compute R^2 and interpret its value.
j. Find a 95% prediction interval for dry drilling time y when drilling begins at a depth of 300 feet. Interpret your result.

10.2   In forestry, the diameter of a tree at breast height (which is fairly easy to measure) is used to predict the height of the tree (a difficult measurement to obtain). Silviculturists working in British Columbia's boreal forest conducted a series of spacing trials to predict the heights of several species of trees. The data in the table at the top of the next page are the breast height diameters (in centimeters) and heights (in meters) for a sample of 36 white spruce trees.

a. Construct a scattergram for the data.
b. Assuming the relationship between the variables is best described by a straight line, use the method of least squares to estimate the y-intercept and slope of the line.
c. Plot the least squares line on your scattergram.
d. Do the data provide sufficient evidence to indicate that the breast height diameter x contributes information for the prediction of tree height y? Test using $\alpha = .05$.
e. Use your least squares line to find a 90% confidence interval for the average height of white spruce trees with a breast height diameter of 20 cm. Interpret the interval.

BREAST HEIGHT DIAMETER x, cm	HEIGHT y, m	BREAST HEIGHT DIAMETER x, cm	HEIGHT y, m	BREAST HEIGHT DIAMETER x, cm	HEIGHT y, m
18.9	20.0	18.5	19.0	14.1	18.5
15.5	16.8	21.5	19.2	10.1	12.1
19.4	20.2	14.8	16.1	5.8	8.0
20.0	20.0	17.7	19.9	20.7	17.4
29.8	20.2	21.0	20.4	17.8	18.4
19.8	18.0	15.9	17.6	11.4	17.3
20.3	17.8	16.6	18.8	14.4	16.6
20.0	19.2	15.5	16.9	13.4	12.9
22.0	22.3	13.7	16.3	17.8	17.5
23.6	18.9	27.5	21.4	20.7	19.4
14.8	13.3	20.3	19.2	13.3	15.5
22.7	20.6	22.9	19.8	22.9	19.2

Source: Scholz, H., Northern Lights College, British Columbia.

10.3 Multinational corporations are firms with both domestic and foreign assets/investments. The foreign revenues (as a percentage of total revenue) generated by each of the top 20 U.S. based multinationals are listed in the table. Is there a positive linear relationship between the foreign revenue (measured as a percentage of total revenue) and the foreign assets (measured as a percentage of total assets) of multinational firms? Test using $\alpha = .10$.

FIRM	FOREIGN REVENUE (%)	FOREIGN ASSETS (%)	FIRM	FOREIGN REVENUE (%)	FOREIGN ASSETS (%)
Exxon	73.2	55.8	Procter & Gamble	39.9	32.2
IBM	58.9	48.6	Philip Morris	19.6	14.8
GM	26.6	25.2	Eastman Kodak	40.9	28.0
Mobil	64.7	51.1	Digital	54.1	44.2
Ford	33.2	26.9	GE	12.4	8.8
Citicorp	52.3	39.4	United Technologies	32.9	26.7
EI duPont	39.8	29.5	Amoco	26.1	32.7
Texaco	42.3	26.6	Hewlitt-Packard	53.3	38.7
ITT	43.3	23.6	Xerox	34.6	25.4
Dow Chemical	54.1	44.9	Chevron	20.5	22.6

Source: Forbes, July 23, 1990, pp. 362–363. Used by permission. © Forbes Inc., 1990.

10.4 A medical item used to administer to a hospital patient is called a *factor*. For example, factors can be intravenous (I.V.) tubing, I.V. fluid, needles, shave kits, bedpans, diapers, dressings, medications, and even code carts. The coronary care unit at Bayonet Point Hospital (St. Petersburg, Florida) investigated the relationship between the number of factors per patient, x, and the patient's length of stay (in days), y. The data for a random sample of 50 coronary care patients are given in the table, followed by the SAS printout of the simple linear regression analysis. (See p. 450.)

a. Construct a scattergram of the data.
b. Find the least squares line for the data and plot it on your scattergram.
c. Define β_1 in the context of this problem.
d. Test the hypothesis that the number of factors per patient (x) contributes no information for the prediction of the patient's length of stay (y) when a linear model is used (use $\alpha = .05$). Draw the appropriate conclusion.

Data for Problem 10.4

NUMBER OF FACTORS x	LENGTH OF STAY y, days	NUMBER OF FACTORS x	LENGTH OF STAY y, days	NUMBER OF FACTORS x	LENGTH OF STAY y, days	NUMBER OF FACTORS x	LENGTH OF STAY y, days
231	9	354	11	78	3	84	3
323	7	142	7	525	9	331	9
113	8	286	9	121	7	302	7
208	5	341	10	248	5	60	2
162	4	201	5	233	8	110	2
117	4	158	11	260	4	131	5
159	6	243	6	224	7	364	4
169	9	156	6	472	12	180	7
55	6	184	7	220	8	134	6
77	3	115	4	383	6	401	15
103	4	202	6	301	9	155	4
147	6	206	5	262	7	338	8
230	6	360	6				

Source: Bayonet Point Hospital, Coronary Care Unit, St. Petersburg, FL.

```
Model: MODEL1
Dependent Variable: Y

                        Analysis of Variance

                        Sum of          Mean
    Source      DF      Squares         Square      F Value      Prob>F

    Model        1      126.58393       126.58393    28.683      0.0001
    Error       48      211.83607         4.41325
    C Total     49      338.42000

        Root MSE        2.10077      R-square      0.3740
        Dep Mean        6.54000      Adj R-sq      0.3610
        C.V.           32.12193

                        Parameter Estimates

                   Parameter      Standard     T for H0:
    Variable  DF    Estimate         Error     Parameter=0    Prob > |T|

    INTERCEP   1    3.306032      0.67297426      4.913         0.0001
    X          1    0.014755      0.00275502      5.356         0.0001


               Dep Var   Predict   Std Err   Lower95%   Upper95%
    Obs    X      Y       Value     Predict   Predict    Predict    Residual

    1     200     .       6.2570     0.302     1.9898    10.5242       .

Sum of Residuals          9.769963E-15
Sum of Squared Residuals     211.8361
Predicted Resid SS (Press)   234.7934
```

e. Find a 90% confidence interval for β_1. Interpret your result.

f. Find the coefficient of correlation for the data. Interpret your result.

g. Find the coefficient of determination for the linear model you constructed in part **b**. Interpret your result.

h. Find a 95% prediction interval for the length of stay of a coronary care patient who is administered a total of $x = 200$ factors.

i. Explain why the prediction interval obtained in part **h** is so wide. How could you reduce the width of the interval?

10.5 Refer to the *Chemosphere* (Vol. 20, 1990) study of Vietnam veterans exposed to Agent Orange (and the dioxin 2,3,7,8-TCDD), discussed in Problem 6.24. The data, reproduced here, give the amounts of 2,3,7,8-TCDD (measured in parts per million, ppm) in both blood plasma and fat tissue drawn from each of the 20 veterans studied.

VETERAN	TCDD LEVELS IN PLASMA	TCDD LEVELS IN FAT TISSUE	VETERAN	TCDD LEVELS IN PLASMA	TCDD LEVELS IN FAT TISSUE
1	2.5	4.9	11	6.9	7.0
2	3.1	5.9	12	3.3	2.9
3	2.1	4.4	13	4.6	4.6
4	3.5	6.9	14	1.6	1.4
5	3.1	7.0	15	7.2	7.7
6	1.8	4.2	16	1.8	1.1
7	6.0	10.0	17	20.0	11.0
8	3.0	5.5	18	2.0	2.5
9	36.0	41.0	19	2.5	2.3
10	4.7	4.4	20	4.1	2.5

Source: Schecter, A., et al. "Partitioning of 2,3,7,8-Chlorinated Dibenzo-*p*-dioxins and Dibenzofurans Between Adipose Tissue and Plasma Lipid of 20 Massachusetts Vietnam Veterans." *Chemosphere*, Vol. 20, Nos. 7–9, 1990, pp. 954–955 (Tables I, II).

One goal of the researchers was to determine the degree of linear association between the levels of dioxin found in blood plasma and in fat tissue. If a linear association between the two variables can be established, the researchers want to build models to (1) predict blood plasma level of 2,3,7,8-TCDD from the observed level of 2,3,7,8-TCDD in fat tissue and (2) predict fat tissue level from the observed blood plasma level.

a. Find the prediction equations for the researchers. Interpret the results.

b. Test the hypothesis that fat tissue level (y) is a useful linear predictor of blood plasma level (x). Use $\alpha = .05$.

c. Test the hypothesis that blood plasma level (x) is a useful linear predictor of fat tissue level (y). Use $\alpha = .05$.

d. Intuitively, why must the results of the tests in parts **b** and **c** agree?

10.6 Refer to Problem 10.5. The blood plasma and fat tissue levels of several other types of dioxin (called *cogeners*) were also measured for each of the 20 Vietnam veterans. For each cogener, a simple linear regression analysis was conducted to predict (1) fat tissue level from blood plasma level and (2) blood plasma level from fat tissue level. The results for three of these cogeners are shown in the table.

COGENER	y = Fat tissue level x = Blood plasma level	y = Blood plasma level x = Fat tissue level	CORRELATION COEFFICIENT
2,3,4,7,8-P_nCDF	$\hat{y} = .8109 + .9713x$	$\hat{y} = .9855 + .7605x$	$r = .8594$
H_xCDD	$\hat{y} = 18.1565 + .7377x$	$\hat{y} = 5.2009 + .9018x$	$r = .8156$
OCDD	$\hat{y} = 118.6057 + .3679x$	$\hat{y} = 167.723 + 1.5752x$	$r = .7612$

Source: Schecter, A., et al. "Partitioning of 2,3,7,8-Chlorinated Dibenzo-*p*-dioxins and Dibenzofurans Between Adipose Tissue and Plasma Lipid of 20 Massachusetts Vietnam Veterans." *Chemosphere*, Vol. 20, Nos. 7–9, 1990, pp. 954–955 (Table III).

a. For the cogener 2,3,4,7,8-P_nCDF, are the two regression models statistically adequate for predicting y? Test both using $\alpha = .05$.

b. Repeat part **a** for the cogener H_xCDD.

c. Repeat part **a** for the cogener OCDD.

d. Use the regression results to predict the level of 2,3,4,7,8-P_nCDF in blood plasma for a veteran with a fat tissue level of 8.0 ppm.

e. Use the regression results to predict the level of H_xCDD in fat tissue for a veteran with a blood plasma level of 24.0 ppm.

f. Use the regression results to predict the level of OCDD in blood plasma for a veteran with a fat tissue level of 776 ppm.

10.7 Each year, *Fortune* ranks the top American cities according to their ability to provide high-quality, low-cost labor for companies that are relocating. One important measure used to form the rankings is the *labor market stress index* (*y*), which indicates the availability of workers in the city. (The higher the index, the tighter the labor market.) A second important variable is the *unemployment rate* (*x*). The values of these two variables for each of the top ten cities in 1990 are listed in the table.

a. Construct a scattergram for the data.
b. Find the least squares prediction equation.
c. Graph the least squares line on the scattergram.
d. Interpret the values of $\hat{\beta}_0$ and $\hat{\beta}_1$.

RANK	CITY	LABOR MARKET STRESS INDEX y	UNEMPLOYMENT RATE x
1	Salt Lake City	107	4.5%
2	Minneapolis–St. Paul	107	3.8%
3	Atlanta	100	5.1%
4	Sacramento	100	4.9%
5	Austin (Texas)	80	5.4%
6	Columbus (Ohio)	100	4.8%
7	Dallas/Fort Worth	100	5.5%
8	Phoenix	93	4.3%
9	Jacksonville (Florida)	87	5.7%
10	Oklahoma City	80	4.6%

Source: *Fortune,* Oct. 22, 1990, pp. 58–63. FORTUNE © 1990 Time Inc. All rights reserved.

10.8 An investigation sought to determine whether there were certain collective behaviors, affective reactions, or performance outcomes associated with the maturity level of small groups (*Small Group Behavior,* May 1988). Fifty-eight undergraduate students at a medium-sized university participated in the experiment. A 10 item questionnaire (see Problem 4.32, p. 183) was used to measure the maturity level, *y*, of the students on a scale of 0–100, where more mature students received higher scores. One of several other variables measured was the number, *x*, of meetings held with their groups outside regular class sessions. The correlation coefficient relating *y* to *x* was found to be $r = .46$. Is this sufficient evidence to indicate a positive correlation between group maturity and outside meetings? Test using $\alpha = .01$.

10.9 Civil engineers often use the straight-line equation $E(y) = \beta_0 + \beta_1 x$ to model the relationship between the mean shear strength $E(y)$ of masonry joints and precompression stress *x*. To test this theory, a series of stress tests was performed on solid bricks arranged in triplets and joined with mortar (*Proceedings of the Institution of Civil Engineers,* Mar. 1990). The precompression stress was varied for each triplet, and the ultimate shear load just before failure (called the *shear strength*) was recorded. The stress results for seven triplets (measured in newtons per square millimeter) are given in the table. Analyze the data.

TRIPLET TEST	1	2	3	4	5	6	7
Shear Strength, y	1.00	2.18	2.24	2.41	2.59	2.82	3.06
Precompression Stress, x	0	.60	1.20	1.33	1.43	1.75	1.75

Source: Riddington, J. R., and Ghazali, M. Z. "Hypothesis for Shear Failure in Masonry Joints." *Proceedings of the Institution of Civil Engineers, Part 2,* Mar. 1990, Vol. 89, p. 96 (Fig. 7).

10.10 To examine potential gender differences in the industrial sales force, a sample of 153 females and 244 males were administered a questionnaire (*Journal of Personal Selling & Sales Management*, Summer 1990). All respondents were either sales managers or salespeople at one of 16 industrial firms located in the southeastern United States. Two variables of interest to the researchers were level of organizational commitment (y) and total months experience in sales (x). For the 244 males in the study, the coefficient of correlation between x and y was $r_{Males} = -.35$. For the 153 females in the study, the correlation coefficient was $r_{Females} = -.06$.

    a. Interpret the value of r_{Males}.
    b. Interpret the value of $r_{Females}$.
    c. For each gender, test the hypothesis of no linear correlation between organizational commitment (y) and experience in months (x).

10.11 An automated system, called AUTOMARK, for marking large numbers of student computer programs, has been used successfully at McMaster University in Ontario, Canada. AUTOMARK takes into account both program correctness and program style when marking student assignments. To evaluate the effectiveness of the automated system, AUTOMARK was used to grade the FORTRAN77 assignments of a class of 33 students. These grades were then compared to the grades assigned by the instructor. The results are given in the table.

AUTOMARK GRADE	INSTRUCTOR GRADE	AUTOMARK GRADE	INSTRUCTOR GRADE	AUTOMARK GRADE	INSTRUCTOR GRADE
x	y	x	y	x	y
12.2	10	18.2	15	19.0	17
10.6	11	15.1	16	19.3	17
15.1	12	17.2	16	19.5	17
16.2	12	17.5	16	19.7	17
16.6	12	18.6	16	18.6	18
16.6	13	18.8	16	19.0	18
17.2	14	17.8	17	19.2	18
17.6	14	18.0	17	19.4	18
18.2	14	18.2	17	19.6	18
16.5	15	18.4	17	20.1	18
17.2	15	18.6	17	19.2	19

Source: Redish, K. A., and Smyth, W. F. "Program Style Analysis: A Natural By-product of Program Compilation." *Communications of the Association for Computing Machinery*, Vol. 29, No. 2, Feb. 1986, p. 132 (Fig. 4).

    a. Assuming instructor grade, y, and AUTOMARK grade, x, are linearly related, hypothesize a model relating y to x.
    b. Fit the model from part **a** to the data using the method of least squares. Give the least squares prediction equation.
    c. Interpret the values of $\hat{\beta}_0$ and $\hat{\beta}_1$.
    d. What assumptions are required to make valid inferences based on the regression results?
    e. Calculate and interpret s, the estimated standard deviation of the model.
    f. Conduct a test to determine whether y and x are positively linearly related. Use $\alpha = .05$.
    g. Calculate a 90% confidence interval for β_1, and interpret the result.
    h. Calculate the coefficient of determination, R^2, and interpret its value.
    i. Do you recommend using the model for estimation and prediction?
    j. Construct a 90% prediction interval for instructor grade, y, for an assignment given an AUTOMARK grade of $x = 18$. Interpret the result.

SIMPLE LINEAR REGRESSION

The computer commands and instructions given in this section produce a simple linear regression on analysis of the P/E ratio–R/S ratio data in Table 10.7 (p. 433). In addition, we give the commands for calculating and testing the correlation coefficient r.

SAS

```
Command
Line
1       DATA FIRMS;  ⎫
2       INPUT Y X;   ⎬  Data entry instructions
3       CARDS;       ⎭
        5.6   .003 ⎫
        7.2   .004 ⎮
         .     .   ⎬  Input data values
         .     .   ⎮  (1 observation per line)
         .     .   ⎮
        5.9   .028 ⎭
4       PROC REG;           ⎫
5       MODEL Y=X/P CLI;    ⎬  Regression analysis/prediction intervals
6       ID X;               ⎭
7       PROC CORR;   ⎫  Correlation analysis
8       VAR X Y;     ⎭
```

COMMAND 4 The REG procedure performs a complete regression analysis on the data.

COMMAND 5 In the MODEL statement, the dependent variable is listed to the left of the equals sign and the independent variable to the right. The option P (following the slash) prints predicted values and residuals, and the option CLI prints corresponding lower and upper 95% prediction limits for all observations in the data set. Specify CLM to obtain 95% confidence intervals for $E(y)$. [*Note:* To predict y for a value of x that is not included in the data set (eg, $x = .07$), you must include an "extra" observation in the data set. This observation has the specified value of x (eg, .07), but a missing value for y (ie, a single decimal point).]

COMMAND 6 The optional ID statement identifies the value of x for each 95% prediction (or confidence) interval.

COMMANDS 7–8 The CORR procedure calculates the correlation coefficient between the variables specified in the VAR statement. The two-tailed p-value for testing H_0: $\rho = 0$ is also produced.

NOTE The printout for this SAS program is displayed in Figure 10.15a (p. 457).

```
Command
   Line
    1      DATA LIST FREE/Y X.⎫
    2      BEGIN DATA.        ⎬ Data entry instructions
           5.6  .003⎫
           7.2  .004 ⎪
            .    .   ⎪  Input data values
            .    .   ⎬  (1 observation per line)
            .    .   ⎪
           5.9  .028⎭
    3      END DATA.
    4      REGRESSION VARIABLES = Y, X/ ⎫
    5                 DEPENDENT = Y/     ⎪
    6                 METHOD = ENTER X/  ⎬ Regression analysis
    7                 STATISTICS=DEFAULTS CI/ ⎪
    8                 CASEWISE=ALL DEPENDENT PRED.⎭
    9      CORRELATION VARIABLES = Y, X.⎬ Correlation analysis
```

COMMANDS 4–6   The REGRESSION procedure in SPSS performs a complete regression analysis on the data. The dependent and independent variables are specified in the DEPENDENT and METHOD subcommands, respectively.

COMMAND 7   The STATISTICS subcommand with the CI option produces 95% confidence intervals for the β coefficients.

COMMAND 8   The CASEWISE subcommand generates predicted values for all observations in the data set.

COMMAND 9   The CORRELATION procedure in SPSS calculates the correlation coefficient between the specified variables and gives the one-tailed p-value for testing H_0: $\rho = 0$.

GENERAL   Confidence intervals for $E(y)$ and prediction intervals for y are not available in the SPSS regression procedure.

NOTE   The printout for the SPSS program is displayed in Figure 10.15b (p. 458).

```
Command
  Line
    1      READ Y IN C1, X IN C2   Data entry instruction
           5.6   .003⎫
           7.2   .004⎪
            .     .  ⎬  Input data values
            .     .  ⎪  (1 observation per line)
            .     .  ⎪
           5.9   .028⎭
    2      NAME C1='Y' C2='X'
    3      REGRESS C1 ON 1 PREDICTOR IN C2;⎫
    4          PREDICT .07.                 ⎬ Regression analysis
    5      CORRELATION C1 C2   Correlation analysis
```

COMMAND 3   The REGRESS procedure in MINITAB performs a complete linear regression analysis on the data. The column in which the values of the dependent variables appear must be specified first (eg, C1), followed by the number of predictors (independent variables) in the model (eg, 1), and the column(s) in which the values of the predictor(s) appear (eg, C2).

COMMAND 4   PREDICT is a subcommand of the main REGRESS command that produces a 95% confidence interval for $E(y)$ and a 95% prediction interval for y for the value of the independent variable specified (eg, .07).

COMMAND 5   The CORRELATION procedure in MINITAB calculates the coefficient of correlation between the variables (columns) specified.

GENERAL   When a subcommand is used in MINITAB, the main command (eg, REGRESS in line 3) must end in a semicolon, followed by the subcommand (eg, PREDICT in line 4), which ends in a period.

NOTE   The printout for the MINITAB program is displayed in Figure 10.15c (p. 459).

FIGURE 10.15a

SAS Output for Computer Lab 1

Analysis of Variance

Source	DF	Sum of Squares	Mean Square	F Value	Prob>F
Model	1	86.40357	86.40357	20.090	0.0003
Error	18	77.41393	4.30077		
C Total	19	163.81750			

Root MSE	2.07383	R-square	0.5274	
Dep Mean	9.52500	Adj R-sq	0.5012	
C.V.	21.77250			

Parameter Estimates

Variable	DF	Parameter Estimate	Standard Error	T for H0: Parameter=0	Prob > |T|
INTERCEP	1	5.977162	0.91737112	6.516	0.0001
X	1	74.067607	16.52478400	4.482	0.0003

Obs	X	Dep Var Y	Predict Value	Std Err Predict	Lower95% Predict	Upper95% Predict	Residual
1	0.003	5.6000	6.1994	0.875	1.4705	10.9282	-0.5994
2	0.004	7.2000	6.2734	0.861	1.5559	10.9909	0.9266
3	0.009	8.1000	6.6438	0.793	1.9795	11.3081	1.4562
4	0.021	9.9000	7.5326	0.642	2.9714	12.0937	2.3674
5	0.023	6.0000	7.6807	0.620	3.1333	12.2282	-1.6807
6	0.03	8.2000	8.1992	0.550	3.6916	12.7068	0.00081
7	0.035	6.3000	8.5695	0.510	4.0826	13.0565	-2.2695
8	0.037	10.0000	8.7177	0.497	4.2371	13.1982	1.2823
9	0.044	8.5000	9.2361	0.468	4.7696	13.7027	-0.7361
10	0.051	13.2000	9.7546	0.467	5.2888	14.2204	3.4454
11	0.058	8.4000	10.2731	0.493	5.7948	14.7514	-1.8731
12	0.058	11.1000	10.2731	0.493	5.7948	14.7514	0.8269
13	0.067	11.1000	10.9397	0.561	6.4262	15.4532	0.1603
14	0.08	13.2000	11.9026	0.705	7.3011	16.5041	1.2974
15	0.08	13.4000	11.9026	0.705	7.3011	16.5041	1.4974
16	0.083	11.5000	12.1248	0.743	7.4969	16.7526	-0.6248
17	0.091	9.8000	12.7173	0.850	8.0087	17.4259	-2.9173
18	0.092	16.1000	12.7914	0.864	8.0716	17.5111	3.3086
19	0.064	7.0000	10.7175	0.535	6.2181	15.2169	-3.7175
20	0.028	5.9000	8.0511	0.568	3.5334	12.5687	-2.1511

Sum of Residuals	-9.76996E-15
Sum of Squared Residuals	77.4139
Predicted Resid SS (Press)	96.2706

CORRELATION ANALYSIS

Pearson Correlation Coefficients / Prob > |R| under Ho: Rho=0 / N = 20

	X	Y
X	1.00000 0.0	0.72625 0.0003
Y	0.72625 0.0003	1.00000 0.0

FIGURE 10.15b

SPSS Output for Computer Lab 1

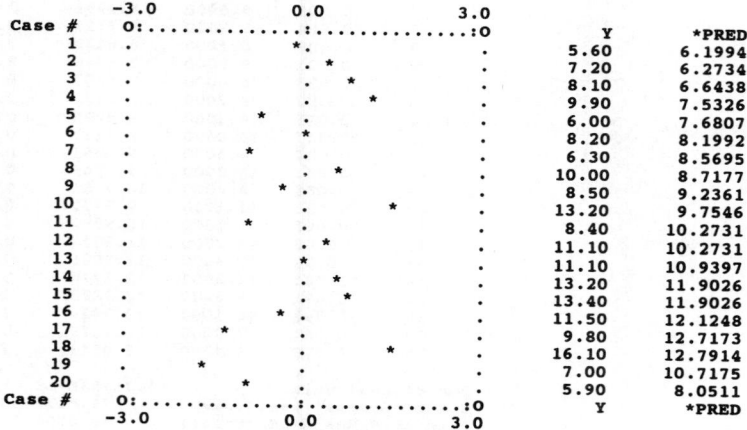

```
Multiple R              .72625
R Square                .52744
Adjusted R Square       .50118
Standard Error         2.07383

Analysis of Variance
                    DF      Sum of Squares     Mean Square
Regression           1           86.40357        86.40357
Residual            18           77.41393         4.30077

F =      20.09024       Signif F =  .0003


---------------------- Variables in the Equation ----------------------------

Variable          B          SE B      95% Confdnce Intrvl B      Beta      T    Sig T

X          74.067607    16.524784      39.350324   108.784890   .726249   4.482  .0003
(Constant)  5.977162      .917371       4.049836     7.904487             6.516  .0000

Casewise Plot of Standardized Residual

*: Selected   M: Missing

              -3.0            0.0             3.0
     Case #    O:...............:...............:O          Y       *PRED
        1      .               * .                .        5.60      6.1994
        2      .               .  *               .        7.20      6.2734
        3      .               .    *             .        8.10      6.6438
        4      .               .       *          .        9.90      7.5326
        5      .          *    .                  .        6.00      7.6807
        6      .               *                  .        8.20      8.1992
        7      .         *     .                  .        6.30      8.5695
        8      .               .  *               .       10.00      8.7177
        9      .          *  . .                  .        8.50      9.2361
       10      .               .        *         .       13.20      9.7546
       11      .         *     .                  .        8.40     10.2731
       12      .               . *                .       11.10     10.2731
       13      .               *                  .       11.10     10.9397
       14      .               . *                .       13.20     11.9026
       15      .               .  *               .       13.40     11.9026
       16      .          *  . .                  .       11.50     12.1248
       17      .      *        .                  .        9.80     12.7173
       18      .               .      *           .       16.10     12.7914
       19      .   *           .                  .        7.00     10.7175
       20      .          *    .                  .        5.90      8.0511
     Case #    O:...............:...............:O          Y       *PRED
              -3.0            0.0             3.0
```

```
Correlations:   X

    Y           .7262**

N of cases:    20          1-tailed Signif:   * - .01   ** - .001
```

FIGURE 10.15c

MINITAB Output for Computer Lab 1

```
The regression equation is
Y = 5.98 + 74.1 X

Predictor       Coef        Stdev      t-ratio        p
Constant      5.9772       0.9174         6.52    0.000
X             74.07        16.52          4.48    0.000

s = 2.074      R-sq = 52.7%      R-sq(adj) = 50.1%

Analysis of Variance

SOURCE         DF          SS           MS          F        p
Regression      1      86.404       86.404      20.09    0.000
Error          18      77.414        4.301
Total          19     163.818


    Fit   Stdev.Fit          95% C.I.            95% P.I.
 11.162       0.590    (  9.921, 12.402)   (  6.631, 15.693)


---------------------------------------------------------------

Correlation of Y and X = 0.726
```

MULTIPLE REGRESSION MODELS

10.4

Most practical applications of regression analysis require models that are more complex than the simple straight-line model. For example, a realistic probabilistic model for a firm's price/earnings ratio, y, would include more variables than the research and development (R&D) expenditures/sales ratio, x, discussed in Section 10.3. Additional variables such as type of firm, the firm's stock rating, and corporate assets might also be related to the P/E ratio. Thus, we would want to incorporate these and other potentially important independent variables into the model if we needed to make accurate predictions of the P/E ratio, y.

A more complex probabilistic model relating y to various independent variables, $x_1, x_2, x_3, \ldots$, is called a **general linear statistical model**, or more simply, a **linear model**.

General linear models are more flexible than straight-line models because they may include more than one independent variable. These models might also include some independent variables of higher orders—for example, terms such as x_1^2, $x_1 x_2$, x_3^3, etc. For example,

$$y = \beta_0 + \beta_1 x_1 + \beta_2 x_2 + \beta_3 x_1 x_2 + \beta_4 x_1^2 + \beta_5 x_2^2 + \epsilon$$

is a linear model. You may wonder why the model is referred to as a linear model if these higher-order terms are present. The model is called *linear* because it represents a linear function of the unknown parameters, $\beta_0, \beta_1, \beta_2, \ldots$. That is, each term contains only one of the β parameters, and each β is a coefficient of the remaining portion of the term. For example, the term $\beta_1 x_1 x_2^2$ satisfies this requirement, but the term $\beta_1 x_1^{\beta_2}$ does not, because it contains two unknown parameters (β_1 and β_2) and also because β_2 appears as an exponent rather than a multiplicative coefficient.

In Sections 10.5–10.8 we will use the method of least squares to fit a general linear model to a set of data. That is, we find the estimated model

$$\hat{y} = \hat{\beta}_0 + \hat{\beta}_1 x_1 + \hat{\beta}_2 x_2 + \cdots + \hat{\beta}_k x_k$$

$$y = \beta_0 + \beta_1 x_1 + \beta_2 x_2 + \cdots + \beta_k x_k + \epsilon$$

where y is the dependent variable, $x_1, x_2, ..., x_k$ are the independent variables,

$$E(y) = \beta_0 + \beta_1 x_1 + \beta_2 x_2 + \cdots + \beta_k x_k \text{ is the deterministic portion of}$$
the model

and β_i determines the contribution of the independent variable x_i.

Note: The symbols $x_1, x_2, ..., x_k$ may represent higher-order terms. For example, x_1 might represent the current interest rate, x_2 might represent x_1^2, and so forth.

---

that minimizes SSE $= \Sigma(y - \hat{y})^2$. This process, along with the estimation and test procedures associated with it, is called a **multiple regression analysis**.

For the statistical tests, confidence intervals, and prediction intervals to be valid, certain assumptions about the random error term must be satisfied. The assumptions for the general linear model, shown in the box, are identical to those for the straight-line model. As with the straight-line model, the assumptions need not hold exactly for the results of a multiple regression analysis to be valid. In fact, in many practical business applications they will be adequately satisfied. Statistical techniques for checking the validity of these assumptions are presented in Chapter 11.

ASSUMPTIONS ABOUT THE RANDOM ERROR TERM IN THE GENERAL LINEAR MODEL

1. The mean of the probability distribution of the random error is 0.
2. The variance σ^2 of the probability distribution of the random error is constant for all settings of the independent variables in the model.
3. The probability distribution of the random error is normal.
4. The errors associated with any two observations are independent.

Because the computations involved in a multiple regression analysis are very complex, almost all regression analyses are performed on a computer.* In the following sections we will present several examples of a multiple regression analysis and, in each case, we will examine and interpret the printouts for one of the statistical computer software packages discussed in this text (SAS, SPSS, and MINITAB).

---

* Performing a multiple regression analysis without a computer requires knowledge of matrices and matrix theory. Consult the references at the end of this chapter for details on the matrix mechanics of multiple regression.

FIRST-ORDER MODELS WITH QUANTITATIVE VARIABLES

10.5

Recall that the straight-line model,

$$E(y) = \beta_0 + \beta_1 x_1$$

of Section 10.3 is a first-order model in a single quantitative variable, x. Similarly, the model

$$E(y) = \beta_0 + \beta_1 x_1 + \beta_2 x_2$$

is a first-order model in two quantitative independent variables, x_1 and x_2. The term *first-order* is derived from the fact that the exponent for any x variable in the model is a "1." A **first-order model** in k quantitative variables is shown in the box.

A FIRST-ORDER MODEL RELATING $E(y)$ TO x_1, x_2, ..., x_k

$$E(y) = \beta_0 + \beta_1 x_1 + \beta_2 x_2 + \cdots + \beta_k x_k$$

where β_i represents the slope of the line relating y to x_i when all other x's are held fixed (ie, β_i measures the change in y for every 1 unit increase in x_i when all other x's are held constant).

In Section 10.3 we learned that in the straight-line model

$$E(y) = \beta_0 + \beta_1 x_1$$

β_0 represents the y-intercept of the line and β_1 represents the slope of the line. Furthermore, β_1 has a practical interpretation—it represents the mean change in y for every 1 unit increase in x. When the independent variables are quantitative (numeric variables), the β parameters in the multiple regression version of the first-order model have similar interpretations. The difference is that when we interpret the β that multiplies one of the variables (eg, x_1), we must be certain to hold the values of the remaining independent variables (eg, x_2, x_3) fixed.

For example, suppose that the mean value $E(y)$ of a response, y, is related to two quantitative independent variables, x_1 and x_2, by the model

$$E(y) = \beta_0 + \beta_1 x_1 + \beta_2 x_2$$

where $\beta_0 = 1$, $\beta_1 = 2$, and $\beta_2 = -1$. In other words,

$$E(y) = 1 + 2x_1 - x_2$$

When $x_2 = 0$, the relationship between $E(y)$ and x_1 is given by

$$E(y) = 1 + 2x_1 - (0) = 1 + 2x_1$$

A graph of this relationship (a straight line) is shown in Figure 10.16. Similar graphs of the relationship between $E(y)$ and x_1 for $x_2 = 1$,

$$E(y) = 1 + 2x_1 - (1) = 2x_1$$

and for $x_2 = 2$,

$$E(y) = 1 + 2x_1 - (2) = -1 + 2x_1$$

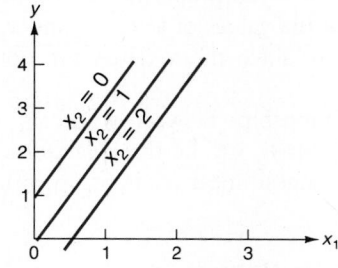

FIGURE 10.16
Graphs of $E(y) = 1 + 2x_1 - x_2$ for $x_2 = 0, 1, 2$

are shown in Figure 10.16. Note that the slopes of the three lines are all equal to $\beta_1 = 2$, the coefficient that multiplies x_1.

Figure 10.16 illustrates a characteristic of all first-order models: If you graph $E(y)$ versus any one variable (say, x_1) for fixed values of the other variables, the response curve will always be a *straight line* with slope equal to β_1. If you repeat the process for other values of the fixed independent variables, you will obtain a set of *parallel straight lines*. This indicates that the effect of the independent variable x_i on $E(y)$ is independent of all the other independent variables in the model, and this effect is measured by the slope β_i.

Consequently, you should hypothesize a first-order model for $E(y)$ in step 1 of a multiple regression analysis if you feel (1) that a linear relationship exists between y and each of the quantitative x's, and (2) that the relationship between y and x_i is independent of all the other x's.

EXAMPLE 10.9 Suppose a real estate investor wants to model the relationship between the sale price, y, of a residential property in a midsize city and the following three quantitative independent variables: x_1 = appraised land value of the property, x_2 = appraised value of improvements on the property (ie, home value), and x_3 = area of living space on the property (ie, home size). The investor theorizes that sale price, y, is linearly related to all three x's and that the relationship between y and any one x is independent of the remaining two x's. To build the model, the investor selects a random sample of $n = 20$ properties from the thousands of properties sold in a recent year. The resulting data are given in Table 10.8. Conduct a complete multiple regression analysis of the data.

Solution

STEP 1   Since the investor believes that sale price is linearly related to x_1, x_2, and x_3, and that the straight-line relationships are independent, the appropriate model is the first-order model:

$$E(y) = \beta_0 + \beta_1 x_1 + \beta_2 x_2 + \beta_3 x_3$$

STEP 2   The investor has collected appraisal data for $n = 20$ properties. Thus, the experimental unit is a residential property. Note that the values of y, x_1, x_2, and x_3 are recorded for each property in Table 10.8. Also, since the x-values are not controlled, the data are observational in nature.

SPSS scatterplots for examining the bivariate relationships between y and x_1, y and x_2, and y and x_3 are shown in Figure 10.17 (p. 464). Of the three variables, appraised improvements (x_2) appears to have the strongest linear relationship with sale price (y).

STEP 3   The first-order model is fit to the data of Table 10.8 using SAS. A portion of the SAS printout is reproduced in Figure 10.18 (p. 465). The least squares estimates of the β parameters appear in the column labeled Parameter Estimate. You can see that $\hat{\beta}_0 = 1{,}470.275919$, $\hat{\beta}_1 = .814490$, $\hat{\beta}_2 = .820445$, and $\hat{\beta}_3 =$

TABLE 10.8
Real Estate Appraisal Data for 20 Properties

PROPERTY Observation	SALE PRICE y, Dollars	LAND VALUE x_1, Dollars	IMPROVEMENTS VALUE x_2, Dollars	AREA x_3, Square Feet
1	68,900	5,960	44,967	1,873
2	48,500	9,000	27,860	928
3	55,500	9,500	31,439	1,126
4	62,000	10,000	39,592	1,265
5	116,500	18,000	72,827	2,214
6	45,000	8,500	27,317	912
7	38,000	8,000	29,856	899
8	83,000	23,000	47,752	1,803
9	59,000	8,100	39,117	1,204
10	47,500	9,000	29,349	1,725
11	40,500	7,300	40,166	1,080
12	40,000	8,000	31,679	1,529
13	97,000	20,000	58,510	2,455
14	45,500	8,000	23,454	1,151
15	40,900	8,000	20,897	1,173
16	80,000	10,500	56,248	1,960
17	56,000	4,000	20,859	1,344
18	37,000	4,500	22,610	988
19	50,000	3,400	35,948	1,076
20	22,400	1,500	5,779	962

13.528650. Therefore, the equation that minimizes the SSE for this data set (ie, the least squares prediction equation) is

$$\hat{y} = 1{,}470.28 + .8145x_1 + .8204x_2 + 13.53x_3$$

With first-order models, we know that β_1 represents the slope of the y–x_1 line for fixed x_2 and x_3. That is, β_1 measures the change in $E(y)$ for every 1 unit increase in x_1 when all other independent variables in the model are held fixed. Similar statements can be made about β_2 and β_3 (eg, β_2 measures the change in $E(y)$ for every 1 unit increase in x_2 when all other x's in the model are held fixed). Consequently, we obtain the following interpretations of the β estimates:

$\hat{\beta}_1 = .8145$: We estimate the mean sale price of a property, $E(y)$, to increase $0.8145 for every $1 increase in appraised land value (x_1) when both appraised improvements (x_2) and area (x_3) are held fixed.

$\hat{\beta}_2 = .8204$: We estimate the mean sale price of a property, $E(y)$, to increase $0.8204 for every $1 increase in appraised improvements (x_2) when both appraised land value (x_1) and area (x_3) are held fixed.

$\hat{\beta}_3 = 13.53$: We estimate the mean sale price of a property, $E(y)$, to increase $13.53 for each additional square foot of living area (x_3) when both appraised land value (x_1) and appraised improvements (x_2) are held fixed.

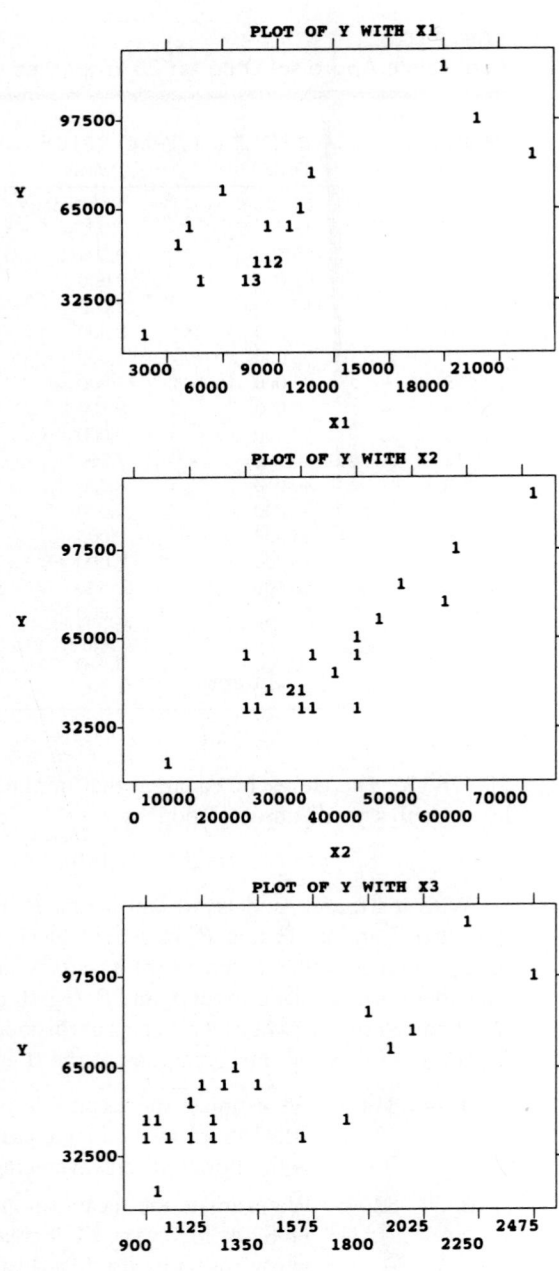

FIGURE 10.17
SPSS Scatterplots for the Data of
Table 10.8

FIGURE 10.18
SAS Output for Sale Price Model

Analysis of Variance

Source	DF	Sum of Squares	Mean Square	F Value	Prob>F
Model	3	8779676740.6	2926558913.5	46.662	0.0001
Error	16	1003491259.4	62718203.714		
C Total	19	9783168000.0			

Root MSE	7919.48254	R-Square	0.8974	
Dep Mean	56660.00000	Adj R-Sq	0.8782	
C.V.	13.97720			

Parameter Estimates

Variable	DF	Parameter Estimate	Standard Error	T for H0: Parameter=0	Prob > |T|
INTERCEP	1	1470.275919	5746.3245832	0.256	0.8013
X1	1	0.814490	0.51221871	1.590	0.1314
X2	1	0.820445	0.21118494	3.885	0.0013
X3	1	13.528650	6.58568006	2.054	0.0567

The value $\hat{\beta}_0 = 1,470.28$ does not have a meaningful interpretation in the example. Note that $\hat{y} = \hat{\beta}_0$ when $x_1 = x_2 = x_3 = 0$. Thus, $\hat{\beta}_0 = 1,470.28$ represents the estimated mean sale price when the values of all the independent variables are set equal to 0. Since a residential property with these characteristics—appraised land value of \$0, appraised improvements of \$0, and 0 square feet of living area—is not realistic, the value of $\hat{\beta}_0$ has no meaningful interpretation. In general, $\hat{\beta}_0$ will not have a practical interpretation unless it makes sense to set the values of the x's simultaneously equal to 0.

> **WARNING**
>
> The interpretation of the β parameters in the general linear model will depend on the terms specified in the model. The interpretations above are for a first-order linear model only. In practice, you should be sure that a first-order model is the correct model for $E(y)$ before making these β interpretations. [We discuss alternative models for $E(y)$ in Sections 10.6–10.7.]

STEP 4   To proceed with model testing, we must assume that the random error term, ϵ, of the probabilistic model has a mean of 0, has constant variance σ^2, and is normally distributed. Also, the error associated with any one residential property is assumed to be independent of the error associated with any other property.

Specification of the probability distribution of ϵ is not complete unless we obtain an estimate of the error variance, σ^2. Recall from Section 10.3 that we can use the SSE to estimate σ^2. The estimator for the straight-line model was $s^2 = \text{SSE}/(n - 2)$. Note that the denominator is

$$n - (\text{Number of estimated } \beta \text{ parameters})$$

which, in the case of the straight-line model, is equal to $n - 2$. Since we must estimate two more parameters, β_2 and β_3, for the first-order model in this example, the estimator of σ^2 is

$$s^2 = \frac{\text{SSE}}{n - 4}$$

That is, the denominator becomes $(n - 4)$ because there are now four β parameters (including β_0) in the model.

From the SAS printout, Figure 10.18, SSE = 1,003,491,259.4. Thus, the estimate of σ^2 for this example is

$$s^2 = \frac{\text{SSE}}{20 - 4} = \frac{1,003,491,259.4}{16} = 62,718,203.7$$

This estimate also appears in the printout as the Mean Square for Error (MSE). Similarly, the standard deviation, $s = 7,919.48$, appears to the right of the heading Root MSE in Figure 10.18.

ESTIMATOR OF σ^2: MULTIPLE REGRESSION

$$s^2 = \frac{\text{SSE}}{n - (\text{Number of estimated } \beta \text{ parameters})}$$

where n is the number of data points.

The interpretation of s in multiple regression is essentially the same as that for simple linear regression. Since s estimates the standard deviation of the errors of prediction, we expect most of the y-values to lie within $2s = 2(7,919.48) = 15,838.96$ of their least squares predicted value, $\hat{y}$. Consequently, we expect the first-order model with appraised land value (x_1), appraised improvements (x_2), and area (x_3) to predict the sale price (y) of a residential property to within about $15,839 of its true value.

STEP 5   The objective of this step is to test the utility of the first-order model—that is, to determine whether the model is really useful for predicting y.

TEST OF OVERALL MODEL UTILITY

One way to determine the usefulness of the model is to conduct individual t tests on each of the β parameters in the model, excluding β_0. For this model, we would test H_0: $\beta_1 = 0$, H_0: $\beta_2 = 0$, and H_0: $\beta_3 = 0$, each at $\alpha = .05$. (We show how to conduct these tests later in this example.) However, conducting ɛ   ɛate t tests on the β's is generally not a good way to determine whether a model is contributing information for the prediction of y. If all three β parameters in the model are in fact equal to 0, you will incorrectly reject the null hypothesis at least once and conclude that some β parameter is nonzero approximately 14% of the time (proof omitted). In other words, the overall probability of a Type I error is about .14, not

.05! Thus, conducting multiple t tests leads to an inflated overall Type I error probability.

A better way to test the overall utility of a linear model is to conduct a test involving all the β parameters (except β_0) simultaneously. That is, test the hypothesis

H_0: $\beta_1 = \beta_2 = \beta_3 = 0$

H_a: At least one of the β parameters in H_0 is nonzero.

Practically speaking, this test for model utility is a comparison of the predictive ability of the estimated general linear model (which uses the predictor $\hat{y} = \hat{\beta}_0 + \hat{\beta}_1 x_1 + \hat{\beta}_2 x_2 + \cdots + \hat{\beta}_k x_k$) with a model that contains no x's (which uses the predictor $\hat{y} = \bar{y}$). If the test shows that at least one of the β's is nonzero, then the value of $\hat{y}$ obtained from the estimated linear model will generally predict a future value of y more accurately than the sample mean, $\bar{y}$.

The test statistic used in the test for model utility is an F statistic. The formula for computing the F statistic is given in the box. However, most statistical computer software packages with regression analysis routines give this F-value. The F-value for the sale price model in the SAS computer printout (Figure 10.18) is $F = 46.662$. To determine whether this F-value is statistically significant, we read the value of the observed significance level given in the SAS printout. The observed significance level for this test, .0001, is located in Figure 10.18 in the column headed Prob > F.

PROCEDURE FOR TESTING WHETHER THE OVERALL MULTIPLE REGRESSION MODEL IS USEFUL FOR PREDICTING y

---

H_0: $\beta_1 = \beta_2 = \cdots = \beta_k = 0$

H_a: At least one of the parameters $\beta_1, \beta_2, ..., \beta_k$ differs from 0.

Test statistic: $F = \dfrac{\text{Mean square for model}}{\text{Mean square for error}}$

$$= \left[\frac{\text{SS(Model)}}{\text{SSE}}\right]\left[\frac{n - (k + 1)}{k}\right]$$

$$= \left(\frac{R^2}{1 - R^2}\right)\left[\frac{n - (k + 1)}{k}\right]$$

Rejection region: $F > F_\alpha$

where

  n = Number of observations

  k = Number of parameters in the model (excluding β_0)

  R^2 = Coefficient of determination

and the distribution of F depends on k numerator degrees of freedom and $n - (k + 1)$ denominator degrees of freedom. Values of F_α for $\alpha = .10, .05, .025,$ and $.01$ are given in Tables 7–10, Appendix A.

This implies that we would reject the null hypothesis for any α level larger than .0001. Thus, we have strong evidence to reject H_0 and to conclude that at least one of the model coefficients, β_1, β_2, and β_3, is nonzero. Since the observed significance level is so small, there is ample evidence to indicate that the first-order model is useful for predicting the sale price of residential properties.

[*Note:* Some software packages do not compute the value of the F statistic for testing the model, and some do not compute its observed significance level. In such cases, you can calculate the F statistic directly using the formula shown in the box and reject H_0: $\beta_1 = \beta_2 = \cdots = \beta_k = 0$ for a given value of α if $F > F_\alpha$.]

WARNING

Rejecting H_0: $\beta_1 = \beta_2 = \cdots = \beta_k = 0$ in a test of overall model adequacy does not necessarily imply that the model is "best" for predicting y. Another model may prove even more useful in terms of providing more reliable estimates and predictions.

---

t TESTS ON INDIVIDUAL β PARAMETERS

After we have determined that the overall model is useful for predicting y using the F test, we may elect to conduct one or more t tests on the individual β parameters. However, the test (or tests) to be conducted should be decided a priori—that is, prior to fitting the model. Also, we should limit the number of t tests conducted in order to avoid the potential problem of making too many Type I errors. Generally, the regression analyst will conduct t tests on only the "most important" β's. These are usually the β's associated with higher-order terms (x_1^2, $x_1 x_2$, etc.), since these terms control the shape of the hypothesized model. (We provide further insight into identifying the most important β's in a linear model in Sections 10.6–10.8.)

To illustrate a t test on an individual β, suppose we decide a priori to test whether the value of appraised improvements, x_2, is useful for predicting sale price, y. Then we require a test of hypothesis

H_0: $\beta_2 = 0$ Appraised improvements not useful for predicting sale price

H_a: $\beta_2 \neq 0$ Appraised improvements is a useful predictor of sale price

This t test is quite similar to the test about the slope of the simple straight-line model (refer to Section 10.3). The details for a test about any β parameter in the general linear model are given in the box at the top of the next page.*

---

* The formula for the estimated standard error of $\hat{\beta}_i$, denoted $s_{\hat{\beta}_i}$, is too complex to present here. However, nearly all statistical software packages report these standard errors in their printouts.

To test the null hypothesis that $\beta_2 = 0$, we again consult the SAS printout for the sale price model. From Figure 10.18, we see that the computed value of the test statistic corresponding to the test of H_0: $\beta_2 = 0$ (located under the column headed T for H0: Parameter = 0) is $t = 3.885$. The two-tailed observed significance level (*p*-value) for the test is given under the column headed Prob > |T| in the row corresponding to X2. [*Note:* One-tailed observed significance levels are obtained by dividing the two-tailed *p*-values in half.] The observed significance level, .0013, implies that we would reject H_0: $\beta_2 = 0$ in favor of H_a: $\beta_2 \neq 0$ at any α level larger than .0013. Thus, there is very strong evidence of at least a linear relationship between sale price (y) and appraised improvements value (x_2) for these residential properties.

Notice that the *p*-value for appraised land value (x_1) is .1314. Since the *p*-value is larger than $\alpha = .05$, we would fail to reject the null hypothesis H_0: $\beta_1 = 0$. Our first inclination might be to assume that $\beta_1 = 0$ and, therefore, that appraised land value is not useful for predicting sales price. However, such a decision is dangerous for two reasons. First, the fact that we are accepting H_0: $\beta_1 = 0$ leaves us vulnerable to making a Type II error with unknown probability of occurrence. Second, if $\beta_1 = 0$, the most we can say is that appraised land value (x_1) is not a useful linear predictor of sale price (y). There may, in fact, be a strong *curvilinear (second-order) relationship* between y and x_1. (We explain in Section 10.6 how to determine whether such a relationship exists.)

WARNING

It is dangerous to conduct t tests on the individual β parameters in a *first-order linear model* for the purpose of determining which independent variables are useful for predicting y and which are not. If you fail to reject H_0: $\beta_i = 0$, three conclusions are possible:

1. There is no relationship between y and x_i.
2. A straight-line relationship between y and x_i exists (holding the other x's in the model fixed), but a Type II error occurred.
3. A relationship between y and x_i (holding the other x's in the model fixed) exists, but is more complex than a straight-line relationship (eg, a curvilinear relationship may be appropriate).

The most you can say about a β parameter test is that there is either sufficient (if you reject H_0: $\beta_i = 0$) or insufficient (if you do not reject H_0: $\beta_i = 0$) evidence of a *linear (straight-line) relationship* between y and x_i.

CONFIDENCE INTERVALS FOR β PARAMETERS

Additional information on the model's utility can be obtained from 95% confidence intervals for the β parameters. A confidence interval for any β parameter in a general linear model is given in the next box.

A $(1 - \alpha)100\%$ CONFIDENCE INTERVAL FOR AN INDIVIDUAL PARAMETER COEFFICIENT IN THE GENERAL LINEAR MODEL

$$\hat{\beta}_i \pm t_{\alpha/2} s_{\hat{\beta}_i}$$

where

n = Number of observations

$s_{\hat{\beta}_i}$ = Estimated standard error of $\hat{\beta}_i$

the distribution of t has degrees of freedom equal to (n − Number of β parameters in the model), and $t_{\alpha/2}$ is the t-value such that $P(t > t_{\alpha/2}) = \alpha/2$.

To illustrate, we will form a 95% confidence interval for β_2. From Figure 10.18, we see that $\hat{\beta}_2 = .820445$. The estimated standard deviations of the model coefficients appear in the SAS printout under the column labeled Standard Error. The estimated standard error of $\hat{\beta}_2$ is $s_{\hat{\beta}_2} = .21118494$. Substituting the values of $\hat{\beta}_2$, $s_{\hat{\beta}_2}$, and $t_{.025} = 2.120$ (based on $n - 4 = 16$ degrees of freedom) into the formula for a confidence interval, we find the 95% confidence interval for β_2 to be

$$\hat{\beta}_2 \pm t_{\alpha/2} s_{\hat{\beta}_2} = .820445 \pm (2.120)(.21118494)$$

or (.372733, 1.268157). This interval can be used to estimate the change in mean sale price as appraised improvements value x_2 is increased, holding the values of x_1 and x_3 fixed. We are 95% confident that for every \$1 increase in appraised improvements value, the mean sale price will increase by an amount between \$0.37 and \$1.27. Note that all values in the interval are positive, reconfirming our test conclusion that β_2 is nonzero.

COEFFICIENT OF DETERMINATION

Another measure of model adequacy is the coefficient of determination, R^2. The value of R^2 for this multiple regression model (obtained from the SAS printout) is $R^2 = .8947$.

Just as for the simple linear model, R^2 represents the proportion of the sum of squares of deviations (SS_{yy}) of the y-values about $\bar{y}$ that can be attributed to the regression model. Thus, $R^2 = 0$ implies a complete lack of fit of the model to the data, and $R^2 = 1$ implies a perfect fit, with the model passing through every data point. In general, the larger the value of R^2, the better the model fits the data.

DEFINITION 10.7

The **multiple coefficient of determination, R^2,** is defined as

$$R^2 = 1 - \frac{SSE}{SS_{yy}} \qquad 0 \le R^2 \le 1$$

where $SSE = \Sigma(y - \hat{y})^2$, $SS_{yy} = \Sigma(y - \bar{y})^2$, and $\hat{y}$ is the predicted value of y for the multiple regression model.

Thus, $R^2 = .8974$ implies that, by using the three independent variables (appraised land value, appraised improvements value, and home size) in a first-order model to predict y, instead of $\bar{y}$, we can reduce the sum of squared prediction errors by approximately 90%. Thus, this large value of R^2 indicates that the model provides a good fit to the $n = 20$ sample data points.

A large value of R^2 computed from the sample data does not necessarily mean that the model provides a good fit to all the data points in the population. For example, a first-order linear model that contains three parameters will provide a perfect fit to a sample of three data points, and R^2 will equal 1. Likewise, you will always obtain a perfect fit ($R^2 = 1$) to a set of n data points if the model contains exactly n parameters. Consequently, if you want to use R^2 as a measure of model utility, it should be based on a sample that contains substantially more data points than the number of parameters in the model.

As an alternative to using R^2 as a measure of model adequacy, the **adjusted multiple coefficient of determination**, denoted R_a^2, is often reported. The formula for R_a^2 is shown in the box at the top of the next page.

Unlike R^2, R_a^2 takes into account (adjusts for) both the sample size n and the number of β parameters in the model. The value of R_a^2 will always be smaller than R^2, and more importantly, cannot be "forced" to equal 1 by simply adding more and more independent variables to the model. Consequently, analysts prefer the more conservative R_a^2 when choosing a measure of model adequacy.

THE ADJUSTED MULTIPLE COEFFICIENT OF DETERMINATION

$$R_a^2 = 1 - \frac{n-1}{n-(k+1)}\left(\frac{SSE}{SS_{yy}}\right)$$

$$= 1 - \frac{n-1}{n-(k+1)}(1 - R^2)$$

For example, the value of R_a^2 is shown in the SAS printout (Figure 10.18) directly under the value of R^2. Note that $R_a^2 = .8782$, a value only slightly smaller than R^2. Our interpretation is that after adjusting for sample size and the number of parameters in the model, approximately 88% of the sample variation in sale price can be explained by the first-order model.

Despite their utility, R^2 and R_a^2 are only sample statistics. Consequently, it is dangerous to judge the usefulness of the model based solely on these values. It is better to conduct the overall F test of model utility first. If the model is deemed adequate based on this test, then R^2 or R_a^2 can provide useful information about the degree to which the model fits the data.

RECOMMENDATIONS FOR CHECKING THE UTILITY OF A MULTIPLE REGRESSION MODEL

1. First, conduct a test of overall model adequacy using the F test; that is, test

   $$H_0: \quad \beta_1 = \beta_2 = \cdots = \beta_k = 0$$

   If the model is deemed adequate (ie, if you reject H_0), then proceed to steps 2 and 3. Otherwise, you should hypothesize and fit another model. The new model may include more independent variables or higher-order terms.

2. Conduct t tests on those β parameters that you are particularly interested in (ie, the most important β's). These usually involve only the β's associated with higher-order terms (x_1^2, $x_1 x_2$, etc.). It is a safe practice to limit the number of β's that are tested. Conducting a series of t tests leads to a high overall Type I error rate.

3. Interpret the value of R^2 (or R_a^2). A low value may imply that a more useful model can be found.

ESTIMATING $E(Y)$ AND PREDICTING Y

STEP 6 Once the model has been deemed useful, we may use it for prediction and estimation. Our methods for prediction and estimation using any general linear model are identical to those discussed in Section 10.3 for the simple straight-line model. We will use the model to form a confidence interval for the mean $E(y)$ for a given value of x, or a prediction interval for a future value of y for a given x.

To form confidence and prediction intervals, we need to know the standard deviation of the sampling distribution for the estimator, $\hat{y}$. For general linear models, the form of this standard deviation is very complex. However, most regression computer packages allow us to obtain these intervals at any given setting of the independent variables. A 95% confidence interval for the mean sale price, $E(y)$, and a 95% prediction interval for y are shown in the SAS printout, Figure 10.19.

FIGURE 10.19

SAS Printout Showing Confidence Interval (Top) and Prediction Interval (Bottom) for $x_1 = 15{,}000$, $x_2 = 50{,}000$, and $x_3 = 1{,}800$

Obs	X1	X2	X3	Y	Predict Value	Residual	Lower95% Mean	Upper95% Mean
21	15000	50000	1800	.	79061.4	.	73380.7	84742.1

Obs	X1	X2	X3	Y	Predict Value	Residual	Lower95% Predict	Upper95% Predict
21	15000	50000	1800	.	79061.4	.	61337.9	96785

The 95% confidence interval for $E(y)$, the mean sale price for all properties with an appraised land value of $x_1 = \$15{,}000$, an appraised improvements value of $x_2 = \$50{,}000$, and a home size of $x_3 = 1{,}800$ square feet, is shown (top of Figure 10.19) to be $73,380.70 to $84,742.10. The corresponding prediction interval (shown at the bottom of Figure 10.19) extends from $61,337.90 to $96,785.00. As expected, the prediction interval for y is wider than the confidence interval for $E(y)$.

Just as in simple linear regression, it is dangerous to use any general linear model for making predictions outside the region in which the sample data fall. Checking the sample data given in Table 10.8, we see that appraised land value (x_1) ranges from $1,500 to $23,000, appraised improvements value (x_2) ranges from $5,779 to $72,827, and home size ($x_3$) ranges from 899 to 2,455 square feet. Consequently, we would not use the estimated model to make estimates or predictions for properties with values of the independent variables outside their respective ranges.* In general, the fitted model might not provide a good model for the relationship between the mean y and the value of x when stretched over a wider range of x-values.

WARNING

Do not use the least squares model to predict a value of y outside the region in which the sample data fall. In other words, do not predict y for values of the independent variables x_1, x_2, ..., x_k that are not within the range of the sample data.

---

* With two or more independent variables in the model, the values of x_1, x_2, etc., *jointly* define the experimental region. An observation with values of the x's that fall within their respective sample ranges may still fall outside the experimental region. For more information on this "hidden extrapolation" problem, consult the references given at the end of this chapter.

In Example 10.9 we have demonstrated the methods of multiple regression analysis by fitting a first-order linear model to a set of data. In the next three sections (Sections 10.6–10.8) we will introduce other, more complex, models that are useful for relating a response variable y to a set of independent variables.

PROBLEMS

10.12　Residential property appraisers make extensive use of multiple regression in their evaluation of property. Typically, the sale price (y) of a property is modeled as a function of several home-related conditions (eg, gross living area, location, number of bedrooms). However, appraisers are not interested in the predicted price, $\hat{y}$. Rather, they use the regression model as a tool for making value adjustments to the property. These adjustments are derived from the parameter estimates of the model. The *Real Estate Appraiser* (Apr. 1992) reported the results of a multiple regression analysis on the price (y) of $n = 157$ residential properties recently sold in a Northern Virginia subdivision. The SAS printout of the analysis is reproduced below. Note that there are 27 independent variables in the model.

Dep Variable: Sale Price

Analysis of Variance

Source	DF	Sum of Squares	Mean Square	F Value	Prob>F
Model	27	24184211898	895711551.79	20.914	0.0001
Error	129	5524834283	42828172.73		
C Total	156	29709046181			

Root MSE	6544.324	R-Square	0.8140	
Dep Mean	173157.5	Adj R-Sq	0.7751	
C.V.	3.779404			

Parameter Estimates

Variable	Parameter Estimate	Standard Error	95% Confidence Interval (@129df=1.98)	T for H0: Parameter=0	Prob > |T|
Intercept	96603	12530	(71794 to 121412)	7.710	.0001
Time	150	123	(-94 to 394)	1.220	.2248
Lot Size	.60	.30	(0.01 to 1.19)	2.022	.0452
Age	381	502	(-613 to 1375)	.758	.4501
GLA	22.40	3.67	(15.13 to 29.67)	6.099	.0001
Bedrooms	2263	1609	(-923 to 5499)	1.407	.1619
Half Baths	5962	2934	(153 to 11771)	2.032	.0442
Corner Lot	-1481	1692	(-4831 to 1869)	-.876	.3829
Cul-de-Sac	-56	2557	(-5119 to 5007)	-.022	.9825
Back to Woods	4086	2044	(39 to 8133)	1.999	.0477
Deck	2408	2167	(-1883 to 6699)	1.111	.2686

Fence	2896	1271	(379 to 5413)	2.279	.0243
Shed	70	1343	(-2589 to 2729)	.052	.9588
Patio	2377	1671	(-932 to 5686)	1.423	.1572
Portico	-906	2963	(-6773 to 4961)	-.306	.7603
Screen Porch	5021	2038	(986 to 9056)	2.463	.0151
In-grnd Pool	7570	3028	(1575 to 13565)	2.500	.0137
Garage	2989	1446	(126 to 5852)	2.068	.0407
Driveway	-1844	3222	(-8224 to 4536)	-.572	.5681
Fireplace	1290	1277	(-1238 to 3818)	1.010	.3144
Brick Facade	-2140	2369	(-6381 to 2551)	-.903	.3680
Updated Kit.	4171	1470	(1260 to 7082)	2.837	.0053
Remodel Kit.	6091	2367	(1404 to 10778)	2.574	.0112
Intercom	1933	2146	(-2316 to 6182)	.901	.3693
Cen. Vacuum	-4636	2166	(-8925 to -347)	-2.140	.0342
Skylights	7744	2622	(2552 to 12936)	-2.954	.0037
Air Filter	874	2506	(-4088 to 5836)	-.349	.7280
Bay Window	-3174	2086	(-7304 to 956)	-1.522	.1305

Source: Gilson, S. J. "A Case Study—Comparing the Results: Multiple Regression Analysis Vs. Matched Pairs in Residential Subdivision." *The Real Estate Appraiser*, Apr. 1992, p. 37 (Table 4).

  a. Interpret the values of F Value, Root MSE, R-Square, and Adj R-Sq shown in the printout.
  b. One of the independent variables in the model is gross living area (GLA), measured in square feet. A 95% confidence interval for the β coefficient associated with GLA is shown in the printout. Interpret this interval.
  c. Note that the independent variables with β coefficients significantly different from 0 (at $\alpha = .05$) are highlighted in color in the printout. The nonsignificant variables are not highlighted. Would you advise the property appraiser to ignore any value adjustments based on nonsignificant independent variables? Explain.

10.13 Is the suicide rate in the United States related to the health of the economy? This question was the topic of research reported in the *American Journal of Economics and Sociology* (Jan. 1992). The annual suicide rate y (measured as number of suicides per 100,000 persons) was recorded over the period 1940–1984 ($n = 45$ years). In addition, the following independent variables were measured each year:

$$x_1 = \text{Gross National Product (GNP) in 1982 dollars}$$

$$x_2 = \text{GNP for the previous year}$$

$$x_3 = \text{Unemployment rate}$$

$$x_4 = \begin{cases} 1 & \text{if World War II (1942–1945)} \\ 0 & \text{if not} \end{cases}$$

$$x_5 = \text{Female labor force participation rate}$$

$$x_6 = \text{Divorce rate}$$

$$x_7 = \text{Proportion of U.S. population that is Catholic}$$

The regression results are summarized below. [*Note:* t-values for β parameters are given in parentheses.] Interpret the regression results.

$$\hat{y} = 1.57 + .48x_1 - .57x_2 + .01x_3 - .06x_4 - .01x_5 + .35x_6 + .01x_7$$
$$(1.65)\ (4.18)\ (-6.34)\ \ (4.14)\ (-2.30)\ (-3.16)\ \ (10.35)\ \ (3.00)$$
$$R^2 = .92 \qquad R_a^2 = .90 \qquad F = 31.9$$

10.14 In a production facility, an accurate estimate of work-hours needed to complete a task is crucial to management in making such decisions as the proper number of workers to hire, an accurate deadline to quote a client, or cost-analysis decisions regarding budgets. A manufacturer of boiler drums wants to use regression analysis to predict the number of work-hours needed to erect the drums for future projects. To accomplish this, data for 35 boilers were collected. In addition to work-hours (y), the variables measured were boiler capacity (x_1 = pounds per hour), boiler design pressure (x_2 = pounds per square inch), boiler type (x_3 = 1 if industry field erected, 0 if utility field erected), and drum type (x_4 = 1 if steam, 0 if mud). The data are provided in the table. A MINITAB printout for the model $E(y) = \beta_0 + \beta_1 x_1 + \beta_2 x_2 + \beta_3 x_3 + \beta_4 x_4$ follows.

WORK-HOURS y	BOILER CAPACITY x_1	DESIGN PRESSURE x_2	BOILER TYPE	DRUM TYPE
3,137	120,000	375	Industrial	Steam
3,590	65,000	750	Industrial	Steam
4,526	150,000	500	Industrial	Steam
10,825	1,073,877	2,170	Utility	Steam
4,023	150,000	325	Industrial	Steam
7,606	610,000	1,500	Utility	Steam
3,748	88,200	399	Industrial	Steam
2,972	88,200	399	Industrial	Steam
3,163	88,200	399	Industrial	Steam
4,065	90,000	1,140	Industrial	Steam
2,048	30,000	325	Industrial	Steam
6,500	441,000	410	Industrial	Steam
5,651	441,000	410	Industrial	Steam
6,565	441,000	410	Industrial	Steam
6,387	441,000	410	Industrial	Steam
6,454	627,000	1,525	Utility	Steam
6,928	610,000	1,500	Utility	Steam
4,268	150,000	500	Industrial	Steam
14,791	1,089,490	2,170	Utility	Steam
2,680	125,000	750	Industrial	Steam
2,974	120,000	375	Industrial	Mud
1,965	65,000	750	Industrial	Mud
2,566	150,000	500	Industrial	Mud
1,515	150,000	250	Industrial	Mud
2,000	150,000	500	Industrial	Mud
2,735	150,000	325	Industrial	Mud
3,698	610,000	1,500	Utility	Mud
2,635	90,000	1,140	Industrial	Mud
1,206	30,000	325	Industrial	Mud
3,775	441,000	410	Industrial	Mud
3,120	441,000	410	Industrial	Mud
4,206	441,000	410	Industrial	Mud
4,006	441,000	410	Industrial	Mud
3,728	627,000	1,525	Utility	Mud
3,211	610,000	1,500	Utility	Mud
1,200	30,000	325	Industrial	Mud

Source: Kelly Uscategui, former graduate student, University of South Florida.

a. Test the hypothesis that boiler capacity (x_1) is positively linearly related to work-hours (y). Use $\alpha = .05$.
b. Test the hypothesis that boiler pressure (x_2) is positively linearly related to work-hours (y). Use $\alpha = .05$.
c. Construct a 95% confidence interval for β_3. (We will learn how to interpret this interval in Section 10.8.)
d. Conduct a test of overall model adequacy.

MINITAB Printout for Problem 10.14

```
The regression equation is
Y = - 3783 + 0.00875 X1 + 1.93 X2 + 3444 X3 + 2093 X4

Predictor       Coef       Stdev     t-ratio        p
Constant       -3783        1205       -3.14    0.004
X1         0.0087490   0.0009035        9.68    0.000
X2            1.9265      0.6489        2.97    0.006
X3            3444.3       911.7        3.78    0.001
X4            2093.4       305.6        6.85    0.000

s = 894.6      R-sq = 90.3%      R-sq(adj) = 89.0%

Analysis of Variance

SOURCE          DF          SS          MS         F        p
Regression       4   230854848    57713712     72.11    0.000
Error           31    24809760      800315
Total           35   255664608

SOURCE          DF      SEQ SS
X1               1   175007136
X2               1      490357
X3               1    17813090
X4               1    37544264

Unusual Observations
Obs.       X1          Y     Fit  Stdev.Fit  Residual   St.Resid
 19   1089490      14791   12022        523      2769      3.81R

R denotes an obs. with a large st. resid.

 Fit  Stdev.Fit        95% C.I.          95% P.I.
1936        239   (  1449,    2424)  (    47,    3825)
```

e. Interpret the value of s shown in the printout.
f. Interpret the value of R_a^2 shown in the printout.
g. Interpret the 95% confidence interval (C.I.) at the bottom of the printout. For this interval, $x_1 = 150,000$, $x_2 = 500$, $x_3 = 1$, and $x_4 = 0$.
h. Interpret the 95% prediction interval (P.I.) at the bottom of the printout. For this interval, $x_1 = 150,000$, $x_2 = 500$, $x_3 = 1$, and $x_4 = 0$.

10.15   Personal computer (PC) technology is changing at a phenomenal rate. As such, the retail price of a PC may vary dramatically depending on when it is purchased and what features it includes. Retail price data were recently collected for IBM and IBM-compatible PCs. The data for $n = 60$ PCs shown in the table (p. 478) were used to fit the multiple regression model

$$E(y) = \beta_0 + \beta_1 x_1 + \beta_2 x_2$$

The printout from an SPSS analysis follows the table, where

$$y = \text{Retail price (dollars)}$$

$$x_1 = \text{Microprocessor speed (megahertz)}$$

$$x_2 = \begin{cases} 1 & \text{if 386 CPU chip} \\ 0 & \text{if 286 CPU chip} \end{cases}$$

a. Write the least squares prediction equation.
b. Is the model adequate for predicting y? Test using $\alpha = .10$.
c. Construct a 90% confidence interval for β_1. Interpret the interval.
d. Is CPU chip (x_2) a useful predictor of price (y) in this model? Test using $\alpha = .10$.

Data for Problem 10.15

RETAIL PRICE y	SPEED MHz	CHIP	RETAIL PRICE y	SPEED MHz	CHIP	RETAIL PRICE y	SPEED MHz	CHIP
$5099	33	386	$3795	33	386	$2095	16	386
3995	25	386	3295	25	386	2695	25	386
2230	20	386	1995	16	386	2295	20	386
4395	33	386	2795	25	386	3445	25	386
6299	25	386	5795	33	386	2445	16	386
2549	16	386	3995	33	386	3795	25	386
3499	16	386	1850	12	286	2395	16	386
2995	16	386	1895	16	386	1595	12	286
1649	10	286	1795	16	286	2095	16	386
5499	20	386	2645	16	386	2995	25	386
1695	12	286	3249	25	386	2895	20	386
2595	20	386	2995	20	386	3995	33	386
3695	33	386	3419	20	386	2595	20	386
3499	33	386	1590	20	386	4995	25	386
2845	20	386	3899	20	386	2695	25	386
4195	33	386	2249	12	286	3990	33	386
2895	20	386	5796	25	386	2795	20	386
2195	12	286	4330	16	286	1995	20	286
5625	25	386	2699	16	386	1595	16	286
2495	20	386	5579	20	386	2875	20	386

Source: Computer Monthly, Computer Shopper, and IBM Corporation flyers. Data compiled by Jerasimos Mantas, University of South Florida business student.

```
* * * *   M U L T I P L E   R E G R E S S I O N   * * * *

Equation Number 1    Dependent Variable..   Y

Multiple R            .63263
R Square              .40022
Adjusted R Square     .37918
Standard Error     953.66516

Analysis of Variance
                     DF      Sum of Squares      Mean Square
Regression            2      34592103.00773   17296051.50386
Residual             57      51840202.92561     909477.24431

F =     19.01757       Signif F =  .0000

----------------- Variables in the Equation ------------------

Variable          B          SE B        Beta       T   Sig T

X2         357.184971   389.422935     .110908     .917   .3629
X1         104.838940    22.362982     .566873    4.688   .0000
(Constant) 648.022624   431.494302                1.502   .1387
```

10.16   As a result of the U.S. surgeon general's warnings about the health hazards of smoking, Congress banned television and radio advertising of cigarettes in January 1971. The banning of prosmoking messages, however, also led to the virtual elimination of antismoking messages. In theory, if these antismoking commercials are more effective than prosmoking commercials, the net effect of the congressional ban will be to increase the consumption of cigarettes and therefore benefit the tobacco industry. To test this hypothesis, researchers at the University of Houston built a cigarette-demand model based on data collected from 46 states over the 18 year period 1963–1980 (*The Review of Economics & Statistics*, Feb. 1986). For each state–year combination, the following independent variables were recorded:

x_1 = Natural logarithm of price of a carton of cigarettes

x_2 = Natural logarithm of minimum price of a carton of cigarettes in any neighboring state (This variable was included to measure the effect of "bootlegging" cigarettes in nearby states with lower tax rates.)

x_3 = Natural logarithm of real disposable income per capita

x_4 = Per capita index of expenditures for cigarette advertising on television and radio (This value is 0 for the years 1971–1980, when the ban was in effect.)

The dependent variable of interest is y, the natural logarithm of per capita consumption of cigarettes by persons of smoking age (14 years and older). The multiple regression model

$$E(y) = \beta_0 + \beta_1 x_1 + \beta_2 x_2 + \beta_3 x_3 + \beta_4 x_4$$

was fit to the $n = 828$ observations (46 states $\times$ 18 years) with the following results:

$$R^2 = .95 \qquad s = .047$$

a. Test the hypothesis that the model is useful for predicting y. (Use $\alpha = .05$.)

b. Give the null and alternative hypotheses appropriate for testing whether a decrease in per capita cigarette advertising expenditures is accompanied by an increase in per capita consumption of cigarettes over the period 1963–1980.

c. The value of $\hat{\beta}_4$ was determined to be .033. Interpret this value.

d. Does the value $\hat{\beta}_4 = .033$ support the alternative hypothesis of part **b**? Explain.

10.17 A major portion of the effort expended in developing commercial computer software is associated with program testing. A study was undertaken to assess the potential usefulness of various product- and process-related variables in identifying error-prone software (*IEEE Transactions on Software Engineering*, Apr. 1985). A multiple regression analysis was conducted to identify the variables related to computer modules (called *metrics*) that are useful for predicting the number y of discovered module defects. For a certain product written in PL/S language, the following model was fit to data collected for $n = 253$ modules:

$$E(y) = \beta_0 + \beta_1 x_1 + \beta_2 x_2$$

where

x_1 = Number of unique operands in the module

x_2 = Number of conditional statements, loops, and Boolean operators in the module

a. Interpret the β parameters in the first-order model.

b. The multiple coefficient of determination of the model was $R^2 = .78$. Is there sufficient evidence to indicate that the model is useful for predicting the number y of defects in modules of the software product? Test using $\alpha = .05$.

10.18 Marketers are keenly interested in the factors that motivate coupon usage by consumers. Three dominant motivational factors are thought to be (1) price reduction, (2) time and effort required to collect coupons, and (3) self-satisfaction. Using questionnaire data collected for a sample of $n = 290$ shoppers, a trio of marketing researchers examined the relationship between coupon usage and these factors (*The Journal of Consumer Marketing*, Spring 1988). The multiple regression model took the form

$$E(y) = \beta_0 + \beta_1 x_1 + \beta_2 x_2 + \beta_3 x_3$$

where

y = Coupon redemption rate

x_1 = Price-consciousness score

x_2 = Time value score

x_3 = Satisfaction/pride score

The results are summarized as follows (t-values for testing β's in parentheses):

$$\hat{\beta}_1 = .09784 \ (1.444) \qquad R^2 = .11671$$
$$\hat{\beta}_2 = -.13134 \ (-1.695) \qquad F = 9.6893$$
$$\hat{\beta}_3 = .20019 \ (2.571)$$

a. Conduct an overall test of model accuracy. Use $\alpha = .10$.
b. In theory, the more price-conscious you are, the higher your coupon redemption rate. Test the theory using $\alpha = .10$.
c. Interpret the negative β estimate for time value score (x_2).

INTERACTION MODELS WITH QUANTITATIVE VARIABLES

10.6

In Section 10.5 we demonstrated the relationship between $E(y)$ and the independent variables in a first-order linear model,

$$E(y) = \beta_0 + \beta_1 x_1 + \beta_2 x_2$$

When $E(y)$ is graphed against any one variable (say, x_1) for fixed values of the other variable (x_2), the result is a set of *parallel* straight lines (see Figure 10.20). When this situation occurs (as it always does for a first-order model), we say that the relationship between $E(y)$ and any one independent variable *does not depend on* the value of the other independent variable(s) in the model—that is, we say that the independent variables **do not interact**.

However, if the relationship between $E(y)$ and x_1 *does depend on the value of x_2* held fixed, then the first-order model is not appropriate for predicting y. In this case, we need another model that will take this dependence into account.

For example, suppose that the mean value $E(y)$ of a response y is related to two quantitative independent variables, x_1 and x_2, by the model

$$E(y) = \beta_0 + \beta_1 x_1 + \beta_2 x_2 + \beta_3 x_1 x_2$$

where $\beta_0 = 1$, $\beta_1 = 2$, $\beta_2 = -1$, and $\beta_3 = 1$. Then we have

$$E(y) = 1 + 2x_1 - x_2 + x_1 x_2$$

Note that this model contains the term $x_1 x_2$ in addition to all the terms of the first-order model discussed in Section 10.5.

Substituting $x_2 = 0$, 1, and 2 into the equation for $E(y)$, we obtain three response lines relating $E(y)$ to x_1—one for each of the values $x_2 = 0$, 1, and 2. For $x_2 = 0$:

$$E(y) = 1 + 2x_1 - (0) + x_1(0) = 1 + 2x_1$$

For $x_2 = 1$:

$$E(y) = 1 + 2x_1 - (1) + x_1(1) = 3x_1$$

For $x_2 = 2$:

$$E(y) = 1 + 2x_1 - (2) + x_1(2) = -1 + 4x_1$$

Note that the slope of each line is represented by $\beta_1 + \beta_3 x_2 = 2 + x_2$. Graphs of these three straight lines are shown in Figure 10.21. The effect of adding a term

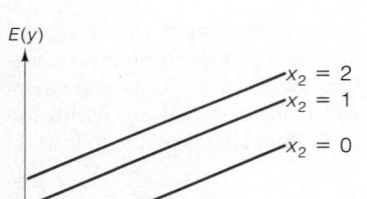

FIGURE 10.20

Graphs of $E(y)$ Versus x_1 for Fixed Values of x_2: First-Order Model

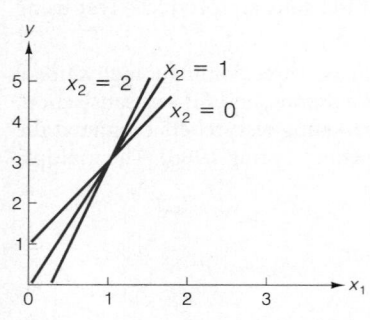

FIGURE 10.21

Graphs of $E(y) = 1 + 2x_1 - x_2 + x_1 x_2$ for $x_2 = 0, 1, 2$

involving the cross-product x_1x_2 can be seen in Figure 10.21. In contrast to Figure 10.20, the lines relating $E(y)$ to x_1 are no longer parallel. The effect on $E(y)$ of a change in x_1 (ie, the slope) now *depends on the value of* x_2. When this situation occurs, we say that x_1 and x_2 **interact**. The cross-product term, $\beta_3x_1x_2$, is called an **interaction term**, and the model $E(y) = \beta_0 + \beta_1x_1 + \beta_2x_2 + \beta_3x_1x_2$ is called an **interaction model** with two quantitative variables (see the box).

AN INTERACTION MODEL RELATING $E(y)$ TO TWO QUANTITATIVE INDEPENDENT VARIABLES

$$E(y) = \beta_0 + \beta_1x_1 + \beta_2x_2 + \beta_3x_1x_2$$

where

$(\beta_1 + \beta_3x_2)$ represents the change in $E(y)$ for every 1 unit increase in x_1, holding x_2 fixed

$(\beta_2 + \beta_3x_1)$ represents the change in $E(y)$ for every 1 unit increase in x_2, holding x_1 fixed

---

EXAMPLE 10.10   Although a regional express delivery service bases the charge for shipping a package on the package weight and distance shipped, its profit per package depends on the package size (volume of space that it occupies) and the size and nature of the load on the delivery truck. The company recently conducted a study to investigate the relationship between the cost, y, of shipment (in dollars) and the variables that control the shipping charge—package weight, x_1 (in pounds), and distance shipped, x_2 (in miles). Twenty packages were randomly selected from among the large number received for shipment. A detailed analysis of the cost of shipment was made for each package, with the results shown in Table 10.9.

a. Suppose the company believes that straight-line relationships exist between mean shipment cost, $E(y)$, and package weight, x_1, and between $E(y)$ and distance

---

TABLE 10.9
Cost of Shipment Data

PACKAGE	x_1	x_2	y	PACKAGE	x_1	x_2	y
1	5.9	47	2.60	11	5.1	240	11.00
2	3.2	145	3.90	12	2.4	209	5.00
3	4.4	202	8.00	13	.3	160	2.00
4	6.6	160	9.20	14	6.2	115	6.00
5	.75	280	4.40	15	2.7	45	1.10
6	.7	80	1.50	16	3.5	250	8.00
7	6.5	240	14.50	17	4.1	95	3.30
8	4.5	53	1.90	18	8.1	160	12.10
9	.60	100	1.00	19	7.0	260	15.50
10	7.5	190	14.00	20	1.1	90	1.70

shipped, x_2, but that the rate of change of $E(y)$ with x_1 depends on x_2, and vice versa. Hypothesize an appropriate linear model for $E(y)$.

b. Fit the model to the data, and graph the prediction equation.
c. Find the value of s and interpret it.
d. Find the value of R_a^2 and interpret it.
e. Is the model useful for the prediction of shipping cost, y? Find the value of the F statistic in the printout shown in Figure 10.22, and give the observed significance level (p-value) for the test.
f. Is there evidence that the interaction term contributes to the prediction of shipping cost, y?

Solution

a. Since the company expects the linear relationship between $E(y)$ and one x-value (say, x_1) to depend on the other x-value (x_2)—that is, since the company expects x_1 and x_2 to interact—the appropriate model is

$$E(y) = \beta_0 + \beta_1 x_1 + \beta_2 x_2 + \beta_3 x_1 x_2$$

b. The SAS printout for fitting the interaction model to $n = 20$ data points is shown in Figure 10.22.

FIGURE 10.22

SAS Printout for Interaction Model

Dep Variable: Y

Analysis of Variance

Source	DF	Sum of Squares	Mean Square	F Value	Prob>F
Model	3	445.45219	148.48406	358.154	0.0001
Error	16	6.63331	0.41458		
C Total	19	452.08550			

Root MSE	0.64388	R-Square	0.9853
Dep Mean	6.33500	Adj R-Sq	0.9826
C.V.	10.16385		

Parameter Estimates

Variable	DF	Parameter Estimate	Standard Error	T for H0: Parameter=0	Prob > |T|
INTERCEP	1	-0.140501	0.64810001	-0.217	0.8311
X1	1	0.019088	0.15821160	0.121	0.9055
X2	1	0.007721	0.00390568	1.977	0.0656
X1X2	1	0.007796	0.00089766	8.684	0.0001

You can see from the printout that the parameter estimates (shaded) are

$$\hat{\beta}_0 = -.140501 \qquad \hat{\beta}_1 = .019088$$
$$\hat{\beta}_2 = .007721 \qquad \hat{\beta}_3 = .007796$$

Therefore, the prediction equation that relates shipping cost, y, to package weight, x_1, and distance shipped, x_2, is

$$\hat{y} = -.140501 + .019088 x_1 + .007721 x_2 + .007796 x_1 x_2$$

Graphs of the least squares lines relating shipping cost (y) to distance shipped (x_2) for several package weight values (x_1) are shown in Figure 10.23. Notice

FIGURE 10.23

Graph of the Least Squares Prediction Equation

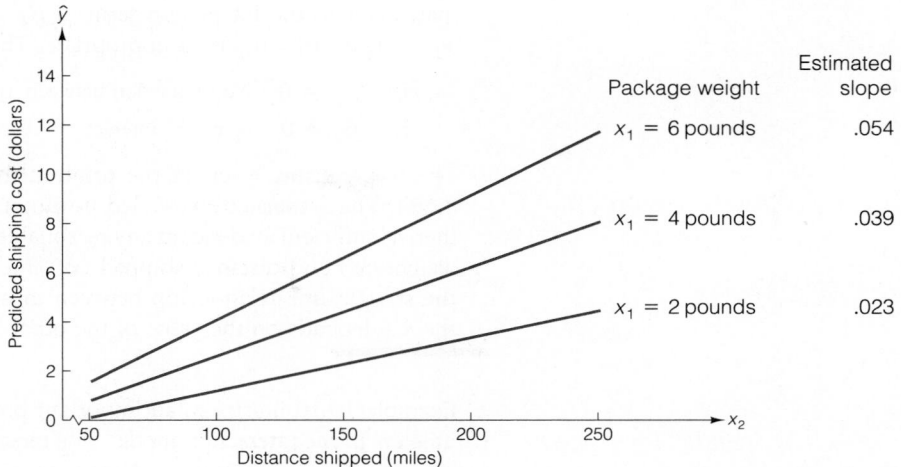

that the lines are not parallel, due to the interaction term. Also, you can see that the rate of increase of mean shipping cost with distance is faster for heavier packages. (The estimated slopes for all three lines are shown in Figure 10.23.)

c. The value of s, given in the printout as Root MSE (shaded), is $s = .64388$. Multiplying this value by 2, we obtain $2s = 2(.64388) = 1.28776$. We expect to predict shipping cost to within approximately $1.29 of its true value using the fitted interaction model.

d. The value of R_a^2 shown in Figure 10.22 (shaded), is .9826. This means that after adjusting for sample size and degrees of freedom, about 98% of the total sample variation in shipping cost (y) is explained by the model; the remainder of the variation is due to random error.

e. To determine whether the overall model is useful for predicting y, we test

$$H_0: \quad \beta_1 = \beta_2 = \beta_3 = 0$$
$$H_a: \quad \text{At least one } \beta_i \neq 0.$$

The test statistic is the value of F (shaded) in the upper-right corner of the SAS printout, $F = 358.154$. Since $n = 20$ and $k = 3$, this F-value depends on $k = 3$ numerator df and $n - (k + 1) = 20 - 4 = 16$ denominator df. The observed significance level (p-value) for the test is shown to the right of the F-value in the printout as Prob>F. This value (shaded) is $p = .0001$. This means that if the model actually contributed no information for the prediction of y, the probability of observing a value of the F statistic as large as 358.154 would be only .0001. Thus, for any value of α larger than .0001, we will reject the null hypothesis and conclude that the model is adequate for predicting shipping cost.

f. Although we have decided that the overall model is useful for predicting y, we have not yet determined whether the interaction term contributes significantly to the model. That is, we do not know whether the relationship between $E(y)$ and x_2 depends on x_1. Consequently, we want to conduct a t test on β_3, the parameter in the interaction term. If $\beta_3 = 0$, then x_1 and x_2 do not interact, and a first-order model is appropriate. Therefore, we want to test

H_0: $\beta_3 = 0$ No interaction between x_1 and x_2

H_a: $\beta_3 \neq 0$ x_1 and x_2 interact

The test statistic, given in the printout in the X1X2 row (shaded), is $t = 8.684$. The associated two-tailed p-value (also shaded) is $p = .0001$. Thus, there is sufficient evidence at any reasonable value of α to indicate that package weight (x_1) and distance shipped (x_2) interact. This means that the slope of the straight-line relationship between mean shipping cost, $E(y)$, and one of the x's depends on the value of the other x (see Figure 10.23).

Example 10.10 illustrates an important point about conducting t tests on the β parameters in the interaction model. The most important β parameter in this model is the interaction coefficient, β_3. Note that this β is also the one associated with the highest-order term in the model, x_1x_2. (When x_1 and x_2 are both quantitative variables, the cross-product x_1x_2 is considered a second-order term by virtue of summing the exponents of x_1 and x_2.) Consequently, we will want to test H_0: $\beta_3 = 0$ after we have determined that the overall model is useful for predicting y. Once interaction is detected, tests on the first-order terms x_1 and x_2 should not be conducted, since they are meaningless tests; the presence of interaction implies that both x's are important.

WARNING

Once interaction has been deemed important in the model $E(y) = \beta_0 + \beta_1x_1 + \beta_2x_2 + \beta_3x_1x_2$, do not conduct t tests on the β coefficients of the first-order terms x_1 and x_2. These terms should be kept in the model regardless of the magnitude of the p-values shown in the printout.

PROBLEMS

10.19   In theory, most academics advocate group decision-making as a way to solve conflicts among a manager's subordinates. Many managers reject this proposition in practice, however, believing that conflict in groups is counterproductive. A study was conducted to examine this contradiction between accepted normative theory and current practice in Australia (*Organizational Behavior & Human Decision Processes*, Vol. 39, 1987). For one part of the study, multiple regression analysis was used to test "the proposition that the effective use of group discussion methods to resolve conflict depends on the manager's ability and willingness to encourage subordinates to confront conflict." A sample of 89 upper-level managers were asked to complete a questionnaire that measured the following variables (on a 7 point Likert scale):

$$y = \text{Average performance of manager's subordinates (ie, subordinate performance)}$$

$$x_1 = \text{Manager's preferred level of subordinate participation in decision-making when conflict is present (ie, group decision method)}$$

$$x_2 = \text{Average of subordinates' perceptions of manager's inclination to legitimize conflict (ie, conflict legitimization)}$$

The interaction model $E(y) = \beta_0 + \beta_1 x_1 + \beta_2 x_2 + \beta_3 x_1 x_2$ was fit to the 89 data points, with the following results (t-values in parentheses):

$$\hat{y} = 7.09 - .44x_1 - .01x_2 + .06x_1 x_2 \qquad R^2 = .22$$
$$\phantom{\hat{y} = 7.09\,} (-1.86) \ \ (-.01) \ \ (1.85)$$

a. Conduct a test to determine whether the model is adequate for predicting subordinate performance, y. Use $\alpha = .10$.
b. Use the least squares prediction equation to graph the estimated relationships between subordinate performance (y) and group decision method (x_1) for low conflict legitimization ($x_2 = 1$) and high conflict legitimization ($x_2 = 7$). Interpret the graphs.
c. Conduct a test to determine whether the relationship between subordinate performance (y) and manager's use of a group decision method (x_1) depends on a manager's legitimization of conflict (x_2). Use $\alpha = .10$.
d. Based on the result of part c, would you recommend that the researchers conduct t tests on β_1 and β_2? Explain.

10.20   Stock market analysts are continually searching for reliable predictors of stock price. Consider the problem of modeling the price per share, y, of electric utility stocks. Two variables that are thought to influence stock price are return on average equity, x_1, and annual rate of dividend, x_2. The stock prices, returns on equity, and dividend rates for a sample of 12 nuclear and 16 nonnuclear electric utility stocks for a randomly selected day are shown in the table. The interaction model

$$E(y) = \beta_0 + \beta_1 x_1 + \beta_2 x_2 + \beta_3 x_1 x_2$$

was fit to the data on each type of stock (nuclear and nonnuclear). The resulting SAS printouts follow.

NUCLEAR STOCKS			NONNUCLEAR STOCKS		
y	x_1	x_2	y	x_1	x_2
21	15.1	2.36	25	15.2	2.60
31	15.0	3.00	20	13.9	2.14
26	11.2	3.00	15	15.8	1.52
11	12.1	1.96	34	12.8	3.12
24	16.3	3.00	20	6.9	2.48
8	11.9	1.40	33	14.6	3.08
18	14.9	1.80	28	15.4	2.92
23	11.8	2.56	30	17.3	2.76
13	13.4	2.06	23	13.7	2.36
14	16.2	1.94	24	12.7	2.36
35	17.1	2.96	25	15.3	2.56
13	13.3	2.20	26	15.2	2.80
			26	12.0	2.72
			20	15.3	1.92
			20	13.7	1.92
			13	13.3	1.60

Source: United Business & Investment Report, Wellesley Hills, MA 02181.

SAS Printout for Problem 10.20:
Nuclear Stocks

Analysis of Variance

Source	DF	Sum of Squares	Mean Square	F Value	Prob>F
Model	3	640.93485	213.64495	13.217	0.0018
Error	8	129.31515	16.16439		
C Total	11	770.25000			

Root MSE	4.02050	R-square	0.8321	
Dep Mean	19.75000	Adj R-sq	0.7692	
C.V.	20.35695			

Parameter Estimates

Variable	DF	Parameter Estimate	Standard Error	T for H0: Parameter=0	Prob > |T|
INTERCEP	1	-17.556340	40.05327713	-0.438	0.6727
X1	1	0.518988	2.93598713	0.177	0.8641
X2	1	10.889423	15.57141358	0.699	0.5042
X1X2	1	0.132215	1.12491646	0.118	0.9093

Obs	X1	X2	Dep Var Y	Predict Value	Std Err Predict	Lower95% Predict	Upper95% Predict	Residual
1	15.1	2.36	21.0000	20.6910	1.447	10.8374	30.5447	0.3090
2	15.0	3.00	31.0000	28.8464	1.898	18.5940	39.0989	2.1536
3	11.2	3.00	26.0000	25.3670	3.234	13.4687	37.2654	0.6330
4	12.1	1.96	11.0000	13.2023	1.918	2.9301	23.4745	-2.2023
5	16.3	3.00	24.0000	30.0368	2.363	19.2826	40.7909	-6.0368
6	11.9	1.40	8.0000	6.0675	3.255	-5.8616	17.9966	1.9325
7	14.9	1.80	18.0000	13.3236	2.292	2.6512	23.9959	4.6764
8	11.8	2.56	23.0000	20.4386	1.993	10.0902	30.7870	2.5614
9	13.4	2.06	13.0000	15.4800	1.347	5.7018	25.2581	-2.4800
10	16.2	1.94	14.0000	16.1320	2.950	4.6325	27.6315	-2.1320
11	17.1	2.96	35.0000	30.2433	2.702	19.0724	41.4141	4.7567
12	13.3	2.20	13.0000	17.1715	1.264	7.4528	26.8903	-4.1715

SAS Printout for Problem 10.20:
Nonnuclear Stocks

Analysis of Variance

Source	DF	Sum of Squares	Mean Square	F Value	Prob>F
Model	3	478.30855	159.43618	60.851	0.0001
Error	12	31.44145	2.62012		
C Total	15	509.75000			

Root MSE	1.61868	R-square	0.9383	
Dep Mean	23.87500	Adj R-sq	0.9229	
C.V.	6.77981			

Parameter Estimates

Variable	DF	Parameter Estimate	Standard Error	T for H0: Parameter=0	Prob > |T|
INTERCEP	1	-44.681773	25.23972659	-1.770	0.1021
X1	1	2.879579	1.74113100	1.654	0.1241
X2	1	25.062181	10.02876655	2.499	0.0280
X1X2	1	-0.959006	0.69103996	-1.388	0.1904

a. Write the least squares prediction equations for the two types of electric utility stocks.
b. Is the model useful for predicting the price of nuclear stocks? Nonnuclear stocks? Test each hypothesis using $\alpha = .05$.
c. Is there evidence of interaction between return on equity and dividend rate in the nuclear stock model? The nonnuclear stock model? Perform each test using $\alpha = .05$.

d. Ninety-five percent prediction intervals for price per share (y) are shown in the SAS printout for nuclear stocks. Locate the lower and upper limits for a 95% prediction interval for y when $x_1 = 13.3$ and $x_2 = 2.20$.

e. Interpret the interval obtained in part **d**.

f. Would you recommend using the model to predict price per share of a nuclear stock with a dividend rate of 1.10? Explain.

10.21 Over the years, Graduate Record Examination (GRE) scores have been used to aid college administrators in the graduate school admission process. Some educators argue, however, that the GRE is biased against minority students, especially blacks, who are often unfairly denied admission to graduate study on the basis of test scores alone. A study was conducted to compare the relationship between GRE scores and performance of black and white graduate students at the University of Florida (*Journal of Negro Education*, Jan. 1985). The initial sample consisted of 75 black graduate students who were enrolled full-time. Each of these black students was matched (by department, age, sex, and tenure) with a white graduate student, giving a combined sample of 150 students (75 white and 75 black). Data collected on GRE score and current grade-point average (GPA) were used to fit the model

$$E(y) = \beta_0 + \beta_1 x_1 + \beta_2 x_2 + \beta_3 x_1 x_2$$

where

$$y = \text{GPA}$$
$$x_1 = \text{GRE score}$$
$$x_2 = \begin{cases} 1 & \text{if black} \\ 0 & \text{if white} \end{cases}$$

The least squares prediction equation and coefficient of determination follow:*

$$\hat{y} = 3.031 + .000498x_1 + .687x_2 - .000983x_1 x_2$$
$$R^2 = .05 \qquad s_{\hat{\beta}_3} = .0003738$$

a. Calculate the test statistic for checking model adequacy. Give the approximate p-value for the test.

b. Write the equation of the fitted line relating GPA to GRE score for white graduate students. [*Hint:* Substitute $x_2 = 0$ into the equation.]

c. Write the equation of the fitted line relating GPA to GRE score for black graduate students. [*Hint:* Substitute $x_2 = 1$ into the equation.]

d. Graph the lines from parts **b** and **c** on the same set of axes. What do you observe?

e. Test the hypothesis that the slopes of the lines relating GPA to GRE score differ for whites and blacks. [*Hint:* Test H_0: $\beta_3 = 0$.]

f. Predict the GPA of a black graduate student with a GRE score of 1200.

10.22 One of the most promising methods for extracting crude oil employs a carbon dioxide (CO_2) flooding technique. When flooded into oil pockets, CO_2 enhances oil recovery by displacing the crude oil. In a microscopic investigation of the CO_2 flooding process, flow tubes were dipped into sample oil pockets containing a known amount of oil. The oil pockets were flooded with CO_2, and the percentage of oil displaced was recorded. The experiment was conducted at three different flow pressures and three different dipping angles. The displacement test data are recorded in the table at the top of the next page.

---

* Scott, R. R., and Shaw, M. E. "Black and White Performance in Graduate School and Policy Implications of the Use of Graduate Record Examination Scores in Admissions." *Journal of Negro Education*, Vol. 54, No. 1, 1985, pp. 14–23. Some of the regression results shown here are approximated based on information provided in the article.

PRESSURE x_1, Pounds per Square Inch	DIPPING ANGLE x_2, Degrees	OIL RECOVERY y, Percentage
1,000	0	60.58
1,000	15	72.72
1,000	30	79.99
1,500	0	66.83
1,500	15	80.78
1,500	30	89.78
2,000	0	69.18
2,000	15	80.31
2,000	30	91.99

Source: Wang, G. C. "Microscopic Investigation of CO_2 Flooding Process." *Journal of Petroleum Technology*, Vol. 34, No. 8, Aug. 1982, pp. 1789–1797. Copyright © 1982, Society of Petroleum Engineers.

a. Plot the sample data in a scattergram, with percentage oil recovery, y, on the vertical axis and pressure, x_1, on the horizontal axis. Connect the points corresponding to the same value of dipping angle, x_2. Based on the scattergram, do you believe that x_1 and x_2 interact?

b. The MINITAB printout for the interaction model

$$E(y) = \beta_0 + \beta_1 x_1 + \beta_2 x_2 + \beta_3 x_1 x_2$$

is provided here. Give the prediction equation for this model.

```
The regression equation is
y = 54.5 + 0.00770 x1 + 0.554 x2 +0.000113 x1x2

Predictor      Coef      Stdev    t-ratio       p
Constant     54.500      5.034      10.83   0.000
x1         0.007697   0.003238       2.38   0.063
x2           0.5541     0.2600       2.13   0.086
x1x2      0.0001133  0.0001672       0.68   0.528

s = 2.508     R-sq = 96.4%    R-sq(adj) = 94.2%

Analysis of Variance

SOURCE       DF         SS         MS        F       p
Regression    3     843.19     281.06    44.67   0.000
Error         5      31.46       6.29
Total         8     874.65
```

c. Construct a plot similar to the scattergram of part a, but use the predicted values from the interaction model on the vertical axis. Compare the two plots. Do you believe the interaction model will provide an adequate fit?

d. Check model adequacy using a statistical test with $\alpha = .05$.

e. Is there evidence of interaction between pressure, x_1, and dipping angle, x_2? Test using $\alpha = .05$.

f. Based on the result from part e, what model would you use to predict oil recovery, y?

10.23   To what degree do the attitudes of your peers influence your behavior? There is general agreement among sociologists and psychologists that your behavior is dependent on the attitudes of and social support from your friends, neighbors, etc. However, it is unclear whether the effects of attitude and social support are additive or interactive. An attempt to resolve this attitude–behavior issue was presented in *Social Psychology Quarterly* (Vol. 50, 1987). The study included a sample of $n = 143$ adult drinkers in an urban setting characterized by high physical availability of alcoholic beverages. The goal of the study was to build a model relating frequency of drinking alcoholic beverages, y, to attitude toward drinking (x_1) and social support (x_2). Consider the interaction model

$$E(y) = \beta_0 + \beta_1 x_1 + \beta_2 x_2 + \beta_3 x_1 x_2$$

a. Interpret the phrase "x_1 and x_2 interact" in terms of the problem.

b. Write the null and alternative hypotheses for determining whether attitude (x_1) and social support (x_2) interact.

c. The reported p-value for the test in part b was $p < .001$. Interpret this result.

SECOND-ORDER (QUADRATIC) MODELS WITH QUANTITATIVE VARIABLES

10.7 All the linear models discussed in the previous sections proposed straight-line relationships between $E(y)$ and each of the independent variables in the model. In this section we consider models that allow for curvature in the relationships. Each of these models is a **second-order model** because it will include an x^2 term.

First, we consider second-order models involving a single independent variable, x. The form of this model, called the **quadratic model**, is

$$y = \beta_0 + \beta_1 x + \beta_2 x^2 + \epsilon$$

Technically, the quadratic model includes only one independent variable, x, but we can think of the model as a general linear model in two independent variables with $x_1 = x$ and $x_2 = x^2$. The term involving x^2, called a **quadratic term** (or **second-order term**), enables us to hypothesize curvature in the graph of the response model relating y to x. Graphs of the quadratic model for two different values of β_2 are shown in Figure 10.24. When the curve opens upward, the sign of β_2 is positive (see Figure 10.24a); when the curve opens downward, the sign of β_2 is negative (see Figure 10.24b).

A QUADRATIC (SECOND-ORDER) MODEL IN A SINGLE QUANTITATIVE INDEPENDENT VARIABLE

$$E(y) = \beta_0 + \beta_1 x + \beta_2 x^2$$

where

β_0 is the y-intercept of the curve

β_1 is a shift parameter

β_2 is the rate of curvature

FIGURE 10.24

Graphs for Two Quadratic Models

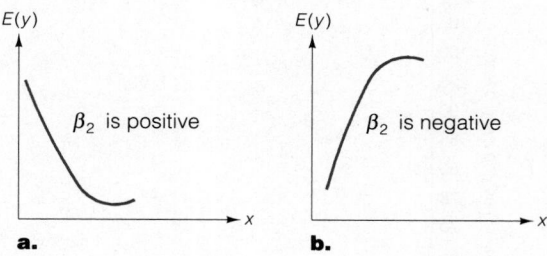

a. β_2 is positive

b. β_2 is negative

EXAMPLE 10.11 Suppose a real estate investor wants to model the relationship between the sale price of a property located in a particular neighborhood and the corresponding appraised improvements value of the property. A random sample of

TABLE 10.10

Sale Price and Appraised
Improvements Value for 10
Properties

SALE PRICE	APPRAISED IMPROVEMENTS
y, Dollars	x, Dollars
48,000	26,563
82,900	58,364
72,000	57,310
126,000	71,486
65,000	45,135
101,000	63,966
43,000	23,459
54,800	40,712
94,000	62,267
108,000	65,718

10 properties in the neighborhood that were sold last year was selected for the analysis. The resulting data are given in Table 10.10.

a. Construct a scattergram for the sale price–appraised improvements value data of Table 10.10.

b. Hypothesize a probabilistic model relating sale price to appraised improvements value for all properties in the neighborhood that were sold last year.

c. Use the method of least squares to estimate the unknown parameters of the model, and graph the prediction equation.

d. Interpret the β estimates.

e. Is the overall model useful for predicting sale price, y?

f. Is there sufficient evidence of upward curvature in the sale price–appraised improvements value relationship?

Solution

a. A plot of the data of Table 10.10 is given in Figure 10.25. You can see that the sale price of the properties appears to increase in a curvilinear manner with appraised improvements value.

b. The apparent curvature in the graph relating appraised improvements value, x, to the sale price, y, provides some support for the inclusion of a quadratic term, x^2, in the response model. Thus, we think that the quadratic model

$$y = \beta_0 + \beta_1 x + \beta_2 x^2 + \epsilon$$

might yield a better prediction equation than one based on the straight-line model of Section 10.3.

FIGURE 10.25

Scattergram of the Sale Price–
Appraised Improvements Value Data

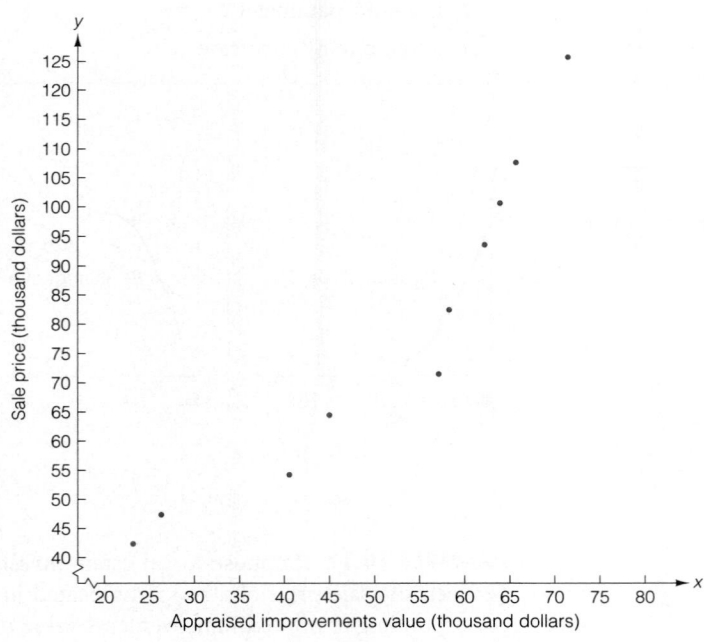

c. The quadratic model was fit to the data using SPSS. Part of the SPSS output is reproduced in Figure 10.26. The least squares estimates of the β parameters appear (shaded) in the SPSS column labeled B. You can see that $\hat{\beta}_0 = 75,769.69820$, $\hat{\beta}_1 = -2.18924$, and $\hat{\beta}_2 = .00004009804$.* Therefore, the equation that minimizes SSE for this data set is

$$\hat{y} = 75,769.698 - 2.189x + .000040098x^2$$

In Figure 10.27 we see that the graph of the quadratic regression model provides a good fit to the data of Table 10.10.

FIGURE 10.26

SPSS Printout for the Quadratic Model

```
Multiple R            .98703
R Square              .97422
Adjusted R Square     .96686
Standard Error     5025.82166

Analysis of Variance
                    DF      Sum of Squares        Mean Square
Regression           2   6682828816.80825   3341414408.40413
Residual             7    176812183.19175     25258883.31311

F =      132.28670      Signif F =   .0000
```

```
------------------ Variables in the Equation ------------------

Variable            B          SE B        Beta        T    Sig T

XX          4.009804E-05  8.06094E-06    2.28636     4.974  .0016
X                -2.18924      .75850    -1.32661    -2.886  .0234
(Constant)   75769.69820  16234.27331                4.667  .0023
```

FIGURE 10.27

Graph of the Least Squares Fit of the Quadratic Model

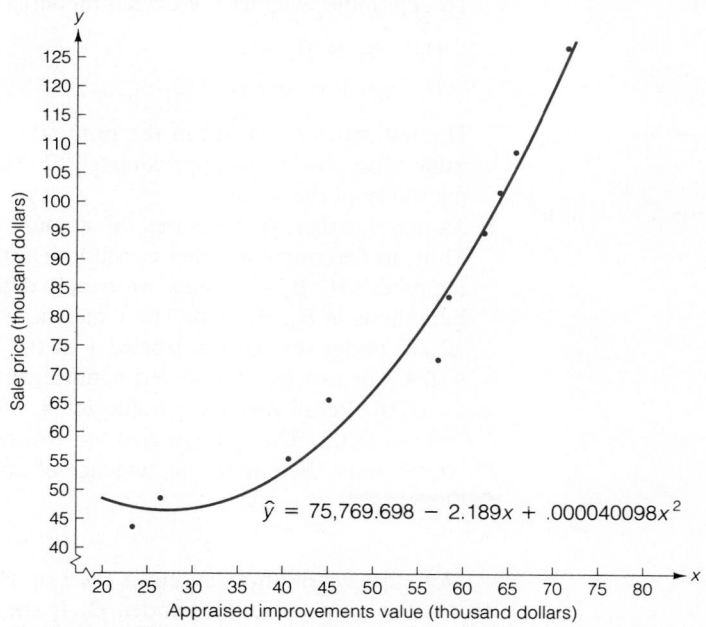

$$\hat{y} = 75,769.698 - 2.189x + .000040098x^2$$

* SPSS uses E notation to indicate that the decimal point for the number shown on the printout should be moved right or left. The notation E − 05 for the value of $\hat{\beta}_2$ requires you to move the decimal 5 places to the left (−). In contrast, E + 02 would require you to move the decimal 2 places to the right (+).

d. According to the preceding box, the β estimates (rounded) have the following interpretations:

$\hat{\beta}_0 = 75,770$ is the estimated y-intercept of the least squares curve shown in Figure 10.27. We also know that $\hat{\beta}_0$ represents the estimate of $E(y)$ when $x = 0$, which is meaningless in this example because a property with an appraised improvements value of $0 is not practical.

$\hat{\beta}_1 = -2.19$ is an estimate of the amount the curve in Figure 10.27 is shifted along the x-axis. This value rarely has a practical interpretation. Note that $\hat{\beta}_1$ is not a slope, and should not be interpreted as such.

$\hat{\beta}_2 = .00004$ is an estimate of the rate of curvature in the least squares curve in Figure 10.27. (Large absolute values of $\hat{\beta}_2$ indicate a faster rate of curvature; small absolute values of $\hat{\beta}_2$ indicate a slower rate of curvature.) The sign of $\hat{\beta}_2$ is positive, which implies upward curvature in the sale price–appraised improvements relationship. We note here that the small value of $\hat{\beta}_2$ does not imply that the curvature is not significant, since the numerical scale of $\hat{\beta}_2$ depends on the scale of measurement. We will test the contribution of the quadratic coefficient in part **f**.

e. To determine whether the overall model is useful for predicting y, we test

H_0: $\beta_1 = \beta_2 = 0$
H_a: At least one $\beta_i \neq 0$.

The test statistic, shaded in the printout, is $F = 132.29$, and its associated p-value (also shaded) is approximately 0. Therefore, there is strong evidence of the utility of the model.

f. As noted earlier, β_2 measures the amount of curvature in the response curve. Thus, to determine whether curvature exists in the population, we test the null hypothesis H_0: $\beta_2 = 0$. Since we want to detect upward curvature, the alternative hypothesis is H_a: $\beta_2 > 0$. The t statistic is given in the SPSS printout (Figure 10.26) under the column labeled T in the XX row. This value (shaded) is $t = 4.974$. The two-tailed observed significance level, given under the Sig T column, is .0016. Recall that the p-value for a one-tailed test is half this value: $p = \frac{.0016}{2} = .0008$. This implies that we will reject H_0 for any α value larger than .0008; thus, there is strong evidence of upward curvature in the population.

Note that we did not conduct a t test on β_1 in the quadratic model in Example 10.11. With the quadratic model, β_2 is the most important β (and also the β associated with the highest-order term in the model—namely, x^2), since it controls whether the relationship between y and x is linear or curvilinear. Once curvature has been detected, there is no need to test a β parameter (eg, β_1) that has no meaningful interpretation and thereby risk making a Type I or II error unnecessarily.

Once curvature has been deemed important in the model $E(y) = \beta_0 + \beta_1 x + \beta_2 x^2$, do not conduct a t test on β_1. It is a safe practice to keep the $\beta_1 x$ term in the model regardless of the magnitude of the p-value shown in the printout.

The quadratic model in Example 10.11 is a second-order model in one quantitative independent variable. A second-order model in two quantitative variables is shown in the next box. Note that the model contains all the possible cross-products (interaction terms) and squares of the independent variables.

**A SECOND-ORDER MODEL IN TWO
QUANTITATIVE INDEPENDENT VARIABLES**

$$E(y) = \beta_0 + \beta_1 x_1 + \beta_2 x_2 + \beta_3 x_1 x_2 + \beta_4 x_1^2 + \beta_5 x_2^2$$

A two-dimensional graph of a second-order model in two quantitative variables will look similar to the graph of a quadratic model, except that there will be one curve for each value of the second independent variable held constant. For example, suppose the mean value $E(y)$ of a response, y, is related to two quantitative independent variables, x_1 and x_2, by the second-order model

$$E(y) = \beta_0 + \beta_1 x_1 + \beta_2 x_2 + \beta_3 x_1 x_2 + \beta_4 x_1^2 + \beta_5 x_2^2$$

where $\beta_0 = 1$, $\beta_1 = 2$, $\beta_2 = -1$, $\beta_3 = 1$, $\beta_4 = 1$, and $\beta_5 = 3$; that is,

$$E(y) = 1 + 2x_1 - x_2 + x_1 x_2 + x_1^2 + 3x_2^2$$

A computer-generated (SAS) graph of the relationship between $E(y)$ and x_1 for $x_2 = 0$, 1, and 2 is shown in Figure 10.28 (p. 494). Note that the response curves in Figure 10.28 rise (or fall) in a manner similar to the lines shown in Figure 10.21. However, the graphs are curvilinear, and the spacing between the curves has changed. These changes were produced by adding the second-order terms (those involving x_1 and x_2) to the model.

How can you choose an appropriate linear model with one or more quantitative independent variables to fit a set of data? Since most relationships in the real world are curvilinear (at least to some extent), a good first choice would be a second-order linear model. If you are fairly certain that the relationships between $E(y)$ and the individual independent variables are approximately first-order and that the independent variables do not interact, you could select a first-order model for the data. If you have information that suggests there is moderate or very little curvature over the region in which the independent variables are measured, you could use the interaction model. However, keep in mind that for all multiple regression models, the number of data points must exceed the number of parameters in the model

FIGURE 10.28

SAS Graph of $E(y) = 1 + 2x_1 - x_2 + x_1x_2 + x_1^2 + 3x_2^2$ for $x_2 = 0, 1, 2$

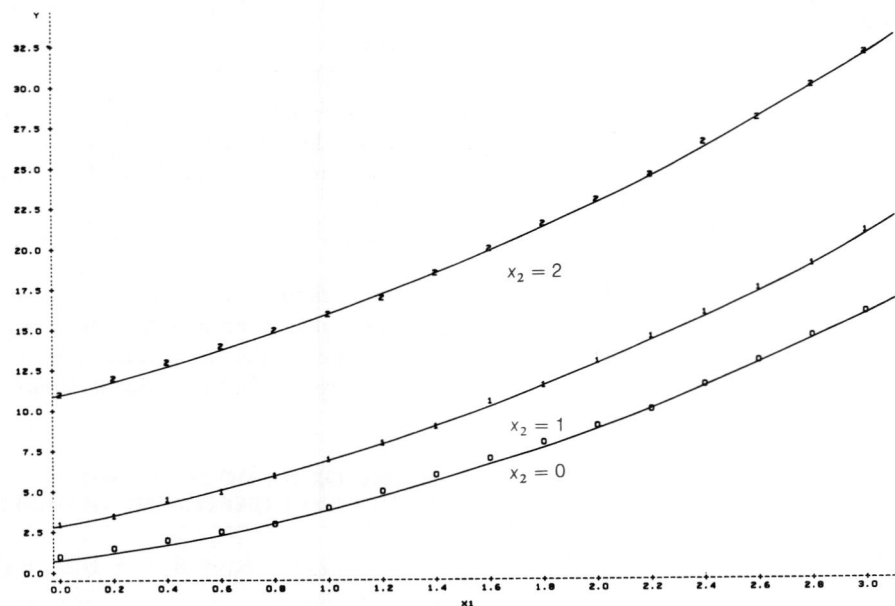

(Section 10.2). Thus, you may be forced to use a first-order model rather than a second-order model simply because you do not have sufficient data to estimate all the parameters in the second-order model.

PROBLEMS

10.24 In the pharmaceutical industry, a new chemical entity (NCE) is defined as a new chemical or biological compound tested in humans for therapeutic purposes for the first time. A study published in *Managerial & Decision Economics* (Sept. 3, 1988) reported that expenditures on research and development (R&D) of NCEs in the United Kingdom has increased dramatically over the 20 years 1964–1984. A plot of R&D expenditures (y) versus year (x) is shown at the top of the next page.

a. Propose a model for $E(y)$ that would seem to fit the data well.
b. What are the expected signs of the β's in the model proposed in part **a**?

10.25 Research on the relationship between job performance and job turnover has yielded conflicting results. Some early studies found a negative relationship (ie, the lower the performance, the greater the likelihood of turnover) among all types of workers, while others detected a positive relationship (ie, the higher the performance, the greater the likelihood of turnover) among those employed in white-collar positions. These early studies, however, focused on the linear (first-order) relationship between these variables. The *Journal of Management* (1986) investigated the possibility of a curvilinear (second-order) relationship between job performance and turnover, both for white-collar workers (accountants) and for blue-collar workers (truck drivers). For each sample of workers, the quadratic model

Scattergram for Problem 10.24

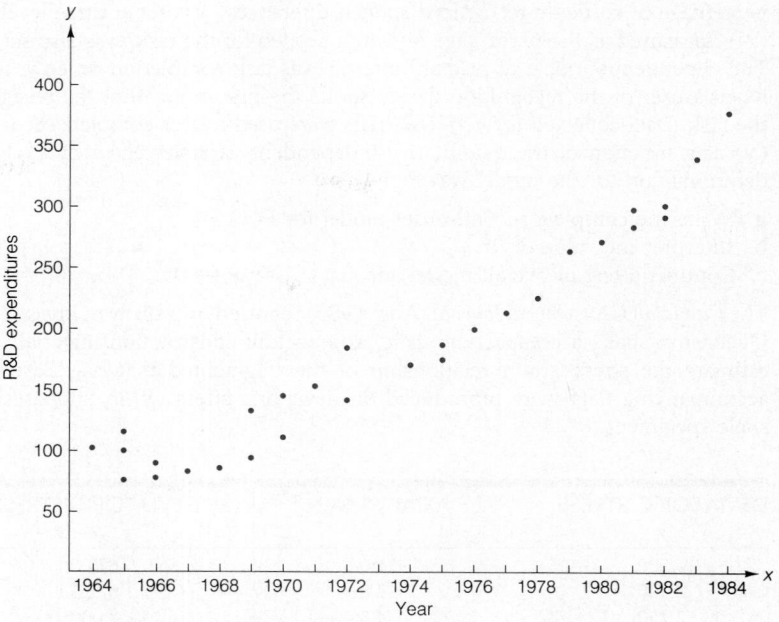

Source: Prentis, R. A., et al. "Pharmaceutical Innovation and R&D Investment in the UK." *Managerial & Decision Economics*, Sept. 3, 1988, p. 198 (Fig. 1).

$E(y) = \beta_0 + \beta_1 x + \beta_2 x^2$ was fit, where

x = Performance rating (1 = poor, ..., 4 = outstanding)

y = Probability of turnover (ie, likelihood of worker leaving job within 1 year)

The results are shown in the table:

ACCOUNTANTS $n = 169$	TRUCK DRIVERS $n = 107$
$\hat{\beta}_1 = -1.40$ ($t = -3.88$)	$\hat{\beta}_1 = -1.50$ ($t = -3.83$)
$\hat{\beta}_2 = 1.13$ ($t = 3.23$)	$\hat{\beta}_2 = 1.22$ ($t = 4.70$)
$R^2 = .114$	$R^2 = .298$

Source: Jackofsky, E. F., Ferris, K. R., and Breckenridge, B. G. "Evidence for a Curvilinear Relationship Between Job Performance and Turnover." *Journal of Management*, Vol. 12, No. 1, 1986, pp. 105–111.

a. Conduct a test of model adequacy for each of the two groups of workers. Use $\alpha = .05$.
b. Interpret the β estimates for each of the two groups of workers. Which of the β's have practical interpretations?
c. Is there evidence of upward curvature in the relationship between turnover and performance for accountants? Use $\alpha = .05$. What is the practical implication of this result?
d. Repeat part **c** for truck drivers.

10.26 A study reported in *Human Factors* (Apr. 1990) investigated the effects of recognizer accuracy and vocabulary size on the performance of a computerized speech recognition device. Accuracy (x_1) of the device, measured as the percentage of correctly recognized spoken utterances, was set at three levels: 90%, 95%, and 99%. Vocabulary size (x_2), measured as the percentage of words needed for the task, was also set at three levels: 75%, 87.5%, and 100%. The dependent variable of primary interest was task completion time (y, in minutes), measured from the moment when a user of the recognition device spoke the first input until the recognizer displayed the last spoken word of the task. Data collected for $n = 162$ trials were used to fit a complete second-order model for task completion time (y) as a function of the quantitative independent variables accuracy (x_1) and vocabulary (x_2). The coefficient of determination for the model was $R^2 = .75$.

a. Write the complete second-order model for $E(y)$.
b. Interpret the value of R^2.
c. Conduct a test of overall model adequacy. Use $\alpha = .05$.

10.27 The *Canadian Geotechnical Journal* (Aug. 1985) reported on a study to investigate the reliability of the use of fragmented Queenston shale, a compaction shale, as a rockfill construction material. In particular, the researchers wanted to estimate the stress–strain relationship of the fragmented material. Based on a graph shown in the paper, the accompanying data were reproduced on deviatoric stress (y, in kilopascals) and axial strain (x, percent) for wet shale specimens.

DEVIATORIC STRESS	AXIAL STRAIN	DEVIATORIC STRESS	AXIAL STRAIN
y	x	y	x
500	1.0	6,000	13.5
2,000	2.8	6,625	16.7
2,750	4.3	7,000	19.8
3,500	6.0	7,125	23.0
4,375	7.5	7,000	26.0
4,875	9.0	7,125	27.5
5,250	10.5		

Source: Caswell, R. H., and Trak, B. "Some Geotechnical Characteristics of Fragmented Queenston Shale." *Canadian Geotechnical Journal,* Vol. 22, No. 3, Aug. 1985, pp. 403–408.

a. Plot the data in a scattergram. What type of relationship appears to exist?
b. The quadratic model $E(y) = \beta_0 + \beta_1 x + \beta_2 x^2$ was fit to the data, with the results shown in the accompanying SAS printout. Test the hypothesis that deviatoric stress y increases with axial strain x at a decreasing rate. Use $\alpha = .05$.

```
Dependent Variable: Y

                        Analysis of Variance

                            Sum of          Mean
    Source        DF       Squares        Square      F Value      Prob>F

    Model          2  57287428.971  28643714.485     802.791      0.0001
    Error         10    356801.79868   35680.17987
    C Total       12  57644230.769

          Root MSE       188.89198     R-square      0.9938
          Dep Mean      4932.69231     Adj R-sq      0.9926
          C.V.             3.82939

                        Parameter Estimates

                      Parameter      Standard     T for H0:
    Variable   DF     Estimate         Error      Parameter=0    Prob > |T|

    INTERCEP    1    248.635810    147.80770576       1.682        0.1235
    X           1    619.763109     25.80667772      24.016        0.0001
    XX          1    -13.752316      0.87153259     -15.779        0.0001
```

c. Give the observed significance level for the test of part **b** and interpret its value.

d. Locate the estimate of σ in the printout, and interpret its value.

10.28 A large data-processing firm rates the performance of each member of its technical staff once a year. Each person is rated on a scale of 0 to 100 by his or her immediate supervisor, and this merit rating is used to help determine the size of the person's pay raise for the coming year. The firm's personnel department is interested in developing a regression model to help forecast the merit rating that an applicant for a technical position will receive after being employed 3 years. The firm proposes to use the following model to forecast the merit ratings of applicants who have just completed their graduate studies and who have no prior related job experience:

$$E(y) = \beta_0 + \beta_1 x_1 + \beta_2 x_2 + \beta_3 x_1 x_2 + \beta_4 x_1^2 + \beta_5 x_2^2$$

where

y = Applicant's merit rating after 3 years

x_1 = Applicant's grade-point average (GPA) in graduate school

x_2 = Applicant's total score (verbal plus quantitative) on the Graduate Record Examination (GRE)

A random sample of $n = 40$ employees who have been on the technical staff of the data-processing firm more than 3 years was selected. Each employee's merit rating after 3 years, graduate school GPA, and total score on the GRE were recorded. The proposed model was fit to the data with the aid of a computer. The following is a portion of the resulting computer printout:

Source	DF	Sum of Squares	Mean Square	F Value
Model	5	4911.56	982.31	18.24
Error	34	1830.44	53.84	
Total	59	6742.00		

a. Identify the appropriate null and alternative hypotheses to test whether the second-order model contributes information for the prediction of y.

b. Conduct the test of hypothesis given in part **a**. Test using $\alpha = .05$. Interpret the results in the context of this problem.

10.29 In the mid-1800's, the U.S. census inquired about the real property and personal wealth of individual households. Using census information from 1860 and 1870, J. R. Kearl and C. L. Pope examined the mobility of Utah households as measured by their wealth (*The Review of Economics and Statistics*, May 1984). Holding occupation, time of entry into the economy, nativity, sex, place of residence, and internal migration constant, Kearl and Pope fit the quadratic model

$$E(y) = \beta_0 + \beta_1 x + \beta_2 x^2$$

where

y = Personal wealth (in dollars) of a Utah household

x = Age (in years) of the head of household

The results of the regression analysis are summarized as follows:

$$\hat{y} = 52.39 + 74.29x - .71x^2$$

$$n > 20,000 \qquad t \text{ (for } \beta_1) = 13.79 \qquad t \text{ (for } \beta_2) = -.15$$

a. Graph the least squares prediction equation.

b. Is there evidence of a quadratic relationship between wealth and age for Utah households during 1860–1870? Test using $\alpha = .10$.

MODELS WITH QUALITATIVE (DUMMY) VARIABLES

10.8

Linear models also can be written to include qualitative (or categorical) independent variables. Since qualitative variables, unlike quantitative variables, cannot be measured on a numerical scale, we need to code the values (called **levels**) of the qualitative variable as numbers before we can fit the model. These coded qualitative variables are called **dummy variables** since the numbers assigned to the various levels are arbitrarily selected.

To illustrate, suppose a female executive at a certain company claims that male executives earn higher salaries, on average, than female executives with the same education, experience, and responsibilities. To support her claim, she wants to model the salary, y, of an executive using a qualitative independent variable representing the gender of an executive (male or female). A convenient method of coding the values of a qualitative variable at two levels involves assigning a value of 1 to one of the levels and a value of 0 to the other. For example, the dummy variable used to describe gender could be coded as follows:

$$x = \begin{cases} 1 & \text{if male} \\ 0 & \text{if female} \end{cases}$$

The choice of which level is assigned to 1 and which is assigned to 0 is arbitrary. The model then takes the following form:

$$E(y) = \beta_0 + \beta_1 x$$

The advantage of using a 0–1 coding scheme is that the β coefficients are easily interpreted. The above model allows us to compare the mean executive salary $E(y)$ for males with the corresponding mean for females:

Males $(x = 1)$: $E(y) = \beta_0 + \beta_1(1) = \beta_0 + \beta_1$

Females $(x = 0)$: $E(y) = \beta_0 + \beta_1(0) = \beta_0$

First, note that β_0 represents the mean salary for females (say, μ_F). When a 0–1 coding convention is used, β_0 will always represent the mean response associated with the level of the qualitative variable assigned the value 0 (called the **base level**). The difference between the mean salary for males and the mean salary for females, $\mu_M - \mu_F$, is represented by β_1, that is,

$$\mu_M - \mu_F = (\beta_0 + \beta_1) - (\beta_0) = \beta_1$$

Therefore, with the 0–1 coding convention, β_1 will always represent the difference between the mean response for the level assigned the value 1 and the mean for the base level. Thus, for the executive salary model, we have

$$\beta_0 = \mu_F \qquad \beta_1 = \mu_M - \mu_F$$

For models that involve qualitative independent variables at more than two levels, additional dummy variables must be created. In general, the number of dummy variables used to describe a qualitative variable will be 1 less than the number of levels of the qualitative variable. The procedure is described in the box.

EXAMPLE 10.12 Refer to the problem described in Example 10.10 (p. 481) of modeling the shipment cost, y, of a regional express delivery service. Suppose we want to model $E(y)$ as a function of cargo type, where cargo type has three levels: fragile, semifragile, and durable. Costs for 15 packages of approximately the same weight and same distance shipped, but of different cargo types, are listed in Table 10.11 (at the top of the next page).

a. Write a linear model relating $E(y)$ to cargo type.
b. Interpret the β coefficients in the model.
c. A MINITAB printout for the model from part **a** is shown in Figure 10.29. Conduct the F test for overall model utility using $\alpha = .05$. Explain the practical significance of the result.

Solution

a. Since the qualitative variable of interest, cargo type, has three levels, we need to create $(3 - 1) = 2$ dummy variables. First, select (arbitrarily) one of the levels to be the base level—say, durable cargo. Then each of the remaining levels is

TABLE 10.11
Data for Example 10.12

PACKAGE	COST y	CARGO TYPE	x_1	x_2
1	$17.20	Fragile	1	0
2	11.10	Fragile	1	0
3	12.00	Fragile	1	0
4	10.90	Fragile	1	0
5	13.80	Fragile	1	0
6	6.50	Semifragile	0	1
7	10.00	Semifragile	0	1
8	11.50	Semifragile	0	1
9	7.00	Semifragile	0	1
10	8.50	Semifragile	0	1
11	2.10	Durable	0	0
12	1.30	Durable	0	0
13	3.40	Durable	0	0
14	7.50	Durable	0	0
15	2.00	Durable	0	0

FIGURE 10.29

MINITAB Printout for Dummy Variable Regression, Example 10.12

```
The regression equation is
Y = 3.26 + 9.74 X1 + 5.44 X2

Predictor       Coef        Stdev     t-ratio       p
Constant       3.260        1.075        3.03     0.010
X1             9.740        1.521        6.41     0.000
X2             5.440        1.521        3.58     0.004

s = 2.404      R-sq = 77.4%      R-sq(adj) = 73.7%

Analysis of Variance

SOURCE        DF          SS          MS        F         p
Regression     2      238.25      119.13    20.61     0.000
Error         12       69.37        5.78
Total         14      307.62
```

assigned the value 1 in one of the two dummy variables as follows:

$$x_1 = \begin{cases} 1 & \text{if fragile} \\ 0 & \text{if not} \end{cases} \qquad x_2 = \begin{cases} 1 & \text{if semifragile} \\ 0 & \text{if not} \end{cases}$$

(Note that for the base level, durable cargo, $x_1 = x_2 = 0$.) The values of x_1 and x_2 for each package are given in Table 10.11. Then, the appropriate model is

$$E(y) = \beta_0 + \beta_1 x_1 + \beta_2 x_2$$

b. To interpret the β's, first write the mean shipment cost, $E(y)$, for each of the three cargo types as a function of the β's:

Fragile $(x_1 = 1, x_2 = 0)$: $E(y) = \beta_0 + \beta_1(1) + \beta_2(0)$
$$= \beta_0 + \beta_1$$
$$= \mu_F$$

$$\text{Semifragile } (x_1 = 0, x_2 = 1): \quad E(y) = \beta_0 + \beta_1(0) + \beta_2(1)$$
$$= \beta_0 + \beta_2$$
$$= \mu_S$$

$$\text{Durable } (x_1 = 0, x_2 = 0): \quad E(y) = \beta_0 + \beta_1(0) + \beta_2(0)$$
$$= \beta_0$$
$$= \mu_D$$

Then we have

$$\beta_0 = \mu_D \quad \text{Mean of the base level}$$
$$\beta_1 = \mu_F - \mu_D$$
$$\beta_2 = \mu_S - \mu_D$$

Note that the β's associated with the nonbase levels of cargo type (fragile and semifragile) represent differences between a pair of means. As always, β_0 represents a single mean—the mean response for the base level (durable).

c. The F test for overall model utility tests the null hypothesis

$$H_0: \quad \beta_1 = \beta_2 = 0$$

Note that $\beta_1 = 0$ implies that $\mu_F = \mu_D$, and $\beta_2 = 0$ implies that $\mu_S = \mu_D$. Therefore, $\beta_1 = \beta_2 = 0$ implies that $\mu_F = \mu_S = \mu_D$. Thus, a test for model utility is equivalent to a test for equality of means, that is,

$$H_0: \quad \mu_F = \mu_S = \mu_D$$

From the MINITAB printout in Figure 10.29, $F = 20.61$. Since the p-value of the test (.000) is less than $\alpha = .05$, the null hypothesis is rejected. Thus, there is evidence of a difference between any two of the three mean shipment costs; that is, cargo type is a useful predictor of shipment cost y.

The linear models described in Sections 10.5–10.8 form the basis for building models with quantitative independent variables and models with qualitative independent variables. More complex models, such as those with interactions between qualitative variables and those with both quantitative and qualitative variables (including interactions), may be required in practice.

PROBLEMS

10.30   The *Academy of Management Journal* (Mar. 1989) reported on a study of the relationship between wives' employment and husbands' well-being for $n = 413$ professional accountants. The researchers used regression to fit the model $E(y) = \beta_0 + \beta_1 x$, where y = husband's job satisfaction (measured on a 5 point scale) and x is a dummy variable for employment status of wife (1 = employed, 0 = unemployed).

a. The estimate of β_1 was negative and statistically significant at $\alpha = .01$. Interpret these results.
b. The value of the coefficient of determination was $R^2 = .02$. Interpret this result.

10.31 The *Sociology of Sport Journal* (1986) investigated the problem of racial discrimination in professional baseball. The objective was to determine whether the salary of a major league baseball player is influenced by race and, if so, whether black players are paid, on average, less than white players, taking into account levels of performance. Using salary data of 212 players (nonpitchers) who started on opening day of 1977, the following multiple regression model was fit:

$$E(y) = \beta_0 + \beta_1 x_1 + \beta_2 x_2 + \beta_3 x_3 + \beta_4 x_4 + \beta_5 x_5 + \beta_6 x_6 + \beta_7 x_7 + \beta_8 x_8$$

where

y = Natural logarithm of 1977 salary

x_1 = Years of experience as a major league ballplayer

x_2 = Number of home runs hit during previous season

x_3 = Batting average (ie, ratio of hits to times at bat) during previous season

$x_4 = \begin{cases} 1 & \text{if player's team made the playoffs during the previous year} \\ 0 & \text{if not} \end{cases}$

$x_5 = \begin{cases} 1 & \text{if infielder or catcher} \\ 0 & \text{if not} \end{cases}$

$x_6 = \begin{cases} 1 & \text{if white} \\ 0 & \text{if not} \end{cases}$

x_7 = Amount (million dollars) paid by local radio and TV for broadcast rights to carry games of player's team

$x_8 = \begin{cases} 1 & \text{if bats left-handed or switch hitter} \\ 0 & \text{if not} \end{cases}$

The results are shown in the table.

SOURCE	DF	SS	MS	F	p-VALUE
Model	8	14.710	1.839	53.2	.001
Error	203	7.018	.035		
Total	211	21.728			

VARIABLE	PARAMETER ESTIMATE	STANDARD ERROR OF ESTIMATE	t-VALUE	p-VALUE (TWO-TAILED)
x_1	.037	.004	9.25	.001
x_2	.014	.002	7.00	.001
x_3	2.009	.303	6.63	.001
x_4	.108	.037	2.92	.010
x_5	.078	.029	2.69	.010
x_6	−.046	.028	−1.64	.100
x_7	.042	.034	1.24	.250
x_8	−.027	.027	−1.00	.350

Source: Christiano, K. J. "Salary Discrimination in Major League Baseball: The Effect of Race." *Sociology of Sport Journal,* Vol. 3, 1986, p. 148.

a. Is the model adequate for predicting y? Interpret the p-value of the test.
b. Calculate s, the estimated standard deviation of the random error. Interpret the result.
c. Calculate R^2 and interpret the result.
d. Calculate a 99% confidence interval for β_6. Interpret the result.
e. Is there evidence of salary discrimination against black baseball players? Test using $\alpha = .01$.

10.32 The liquefaction of coal is a major contributor of synthetic fuels. An experiment was conducted to evaluate the performance of a diesel engine run on synthetic (coal-derived) and petroleum-derived fuel oil (*Journal of Energy Resources Technology*, Mar. 1990). The petroleum-derived fuel was a number 2 diesel fuel (DF-2) obtained from Phillips Chemical Company. Two synthetic fuels were used: a blended fuel (50% coal-derived and 50% DF-2) and a blended fuel with advanced timing. The brake power (x_1, in kilowatts) and fuel type were varied in test runs, and engine performance was measured. The table gives the experimental results for the performance measure, y, mass burning rate per degree of crank angle. Initially, the researchers fit the first-order, main effects model

$$E(y) = \beta_0 + \beta_1 x_1 + \beta_2 x_2 + \beta_3 x_3$$

where

$$y = \text{Mass burning rate}$$
$$x_1 = \text{Brake power}$$
$$x_2 = \begin{cases} 1 & \text{if DF-2 fuel} \\ 0 & \text{if not} \end{cases}$$
$$x_3 = \begin{cases} 1 & \text{if blended fuel} \\ 0 & \text{if not} \end{cases}$$

Interpret the results shown in the following MINITAB printout.

BRAKE POWER x_1	FUEL TYPE	MASS BURNING RATE y
4	DF-2	13.2
4	Blended	17.5
4	Advanced timing	17.5
6	DF-2	26.1
6	Blended	32.7
6	Advanced timing	43.5
8	DF-2	25.9
8	Blended	46.3
8	Advanced timing	45.6
10	DF-2	30.7
10	Blended	50.8
10	Advanced timing	68.9
12	DF-2	32.3
12	Blended	57.1

Source: Litzinger, T. A., and Buzza, T. G. "Performance and Emissions of a Diesel Engine Using a Coal-Derived Fuel." *Journal of Energy Resources Technology*, Vol. 112, Mar. 1990, p. 32 (Table 3).

```
The regression equation is
Y = 13.3 + 4.36 X1 - 22.6 X2 - 7.36 X3

Predictor     Coef      Stdev    t-ratio       p
Constant    13.320      6.931       1.92   0.084
X1          4.3650      0.8057      5.42   0.000
X2         -22.600      5.464      -4.14   0.002
X3          -7.360      5.464      -1.35   0.208

s = 8.057      R-sq = 81.2%      R-sq(adj) = 75.6%
```

```
Analysis of Variance

SOURCE       DF        SS         MS        F        p
Regression    3     2807.90     935.97    14.42    0.001
Error        10      649.09      64.91
Total        13     3456.99

SOURCE       DF      SEQ SS
X1            1     1603.93
X2            1     1086.22
X3            1      117.76

Unusual Observations
Obs.     X1         Y       Fit  Stdev.Fit  Residual   St.Resid
  3     4.0      17.50     30.78     4.70     -13.28     -2.03R

R denotes an obs. with a large st. resid.
```

10.33 Research has found that home ownership is a key factor in the exacerbation and perpetuation of racial/ethnic inequality. A study employed multiple regression analysis to examine the variables that are related to differences in home ownership between the Hispanic and Anglo populations in the United States (*Social Problems*, Apr. 1986). The dependent variable in the analysis was the probability of home ownership, y, for a head of household.

    a. One independent variable used to model y was the qualitative variable ethnic identity (Hispanic or Anglo). Write a model for $E(y)$ as a function of ethnic identity.

    b. Interpret the β's in the model from part **a**.

    c. A second independent variable used to model y was region of residence (Northeast, North Central, South, or West). Write a model for $E(y)$ as a function of region.

    d. Interpret the β's in the model from part **c**.

10.34 Refer to the *Real Estate Appraiser* study discussed in Problem 10.12 (p. 474). Interpret the 95% confidence intervals associated with the following independent variables: back to woods, fence, screen porch, in-ground pool, garage, updated kitchen, remodeled kitchen, and skylights. [*Note:* Each of these variables is a dummy variable coded as 1 if yes and 0 if no.]

10.35 R. H. Brockhaus (St. Louis University) conducted a study to determine whether entrepreneurs, newly hired (transferred) managers, and newly promoted managers differ in their risk-taking propensities (*Academy of Management Journal*, Sept. 1980). For the purposes of this study, entrepreneurs were defined as individuals who, within 3 months prior to the study, had ceased working for their employers to own and manage business ventures. Thirty-one individuals from each of the three groups were randomly selected to participate in the study. Each was administered a questionnaire that required the respondent to choose between a safe alternative and a more attractive but risky one. Test scores were designed to measure risk-taking propensity. (Lower scores are associated with greater conservatism in risk-taking situations.) The test scores for the three groups are summarized below:

GROUP	SAMPLE SIZE	SAMPLE MEAN
Entrepreneurs	31	71.00
Transferred managers	31	72.52
Promoted managers	31	66.97
	93	

Suppose you were to fit the following model to the $n = 93$ data points:

$$E(y) = \beta_0 + \beta_1 x_1 + \beta_2 x_2$$

where

$$y = \text{Test score}$$

$$x_1 = \begin{cases} 1 & \text{if entrepreneur} \\ 0 & \text{if not} \end{cases}$$

$$x_2 = \begin{cases} 1 & \text{if transferred manager} \\ 0 & \text{if not} \end{cases}$$

Base level = Promoted manager

a. Use the given information to find the least squares prediction equation.

b. How would you test the hypothesis that there are no differences among the mean risk-taking propensities of the three groups of managers?

COMPUTER LAB 2

MULTIPLE REGRESSION

The sample programs in this section give the commands or instructions for analyzing multiple regression models. Specifically, we consider the model

$$E(y) = \beta_0 + \beta_1 x_1 + \beta_2 x_2 + \beta_3 x_1 x_2 + \beta_4 x_1^2$$

where

$$y = \text{Shipping cost (in dollars)}$$

$$x_1 = \text{Package weight (in pounds)}$$

$$x_2 = \begin{cases} 1 & \text{if fragile package} \\ 0 & \text{if not} \end{cases}$$

The data for the analysis are provided in Table 10.12.

Note that in each program, the higher-order terms specified in the model (eg, x_1^2 and $x_1 x_2$) must be created through data transformation statements.

TABLE 10.12
Cost of Shipment Data

PACKAGE	x_1	x_2	y	PACKAGE	x_1	x_2	y
1	5.9	0	2.60	11	5.1	0	11.00
2	3.2	1	3.90	12	2.4	1	5.00
3	4.4	1	8.00	13	.3	0	2.00
4	6.6	1	9.20	14	6.2	1	6.00
5	.75	0	4.40	15	2.7	1	1.10
6	.7	0	1.50	16	3.5	0	8.00
7	6.5	1	14.50	17	4.1	0	3.30
8	4.5	0	1.90	18	8.1	1	12.10
9	.60	1	1.00	19	7.0	1	15.50
10	7.5	0	14.00	20	1.1	0	1.70

SAS

```
1    DATA SHIP;
2    INPUT Y X1 X2;
3    X1X2=X1*X2;           Data entry instructions
4    X1SQ=X1*X1;
5    CARDS;
     2.60 5.9 0
     3.90 3.2 1
      .    .  .            Input data values
      .    .  .            (1 observation per line)
      .    .  .
     1.70 1.1 0
6    PROC REG;
7    MODEL Y=X1 X2 X1X2 X1SQ/P CLI;    Multiple regression analysis
8    ID X1 X2;
```

COMMANDS 3–4   Independent variables representing interactions and higher-order terms (eg, X1SQ) must be created in the DATA step prior to running the regression analysis.

COMMAND 6   The REG procedure fits general linear models.

COMMAND 7   In the MODEL statement, the dependent variable is listed to the left of the equals sign and the independent variables to the right. The option P (following the slash) prints predicted values and residuals, and the option CLI prints corresponding lower and upper 95% prediction limits. Specify CLM to obtain 95% confidence intervals for $E(y)$.

NOTE   The output for this SAS program is displayed in Figure 10.30a (p. 509).

```
Command
  Line
    1     DATA LIST FREE/Y X1 X2.  ⎫
    2     COMPUTE X1X2=X1*X2.      ⎬  Data entry instructions
    3     COMPUTE X1SQ=X1*X1.      ⎭
    4     BEGIN DATA.
          2.60 5.9 0  ⎫
          3.90 3.2 1  ⎪
           .    .  .  ⎬  Input data values
           .    .  .  ⎪  (1 observation per line)
           .    .  .  ⎪
          1.70 1.1 0  ⎭
    5     END DATA.
    6     REGRESSION VARIABLES=Y, X1, X2, X1*X2, X1SQ/  ⎫
    7                CRITERIA=TOLERANCE(.00001)/         ⎪
    8                DEPENDENT=Y/                        ⎬  Multiple regression analysis
    9                METHOD=ENTER/                       ⎪
   10                STATISTICS=DEFAULT CI/              ⎪
   11                CASEWISE=ALL DEPENDENT PRED SEPRED. ⎭
```

COMMANDS 2–3 Independent variables representing interactions and higher-order terms (eg, X1SQ) must be created with COMPUTE statements prior to running the regression analysis.

COMMAND 6 The REGRESSION command fits general linear models. All variables analyzed, both dependent and independent, are listed on the VARIABLES subcommand.

COMMAND 7 A low tolerance level (.00001) is specified to guarantee that all the independent variables will be entered into the regression equation. (SPSS will omit an independent variable from the model if its tolerance* is less than the level specified.)

COMMAND 10 The CI option of the STATISTICS subcommand produces a 95% confidence interval for the β coefficient of each independent variable in the model.

COMMAND 11 The CASEWISE subcommand produces a list of the predicted values and their corresponding standard errors for all observations used in the analysis.

NOTE The output for this SPSS program is displayed in Figure 10.30b (p. 510).

```
Command
Line
1      READ C1 C2 C3    Data entry instruction
       2.60 5.9 0  ⎤
       3.90 3.2 1  ⎥
        ·   ·  ·   ⎬  Input data values
        ·   ·  ·   ⎥  (1 observation per line)
        ·   ·  ·   ⎥
       1.70 1.1 0  ⎦
2      LET C4=C2*C3
3      LET C5=C2*C2
4      NAME C1='Y' C2='X1' C3='X2' C4='X1X2' C5='X1SQ'
5      REGRESS C1 4 C2-C5;  ⎤
6         PREDICT 3 0 0 9.  ⎬  Multiple regression analysis
```

COMMANDS 2–3 Independent variables representing interactions and higher-order terms must be created prior to running the regression analysis.

COMMAND 5 The REGRESS command fits general linear models. The column number of the dependent variable is listed first, followed by the number of predictors in the model and the columns where the independent variables are located.

COMMAND 6 The PREDICT subcommand produces a 95% confidence interval and prediction interval for an observation with the x-values specified in column order (eg, $x_1 = 3$, $x_2 = 0$, $x_1 x_2 = 0$, $x_1^2 = 9$).

NOTE The output for this MINITAB program is displayed in Figure 10.30c (p. 510).

FIGURE 10.30a

SAS Printout for Computer Lab 2

Analysis of Variance

Source	DF	Sum of Squares	Mean Square	F Value	Prob>F
Model	4	293.42443	73.35611	6.935	0.0023
Error	15	158.66107	10.57740		
C Total	19	452.08550			

Root MSE	3.25229	R-square	0.6490
Dep Mean	6.33500	Adj R-sq	0.5555
C.V.	51.33847		

Parameter Estimates

Variable	DF	Parameter Estimate	Standard Error	T for H0: Parameter=0	Prob > |T|
INTERCEP	1	2.213435	2.05476880	1.077	0.2984
X1	1	0.103948	1.17649081	0.088	0.9308
X2	1	-1.108612	3.15564605	-0.351	0.7302
X1X2	1	0.395886	0.67899079	0.583	0.5685
X1SQ	1	0.146911	0.15533301	0.946	0.3592

SAS

Obs	X1	X2	Dep Var Y	Predict Value	Std Err Predict	Lower95% Predict	Upper95% Predict	Residual
1	5.9	0	2.6000	7.9407	1.508	0.3001	15.5812	-5.3407
2	3.2	1	3.9000	4.2087	1.388	-3.3286	11.7459	-0.3087
3	4.4	1	8.0000	6.1483	1.351	-1.3584	13.6550	1.8517
4	6.6	1	9.2000	10.8032	1.314	3.3264	18.2799	-1.6032
5	0.75	0	4.4000	2.3740	1.551	-5.3058	10.0538	2.0260
6	0.7	0	1.5000	2.3582	1.576	-5.3444	10.0608	-0.8582
7	6.5	1	14.5000	10.5607	1.296	3.0984	18.0230	3.9393
8	4.5	0	1.9000	5.6561	1.361	-1.8587	13.1710	-3.7561
9	0.6	1	1.0000	1.4576	2.543	-7.3425	10.2577	-0.4576
10	7.5	0	14.0000	11.2568	2.594	2.3893	20.1243	2.7432
11	5.1	0	11.0000	6.5647	1.372	-0.9590	14.0884	4.4353
12	2.4	1	5.0000	3.1506	1.483	-4.4679	10.7691	1.8494
13	0.3	0	2.0000	2.2578	1.819	-5.6852	10.2009	-0.2578
14	6.2	1	6.0000	9.8510	1.264	2.4136	17.2885	-3.8510
15	2.7	1	1.1000	3.5254	1.431	-4.0478	11.0985	-2.4254
16	3.5	0	8.0000	4.3769	1.360	-3.1371	11.8909	3.6231
17	4.1	0	3.3000	5.1092	1.365	-2.4086	12.6270	-1.8092
18	8.1	1	12.1000	14.7923	2.172	6.4570	23.1276	-2.6923
19	7	1	15.5000	11.8023	1.432	4.2278	19.3768	3.6977
20	1.1	0	1.7000	2.5055	1.413	-5.0524	10.0635	-0.8055

FIGURE 10.30b

SPSS Printout for Computer Lab 2

```
Multiple R            .80563
R Square              .64905
Adjusted R Square     .55546
Standard Error        3.25229

Analysis of Variance
                 DF     Sum of Squares      Mean Square
Regression        4        293.42443         73.35611
Residual         15        158.66107         10.57740

F =      6.93517      Signif F =   .0023


--------------------- Variables in the Equation ----------------------

Variable        B           SE B     95% Confdnce Intrvl B      Beta        T    Sig T

X1SQ        .146911      .155333     -.184174      .477995    .624794    .946    .3592
X2        -1.108612     3.155646    -7.834712     5.617489   -.116588   -.351    .7302
X1X2       .395886      .678991    -1.051349     1.843121    .241408    .583    .5685
X1         .103948     1.176491    -2.403683     2.611579    .053852    .088    .9308
(Constant) 2.213435     2.054769    -2.166201     6.593071              1.077    .2984


Casewise Plot of Standardized Residual

*: Selected    M: Missing

               -3.0       0.0        3.0
    Case #     O:.......:.......:O         Y        *PRED      *SEPRED
       1       .    *     .         .      2.60      7.9407     1.5075
       2       .          *         .      3.90      4.2087     1.3883
       3       .          . *       .      8.00      6.1483     1.3514
       4       .          *.        .      9.20     10.8032     1.3143
       5       .          . *       .      4.40      2.3740     1.5508
       6       .          *.        .      1.50      2.3582     1.5755
       7       .          .  *      .     14.50     10.5607     1.2962
       8       .      *   .         .      1.90      5.6561     1.3613
       9       .          *         .      1.00      1.4576     2.5434
      10       .          . *       .     14.00     11.2568     2.5944
      11       .          . *       .     11.00      6.5647     1.3721
      12       .          . *       .      5.00      3.1506     1.4828
      13       .          *         .      2.00      2.2578     1.8194
      14       .      *   .         .      6.00      9.8510     1.2643
      15       .     *    .         .      1.10      3.5254     1.4307
      16       .          . *       .      8.00      4.3769     1.3603
      17       .      *   .         .      3.30      5.1092     1.3649
      18       .     *    .         .     12.10     14.7923     2.1716
      19       .          . *       .     15.50     11.8023     1.4323
      20       .         *.         .      1.70      2.5055     1.4129
    Case #     O:.......:.......:O         Y        *PRED      *SEPRED
               -3.0       0.0        3.0
```

FIGURE 10.30c

MINITAB Printout for Computer Lab 2

```
The regression equation is
Y = 2.21 + 0.10 X1 - 1.11 X2 + 0.396 X1X2 + 0.147 X1SQ

Predictor      Coef       Stdev     t-ratio         p
Constant      2.213       2.055       1.08       0.298
X1            0.104       1.176       0.09       0.931
X2           -1.109       3.156      -0.35       0.730
X1X2         0.3959      0.6790       0.58       0.569
X1SQ         0.1469      0.1553       0.95       0.359

s = 3.252       R-sq = 64.9%      R-sq(adj) = 55.5%

Analysis of Variance

SOURCE       DF        SS           MS         F         p
Regression    4      293.42       73.36      6.94      0.002
Error        15      158.66       10.58
Total        19      452.09


      Fit   Stdev.Fit      95% C.I.            95% P.I.
     3.847     1.340   ( 0.991,  6.703)   ( -3.652, 11.346)
```

NONPARAMETRIC REGRESSION

10.9 In Chapter 11 we will discuss how to modify the regression analysis when the assumptions about the random error term ϵ are violated. An alternative procedure is to conduct a **nonparametric regression analysis** of the data. In nonparametric regression, tests of model adequacy do not require any assumptions about the probability distribution of ϵ; thus, they are distribution-free. Although the tests are intuitively appealing, they can become quite difficult to apply in practice, especially when the number of observations is large. (For this reason, most analysts prefer to use the techniques of Chapter 11 when the standard regression assumptions are violated.)

In this section we provide brief descriptions of the nonparametric alternatives to the parametric simple linear regression tests of Section 10.3. Specifically, we discuss a nonparametric test for (1) linear correlation and (2) the slope parameter of the straight-line model.

SPEARMAN'S RANK CORRELATION

As an alternative to the Pearson product moment correlation coefficient, r (Sections 3.10 and 10.3), we can compute a correlation coefficient based on ranks. **Spearman's rank correlation coefficient**, denoted r_s, can then be used to test for linear correlation between two variables, y and x.

To illustrate, suppose a large manufacturing firm wants to determine whether the number, y, of work-hours an employee misses per year is correlated with the employee's annual wages, x (in thousands of dollars). A sample of 15 employees produced the data shown in Table 10.13.

Spearman's rank correlation coefficient is found by first ranking the values of each variable separately. (Ties are treated by averaging the tied ranks.) Then r_s is

TABLE 10.13
Work-Hours Missed, Annual Wages, and Ranks for 15 Employees

EMPLOYEE	HOURS MISSED y	ANNUAL WAGES x	y-RANK	x-RANK	DIFFERENCE d_i	d_i^2
1	49	15.8	6	11	-5	25
2	36	17.5	4	12	-8	64
3	127	11.3	13	2	11	121
4	91	13.2	12	6	6	36
5	72	13.0	9	5	4	16
6	34	14.5	3	9	-6	36
7	155	11.8	14	3	11	121
8	11	20.2	2	14	-12	144
9	191	10.8	15	1	14	196
10	6	18.8	1	13	-12	144
11	63	13.8	8	7	1	1
12	79	12.7	10	4	6	36
13	43	15.1	5	10	-5	25
14	57	24.2	7	15	-8	64
15	82	13.9	11	8	3	9
					$\Sigma \, d_i^2 =$	1,038

computed in exactly the same way as the Pearson correlation coefficient r; the only difference is that the values of x and y that appear in the formula for r are replaced by their ranks. That is, the *ranks* of the raw data are used to compute r_s rather than the raw data themselves. When there are no (or few) ties in the ranks, this formula reduces to the simple expression

$$r_s = 1 - \frac{6 \sum d_i^2}{n(n^2 - 1)}$$

where d_i is the difference between the rank of y and x for the ith observation.

The ranks of y and x, the differences between the ranks, and the squared differences for each of the 15 employees are also shown in Table 10.13. Note that the sum of the squared differences is $\sum d_i^2 = 1{,}038$. Substituting this value into the formula for r_s, we obtain

$$r_s = 1 - \frac{6 \sum d_i^2}{n(n^2 - 1)} = 1 - \frac{6(1{,}038)}{15(224)} = -.854$$

This large negative value of r_s implies that a fairly strong negative correlation exists between work-hours missed, y, and annual wages, x, in the sample.

To determine whether a negative correlation exists in the population, we would test $H_0: \rho = 0$ against $H_a: \rho < 0$ using r_s as a test statistic. As you would expect, we reject H_0 for small values of r_s. Upper-tailed critical values of Spearman's r_s are provided in Table 15, Appendix A. This table is partially reproduced in Table 10.14. Since the distribution of r_s is symmetric around 0, the lower-tailed critical value is the negative of the corresponding upper-tailed critical value. For, say, $\alpha = .01$ and $n = 15$, the critical value (shaded in Table 10.14) is $r_{.01} = .623$. Thus, the rejection region for the test is

Reject H_0 if $r_s < -.623$

TABLE 10.14

A Portion of the Spearman's r_s Table (Table 15, Appendix A)

The α-values correspond to a one-tailed test of H_0.
The value should be doubled for two-tailed tests.

n	$\alpha = .05$	$\alpha = .025$	$\alpha = .01$	$\alpha = .005$
15	.441	.525	.623	.689
16	.425	.507	.601	.666
17	.412	.490	.582	.645
18	.399	.476	.564	.625
19	.388	.462	.549	.608
20	.377	.450	.534	.591
21	.368	.438	.521	.576
22	.359	.428	.508	.562
23	.351	.418	.496	.549
24	.343	.409	.485	.537
25	.336	.400	.475	.526

Since the test statistic, $r_s = -.854$, falls in the rejection region, there is sufficient evidence (at $\alpha = .01$) of negative correlation between work-hours missed, y, and annual wages, x, in the population.

Spearman's nonparametric test for rank correlation in the population is summarized in the following box:

SPEARMAN'S NONPARAMETRIC TEST FOR RANK CORRELATION

ONE-TAILED TEST

H_0: $\rho = 0$

H_a: $\rho > 0$

[or H_a: $\rho < 0$]

TWO-TAILED TEST

H_0: $\rho = 0$

H_a: $\rho \neq 0$

Test statistic: $r_s = 1 - \dfrac{6 \sum d_i^2}{n(n^2 - 1)}$

where d_i is the difference between the y-rank and x-rank for the ith observation

Note: In the case of ties, calculate r_s by substituting the ranks of the y's and the ranks of the x's for the actual y-values and x-values in the formula for r given in Section 3.10.

Rejection region: $r_s > r_\alpha$
[or $r_s < -r_\alpha$]

Rejection region: $|r_s| > r_{\alpha/2}$

where the values of r_α and $r_{\alpha/2}$ are given in Table 15, Appendix A.

Assumptions: None

THEIL TEST FOR ZERO SLOPE

Alternatively, we can test for linear correlation in the population by testing the slope parameter β_1 in the simple linear regression model

$$y = \beta_0 + \beta_1 x + \epsilon$$

That is, we can test H_0: $\beta_1 = 0$ against H_a: $\beta_1 \neq 0$. A distribution-free test for the slope is the **Theil C test**. To conduct this nonparametric test, we first rank the x-values in increasing order and list the ordered x–y pairs, as shown in Table 10.15 (p. 514). Next, we calculate all possible differences $y_j - y_i$, $i < j$ (where i and j represent the ith- and jth-ranked observations), and note the sign (positive or negative) of each difference.

For example, the y-value for the employee ranked 2, $y_2 = 127$, is compared to the y-value for each employee with a lower rank. In this case, the only employee ranked lower is employee 1, with $y_1 = 191$ (see Table 10.15). The difference

$$y_2 - y_1 = 127 - 191 = -64$$

is negative, and is noted as such in Table 10.15. Similarly, we compare the y-value of the employee ranked 3, $y_3 = 155$, to the y-values of employees of lower rank,

TABLE 10.15
Data of Table 10.13 Ranked by Annual Wages, x

RANKED EMPLOYEE	HOURS MISSED y	ANNUAL WAGES x	DIFFERENCES, $y_j - y_i$ $(i < j)$ Number of Negatives	Number of Positives
1	191	10.8	—	—
2	127	11.3	1	0
3	155	11.8	1	1
4	79	12.7	3	0
5	72	13.0	4	0
6	91	13.2	3	2
7	63	13.8	6	0
8	82	13.9	4	3
9	34	14.5	8	0
10	43	15.1	8	1
11	49	15.8	8	2
12	36	17.5	10	1
13	6	18.8	12	0
14	11	20.2	12	1
15	57	24.2	8	6
			Totals 98	17

$y_2 = 127$ and $y_1 = 191$, by the differences

$$y_3 - y_2 = 155 - 127 = 28$$

and

$$y_3 - y_1 = 155 - 191 = -36$$

This results in one positive and one negative difference. Continuing in this manner, we obtain a total of 17 positive differences and 98 negative differences, as shown in Table 10.15.

The test statistic C is obtained by scoring each positive difference as a $+1$ and each negative difference as a -1 (0 differences are assigned a score of 0) and summing the scores. Therefore, for the data of Table 10.15 we obtain the test statistic

$$C = (+1)(17) + (-1)(98) = -81$$

The observed significance level (p-value) of the test is obtained from Table 16, Appendix A. For this lower-tailed test (ie, a test for a negative slope), the p-value is $P(C \le -81)$. Searching the $n = 15$ column and the $c = 81$ row of Table 16, Appendix A, we obtain the p-value ≈ 0. Thus, there is strong evidence to reject H_0 and conclude that work-hours missed, y, is negatively linearly related to annual wages, x, at this firm.

Theil's test for zero slope in a straight-line model is described, in general, in the following box. A nonparametric confidence interval for the slope β_1 based on the Theil test also can be formed. Consult the references if you want to learn how to construct this interval.

Nonparametric tests are also available for multiple regression models. These tests are very sophisticated, however, and require the use of specialized statistical computer software not yet available on a commercial basis. Consult the references if you want to learn more about these nonparametric techniques.

PROBLEMS

10.36   Housing planners, insurance companies, and credit institutions have shown great interest in measuring factors related to the risk of default in home mortgages. Typically, the default rate (ie, the probability of defaulting on a home loan) is used as the standard measure of risk. Another, possibly superior, measure of risk is the expected loss for a home loan (ie, the dollar loss expected on a default). A study was conducted to compare the two measures of mortgage default risk. The default rate and expected loss (measured as a percentage of loan value) for 16 different FHA categories of home mortgages are recorded in the table at the top of the next page.

a. Calculate Spearman's rank correlation coefficient between the two measures of mortgage default risk.
b. Is there sufficient evidence to indicate that default rate and expected loss are positively correlated? Test using $\alpha = .01$.
c. Analyze the data in the table using Theil's test for zero slope. Do the results agree with part b?

Data for Problem 10.36

	LOAN CATEGORY			DEFAULT RATE %	EXPECTED LOSS %
Loan Size	Loan Value	Race	Location		
GT $20,750	GT 95%	White	Other city	3.44	.948
GT $20,750	GT 95%	White	Suburb	5.20	1.181
GT $20,750	GT 95%	Black	Other city	12.50	3.178
GT $20,750	GT 95%	Black	Suburb	16.95	2.696
LT $20,750	GT 95%	White	Other city	3.89	1.256
LT $20,750	GT 95%	White	Suburb	4.85	1.578
LT $20,750	GT 95%	Black	Other city	13.40	6.453
LT $20,750	GT 95%	Black	Suburb	14.67	4.025
GT $20,750	90–95%	White	Other city	2.15	.558
GT $20,750	90–95%	White	Suburb	2.66	.630
GT $20,750	90–95%	Black	Other city	5.60	1.448
GT $20,750	90–95%	Black	Suburb	7.95	2.304
LT $20,750	90–95%	White	Other city	2.41	.674
LT $20,750	90–95%	White	Suburb	2.60	.897
LT $20,750	90–95%	Black	Other city	10.27	4.836
LT $20,750	90–95%	Black	Suburb	5.66	1.579

Source: Evans, R. D., Maris, B. A., and Weinstein, R. I. "Expected Loss and Mortgage Default Risk." *Quarterly Journal of Business and Economics,* Vol. 24, No. 1, Winter 1985, pp. 75–92.

Note: GT = greater than; LT = less than.

10.37 What are the top graduate business schools in the United States? *Business Week* polled a random sample of approximately 3,000 graduates of the schools that most often make top 20 lists. The graduates assessed the quality of the teaching, curriculum, environment, and job placement efforts on a scale of 1 to 10, and the schools were awarded an average score. Based on those average scores, *Business Week* compiled the list of top 20 business schools in the United States given in the table. In addition, the table reports the average starting pay of the schools' graduates. Is there evidence of a positive correlation between the business school's rank and average starting salary of its graduates? Test using $\alpha = .05$.

BUSINESS SCHOOL	BUSINESS WEEK RANK	AVERAGE STARTING PAY	BUSINESS SCHOOL	BUSINESS WEEK RANK	AVERAGE STARTING PAY
Northwestern	1	$53,031	Chicago	11	$54,772
Harvard	2	64,112	Indiana	12	38,407
Dartmouth	3	62,681	Carnegie-Mellon	13	49,109
Wharton	4	55,183	Columbia	14	49,397
Cornell	5	52,339	MIT	15	60,860
Michigan	6	43,976	UCLA	16	45,378
Virginia	7	50,554	California (Berkeley)	17	45,083
North Carolina	8	44,941	NYU	18	47,037
Stanford	9	65,176	Yale	19	46,455
Duke	10	48,740	Rochester	20	39,990

Source: Business Week, Nov. 28, 1988, pp. 78–79. Reprinted from Nov. 28, 1988 issue of *Business Week* by special permission, copyright © 1988 by McGraw-Hill, Inc. Used with permission.

10.38 Refer to Problem 10.7 and *Fortune* magazine's ranking of the top 10 American cities with respect to their ability to provide high-quality, low-cost labor. The data on labor market stress index (y) and unemployment rate (x) are reproduced in the table at the top of the next page. Consider the straight-line model $E(y) = \beta_0 + \beta_1 x$.

RANK	CITY	LABOR MARKET STRESS INDEX y	UNEMPLOYMENT RATE x
1	Salt Lake City	107	4.5%
2	Minneapolis–St. Paul	107	3.8%
3	Atlanta	100	5.1%
4	Sacramento	100	4.9%
5	Austin (Texas)	80	5.4%
6	Columbus (Ohio)	100	4.8%
7	Dallas/Fort Worth	100	5.5%
8	Phoenix	93	4.3%
9	Jacksonville (Florida)	87	5.7%
10	Oklahoma City	80	4.6%

a. Calculate Theil's test statistic for a test of zero slope.

b. Is there evidence of a linear relationship between labor market stress index and unemployment rate? Test using $\alpha = .01$.

10.39 Refer to the *Proceedings of the Institution of Civil Engineers* study of stress in masonry joints, Problem 10.9. The data on shear strength (y) and precompression stress (x) are reproduced in the table. Conduct a nonparametric test of $H_0: \beta_1 = 0$ against $H_a: \beta_1 > 0$. Test using $\alpha = .05$.

TRIPLET TEST	1	2	3	4	5	6	7
Shear Strength, y	1.00	2.18	2.24	2.41	2.59	2.82	3.06
Precompression Stress, x	0	.60	1.20	1.33	1.43	1.75	1.75

Source: Riddington, J. R., and Ghazali, M. Z. "Hypothesis for Shear Failure in Masonry Joints." *Proceedings of the Institution of Civil Engineers, Part 2*, Mar. 1990, Vol. 89, p. 96 (Fig. 7).

10.40 The data for Problem 10.11 are reproduced below. Conduct a nonparametric test to determine whether instructor grade, y, and AUTOMARK grade, x, are positively linearly related. Test at $\alpha = .01$.

AUTOMARK GRADE x	INSTRUCTOR GRADE y	AUTOMARK GRADE x	INSTRUCTOR GRADE y	AUTOMARK GRADE x	INSTRUCTOR GRADE y
12.2	10	18.2	15	19.0	17
10.6	11	15.1	16	19.3	17
15.1	12	17.2	16	19.5	17
16.2	12	17.5	16	19.7	17
16.6	12	18.6	16	18.6	18
16.6	13	18.8	16	19.0	18
17.2	14	17.8	17	19.2	18
17.6	14	18.0	17	19.4	18
18.2	14	18.2	17	19.6	18
16.5	15	18.4	17	20.1	18
17.2	15	18.6	17	19.2	19

Source: Redish, K. A., and Smyth, W. F. "Program Style Anaiysis: A Natural By-product of Program Compilation." *Communications of the Association for Computing Machinery*, Vol. 29, No. 2, Feb. 1986, p. 132 (Fig. 4).

- The variable y to be predicted (or modeled) in a **regression analysis** is called the **dependent** (or **response**) **variable**.
- A **probabilistic model** for y is $y = E(y) + \epsilon$, where $E(y)$ represents the mean (or expected) value of y and ϵ represents random error.
- The variables used to model the mean, $E(y)$, are called **independent variables** and are denoted by the symbols x_1, x_2, x_3, etc.
- A **deterministic model** for $E(y)$ takes the form $E(y) = \beta_0 + \beta_1 x_1 + \beta_2 x_2 + \cdots + \beta_k x_k$, where the constant β_i determines the contribution of the independent variable x_i to the mean response.
- **Simple linear regression** describes the analysis of the simple **straight-line model** $y = \beta_0 + \beta_1 x + \epsilon$.
- **Multiple regression** describes the analysis of the **general linear model** $y = \beta_0 + \beta_1 x_1 + \beta_2 x_2 + \cdots + \beta_k x_k + \epsilon$.

  Regression modeling consists, at the minimum, of the following six steps:

  STEP 1 Hypothesize the form of the model.

  STEP 2 Collect the sample data.

  STEP 3 Use the sample data to estimate unknown parameters in the model.

  STEP 4 Specify the probability distribution of the random error term, and estimate any unknown parameters of this distribution.

  STEP 5 Statistically check the usefulness of the model.

  STEP 6 When satisfied that the model is useful, use it for prediction, estimation, and so on.

- The data collection phase (step 2) involves collecting observations on both the dependent variable, y, and the independent variables x_1, x_2, ..., x_k, for each experimental unit in the sample.
- **Observational data** are collected when the values of the independent variables (x-values) are uncontrolled by the researcher.
- **Experimental data** require the researcher to preset the values of the independent variables prior to observing y.
- In regression, the sample size should be large enough so that the β's are both estimable and testable. This requires that n be at least as large as the number of β parameters included in the model for $E(y)$. **A good rule of thumb is to select n greater than or equal to 10 times the number of β parameters in the model**.
- The **sum of squared errors (SSE)** for an estimated model is $SSE = \Sigma(y - \hat{y})^2$, where $\hat{y}$ is the predicted value of y obtained from the model.
- The **method of least squares** is used to obtain estimates of the β parameters in the hypothesized model (step 3). This method produces an estimated model that has a smaller SSE than any other estimated model with a sum of errors (SE) of 0.
- Four basic assumptions about the general form of the probability distribution of ϵ (step 4) are required to make parametric inferences about the regression model:

Assumption 1: The mean of the probability distribution of ϵ is 0.

Assumption 2: The variance of the probability distribution of ϵ, denoted σ^2, is constant for all settings of the x's.

Assumption 3: The probability distribution of ϵ is normal.

Assumption 4: The errors are independent.

■ The estimate of σ^2 for any regression model is given by

$$s^2 = \frac{\text{SSE}}{\text{Degrees of freedom for error}} = \frac{\text{SSE}}{n - (\text{Number of } \beta \text{ parameters in model})}$$

■ A practical interpretation of s, the estimated standard deviation of ϵ, is obtained by multiplying s by 2. Then we can expect most of the observed y-values to lie within $2s$ of their respective least squares predicted values, $\hat{y}$.

■ The **coefficient of determination (R^2)** for a model is

$$R^2 = \frac{\text{SS}_{yy} - \text{SSE}}{\text{SS}_{yy}} = 1 - \frac{\text{SSE}}{\text{SS}_{yy}} \qquad \text{where SS}_{yy} = \Sigma(y - \bar{y})^2$$

Since $0 \leq R^2 \leq 1$, it represents the proportion of the sum of squares of deviations of the y-values about their mean that can be explained by the independent variables in the model.

■ The **adjusted coefficient of determination (R_a^2)** is

$$R_a^2 = 1 - \frac{n - 1}{n - (k + 1)}(1 - R^2)$$

Note that $R_a^2 \leq R^2$. Most analysts prefer the more conservative R_a^2 to R^2 in measuring model adequacy.

■ A **test statistic and confidence interval for an individual β parameter** of a model are given as follows:

Test statistic for H_0: $\beta_i = 0$: $t = \dfrac{\hat{\beta}_i}{s_{\hat{\beta}_i}}$

Confidence interval for β_i: $\hat{\beta}_i \pm t_{\alpha/2} s_{\hat{\beta}_i}$

where $s_{\hat{\beta}_i}$ is the estimated standard error of $\hat{\beta}_i$, and the distribution of t depends on $\nu = n - (\text{Total number of } \beta \text{ parameters in model})$ degrees of freedom.

■ The test statistic for **testing overall model adequacy**—that is, testing whether all β parameters in the model (excluding β_0) equal 0—is

$$F = \frac{\text{MS(Model)}}{\text{MSE}} = \left[\frac{\text{SS(Model)}}{\text{SSE}}\right]\left[\frac{n - (k + 1)}{k}\right] = \left(\frac{R^2}{1 - R^2}\right)\left[\frac{n - (k + 1)}{k}\right]$$

where $k = $ number of β parameters in model (excluding β_0), and the distribution of F depends on $\nu_1 = k$ numerator and $\nu_2 = n - (k + 1)$ denominator degrees of freedom.

■ The following procedure is recommended for checking the utility of a model (step 5):

CHECK 1 Conduct a test of overall model adequacy using the F test; that is, test H_0: $\beta_1 = \beta_2 = \cdots = \beta_k = 0$. If the model is deemed adequate (ie, if you reject H_0), then proceed to checks 2 and 3. Otherwise, you should hypothesize and fit another model. The new model may include more independent variables or higher-order terms.

CHECK 2 Conduct t tests on only the most important β parameters. These usually involve only the β's associated with higher-order terms (x_1^2, $x_1 x_2$, etc.). It is a safe practice to limit the number of β's that are tested. Conducting a series of t tests leads to a high overall Type I error rate.

CHECK 3 Interpret the value of R^2 or R_a^2. A low R^2 value may imply that a more useful model can be found.

- A **confidence interval for $E(y)$** for a specified set of x-values (step 6) gives lower and upper confidence limits on the mean value of y for all experimental units with similar x-values.

- A **prediction interval for y** for a specified set of x-values (step 6) gives lower and upper confidence limits on the y-value for an individual experimental unit with similar x-values.

- Using the least squares prediction equation to estimate $E(y)$ or to predict y for values of x that fall **outside the range of the sample data** may lead to errors that are much larger than expected. Although the least squares model may provide a very good fit to the data over the range of x-values contained in the sample, **it could give a poor representation of the true model for values of x outside this region.**

- A **first-order (straight-line) model** for $E(y)$ in one quantitative independent variable is given by the equation

$$E(y) = \beta_0 + \beta_1 x$$

where

$\beta_0 = $ **y-intercept** of the line (ie, the point at which the line cuts through the y-axis)

$\beta_1 = $ **Slope** of the line (ie, the change in $E(y)$ for every 1 unit increase in x)

- A **first-order model** for $E(y)$ in two quantitative independent variables is given by the equation

$$E(y) = \beta_0 + \beta_1 x_1 + \beta_2 x_2$$

where

$\beta_1 = $ Change in $E(y)$ for every 1 unit increase in x_1 (holding x_2 constant)

$\beta_2 = $ Change in $E(y)$ for every 1 unit increase in x_2 (holding x_1 constant)

- An **interaction model** for $E(y)$ in two quantitative independent variables is given by the equation

$$E(y) = \beta_0 + \beta_1 x_1 + \beta_2 x_2 + \beta_3 x_1 x_2$$

where

$(\beta_1 + \beta_3 x_2)$ = Change in $E(y)$ for every 1 unit increase in x_1 (holding x_2 constant)

$(\beta_2 + \beta_3 x_1)$ = Change in $E(y)$ for every 1 unit increase in x_2 (holding x_1 constant)

- A **second-order (quadratic) model** for $E(y)$ in one quantitative independent variable is given by the equation

$$E(y) = \beta_0 + \beta_1 x + \beta_2 x^2$$

where

β_0 = **y-intercept** of the curve

β_1 = **Shift parameter** of the curve

β_2 = **Rate of curvature**   Positive values imply **upward** curvature, while negative values imply **downward** curvature.

- A **complete second-order model** for $E(y)$ in two quantitative independent variables is given by the equation

$$E(y) = \beta_0 + \beta_1 x_1 + \beta_2 x_2 + \beta_3 x_1 x_2 + \beta_4 x_1^2 + \beta_5 x_2^2$$

- A **dummy variable model** for $E(y)$ in a qualitative variable at three levels (A, B, and C) is given by the equation

$$E(y) = \beta_0 + \beta_1 x_1 + \beta_2 x_2$$

where

$$x_1 = \begin{cases} 1 & \text{if level A} \\ 0 & \text{if not} \end{cases}$$

$$x_2 = \begin{cases} 1 & \text{if level B} \\ 0 & \text{if not} \end{cases}$$

Base level = C

$\beta_0 = \mu_C$ The mean of y at level C

$\beta_1 = \mu_A - \mu_C$

$\beta_2 = \mu_B - \mu_C$

- **Spearman's rank correlation coefficient (r_s)** is used to conduct a nonparametric test for linear correlation between two variables, y and x.
- **Theil's zero-slope test** is used to conduct a nonparametric test for the slope parameter of the straight-line model $E(y) = \beta_0 + \beta_1 x$.

LOOKING AHEAD

Our discussion of regression analysis continues in Chapter 11, where the focus is on model building, model diagnostics, and residual analysis.

THE SALARY RACE: MALES VERSUS FEMALES

Upon graduation from college, you will embark upon a career in your chosen field of study. Once you accept a job, you'll join the ranks of workers who are preoccupied with the size of their paychecks. Are you being fairly compensated? Why does your friend in another city receive a larger salary for a less demanding job? What can you do to get a raise?

Certainly, we expect our compensation to be tied to our qualifications. Graduates with engineering degrees expect to be paid more than nursing graduates. Graduates with PhD degrees expect higher starting salaries than graduates with bachelor degrees. But, will your starting salary depend on your gender?

We can obtain a partial answer to this question by examining a data set extracted from a recent Career Resource Center (CRC), University of Florida, questionnaire. The data set contains the starting salaries of approximately 900 graduates (bachelor degree) of the University of Florida in five different colleges: Business Administration, Engineering, Journalism, Liberal Arts and Sciences, and Nursing. In addition to starting salary and college, the gender (male or female) of the graduate was recorded.

Consider a multiple regression model relating starting salary y to the two qualitative independent variables, college (at 5 levels) and gender (at 2 levels). From Section 10.8, we require four dummy variables for college and one for gender. These are defined as follows:

$$College: \quad x_1 = \begin{cases} 1 & \text{if Business Administration} \\ 0 & \text{if not} \end{cases}$$

$$x_2 = \begin{cases} 1 & \text{if Engineering} \\ 0 & \text{if not} \end{cases}$$

$$x_3 = \begin{cases} 1 & \text{if Liberal Arts and Sciences} \\ 0 & \text{if not} \end{cases}$$

$$x_4 = \begin{cases} 1 & \text{if Journalism} \\ 0 & \text{if not} \end{cases}$$

$$Gender: \quad x_5 = \begin{cases} 1 & \text{if female} \\ 0 & \text{if male} \end{cases}$$

Note that we have arbitrarily selected nursing and male as the base levels for college and gender, respectively. A model relating mean starting salary, $E(y)$, to these two independent variables takes the form

$$E(y) = \beta_0 + \underbrace{\beta_1 x_1 + \beta_2 x_2 + \beta_3 x_3 + \beta_4 x_4}_{\substack{\text{College} \\ \text{terms}}} + \underbrace{\beta_5 x_5}_{\substack{\text{Gender} \\ \text{term}}}$$

a. Write the equation relating mean starting salary, $E(y)$, to college, for male graduates only.

b. Interpret β_1 in the model from part **a**.

c. Interpret β_2 in the model from part **a**.

d. Interpret β_3 in the model from part **a**.

e. Interpret β_4 in the model from part **a**.

f. Write the equation relating mean starting salary, $E(y)$, to college, for female graduates only.

g. Interpret β_1 in the model from part **f**. Compare to your answer to part **b**.

h. Interpret β_2 in the model from part **f**. Compare to your answer to part **c**.

i. Interpret β_3 in the model from part **f**. Compare to your answer to part **d**.

j. Interpret β_4 in the model from part **f**. Compare to your answer to part **e**.

k. For a given college, interpret the value of β_5 in the model.

l. The SAS printout of the multiple regression analysis is displayed in Figure 10.31. Interpret the results. Part of your answer should include a statement about whether gender has an effect on average starting salary.

FIGURE 10.31

SAS Printout for the Model Relating Salary to College and Gender

Dependent Variable: SALARY

Analysis of Variance

Source	DF	Sum of Squares	Mean Square	F Value	Prob>F
Model	5	13609836905	2721967380.9	90.022	0.0001
Error	896	27092165483	30236791.833		
C Total	901	40702002387			

Root MSE	5498.79913	R-square	0.3344	
Dep Mean	26020.20510	Adj R-sq	0.3307	
C.V.	21.13280			

Parameter Estimates

Variable	DF	Parameter Estimate	Standard Error	T for H0: Parameter=0	Prob > |T|
INTERCEP	1	29215	739.33031785	39.515	0.0001
X1	1	-3928.938467	731.13739384	-5.374	0.0001
X2	1	1845.020611	778.46344679	2.370	0.0180
X3	1	-8375.343226	902.00089218	-9.285	0.0001
X4	1	-7349.696165	795.38316872	-9.240	0.0001
X5	1	-1142.171471	419.57634068	-2.722	0.0066

REFERENCES

Mendenhall, W., and Sincich, T. *A Second Course in Business Statistics: Regression Analysis*, 4th ed. New York: Dellen/Macmillan, 1993.

Montgomery, D. C., and Peck, E. A. *Introduction to Linear Regression Analysis*. New York: Wiley, 1982.

Neter, J., Wasserman, W., and Kutner, M. H. *Applied Linear Statistical Models*, 3d ed. Homewood, IL: Irwin, 1989.

CHAPTER 11   MODEL BUILDING AND MODEL DIAGNOSTICS: REGRESSION (PART II)

To deter bid-rigging in the road construction industry, the Florida Attorney General relies on sophisticated regression models designed to predict the competitive cost of a road contract. In this chapter, we utilize the foundation established in Chapter 10 to build regression models. Methods for determining the "best" model among a set of models are presented, as well as several diagnostic checks of the model. These techniques are applied to data on 235 Florida road construction contracts in the chapter case study.

MODEL BUILDING

11.1

We have emphasized in Chapter 10 that one of the first steps in regression analysis is to hypothesize the form of the deterministic portion of the model, $E(y)$. This model-construction stage is the key to the success (or failure) of the regression analysis. If the hypothesized model does not reflect, at least approximately, the true nature of the relationship between the mean response $E(y)$ and the independent variables $x_1, x_2, ..., x_k$, the modeling effort will usually be unrewarded.

Successful researchers rarely propose a single model for $E(y)$. Most adopt a **model-building** approach. By model-building, we mean proposing a series of candidate models for $E(y)$ based on prevailing and/or new theories. These models are fit to the sample data and the best model is selected based on the regression results. With this model-building approach, the pitfall of making inferences based on the analysis of a single model can be avoided.

DEFINITION 11.1

In regression, **model-building** implies proposing and testing a series of candidate models for the mean response, $E(y)$.

To illustrate how such pitfalls can occur, consider the following. Several years ago, a nationally recognized education research group issued a report concerning the variables related to academic achievement for a certain type of college student. The researchers selected a random sample of students and recorded a measure of academic achievement, y, at the end of the senior year, along with data on an extensive list of independent variables, $x_1, x_2, ..., x_k$, which they thought were related to y. Among these independent variables were the student's IQ, scores on mathematics and verbal achievement examinations, rank in class, etc. They fit only one model,

$$E(y) = \beta_0 + \beta_1 x_1 + \beta_2 x_2 + \cdots + \beta_k x_k$$

to the data, analyzed the results, and reached the conclusion that none of the independent variables are significantly related to y. The **goodness of fit** of the model, measured by the coefficient of determination R^2, was not particularly good, and t tests on individual parameters did not lead to rejection of the null hypotheses that these parameters equaled 0.

How could the researchers have reached the conclusion that there is no significant relationship, when it is evident, just as a matter of experience, that some of the independent variables studied are related to academic achievement? For example, achievement on a college mathematics placement test should be related to achievement in college mathematics. Certainly, many other variables will affect achievement—motivation, environmental conditions, and so forth—but generally speaking, there will be a positive correlation between entrance achievement test scores and college academic achievement. So, what went wrong with the educational researchers' study?

Although you can never discard the possibility of computing error as a reason for erroneous answers, most likely the difficulties in the results of the educational study were caused by the use of an improperly constructed model. For example, the model

$$E(y) = \beta_0 + \beta_1 x_1 + \beta_2 x_2 + \cdots + \beta_k x_k$$

assumes that the independent variables x_1, x_2, ..., x_k affect mean achievement $E(y)$ independently of each other.* Thus, if you hold all the other independent variables constant and vary only x_1, $E(y)$ will increase by the amount β_1 for every unit increase in x_1. Similarly, a 1 unit change in any of the other independent variables will increase $E(y)$ by the value of the corresponding β parameter for that variable.

Do the assumptions implied by the model agree with your knowledge about academic achievement? First, is it reasonable to assume that the effect of time spent on study is independent of native intellectual ability? We think not. No matter how much effort some students invest in a particular subject, their rate of achievement is low. For others, it may be high. Therefore, assuming that these two variables—effort and native intellectual ability—affect $E(y)$ independently of each other is likely to be an erroneous assumption. Second, suppose that x_5 is the amount of time a student devotes to study. Is it reasonable to expect that a 1 unit increase in x_5 will always produce the same change β_5 in $E(y)$? The changes in $E(y)$ for a 1 unit increase in x_5 might depend on the value of x_5 (for example, the law of diminishing returns). Consequently, it is quite likely that the assumption of a constant rate of change in $E(y)$ for 1 unit increases in the independent variables will not be satisfied.

Clearly, the model

$$E(y) = \beta_0 + \beta_1 x_1 + \beta_2 x_2 + \cdots + \beta_k x_k$$

was a poor choice in view of the researchers' prior knowledge of some of the variables involved. Terms have to be added to the model to account for interrelationships among the independent variables and for curvature in the response function. Failure to include needed terms causes inflated values of SSE, nonsignificance in statistical tests, and, often, erroneous practical conclusions.

In this chapter, we present several model-building techniques as well as methods for diagnosing the goodness of fit of the selected model, including checking the standard regression assumptions listed in Section 10.3. The steps involved in conducting a regression analysis using the model-building approach are listed in the box.

STEP 1   Identify and select the independent variables x_1, x_2, ..., x_k to be used in the model-building procedure.

STEP 2   Propose several candidate models for $E(y)$.

(continued)

---

* Keep in mind that we are discussing the deterministic portion of the model and that the word *independent* is used in a mathematical rather than a probabilistic sense.

STEP 3   Collect the data.

STEP 4   Fit each model to the data using the method of least squares.

STEP 5   Determine the best model based on the regression results.

STEP 6   Check for violations of the standard regression assumptions and make modifications to the model, if necessary.

STEP 7   Use the model for making inferences.

STEPWISE REGRESSION

11.2 Perhaps the biggest problem in building a model is choosing the important independent variables to be included in the model (step 1). The list of potentially important variables can be extremely long (depending on the application), and we need some objective method of screening out those that are not as important. A systematic approach to building a model with a large number of independent variables is difficult because the interpretation of multivariable interactions and higher-order terms (squared terms, cubic terms, etc.) is tedious. In this situation, we turn to a screening procedure known as **stepwise regression**.

The most commonly used stepwise regression procedure, available in most statistical software packages, works as follows. The user first identifies the response, y, and the set of potentially important independent variables, x_1, x_2, ..., x_k, where k generally will be large. (Note that this set of variables could represent both first- and higher-order terms, as well as any interaction terms that might contribute important information.) The response and independent variables are then entered into the computer, and the stepwise procedure begins.

STEP 1   The computer automatically fits all possible one-variable models of the form

$$E(y) = \beta_0 + \beta_1 x_i$$

to the data. For each model, the test of the null hypothesis,

H_0: $\beta_1 = 0$

against the alternative hypothesis,

H_a: $\beta_1 \neq 0$

is conducted using the t test for a single β parameter. [Some software packages report an F test, rather than the t test. It can be shown (proof omitted) that an F test on a single β parameter is equivalent to the t test for the β. In fact, $F = t^2$.] The independent variable that produces the largest (absolute) t-value is declared the best one-variable predictor of y. Call this independent variable x_1.

STEP 2   The stepwise program now begins to search through the remaining $(k - 1)$ independent variables for the best two-variable model of the form

$$E(y) = \beta_0 + \beta_1 x_1 + \beta_2 x_i$$

This is done by fitting all two-variable models containing x_1 and each of the other

$(k - 1)$ options for the second variable x_i. The t-values for the test $H_0: \beta_2 = 0$ are computed for each of the $(k - 1)$ models (corresponding to the remaining independent variables $x_i = 2, 3, ..., k$), and the variable having the largest t-value is retained. Call this variable x_2.

At this point, some software packages diverge in methodology. The better packages now go back and check the t-value of β_1 *after $\beta_2 x_2$ has been added to the model.* If the t-value has become nonsignificant at some specified α level (say, $\alpha = .10$), the variable x_1 is removed and a search is made for the independent variable with a β parameter that will yield the most significant t-value in the presence of $\beta_2 x_2$. Other packages do not recheck β_1, but proceed directly to step 3.

The best-fitting model may yield a different value for $\hat{\beta}_1$ than that obtained in step 1, because x_1 and x_2 may be correlated. (In Section 11.4, we discuss in detail the problems with correlated independent variables.) Thus, both the value of β_1 and, therefore, its significance will usually change from step 1 to step 2. For this reason, the software packages that recheck the t-values at each step are preferred.

STEP 3 The stepwise procedure now checks for a third independent variable to include in the model with x_1 and x_2. That is, we seek the best model of the form

$$E(y) = \beta_0 + \beta_1 x_1 + \beta_2 x_2 + \beta_3 x_i$$

To do this, the computer fits all the $(k - 2)$ models using x_1, x_2, and each of the $(k - 2)$ remaining variables, x_i, as a possible x_3. Again the criterion is to include the independent variable with the largest t-value. Call this best third variable x_3.

The better programs now recheck the t-values corresponding to the x_1 and x_2 coefficients, replacing the variables that have t-values that have become nonsignificant. This procedure is continued until no further independent variables can be found that yield significant t-values (at the specified α level) in the presence of the variables already in the model.

The result of the stepwise procedure is a model containing only the terms with t-values that are significant at the specified α level. Thus, in most practical situations, only several of the large number of independent variables will remain. However, it is very important not to jump to the conclusion that all the independent variables important for predicting y have been identified or that the unimportant independent variables have been eliminated. Remember, the stepwise procedure is using only sample estimates of the true model coefficients (β's) to select the important variables. An extremely large number of single β parameter t tests have been conducted, and the probability is very high that one or more errors have been made in including or excluding variables. That is, we have very probably included some unimportant independent variables in the model (Type I errors) and eliminated some important ones (Type II errors).

There is a second reason why we might not have arrived at a good model. When we choose the variables to be included in the stepwise regression, we often may omit high-order terms (to keep the number of variables manageable). Consequently, we may have initially omitted several important terms from the model. Thus, we should recognize stepwise regression for what it is—an objective screening procedure. Successful model-builders will now consider interactions and quadratic terms (for quantitative variables) among variables screened by the stepwise procedure.

EXAMPLE 11.1 In Example 10.1 we discussed the need for building a multiple regression model for executive salaries as a function of experience, education, etc. A preliminary step in the construction of this model is to determine the most important independent variables. At one large firm, the 10 independent variables (7 quantitative and 3 qualitative) shown in Table 11.1 were measured for each corporate executive in a sample of $n = 100$.

TABLE 11.1

Candidate Independent Variables in the Executive Salary Model, Example 11.1

INDEPENDENT VARIABLE	DESCRIPTION
x_1	Experience (years)—quantitative
x_2	Education (years)—quantitative
x_3	Gender (1 if male, 0 if female)—qualitative
x_4	Number of employees supervised—quantitative
x_5	Corporate assets (million dollars)—quantitative
x_6	Board member (1 if yes, 0 if no)—qualitative
x_7	Age (years)—quantitative
x_8	Company profits (past 12 months, million dollars)—quantitative
x_9	Has international responsibility (1 if yes, 0 if no)—qualitative
x_{10}	Company's total sales (past 12 months, million dollars)—quantitative

a. Why would it be very difficult to construct a second-order model with these 10 independent variables?
b. Use the sample data to decide which of the 10 variables should be included in the construction of the final model for executive salaries.

Solution

a. One way to show the difficulty of fitting a second-order model in 10 independent variables to the data is to write out the complete model. First, we begin with the 7 quantitative variables, $x_1, x_2, x_4, x_5, x_7, x_8$, and x_{10}. The model is proposed as follows:

$$E(y) = \underbrace{\beta_0 + \beta_1 x_1 + \beta_2 x_2 + \beta_3 x_4 + \beta_4 x_5 + \beta_5 x_7 + \beta_6 x_8 + \beta_7 x_{10}}_{\text{First-order terms}}$$

$$\underbrace{\begin{aligned} &+ \beta_8 x_1 x_2 + \beta_9 x_1 x_4 + \beta_{10} x_1 x_5 + \beta_{11} x_1 x_7 + \beta_{12} x_1 x_8 + \beta_{13} x_1 x_{10} \\ &+ \beta_{14} x_2 x_4 + \beta_{15} x_2 x_5 + \beta_{16} x_2 x_7 + \beta_{17} x_2 x_8 + \beta_{18} x_2 x_{10} + \beta_{19} x_4 x_5 \\ &+ \beta_{20} x_4 x_7 + \beta_{21} x_4 x_8 + \beta_{22} x_4 x_{10} + \beta_{23} x_5 x_7 + \beta_{24} x_5 x_8 + \beta_{25} x_5 x_{10} \\ &+ \beta_{26} x_7 x_8 + \beta_{27} x_7 x_{10} + \beta_{28} x_8 x_{10} \end{aligned}}_{\text{Interaction terms}}$$

$$\underbrace{+ \beta_{29} x_1^2 + \beta_{30} x_2^2 + \beta_{31} x_4^2 + \beta_{32} x_5^2 + \beta_{33} x_7^2 + \beta_{34} x_8^2 + \beta_{35} x_{10}^2}_{\text{Quadratic terms}}$$

Now, we add **main effects** and **interactions** for the three qualitative variables, x_3, x_6, and x_9:

$$\underbrace{+\ \beta_{36}x_3 + \beta_{37}x_6 + \beta_{38}x_9}_{\text{Main effects}}$$

$$\underbrace{+\ \beta_{39}x_3x_6 + \beta_{40}x_3x_9 + \beta_{41}x_6x_9}_{\text{Two-way interaction}} \underbrace{+\ \beta_{42}x_3x_6x_9}_{\text{Three-way interaction}}$$

Note that there are 35 terms in the quantitative portion of the model (excluding β_0) and 7 terms in the qualitative portion of the model. To be complete, we would add interactions between each term in the quantitative portion and each term in the qualitative portion—a total of $35 \times 7 = 245$ more terms! Obviously, we cannot fit such a large model with only $n = 100$ data points. Even if we had a sufficiently large sample to fit the model, the model would be impossible to interpret and very unwieldy to use in practice.

b. We will use stepwise regression with the first-order terms of the 7 quantitative independent variables and the main effects of the 3 qualitative independent variables to identify the most important variables. The dependent variable y is the natural logarithm* of the executive salaries. The SAS stepwise regression printout is shown in Figure 11.1. Note that the first variable included in the

FIGURE 11.1
SAS Stepwise Regression for Example 11.1

```
STEP 1
    Variable X4 Entered        R-Square = 0.42071677      C(P) = 1274.7576

                    DF      Sum of Squares   Mean Square      F     Prob > F

    Regression       1        11.46854285    11.46854285   71.17    0.0001
    Error           98        15.79113802     0.16113696
    Total           99        27.25977087

                             B Value         Std Error       F     Prob > F

    Intercept               10.20077500
    X4                       0.00057284      0.00006790    71.17    0.0001
------------------------------------------------------------------------------
STEP 2
    Variable X5 Entered        R-Square = 0.78299675      C(P) = 419.4947

                    DF      Sum of Squares   Mean Square      F     Prob > F

    Regression       2        21.34431198    10.67215599  175.00    0.0001
    Error           97         5.91545889     0.06098411
    Total           99        27.25977087

                             B Value         Std Error       F     Prob > F

    Intercept                9.87702903
    X4                       0.00058353      0.00004178   195.06    0.0001
    X5                       0.00183730      0.00014438   161.94    0.0001
------------------------------------------------------------------------------
```

(*continued*)

---

* We discuss the use of the natural logarithm and other variable transformations in detail in Section 11.3.

FIGURE 11.1 (Continued)

STEP 3
    Variable X1 Entered   R-Square = 0.89667614   C(P) = 152.4952

	DF	Sum of Squares	Mean Square	F	Prob > F
Regression	3	24.44318616	8.14772872	277.71	0.0001
Error	96	2.81658471	0.02933942		
Total	99	27.25977087			

	B Value	Std Error	F	Prob > F
Intercept	9.66449288			
X4	0.00055251	0.00002914	359.59	0.0001
X5	0.00191195	0.00010041	362.60	0.0001
X1	0.01870784	0.00182032	105.62	0.0001

STEP 4
    Variable X3 Entered   R-Square = 0.94815717   C(P) = 32.6757

	DF	Sum of Squares	Mean Square	F	Prob > F
Regression	4	25.84654710	8.46163678	434.37	0.0001
Error	95	1.41322377	0.01487604		
Total	99	27.25977087			

	B Value	Std Error	F	Prob > F
Intercept	9.40077349			
X4	0.00055288	0.00002075	710.15	0.0001
X5	0.00190876	0.00007150	712.74	0.0001
X1	0.02074868	0.00131310	249.68	0.0001
X3	0.30011726	0.03089939	94.34	0.0001

STEP 5
    Variable X2 Entered   R-Square = 0.96039323   C(P) = 5.7215

	DF	Sum of Squares	Mean Square	F	Prob > F
Regression	5	26.18009940	5.23601988	455.87	0.0001
Error	94	1.07967147	0.01148587		
Total	99	27.25977087			

	B Value	Std Error	F	Prob > F
Intercept	8.85387930			
X4	0.00056061	0.00001829	939.84	0.0001
X5	0.00193684	0.00006304	943.98	0.0001
X1	0.02141724	0.00116047	340.61	0.0001
X3	0.31927842	0.02738298	135.95	0.0001
X2	0.03315807	0.00615303	29.04	0.0001

STEP 6
    Variable X6 Entered   R-Square = 0.96100666   C(P) = 6.2699

	DF	Sum of Squares	Mean Square	F	Prob > F
Regression	6	26.19682148	4.36613691	382.00	0.0001
Error	93	1.06294939	0.01142956		
Total	99	27.25977087			

	B Value	Std Error	F	Prob > F
Intercept	8.87509152			
X4	0.00055820	0.00001835	925.32	0.0001
X5	0.00193764	0.00006289	949.31	0.0001
X1	0.02133460	0.00115963	338.48	0.0001
X3	0.31093801	0.02817264	121.81	0.0001
X2	0.03272195	0.00614851	28.32	0.0001
X6	0.03866226	0.03196369	1.46	0.2295

(continued)

FIGURE 11.1 (Continued)

STEP 7
Variable X6 Removed   R-Square = 0.96039323   C(P) = 5.7215

	DF	Sum of Squares	Mean Square	F	Prob > F
Regression	5	26.18009940	5.23601988	455.87	0.0001
Error	94	1.07967147	0.01148587		
Total	99	27.25977087			

	B Value	Std Error	F	Prob > F
Intercept	8.85387930			
X4	0.00056061	0.00001829	939.84	0.0001
X5	0.00193684	0.00006304	943.98	0.0001
X1	0.02141724	0.00116047	340.61	0.0001
X3	0.31927842	0.02738298	135.95	0.0001
X2	0.03315807	0.00615303	29.04	0.0001

model is x_4, number of employees supervised by the executive. At the second step, x_5, corporate assets, enters the model. At the sixth step, x_6, a dummy variable for the qualitative variable board member or not, is brought into the model. However, because the significance (.2295) of the F statistic (SAS uses the $F = t^2$ statistic in the stepwise procedure rather than the t statistic) for x_6 exceeds the preassigned $\alpha = .10$, x_6 is then removed from the model. Thus, at step 7 the procedure indicates that the five-variable model including x_1, x_2, x_3, x_4, and x_5 is best. That is, none of the other independent variables can meet the $\alpha = .10$ criterion for admission to the model.

Thus, we should concentrate on these five independent variables in our effort to build a model for executive salary.

Remember, do not be deceived by the impressive-looking t-values (or F-values) that result from the stepwise procedure; it has retained only the independent variables with the largest t-values. Also, be certain to consider curvilinear and interaction terms in systematically developing the prediction model. The first-order model given by the stepwise procedure may be greatly improved by the addition of interaction and quadratic terms.

WARNING

Be cautious when using the results of stepwise regression to make inferences about the relationship between $E(y)$ and the independent variables in the resulting first-order model. First, an extremely large number of t tests have been conducted, leading to a high probability of making either one or more Type I or Type II errors. Second, the stepwise model does not include any higher-order or interaction terms. Stepwise regression should be used only when necessary, that is, when you want to determine which of a large number of potentially important independent variables should be used in the model-building process.

Because of the problems stated above, successful model-builders avoid using stepwise regression, if possible. It is advisable to use the stepwise technique only when the number of potential independent variables is large. Keep in mind that if you do employ stepwise regression, it is only the first step in the model-building process.

PROBLEMS

11.1 There are six independent variables, x_1, x_2, x_3, x_4, x_5, and x_6, that might be useful in predicting a response y. A total of $n = 50$ observations are available, and it is decided to employ stepwise regression to help in selecting the independent variables that appear to be useful. The computer fits all possible one-variable models of the form

$$E(y) = \beta_0 + \beta_1 x_i$$

where x_i is the ith independent variable, $i = 1, 2, ..., 6$. The information in the table is obtained from the computer printout.

INDEPENDENT VARIABLE	$\hat{\beta}_i$	$s_{\hat{\beta}_i}$
x_1	1.6	.42
x_2	−.9	.01
x_3	3.4	1.14
x_4	2.5	2.06
x_5	−4.4	.73
x_6	.3	.35

a. Which independent variable is declared the best one-variable predictor of y? Explain.
b. Would this variable be included in the model at this stage? Explain.
c. Describe the next phase that a stepwise procedure would execute.

11.2 Many power plants dump hot wastewater into surrounding rivers, streams, and oceans, an action that may have an adverse effect on the marine life in the dumping areas. A marine biologist was hired by the Environmental Protection Agency (EPA) to determine whether the hot water runoff from a particular power plant located near a large gulf is having an adverse effect on the marine life in the area. In the initial phase of the study, the biologist's goal is to acquire a prediction equation for the number of marine animals located at certain predesignated areas, or stations, in the gulf. Based on past experience, the biologist considered the following environmental factors as predictors for the number of animals at a particular station:

x_1 = Temperature of water (TEMP)

x_2 = Salinity of water (SAL)

x_3 = Dissolved oxygen content of water (DO)

x_4 = Turbidity index, a measure of the turbidity of the water (TI)

x_5 = Depth of the water at the station (ST_DEPTH)

x_6 = Total weight of sea grasses in sampled area (TGRSWT)

As a preliminary step in the construction of this model, the biologist used a stepwise regression procedure to identify the most important of these six variables. A total of 716 samples were taken at different stations in the gulf, producing the accompanying SAS printout. (The response measured was y, the natural logarithm of the number of marine animals found in the sampled area.)

a. According to the SAS printout, which of the six independent variables should be used in the model? (Use $\alpha = .10$.)

b. Are we able to assume that the marine biologist has identified all the important independent variables for the prediction of y? Why?

c. Using the variables identified in part **a**, write the first-order model with interaction that may be used to predict y.

d. How would the marine biologist determine whether the model specified in part **c** was better than the first-order model?

e. Note the small value of R^2. What action might the biologist take to improve the model?

SAS Printout for Problem 11.2

STEP 1
Variable ST_DEPTH Entered   R-Square = 0.1223

	DF	Sum of Squares	Mean Square	F	Prob > F
Regression	1	57.44	57.44	99.47	0.0001
Error	714	412.33	0.58		
Total	715	469.77			

	B Value	Std Error	F	Prob > F
Intercept	8.38559			
ST_DEPTH	-0.43678	0.04379	99.47	0.0001

STEP 2
Variable TGRSWT Entered   R-Square = 0.1821

	DF	Sum of Squares	Mean Square	F	Prob > F
Regression	2	85.55	42.78	79.38	0.0001
Error	713	384.22	0.54		
Total	715	469.77			

	B Value	Std Error	F	Prob > F
Intercept	8.07682			
ST_DEPTH	-0.35355	0.04385	65.02	0.0001
TGRSWT	0.00271	0.00038	52.16	0.0001

STEP 3
Variable TI Entered   R-Square = 0.1870

	DF	Sum of Squares	Mean Square	F	Prob > F
Regression	3	87.85	29.28	54.59	0.0001
Error	712	381.92	0.54		
Total	715	469.77			

	B Value	Std Error	F	Prob > F
Intercept	7.38864			
TI	0.65774	0.31783	4.28	0.0389
ST_DEPTH	-0.31451	0.47641	43.58	0.0001
TGRSWT	0.00261	0.00038	47.73	0.0001

STEP 4
Variable DO Entered   R-Square = 0.1889

	DF	Sum of Squares	Mean Square	F	Prob > F
Regression	4	88.75	22.19	41.40	0.0001
Error	711	381.02	0.54		
Total	715	469.77			

	B Value	Std Error	F	Prob > F
Intercept	7.22576			
DO	0.01769	0.01363	1.69	0.1946
TI	0.67347	0.31791	4.49	0.0345
ST_DEPTH	-0.30417	0.04828	39.69	0.0001
TGRSWT	0.00267	0.00038	49.23	0.0001

(*continued*)

```
STEP 5
     Variable DO Removed          R-Square = 0.1870

                          DF    Sum of Squares   Mean Square       F    Prob > F

          Regression       3             87.85         29.28   54.59     0.0001
          Error          712            381.92          0.54
          Total          715            469.77

                                B Value       Std Error         F    Prob > F

          Intercept             7.38864
          TI                    0.65774         0.31783      4.28      0.0389
          ST_DEPTH             -0.31451         0.04764     43.58      0.0001
          TGRSWT                0.00261         0.00038     47.73      0.0001
```

11.3 A study reported in the *Appraisal Journal* used stepwise regression to identify a number of important variables that can be used to predict rural property values. The results were obtained by analyzing a sample of 105 properties from 7 counties in Georgia. The findings are duplicated in the table. The variable names are listed in the order in which the stepwise regression procedure identified their importance, and the *t*-values found at each step are given for each variable. Note that both qualitative and quantitative variables have been included. Since each qualitative variable is at two levels, only one main-effect term (ie, dummy variable) could be included in the model for each factor.

Stepwise Regression of Price per Acre, y

VARIABLE NAME	t-VALUES
Residential land (yes–no)	10.466
Seedlings and saplings (number)	6.692
Percent ponds (percent)	4.141
Distance to state park (miles)	3.985
Branches or springs (yes–no)	3.855
Site index (ratio)	3.160
Size (acres)	1.142
Farmland (yes–no)	2.288

Source: Wise, J. O., and Dover, H. J. "An Evaluation of a Statistical Method of Appraising Rural Property." *Appraisal Journal*, Jan. 1974, Vol. 42, pp. 103–113.

a. Which of the eight variables listed in the table would you use to model rural property value, y?

b. Based on your answer to part **a**, propose a complete model for $E(y)$.

11.4 In any production process in which one or more workers are engaged in a variety of tasks, the total time spent in production varies as a function of the size of the work pool and the level of output of the various activities. For example, in a large metropolitan department store, the number of hours worked (y) per day by the clerical staff may depend on the following variables:

x_1 = Number of pieces of mail processed (open, sort, etc.)

x_2 = Number of money orders and gift certificates sold

x_3 = Number of window payments (customer charge accounts) transacted

x_4 = Number of change-order transactions processed

x_5 = Number of checks cashed

x_6 = Number of pieces of miscellaneous mail processed on "as available" basis

x_7 = Number of bus tickets sold

The table of observations gives the output counts for these activities on each of 52 working days.

Data for Problem 11.4

OBS	DAY OF WEEK	y	x_1	x_2	x_3	x_4	x_5	x_6	x_7
1	M	128.5	7781	100	886	235	644	56	737
2	T	113.6	7004	110	962	388	589	57	1029
3	W	146.6	7267	61	1342	398	1081	59	830
4	Th	124.3	2129	102	1153	457	891	57	1468
5	F	100.4	4878	45	803	577	537	49	335
6	S	119.2	3999	144	1127	345	563	64	918
7	M	109.5	11777	123	627	326	402	60	335
8	T	128.5	5764	78	748	161	495	57	962
9	W	131.2	7392	172	876	219	823	62	665
10	Th	112.2	8100	126	685	287	555	86	577
11	F	95.4	4736	115	436	235	456	38	214
12	S	124.6	4337	110	899	127	573	73	484
13	M	103.7	3079	96	570	180	428	59	456
14	T	103.6	7273	51	826	118	463	53	907
15	W	133.2	4091	116	1060	206	961	67	951
16	Th	111.4	3390	70	957	284	745	77	1446
17	F	97.7	6319	58	559	220	539	41	440
18	S	132.1	7447	83	1050	174	553	63	1133
19	M	135.9	7100	80	568	124	428	55	456
20	T	131.3	8035	115	709	174	498	78	968
21	W	150.4	5579	83	568	223	683	79	660
22	Th	124.9	4338	78	900	115	556	84	555
23	F	97.0	6895	18	442	118	479	41	203
24	S	114.1	3629	133	644	155	505	57	781
25	M	88.3	5149	92	389	124	405	59	236
26	T	117.6	5241	110	612	222	477	55	616
27	W	128.2	2917	69	1057	378	970	80	1210
28	Th	138.8	4390	70	974	195	1027	81	1452
29	F	109.5	4957	24	783	358	893	51	616
30	S	118.9	7099	130	1419	374	609	62	957
31	M	122.2	7337	128	1137	238	461	51	968
32	T	142.8	8301	115	946	191	771	74	719
33	W	133.9	4889	86	750	214	513	69	489
34	Th	100.2	6308	81	461	132	430	49	341
35	F	116.8	6908	145	864	164	549	57	902
36	S	97.3	5345	116	604	127	360	48	126
37	M	98.0	6994	59	714	107	473	53	726
38	T	136.5	6781	78	917	171	805	74	1100
39	W	111.7	3142	106	809	335	702	70	1721
40	Th	98.6	5783	27	546	126	455	52	502
41	F	116.2	4931	174	891	129	481	71	737
42	S	108.9	6501	69	643	129	334	47	473
43	M	120.6	5678	94	828	107	384	52	1083
44	T	131.8	4619	100	777	164	834	67	841
45	W	112.4	1832	124	626	158	571	71	627
46	Th	92.5	5445	52	432	121	458	42	313
47	F	120.0	4123	84	432	153	544	42	654
48	S	112.2	5884	89	1061	100	391	31	280
49	M	113.0	5505	45	562	84	444	36	814
50	T	138.7	2882	94	601	139	799	44	907
51	W	122.1	2395	89	637	201	747	30	1666
52	Th	86.6	6847	14	810	230	547	40	614

Source: Adapted from Smith, G. L., *Work Measurement.* Columbus, OH: Grid Publishing Co., 1978 (Table 3–1).

a. Conduct a stepwise regression analysis of the data using a computer. (The data are available on floppy or microdisk from the publisher; see the Preface.)

b. Interpret the β estimates in the resulting stepwise model.

c. What are the dangers of drawing inferences from the stepwise model?

VARIABLE TRANSFORMATIONS

11.3 The word *transform* means to change the form of some object or thing. Consequently, the phrase *data transformation* indicates a change in the form of the data. For example, if one of the independent variables in a model is the price p of a commodity, we might choose to introduce this variable into the model as $x = 1/p$, $x = \sqrt{p}$, or $x = e^{-p}$.* Thus, if we were to let $x = \sqrt{p}$, we would compute the square root of each price value, and these square roots would be the values of x that would be used in the regression analysis.

Data transformations are performed on the y-values to make them more nearly satisfy the assumptions of Section 10.3 and, sometimes, to make the deterministic portion of the model a better approximation to the mean value of the transformed response. Transformations of the values of the independent variables are performed solely for the latter reason—that is, to achieve a model that provides a better approximation to $E(y)$. The purpose of this section is to present variable transformations that may improve the fit of our model for $E(y)$. (Transformations on the y-values for the purpose of satisfying the assumptions will be discussed in Section 11.6.)

Suppose you want to fit a model relating the demand y for a product to its price p. Also, suppose the product is a nonessential item, and you expect the mean demand to decrease as price p increases and then to decrease more slowly as p gets larger (see Figure 11.2). What function of p will provide a good approximation to $E(y)$?

To answer this question, you need to know the graphs of some elementary mathematical functions—there is a one-to-one relationship between mathematical functions and graphs. If we want to model a relationship similar to the one indicated in Figure 11.2, we need to be able to select a mathematical function that will possess a graph similar to the curve shown.

Portions of some curves corresponding to mathematical functions that decrease as p increases are shown in Figure 11.3. Of the four functions shown, the decreasing graphs in Figures 11.3c and 11.3d will probably provide the best approximations to $E(y)$. This is because both provide graphs that show $E(y)$ decreasing and approaching (but never reaching) 0 as p increases. This suggests that the independent variable, price, should be transformed using either $x = 1/p$ or $x = e^{-p}$. Then you might try fitting the model

$$E(y) = \beta_0 + \beta_1 x$$

using the transformed data.

The functions shown in Figure 11.3 produce curves that either rise or fall, depending on the sign of the parameter β_1 in parts a, c, and d, and depending on β_2 and the portion of the curve used in part b. When you choose a model for a regression analysis, you do not have to specify the sign of the parameter(s). The least squares procedure will choose as estimates of the parameters those that minimize the sum of squares of the residuals. Consequently, if you were to fit the model

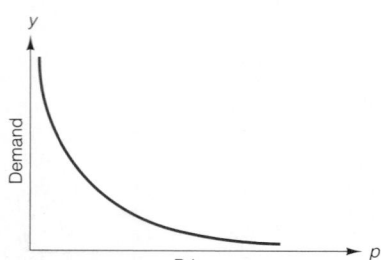

FIGURE 11.2

Hypothetical Relation Between Demand y and Price p

---

* Students of calculus will recall that the symbol e represents Euler's constant; $e = 2.7182818. \ldots$

FIGURE 11.3

Graphs of Some Mathematical Functions Relating $E(y)$ to p

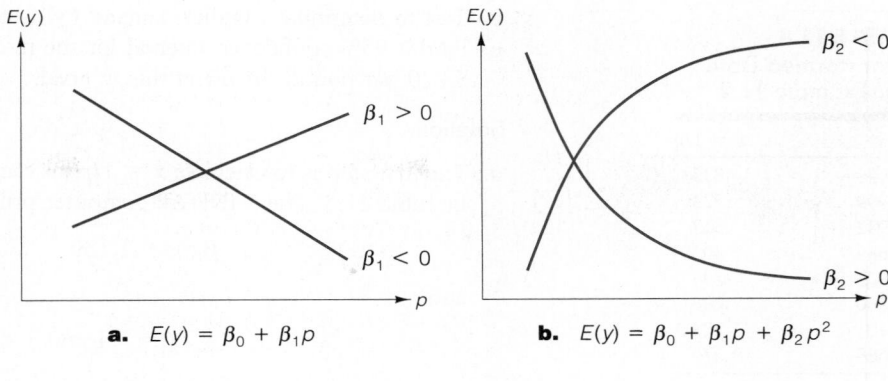

a. $E(y) = \beta_0 + \beta_1 p$

b. $E(y) = \beta_0 + \beta_1 p + \beta_2 p^2$

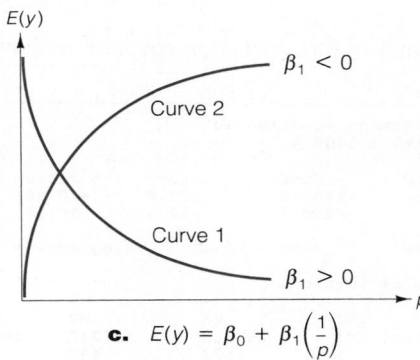

c. $E(y) = \beta_0 + \beta_1 \left(\dfrac{1}{p}\right)$

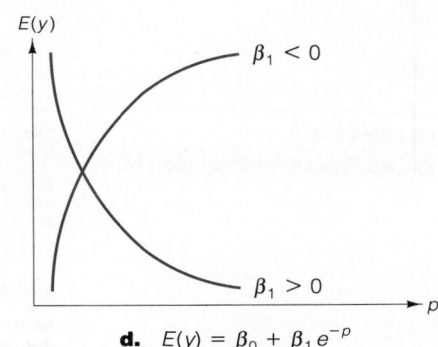

d. $E(y) = \beta_0 + \beta_1 e^{-p}$

shown in Figure 11.3c to a set of y-values that increase in value as p increases, the least squares estimate of β_1 would be negative, and a graph of y would produce a curve similar to curve 2 in Figure 11.3c. If the y-values decrease as p increases, the estimate of β_1 will be positive, and the curve will be similar to curve 1 in Figure 11.3c. All the curves in Figure 11.3 shift upward or downward depending on the value of β_0.

TABLE 11.2

Data for Example 11.2

DEMAND	PRICE
y, Pounds	p, Dollars
1,120	3.00
999	3.10
932	3.20
884	3.30
807	3.40
760	3.50
701	3.60
688	3.70

EXAMPLE 11.2 A supermarket chain conducted an experiment to investigate the effect of price p on the weekly demand (in pounds) for a house brand of coffee. Eight supermarket stores that had nearly equal past records of demand for the product were used in the experiment. Eight prices were randomly assigned to the stores and were advertised using the same procedures. The number of pounds of coffee sold during the following week was recorded for each of the stores. The results are shown in Table 11.2.

a. Fit the model

$$E(y) = \beta_0 + \beta_1 x$$

to the data, letting $x = 1/p$.

TABLE 11.3
Transformed Data
for Example 11.2

y	x = 1/p
1,120	.333
999	.323
932	.313
884	.303
807	.294
760	.286
701	.278
688	.270

b. Test to determine whether demand (y) is negatively related to price (p).

c. Find a 95% confidence interval for the mean demand when the price is set at $3.20 per pound. Interpret this interval.

Solution

a. The first step is to calculate $x = 1/p$ for each data point. These values are given in Table 11.3. The MINITAB computer printout* shown in Figure 11.4 gives

$$\hat{\beta}_0 = -1{,}180 \qquad \hat{\beta}_1 = 6{,}808$$

and

$$\hat{y} = -1{,}180 + 6{,}808x$$
$$= -1{,}180 + 6{,}808\left(\frac{1}{p}\right)$$

A graph of this prediction equation is shown in Figure 11.5.

FIGURE 11.4
MINITAB Prinout for Example 11.2

```
The regression equation is
Y = - 1180 + 6808 X

Predictor       Coef        Stdev      t-ratio        p
Constant     -1180.5        107.7       -10.96    0.000
X             6808.1        358.4        19.00    0.000

s = 20.90       R-sq = 98.4%      R-sq(adj) = 98.1%

Analysis of Variance

SOURCE         DF          SS          MS        F        p
Regression      1      157718      157718   360.94    0.000
Error           6        2622         437
Total           7      160340

Unusual Observations
Obs.      X         Y       Fit   Stdev.Fit   Residual   St.Resid
  1   0.333   1120.00   1088.89       14.07      31.11      2.01R

R denotes an obs. with a large st. resid.

     Fit   Stdev.Fit        95% C.I.           95% P.I.
  947.05        8.66   ( 925.86, 968.24)   ( 891.67,1002.43)
```

b. If demand (y) is negatively related to price (p), then demand will be positively related to the transformed variable x, since $x = 1/p$. Consequently, we want to test

$$H_0: \quad \beta_1 = 0 \quad \text{versus} \quad H_a: \quad \beta_1 > 0$$

The test statistic (given in the MINITAB printout) is $t = 19.00$, and the corresponding two-tailed p-value is approximately 0. Therefore, the one-tailed p-value is also approximately 0. This provides sufficient evidence (at any reasonable α) to reject H_0 in favor of H_a. It appears that demand (y) is negatively related to price (p) at any selected level of significance α.

---

* The MINITAB program uses full decimal accuracy for $x = 1/p$. Hence, the results shown in Figure 11.4 differ from results that would be calculated using the three-decimal-place values for $x = 1/p$ given in Table 11.3.

FIGURE 11.5

Graph of the Demand–Price Curve for Example 11.2

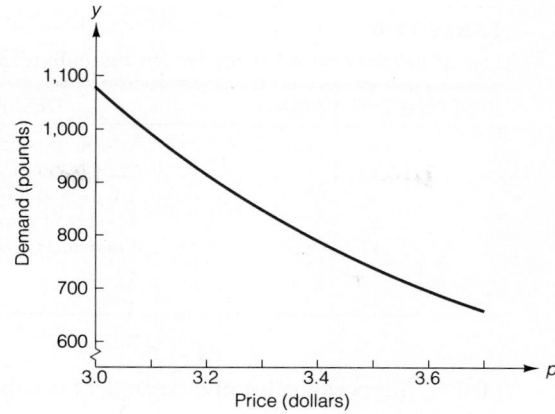

c. A 95% confidence interval for mean demand, $E(y)$, when price is $p = 3.20$, is shaded at the bottom of the MINITAB printout shown in Figure 11.4. (Note that when $p = 3.20$, $x = 1/p = .3125$.) The interval is (926, 968). Thus, we are 95% confident that the mean weekly demand will fall between 926 and 968 pounds when the price is set at $3.20 per pound.

The transformations of Figure 11.3 and Example 11.2 are all transformations of the independent variables. As stated earlier, a transformation of the dependent variable, y, also may improve the fit of the model. A transformation that works well with economic data is the natural logarithm, denoted $\log y$.* The model, called the **log model**, takes the form

$$\log y = \beta_0 + \beta_1 x_1 + \beta_2 x_2 + \cdots + \beta_k x_k + \epsilon$$

A graph of the relationship between y and x in the log model is shown in Figure 11.6. Note that the relationship is curvilinear in nature. Consequently, the log model,

$$\log y = \beta_0 + \beta_1 x + \epsilon$$

is often used as an alternative to the second-order (quadratic) model

$$y = \beta_0 + \beta_1 x + \beta_2 x^2 + \epsilon$$

Researchers have found log models to be useful when the change in the response y, for every 1 unit change in an independent variable x, is better represented by a percentage increase (or decrease) rather than a constant amount increase (or decrease). The next example illustrates this idea.

EXAMPLE 11.3 Let us return to the executive compensation example discussed in Examples 10.1 and 11.1. The management consultant firm of Towers, Perrin, Forster & Crosby (TPF&C) uses a multiple regression model to project executive

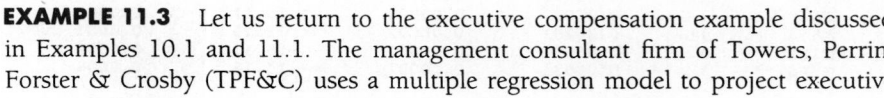

FIGURE 11.6

Graph of $\log y = \beta_0 + \beta_1 x$

---

* The natural logarithm of y is denoted by the expression $\log_e y$. In this text, we use the simpler notation, $\log y$, to represent the natural logarithm, since no confusion will result. An alternative, accepted expression is $\ln y$.

TABLE 11.4

List of Independent Variables for Executive Compensation Example

INDEPENDENT VARIABLE	DESCRIPTION
x_1	Years of experience
x_2	Years of education
x_3	1 if male, 0 if female
x_4	Number of employees supervised
x_5	Corporate assets (million dollars)
x_6	x_1^2
x_7	$x_3 x_4$

salaries. Suppose the list of independent variables given in Table 11.4 is to be used to build a model for the salary, y, of a corporate executive. TPF&C has found that executive compensation models that use the natural logarithm of salary as the dependent variable provide better predictive models than those using the salary as the dependent variable. This is probably because salaries tend to be incremented in percentages rather than dollar values. Thus, the log model we propose (in its linear form) is

$$\log y = \beta_0 + \beta_1 x_1 + \beta_2 x_2 + \beta_3 x_3 + \beta_4 x_4 + \beta_5 x_5 + \beta_6 x_1^2 + \beta_7 x_3 x_4 + \epsilon$$

FIGURE 11.7

Portion of SAS Printout for Executive Compensation Example

Analysis of Variance

Source	DF	Sum of Squares	Mean Square	F Value	Prob>F
Model	7	27.06425	3.86632	1823.73	0.0001
Error	92	0.19551	0.00212		
C Total	99	27.25976			

Root MSE	0.0461	R-square	0.9928	
Dep Mean	12.570	Adj R-sq	0.9923	
C.V.	0.3660			

Parameter Estimates

Variable	DF	Parameter Estimate	Standard Error	T for H0: Parameter=0	Prob > |T|
INTERCEP	1	8.87878	0.04612	192.49	0.0001
X1	1	0.04460	0.00166	26.83	0.0001
X2	1	0.03326	0.00270	12.31	0.0001
X3	1	0.11892	0.01724	6.89	0.0001
X4	1	0.00033	0.00001	19.97	0.0001
X5	1	0.00201	0.00002	73.25	0.0001
X1X1	1	-0.00071	0.00004	-15.11	0.0001
X3X4	1	0.00031	0.00002	16.16	0.0001

Obs	X1	X2	X3	X4	X5	Dep Var Y	Predict Value	Std Err Predict	Lower95% Predict	Upper95% Predict	Residual
100	1	12	16	0	160.1		10.2977	.0483	10.2030	10.3924	

Note that we have included a second-order term, x_1^2, to account for a possible curvilinear relationship between log(Salary) and years of experience, x_1. Also, the interaction term $x_3 x_4$ is included to account for the fact that the relationship between the number of employees supervised, x_4, and corporate salary may depend on gender, x_3. For example, as the number of supervised employees increases, a male's salary (with all other factors being equal) might rise more rapidly than a female's. (If this is found to be true, the firm will take steps to remove the apparent discrimination against female executives.)

A sample of 100 executives is selected, and the variables y and $x_1, x_2, ..., x_5$ are recorded. The sample is then used as input for the SAS regression routine; the output is shown in Figure 11.7.

a. Find the least squares prediction equation, and interpret the estimate of β_2.
b. Locate the estimate of s and interpret its value.
c. Locate R_a^2 and interpret its value.
d. Conduct a test of overall model utility.
e. Test for evidence of gender discrimination at the firm.
f. Use the model to predict the salary of an executive with the characteristics shown in Table 11.5.

TABLE 11.5
Values of Independent Variables
for a Particular Executive

$x_1 = 12$ years of experience
$x_2 = 16$ years of education
$x_3 = 0$ (female)
$x_4 = 400$
$x_5 = \$160.1$ million (the firm's asset value)
$x_6 = 144$
$x_7 = 0$

Solution
a. The least squares model is

$$\widehat{\log y} = 8.88 + .045x_1 + .033x_2 + .119x_3 + .00033x_4 + .002x_5 \\ - .00071x_1^2 + .00031x_3x_4$$

Because we are using the logarithm of salary as the dependent variable, the β estimates have different interpretations from those previously discussed. In general, a parameter β in a log model represents the percentage increase (or decrease) in the dependent variable for a 1 unit increase in the corresponding independent variable. The percentage change is calculated by taking the antilogarithm of the β estimate and subtracting 1, that is, $e^\beta - 1$ (proof omitted). For example, the percentage change in executive compensation associated with a 1 unit (ie, 1 year) increase in years of education x_2 is $e^{\beta_2} - 1 = e^{.033} - 1 = .034$. Thus, when all other independent variables are held constant, we estimate that executive salary will increase 3.4% for each additional year of education.

b. The estimate of the variance σ^2 is given in the SAS printout as

$$s^2 = \text{MSE} = \frac{\text{SSE}}{n - (k + 1)} = \frac{\text{SSE}}{10 - (7 + 1)} = .00212$$

and the estimate of the standard deviation σ, also given in the SAS printout as Root MSE, is $s = \sqrt{s^2} = .046$. Our interpretation is that most of the observed log y values (logarithms of salaries) lie within $2s = 2(.046) = .092$ of their least squares predicted values, $\widehat{\log y}$. A more practical interpretation (in terms of salaries) is obtained, however, if we take the antilog of this value and subtract 1, similar to the manipulation in part **a**. That is, we expect most of the observed executive salaries to lie within $e^{2s} - 1 = e^{.092} - 1 = .096$, or 9.6%, of their respective least squares predicted values.

c. The adjusted R^2 value given in the SAS printout is $R_a^2 = .9923$. This implies that, after taking into account sample size and the number of independent variables, over 99% of the variation in the logarithm of salaries for these 100 sampled executives is accounted for by the model.

d. The test for overall model utility is conducted as follows:

H_0: $\beta_1 = \beta_2 = \cdots = \beta_7 = 0$

H_a: At least one of the model coefficients is nonzero.

Test statistic: $\quad F = \dfrac{\text{Mean square for model}}{\text{MSE}}$

$\qquad\qquad\qquad = 1,823.73 \quad$ See Figure 11.7

p-Value: $\quad p = .0001 \quad$ See Figure 11.7

Since the observed significance level of the test, $p = .0001$, is small, there is sufficient evidence to conclude that the model is useful for predicting executive salary.

e. If the firm is (knowingly or unknowingly) discriminating against female executives, then the mean salary for females (denoted μ_F) will be less than the mean salary for males (denoted μ_M) with the same qualifications (eg, years of experience, years of education, etc.). From our earlier discussion of dummy variables, this difference will be represented by β_3, the β coefficient multiplied by x_3. Since $x_3 = 1$ if male, 0 if female, then $\beta_3 = (\mu_M - \mu_F)$ for fixed values of x_1, x_2, and x_5, and for $x_4 = 0$. Consequently, a test of

H_0: $\beta_3 = 0 \qquad$ versus $\qquad H_a$: $\beta_3 > 0$

is one way to test the discrimination hypothesis.* The *p*-value for this one-tailed test is half the *p*-value shown in the SAS printout, that is, $\frac{.0001}{2} = .00005$. With such a small *p*-value, there is strong evidence to reject H_0 and claim that some form of gender discrimination exists at the firm.

f. The least squares model can be used to obtain a predicted value for the natural logarithm of salary. Substituting the *x*-values shown in Table 11.5, we obtain

$$\log y = \hat{\beta}_0 + \hat{\beta}_1(12) + \hat{\beta}_2(16) + \hat{\beta}_3(0) + \hat{\beta}_4(400) + \hat{\beta}_5(160.1)$$
$$+ \hat{\beta}_6(144) + \hat{\beta}_7(0)$$

This predicted value is given at the bottom of the SAS printout, Figure 11.7, as $\log y = 10.298$. The 95% prediction interval, from 10.203 to 10.392, is also given. To predict the salary of an executive with these characteristics, we take the antilog of these values. That is, the predicted salary is $e^{10.298} = \$29,700$ (rounded to the nearest hundred), and the 95% prediction interval is from $e^{10.203}$ to $e^{10.392}$ (or from \$27,000 to \$32,600). Thus, an executive with the characteristics

---

*A test for discrimination also could include testing the interaction term $\beta_7 x_3 x_4$. If, as number of employees supervised (x_4) increases, the rate of increase in salary for males exceeds the rate for females, then $\beta_7 > 0$. Thus, rejecting H_0: $\beta_7 = 0$ in favor of H_a: $\beta_7 > 0$ would also suggest discrimination against female executives.

in Table 11.5 should be paid between $27,000 and $32,600 to be consistent with the sample data.

The variable transformations presented in this section, coupled with the different types of models discussed in Chapter 10, provide you with a great variety of mathematical functions to employ as candidate models in model-building.

PROBLEMS

11.5   The demand–price data of Table 11.2 are reproduced below. Recall that we fit the model $E(y) = \beta_0 + \beta_1 x$, where $x = 1/p$, in Example 11.2.

DEMAND y, Pounds	PRICE p, Dollars
1,120	3.00
999	3.10
932	3.20
884	3.30
807	3.40
760	3.50
701	3.60
688	3.70

a. Propose at least one other transformation on price, p, that may provide a good fit to the data.
b. Fit the model from part **a**. Interpret the results.
c. Consider the dependent variable transformation, $y^* = \log y$. The model $E(y^*) = \beta_0 + \beta_1 p$ is fit to the data; the MINITAB printout is shown below. Assess the adequacy of the log model.
d. Refer to part **c**. Interpret the estimate of β_1.

MINITAB Output for Problem 11.5

```
The regression equation is
LOGY = 9.09 - 0.701 P

Predictor        Coef       Stdev     t-ratio        p
Constant       9.0925      0.1176       77.31    0.000
P             -0.70065     0.03502      -20.00    0.000

s = 0.02270     R-sq = 98.5%     R-sq(adj) = 98.3%

Analysis of Variance

SOURCE        DF        SS          MS          F        p
Regression     1     0.20618     0.20618     400.18    0.000
Error          6     0.00309     0.00052
Total          7     0.20927
```

11.6   Consider the data shown in the table.

x	54	42	28	38	25	70	48	41	20	52	65
y	6	16	33	18	41	3	10	14	45	9	5

a. Plot the points in a scattergram. What type of relationship appears to exist between x and y?

b. For each observation, calculate log x and log y. Plot the log-transformed data points in a scattergram. What type of relationship appears to exist between log x and log y?

c. The scattergram from part **b** suggests that the transformed model

$$\log y = \beta_0 + \beta_1(\log x) + \epsilon$$

may be appropriate. Fit the transformed model to the data. Is the model adequate? Test using $\alpha = .05$.

d. Use the transformed model to predict the value of y when $x = 30$. [*Hint:* Use the inverse transformation $y = e^{\log y}$.]

MULTICOLLINEARITY

11.4

Often, two or more of the independent variables used in the model for $E(y)$ will contribute redundant information. That is, the independent variables will be correlated with each other. For example, suppose we want to construct a model to predict the gasoline mileage rating, y, of a truck as a function of its load, x_1, and the horsepower, x_2, of its engine. In general, you would expect heavier loads to require greater horsepower and to result in lower mileage ratings. Thus, although both x_1 and x_2 contribute information for the prediction of mileage rating, some of the information is overlapping, because x_1 and x_2 are correlated. When two or more independent variables are correlated, we say that **multicollinearity** exists. In practice, it is not uncommon to observe correlations among the independent variables. However, a few problems arise when serious multicollinearity is present in the regression analysis.

> **DEFINITION 11.2**
>
> **Multicollinearity** exists when two or more of the independent variables used in regression are correlated.

First, high correlations among the independent variables increase the likelihood of rounding errors in the calculations of the β estimates, standard errors, and so forth. Second, and more important, the regression results may be confusing and misleading.

To illustrate, if the gasoline mileage rating model

$$E(y) = \beta_0 + \beta_1 x_1 + \beta_2 x_2$$

were fit to a set of data, we might find that the t-values for both β_1 and β_2 are nonsignificant. However, the F test for H_0: $\beta_1 = \beta_2 = 0$ would probably be highly significant. The tests may seem to be contradictory, but really they are not. The t tests indicate that the contribution of one variable, say $x_1 =$ load, is not significant after accounting for the effect of $x_2 =$ horsepower (because x_2 is also in the model). The significant F test, on the other hand, tells us that at least one of the two variables is making a contribution to the prediction of y (ie, either β_1, β_2, or both differ from 0). In fact, both are probably contributing, but the contribution of one overlaps with that of the other.

Multicollinearity also can have an effect on the signs of the parameter estimates. More specifically, a value of $\hat{\beta}_i$ may have the opposite sign from what is expected. For example, we expect the signs of both the parameter estimates for the gasoline mileage rating model to be negative, yet the regression analysis for the model might yield the estimates $\hat{\beta}_1 = .2$ and $\hat{\beta}_2 = -.7$. The positive value of $\hat{\beta}_1$ seems to contradict our expectation that heavy loads will result in lower mileage ratings. This is the danger of interpreting a β coefficient when the independent variables are correlated. Because the variables contribute redundant information, the effect of load x_1 on mileage rating is measured only partially by β_1.

How can you avoid the problems of multicollinearity in regression analysis? One way is to conduct a designed experiment so that the levels of the x variables are uncorrelated. (Designed experiments are the topic of Chapter 13.) Unfortunately, time and cost constraints may prevent you from collecting data in this manner. For these and other reasons, most data collected in business studies are observational (ie, the sample is selected and the values of the independent variables are observed, with no attempt to control their values). Since observational data frequently consist of correlated independent variables, you will need to recognize when multicollinearity is present and, if necessary, make modifications in the analysis.

Several methods are available for detecting multicollinearity in regression. A simple technique is to calculate the coefficient of correlation, r, between each pair of independent variables in the model and use the procedure outlined in Section 10.3 to test for evidence of positive or negative correlation. If one or more of the r-values is statistically different from 0, the variables in question are correlated, and a severe multicollinearity problem may exist.* Other indications of the presence of multicollinearity include those mentioned in the beginning of this section—namely, nonsignificant t tests for the individual β parameters when the F test for overall model adequacy is significant, and estimates with opposite signs from what is expected.

A more formal method for detecting multicollinearity involves the calculation of **variance inflation factors** for the individual β parameters. One reason why the t tests on the individual β parameters are nonsignificant is because the standard errors of the estimates, $s_{\hat{\beta}_i}$, are inflated in the presence of multicollinearity. When the dependent and independent variables are appropriately transformed,† it can be shown that

$$s_{\hat{\beta}_i}^2 = s^2 \left(\frac{1}{1 - R_i^2} \right)$$

where s^2 is the estimate of σ^2, the variance of ϵ, and R_i^2 is the multiple coefficient of determination for the model that regresses the independent variable, x_i,

---

* Remember that r measures only the pairwise correlation between x-values. Three variables, x_1, x_2, and x_3, may be highly correlated as a group, but may not exhibit large pairwise correlations. Thus, multicollinearity may be present even when all pairwise correlations are not significantly different from 0.

† The transformed variables are obtained as

$$y_i^* = (y_i - \bar{y})/s_y, \qquad x_{1i}^* = (x_{1i} - \bar{x}_1)/s_1, \qquad x_{2i}^* = (x_{2i} - \bar{x}_2)/s_2$$

and so on, where $\bar{y}, \bar{x}_1, \bar{x}_2, ...,$ and $s_y, s_1, s_2, ...,$ are the sample means and standard deviations, respectively, of the original variables.

on the remaining independent variables, $x_1, x_2, ..., x_{i-1}, x_{i+1}, ..., x_k$. The quantity $1/(1 - R_i^2)$ is called the **variance inflation factor** for the parameter β_i and is denoted $(VIF)_i$. Note that $(VIF)_i$ will be large when R_i is large—that is, when the independent variable, x_i, is strongly related to the other independent variables.

Various authors maintain that, in practice, a severe multicollinearity problem exists if the largest of the variance inflation factors for the β's is greater than 10 or, equivalently, if the largest multiple coefficient of determination R_i^2 is greater than .90.* Most statistical software packages have options for calculating variance inflation factors in regression.†

The methods for detecting multicollinearity are summarized in the box. We illustrate the use of these statistics in Example 11.4.

DETECTING MULTICOLLINEARITY IN REGRESSION

The following are indicators of multicollinearity in the model:

$$E(y) = \beta_0 + \beta_1 x_1 + \beta_2 x_2 + \cdots + \beta_k x_k$$

1. Significant correlations between pairs of independent variables in the model
2. Nonsignificant t tests for all (or nearly all) the individual β parameters when the F test for overall model adequacy, $H_0: \beta_1 = \beta_2 = \cdots = \beta_k = 0$, is significant
3. Opposite signs (from what is expected) in the estimated parameters
4. A variance inflation factor (VIF) for a β parameter greater than 10, where

$$(VIF)_i = \frac{1}{1 - R_i^2} \qquad i = 1, 2, ..., k$$

and R_i is the multiple coefficient of determination for the model

$$E(x_i) = \alpha_0 + \alpha_1 x_1 + \alpha_2 x_2 + \cdots + \alpha_{i-1} x_{i-1} + \alpha_{i+1} x_{i+1} + \cdots + \alpha_k x_k$$

EXAMPLE 11.4 The Federal Trade Commission (FTC) annually ranks varieties of domestic cigarettes according to their tar, nicotine, and carbon monoxide contents. The U.S. surgeon general considers each of these three substances hazardous to a smoker's health. Past studies have shown that increases in the tar and nicotine contents of a cigarette are accompanied by an increase in the carbon monoxide

---

* See, for example, Montgomery and Peck (1982) or Neter, Wasserman, and Kutner (1989).

† Some software packages (eg, SPSS) calculate an equivalent statistic, called the *tolerance*. The tolerance for a β coefficient is the reciprocal of the variance inflation factor, that is,

$$(TOL)_i = \frac{1}{(VIF)_i} = 1 - R_i^2$$

For $R_i^2 > .90$ (the extreme multicollinearity case), $(TOL)_i < .10$. These software packages allow the user to set tolerance limits, so that any independent variable with a value of $(TOL)_i$ below the tolerance limit will not be allowed to enter into the model.

TABLE 11.6
FTC Cigarette Data

BRAND	TAR x_1, Milligrams	NICOTINE x_2, Milligrams	WEIGHT x_3, Grams	CARBON MONOXIDE y, Milligrams
Alpine	14.1	.86	.9853	13.6
Benson & Hedges	16.0	1.06	1.0938	16.6
Bull Durham	29.8	2.03	1.1650	23.5
Camel Lights	8.0	.67	.9280	10.2
Carlton	4.1	.40	.9462	5.4
Chesterfield	15.0	1.04	.8885	15.0
Golden Lights	8.8	.76	1.0267	9.0
Kent	12.4	.95	.9225	12.3
Kool	16.6	1.12	.9372	16.3
L&M	14.9	1.02	.8858	15.4
Lark Lights	13.7	1.01	.9643	13.0
Marlboro	15.1	.90	.9316	14.4
Merit	7.8	.57	.9705	10.0
Multifilter	11.4	.78	1.1240	10.2
Newport Lights	9.0	.74	.8517	9.5
Now	1.0	.13	.7851	1.5
Old Gold	17.0	1.26	.9186	18.5
Pall Mall Light	12.8	1.08	1.0395	12.6
Raleigh	15.8	.96	.9573	17.5
Salem Ultra	4.5	.42	.9106	4.9
Tareyton	14.5	1.01	1.0070	15.9
True	7.3	.61	.9806	8.5
Viceroy Rich Lights	8.6	.69	.9693	10.6
Virginia Slims	15.2	1.02	.9496	13.9
Winston Lights	12.0	.82	1.1184	14.9

Source: Federal Trade Commission.

emitted from the cigarette smoke. Table 11.6 presents data on tar, nicotine, and carbon monoxide contents (in milligrams) and weight (in grams) for a sample of 25 (filter) brands tested. Suppose we want to model carbon monoxide content, y, as a function of tar content, x_1, nicotine content, x_2, and weight, x_3, using the model

$$E(y) = \beta_0 + \beta_1 x_1 + \beta_2 x_2 + \beta_3 x_3$$

The model is fit to the 25 data points in Table 11.6, and a portion of the resulting SAS printout is shown in Figure 11.8 (p. 550). Examine the printout. Do you detect any signs of multicollinearity?

Solution First, notice that a test of

$$H_0: \quad \beta_1 = \beta_2 = \beta_3 = 0$$

is highly significant. The F-value (shaded in the printout) is very large ($F = 78.984$), and the observed significance level of the test (also shaded) is small ($p = .0001$). Therefore, we can reject H_0 for any α greater than .0001 and conclude that at least one of the parameters β_1, β_2, and β_3 is nonzero. The t tests for two of the three

FIGURE 11.8

Portion of the SAS Printout

Dependent Variable: CO

Analysis of Variance

Source	DF	Sum of Squares	Mean Square	F Value	Prob>F
Model	3	495.25781	165.08594	78.984	0.0001
Error	21	43.89259	2.09012		
C Total	24	539.15040			

Root MSE	1.44573	R-square	0.9186	
Dep Mean	12.52800	Adj R-sq	0.9070	
C.V.	11.53996			

Parameter Estimates

Variable	DF	Parameter Estimate	Standard Error	T for H0: Parameter=0	Prob > |T|	Variance Inflation
INTERCEP	1	3.202190	3.46175473	0.925	0.3655	0.00000000
TAR	1	0.962574	0.24224436	3.974	0.0007	21.63070592
NICOTINE	1	-2.631661	3.90055745	-0.675	0.5072	21.89991722
WEIGHT	1	-0.130482	3.88534182	-0.034	0.9735	1.33385886

individual β's, however, are nonsignificant. (The p-values for these tests are shaded in the printout.) Unless tar is the only one of the three variables useful for predicting carbon monoxide content, these results are the first indication of a potential multicollinearity problem.

The negative values for $\hat{\beta}_2$ and $\hat{\beta}_3$ (shaded in the printout) are a second clue to the presence of multicollinearity:

$$\hat{\beta}_2 = -2.63 \qquad \hat{\beta}_3 = -.130$$

From past studies, the FTC expects carbon monoxide content, y, to increase when either nicotine content, x_2, or weight, x_3, increases—that is, the FTC expects *positive* relationships between y and x_2 and y and x_3, not negative ones.

A more formal procedure for detecting multicollinearity is to examine the variance inflation factors. Figure 11.8 shows the variance inflation factors (shaded) for each of the three parameters under the column labeled Variance Inflation. Note that the variance inflation factors for both the tar and nicotine parameters are greater than 10. The variance inflation factor for the tar parameter, $(VIF)_1 = 21.63$, implies that a model relating tar content, x_1, to the remaining two independent variables, nicotine content, x_2, and weight, x_3, results in a coefficient of determination

$$R_1^2 = 1 - \frac{1}{(VIF)_1}$$

$$= 1 - \frac{1}{21.63} = .954$$

All signs indicate that a serious multicollinearity problem exists. To confirm our suspicions, we calculate the coefficient of correlation, r, for each of the three pairs of independent variables in the model. These values are given in Table 11.7. You can see that tar content, x_1, and nicotine content, x_2, appear to be highly correlated ($r = .977$), while weight, x_3, appears to be moderately correlated with both tar content ($r = .491$) and nicotine content ($r = .500$). In fact, all three sample

TABLE 11.7

Correlation Coefficients for the Three Pairs of Independent Variables

PAIR	r
x_1, x_2	.977
x_1, x_3	.491
x_2, x_3	.500

correlations exceed the critical t-value for a two-tailed test of $H_0: \rho = 0$ conducted at $\alpha = .05$ with $n - 2 = 23$ df.

Once you have detected that a multicollinearity problem exists, there are several alternative measures available for solving the problem. The appropriate measure to take depends on the severity of the multicollinearity and the ultimate goal of the regression analysis.

Some researchers, when confronted with highly correlated independent variables, choose to include only one of the correlated variables in the final model. One way of deciding which variable to include is to use stepwise regression (see Section 11.2). Generally, only one (or a small number) of a set of multicollinear independent variables will be included in the regression model by the stepwise regression procedure, since this procedure tests the parameter associated with each variable in the presence of all the variables already in the model. For example, in fitting the gasoline mileage rating model introduced earlier, if at one step the variable representing truck load is included as a significant variable in the prediction of the mileage rating, the variable representing horsepower will probably not be added in a future step. Thus, if a set of independent variables is thought to be multicollinear, some screening by stepwise regression may be helpful.

If you are interested only in using the model for estimation and prediction, you may decide not to drop any of the independent variables from the model. In the presence of multicollinearity, we have seen that it is dangerous to interpret the individual β's. However, confidence intervals for $E(y)$ and prediction intervals for y generally remain unaffected as long as the values of the independent variables used to predict y follow the same pattern of multicollinearity exhibited in the sample data. That is, you must take strict care to ensure that the values of the x variables fall within the range of the sample data.

When fitting higher-order regression models [for example, the second-order model $E(y) = \beta_0 + \beta_1 x + \beta_2 x^2$], the independent variables $x_1 = x$ and $x_2 = x^2$

SOLUTIONS TO SOME PROBLEMS CREATED BY MULTICOLLINEARITY

1. Drop one or more of the correlated independent variables from the final model. Use a screening procedure such as stepwise regression to determine which variables to drop.

2. If you decide to keep all the independent variables in the model:
   a. Avoid making inferences about the individual β parameters based on the t statistics.
   b. Restrict inferences about $E(y)$ and future y-values to values of the independent variables that fall within the range of the sample data.

3. To reduce rounding errors in higher-order regression models, code the independent variables so that first-, second-, and higher-order terms for a particular x variable are not highly correlated.

will often be correlated. If the correlation is high, the computer solution may result in extreme rounding errors. For this model, the solution is not to drop one of the independent variables but to transform the x variable in such a way that the correlation between the coded x- and x^2-values is substantially reduced. One transformation that works reasonably well is the z-transform. That is, replace the variable x with its z-score:

$$z_x = \frac{x - \bar{x}}{s}$$

PROBLEMS

11.7 A firm that sells a special skin cream exclusively through drug stores currently operates in 15 marketing districts. As part of an expansion feasibility study, the company wants to model district sales (y) as a function of target population (x_1), per capita income (x_2), and the number of drug stores (x_3) in the district. Data collected for each of the 15 districts were used to fit the first-order model,

$$E(y) = \beta_0 + \beta_1 x_1 + \beta_2 x_2 + \beta_3 x_3$$

A summary of the regression results follows:

$$\hat{y} = -3,000 + 3.2x_1 - .4x_2 - 1.1x_3 \qquad R^2 = .93$$
$$s_{\hat{\beta}_1} = 2.4 \qquad s_{\hat{\beta}_2} = .6 \qquad s_{\hat{\beta}_3} = .8$$
$$r_{12} = .92 \qquad r_{13} = .87 \qquad r_{23} = .81$$

Based on these results, the company concludes that none of the three independent variables, x_1, x_2, and x_3, is a useful predictor of district sales, y. Do you agree with this statement? Explain.

11.8 Refer to the FTC cigarette data of Example 11.4. Recall that y = carbon monoxide level, x_1 = tar content, x_2 = nicotine content, and x_3 = weight. The following three straight-line models were fit to the data using MINITAB:

MODEL 1 $E(y) = \beta_0 + \beta_1 x_1$
MODEL 2 $E(y) = \beta_0 + \beta_1 x_2$
MODEL 3 $E(y) = \beta_0 + \beta_1 x_3$

The MINITAB printouts follow:

```
The regression equation is
Y = 2.74 + 0.801 X1

Predictor       Coef        Stdev      t-ratio        p
Constant      2.7433       0.6752         4.06    0.000
X1            0.80098      0.05032        15.92    0.000

s = 1.397       R-sq = 91.7%      R-sq(adj) = 91.3%

Analysis of Variance

SOURCE        DF          SS          MS         F        p
Regression     1      494.28      494.28    253.37    0.000
Error         23       44.87        1.95
Total         24      539.15
```

(*continued*)

```
The regression equation is
Y = 1.66 + 12.4 X2

Predictor       Coef       Stdev      t-ratio       p
Constant       1.6647     0.9936       1.68       0.107
X2            12.395      1.054       11.76       0.000

s = 1.828      R-sq = 85.7%      R-sq(adj) = 85.1%

Analysis of Variance

SOURCE          DF          SS          MS          F          p
Regression       1        462.26      462.26      138.27     0.000
Error           23         76.89        3.34
Total           24        539.15
```

```
The regression equation is
Y = - 11.8 + 25.1 X3

Predictor       Coef       Stdev      t-ratio       p
Constant      -11.795      9.722      -1.21       0.237
X3            25.068       9.980       2.51       0.019

s = 4.289      R-sq = 21.5%      R-sq(adj) = 18.1%

Analysis of Variance

SOURCE          DF          SS          MS          F          p
Regression       1        116.06      116.06       6.31      0.019
Error           23        423.09       18.40
Total           24        539.15
```

a. Based on model 1, is there evidence that tar content, x_1, is useful for predicting carbon monoxide content, y?

b. Based on model 2, is there evidence that nicotine content, x_2, is useful for predicting carbon monoxide content, y?

c. Based on model 3, is there evidence that weight, x_3, is useful for predicting carbon monoxide content, y?

d. Compare the signs of β_1, β_2, and β_3 in the models of parts **a**, **b**, and **c**, respectively, to the signs of the β's in the multiple regression model fit in Example 11.4. The fact that the β's change dramatically when the independent variables are removed from the model is another indication of a serious multicollinearity problem.

11.9 A firm wants to use multiple regression in a cost analysis of its shipping department. Since most of the costs incurred by shipping result from direct labor, the firm will model weekly hours of labor (y) as a function of total weight shipped (x_1), percentage of units shipped by truck (x_2), and average weight per shipment (x_3). Data collected from the firm's accounting and production records for a 20 week period are shown in the table. The SAS computer printout for the model $E(y) = \beta_0 + \beta_1 x_1 + \beta_2 x_2 + \beta_3 x_3$ follows. The firm is concerned about the problems that occur in regression analysis when multicollinearity is present. Examine the SAS printout. Do you detect any signs of multicollinearity?

WEEK	HOURS OF LABOR y	THOUSAND POUNDS SHIPPED x_1	PERCENTAGE OF UNITS SHIPPED BY TRUCK x_2	AVERAGE NUMBER OF POUNDS PER SHIPMENT x_3
1	100	5.1	90	20
2	85	3.8	99	22
3	108	5.3	58	19
4	116	7.5	16	15
5	92	4.5	54	20
6	63	3.3	42	26
7	79	5.3	12	25
8	101	5.9	32	21
9	88	4.0	56	24

(continued)

WEEK	HOURS OF LABOR y	THOUSAND POUNDS SHIPPED x_1	PERCENTAGE OF UNITS SHIPPED BY TRUCK x_2	AVERAGE NUMBER OF POUNDS PER SHIPMENT x_3
10	71	4.2	64	29
11	122	6.8	78	10
12	85	3.9	90	30
13	50	3.8	74	28
14	114	7.5	89	14
15	104	4.5	90	21
16	111	6.0	40	20
17	110	8.1	55	16
18	100	2.9	64	19
19	82	4.0	35	23
20	85	4.8	58	25

SAS Printout for Problem 11.9

Dependent Variable: LABOR

Analysis of Variance

Source	DF	Sum of Squares	Mean Square	F Value	Prob>F
Model	3	5158.31383	1719.43794	17.866	0.0001
Error	16	1539.88617	96.24289		
C Total	19	6698.20000			

Root MSE	9.81035	R-square	0.7701	
Dep Mean	93.30000	Adj R-sq	0.7270	
C.V.	10.51484			

Parameter Estimates

Variable	DF	Parameter Estimate	Standard Error	T for H0: Parameter=0	Prob > |T|	Variance Inflation
INTERCEP	1	131.924252	25.69321439	5.135	0.0001	0.00000000
WEIGHT	1	2.726090	2.27500488	1.198	0.2483	2.25045709
TRUCK	1	0.047218	0.09334856	0.506	0.6199	1.09294182
AVGSHIP	1	-2.587444	0.64281819	-4.025	0.0010	2.16626650

11.10 D. Hamilton illustrated the multicollinearity problem with an example using the data shown in the table. The values of x_1, x_2, and y in the table represent appraised land value, appraised improvements value, and sale price, respectively, of a randomly selected residential property. (All measurements are in thousands of dollars.)

x_1	x_2	y	x_1	x_2	y	x_1	x_2	y
22.3	96.6	123.7	28.3	85.2	130.3	33.9	50.5	112.0
25.7	89.4	126.6	30.2	80.4	131.3	23.5	85.1	115.6
38.7	44.0	120.0	21.4	90.5	114.4	27.6	65.9	108.3
31.0	66.4	119.3	30.4	77.1	128.6	39.0	49.0	126.3
33.9	49.1	110.6	32.6	51.1	108.4	31.6	69.6	124.6

Source: Hamilton, D. "Sometimes $R^2 > r_{yx_1} + r_{yx_2}$: Correlated Variables Are Not Always Redundant." *The American Statistician,* Vol. 41, No. 2, May 1987, pp. 129–132. Reprinted with permission from *The American Statistician.* Copyright 1987 by the American Statistical Association. All rights reserved.

a. Calculate the coefficient of correlation between y and x_1. Is there evidence of a linear relationship between sale price and appraised land value?

b. Calculate the coefficient of correlation between y and x_2. Is there evidence of a linear relationship between sale price and appraised improvements value?

c. Based on the results in parts **a** and **b**, do you think the model $E(y) = \beta_0 + \beta_1 x_1 + \beta_2 x_2$ will be useful for predicting sale price?

d. Use a statistical computer program package to fit the model in part **c**, and conduct a test of model adequacy. In particular, note the value of R^2. Does the result agree with your answer to part **c**?

e. Calculate the coefficient of correlation between x_1 and x_2. What does the result imply?

f. Many researchers avoid the problems of multicollinearity by always omitting all but one of the "redundant" variables from the model. Would you recommend this strategy for this example? Explain. (Hamilton notes that in this case, such a strategy "can amount to throwing out the baby with the bathwater.")

TESTS FOR COMPARING NESTED MODELS

11.5

In step 5 of model-building (see Section 11.1), we require a statistical model that will allow us to determine (with a high degree of confidence) which one among a set of candidate models best fits the data. In this section, we present such a technique for **nested models**.

> ### DEFINITION 11.3
>
> Two models are **nested** if one model contains all the terms of the second model, and at least one additional term.

To illustrate the idea of nested models, consider the problem of modeling the shipping cost (y) of an express delivery package. In Example 10.10 (p. 481), we fit the straight-line interaction model for $E(y)$ as a function of two quantitative variables, package weight (x_1) and distance shipped (x_2). The interaction model was

$$E(y) = \beta_0 + \beta_1 x_1 + \beta_2 x_2 + \beta_3 x_1 x_2$$

However, if we assume that the relationship between shipment cost (y), package weight (x_1), and distance shipped (x_2) is curvilinear, then the curvilinear model is more appropriate:

$$E(y) = \beta_0 + \beta_1 x_1 + \beta_2 x_2 + \beta_3 x_1 x_2 + \beta_4 x_1^2 + \beta_5 x_2^2$$

Note that the curvilinear model contains quadratic terms for x_1 and x_2 as well as all the terms in the interaction model. Consequently, these are nested models. Since the interaction model is the simpler of the two, we say that *the interaction model is nested within the more complex curvilinear model*.

In general, the more complex of two nested models is called the **complete model**, and the simpler of the two is called the **reduced model**. In this case, the curvilinear model is the complete model, and the interaction model is the reduced model.

Now, suppose we wanted to test whether the curvilinear terms in the complete model contribute information for the prediction of y. This can be done by testing the hypothesis that the parameters for the quadratic terms x_1^2 and x_2^2 equal 0:

H_0: $\beta_4 = \beta_5 = 0$

H_a: At least one of the two parameters, β_4 and β_5, is nonzero.

In Chapter 10, we presented both the t test for a single β parameter and the F test for all the β parameters (except β_0) in the model. We now need a test for a *subset* of the β parameters in the model. The test procedure is intuitive. First, we use the method of least squares to fit the reduced model, and calculate the corresponding sum of squares for error, SSE_R (the sum of squares of the deviations between observed and predicted y-values). Next, we fit the complete model, and calculate its sum of squares for error, SSE_C. Then, we compare SSE_R to SSE_C by calculating the difference, $SSE_R - SSE_C$. If the curvature terms contribute to the model, then SSE_C should be much smaller than SSE_R, and the difference $SSE_R - SSE_C$ will be large. The larger the difference, the greater the evidence that the variables package weight and distance shipped affect the mean shipment cost in a curvilinear manner.

The sum of squares for error will always decrease when new terms are added to the model since the total sum of squares, $SS_{yy} = \Sigma(y - \bar{y})^2$, remains the same. The question is whether this decrease is large enough to conclude that it is due to more than just an increase in the number of model terms and to chance. To test the null hypothesis that the curvature coefficients β_4 and β_5 simultaneously equal 0, we use an F statistic calculated as follows:

$$F = \frac{\text{Drop in SSE/Number of } \beta \text{ parameters being tested}}{s^2 \text{ for complete model}}$$

$$= \frac{(SSE_R - SSE_C)/2}{SSE_C/[n - (5 + 1)]}$$

When the assumptions about the random error term are satisfied and the β parameters for curvature are all 0 (H_0 is true), this F statistic has an F distribution with $\nu_1 = 2$ and $\nu_2 = n - 6$ df. Note that ν_1 is the number of β parameters being tested and ν_2 is the number of degrees of freedom associated with s^2 in the complete model.

If the quadratic terms do contribute to the model (H_a is true), we expect the F statistic to be large. Thus, we use a one-tailed test and reject H_0 when F exceeds some critical value, F_α, as shown in Figure 11.9.

Figure 11.10 shows the SAS printout for the curvilinear (complete) model fit to the same $n = 20$ data points as the interaction (reduced) model in Example 10.10. Referring to the printout, we find the following:

Interaction model (reduced model): $SSE_R = 6.63331$

Curvilinear model (complete model): $SSE_C = 2.74474$

The test statistic is

$$F = \frac{(SSE_R - SSE_C)/2}{SSE_C/(20 - 6)} = \frac{(6.63331 - 2.74474)/2}{2.74474/14} = \frac{1.94428}{.19605} = 9.92$$

The critical value of F for $\alpha = .05$, $\nu_1 = 2$, and $\nu_2 = 14$ is found in Table 8, Appendix A, to be $F_{.05} = 3.74$. Since the calculated $F = 9.92$ exceeds 3.74, we reject H_0. Thus, we are confident in concluding that the quadratic terms contribute to the prediction of y, shipment cost per package; the curvature terms should be retained in the model.

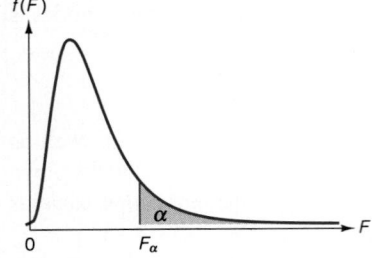

FIGURE 11.9

Rejection Region for the F Test of H_0: $\beta_4 = \beta_5 = 0$

Analysis of Variance

Source	DF	Sum of Squares	Mean Square	F Value	Prob>F
Model	5	449.34076	89.86815	458.388	0.0001
Error	14	2.74474	0.19605		
C Total	19	452.08550			

Root MSE	0.44278	R-square	0.9939	
Dep Mean	6.33500	Adj R-sq	0.9918	
C.V.	6.98940			

Parameter Estimates

Variable	DF	Parameter Estimate	Standard Error	T for H0: Parameter=0	Prob > |T|
INTERCEP	1	0.827016	0.70228935	1.178	0.2586
X1	1	-0.609137	0.17990408	-3.386	0.0044
X2	1	0.004021	0.00799842	0.503	0.6230
X1X2	1	0.007327	0.00063743	11.495	0.0001
X1SQ	1	0.089751	0.02020542	4.442	0.0006
X2SQ	1	0.000015070	0.00002243	0.672	0.5127

The F test described above can be used to determine whether any subset of terms should be included in a complete model by testing the null hypothesis that a particular set of β parameters simultaneously equal 0. For example, we may want to test to determine whether a set of interaction terms for quantitative variables or a set of dummy variable terms for a qualitative variable should be included in a model. If we reject H_0, the complete model is the better of the two nested models; otherwise, the reduced model is better. The F test appropriate for comparing nested models is summarized in the box.

F TEST FOR COMPARING NESTED MODELS

Reduced model: $\quad E(y) = \beta_0 + \beta_1 x_1 + \cdots + \beta_g x_g$

Complete model: $\quad E(y) = \beta_0 + \beta_1 x_1 + \cdots + \beta_g x_g + \beta_{g+1} x_{g+1} + \cdots + \beta_k x_k$

H_0: $\quad \beta_{g+1} = \beta_{g+2} = \cdots = \beta_k = 0$

H_a: $\quad$ At least one of the β parameters under test is nonzero.

Test statistic: $\quad F = \dfrac{(\text{SSE}_R - \text{SSE}_C)/(k - g)}{\text{SSE}_C/[n - (k + 1)]}$

$$= \frac{(\text{SSE}_R - \text{SSE}_C)/\text{Number of }\beta\text{ parameters tested in } H_0}{\text{MSE}_C}$$

where

$\quad \text{SSE}_R$ = Sum of squared errors for the reduced model

$\quad \text{SSE}_C$ = Sum of squared errors for the complete model

$\quad \text{MSE}_C$ = Mean square error (s^2) for the complete model

$\quad k - g$ = Number of β parameters specified in H_0 (ie, number of β parameters tested)

(continued)

$k + 1 =$ Number of β parameters in the complete model (including β_0)

$n =$ Total sample size

Rejection region: $F > F_\alpha$

where F is based on

$\nu_1 = k - g$ numerator degrees of freedom

$\nu_2 = n - (k + 1)$ denominator degrees of freedom

EXAMPLE 11.5 Consider the problem of modeling the price charged for motor transport service (such as trucking) in a particular state. In the early 1980's, several states removed regulatory constraints on the rate charged for intrastate trucking services. (Florida was the first state to embark on a deregulation policy on July 1, 1980.) One of the goals of the regression analysis is to assess the impact of state deregulation on the supply price, y, charged per ton–mile. The following independent variables were selected:

$$x_1 = \text{Distance shipped}$$

$$x_2 = \text{Weight of product}$$

$$x_3 = \begin{cases} 1 & \text{if deregulation in effect} \\ 0 & \text{if not} \end{cases}$$

$$x_4 = \begin{cases} 1 & \text{if large market} \\ 0 & \text{if small market} \end{cases}$$

Data collected for $n = 132$ shipments were used to fit the three candidate models shown below. The results are summarized in Table 11.8.

TABLE 11.8
Summary of Regression Results

MODEL	SSE	R^2	df(ERROR)
1	203,570	.83	108
2	227,520	.81	116
3	395,165	.67	123

MODEL 1 $E(y) = \beta_0 + \beta_1 x_1 + \beta_2 x_2 + \beta_3 x_1 x_2 + \beta_4 x_1^2 + \beta_5 x_2^2 + \beta_6 x_3$
$+ \beta_7 x_4 + \beta_8 x_3 x_4 + \beta_9 x_1 x_3 + \beta_{10} x_1 x_4 + \beta_{11} x_1 x_3 x_4$
$+ \beta_{12} x_2 x_3 + \beta_{13} x_2 x_4 + \beta_{14} x_2 x_3 x_4 + \beta_{15} x_1 x_2 x_3$
$+ \beta_{16} x_1 x_2 x_4 + \beta_{17} x_1 x_2 x_3 x_4 + \beta_{18} x_1^2 x_3 + \beta_{19} x_1^2 x_4$
$+ \beta_{20} x_1^2 x_3 x_4 + \beta_{21} x_2^2 x_3 + \beta_{22} x_2^2 x_4 + \beta_{23} x_2^2 x_3 x_4$

MODEL 2 $E(y) = \beta_0 + \beta_1 x_1 + \beta_2 x_2 + \beta_3 x_1 x_2 + \beta_4 x_3 + \beta_5 x_4 + \beta_6 x_3 x_4$
$+ \beta_7 x_1 x_3 + \beta_8 x_1 x_4 + \beta_9 x_1 x_3 x_4 + \beta_{10} x_2 x_3 + \beta_{11} x_2 x_4$
$+ \beta_{12} x_2 x_3 x_4 + \beta_{13} x_1 x_2 x_3 + \beta_{14} x_1 x_2 x_4 + \beta_{15} x_1 x_2 x_3 x_4$

MODEL 3 $E(y) = \beta_0 + \beta_1 x_1 + \beta_2 x_2 + \beta_3 x_1 x_2 + \beta_4 x_4 + \beta_5 x_1 x_4$
$+ \beta_6 x_2 x_4 + \beta_7 x_1 x_2 x_4$

a. Identify the nested models in the set of candidate models.
b. What null hypothesis would you test to compare models 1 and 2?
c. Conduct the test specified in part **b**. Use $\alpha = .05$.

d. Based on the result in part **c**, conduct a test to determine whether deregulation has an impact on the mean price change. Use $\alpha = .05$.

Solution

a. Close examination of the terms in the three models reveals that model 1 contains all terms in model 2 and in model 3, and additional terms. Thus, both model 2 and model 3 are nested within model 1. Also, model 2 contains all terms in model 3, plus several more terms; thus, model 3 is also nested within model 2.

b. Model 1 contains first-order, interaction, and quadratic terms for the two quantitative variables, x_1 and x_2, as well as main-effect and interaction terms for the two qualitative variables, x_3 and x_4. Model 2 contains terms identical to those in model 1, except it lacks the quadratic terms for x_1 and x_2. Specifically, the terms $x_1^2, x_2^2, x_1^2 x_3, x_2^2 x_3, x_1^2 x_4, x_2^2 x_4, x_1^2 x_3 x_4, x_2^2 x_3, x_2^2 x_4$, and $x_2^2 x_3 x_4$ are omitted. Thus, a test to compare models 1 and 2 is a test for the importance of these 10 quadratic (or curvature) terms. The appropriate null hypothesis is

$$H_0: \quad \beta_4 = \beta_5 = \beta_{18} = \beta_{19} = \beta_{20} = \beta_{21} = \beta_{22} = \beta_{23} = \beta_{24} = 0$$

c. For this test, model 1 is the complete model and model 2 is the reduced model. The test statistic is

$$F = \frac{(\text{SSE}_2 - \text{SSE}_1)/\text{Number of }\beta \text{ parameters tested in } H_0}{\text{SSE}_1/\text{df(Error) for model 1}}$$

where (from Table 11.8) $\text{SSE}_1 = 203{,}570$, $\text{SSE}_2 = 227{,}520$, and df(Error) for model 1 is 108. Substituting these values into the formula, we obtain

$$F = \frac{(227{,}520 - 203{,}570)/10}{203{,}570/108} = 1.27$$

The rejection region for the test is $F > F_{.05}$, where $F_{.05}$ is based on 10 numerator and 108 denominator degrees of freedom. From Table 8, Appendix A, $F_{.05} = 1.83$. Therefore, we reject H_0 if $F > 1.83$. Since the test statistic, $F = 1.27$, falls below the critical value, 1.83, we fail to reject H_0. At $\alpha = .05$, there is insufficient evidence to say that the curvature terms contribute information for the prediction of supply price, y.

Although we must be cautious about accepting H_0, most practitioners of regression analysis adopt the principle of **parsimony**. That is, in situations where two competing models are found to have essentially the same predictive power (as in this case), the model with the fewest number of β's (ie, the more **parsimonious model**) is selected. Based on this principle, we would drop the 10 curvature terms and select model 2 over model 1.

d. If deregulation has no impact on the mean supply price, $E(y)$, the β parameters associated with x_3 in model 2 will all equal 0. These eight β's are $\beta_4, \beta_6, \beta_7, \beta_9, \beta_{10}, \beta_{12}, \beta_{13}$, and β_{15}. If deregulation does have an impact, at least one of these β's will be nonzero. Thus, we want to test

$$H_0: \quad \beta_4 = \beta_6 = \beta_7 = \beta_9 = \beta_{10} = \beta_{12} = \beta_{13} = \beta_{15} = 0$$

H_a: At least one of the above β's is nonzero.

Since model 3 is nested within model 2, model 2 is now the complete model for the test, and model 3 is the reduced model. The test statistic is

$$F = \frac{(SSE_3 - SSE_2)/\text{Number of }\beta\text{ parameters tested in }H_0}{SSE_2/df(\text{Error}) \text{ for model 2}}$$

$$= \frac{(395{,}165 - 227{,}520)/8}{227{,}520/116} = 10.68$$

and the rejection region is $F > F_{.05} \approx 2.02$ (where $F_{.05} \approx 2.02$ is based on 8 numerator and 116 denominator degrees of freedom). Since the test statistic falls into the rejection region, we reject H_0 at $\alpha = .05$; there is sufficient evidence to indicate that the deregulation terms (ie, terms involving x_3) are useful for predicting y. This implies that model 3 is the more useful model.

DEFINITION 11.4

A **parsimonious model** is a general linear model with a small number of β parameters. In situations where two competing models have essentially the same predictive power (as determined by an F test), choose the more parsimonious of the two.

When the candidate models in model-building are nested models, the F test developed in this section is the appropriate procedure to apply to compare the models. However, if the models are not nested, this F test is not applicable. In this situation, the analyst must base the choice of the best model on statistics such as R_a^2 and s. It is important to remember that decisions based on these and other numerical descriptive measures of model adequacy cannot be supported with a measure of reliability and are often very subjective in nature.

PROBLEMS

11.11 Since 1978, when the U.S. airline industry was deregulated, researchers have questioned whether the deregulation has ensured a truly competitive environment. If so, the profitability of any major airline would be related to overall industry conditions (eg, disposable income and market share) but not to any unchanging feature of that airline. This profitability hypothesis was tested using multiple regression (*Transportation Journal*, Winter 1990). Data for $n = 234$ carrier–years were used to fit the model

$$E(y) = \beta_0 + \beta_1 x_1 + \beta_2 x_2 + \beta_3 x_3 + \cdots + \beta_{30} x_{30}$$

where

y = Profit rate

x_1 = Real personal disposable income

x_2 = Industry market share

x_3–x_{30} = Dummy variables (coded 0–1) for the 29 air carriers investigated in the study

---

The results of the regression are summarized in the table. Interpret the results. Is the profitability hypothesis supported?

VARIABLE	β ESTIMATE	t-VALUE	p-VALUE
Intercept	1.2642	0.09	.9266
x_1	−0.0022	−0.99	.8392
x_2	4.8405	3.57	.0003
x_3–x_{30}	(Not given)	—	—
$R^2 = .3402$	F(Full model) $= 3.49$		p-Value $= .0001$
	F(For testing carrier dummies) $= 3.59$		p-Value $= .0001$

Source: Leigh, L. E. "Contestability in Deregulated Airline Markets: Some Empirical Tests." *Transportation Journal*, Winter 1990, p. 55 (Table 4). Reprinted from the Winter 1990 issue of *Transportation Journal* with the express permission of the publisher, the American Society of Transportation and Logistics, Inc., for educational purposes only.

11.12 Refer to Problem 10.10 (p. 000) and the *Journal of Personal Selling & Sales Management* (Summer 1990) study of gender differences in the industrial sales force. Recall that a sample of 244 male and 153 female sales managers participated in the survey. One objective of the research was to assess how supervisory behavior affects intrinsic job satisfaction. Initially, the researchers fit the following reduced model to the data on each gender group:

$$E(y) = \beta_0 + \beta_1 x_1 + \beta_2 x_2 + \beta_3 x_3 + \beta_4 x_4$$

where

  y = Intrinsic job satisfaction (measured on a scale of 0 to 40)

  x_1 = Age (years)

  x_2 = Education level (years)

  x_3 = Firm experience (months)

  x_4 = Sales experience (months)

To determine the effects of supervisory behavior, four variables (all measured on a scale of 0 to 50) were added to the model: x_5 = contingent reward behavior, x_6 = noncontingent reward behavior, x_7 = contingent punishment behavior, and x_8 = noncontingent punishment behavior. Thus, the complete model is

$$E(y) = \beta_0 + \beta_1 x_1 + \beta_2 x_2 + \beta_3 x_3 + \beta_4 x_4 + \beta_5 x_5 + \beta_6 x_6 + \beta_7 x_7 + \beta_8 x_8$$

a. For each gender, specify the null hypothesis and rejection region ($\alpha = .05$) for testing whether any of the four supervisory behavior variables affect intrinsic job satisfaction.

b. The R^2 values for the four models (reduced and complete models for each sample) are given in the table. Interpret the results. For each gender, does it appear that the supervisory behavior variables have an impact on intrinsic job satisfaction? Explain.

MODEL	R^2	
	Males	Females
Reduced	.218	.268
Complete	.408	.496

Source: Schul, P. L., et al. "Assessing Gender Differences in Relationships Between Supervisory Behaviors and Job-Related Outcomes in Industrial Sales Force." *Journal of Personal Selling & Sales Management*, Vol. X, Summer 1990, p. 9 (Table 4).

c. The F statistics for comparing the two models are $F_{\text{Males}} = 13.00$ and $F_{\text{Females}} = 9.05$. Conduct the tests from part **a** and interpret the results.

11.13   Research was undertaken to examine the effect of several factors on managerial performance (*Journal of Vocational Behavior*, Vol. 29, Oct. 1986). A sample of 100 management personnel from several divisions within a government agency took part in the study. Each manager completed a questionnaire designed to measure the following variables:

y = Performance rating (1 = unacceptable, ..., 5 = outstanding)

$$x_1 = \begin{cases} 1 & \text{if male} \\ 0 & \text{if female} \end{cases}$$

x_2 = Job tenure (years)

x_3 = Manager–subordinate work relationship rating
(1 = unsatisfactory, ..., 5 = excellent)

x_4 = Effort level (average number of hours per week invested in job)

$$x_5 = \begin{cases} 1 & \text{if middle or upper-level manager} \\ 0 & \text{if lower-level manager} \end{cases}$$

x_6 = Subordinate-related managerial behavior score (low scores indicate little or no effort spent on counseling, evaluating, and training subordinates)

The data collected on the 100 managers were used to fit several regression models of managerial performance.

a. Initially, the model

$$E(y) = \beta_0 + \beta_1 x_1 + \beta_2 x_2 + \beta_3 x_3 + \beta_4 x_4$$

was considered to account for the influence of gender, job tenure, manager–subordinate work relationship, and effort level on performance rating. For this model, SSE = 352 and R^2 = .11. Calculate the F statistic for testing model adequacy. Is the model useful for predicting performance rating, y? (Use α = .05.)

b. Terms for managerial level and subordinate-related behavior (ie, $\beta_5 x_5 + \beta_6 x_6$) were added to the model of part **a**, resulting in SSE = 341 and R^2 = .14. Do these terms contribute additional information for the prediction of performance rating, y? (Test using α = .05.)

c. A third model was also considered:

$$E(y) = \beta_0 + \beta_1 x_1 + \beta_2 x_2 + \beta_3 x_3 + \beta_4 x_4 + \beta_5 x_5 + \beta_6 x_6 + \beta_7 x_5 x_6$$

The model resulted in SSE = 321 and R^2 = .19. Test the hypothesis that the interaction between managerial level (x_5) and subordinate-related behavior (x_6) is not important; that is, test H_0: β_7 = 0. Use α = .05.

d. Interpret the result of part **c** in terms of this problem.

11.14   Refer to Problem 10.32 (p. 503) and the *Journal of Energy Resources Technology* study of diesel engines. Recall that the researchers fit the model

$$E(y) = \beta_0 + \beta_1 x_1 + \beta_2 x_2 + \beta_3 x_3$$

where

$$y = \text{Mass burning rate}$$
$$x_1 = \text{Brake power}$$
$$x_2 = \begin{cases} 1 & \text{if DF-2 fuel} \\ 0 & \text{if not} \end{cases}$$
$$x_3 = \begin{cases} 1 & \text{if blended fuel} \\ 0 & \text{if not} \end{cases}$$

The interaction model

$$E(y) = \beta_0 + \beta_1 x_1 + \beta_2 x_2 + \beta_3 x_3 + \beta_4 x_1 x_2 + \beta_5 x_1 x_3$$

was also fit using MINITAB, with the results shown in the following printout. Conduct a test to determine whether brake power and fuel type interact. Test using α = .01.

MINITAB Printout for Problem 11.14
(Interaction Model)

```
The regression equation is
Y = - 10.8 + 7.82 X1 + 19.4 X2 + 12.8 X3 - 5.68 X1X2 - 2.95 X1X3

Predictor        Coef       Stdev      t-ratio        p
Constant      -10.830       8.277       -1.31      0.227
X1              7.815       1.126        6.94      0.000
X2             19.35       10.69         1.81      0.108
X3             12.79       10.69         1.20      0.266
X1X2           -5.675       1.380       -4.11      0.003
X1X3           -2.950       1.380       -2.14      0.065

s = 5.037      R-sq = 94.1%      R-sq(adj) = 90.5%

Analysis of Variance

SOURCE        DF          SS          MS         F         p
Regression     5     3253.98      650.80     25.65     0.000
Error          8      203.01       25.38
Total         13     3456.99
```

11.15 A chain of drug stores wants to model mean profit per week, $E(y)$, as a function of three advertising factors: type of design, choice of newspaper, and percentage discount offered on sale items. A first proposal is the model

$$E(y) = \beta_0 + \beta_1 x_1 + \beta_2 x_1^2 + \beta_3 x_2 + \beta_4 x_3 + \beta_5 x_2 x_3 + \beta_6 x_1 x_2 + \beta_7 x_1 x_3 + \beta_8 x_1 x_2 x_3 + \beta_9 x_1^2 x_2 + \beta_{10} x_1^2 x_3 + \beta_{11} x_1^2 x_2 x_3$$

where

$$x_1 = \text{Percentage discount}$$

$$x_2 = \begin{cases} 1 & \text{if design D}_1 \\ 0 & \text{if design D}_2 \end{cases}$$

$$x_3 = \begin{cases} 1 & \text{if newspaper N}_1 \\ 0 & \text{if newspaper N}_2 \end{cases}$$

a. Specify the parameters that would be involved in a test of the hypothesis, "The design of the advertising and the choice of newspaper have no effect on the mean value of the weekly profits."

b. Refer to part **a**. State the hypothesis that you would make regarding the parameter values.

c. Give the parameters that would be involved in a test of the hypothesis, "The relationship between mean weekly profit and percentage discount for each of the combinations of newspaper and design is first-order (ie, a straight line)."

11.16 Real estate appraisers, tax assessors, real estate investors, and home buyers are interested in the relationship between the appraised value of a property and its sale price. A data set obtained from the Alachua County (Florida) property appraiser's office contains the appraised land and improvements values and the sale prices for 651 residential properties sold in 6 neighborhoods in the county. The data will be used to develop a model for sale price, y, recorded in thousands of dollars. Consider the following four candidate models, where

$$x_1 = \text{Appraised land value}$$

$$x_2 = \text{Appraised improvements value}$$

$$x_3 = \begin{cases} 1 & \text{if neighborhood A} \\ 0 & \text{if not} \end{cases}$$

$$x_4 = \begin{cases} 1 & \text{if neighborhood B} \\ 0 & \text{if not} \end{cases}$$

$$\vdots$$

$$x_7 = \begin{cases} 1 & \text{if neighborhood E} \\ 0 & \text{if not} \end{cases}$$

MODEL 1 $\quad E(y) = \beta_0 + \beta_1 x_1 + \beta_2 x_2$

MODEL 2 $\quad E(y) = \beta_0 + \beta_1 x_1 + \beta_2 x_2 + \beta_3 x_3 + \beta_4 x_4 + \beta_5 x_5 + \beta_6 x_6 + \beta_7 x_7 + \beta_8 x_1 x_3 + \beta_9 x_1 x_4 + \cdots$
$\qquad + \beta_{12} x_1 x_7 + \beta_{13} x_2 x_3 + \beta_{14} x_2 x_4 + \cdots + \beta_{17} x_2 x_7$

MODEL 3 $\quad E(y) = \beta_0 + \beta_1 x_1 + \beta_2 x_2 + \beta_3 x_1 x_2 + \beta_4 x_1^2 + \beta_5 x_2^2 + \beta_6 x_3 + \beta_7 x_4 + \beta_8 x_5 + \beta_9 x_6 + \beta_{10} x_7$
$\qquad + \beta_{11} x_3 x_1 + \beta_{12} x_3 x_2 + \beta_{13} x_3 x_1 x_2 + \beta_{14} x_3 x_1^2 + \beta_{15} x_3 x_2^2 + \beta_{16} x_4 x_1 + \beta_{17} x_4 x_2 + \beta_{18} x_4 x_1 x_2$
$\qquad + \beta_{19} x_4 x_1^2 + \beta_{20} x_4 x_2^2 + \cdots + \beta_{31} x_7 x_1 + \beta_{32} x_7 x_2 + \beta_{33} x_7 x_1 x_2 + \beta_{34} x_7 x_1^2 + \beta_{35} x_7 x_2^2$

MODEL 4 $\quad E(y) = \beta_0 + \beta_1 x_1 + \beta_2 x_2 + \beta_3 x_1 x_2 + \beta_4 x_1^2 + \beta_5 x_2^2$

a. Determine and list the pairs of nested models.
b. All four models were fit to the 651 data points. The sums of squares for error and their respective degrees of freedom for the four models are listed in the table. Compare the models using nested F tests. Which one of the four do you recommend for predicting sale price, y?

MODEL	SSE	df(ERROR)
1	93,233	648
2	71,998	633
3	54,178	615
4	76,356	645

RESIDUAL ANALYSIS

11.6 An analysis of **residuals**, the differences $(y - \hat{y})$ between the y-values and their corresponding predicted values, often provides information that can lead to modifications and improvements in a regression model. These modifications may result from any one of three reasons: (1) the model itself has been misspecified, (2) one or more of the assumptions about ϵ is violated, and (3) the data used to fit the model contain one or more unusual values.

DEFINITION 11.5

A regression **residual** is defined as the difference between an observed y-value and its corresponding predicted value:

$$\text{Residual} = (y - \hat{y})$$

DETECTING MODEL MISSPECIFICATION

One method for analyzing the residuals in a regression analysis is to plot the value of each residual versus the corresponding value of the independent variable, x. (If the model contains more than one independent variable, a plot would be constructed for each of the independent variables.) This plot will help detect whether you have misspecified the model, as the following example illustrates.

EXAMPLE 11.6 Fit the first-order linear model $E(y) = \beta_0 + \beta_1 x$ to the data shown in Table 11.9. Calculate the residuals, plot the residuals versus x, and analyze the plot.

TABLE 11.9
Data for Example 11.6

x	0	1	2	3	4	5	6	7
y	1	4	6	8	9	10	10	8

Solution   The MINITAB printout for the simple linear regression is shown in Figure 11.11

FIGURE 11.11
MINITAB Printout for the Simple Linear Model

```
The regression equation is
Y = 3.17 + 1.10 X

Predictor      Coef         Stdev       t-ratio
Constant       3.167        1.167        2.71
X              1.0952       0.2790       3.93

s = 1.808       R-sq = 72.0%       R-sq(adj) = 67.3%

Analysis of Variance

SOURCE        DF          SS           MS
Regression    1           50.381       50.381
Error         6           19.619       3.270
Total         7           70.000

Unusual Observations
Obs.      X         Y         Fit  Stdev.Fit  Residual    St.Resid
  8     7.00     8.000     10.833    1.167     -2.833      -2.05R

R denotes an obs. with a large st. resid.
```

You can see that the resulting prediction equation is

$$\hat{y} = 3.167 + 1.0952x$$

Substituting each value of x into this prediction equation, we can calculate $\hat{y}$ and the corresponding residual, $y - \hat{y}$. The value of x, the predicted value $\hat{y}$, and the residual $(y - \hat{y})$ are listed in Table 11.10 for each of the data points.

A plot of the residuals versus the independent variable x is shown in Figure 11.12a. If the model were correctly specified, we would expect the residuals to vary randomly as x increases. Instead, the values of the residuals in Figure 11.12a cycle from negative to positive to negative as x increases. This cyclical behavior occurs because we have fit a first-order (straight-line) linear model to data for which a second-order model is appropriate—that is, we have misspecified the model. A plot of the data points on a graph of $\hat{y}$ versus x is shown in Figure 11.12b.

The residuals, the vertical bars between the data points, and the fitted line are shown in color. Those below the $\hat{y}$ line are negative; those above it are positive. Figure 11.12 shows why fitting the wrong model to a data set can produce patterns in the residuals when they are plotted versus an independent variable. For this simple example, the nonrandom (in this case, cyclical) behavior of the residuals can be eliminated by fitting the second-order model $E(y) = \beta_0 + \beta_1 x + \beta_2 x^2$ to the data. In general, certain patterns in the values of the residuals may suggest a need

TABLE 11.10
Calculation of the Residuals for the Simple Linear Regression Analysis

x	y	$\hat{y}$	$(y - \hat{y})$
0	1	3.167	−2.167
1	4	4.262	−.262
2	6	5.357	.643
3	8	6.452	1.548
4	9	7.548	1.452
5	10	8.643	1.357
6	10	9.738	.262
7	8	10.833	−2.833

FIGURE 11.12
Plots of Residuals and Predicted
Values

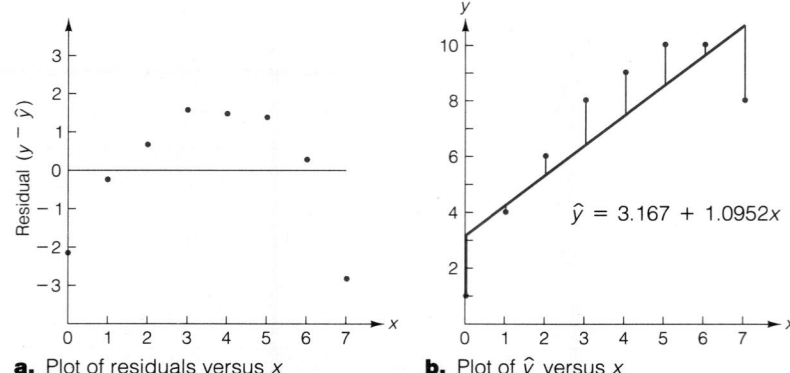

a. Plot of residuals versus x **b.** Plot of $\hat{y}$ versus x

to modify the deterministic portion of the regression model, but the exact change may not always be obvious.

A check for model misspecification is equivalent to graphically testing the assumption that $E(\epsilon) = 0$. To see this, suppose the true model for $E(y)$ is given by the second-order model,

$$E(y) = \beta_0 + \beta_1 x + \beta_2 x^2$$

but we specify the first-order probabilistic model

$$y = \beta_0 + \beta_1 x + \epsilon$$

For our hypothesized model, we can write

$$\epsilon = y - (\beta_0 + \beta_1 x)$$

Then it can be shown that

$$E(\epsilon) = E(y) - (\beta_0 + \beta_1 x)$$

Substituting the expression for $E(y)$ above, we obtain

$$E(\epsilon) = \beta_0 + \beta_1 x + \beta_2 x^2 - (\beta_0 + \beta_1 x)$$
$$= \beta_2 x^2$$

When $\beta_2 \neq 0$ and $x \neq 0$, $E(\epsilon)$ will be nonzero; consequently, the 0 mean assumption will be violated.

DETECTING UNEQUAL VARIANCES

A plot of the residuals also can be used to check the assumption of a constant error variance. For example, a plot of the residuals for the model $E(y) = \beta_0 + \beta_1 x$ may display a pattern as shown in Figure 11.13. In the figure, the range in values of the residuals increases as x increases, indicating that the variance of the response variable y (and the random error ϵ) becomes larger as x increases in value.*

---

* It can be shown (proof omitted) that for any regression model, Variance (y) = Variance (ϵ) = σ^2.

FIGURE 11.13

Residual Plot Showing Changes in
the Variance of y

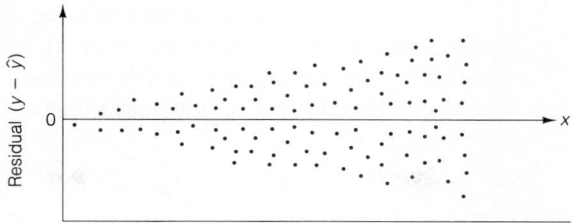

Residual plots of the type shown in Figure 11.13 are not uncommon, because the variance of y often depends on the mean value of y. Variables that represent counts per unit of area, volume, time, etc. (called **Poisson random variables**) are cases in point. For a Poisson random variable, the variance of y is equal to $E(y) = \mu$, that is, $\sigma_y^2 = \mu$.

Since $\hat{y}$ is an estimator of $E(y)$, a plot of the residuals versus $\hat{y}$ may indicate how the range of the residuals (and hence, σ_y^2) varies as $E(y)$ increases. If the plot assumes the pattern shown in Figure 11.14a, and if you think it is possible that y is approximately a Poisson random variable, you may be able to stabilize the variance of the response by using the transformation $y^* = \sqrt{y}$ and fitting y^* (instead of y) to the independent variables.

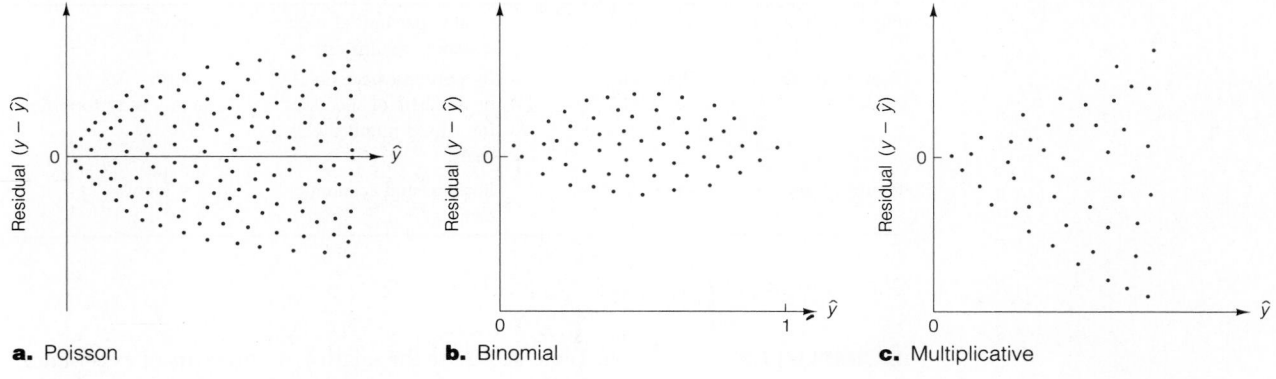

a. Poisson   **b.** Binomial   **c.** Multiplicative

FIGURE 11.14

Plots of the Residuals Versus $\hat{y}$ for
Poisson, Binomial, and Multiplicative
Response Variables

Similarly, if y is a binomial percentage or proportion, $0 \le y \le 1$, we would expect $\sigma_y^2 = y(1 - y)/n$ to be small when y is near 0 or 1 and to reach a maximum when y is equal to .5. A plot of the residuals versus $\hat{y}$ for this type of data (ie, binomial data) would appear as shown in Figure 11.14b. To stabilize the variance for this type of data, use the transformation $y^* = \sin^{-1}\sqrt{y}$, where y is expressed in radians.

A third situation that requires a variance-stabilizing transformation occurs with business and economic data where the response variable, y, follows a **multiplicative model**. Unlike the additive models discussed so far, in the multiplicative model, the dependent variable is written as the *product* of its mean and the random error component:

Multiplicative model: $\quad y = [E(y)] \cdot \epsilon$

The variance of this response will grow proportionally to the square of the mean, that is, $\sigma_y^2 = [E(y)]^2 \sigma^2$, where σ^2 is the variance of the random error. Data subject to multiplicative errors produce a pattern of residuals about $\hat{y}$ like that shown in Figure 11.14c. The appropriate transformation for this type of data is $y^* = \log y$. Thus, the natural logarithm model discussed in Section 11.3 is useful for satisfying assumptions as well as for improving the fit of the model.

The three variance-stabilizing transformations we have discussed are summarized in Table 11.11.

TABLE 11.11
Transformations to Stabilize the Variance of a Response

RESIDUAL PLOT	TYPE OF DATA	CHARACTERISTICS	TRANSFORMATION
Figure 11.14a	Poisson	Counts per unit of time, distance, volume, etc.	$y^* = \sqrt{y}$
Figure 11.14b	Binomial	Proportions, percentages, or numbers of successes for a fixed number n of trials	$y^* = \sin^{-1}\sqrt{y}$ where y is a proportion
Figure 11.14c	Multiplicative	Business and economic data	$y^* = \log y$

EXAMPLE 11.7 The data in Table 11.12 are the salaries, y, and years of experience, x, for a sample of 50 auditors. The first-order model $E(y) = \beta_0 + \beta_1 x$ was fit to the data using MINITAB. The MINITAB printout is shown in Figure 11.15, followed by a plot of the residuals versus $\hat{y}$ in Figure 11.16. Interpret the results. Should the model be modified? If so, how?

Solution   The MINITAB printout in Figure 11.15 suggests that the first-order model provides an adequate fit to the data. The R^2-value indicates that the model explains 78.7% of the sample variation in salaries. The t-value for testing β_1, 13.31, is highly significant (p-value ≈ 0) and indicates that the model contributes information for

TABLE 11.12
Salary Data for Example 11.7

YEARS OF EXPERIENCE	SALARY	YEARS OF EXPERIENCE	SALARY	YEARS OF EXPERIENCE	SALARY
x	y	x	y	x	y
7	$26,075	21	$43,628	28	$99,139
28	79,370	4	16,105	23	52,624
23	65,726	24	65,644	17	50,594
18	41,983	20	63,022	25	53,272
19	62,308	20	47,780	26	65,343
15	41,154	15	38,853	19	46,216
24	53,610	25	66,537	16	54,288
13	33,697	25	67,447	3	20,844
2	22,444	28	64,785	12	32,586
8	32,562	26	61,581	23	71,235
20	43,076	27	70,678	20	36,530
21	56,000	20	51,301	19	52,745
18	58,667	18	39,346	27	67,282
7	22,210	1	24,833	25	80,931
2	20,521	26	65,929	12	32,303
18	49,727	20	41,721	11	38,371
11	33,233	26	82,641		

FIGURE 11.15
MINITAB Analysis for Example 11.7

```
The regression equation is
Y = 11369 + 2141 X

Predictor        Coef       Stdev     t-ratio        p
Constant        11369        3160        3.60    0.001
X              2141.3       160.8       13.31    0.000

s = 8642       R-sq = 78.7%      R-sq(adj) = 78.2%

Analysis of Variance

SOURCE       DF           SS           MS         F        p
Regression    1  13238774784  13238774784   177.25    0.000
Error        48   3585073152     74689024
Total        49  16823847936

Unusual Observations
Obs.       X          Y      Fit Stdev.Fit   Residual   St.Resid
  31     1.0      24833    13511      3013      11322      1.40 X
  35    28.0      99139    71326      2005      27813      3.31R
  45    20.0      36530    54196      1259     -17666     -2.07R
R denotes an obs. with a large st. resid.
X denotes an obs. whose X value gives it large influence.
```

FIGURE 11.16
MINITAB Residual Plot for the Data of Example 11.7

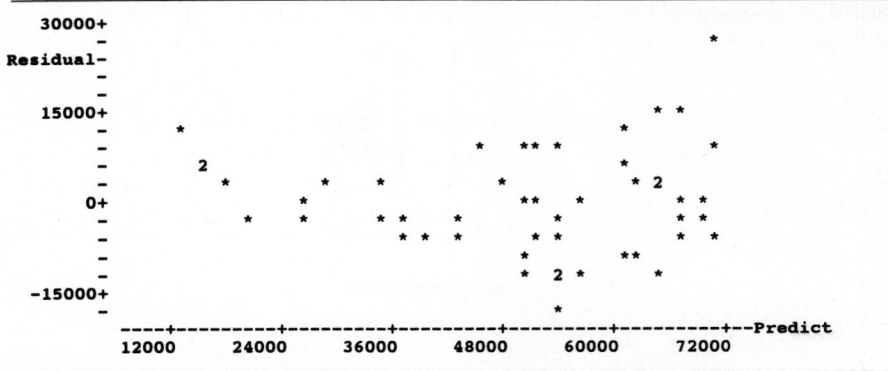

569

the prediction of y. However, an examination of the residuals plotted against $\hat{y}$ (Figure 11.16) reveals a potential problem. Note the cone shape of the residual variability; the size of the residuals increases as the estimated mean salary increases. This residual plot indicates the possibility of a multiplicative model and suggests we employ the variance-stabilizing transformation $y^* = \log y$.

DETECTING NONNORMALITY

Of the four standard regression assumptions about the random error ϵ, the assumption that ϵ is normally distributed is the least restrictive when we apply regression analysis in practice. That is, moderate departures from the assumption of normality have very little effect on the validity of the statistical tests, confidence intervals, and prediction intervals. In this case, we say that regression is **robust** with respect to nonnormality. However, great departures from normality cast doubt on any inferences derived from the regression analysis.

The simplest way to determine whether the data grossly violate the assumption of normality is to use one of the graphical checks for normality presented in Section 4.5, that is, a relative frequency histogram, a stem-and-leaf display, or a normal probability plot of the residuals.

TABLE 11.13

Residuals for Curvilinear Model Fit to $n = 20$ Data Points (from Section 11.5)

RESIDUALS			
−.011	.230	.144	−.153
−.196	.577	−.056	.090
.176	−.006	−.033	−.207
−.283	−.486	−.386	−.860
.133	.943	.162	.225

EXAMPLE 11.8 Refer to the curvilinear model for shipping cost (y) fit in Section 11.5. The residuals for the model (obtained by computer) are provided in Table 11.13. Construct a stem-and-leaf display for the residuals. Interpret the plot.

Solution   A computer-generated (MINITAB) stem-and-leaf display for the residuals is shown in Figure 11.17. Recall from Chapter 3 that if you turn the stem-and-leaf display on its side, it will look very much like a frequency histogram. You can see from Figure 11.17 that the distribution of the residuals is mound-shaped and reasonably symmetric about 0. Consequently, it is unlikely that the normality assumption would be violated using these data.

FIGURE 11.17

MINITAB Stem-and-Leaf Display of the Residuals Listed in Table 11.13

```
Stem-and-leaf of RESID      N  = 20
Leaf Unit = 0.10

      1     -0  8
      1     -0
      2     -0  4
      5     -0  322
    (6)     -0  110000
      9      0  01111
      4      0  22
      2      0  5
      1      0
      1      0  9
```

When nonnormality of the random error term is detected, it often can be rectified by applying one of the transformations listed in Table 11.11. For example, if the relative frequency distribution (or stem-and-leaf display) of the residuals is highly skewed to the right (as it usually is for Poisson data), the square root transformation on y will stabilize (approximately) the variance and, at the same time, will reduce skewness in the distribution of residuals. Nonnormality may also be due to outliers, which are discussed next.

DETECTING OUTLIERS

Residual plots also can be used to detect **outliers**, that is, values of y that appear to be in disagreement with the model. Since almost all values of y should lie within 3σ of $E(y)$, the mean value of y, we would expect most of them to lie within $3s$ of $\hat{y}$. If a residual is larger than $3s$ (in absolute value), we consider it an outlier and seek background information that might explain the reason for its large value. (Note that this definition is consistent with the definition of an outlier given in Section 3.9.)

> **DEFINITION 11.6**
>
> A regression residual that is larger than $3s$ (in absolute value) is considered to be an **outlier**.

To detect outliers we can construct horizontal lines located a distance of $3s$ above and below 0 on a residual plot (see Figure 11.18). Any residual falling outside the band formed by these lines would be considered an outlier. We would then try to find out why these observations depart from expected behavior.

FIGURE 11.18
$3s$ Lines Used to Locate Outliers

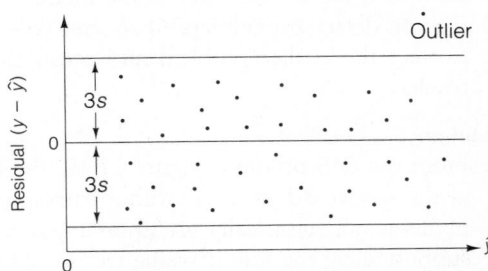

EXAMPLE 11.9 Table 11.14 lists the sales, y (in thousand dollars per week), for fast-food outlets in each of four cities. The objective is to model sales y as a function of traffic flow, adjusting for city-to-city variations that might be due to size or other

TABLE 11.14
Data for Fast-Food Sales, Example 11.9

CITY	TRAFFIC FLOW Thousand Cars	WEEKLY SALES y, Thousand Dollars	CITY	TRAFFIC FLOW Thousand Cars	WEEKLY SALES y, Thousand Dollars
1	59.3	6.3	3	75.8	8.2
1	60.3	6.6	3	48.3	5.0
1	82.1	7.6	3	41.4	3.9
1	32.3	3.0	3	52.5	5.4
1	98.0	9.5	3	41.0	4.1
1	54.1	5.9	3	29.6	3.1
1	54.4	6.1	3	49.5	5.4
1	51.3	5.0	4	73.1	8.4
1	36.7	3.6	4	81.3	9.5
2	23.6	2.8	4	72.4	8.7
2	57.6	6.7	4	88.4	10.6
2	44.6	5.2	4	23.2	3.3

market conditions. In theory, a linear relationship exists between mean sales, $E(y)$, and traffic flow. Also, although the level of mean sales will differ from city to city, the change in $E(y)$ per unit increase in traffic flow is expected to remain the same for all four cities. Consequently, the first-order, noninteraction model is proposed:

$$E(y) = \beta_0 + \beta_1 x_1 + \beta_2 x_2 + \beta_3 x_3 + \beta_4 x_4$$

where

$$x_1 = \begin{cases} 1 & \text{if city 1} \\ 0 & \text{if not} \end{cases} \qquad x_2 = \begin{cases} 1 & \text{if city 2} \\ 0 & \text{if not} \end{cases}$$

$$x_3 = \begin{cases} 1 & \text{if city 3} \\ 0 & \text{if not} \end{cases} \qquad x_4 = \text{Traffic flow}$$

The SAS printout of the regression results is shown in Figure 11.19.
a. Comment on the adequacy of the model.
b. Do you detect any outliers? If so, can you determine the cause?
c. Correct the outlier problem and rerun the regression analysis. Interpret the results.

Solution
a. From the SAS printout, Figure 11.19, the F-value for testing the global utility of the model is $F = 1.67$, with a corresponding p-value of .1996. Clearly, the model is not statistically useful (at any $\alpha \le .10$) for predicting sales, y. This is supported by the low R^2-value ($R^2 = .259$) and the large value of Root MSE ($s = 14.86$).
b. The residuals are listed in the bottom portion of the printout (Figure 11.19). By definition, an outlier is a residual that exceeds $3s = 3(14.86) = 44.58$ in absolute value. You can see that observation 13 (denoted y_{13}), with a residual of 56.46, is the only outlier. The cause of this outlier can be determined by comparing

FIGURE 11.19

SAS Regression Printout for Model of Fast-Food Sales, Example 11.9

Analysis of Variance

Source	DF	Sum of Squares	Mean Square	F Value	Prob>F
Model	4	1469.76287	367.44072	1.665	0.1996
Error	19	4194.22671	220.74877		
C Total	23	5663.98958			

Root MSE	14.85762	R-square	0.2595	
Dep Mean	9.07083	Adj R-sq	0.1036	
C.V.	163.79550			

Parameter Estimates

Variable	DF	Parameter Estimate	Standard Error	T for H0: Parameter=0	Prob > |T|
INTERCEP	1	-16.459248	13.16399794	-1.250	0.2264
X1	1	1.106092	8.42256884	0.131	0.8969
X2	1	6.142771	11.67996860	0.526	0.6050
X3	1	14.489623	9.28839086	1.560	0.1353
X4	1	0.362873	0.16790819	2.161	0.0437

Obs	CITY	X4	Dep Var Y	Predict Value	Residual
1	1	59.3	6.3000	6.1652	0.1348
2	1	60.3	6.6000	6.5281	0.0719
3	1	82.1	7.6000	14.4387	-6.8387
4	1	32.3	3.0000	-3.6324	6.6324
5	1	98	9.5000	20.2084	-10.7084
6	1	54.1	5.9000	4.2783	1.6217
7	1	54.4	6.1000	4.3871	1.7129
8	1	51.3	5.0000	3.2622	1.7378
9	1	36.7	3.6000	-2.0357	5.6357
10	2	23.6	2.8000	-1.7527	4.5527
11	2	57.6	6.7000	10.5850	-3.8850
12	2	44.6	5.2000	5.8677	-0.6677
13	3	75.8	82.0000	25.5362	56.4638
14	3	48.3	5.0000	15.5571	-10.5571
15	3	41.4	3.9000	13.0533	-9.1533
16	3	52.5	5.4000	17.0812	-11.6812
17	3	41	4.1000	12.9082	-8.8082
18	3	29.6	3.1000	8.7714	-5.6714
19	3	49.5	5.4000	15.9926	-10.5926
20	4	73.1	8.4000	10.0668	-1.6668
21	4	81.3	9.5000	13.0423	-3.5423
22	4	72.4	8.7000	9.8128	-1.1128
23	4	88.4	10.6000	15.6187	-5.0187
24	4	23.2	3.3000	-8.0406	11.3406

Sum of Residuals	1.261213E-13
Sum of Squared Residuals	4194.2267
Predicted Resid SS (Press)	7303.4839

the value of y_{13} shown in the SAS printout with the value listed in Table 11.14. You can see that the printout value, 82.0, does not agree with the value, 8.2, in the table. Evidently, the decimal point was inadvertently dropped when the data were entered into the computer.

c. If the correct y_{13}-value, 8.2, is substituted for 82.0, we obtain the regression printout shown in Figure 11.20. The corrected SAS printout indicates the dramatic effect that a single outlier can have on the regression analysis. The test for overall model utility has an F-value of 222.17 with a p-value of .0001, indicating that the model is adequate for predicting y. Also, R^2 has increased dramatically (from .259 to .979) and s has decreased dramatically (from 14.86 to .36).

Analysis of Variance

Source	DF	Sum of Squares	Mean Square	F Value	Prob>F
Model	4	116.65552	29.16388	222.173	0.0001
Error	19	2.49407	0.13127		
C Total	23	119.14958			

Root MSE	0.36231	R-square	0.9791
Dep Mean	5.99583	Adj R-sq	0.9747
C.V.	6.04265		

Parameter Estimates

Variable	DF	Parameter Estimate	Standard Error	T for H0: Parameter=0	Prob > |T|
INTERCEP	1	1.083388	0.32100795	3.375	0.0032
X1	1	-1.215762	0.20538681	-5.919	0.0001
X2	1	-0.530757	0.28481946	-1.863	0.0779
X3	1	-1.076525	0.22650014	-4.753	0.0001
X4	1	0.103673	0.00409449	25.320	0.0001

Obs	CITY	X4	Dep Var Y	Predict Value	Residual
1	1	59.3	6.3000	6.0155	0.2845
2	1	60.3	6.6000	6.1191	0.4809
3	1	82.1	7.6000	8.3792	-0.7792
4	1	32.3	3.0000	3.2163	-0.2163
5	1	98	9.5000	10.0276	-0.5276
6	1	54.1	5.9000	5.4764	0.4236
7	1	54.4	6.1000	5.5075	0.5925
8	1	51.3	5.0000	5.1861	-0.1861
9	1	36.7	3.6000	3.6724	-0.0724
10	2	23.6	2.8000	2.9993	-0.1993
11	2	57.6	6.7000	6.5242	0.1758
12	2	44.6	5.2000	5.1765	0.0235
13	3	75.8	8.2000	7.8653	0.3347
14	3	48.3	5.0000	5.0143	-0.0143
15	3	41.4	3.9000	4.2989	-0.3989
16	3	52.5	5.4000	5.4497	-0.0497
17	3	41	4.1000	4.2575	-0.1575
18	3	29.6	3.1000	3.0756	0.0244
19	3	49.5	5.4000	5.1387	0.2613
20	4	73.1	8.4000	8.6619	-0.2619
21	4	81.3	9.5000	9.5120	-0.0120
22	4	72.4	8.7000	8.5893	0.1107
23	4	88.4	10.6000	10.2481	0.3519
24	4	23.2	3.3000	3.4886	-0.1886

Sum of Residuals	1.332268E-14
Sum of Squared Residuals	2.4941
Predicted Resid SS (Press)	3.8772

Although some analysts advocate elimination of outliers, regardless of whether cause can be assigned, others encourage the correction of only those outliers that can be traced to specific causes. The best philosophy is probably a compromise between these extremes. For example, before deciding the fate of an outlier, you may want to determine how much influence it has on the regression analysis. When an accurate outlier (ie, an outlier that is not due to recording or measurement error) is found to have a dramatic effect on the regression analysis, it may be the model and not the outlier that is suspect. Omission of important independent variables or higher-order terms could be the reason why the model is not predicting well for the outlying observation. Several numerical techniques for identifying outlying influential observations are presented in Section 11.7.

DETECTING CORRELATED ERRORS

The assumption that the random errors are independent (uncorrelated) is most often violated when the data employed in a regression analysis are a **time series**. With time series data, the experimental units in the sample are time periods (eg, years, months, or days) in consecutive time order.

For most business and economic time series, there is a tendency for the regression residuals to have positive and negative runs over time. For example, consider fitting a straight-line regression model to yearly time series data. The model takes the form

$$E(y) = \beta_0 + \beta_1 t$$

where y is the value of the time series in year t. A sequence plot of the yearly residuals may appear as shown in Figure 11.21. Note that if the residual for year t is positive (or negative), there is a tendency for the residual for year $(t + 1)$ to be positive (or negative). That is, neighboring residuals tend to have the same sign and appear to be correlated. Thus, the assumption of independent errors is likely to be violated, and any inferences derived from the model are suspect.*

Remedial measures for this problem involve proposing complex time series models that include a model for both the deterministic and random error components. Time series models are the subject of Chapter 12.

FIGURE 11.21

Residual Plot for Yearly Time Series Model

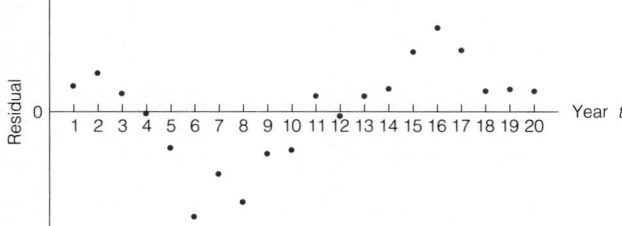

A SUMMARY OF STEPS TO FOLLOW IN A RESIDUAL ANALYSIS

STEP 1   Check for a **misspecified model** by plotting the residuals $(y - \hat{y})$ against each independent variable in the model. A curvilinear trend detected in a plot implies that a quadratic term for that particular x variable will probably improve model adequacy.

STEP 2   Check for **unequal variances** by plotting the residuals against the predicted values ($\hat{y}$). If you detect a pattern similar to one of those shown in Figure 11.14, refit the model using the appropriate variance-stabilizing transformation on y (see Table 11.11).

STEP 3   Check for **nonnormal errors** by constructing a stem-and-leaf display (or histogram) for the residuals. If you detect extreme skewness in the data, then either apply one of the transformations listed in Table 11.11 or look for one or more outliers (see step 4).

(continued)

---

* A test for residual correlation is presented in Chapter 12.

STEP 4   Check for **outliers** by locating residuals that lie a distance of 3s or more above or below 0 on a residual plot versus $\hat{y}$. Before eliminating an outlier from the analysis, you should conduct an investigation to determine its cause. If the outlier is found to be the result of a coding or recording error, fix it or remove it. Otherwise, you may want to determine how influential the outlier is before deciding its fate. (See Section 11.7.)

STEP 5   Check for **correlated errors** by plotting the residuals in time order. If you detect runs of positive and negative residuals, propose a time series model to account for the residual correlation (see Chapter 12).

PROBLEMS

11.17   Identify the problem(s) in each of the following residual plots:

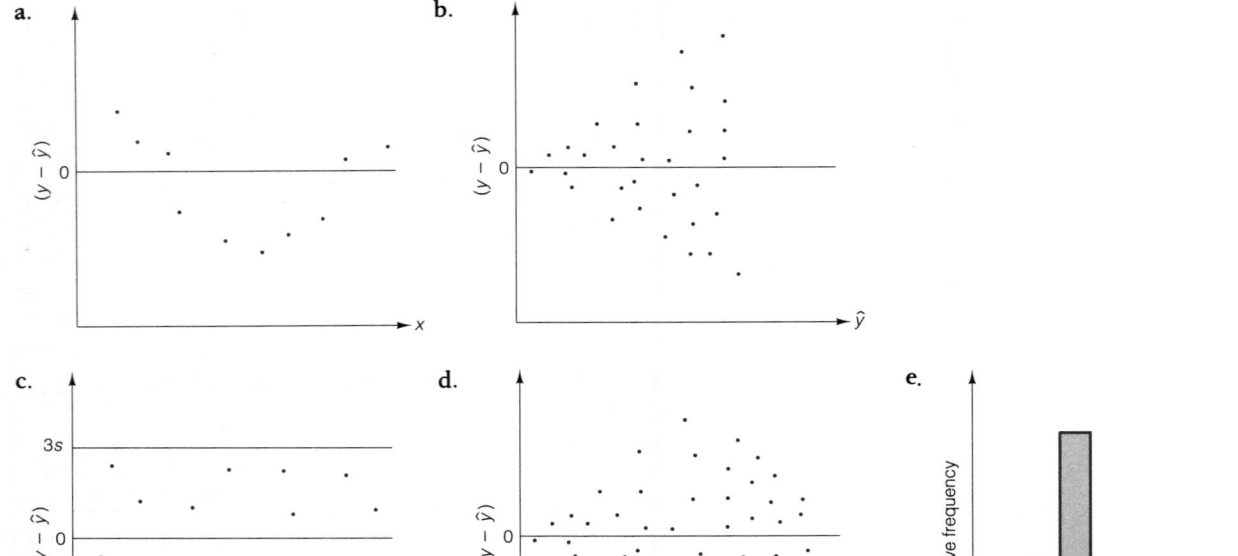

11.18   The data in the table, extracted from *The Real Estate Appraiser and Analyst*, were collected from $n = 10$ home sales. Property appraisers used the data to fit the model $E(y) = \beta_0 + \beta_1 x_1 + \beta_2 x_2$, where

$$y = \text{Sale price (thousand dollars)}$$
$$x_1 = \text{Home size (hundred square feet)}$$
$$x_2 = \text{Condition rating (1–10)}$$

The resulting least squares prediction equation is

$$\hat{y} = 9.782 + 1.871x_1 + 1.278x_2$$

SALE PRICE	HOME SIZE	CONDITION RATING	SALE PRICE	HOME SIZE	CONDITION RATING
y	x_1	x_2	y	x_1	x_2
60.0	23	5	55.3	21	4
32.7	11	2	64.5	24	7
57.7	20	9	42.6	13	6
45.5	17	3	54.5	19	7
47.0	15	8	57.5	25	2

Source: Andrews, R. L., and Ferguson, J. T. "Integrating Judgment with a Regression Appraisal." *The Real Estate Appraiser and Analyst,* Vol. 52, No. 2, Spring 1986, Table 1.

a. Calculate the residuals for the model.
b. Plot the residuals versus x_1. Do you detect any trends? If so, what does the pattern suggest about the model?
c. Plot the residuals versus x_2. Do you detect any trends? If so, what does the pattern suggest about the model?

11.19 Breakdowns of machines that produce steel cans are very costly. The more breakdowns, the fewer cans produced, and the smaller the company's profits. To help anticipate profit loss, the owners of a can company would like to find a model that will predict the number of breakdowns on the assembly line. The model proposed by the company's statistician is the following:

$$y = \beta_0 + \beta_1 x_1 + \beta_2 x_2 + \beta_3 x_3 + \beta_4 x_4 + \epsilon$$

where

$y =$ Number of breakdowns per 8 hour shift

$$x_1 = \begin{cases} 1 & \text{if afternoon shift} \\ 0 & \text{otherwise} \end{cases}$$

$$x_2 = \begin{cases} 1 & \text{if midnight shift} \\ 0 & \text{otherwise} \end{cases}$$

$x_3 =$ Temperature of the plant (°F)

$x_4 =$ Number of inexperienced personnel working on the assembly line

After the model is fit using the least squares procedure, the residuals are plotted against $\hat{y}$, as shown in the figure:

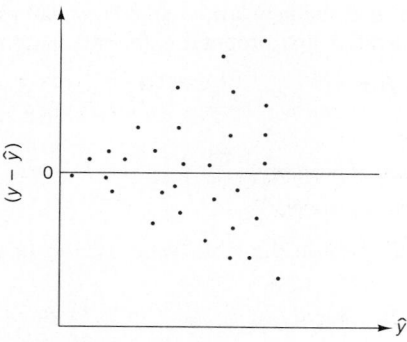

a. Do you detect a pattern in the residual plot? What does this suggest about the least squares assumptions?

b. Given the nature of the response variable y and the pattern detected in part **a**, what model adjustments would you recommend?

11.20 A certain type of rare gem serves as a status symbol for many of its owners. In theory, as the price of the gem varies, the demand will decrease at low prices, level off at moderate prices, and increase at high prices due to the status the owners believe they gain by obtaining the gem. Although a quadratic model would seem to match the theory, the model proposed to explain the demand for the gem in relation to its price is the first-order model

$$y = \beta_0 + \beta_1 x + \epsilon$$

where y is the demand (in thousands) and x is the retail price per carat (in dollars). This model was fit to the 12 data points given in the table. The SPSS printout of the analysis is shown below.

x	100	700	450	150	500	800	70	50	300	350	750	700
y	130	150	60	120	50	200	150	160	50	40	180	130

SPSS Printout for Straight-Line Model

```
Multiple R              .23064
R Square                .05319
Adjusted R Square      -.04149
Standard Error        56.20658

Analysis of Variance
                       DF      Sum of Squares      Mean Square
Regression              1         1774.86785       1774.86785
Residual               10        31591.79882       3159.17988

F =         .56181        Signif F =   .4708

------------------ Variables in the Equation ------------------

Variable             B          SE B        Beta        T     Sig T

X                 .04516       .06025      .23064      .750   .4708
(Constant)      99.81690     29.55565                 3.377   .0070
```

a. Use the least squares prediction equation to calculate the regression residuals.

b. Plot the residuals against retail price per carat, x.

c. Can you detect any trends in the residual plot? What does this imply?

11.21 Condemnation proceedings are underway in Hawaii to enable private citizens to own the property their homes are built on. Prior to 1980, only estates were permitted to own land, and homeowners leased the land from the estate (a law that dates back to the feudal period in Hawaii). To comply with the new law, a large Hawaiian estate wants to use regression analysis to estimate the fair market value of its land. A first proposal is the quadratic model

$$E(y) = \beta_0 + \beta_1 x + \beta_2 x^2$$

where

$$y = \text{Leased fee value (ie, sale price of property)}$$
$$x = \text{Size of property (in thousand square feet)}$$

Data collected for 20 property sales in a particular neighborhood, given in the table, were used to fit the model. The least squares prediction equation is

$$\hat{y} = -44.0947 + 11.5339x - .06378x^2$$

PROPERTY	LEASED FEE VALUE y, Thousand Dollars	SIZE x	PROPERTY	LEASED FEE VALUE y, Thousand Dollars	SIZE x
1	70.7	13.5	11	148.0	14.5
2	52.7	9.6	12	85.0	10.2
3	87.6	17.6	13	171.2	18.7
4	43.2	7.9	14	97.5	13.2
5	103.8	11.5	15	158.1	16.3
6	45.1	8.2	16	74.2	12.3
7	86.8	15.2	17	47.0	7.7
8	73.3	12.0	18	54.7	9.9
9	144.3	13.8	19	68.0	11.2
10	61.3	10.0	20	75.2	12.4

a. Calculate the predicted values and corresponding residuals for the model.

b. Plot the residuals versus $\hat{y}$. Do you detect any trends? If so, what does the pattern suggest about the model?

c. Based on your results, how should the estate proceed?

11.22 A study* investigated the geopolitical and socioeconomic processes that shape the urban size distributions of the world's nations. One of the goals of the study was to determine the factors that influence population size in each nation's largest city. Based on data collected for a sample of 126 countries, the following model was fit:

$$E(y) = \beta_0 + \beta_1 x_1 + \beta_2 x_2 + \beta_3 x_3 + \beta_4 x_4 + \beta_5 x_5 + \beta_6 x_6 + \beta_7 x_7 + \beta_8 x_8 + \beta_9 x_9 + \beta_{10} x_{10}$$

where

y = Logarithm of population (in thousands) of largest city in country

x_1 = Logarithm of area (in thousand square kilometers) of country

x_2 = Logarithm of radius (in hundred kilometers) of city limits

x_3 = Logarithm of national population (in thousands)

x_4 = Percentage annual change in national population (1960–1970)

x_5 = Logarithm of energy consumption per capita (in kilograms of coal equivalent)

x_6 = Percentage of nation's population in urban areas

x_7 = Logarithm of population (in thousands) of second largest city in country

$x_8 = \begin{cases} 1 & \text{if seaport city} \\ 0 & \text{if not} \end{cases}$

$x_9 = \begin{cases} 1 & \text{if capital city} \\ 0 & \text{if not} \end{cases}$

$x_{10} = \begin{cases} 1 & \text{if city data are for metropolitan area} \\ 0 & \text{if not} \end{cases}$

[*Note:* All logarithms are log to the base 10.] The regression resulted in $R^2 = .879$ and MSE $= .036$.

a. Conduct a test for model adequacy. (Use $\alpha = .05$.)

b. A computer-generated (SAS) stem-and-leaf plot of all the residuals is shown on p. 580. Does it appear that the assumption of normal errors is satisfied?

c. A computer-generated (SAS) plot of the regression residuals versus $\hat{y}$ is shown on p. 580. Identify any outliers on the plot.

---

* Source: DeCola, L. "Statistical Determinants of the Population of a Nation's Largest City." *Economic Development and Cultural Change*, Vol. 33, No. 1, Oct. 1984, pp. 71–98.

SAS Stem-and-Leaf Plot of Residuals
for Problem 11.22

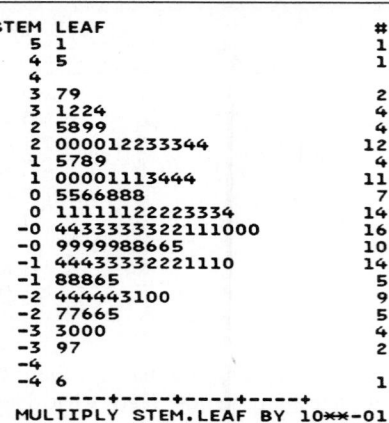

```
STEM  LEAF                                    #
   5  1                                        1
   4  5                                        1
   4
   3  79                                       2
   3  1224                                     4
   2  5899                                     4
   2  000012233344                            12
   1  5789                                     4
   1  00001113444                             11
   0  5566888                                  7
   0  11111122223334                          14
  -0  4433333322111000                        16
  -0  9999988665                              10
  -1  44433332221110                          14
  -1  88865                                    5
  -2  444443100                                9
  -2  77665                                    5
  -3  3000                                     4
  -3  97                                       2
  -4
  -4  6                                        1
      ----+----+----+----+
MULTIPLY STEM.LEAF BY 10**-01
```

SAS Residual Plot for Problem 11.22

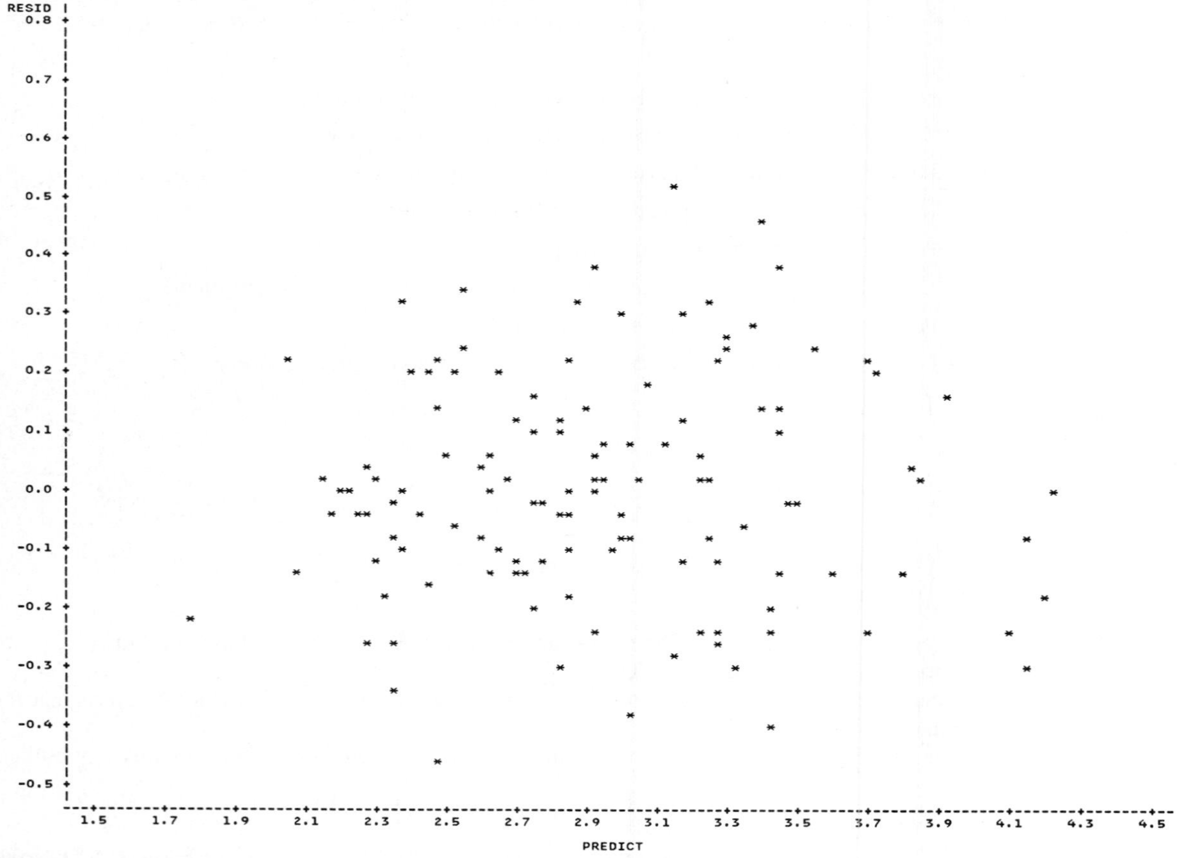

RESID scatter plot with vertical axis labeled RESID from -0.5 to 0.8 and horizontal axis labeled PREDICT from 1.5 to 4.5.

NOTE: 2 OBS HIDDEN

11.23 A large manufacturing firm wants to determine whether a relationship exists between the number of work-hours an employee misses per year, y, and the employee's annual wages, x (in thousand dollars). A sample of 15 employees produced the data in the table. A first-order model was fit to the data with the following results:

$$\hat{y} = 222.64 - 9.60x \qquad R^2 = .073$$

EMPLOYEE	y	x	EMPLOYEE	y	x
1	49	12.8	9	191	7.8
2	36	14.5	10	6	15.8
3	127	8.3	11	63	10.8
4	91	10.2	12	79	9.7
5	72	10.0	13	543	12.1
6	34	11.5	14	57	21.2
7	155	8.8	15	82	10.9
8	11	17.2			

a. Interpret the value of R^2.

b. Calculate and plot the regression residuals. What do you notice?

c. After searching through its employees' files, the firm has found that employee 13 had been fired but that his name had not been removed from the active employee payroll. This explains the large accumulation of work-hours missed (543) by that employee. In view of this fact, what is your recommendation concerning this outlier?

d. Refit the model to the data, excluding the outlier, and find the least squares line. Calculate R^2 and comment on model adequacy.

INFLUENTIAL OBSERVATIONS

11.7

In Section 11.6 we discussed the importance of identifying outliers in regression. Once an outlier is detected, it is wise to measure its influence on the regression results. If the outlier has a dramatic effect on the regression analysis, it is labeled an **influential observation**. In this section, we briefly discuss several sophisticated numerical methods for identifying influential observations.

> **DEFINITION 11.7**
>
> An outlier that has a dramatic effect on the regression results is called an **influential observation**.

LEVERAGE

This procedure is based on a result (proof omitted) in regression analysis that states that the predicted value for the ith observation, $\hat{y}_i$, can be written as a linear combination of the n observed values, $y_1, y_2, ..., y_n$:

$$\hat{y}_i = h_1 y_1 + h_2 y_2 + \cdots + h_i y_i + \cdots + h_n y_n \qquad i = 1, 2, ..., n$$

where the weights $h_1, h_2, ..., h_n$ of the observed values are functions of the independent variables. In particular, the coefficient h_i measures the influence of the observed value y_i on its own predicted value $\hat{y}_i$. This value, h_i, is called the **leverage** of the ith observation (with respect to the values of the independent variables). Thus, leverage values can be used to identify influential observations—the larger the leverage value, the more influence the observed y value has on its predicted value.

Leverage values are extremely difficult to calculate without the aid of a computer. Fortunately, most of the statistical software packages discussed in this text have options that give the leverage associated with each observation. The leverage value for an observation is usually compared with the average leverage value of all n observations, $\overline{h}$, where*

$$\overline{h} = \frac{k+1}{n} = \frac{\text{Number of } \beta \text{ parameters in the model, including } \beta_0}{n}$$

A good rule of thumb identifies an observation y_i as influential if its leverage value h_i is more than twice as large as $\overline{h}$, that is, if

$$h_i > \frac{2(k+1)}{n}$$

DEFINITION 11.8

The **leverage** of the ith observation, denoted h_i, measures the influence of the x-values on the predicted value $\hat{y}_i$. The observation is considered influential (with respect to the independent variables) if

$$h_i > \frac{2(k+1)}{n}$$

where k is the number of x variables in the model.

THE JACKKNIFE   Another technique for identifying influential observations requires that you delete the observations one at a time, each time refitting the regression model based on only the remaining $n - 1$ observations. This method is based on a statistical procedure, called the **jackknife**,† which is gaining increasing acceptance among practitioners. The basic principle of the jackknife when applied to regression is to compare the regression results using all n observations to the results with the ith observation deleted to ascertain how much influence a particular observation has on the analysis. Using the jackknife, several alternative influence measures can be calculated.

The **deleted residual,** $d_i = y_i - \hat{y}_{(i)}$, measures the difference between the observed value y_i and the predicted value $\hat{y}_{(i)}$ based on the model with the ith observation deleted. [The notation (i) is generally used to indicate that the observed value y_i

---

* The proof of this result is beyond the scope of this text. Consult the references given at the end of this chapter. See Neter, Wasserman, and Kutner (1989).

† The procedure derives its name from the Boy Scout jackknife, which serves as a handy tool in a variety of situations when specialized techniques may not be applicable. See Belsley, Kuh, and Welsch (1980).

was deleted from the regression analysis.] An observation with a deleted residual that is unusually large (in absolute value) is considered to have large influence on the fitted model.

DEFINITION 11.9

A **deleted residual**, denoted d_i, for the ith observation is

$$d_i = y_i - \hat{y}_{(i)}$$

where y_i is the observed y-value and $\hat{y}_{(i)}$ is the predicted value based on the model with the ith observation deleted.

A measure closely related to the deleted residual is the difference between the predicted value based on the model fit to all n observations and the predicted value obtained when y_i is deleted. If $\hat{y}_i - \hat{y}_{(i)}$ is large relative to the predicted value $\hat{y}_i$, the observation y_i is said to influence the regression fit.

A third way to identify an influential observation using the jackknife is to calculate, for each β parameter in the model, the difference between the parameter estimate based on all n observations and the estimate based on only $n - 1$ observations (with the observation in question deleted). Consider, for example, the straight-line model $E(y) = \beta_0 + \beta_1 x$. The differences $\hat{\beta}_0 - \hat{\beta}_0^{(i)}$ and $\hat{\beta}_1 - \hat{\beta}_1^{(i)}$ measure how influential the ith observation y_i is on the parameter estimates. [Using the (i) notation defined earlier, $\hat{\beta}^{(i)}$ represents the estimate of the β coefficient when the ith observation is omitted from the analysis.] If the parameter estimates change drastically, that is, if the absolute differences are large, y_i is deemed an influential observation.

Each of the statistical software packages discussed in this text has a jackknife routine that produces one or more of the measures described above.

COOK'S DISTANCE   A measure of the overall influence an outlying observation has on the estimated β coefficients was proposed by Cook (1979). **Cook's distance, D_i,** is calculated for the ith observation as follows:

$$D_i = \frac{(y_i - \hat{y}_i)^2}{(k+1)\text{MSE}} \left[\frac{h_i}{(1 - h_i)^2} \right]$$

Note that D_i depends on both the residual $(y_i - \hat{y}_i)$ and the leverage h_i for the ith observation. A large value of D_i indicates that the observed y_i-value has strong influence on the estimated β coefficients (since the residual, the leverage, or both will be large). Values of D_i can be compared to the values of the F distribution with $\nu_1 = k + 1$ and $\nu_2 = n - (k + 1)$ degrees of freedom. Usually, an observation with a value of D_i that falls at or above the 50th percentile of the F distribution is considered to be an influential observation. Like the other numerical measures of influence, options for calculating Cook's distance are available in most statistical software packages.

EXAMPLE 11.10 Refer to the fast-food sales model discussed in Example 11.9. Recall that the outlier was due to an error in coding the weekly sales value for observation 13 (denoted y_{13}). The SAS regression analysis is rerun using the original (miscoded) data with options for producing influence diagnostics. (An **influence diagnostic** is a number that measures how much influence an observation has on the regression analysis.) The resulting SAS printout is shown in Figure 11.22. Locate and interpret the measures of influence of y_{13} in the printout.

Solution The influence diagnostics are shown in the last portion of the SAS printout in Figure 11.22. Leverage values for each observation are given under the column heading Hat Diag H. The leverage value for y_{13} (shaded in the printout) is $h_{13} = .2394$, whereas the average leverage for all $n = 24$ observations is

$$\bar{h} = \frac{k+1}{n} = \frac{5}{24} = .2083$$

Since the leverage value .2394 does not exceed $2\bar{h} = .4166$, we would not identify y_{13} as an influential observation. At first, this result may seem confusing since we already know the dramatic effect the incorrectly coded value of y_{13} had on the regression analysis. Remember, however, that the leverage values, $h_1, h_2, ..., h_{24}$, are functions of the independent variables only. Since we know that the values of x_1, x_2, x_3, and x_4 were coded correctly, the relatively small leverage value of .2394 simply indicates that observation 13 is not an outlier with respect to the values of the independent variables.

A better overall measure of the influence of y_{13} on the fitted regression model is Cook's distance, D_{13}. Recall that Cook's distance is a function of both leverage and the magnitude of the residual. This value, $D_{13} = 1.189$ (shaded in the printout) is given in the column labeled Cook's D located on the right side of the printout. You can see that the value is extremely large relative to the other values of D_i in the printout. [In fact, $D_{13} = 1.189$ falls in the 65th percentile of the F distribution with $\nu_1 = k + 1 = 5$ and $\nu_2 = n - (k + 1) = 24 - 5 = 19$ degrees of freedom.] This implies that the observed value y_{13} has substantial influence on the estimates of the model parameters.

A statistic related to the deleted residual of the jackknife procedure is the **Studentized deleted residual** given under the column heading Rstudent. The Studentized deleted residual, denoted d_i^*, is calculated by dividing the deleted residual d_i by its standard error s_{d_i}:

$$d_i^* = \frac{d_i}{s_{d_i}}$$

The Studentized deleted residual for y_{13} (shaded in the printout) is $d_{13}^* = 53.8929$. This extremely large value* is another indication that y_{13} is an influential observation.

---

* Under the assumptions of Section 10.4, the Studentized deleted residual d_i^* has a sampling distribution that is approximated by a Student's t distribution with $(n - 1) - (k + 1)$ df.

Analysis of Variance

Source	DF	Sum of Squares	Mean Square	F Value	Prob>F
Model	4	1423.32470	355.83118	1.582	0.2199
Error	19	4274.47488	224.97236		
C Total	23	5697.79958			

Root MSE	14.99908	R-square	0.2498	
Dep Mean	8.87917	Adj R-sq	0.0919	
C.V.	168.92440			

Parameter Estimates

Variable	DF	Parameter Estimate	Standard Error	T for H0: Parameter=0	Prob > |T|
INTERCEP	1	-15.529711	13.28933470	-1.169	0.2570
X1	1	0.471952	8.50276160	0.056	0.9563
X2	1	5.789159	11.79117565	0.491	0.6291
X3	1	14.223452	9.37682727	1.517	0.1458
X4	1	0.349139	0.16950687	2.060	0.0534

Obs	Dep Var Y	Predict Value	Std Err Predict	Residual	Std Err Residual	Student Residual	-2-1-0 1 2	Cook's D
1	6.3000	5.6462	5.001	0.6538	14.141	0.046		0.000
2	6.6000	5.9953	5.007	0.6047	14.139	0.043		0.000
3	3.0000	13.6065	6.380	-10.6065	13.575	-0.781	* |	0.027
4	3.0000	-3.7806	6.712	6.7806	13.413	0.506	| *	0.013
5	9.5000	19.1578	8.326	-9.6578	12.476	-0.774	* |	0.053
6	5.9000	3.8306	5.061	2.0694	14.120	0.147		0.001
7	6.1000	3.9354	5.053	2.1646	14.122	0.153		0.001
8	5.0000	2.8531	5.156	2.1469	14.085	0.152		0.001
9	3.6000	-2.2444	6.240	5.8444	13.640	0.428		0.008
10	2.8000	-1.5009	9.200	4.3009	11.846	0.363		0.016
11	6.7000	10.3698	9.058	-3.6698	11.955	-0.307		0.011
12	5.2000	5.8310	8.672	-0.6310	12.238	-0.052		0.000
13	82.0000	25.1585	7.339	56.8415	13.081	4.345	|******	1.189
14	5.0000	15.5571	5.669	-10.5571	13.886	-0.760	* |	0.019
15	3.9000	13.1481	5.789	-9.2481	13.837	-0.668	* |	0.016
16	5.4000	17.0235	5.714	-11.6235	13.868	-0.838	* |	0.024
17	4.1000	13.0084	5.803	-8.9084	13.831	-0.644	* |	0.015
18	3.1000	9.0282	6.495	-5.9282	13.520	-0.438		0.009
19	5.4000	15.9761	5.673	-10.5761	13.885	-0.762	* |	0.019
20	8.4000	9.9923	6.770	-1.5923	13.384	-0.119		0.001
21	9.5000	12.8553	7.094	-3.3553	13.215	-0.254		0.004
22	8.7000	9.7479	6.755	-1.0479	13.392	-0.078		0.000
23	10.6000	15.3342	7.572	-4.7342	12.948	-0.366		0.009
24	3.3000	-7.4297	10.092	10.7297	11.096	0.967	| *	0.155

Obs	Rstudent	Hat Diag H	Cov Ratio	Dffits	INTERCEP Dfbetas	X1 Dfbetas	X2 Dfbetas	X3 Dfbetas	X4 Dfbetas
1	0.0450	0.1112	1.4734	0.0159	-0.0003	0.0094	0.0001	0.0001	0.0003
2	0.0416	0.1114	1.4740	0.0147	-0.0007	0.0088	0.0003	0.0003	0.0008
3	-0.7730	0.1809	1.3588	-0.3633	0.1948	-0.2077	-0.0835	-0.0791	-0.2257
4	0.4954	0.2003	1.5313	0.2479	0.1428	0.0790	-0.0612	-0.0579	-0.1654
5	-0.7656	0.3081	1.6136	-0.5110	0.3527	-0.2534	-0.1512	-0.1431	-0.4086
6	0.1427	0.1138	1.4704	0.0512	0.0068	0.0283	-0.0029	-0.0028	-0.0079
7	0.1493	0.1135	1.4691	0.0534	0.0067	0.0297	-0.0029	-0.0027	-0.0077
8	0.1485	0.1181	1.4769	0.0543	0.0114	0.0286	-0.0049	-0.0046	-0.0133
9	0.4191	0.1731	1.5095	0.1917	0.0990	0.0698	-0.0425	-0.0402	-0.1147
10	0.3546	0.3763	2.0290	0.2754	0.0803	-0.0166	0.1560	-0.0326	-0.0930
11	-0.2995	0.3647	2.0120	-0.2269	0.0574	-0.0119	-0.1840	-0.0233	-0.0665
12	-0.0502	0.3342	1.9669	-0.0356	0.0016	-0.0003	-0.0268	-0.0006	-0.0019
13	53.8929	0.2394	0.0000	30.2389	-16.5793	3.4296	7.1084	20.8497	19.2053
14	-0.7515	0.1429	1.3100	-0.3068	-0.0000	0.0000	0.0000	-0.1855	0.0000
15	-0.6583	0.1489	1.3670	-0.2754	-0.0480	0.0099	0.0206	-0.1436	0.0556
16	-0.8313	0.1451	1.2697	-0.3425	0.0368	-0.0076	-0.0158	-0.2204	-0.0427
17	-0.6339	0.1497	1.3800	-0.2659	-0.0490	0.0101	0.0210	-0.1372	0.0567
18	-0.4290	0.1875	1.5329	-0.2061	-0.0868	0.0180	0.0372	-0.0735	0.1006
19	-0.7530	0.1430	1.3095	-0.3076	0.0095	-0.0020	-0.0041	-0.1897	-0.0110
20	-0.1158	0.2038	1.6396	-0.0586	-0.0224	0.0444	0.0301	0.0387	-0.0080
21	-0.2475	0.2237	1.6596	-0.1329	-0.0261	0.0914	0.0555	0.0747	-0.0432
22	-0.0762	0.2028	1.6412	-0.0384	-0.0153	0.0293	0.0200	0.0257	-0.0046
23	-0.3571	0.2548	1.6975	-0.2089	-0.0098	0.1287	0.0694	0.0984	-0.0969
24	0.9652	0.4527	1.8603	0.8778	0.8607	-0.5774	-0.5747	-0.6471	-0.6558

FIGURE 11.22

SAS Regression Analysis with Influence Diagnostics

The Dffits column gives the difference between the predicted value when all 24 observations are used and when the ith observation is deleted. The difference, $\hat{y}_i - \hat{y}_{(i)}$, is divided by its standard error so that the differences can be compared more easily. For observation 13, this scaled difference (shaded in the printout) is $\hat{y}_{13} - \hat{y}_{(13)} = 30.2389$, an extremely large value relative to the other differences in predicted values. Similarly, the changes in the parameter estimates when observation 13 is deleted are given in the Dfbetas columns immediately to the right of Dffits in the printout. (Each difference is also divided by the appropriate standard error.) The large magnitude of these differences provides further evidence that y_{13} is very influential on the regression analysis.

PROBLEMS

11.24 PCBs make up a family of hazardous chemicals that are often dumped (illegally) by industrial plants into the surrounding streams, rivers, or bays. The table reports the 1984 and 1985 concentrations of PCBs (measured in parts per billion) in water samples collected from 37 U.S. bays and estuaries. An official from the Environmental Protection Agency (EPA) wants to model the 1985 PCB concentration (y) of a bay as a function of the 1984 PCB concentration (x). Consider the first-order model $E(y) = \beta_0 + \beta_1 x$. The SAS printout of the analysis, with residuals, is shown on the next page.

BAY	STATE	PCB CONCENTRATION 1984	PCB CONCENTRATION 1985	BAY	STATE	PCB CONCENTRATION 1984	PCB CONCENTRATION 1985
Casco Bay	ME	95.28	77.55	Mississippi River Delta	LA	34	30.14
Merrimack River	MA	52.97	29.23	Barataria Bay	LA	0	0
Salem Harbor	MA	533.58	403.1	San Antonio Bay	TX	0	0
Boston Harbor	MA	17,104.86	736	Corpus Christi Bay	TX	0	0
Buzzards Bay	MA	308.46	192.15	San Diego Harbor	CA	422.1	531.67
Narragansett Bay	RI	159.96	220.6	San Diego Bay	CA	6.74	9.3
East Long Island Sound	NY	10	8.62	Dana Point	CA	7.06	5.74
West Long Island Sound	NY	234.43	174.31	Seal Beach	CA	46.71	46.47
Raritan Bay	NJ	443.89	529.28	San Pedro Canyon	CA	159.56	176.9
Delaware Bay	DE	2.5	130.67	Santa Monica Bay	CA	14	13.69
Lower Chesapeake Bay	VA	51	39.74	Bodega Bay	CA	4.18	4.89
Pamlico Sound	NC	0	0	Coos Bay	OR	3.19	6.6
Charleston Harbor	SC	9.1	8.43	Columbia River Mouth	OR	8.77	6.73
Sapelo Sound	GA	0	0	Nisqually Beach	WA	4.23	4.28
St. Johns River	FL	140	120.04	Commencement Bay	WA	20.6	20.5
Tampa Bay	FL	0	0	Elliott Bay	WA	329.97	414.5
Apalachicola Bay	FL	12	11.93	Lutak Inlet	AK	5.5	5.8
Mobile Bay	AL	0	0	Nahku Bay	AK	6.6	5.08
Round Island	MS	0	0				

Source: Environmental Quality, 1987–1988.

Printout for Problem 11.24

Analysis of Variance

Source	DF	Sum of Squares	Mean Square	F Value	Prob>F
Model	1	462349.85512	462349.85512	21.772	0.0001
Error	35	743254.18292	21235.83380		
C Total	36	1205604.0380			

Root MSE	145.72520	R-square	0.3835	
Dep Mean	107.13351	Adj R-sq	0.3659	
C.V.	136.02205			

Parameter Estimates

Variable	DF	Parameter Estimate	Standard Error	T for H0: Parameter=0	Prob > |T|
INTERCEP	1	85.013798	24.42159452	3.481	0.0014
PCB84	1	0.040454	0.00866978	4.666	0.0001

Obs	BAY	PCB84	Dep Var PCB85	Predict Value	Residual
1	Casco	95.28	77.5500	88.8682	-11.3182
2	Merrmack	52.97	29.2300	87.1566	-57.9266
3	Salem	533.58	403.1	106.6	296.5
4	Boston	17104.86	736.0	777.0	-40.9695
5	Buzzards	308.46	192.2	97.5	94.7
6	Narragan	159.96	220.6	91.4848	129.1
7	ELongIsl	10	8.6200	85.4183	-76.7983
8	WLongIsl	234.43	174.3	94.5	79.8126
9	Raritan	443.89	529.3	103.0	426.3
10	Delaware	2.5	130.7	85.1149	45.5551
11	LChesapk	51	39.7400	87.0769	-47.3369
12	Pamilico	0	0	85.0138	-85.0138
13	Charlest	9.1	8.4300	85.3819	-76.9519
14	Sapelo	0	0	85.0138	-85.0138
15	StJohns	140	120.0	90.6773	29.3627
16	Tampa	0	0	85.0138	-85.0138
17	Apalach	12	11.9300	85.4992	-73.5692
18	Mobile	0	0	85.0138	-85.0138
19	RoundIsl	0	0	85.0138	-85.0138
20	MissRiv	34	30.1400	86.3892	-56.2492
21	Baratara	0	0	85.0138	-85.0138
22	SanAnton	0	0	85.0138	-85.0138
23	CorpusCh	0	0	85.0138	-85.0138
24	SDiegoHa	422.1	531.7	102.1	429.6
25	SDiegoBa	6.74	9.3000	85.2865	-75.9865
26	DanaPt	7.06	5.7400	85.2994	-79.5594
27	SealBch	46.71	46.4700	86.9034	-40.4334
28	SanPedro	159.56	176.9	91.4686	85.4314
29	SantaMon	14	13.6900	85.5802	-71.8902
30	Bodega	4.18	4.8900	85.1829	-80.2929
31	Coos	3.19	6.6000	85.1428	-78.5428
32	Columbia	8.77	6.7300	85.3686	-78.6386
33	Nisquall	4.23	4.2800	85.1849	-80.9049
34	Commence	20.6	20.5000	85.8471	-65.3471
35	Elliot	329.97	414.5	98.4	316.1
36	Lutak	5.5	5.8000	85.2363	-79.4363
37	Nahku	6.6	5.0800	85.2808	-80.2008

a. Is the model adequate for predicting y? Explain.
b. Construct a residual plot for the data. Do you detect any outliers? If so, identify them.
c. Refer to part b. Although the residual for Boston Harbor is not, by definition, an outlier, the EPA believes that it has strong influence on the regression due to its large y-value. Remove the observation for Boston Harbor from the data and refit the model. Has model adequacy improved?

d. An alternative approach is to use the log transformations $y^* = $ natural $\log(y + 1)$ and $x^* = $ natural $\log(x + 1)$, and fit the model $E(y^*) = \beta_0 + \beta_1 x^*$. The SAS printout for this model follows. Conduct a test for model adequacy and perform a residual analysis. Interpret the results. In particular, comment on the residual value for Boston Harbor.

Printout for Problem 11.24, Transformed Data

Analysis of Variance

Source	DF	Sum of Squares	Mean Square	F Value	Prob>F
Model	1	145.58169	145.58169	251.172	0.0001
Error	35	20.28631	0.57961		
C Total	36	165.86800			

Root MSE	0.76132	R-square	0.8777
Dep Mean	2.94451	Adj R-sq	0.8742
C.V.	25.85556		

Parameter Estimates

Variable	DF	Parameter Estimate	Standard Error	T for H0: Parameter=0	Prob > |T|
INTERCEP	1	0.425110	0.20232699	2.101	0.0429
LNPCB84	1	0.850826	0.05368523	15.848	0.0001

Obs	BAY	LNPCB84	Dep Var LNPCB85	Predict Value	Residual
1	Casco	4.567261	4.3637	4.3111	0.0527
2	Merrmack	3.988428	3.4088	3.8186	-0.4097
3	Salem	6.281481	6.0017	5.7696	0.2321
4	Boston	9.747176	6.6026	8.7183	-2.1157
5	Buzzards	5.734829	5.2635	5.3045	-0.0410
6	Narragan	5.081156	5.4009	4.7483	0.6526
7	ELongIsl	2.397895	2.2638	2.4653	-0.2015
8	WLongIsl	5.461414	5.1666	5.0718	0.0947
9	Raritan	6.097827	6.2734	5.6133	0.6601
10	Delaware	1.252763	4.8803	1.4910	3.3893
11	LChesapk	3.951244	3.7072	3.7869	-0.0797
12	Pamilico	0	0	0.4251	-0.4251
13	Charlest	2.312535	2.2439	2.3927	-0.1488
14	Sapelo	0	0	0.4251	-0.4251
15	StJohns	4.94876	4.7961	4.6356	0.1605
16	Tampa	0	0	0.4251	-0.4251
17	Apalach	2.564949	2.5596	2.6074	-0.0479
18	Mobile	0	0	0.4251	-0.4251
19	RoundIsl	0	0	0.4251	-0.4251
20	MissRiv	3.555348	3.4385	3.4501	-0.0116
21	Baratara	0	0	0.4251	-0.4251
22	SanAnton	0	0	0.4251	-0.4251
23	CorpusCh	0	0	0.4251	-0.4251
24	SDiegoHa	6.047609	6.2779	5.5706	0.7073
25	SDiegoBa	2.046402	2.3321	2.1662	0.1659
26	DanaPt	2.086914	1.9081	2.2007	-0.2926
27	SealBch	3.865141	3.8601	3.7137	0.1464
28	SanPedro	5.078668	5.1812	4.7462	0.4351
29	SantaMon	2.70805	2.6872	2.7292	-0.0420
30	Bodega	1.644805	1.7733	1.8246	-0.0513
31	Coos	1.432701	2.0281	1.6441	0.3841
32	Columbia	2.279316	2.0451	2.3644	-0.3193
33	Nisquall	1.654411	1.6639	1.8327	-0.1688
34	Commence	3.072693	3.0681	3.0394	0.0286
35	Elliot	5.802028	6.0295	5.3616	0.6679
36	Lutak	1.871802	1.9169	2.0177	-0.1008
37	Nahku	2.028148	1.8050	2.1507	-0.3457

11.25 *The New England Journal of Medicine* (Sept. 1990) reported on a study of passive exposure to environmental tobacco smoke in children with cystic fibrosis. The researchers investigated the correlation between a child's weight percentile (y) and number of cigarettes smoked per day in the child's home (x). The data for the 25 boys are listed in the table.

WEIGHT PERCENTILE y	NUMBER OF CIGARETTES SMOKED PER DAY x	WEIGHT PERCENTILE y	NUMBER OF CIGARETTES SMOKED PER DAY x
6	0	43	0
6	15	49	0
2	40	50	0
8	23	49	22
11	20	46	30
17	7	54	0
24	3	58	0
25	0	62	0
17	25	66	0
25	20	66	23
25	15	83	0
31	23	87	44
35	10		

Source: Rubin, B. K. "Exposure of Children with Cystic Fibrosis to Environmental Tobacco Smoke." *The New England Journal of Medicine*, Sept. 20, 1990, Vol. 323, No. 12, p. 785 (data extracted from Fig. 3).

a. The SAS regression printout (with residuals) for the straight-line model relating y to x is shown below. Examine the residuals. Do you detect any outliers?

b. Influence diagnostics are also given in the SAS printout. Interpret these results.

Printout for Problem 11.25

Dependent Variable: Y

Analysis of Variance

Source	DF	Sum of Squares	Mean Square	F Value	Prob>F
Model	1	304.88209	304.88209	0.500	0.4864
Error	23	14011.11791	609.17904		
C Total	24	14316.00000			

Root MSE	24.68155	R-square	0.0213	
Dep Mean	37.80000	Adj R-sq	-0.0213	
C.V.	65.29511			

Parameter Estimates

Variable	DF	Parameter Estimate	Standard Error	T for H0: Parameter=0	Prob > |T|
INTERCEP	1	41.152655	6.84296599	6.014	0.0001
X	1	-0.261926	0.37024180	-0.707	0.4864

(continued)

Obs	Dep Var Y	Predict Value	Std Err Predict	Residual	Std Err Residual	Student Residual	-2-1-0 1 2	Cook's D
1	6.0000	41.1527	6.843	-35.1527	23.714	-1.482	**	0.091
2	43.0000	41.1527	6.843	1.8473	23.714	0.078		0.000
3	6.0000	37.2238	5.003	-31.2238	24.169	-1.292	**	0.036
4	49.0000	41.1527	6.843	7.8473	23.714	0.331		0.005
5	2.0000	30.6756	11.215	-28.6756	21.986	-1.304	**	0.221
6	50.0000	41.1527	6.843	8.8473	23.714	0.373		0.006
7	8.0000	35.1284	6.215	-27.1284	23.886	-1.136	**	0.044
8	49.0000	35.3903	5.997	13.6097	23.942	0.568	*	0.010
9	11.0000	35.9141	5.610	-24.9141	24.036	-1.037	**	0.029
10	46.0000	33.2949	8.057	12.7051	23.329	0.545	*	0.018
11	17.0000	39.3192	5.383	-22.3192	24.087	-0.927	*	0.021
12	54.0000	41.1527	6.843	12.8473	23.714	0.542	*	0.012
13	24.0000	40.3669	6.126	-16.3669	23.909	-0.685	*	0.015
14	58.0000	41.1527	6.843	16.8473	23.714	0.710	*	0.021
15	25.0000	41.1527	6.843	-16.1527	23.714	-0.681	*	0.019
16	62.0000	41.1527	6.843	20.8473	23.714	0.879	*	0.032
17	17.0000	34.6045	6.691	-17.6045	23.757	-0.741	*	0.022
18	66.0000	41.1527	6.843	24.8473	23.714	1.048	**	0.046
19	25.0000	35.9141	5.610	-10.9141	24.036	-0.454		0.006
20	66.0000	35.1284	6.215	30.8716	23.886	1.292	**	0.057
21	25.0000	37.2238	5.003	-12.2238	24.169	-0.506	*	0.005
22	83.0000	41.1527	6.843	41.8473	23.714	1.765	***	0.130
23	31.0000	35.1284	6.215	-4.1284	23.886	-0.173		0.001
24	87.0000	29.6279	12.562	57.3721	21.246	2.700	*****	1.275
25	35.0000	38.5334	5.044	-3.5334	24.161	-0.146		0.000

Obs	Rstudent	Hat Diag H	Cov Ratio	Dffits	INTERCEP Dfbetas	X Dfbetas
1	-1.5244	0.0769	0.9686	-0.4399	-0.4399	0.3046
2	0.0762	0.0769	1.1834	0.0220	0.0220	-0.0152
3	-1.3120	0.0411	0.9804	-0.2716	-0.1627	-0.0442
4	0.3244	0.0769	1.1727	0.0936	0.0936	-0.0648
5	-1.3255	0.2065	1.1812	-0.6762	0.2058	-0.6072
6	0.3660	0.0769	1.1697	0.1056	0.1056	-0.0731
7	-1.1433	0.0634	1.0398	-0.2975	-0.0453	-0.1808
8	0.5599	0.0590	1.1292	0.1403	0.0281	0.0797
9	-1.0383	0.0517	1.0474	-0.2424	-0.0741	-0.1152
10	0.5361	0.1066	1.1920	0.1852	-0.0195	0.1463
11	-0.9236	0.0476	1.0635	-0.2064	-0.1936	0.0823
12	0.5333	0.0769	1.1540	0.1539	0.1539	-0.1066
13	-0.6764	0.0616	1.1178	-0.1733	-0.1718	0.1027
14	0.7026	0.0769	1.1326	0.2027	0.2027	-0.1404
15	-0.6730	0.0769	1.1367	-0.1942	-0.1942	0.1345
16	0.8746	0.0769	1.1058	0.2524	0.2524	-0.1748
17	-0.7335	0.0735	1.1240	-0.2066	-0.0134	-0.1395
18	1.0501	0.0769	1.0737	0.3030	0.3030	-0.2099
19	-0.4461	0.0517	1.1319	-0.1041	-0.0318	-0.0495
20	1.3126	0.0634	1.0036	0.3415	0.0520	0.2075
21	-0.4974	0.0411	1.1146	-0.1030	-0.0617	-0.0168
22	1.8561	0.0769	0.8851	0.5356	0.5356	-0.3709
23	-0.1691	0.0634	1.1639	-0.0440	-0.0067	-0.0267
24	3.1959	0.2590	0.6880	1.8896	-0.6678	1.7376
25	-0.1431	0.0418	1.1385	-0.0299	-0.0253	0.0061

11.26 Refer to *The Real Estate Appraiser and Analyst* data given in Problem 11.18 (p. 576). Use a computer to generate influence diagnostics and interpret the results.

11.27 Refer to the leased fee value data given in Problem 11.21 (p. 578). Use a computer to generate influence diagnostics and interpret the results.

STEPWISE REGRESSION, RESIDUALS, AND REGRESSION DIAGNOSTICS

In this Computer Lab we give the commands for conducting a stepwise regression and a residual analysis, and for computing variance inflation factors and influence diagnostics. To illustrate, we use the fast-food sales data in Table 11.14.

SAS

Command
Line

```
1    DATA FOOD;                              ⎫
2    INPUT Y X1 X2 X3 X4;                    ⎬  Data entry instructions
3    CARDS;                                  ⎭
     6.3   1   0   0   59.3  ⎫
     6.6   1   0   0   60.3  ⎪
      .    .   .   .    .    ⎬  Input data values
      .    .   .   .    .    ⎪  (1 observation per line)
      .    .   .   .    .    ⎪
     3.3   0   0   0   23.2  ⎭
4    PROC REG;                                       ⎫
5    MODEL Y = X1 X2 X3 X4/VIF R INFLUENCE;          ⎬  Regression analysis
6    OUTPUT OUT=RESIDS P=YHAT R=RESID;               ⎭  with diagnostics
7    PROC PLOT;                              ⎫
8    PLOT RESID*(YHAT X4);                   ⎬  Residual plots
9    PROC UNIVARIATE NORMAL PLOT;            ⎫  Histogram of residuals
10   VAR RESID;                              ⎬  Normal probability plot
11   PROC STEPWISE;                          ⎫
12   MODEL Y = X1 X2 X3 X4;                  ⎬  Stepwise regression
```

COMMAND 5 The option VIF produces variance inflation factors for the independent variables in the model. The R option produces a list of residuals, predicted values, Studentized residuals, the Cook's D statistic for all observations in the analysis. The INFLUENCE option requests a detailed analysis of the influence of each observation on the β estimates. This includes leverage values and Studentized deleted residuals.

COMMANDS 7–8 Two plots are produced: residuals versus predicted $(\hat{y})$ and residuals versus quantitative x (x_4).

COMMANDS 9–10 The UNIVARIATE procedure is used to produce a histogram (or stem-and-leaf display) and a normal probability plot for the regression residuals.

COMMANDS 11–12 The STEPWISE procedure conducts a stepwise regression analysis of the independent variables listed in the MODEL statement.

NOTE The output for this SAS program is displayed in Figure 11.23 (p. 594).

SPSS

```
Command
  Line
   1     DATA LIST FREE/Y X1 X2 X3 X4.   Data entry instruction
   2     BEGIN DATA.
         6.3  1   0   0   59.3⎫
         6.6  1   0   0   60.3⎬  Input data values
          .    .   .   .    .   ⎬  (1 observation per line)
          .    .   .   .    .   ⎬
          .    .   .   .    .   ⎭
         3.3  0   0   0   23.2
   3     END DATA.
   4     REGRESSION VARIABLES = Y, X1, X2, X3, X4/ ⎫
   5        STATISTICS=DEFAULTS TOL/                ⎬  Regression analysis
   6        CRITERIA=TOLERANCE(.00001)/             ⎬  with diagnostics
   7        DEPENDENT=Y/METHOD=ENTER/               ⎭
   8        RESIDUALS/                              ⎫  Residual analysis
   9        CASEWISE=ALL DEFAULT SDRESID COOK LEVER/ ⎭
  10        SCATTERPLOT=(*RESID, *PRED)(*RESID,X4).
  11     REGRESSION VARIABLES=Y, X1, X2, X3, X4/ ⎫  Stepwise regression
  12        DEPENDENT=Y/METHOD=STEPWISE.          ⎭
```

COMMAND 5 The TOL option of the STATISTICS command generates variance inflation factors and tolerance limits for each independent variable in the model.

COMMAND 8 The RESIDUALS subcommand produces a histogram (or stem-and-leaf display) and normal probability plot of the residuals.

COMMAND 9 The CASEWISE subcommand produces a list of the residuals and predicted values (DEFAULT), Studentized deleted residuals (SDRESID), Cook's distances (COOK), and leverage values (LEVER) for all observations (ALL) used in the analysis.

COMMAND 10 Two residual plots are produced: residuals versus predicted ($\hat{y}$) and residuals versus the quantitative x (x_4).

COMMANDS 11–12 Specify STEPWISE in the METHOD subcommand to conduct a stepwise regression of the independent variables listed in the VARIABLES subcommand.

NOTE The output for this SPSS program is displayed in Figure 11.24 (p. 601).

MINITAB

```
 1    READ C1-C5   Data entry instruction
      6.3  1   0   0   59.3⎫
      6.6  1   0   0   60.3⎪   Input data values
       •   •   •   •     •   ⎬   (1 observation per line)
       •   •   •   •     •   ⎪
       •   •   •   •     •   ⎪
      3.3  0   0   0   23.2⎭
 2    NAME C1='Y' C2='X1' C3='X2' C4='X3' C5='X4'
 3    REGRESS C1 4 C2-C5 PRED IN C6;⎫
 4       VIF;                        ⎪
 5       RESIDUALS C7;               ⎬   Regression analysis with diagnostics
 6       HI C8;                      ⎪
 7       TRESIDUALS C9;              ⎪
 8       COOKD C10.                  ⎭
 9    NAME C6='PRED' C7='RESID' C8='LEVERAGE' C9='STUDRES' C10='COOKD'
10    PRINT C6-C10
11    PLOT C7 VS. C6 ⎫
12    PLOT C7 VS. C5 ⎭   Residual plots
13    STEM-AND-LEAF C7   Stem-and-leaf residuals
14    STEPWISE C1 C2-C5  Stepwise regression
```

COMMAND 3 The predicted values for the regression are stored in the last column specified (C6).

COMMAND 4 The VIF subcommand produces variance inflation factors for the independent variables in the model.

COMMAND 5 The RESIDUALS subcommand stores residuals in the assigned column (C7).

COMMAND 6 The HI subcommand stores leverage values in the assigned column (C8).

COMMAND 7 The TRESIDUALS subcommand stores Studentized deleted residuals in the assigned column (C9).

COMMAND 8 The COOKD subcommand stores Cook's distance values in the assigned column (C10).

COMMANDS 11–12   Two residual plots are produced: residuals versus predicted and residuals versus quantitative x, x_4.

COMMAND 13   A stem-and-leaf display of the residuals is produced.

COMMAND 14   The STEPWISE command conducts a stepwise regression of the independent variables listed. Note that the dependent variable must be listed first.

NOTE   The output for this MINITAB program is displayed in Figure 11.25 (p. 606).

FIGURE 11.23

SAS Output for Computer Lab

Analysis of Variance

Source	DF	Sum of Squares	Mean Square	F Value	Prob>F
Model	4	116.65552	29.16388	222.173	0.0001
Error	19	2.49407	0.13127		
C Total	23	119.14958			

Root MSE	0.36231	R-square	0.9791
Dep Mean	5.99583	Adj R-sq	0.9747
C.V.	6.04265		

Parameter Estimates

Variable	DF	Parameter Estimate	Standard Error	T for H0: Parameter=0	Prob > |T|	Variance Inflation
INTERCEP	1	1.083388	0.32100795	3.375	0.0032	0.00000000
X1	1	−1.215762	0.20538681	−5.919	0.0001	1.80764591
X2	1	−0.530757	0.28481946	−1.863	0.0779	1.62223720
X3	1	−1.076525	0.22650014	−4.753	0.0001	1.93784208
X4	1	0.103673	0.00409449	25.320	0.0001	1.22352730

Obs	Dep Var Y	Predict Value	Std Err Predict	Residual	Std Err Residual	Student Residual	−2−1−0 1 2	Cook's D
1	6.3000	6.0155	0.121	0.2845	0.342	0.833	| *	0.017
2	6.6000	6.1191	0.121	0.4809	0.342	1.408	| **	0.050
3	7.6000	8.3792	0.154	−0.7792	0.328	−2.376	**** |	0.249
4	3.0000	3.2163	0.162	−0.2163	0.324	−0.668	* |	0.022
5	9.5000	10.0276	0.201	−0.5276	0.301	−1.751	*** |	0.273
6	5.9000	5.4764	0.122	0.4236	0.341	1.242	| **	0.040
7	6.1000	5.5075	0.122	0.5925	0.341	1.737	| ***	0.077
8	5.0000	5.1861	0.125	−0.1861	0.340	−0.547	* |	0.008
9	3.6000	3.6724	0.151	−0.0724	0.329	−0.220	|	0.002
10	2.8000	2.9993	0.222	−0.1993	0.286	−0.697	* |	0.059
11	6.7000	6.5242	0.219	0.1758	0.289	0.609	| *	0.043
12	5.2000	5.1765	0.209	0.0235	0.296	0.080	|	0.001
13	8.2000	7.8653	0.177	0.3347	0.316	1.059	| **	0.071
14	5.0000	5.0143	0.137	−0.0143	0.335	−0.043	|	0.000
15	3.9000	4.2989	0.140	−0.3989	0.334	−1.194	** |	0.050
16	5.4000	5.4497	0.138	−0.0497	0.335	−0.148	|	0.001
17	4.1000	4.2575	0.140	−0.1575	0.334	−0.471	|	0.008
18	3.1000	3.0756	0.157	0.0244	0.327	0.075	|	0.000
19	5.4000	5.1387	0.137	0.2613	0.335	0.779	| *	0.020
20	8.4000	8.6619	0.164	−0.2619	0.323	−0.810	* |	0.034
21	9.5000	9.5120	0.171	−0.0120	0.319	−0.038	|	0.000
22	8.7000	8.5893	0.163	0.1107	0.323	0.342	|	0.006
23	10.6000	10.2481	0.183	0.3519	0.313	1.125	| **	0.087
24	3.3000	3.4886	0.244	−0.1886	0.268	−0.704	* |	0.082

(continued)

FIGURE 11.23

SAS Output (*Continued*)

Obs	Rstudent	Hat Diag H	Cov Ratio	Dffits	INTERCEP Dfbetas	X1 Dfbetas	X2 Dfbetas	X3 Dfbetas	X4 Dfbetas
1	0.8260	0.1112	1.2240	0.2921	-0.0049	0.1728	0.0021	0.0020	0.0057
2	1.4481	0.1114	0.8500	0.5128	-0.0236	0.3060	0.0101	0.0096	0.0274
3	-2.7590	0.1809	0.2743	-1.2967	0.6953	-0.7414	-0.2981	-0.2822	-0.8054
4	-0.6575	0.2003	1.4552	-0.3290	-0.1895	-0.1049	0.0813	0.0769	0.2195
5	-1.8608	0.3081	0.7859	-1.2418	0.8572	-0.6158	-0.3675	-0.3479	-0.9930
6	1.2613	0.1138	0.9682	0.4521	0.0604	0.2501	-0.0259	-0.0245	-0.0700
7	1.8434	0.1135	0.6226	0.6596	0.0826	0.3667	-0.0354	-0.0335	-0.0956
8	-0.5365	0.1181	1.3726	-0.1964	-0.0414	-0.1034	0.0177	0.0168	0.0479
9	-0.2143	0.1731	1.5646	-0.0980	-0.0506	-0.0357	0.0217	0.0205	0.0586
10	-0.6868	0.3763	1.8460	-0.5335	-0.1555	0.0322	-0.3021	0.0631	0.1802
11	0.5983	0.3647	1.8692	0.4533	-0.1147	0.0237	0.3675	0.0466	0.1329
12	0.0775	0.3342	1.9650	0.0549	-0.0025	0.0005	0.0413	0.0010	0.0029
13	1.0629	0.2394	1.2708	0.5964	-0.3270	0.0676	0.1402	0.4112	0.3788
14	-0.0415	0.1429	1.5281	-0.0169	-0.0000	0.0000	0.0000	-0.0102	0.0000
15	-1.2079	0.1489	1.0428	-0.5053	-0.0881	0.0182	0.0378	-0.2634	0.1021
16	-0.1445	0.1451	1.5240	-0.0595	0.0064	-0.0013	-0.0027	-0.0383	-0.0074
17	-0.4615	0.1497	1.4530	-0.1936	-0.0356	0.0074	0.0153	-0.0999	0.0413
18	0.0728	0.1875	1.6105	0.0350	0.0147	-0.0030	-0.0063	0.0125	-0.0171
19	0.7707	0.1430	1.3000	0.3149	-0.0097	0.0020	0.0042	0.1942	0.0113
20	-0.8025	0.2038	1.3805	-0.4059	-0.1555	0.3075	0.2084	0.2684	-0.0551
21	-0.0367	0.2237	1.6874	-0.0197	-0.0039	0.0135	0.0082	0.0111	-0.0064
22	0.3340	0.2028	1.5938	0.1685	0.0672	-0.1284	-0.0878	-0.1127	0.0200
23	1.1335	0.2548	1.2457	0.6629	0.0310	-0.4084	-0.2203	-0.3124	0.3075
24	-0.6940	0.4527	2.0981	-0.6312	-0.6188	0.4152	0.4132	0.4653	0.4715

(*continued*)

FIGURE 11.23
SAS Output (*Continued*)

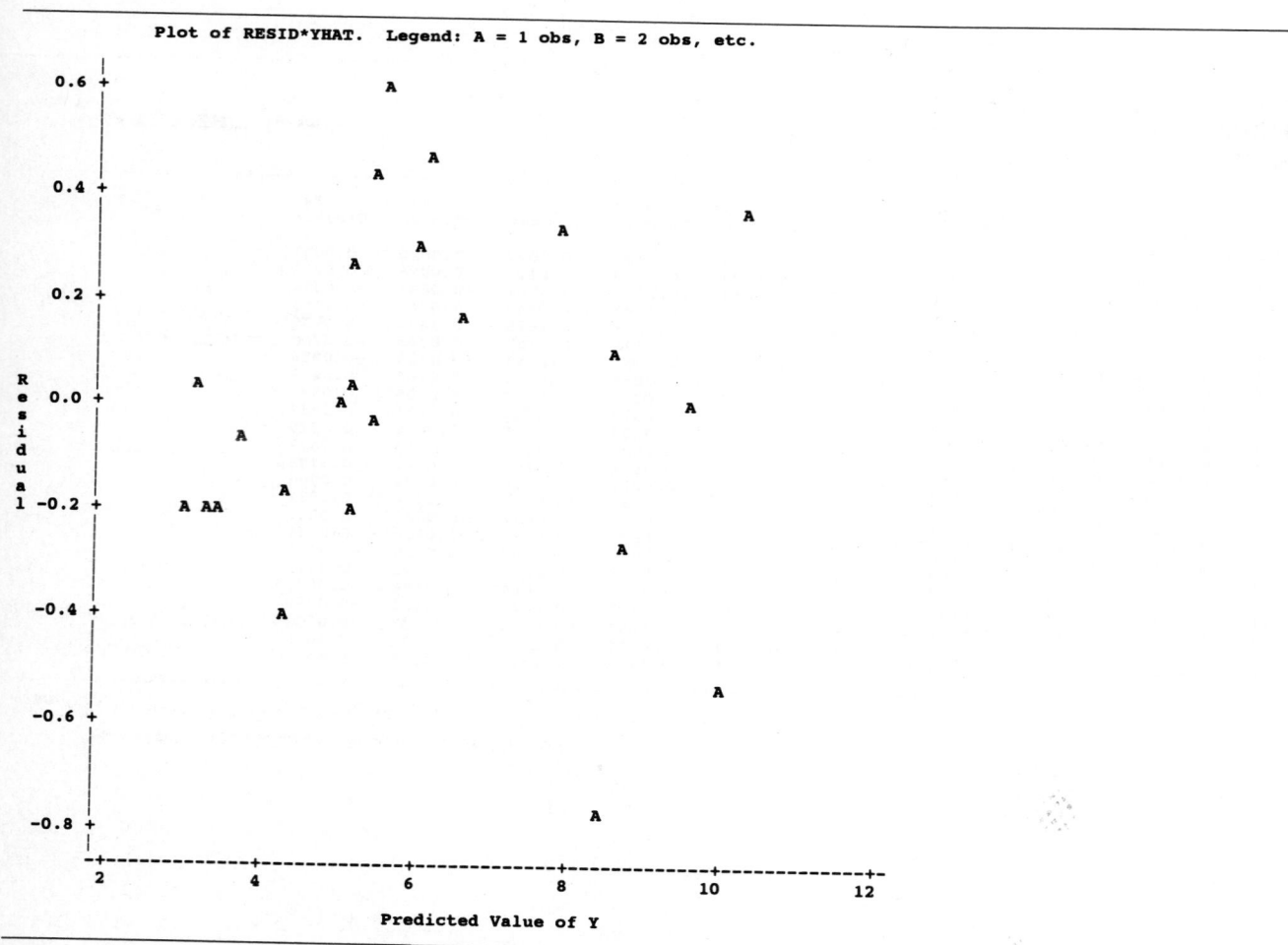

Plot of RESID*YHAT.   Legend: A = 1 obs, B = 2 obs, etc.

(*continued*)

FIGURE 11.23
SAS Output (*Continued*)

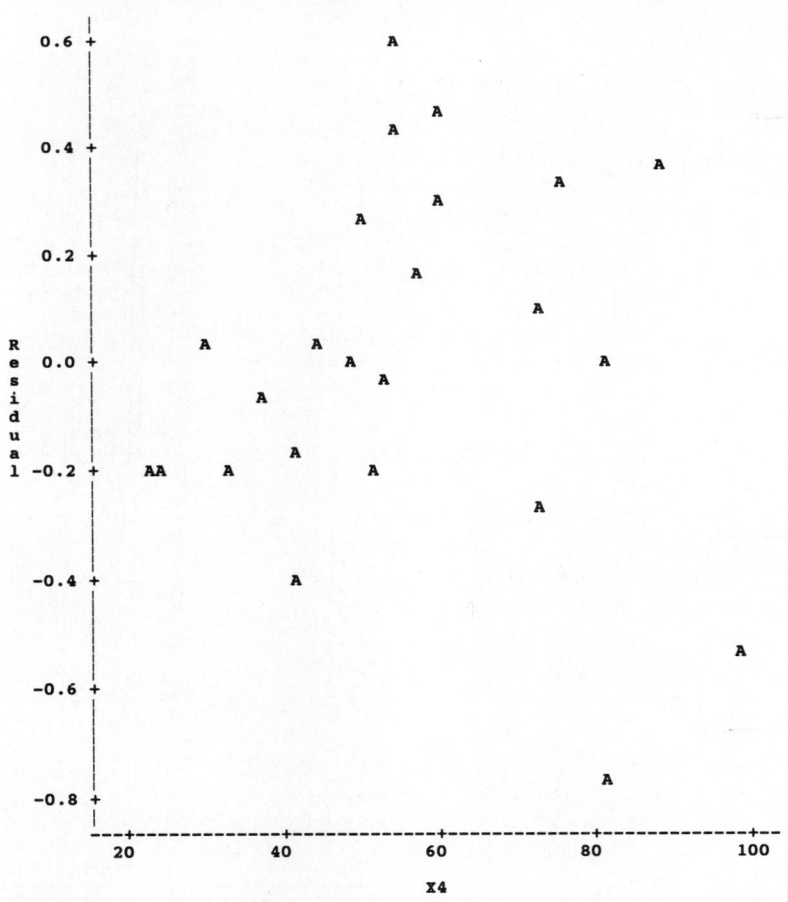

SAS

Plot of RESID*X4.   Legend: A = 1 obs, B = 2 obs, etc.

(continued)

FIGURE 11.23

SAS Output (*Continued*)

```
                    UNIVARIATE PROCEDURE

        Variable=RESID              Residual

                      Moments

        N                    24  Sum Wgts             24
        Mean                  0  Sum                   0
        Std Dev        0.329299  Variance       0.108438
        Skewness      -0.28293   Kurtosis       0.081055
        USS            2.494066  CSS            2.494066
        CV                    .  Std Mean       0.067218
        T:Mean=0              0  Prob>|T|         1.0000
        Sgn Rank             2   Prob>|S|         0.9559
        Num ^= 0            24
        W:Normal      0.980141   Prob<W           0.8893

                    Quantiles(Def=5)

        100% Max    0.592544        99%  0.592544
         75% Q3     0.272925        95%  0.480871
         50% Med   -0.01316         90%  0.423646
         25% Q1    -0.19397         10%  -0.39894
          0% Min   -0.77921          5%  -0.52761
                                     1%  -0.77921
        Range       1.371752
        Q3-Q1       0.466891
        Mode       -0.77921

                      Extremes

        Lowest     Obs       Highest     Obs
       -0.77921(      3)   0.334697(      13)
       -0.52761(      5)   0.351888(      23)
       -0.39894(     15)   0.423646(       6)
       -0.26191(     20)   0.480871(       2)
       -0.21628(      4)   0.592544(       7)


   Stem Leaf                     #          Boxplot
      4 289                      3             |
      2 6835                     4             |
      0 2218                     4          +-----+
     -0 9967511                  7          |  +  |
     -2 620                      3          *-----*
     -4 30                       2             |
     -6 8                        1             |
        ----+----+----+----+
   Multiply Stem.Leaf by 10**-1


   Variable=RESID              Residual

                Normal Probability Plot
   0.5+                                 *+++++++*
      |                             **+*++++
  -0.1+                       ++*****++
      |              *******  *
      |          *+***++
  -0.7+ +++++*
      +----+----+----+----+----+----+----+----+----+----+
         -2        -1         0        +1        +2
```

FIGURE 11.23

SAS Output (*Continued*)

```
                  Stepwise Procedure for Dependent Variable Y
Step 1    Variable X4 Entered        R-square = 0.93447459   C(p) = 39.47685536

                     DF      Sum of Squares     Mean Square        F    Prob>F

Regression            1       111.34225798     111.34225798    313.75   0.0001
Error                22         7.80732535       0.35487842
Total                23       119.14958333

                 Parameter        Standard        Type II
Variable          Estimate          Error     Sum of Squares       F    Prob>F

INTERCEP         0.01794982      0.35872576       0.00088854     0.00    0.9605
X4               0.10780674      0.00608633     111.34225798   313.75    0.0001

Bounds on condition number:             1,            1
--------------------------------------------------------------------------------

Step 2    Variable X1 Entered        R-square = 0.95345047   C(p) = 24.25260838

                     DF      Sum of Squares     Mean Square        F    Prob>F

Regression            2       113.60322655      56.80161327    215.07   0.0001
Error                21         5.54635679       0.26411223
Total                23       119.14958333

                 Parameter        Standard        Type II
Variable          Estimate          Error     Sum of Squares       F    Prob>F

INTERCEP         0.14868449      0.31267801       0.05972074     0.23    0.6393
X1              -0.63915961      0.21845215       2.26096856     8.56    0.0081
X4               0.10977157      0.00529338     113.57986543   430.04    0.0001

Bounds on condition number:     1.016358,     4.065431
--------------------------------------------------------------------------------

Step 3    Variable X3 Entered        R-square = 0.97524205   C(p) =  6.47257601

                     DF      Sum of Squares     Mean Square        F    Prob>F

Regression            3       116.19968440      38.73322813    262.61   0.0001
Error                20         2.94989894       0.14749495
Total                23       119.14958333

                 Parameter        Standard        Type II
Variable          Estimate          Error     Sum of Squares       F    Prob>F

INTERCEP         0.72048655      0.27050333       1.04636615     7.09    0.0149
X1              -1.01869682      0.18663627       4.39415057    29.79    0.0001
X3              -0.85002677      0.20259584       2.59645785    17.60    0.0004
X4               0.10649743      0.00403198     102.90089471   697.66    0.0001

                              SAS
Bounds on condition number:     1.379811,     11.29245
--------------------------------------------------------------------------------
```

(*continued*)

FIGURE 11.23

SAS Output (*Continued*)

```
Step 4    Variable X2 Entered       R-square = 0.97906778   C(p) =  5.00000000

                DF       Sum of Squares      Mean Square        F     Prob>F

Regression       4       116.65551769       29.16387942     222.17   0.0001
Error           19         2.49406564        0.13126661
Total           23       119.14958333

                Parameter        Standard          Type II
Variable         Estimate           Error     Sum of Squares        F     Prob>F

INTERCEP        1.08338756       0.32100795       1.49516933     11.39   0.0032
X1             -1.21576160       0.20538681       4.59945110     35.04   0.0001
X2             -0.53075677       0.28481946       0.45583329      3.47   0.0779
X3             -1.07652473       0.22650014       2.96527761     22.59   0.0001
X4              0.10367335       0.00409449      84.15672801    641.11   0.0001

Bounds on condition number:     1.937842,      26.36501
--------------------------------------------------------------------------

All variables in the model are significant at the 0.1500 level.
No other variable met the 0.1500 significance level for entry into the model.

          Summary of Stepwise Procedure for Dependent Variable Y

         Variable          Number    Partial    Model
Step    Entered Removed      In       R**2      R**2      C(p)           F     Prob>F

  1     X4                    1      0.9345    0.9345   39.4769    313.7476   0.0001
  2     X1                    2      0.0190    0.9535   24.2526      8.5606   0.0081
  3     X3                    3      0.0218    0.9752    6.4726     17.6037   0.0004
  4     X2                    4      0.0038    0.9791    5.0000      3.4726   0.0779
```

FIGURE 11.24
SPSS Output for Computer Lab

```
Multiple R              .98948      Analysis of Variance
R Square                .97907                      DF     Sum of Squares     Mean Square
Adjusted R Square       .97466      Regression       4          116.65552        29.16388
Standard Error          .36231      Residual        19            2.49407          .13127

                                    F =    222.17286     Signif F =   .0000

---------------------------- Variables in the Equation ----------------------------

Variable            B         SE B      Beta   Tolerance      VIF         T    Sig T

X4            .103673     .004094   .929619    .817309     1.224    25.320    .0000
X1          -1.215762     .205387  -.264158    .553206     1.808    -5.919    .0000
X2           -.530757     .284819  -.078780    .616433     1.622    -1.863    .0779
X3          -1.076525     .226500  -.219607    .516038     1.938    -4.753    .0001
(Constant)   1.083388     .321008                                    3.375    .0032


Casewise Plot of Standardized Residual

*: Selected   M: Missing

           -3.0            0.0            3.0
Case #    0:..............:..............:0      Y     *PRED   *RESID  *SDRESID  *LEVER  *COOK D
    1     .               .        *    .      6.30    6.0155   .2845    .8260    .0695   .0174
    2     .       *       .          *  .      6.60    6.1191   .4809   1.4481    .0698   .0497
    3     .       *       .             .      7.60    8.3792  -.7792  -2.7590    .1392   .2495
    4     .               *  .          .      3.00    3.2163  -.2163   -.6575    .1586   .0223
    5     .         *     .             .      9.50   10.0276  -.5276  -1.8608    .2665   .2730
    6     .               .      *      .      5.90    5.4764   .4236   1.2613    .0722   .0396
    7     .               .        *    .      6.10    5.5075   .5925   1.8434    .0718   .0773
    8     .               *  .          .      5.00    5.1861  -.1861   -.5365    .0765   .0080
    9     .               .  *.         .      3.60    3.6724  -.0724   -.2143    .1314   .0020
   10     .               * .           .      2.80    2.9993  -.1993   -.6868    .3346   .0585
   11     .               .  *          .      6.70    6.5242   .1758    .5983    .3230   .0425
   12     .               *.            .      5.20    5.1765   .0235    .0775    .2926   .0006
   13     .               .  *          .      8.20    7.8653   .3347   1.0629    .1978   .0707
   14     .               *.            .      5.00    5.0143  -.0143   -.0415    .1012   .0001
   15     .          *    .             .      3.90    4.2989  -.3989  -1.2079    .1073   .0499
   16     .               *.            .      5.40    5.4497  -.0497   -.1445    .1034   .0007
   17     .             * .             .      4.10    4.2575  -.1575   -.4615    .1080   .0078
   18     .               *             .      3.10    3.0756   .0244    .0728    .1459   .0003
   19     .               .  *          .      5.40    5.1387   .2613    .7707    .1014   .0203
   20     .          *    .             .      8.40    8.6619  -.2619   -.8025    .1621   .0336
   21     .               *             .      9.50    9.5120  -.0120   -.0367    .1820   .0001
   22     .               . *           .      8.70    8.5893   .1107    .3340    .1612   .0060
   23     .               .   *         .     10.60   10.2481   .3519   1.1335    .2132   .0866
   24     .          *    .             .      3.30    3.4886  -.1886   -.6940    .4110   .0819
Case #    0:..............:..............:0      Y     *PRED   *RESID  *SDRESID  *LEVER  *COOK D
           -3.0            0.0            3.0
```

(continued)

FIGURE 11.24

SPSS Output (*Continued*)

```
Outliers - Standardized Residual

   Case #        *ZRESID

       3        -2.15068
       7         1.63547
       5        -1.45626
       2         1.32725
       6         1.16930
      15        -1.10111
      23          .97124
      13          .92379
       1          .78537
      20         -.72289
```

```
Histogram - Standardized Residual

NExp N        (* = 1 Cases,      . : = Normal Curve)
0   .02   Out
0   .04   3.00
0   .09   2.67
0   .21   2.33
0   .44   2.00
1   .80   1.67 :
2  1.32   1.33 :*
2  1.94   1.00 *:
2  2.55    .67 **.
2  3.01    .33 **.
5  3.18    .00 **:**
2  3.01   -.33 **.
5  2.55   -.67 **:**
1  1.94  -1.00 *.
1  1.32  -1.33 :
0   .80  -1.67 .
1   .44  -2.00 *
0   .21  -2.33
0   .09  -2.67
0   .04  -3.00
0   .02   Out
```

Normal Probability (P-P) Plot
Standardized Residual

(continued)

FIGURE 11.24
SPSS Output (*Continued*)

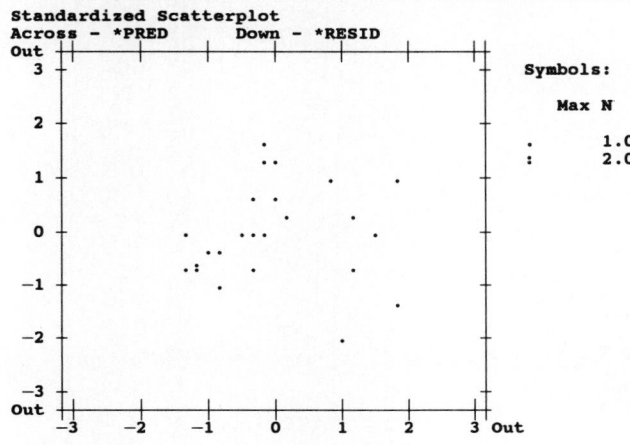

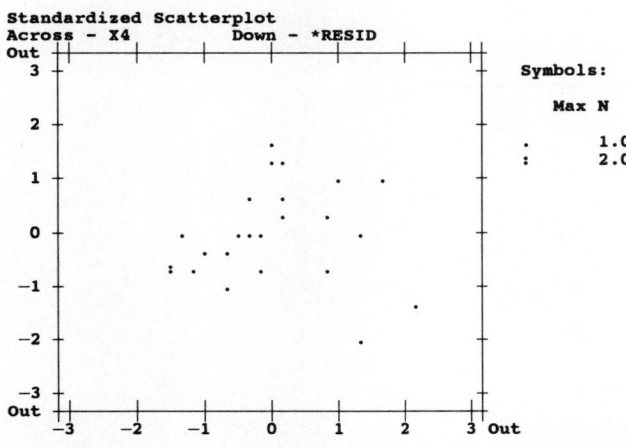

(continued)

FIGURE 11.24
SPSS Output (*Continued*)

```
Block Number   1.  Method: Stepwise     Criteria  PIN  .0500   POUT  .1000
--------------------------------------------------------------------------------
Equation Number 1    Dependent Variable..    Y

Variable(s) Entered on Step Number
   1..    X4

Multiple R              .96668
R Square                .93447
Adjusted R Square       .93150
Standard Error          .59572

Analysis of Variance
                   DF       Sum of Squares        Mean Square
Regression          1          111.34226           111.34226
Residual           22            7.80733              .35488

F =      313.74761       Signif F =  .0000

------------------ Variables in the Equation ------------------

Variable             B          SE B        Beta         T    Sig T

X4               .107807     .006086      .966682    17.713   .0000
(Constant)       .017950     .358726                   .050   .9605

------------- Variables not in the Equation -------------

Variable    Beta In   Partial  Min Toler       T   Sig T

X1         -.138875 -.538141    .983905    -2.926   .0081
X2          .065586  .247698    .934614     1.172   .2545
X3         -.064068 -.243595    .947264    -1.151   .2627
--------------------------------------------------------------------------------

Variable(s) Entered on Step Number
   2..    X1

Multiple R              .97645
R Square                .95345
Adjusted R Square       .94902
Standard Error          .51392

Analysis of Variance
                   DF       Sum of Squares        Mean Square
Regression          2          113.60323            56.80161
Residual           21            5.54636              .26411

F =      215.06620       Signif F =  .0000

------------------ Variables in the Equation ------------------

Variable             B          SE B        Beta         T    Sig T

X4               .109772     .005293      .984301    20.738   .0000
X1              -.639160     .218452     -.138875    -2.926   .0081
(Constant)       .148684     .312678                   .476   .6393

------------- Variables not in the Equation -------------

Variable    Beta In   Partial  Min Toler       T   Sig T

X2          .029044  .125253    .865734      .565   .5786
X3         -.173402 -.684206    .724737    -4.196   .0004
```

(continued)

FIGURE 11.24

SPSS Output (*Continued*)

```
Variable(s) Entered on Step Number
   3..    X3

Multiple R            .98754
R Square              .97524
Adjusted R Square     .97153
Standard Error        .38405

Analysis of Variance
                    DF      Sum of Squares        Mean Square
Regression           3        116.19968            38.73323
Residual            20          2.94990              .14749

F =      262.60715       Signif F =   .0000

------------------ Variables in the Equation ------------------

Variable             B        SE B        Beta         T    Sig T

X4            .106497     .004032     .954942     26.413   .0000
X1          -1.018697     .186636    -.221340     -5.458   .0000
X3           -.850027     .202596    -.173402     -4.196   .0004
(Constant)    .720487     .270503                  2.664   .0149

------------ Variables not in the Equation -------------

Variable    Beta In  Partial  Min Toler       T   Sig T

X2         -.078780 -.393097    .516038    -1.863   .0779


End Block Number   1  PIN =       .050 Limits reached.
```

(continued)

FIGURE 11.25

MINITAB Output for Computer Lab

```
The regression equation is
Y = 1.08 - 1.22 X1 - 0.531 X2 - 1.08 X3 + 0.104 X4

Predictor       Coef       Stdev     t-ratio       p       VIF
Constant      1.0834      0.3210        3.37    0.003
X1           -1.2158      0.2054       -5.92    0.000       1.8
X2           -0.5308      0.2848       -1.86    0.078       1.6
X3           -1.0765      0.2265       -4.75    0.000       1.9
X4           0.103673    0.004094      25.32    0.000       1.2


s = 0.3623      R-sq = 97.9%      R-sq(adj) = 97.5%

Analysis of Variance

SOURCE        DF         SS          MS          F        p
Regression     4     116.656      29.164     222.17    0.000
Error         19       2.494       0.131
Total         23     119.150

Unusual Observations
Obs.      X1        Y       Fit Stdev.Fit  Residual   St.Resid
   3    1.00   7.6000    8.3792    0.1541    -0.7792      -2.38R

R denotes an obs. with a large st. resid.
```

```
ROW      PRED      RESID     LEVERAGE    STUDRES        COOKD

  1    0.83303   0.284544   0.111154    0.82603     0.017356
  2    1.40801   0.480871   0.111429    1.44808     0.049722
  3   -2.37635  -0.779208   0.180911   -2.75904     0.249450
  4   -0.66751  -0.216275   0.200274   -0.65746     0.022317
  5   -1.75078  -0.527615   0.308144   -1.86078     0.273044
  6    1.24214   0.423646   0.113840    1.26130     0.039642
  7    1.73701   0.592544   0.113497    1.84337     0.077257
  8   -0.54689  -0.186069   0.118147   -0.53654     0.008014
  9   -0.21986  -0.072438   0.173051   -0.21427     0.002023
 10   -0.69659  -0.199322   0.376260   -0.68684     0.058542
 11    0.60870   0.175784   0.364681    0.59833     0.042537
 12    0.07962   0.023538   0.334242    0.07751     0.000637
 13    1.05927   0.334697   0.239442    1.06288     0.070651
 14   -0.04259  -0.014286   0.142857   -0.04145     0.000060
 15   -1.19357  -0.398940   0.148938   -1.20791     0.049862
 16   -0.14840  -0.049714   0.145110   -0.14453     0.000748
 17   -0.47133  -0.157470   0.149663   -0.46147     0.007820
 18    0.07473   0.024406   0.187518    0.07275     0.000258
 19    0.77910   0.261306   0.143041    0.77073     0.020264
 20   -0.81012  -0.261909   0.203752   -0.80250     0.033588
 21   -0.03769  -0.012032   0.223692   -0.03669     0.000082
 22    0.34210   0.110662   0.202845    0.33400     0.005956
 23    1.12512   0.351889   0.254831    1.13353     0.086582
 24   -0.70367  -0.188609   0.452682   -0.69400     0.081906
```

```
         -
         -                                                    *
   0.50+                                                *
         -                                         *  *  *
RESID    -                                    2   *
         -                                  *
         -                               *
   0.00+                          ***2
         -                      *
         -                2***
         -              *
         -
  -0.50+        *
         -
         -    *
         -
         --+---------+---------+---------+---------+---------+----PRED
         -2.40     -1.60     -0.80      0.00      0.80      1.60
```

FIGURE 11.25
MINITAB Output (*Continued*)

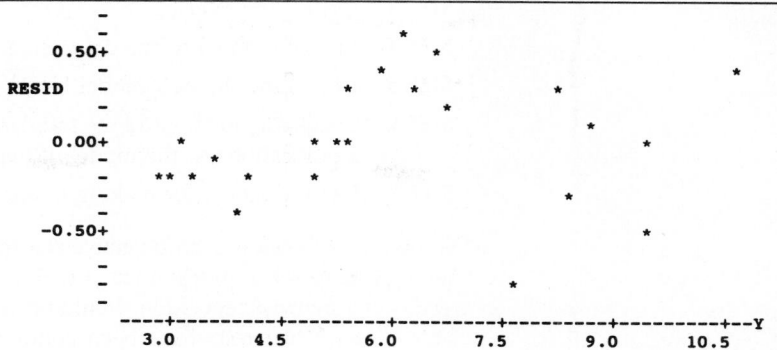

```
Stem-and-leaf of RESID     N  = 24
Leaf Unit = 0.010

     1    -7  7
     1    -6
     2    -5  2
     2    -4
     3    -3  9
     5    -2  61
     9    -1  9885
    (4)   -0  7411
    11     0  22
     9     1  17
     7     2  68
     5     3  35
     3     4  28
     1     5  9
```

```
STEPWISE REGRESSION OF       Y      ON  4 PREDICTORS, WITH N =    24

    STEP          1         2  ╲       3
CONSTANT    0.01795   0.14868   0.72049

X4           0.1078    0.1098    0.1065
T-RATIO       17.71     20.74     26.41

X1                     -0.64     -1.02
T-RATIO                -2.93     -5.46

X3                               -0.85
T-RATIO                          -4.20

S            0.596     0.514     0.384
R-SQ         93.45     95.35     97.52
```

CHAPTER NOTES

■ **Model-building** involves proposing and testing a series of models for $E(y)$.
■ The steps involved in model-building are:

STEP 1 Identify and select the independent variables $x_1, x_2, ..., x_k$ to be used in the model-building procedure.

STEP 2 Propose several candidate models for $E(y)$.

STEP 3   Collect the data.

STEP 4   Fit each model to the data using the method of least squares.

STEP 5   Determine the best model based on the regression results.

STEP 6   Check for violations of the standard regression assumptions and make modifications to the model, if necessary.

STEP 7   Use the model for making inferences.

- **Stepwise regression** is an objective screening procedure for determining which among a large set of independent variables are most useful for predicting y. The results of a stepwise regression should be used with caution since (1) an extremely large number of t tests have been conducted (leading to a high probability of making either one or more Type I or Type II errors) and (2) the final stepwise model will usually not include any higher-order or interaction terms.
- **Variable transformations** can be used to improve the fit of a model.
- **Multicollinearity** exists when two or more of the independent variables used in the regression are correlated. In the presence of multicollinearity, the regression results can be confusing and misleading. The following are indicators of multicollinearity:

  1. Significant correlations between pairs of independent variables in the model
  2. Nonsignificant t tests for all (or nearly all) of the individual β parameters in the presence of a significant overall F test
  3. Opposite signs (from what is expected) in the estimated parameters
  4. Large **variance inflation factors (VIF)** for the β parameters

- Employ one or more of the following to solve the problems created by multicollinearity:
  1. Drop one or more of the correlated independent variables from the final model.
  2. If you decide to keep all the independent variables in the model:
     a. Avoid making inferences about the individual β parameters based on the t statistics.
     b. Restrict inferences about $E(y)$ and future y-values to values of the independent variables that fall within the range of the sample data.
  3. To reduce rounding errors in higher-order regression models, code the independent variables so that first-, second-, and higher-order terms for a particular x variable are not highly correlated.

- Model A is **nested within** model B if model B contains all the terms in model A, plus additional terms.
- A **test statistic for comparing nested models** is given by

$$F = \frac{(\text{SSE}_R - \text{SSE}_C)/\text{Number of } \beta \text{ parameters tested in } H_0}{\text{MSE}_C}$$

where SSE_R = SSE for the reduced model, SSE_C = SSE for the complete model, MSE_C = MSE for the complete model, and the distribution of F depends on ν_1 = (number of β's tested) numerator and $\nu_2 = n - $ (total number of β's in complete model) denominator degrees of freedom.

- A **parsimonious model** is a general linear model with a low number of β parameters. In situations where two competing models have essentially the same predictive power (as determined by an F test), choose the more parsimonious of the two.
- A regression **residual** is defined as the difference between an observed y-value and its corresponding predicted value, that is, $(y - \hat{y})$. Residual plots can help identify situations when the model assumptions are violated.
- A regression residual that is larger than $3s$ (in absolute value) is considered to be an **outlier**.
- Perform the following checks when conducting a **residual analysis**:

CHECK 1   Plot the residuals against each independent variable in the model. If you detect a trend in one or more of the plots, the model has been **misspecified**. (For example, a curvilinear trend implies that a quadratic term for that particular x variable will improve model adequacy.)

CHECK 2   Plot the residuals against the predicted values. If you detect a pattern of **unequal variances**, refit the model using the appropriate variance-stabilizing transformation on y (see Table 11.11).

CHECK 3   Construct a stem-and-leaf display, histogram, or normal probability plot for the residuals. If you detect extreme **nonnormality** in the data, then either apply one of the transformations listed in Table 11.11 or look for outliers.

CHECK 4   Look for **outliers** by locating residuals that lie a distance of $3s$ or more above or below 0 on a residual plot versus $\hat{y}$. Before eliminating an outlier from the analysis, you should conduct an investigation to determine its cause and/or its influence.

CHECK 5   If your data constitute a **time series** (ie, if data are recorded sequentially over time), plot the residuals in time order. If you detect runs of positive and negative residuals, a time series model is needed to account for the **residual correlation** (see Chapter 12).

- An **influential observation** is an outlier that has a dramatic effect on the regression results when it is removed from the analysis.
- The **leverage**, h_i, of an observation measures the influence of the x-values on its predicted value. If

$$h_i > \frac{2(\text{Number of } \beta\text{'s in model, including } \beta_0)}{n}$$

then the observation is considered influential.
- A **deleted residual**, d_i, for an observation is the difference between the observed y-value and the predicted value obtained when the observation is omitted from the analysis. A **Studentized deleted residual**, d_i^*, is d_i divided by its standard error. If d_i^* is large in absolute value (say, $|d_i^*| > 3$), the observation is considered influential.
- A measure of the influence of an observation with respect to both its x-values and its y-value is **Cook's distance**, D_i. If D_i exceeds the 50th percentile of an F distribution with $\nu_1 = k + 1$ and $\nu_2 = n - (k + 1)$ degrees of freedom, the observation is considered influential.

When the data for a regression analysis are collected sequentially over time (ie, time series data), the assumption of independent errors is likely to be violated. In Chapter 12 we demonstrate how to build **time series forecasting models** that account for this residual correlation.

CASE STUDY

BUILDING A MODEL FOR ROAD CONSTRUCTION COSTS

In the United States, commercial contractors bid for the right to construct state highways and roads. A state government agency, usually the Department of Transportation (DOT), notifies various contractors of the state's intent to build a highway. Sealed bids are submitted by the contractors, and the contractor with the lowest bid (building cost) is awarded the road construction contract. The bidding process works extremely well in competitive markets, but has the potential to increase construction costs if the markets are noncompetitive or if collusive practices are present. The latter occurred in the 1970's and 1980's in Florida. Numerous contractors either admitted or were found guilty of price-fixing, that is, setting the cost of construction above the fair, or competitive, cost through bid-rigging or other means.

In this case study, we apply multiple regression to a data set obtained from the office of the Florida Attorney General. Our objective is to build and test the adequacy of a model designed to predict the cost y of a road construction contract awarded using the sealed-bid system in Florida.

Based on the opinions of several experts in road construction and bid-rigging, a list of potential predictors of contract cost y was developed. This list is given in Table 11.15. Data collected on these eight potential predictors and contract cost for a sample of $n = 235$ contracts are listed in Table 11.16.

TABLE 11.15
Description of Several Potential Predictors of Contract Cost

VARIABLE	DESCRIPTION
DOTEST (x_1)	DOT engineer's estimate of construction cost
B2B1RAT (x_2)	Ratio of second lowest bid to lowest bid
B3B1RAT (x_3)	Ratio of third lowest bid to lowest bid
BHB1RAT (x_4)	Ratio of highest bid to lowest bid
STATUS (x_5)	1 if fixed contract, 0 if competitive contract
DISTRICT (x_6)	1 if contract awarded in South Florida District, 0 if not
BTPRATIO (x_7)	Ratio of number of bidders to number of planholders
DAYSEST (x_8)	Engineer's estimate of number of work days required

TABLE 11.16
Data for Bid-Rigging Case Study

OBS	COST	DOTEST	B2B1RAT	B3B1RAT	BHB1RAT	STATUS	DISTRICT	BTPRATIO	DAYSEST
1	1379.43	1386.29	1.01397	1.03303	1.06121	1	0	0.33333	250
2	134.03	85.71	1.00995	1.01092	1.01092	1	1	0.75000	45
3	202.33	248.89	1.12084	1.22498	1.30546	0	0	0.50000	120
4	397.12	467.49	1.00588	1.11035	1.26733	0	0	0.50000	180
5	158.54	117.72	1.01053	1.10247	1.10247	1	0	0.37500	80
6	1128.11	1008.91	1.06208	1.09137	1.09137	1	0	0.60000	200
7	400.33	472.98	1.10275	1.13560	1.13560	1	1	0.60000	70
8	581.64	785.39	1.09346	1.16794	1.33349	0	0	0.50000	200
9	353.96	370.02	1.05063	1.28312	1.47836	0	1	0.57143	75
10	138.71	174.25	1.07047	1.19279	1.27559	0	0	0.83333	70
11	383.66	410.95	1.07508	1.13970	1.13970	1	1	0.42857	60
12	3910.94	3405.94	1.02768	1.04733	1.07683	1	1	0.45455	350
13	362.92	385.96	1.01691	1.04658	1.04658	0	1	0.37500	100
14	196.50	235.41	1.16398	1.19491	1.62532	0	0	0.70000	120
15	637.99	627.41	1.07043	1.16355	1.58125	0	0	0.50000	140
16	152.06	175.40	1.07504	1.24451	1.24451	1	1	0.50000	75
17	375.00	432.33	1.05025	1.20642	1.30949	0	0	0.57143	120
18	2284.56	1499.04	1.01600	1.20033	1.20033	1	0	0.60000	270
19	551.45	497.74	1.06668	1.10932	1.10932	1	1	0.60000	100
20	239.67	194.65	1.02302	1.21276	1.21276	1	1	0.60000	65
21	207.87	167.99	1.05143	1.08977	1.15240	1	1	0.66667	60
22	640.48	767.80	1.06059	1.08447	1.27066	0	0	0.40000	90
23	230.54	260.30	1.11029	1.12570	1.12570	1	1	0.42857	125
24	299.87	247.04	1.08411	1.10180	1.10180	1	1	0.60000	80
25	2368.84	2456.77	1.17209	1.18020	1.48550	0	0	0.30769	320
26	496.49	879.40	1.00453	1.17145	1.38498	0	0	0.58333	140
27	1564.87	1303.40	1.00374	1.04983	1.04983	1	0	0.33333	200
28	7387.03	6107.93	1.01878	1.05413	1.05718	0	1	0.66667	340
29	195.68	199.09	1.04290	1.27466	1.27466	0	1	0.60000	50
30	830.47	715.46	1.01755	1.02450	1.08833	1	0	0.57143	135
31	179.06	208.72	1.02474	1.03067	1.60580	0	1	0.62500	90
32	150.35	199.09	1.00893	1.06483	1.55218	0	0	0.63636	100
33	240.06	429.24	1.10055	1.16394	1.72898	0	0	0.71429	120
34	586.81	709.85	1.01241	1.08838	1.38652	0	0	0.60000	120
35	537.17	676.41	1.03962	1.06037	1.25739	0	0	0.72727	225
36	392.69	490.55	1.07153	1.12770	1.64803	0	1	0.50000	180
37	216.47	406.47	1.05636	1.13153	1.57543	0	1	0.82353	130
38	1559.37	1925.31	1.07850	1.08130	1.60339	0	1	0.47619	250
39	88.31	143.07	1.09813	1.26329	1.50073	0	0	0.71429	55
40	268.45	308.09	1.14764	1.17190	1.32518	0	1	0.66667	75
41	189.02	269.55	1.00993	1.14649	1.95409	0	0	0.85714	115
42	192.81	227.70	1.04378	1.15395	1.45160	0	1	0.83333	60
43	256.22	436.79	1.00000	1.09973	1.89401	0	0	0.88235	125
44	113.61	132.39	1.01195	1.01307	1.60670	0	0	0.69231	70
45	124.99	121.61	1.00000	1.11019	1.26999	0	0	0.57143	40
46	116.57	114.21	1.00000	1.21566	1.91806	0	0	0.57143	35
47	143.13	172.71	1.08608	1.13900	1.38149	0	0	0.60000	50
48	36.19	64.44	1.25303	1.31504	1.49919	0	1	0.62500	60
49	2518.39	3124.39	1.02196	1.04278	1.31920	0	0	0.57143	255
50	1353.51	1617.53	1.12729	1.22658	1.40600	0	1	0.41176	200
51	332.82	376.37	1.00024	1.05449	1.53705	0	0	0.61538	140
52	202.50	300.32	1.18810	1.23180	1.92381	0	0	0.41667	100
53	6043.31	7074.99	1.02471	1.02528	1.22949	0	0	0.57895	350
54	2280.81	2823.87	1.08084	1.09406	1.39083	0	0	0.53333	330
55	99.92	118.99	1.16879	1.29648	1.58897	1	0	0.55556	70
56	1461.59	1774.72	1.01678	1.16689	1.54772	0	1	0.57143	220
57	1217.57	1341.08	1.01074	1.01149	1.39080	0	0	0.91667	350
58	258.44	306.44	1.00453	1.01727	1.25857	0	0	0.70000	75
59	115.42	117.94	1.06379	1.09767	1.44878	0	1	0.85714	65
60	463.93	540.01	1.07317	1.10858	1.35774	0	1	0.62500	120
61	728.86	763.02	1.02446	1.03732	1.44687	0	0	0.73333	200
62	3929.92	3941.57	1.00506	1.06041	1.23232	0	0	0.66667	400
63	181.69	194.82	1.08679	1.16042	1.37565	0	1	0.62500	60
64	479.47	487.17	1.00000	1.04831	1.35510	0	0	0.53333	140
65	93.48	92.36	1.00468	1.02595	1.19858	0	0	0.83333	60
66	2301.07	2505.60	1.06746	1.09047	1.38057	0	0	0.77778	400
67	136.06	181.09	1.13520	1.23219	1.23219	0	1	0.33333	100
68	144.06	252.92	1.30227	1.30894	1.71178	0	1	0.66667	90
69	65.17	84.75	1.20310	1.36565	1.96397	0	0	0.53846	60
70	161.33	164.03	1.07334	1.09596	1.47418	0	1	0.80000	100
71	1138.54	1254.62	1.00892	1.03438	1.37670	0	0	0.68421	200
72	84.79	97.63	1.05202	1.10115	1.36417	0	0	0.60000	50
73	749.13	859.34	1.00000	1.04832	1.49429	0	0	0.92857	180
74	43.67	41.09	1.00048	1.21624	1.33987	0	1	0.80000	30
75	2920.71	2812.50	1.05215	1.11637	1.22283	0	0	0.50000	315
76	32.63	40.05	1.06642	1.25626	2.08540	0	0	0.70000	35
77	1115.12	1148.53	1.00244	1.08541	1.45950	0	0	0.64286	250
78	50.66	59.86	1.29181	1.63089	2.39326	0	0	0.57143	50
79	2229.34	2434.60	1.00386	1.09355	1.21600	0	0	0.46154	450
80	2159.85	2698.59	1.00454	1.05874	1.32056	0	0	0.50000	360
81	45.91	61.89	1.14934	1.51780	2.10760	0	1	0.57143	60
82	127.31	137.52	1.07749	1.11993	1.38302	0	0	0.66667	30

(continued)

TABLE 11.16 (Continued)

OBS	COST	DOTEST	B2B1RAT	B3B1RAT	BHB1RAT	STATUS	DISTRICT	BTPRATIO	DAYSEST
83	147.81	143.34	1.00567	1.16406	1.16406	1	0	0.60000	50
84	470.71	447.75	1.00000	1.01164	1.37056	0	0	0.57143	150
85	188.67	202.46	1.00000	1.09388	1.69629	0	0	0.53846	120
86	4765.17	5035.94	1.00785	1.04760	1.27208	0	0	0.52381	300
87	168.53	163.67	1.05127	1.08435	1.30180	0	0	0.80000	30
88	95.86	95.63	1.06483	1.09471	1.40106	0	0	0.80000	30
89	106.92	107.89	1.03253	1.07409	1.28517	0	0	0.70000	30
90	698.48	646.43	1.01875	1.10615	1.64604	0	0	0.58333	180
91	796.00	969.69	1.14418	1.16051	1.28223	0	0	0.63636	175
92	689.73	801.61	1.06850	1.14537	1.27266	0	0	0.38462	210
93	831.84	906.84	1.00519	1.03516	1.22892	0	1	0.64286	190
94	2150.15	2161.37	1.04553	1.06808	1.29205	0	0	0.62500	400
95	169.75	187.32	1.11882	1.19117	1.19117	0	0	0.75000	100
96	923.58	887.37	1.00000	1.00012	1.29230	0	0	0.87500	130
97	2527.47	2616.81	1.01785	1.14500	1.40809	0	1	0.50000	350
98	726.58	778.27	1.04401	1.08922	1.21345	0	1	0.45455	220
99	1187.10	1573.45	1.05288	1.10879	1.35808	0	1	0.50000	230
100	138.02	149.28	1.04753	1.27350	1.30600	0	0	0.83333	40
101	147.56	162.23	1.02199	1.24037	1.26737	0	0	0.66667	40
102	94.24	116.09	1.13259	1.15708	1.54419	0	0	0.58333	75
103	580.52	675.41	1.00626	1.08359	1.37753	0	0	0.75000	225
104	445.52	435.03	1.13385	1.21180	1.41720	0	0	0.63636	150
105	110.46	120.07	1.08633	1.13347	1.96465	0	0	0.71429	70
106	45.17	68.28	1.12017	1.13175	1.13175	0	0	0.75000	65
107	800.60	1031.45	1.20374	1.23253	1.45298	0	0	0.72727	425
108	495.47	541.81	1.00323	1.13667	1.24085	0	0	0.83333	140
109	1370.06	1377.92	1.04485	1.10819	1.32836	0	0	0.58333	400
110	607.51	809.09	1.01111	1.05622	1.16072	0	0	0.66667	185
111	152.72	161.24	1.02685	1.10447	1.39143	0	0	0.75000	155
112	728.20	916.97	1.02795	1.09383	1.17993	0	0	0.66667	185
113	181.59	146.46	1.01158	1.43074	1.43074	0	0	0.75000	135
114	462.92	504.79	1.06679	1.07253	1.20283	0	0	0.50000	175
115	169.38	144.51	1.00382	1.02281	1.02281	0	1	0.50000	145
116	2473.26	2618.24	1.01709	1.04063	1.05926	0	1	0.33333	630
117	2346.77	2447.81	1.08238	1.08388	1.34398	0	0	0.80000	455
118	170.42	196.75	1.00000	1.03571	1.06790	0	0	0.75000	75
119	77.85	109.91	1.12864	1.16302	1.16302	0	0	0.60000	80
120	4770.88	7511.33	1.04645	1.11915	1.42217	0	1	0.52000	600
121	303.34	341.22	1.09503	1.20479	1.40115	0	0	0.77778	210
122	395.98	419.00	1.21029	1.25946	1.25946	0	0	0.42857	185
123	150.55	174.48	1.05048	1.73452	1.73452	0	0	0.50000	110
124	1404.08	1573.83	1.02724	1.04925	1.24881	0	0	0.58333	550
125	1691.66	1627.08	1.03387	1.11274	1.11898	0	0	0.62500	600
126	5196.22	6365.13	1.02538	1.06196	1.30446	0	1	0.42857	805
127	3815.88	4960.82	1.01846	1.04353	1.07254	0	1	0.18182	450
128	122.62	95.38	1.04459	1.05195	1.07457	0	0	0.40000	120
129	1571.15	1759.21	1.01214	1.12645	1.27038	0	1	0.62500	385
130	4385.47	5556.82	1.12799	1.16978	1.72492	0	1	0.31818	600
131	4497.56	5186.30	1.00691	1.33380	1.51646	0	1	0.26316	750
132	23.67	32.54	1.05197	1.18120	2.22753	0	0	0.77778	60
133	1048.86	1040.53	1.05138	1.07009	1.27610	0	0	0.66667	300
134	239.51	315.11	1.05008	1.07829	1.17735	0	1	0.80000	100
135	260.64	351.80	1.02397	1.04081	1.17632	0	1	0.80000	120
136	138.89	123.31	1.00729	1.07116	1.07116	0	1	0.50000	150
137	128.38	151.89	1.00059	1.12683	1.12683	0	1	0.60000	75
138	284.98	315.97	1.04283	1.10622	1.10622	0	1	0.50000	110
139	77.32	101.04	1.00690	1.30480	1.30480	0	0	0.50000	90
140	5411.51	5086.25	1.02548	1.05641	1.29599	0	1	0.38889	815
141	3864.60	3991.03	1.02963	1.03230	1.48893	0	1	0.41176	800
142	2976.03	2832.43	1.06799	1.17414	1.56334	0	1	0.37500	440
143	257.51	205.86	1.01018	1.04526	1.05595	1	1	0.80000	130
144	36.44	42.04	1.02332	1.09791	1.09791	0	1	0.75000	45
145	182.52	223.13	1.00000	1.26493	1.26493	0	0	0.40000	90
146	1367.07	1433.62	1.07465	1.08446	1.35155	0	0	0.80000	475
147	76.81	75.25	1.01507	1.05527	1.05527	1	1	0.75000	90
148	1747.88	1493.45	1.01231	1.19420	1.31394	0	0	0.54545	445
149	5734.42	5427.31	1.02020	1.02571	1.32330	0	1	0.88889	700
150	5884.70	6097.41	1.03037	1.08206	1.26745	0	1	0.38889	900
151	346.52	331.10	1.12303	1.12316	1.47592	0	0	0.62500	190
152	646.40	818.54	1.29112	1.38469	1.59691	0	1	0.45455	400
153	760.84	718.24	1.02365	1.05158	1.05158	1	0	0.50000	185
154	169.77	175.95	1.02389	1.02754	1.05433	1	0	0.44444	125
155	138.79	151.62	1.00853	1.08094	1.08094	0	1	0.75000	60
156	346.76	394.21	1.10806	1.11556	1.11556	0	0	0.37500	150
157	1082.17	1085.87	1.07610	1.08797	1.34776	0	1	0.66667	400
158	253.68	270.93	1.07228	1.34120	1.34120	0	0	0.60000	200
159	433.15	545.26	1.00422	1.18435	1.24967	0	0	0.71429	230
160	10270.45	10467.40	1.03748	1.04612	1.28400	0	1	0.40000	720
161	1398.03	1414.73	1.09989	1.12889	1.22787	0	0	0.71429	460
162	2140.88	2152.01	1.00491	1.02566	1.02566	0	1	0.42857	400
163	6584.11	5949.35	1.02135	1.03414	1.37884	0	1	0.50000	675
164	666.77	641.52	1.14124	1.24950	1.31278	0	0	0.55556	240
165	108.09	99.56	1.08943	1.21201	1.21201	0	0	0.50000	65

TABLE 11.16 (Continued)

OBS	COST	DOTEST	B2B1RAT	B3B1RAT	BHB1RAT	STATUS	DISTRICT	BTPRATIO	DAYSEST
166	106.10	95.29	1.00661	1.07263	1.33137	0	0	0.85714	125
167	549.64	413.08	1.02910	1.12878	1.12878	1	1	0.60000	120
168	1272.04	949.46	1.01918	1.02475	1.10157	1	0	0.55556	450
169	122.82	132.26	1.06736	1.30510	1.30510	0	0	0.30000	130
170	359.45	333.45	1.03525	1.04301	1.29319	0	1	0.50000	190
171	1731.47	1672.53	1.19267	1.21635	1.21635	0	1	0.33333	400
172	31.72	28.30	1.06263	1.22120	1.22120	0	0	0.50000	60
173	3299.96	2805.89	1.00757	1.05891	1.08968	1	1	0.44444	525
174	480.56	480.31	1.13607	1.34698	1.36586	0	0	0.66667	125
175	673.09	655.81	1.00000	1.08450	1.10744	0	0	0.83333	100
176	116.99	99.94	1.04192	1.07735	1.07735	1	0	0.75000	100
177	1157.39	891.21	1.01295	1.09076	1.09076	1	0	0.75000	450
178	166.80	131.99	1.07707	1.08335	1.08335	1	0	0.42857	120
179	668.53	596.89	1.03133	1.05542	1.05542	1	1	0.75000	120
180	7622.16	7871.19	1.06781	1.08947	1.18429	0	1	0.37500	700
181	201.32	182.94	1.04814	1.07143	1.07143	0	0	0.42857	90
182	1270.08	1306.33	1.02258	1.07352	1.07352	1	1	0.75000	195
183	1055.14	1148.65	1.03627	1.10087	1.33284	0	1	0.45455	400
184	5212.23	5090.86	1.01774	1.01786	1.25398	0	1	0.56250	500
185	5654.86	5447.59	1.04491	1.06438	1.06438	1	1	0.37500	500
186	856.46	938.14	1.06181	1.15976	1.23706	0	1	0.50000	375
187	88.98	66.06	1.15552	1.18257	1.19208	1	1	0.50000	90
188	200.00	168.99	1.10151	1.12477	1.12477	1	1	0.75000	90
189	234.04	179.74	1.03977	1.04869	1.07225	0	0	0.80000	170
190	116.56	125.85	1.05611	1.07894	1.07894	0	1	0.75000	80
191	82.11	93.04	1.00000	1.15889	1.39368	0	0	0.75000	100
192	207.81	214.25	1.07698	1.09489	1.09489	0	0	0.50000	155
193	463.28	474.89	1.00903	1.04904	1.18654	0	0	0.88889	215
194	7385.55	8460.87	1.04472	1.05852	1.05852	0	0	0.23077	505
195	91.66	100.31	1.02867	1.12586	1.18879	0	1	0.57143	90
196	546.16	622.92	1.00235	1.07635	1.07635	0	0	0.37500	165
197	740.30	810.26	1.00000	1.03483	1.14590	0	0	0.44444	175
198	888.44	883.30	1.01844	1.03710	1.18272	1	0	0.83333	250
199	656.75	750.82	1.03327	1.06556	1.11905	1	1	0.44444	180
200	1884.39	1550.49	1.01914	1.08680	1.08680	1	1	0.42857	350
201	4448.13	4197.79	1.01046	1.02215	1.02215	1	0	0.50000	660
202	258.20	181.95	1.00732	1.02541	1.04932	1	1	0.80000	130
203	1949.63	1880.83	1.05165	1.10803	1.17919	1	1	0.44444	330
204	235.28	230.75	1.01587	1.08762	1.12906	1	0	0.83333	90
205	35.18	39.21	1.03338	1.39979	1.39979	0	1	0.60000	45
206	244.76	221.88	1.00543	1.02878	1.17723	1	0	0.80000	90
207	648.92	563.88	1.02119	1.02659	1.02659	1	0	0.60000	140
208	391.47	358.53	1.02829	1.09437	1.09437	1	0	0.60000	100
209	267.78	249.91	1.03914	1.06844	1.11820	1	0	0.36364	255
210	2130.04	2019.87	1.10956	1.16759	1.19220	0	1	0.71429	450
211	301.23	303.19	1.07610	1.10834	1.10834	1	0	0.60000	110
212	1077.90	878.72	1.04175	1.06434	1.06768	1	0	0.80000	190
213	927.38	902.03	1.11036	1.16285	1.16285	0	1	0.25000	400
214	241.70	243.97	1.04946	1.16941	1.16941	1	1	0.75000	45
215	65.79	82.36	1.18645	1.20456	1.22890	0	1	0.44444	60
216	1208.44	1230.33	1.00000	1.30919	1.49820	0	0	0.30769	295
217	9453.35	9479.73	1.02255	1.03217	1.14419	0	1	0.31579	500
218	7098.11	8296.80	1.00855	1.03726	1.19543	0	1	0.50000	510
219	912.06	1137.65	1.00000	1.28672	1.28672	0	0	0.33333	220
220	259.99	319.59	1.00717	1.06833	1.06854	1	0	0.80000	90
221	8992.25	10743.60	1.03058	1.05344	1.36599	0	1	0.45455	650
222	339.88	428.82	1.20245	1.23939	1.23939	0	1	0.37500	165
223	833.66	859.74	1.05191	1.06098	6.04598	1	0	0.33333	450
224	4833.82	6225.04	1.00000	1.06601	1.37437	0	0	0.53333	520
225	271.94	223.89	1.01232	1.03402	1.10971	1	1	0.66667	110
226	2966.28	4433.47	1.07730	1.30852	1.51367	0	0	0.25000	720
227	577.37	701.07	1.00000	1.25713	1.25713	0	0	0.25000	150
228	10480.32	10276.29	1.02502	1.03832	1.30423	0	1	0.68750	570
229	462.39	444.19	1.04262	1.04489	1.05778	0	1	0.80000	120
230	2558.19	2741.05	1.14482	1.16483	1.19685	0	1	0.44444	365
231	2814.91	2816.73	1.02002	1.11954	1.26368	0	0	0.54545	540
232	119.81	122.16	1.00000	1.06686	1.29526	0	0	0.66667	90
233	3184.86	3373.04	1.00000	1.02879	1.35838	0	1	0.58333	240
234	473.20	548.01	1.11100	1.12516	1.12516	0	0	0.37500	130
235	400.48	496.68	1.06915	1.08216	1.18507	0	1	0.50000	90

a. Since the number of potential predictors is large, stepwise regression is employed to aid in the variable selection process. The SAS printout for the stepwise regression is shown in Figure 11.26 (p. 614). Interpret the results.

b. Explain why we should avoid using the final stepwise regression model as the best model for cost, y.

FIGURE 11.26

SAS Stepwise Regression Printout for
Contract Cost

Stepwise Procedure for Dependent Variable COST

Step 1   Variable DOTEST Entered   R-square = 0.97424702   C(p) = 15.18496446

	DF	Sum of Squares	Mean Square	F	Prob>F
Regression	1	864035547.29525	864035547.29525	8814.50	0.0001
Error	233	22839676.680072	98024.36343379		
Total	234	886875223.97532			

Variable	Parameter Estimate	Standard Error	Type II Sum of Squares	F	Prob>F
INTERCEP	20.90684416	24.36729323	72159.98186400	0.74	0.3918
DOTEST	0.92628789	0.00986614	864035547.29525	8814.50	0.0001

Step 2   Variable STATUS Entered   R-square = 0.97545236   C(p) = 5.66262181

	DF	Sum of Squares	Mean Square	F	Prob>F
Regression	2	865104526.39042	432552263.19521	4609.50	0.0001
Error	232	21770697.584902	93839.21372803		
Total	234	886875223.97532			

Variable	Parameter Estimate	Standard Error	Type II Sum of Squares	F	Prob>F
INTERCEP	-20.53871363	26.81797336	55040.06386988	0.59	0.4445
DOTEST	0.93077968	0.00974453	856162794.59683	9123.72	0.0001
STATUS	166.35513274	49.28829319	1068979.0951699	11.39	0.0009

All variables in the model are significant at the 0.1500 level.
No other variable met the 0.0500 significance level for entry into the model.

Summary of Stepwise Procedure for Dependent Variable COST

Step	Variable Entered Removed	Number In	Partial R**2	Model R**2	C(p)	F	Prob>F
1	DOTEST	1	0.9742	0.9742	15.1850	8814.4979	0.0001
2	STATUS	2	0.0012	0.9755	5.6626	11.3916	0.0009

c. Using the two variables selected by the stepwise regression, a good initial choice for a candidate model is the complete second-order model shown below:

$$E(y) = \beta_0 + \beta_1 x_1 + \beta_2 x_1^2 + \beta_3 x_5 + \beta_4 x_1 x_5 + \beta_5 x_1^2 x_5$$

where x_1 = DOTEST and x_5 = STATUS. The SAS regression printout of this model is shown in Figure 11.27. Interpret the results.

d. Can the model be simplified by dropping the curvilinear terms, $\beta_2 x_1^2$ and $\beta_5 x_1^2 x_5$? Set up the null and alternative hypotheses for testing whether these curvilinear terms are statistically significant.

e. Identify the complete and reduced models for testing the hypothesis from part **d**.

f. The SAS printout for the model $E(y) = \beta_0 + \beta_1 x_1 + \beta_3 x_5 + \beta_4 x_1 x_5$ is shown in Figure 11.28. Interpret the results.

g. Use the information contained in the SAS printouts (Figures 11.27 and 11.28) to conduct the test from part **d**. (Use $\alpha = .01$.) Which model do you recommend?

FIGURE 11.27
SAS Printout for Complete Second-Order Model

Dependent Variable: COST

Analysis of Variance

Source	DF	Sum of Squares	Mean Square	F Value	Prob>F
Model	5	866723465.17	173344693.03	1969.850	0.0001
Error	229	20151758.803	87998.94674		
C Total	234	886875223.98			

Root MSE	296.64616	R-square	0.9773
Dep Mean	1268.70217	Adj R-sq	0.9768
C.V.	23.38186		

Parameter Estimates

Variable	DF	Parameter Estimate	Standard Error	T for H0: Parameter=0	Prob > |T|
INTERCEP	1	-2.975454	30.89143173	-0.096	0.9234
DOTEST	1	0.915530	0.02917084	31.385	0.0001
DOTEST2	1	0.000000719	0.00000340	0.211	0.8330
STATUS	1	-36.724712	74.77308250	-0.491	0.6238
STA_DOT	1	0.324213	0.11917429	2.720	0.0070
STA_DOT2	1	-0.000035759	0.00002478	-1.443	0.1504

FIGURE 11.28
SAS Printout for Reduced Model

Dependent Variable: COST

Analysis of Variance

Source	DF	Sum of Squares	Mean Square	F Value	Prob>F
Model	3	866540269.49	288846756.50	3281.227	0.0001
Error	231	20334954.484	88030.10599		
C Total	234	886875223.98			

Root MSE	296.69868	R-square	0.9771
Dep Mean	1268.70217	Adj R-sq	0.9768
C.V.	23.38600		

Parameter Estimates

Variable	DF	Parameter Estimate	Standard Error	T for H0: Parameter=0	Prob > |T|
INTERCEP	1	-6.428954	26.20854879	-0.245	0.8064
DOTEST	1	0.921336	0.00972347	94.754	0.0001
STATUS	1	28.670505	58.66231493	0.489	0.6255
STA_DOT	1	0.163282	0.04043122	4.039	0.0001

h. Based on the model you selected in part **g**, conduct a test to determine whether DOTEST (x_1) and STATUS (x_5) interact. Use $\alpha = .01$.

i. Explain why no further reductions of the model shown in Figure 11.28 should be considered.

j. Sketch, in a two-dimensional plot, the least squares lines for the reduced model in Figure 11.28. [*Hint:* Substitute $x_5 = 0$ and $x_5 = 1$ into the prediction equation to obtain the equations of two straight lines.]

k. Use the results in the SAS printouts shown in Figure 11.29 to conduct a residual analysis of the reduced model. Are any modifications recommended?

FIGURE 11.29

SAS Printouts for Residual Analysis

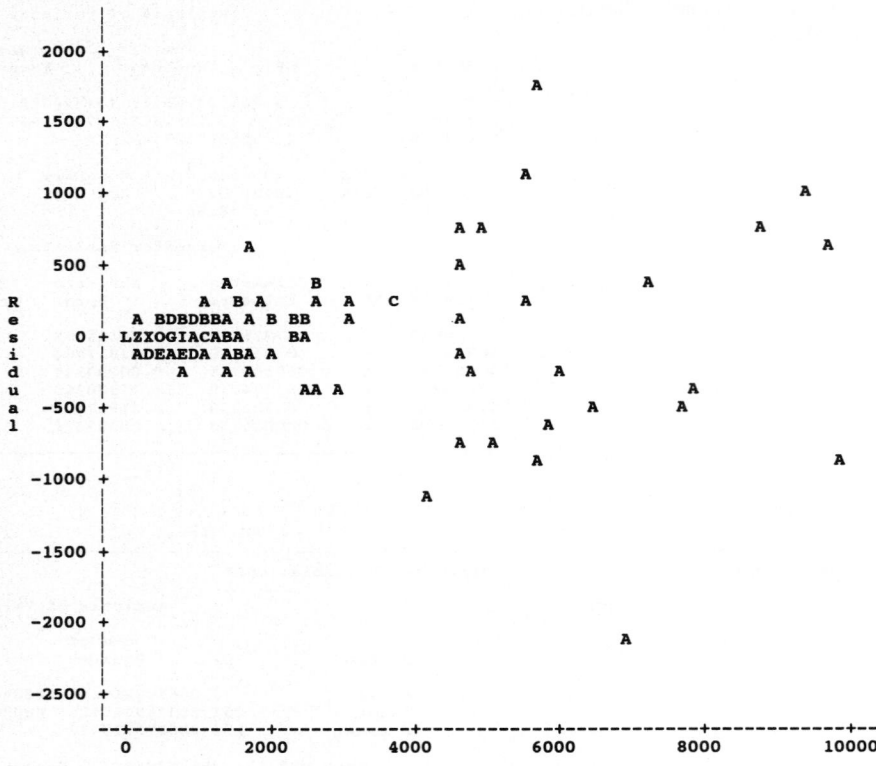

Plot of RESID*YHAT.   Legend: A = 1 obs, B = 2 obs, etc.

NOTE: 36 obs hidden.

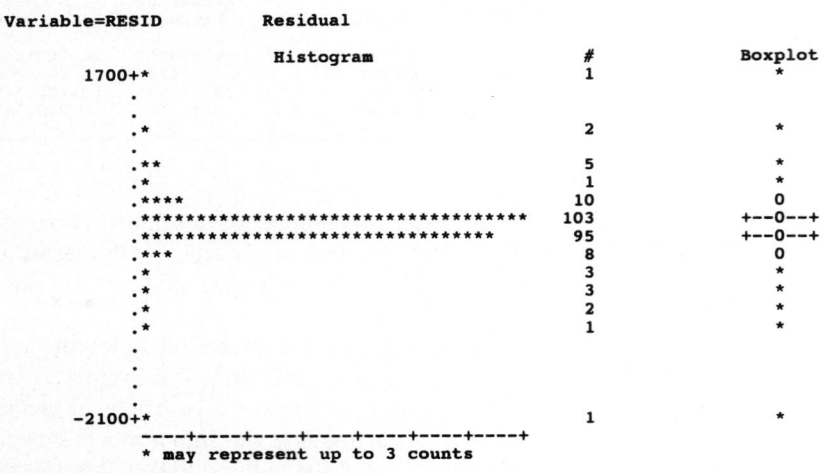

Variable=RESID   Residual

* may represent up to 3 counts

REFERENCES

Barnett, V., and Lewis, T. *Outliers in Statistical Data*. New York: Wiley, 1978.

Belsley, D. A., Kuh, E., and Welsch, R. E. *Regression Diagnostics: Identifying Influential Data and Sources of Collinearity*. New York: Wiley, 1980.

Cook, R. D. "Influential Observations in Linear Regression." *Journal of the American Statistical Association*, 1979, Vol. 74, pp. 169–174.

Mendenhall, W., and Sincich, T. *A Second Course in Business Statistics: Regression Analysis*, 4th ed. New York: Dellen/Macmillan, 1993.

Montgomery, D. C., and Peck, E. A. *Introduction to Linear Regression Analysis*. New York: Wiley, 1982.

Neter, J., Wasserman, W., and Kutner, M. H. *Applied Linear Statistical Models*, 3d ed. Homewood, IL: Irwin, 1989.

Rousseeuw, P. J., and Leroy, A. M. *Robust Regression and Outlier Detection*. New York: Wiley, 1987.

SAMPLE EXAM QUESTIONS: CHAPTERS 10–11

(1–5) An extensive study was undertaken at Utah State University to find the strongest predictor of a student athlete's academic performance (*Sociology of Sport Journal*, Vol. 3, 1986). Data collected for a sample of $n = 519$ student athletes included 15 independent variables. A stepwise regression was performed and the following regression model was fit:

$$E(y) = \beta_0 + \beta_1 x_1 + \beta_2 x_2 + \beta_3 x_3 + \beta_4 x_4 + \beta_5 x_5$$

where

y = University grade-point average (GPA)

x_1 = Ratio of number of years the athlete lettered to number of years participated in sport

x_2 = Standardized score on college entrance exam (SAT or ACT)

x_3 = high school GPA

$x_4 = \begin{cases} 1 & \text{if female} \\ 0 & \text{if male} \end{cases}$

$x_5 = \begin{cases} 1 & \text{if minority} \\ 0 & \text{if white} \end{cases}$

The β estimates, standard errors, and corresponding t ratios are given in the table:

	VARIABLE	$\hat{\beta}$	$s_{\hat{\beta}}$	t
Letter ratio	x_1	.152	.05	3.04
College entrance score	x_2	1.653	.22	7.51
High school GPA	x_3	.331	.06	5.52
Sex	x_4	.120	.05	2.40
Race	x_5	−.249	.06	−4.15

1. Identify the experimental unit for this regression.
2. Interpret the β estimates in the model.
3. Construct a 95% confidence interval for β_3. Interpret the result.
4. Test the hypothesis that letter ratio (x_1) is a useful linear predictor of university GPA (y). Use $\alpha = .05$.
5. Would you recommend using this stepwise model for predicting y without considering any other models? Explain.

(6–10)   Researchers at Upjohn utilized multiple regression analysis in the development of a sustained release tablet.* One of the objectives of the research was to develop a model relating the dissolution, y, of a tablet (ie, the percentage of the tablet dissolved over a period of time) to the following independent variables:

x_1 = Excipient level   Amount of nondrug ingredient in the tablet

x_2 = Process variable   For example, machine setting under which tablet is processed

6. Write a complete second-order model for $E(y)$.
7. Write a model that hypothesizes straight-line relationships between $E(y)$, x_1, and x_2. Assume that the lines relating $E(y)$ to x_1 for different values of x_2 are parallel.
8. What does it mean to say that x_1 and x_2 interact? Incorporate interaction into the model of Question 7.
9. In terms of the β's of the interaction model, what is the amount increase (or decrease) in $E(y)$ for every 1 unit increase in x_1 for a fixed value of x_2?
10. Now consider the simple, first-order model $E(y) = \beta_0 + \beta_1 x_1 + \beta_2 x_2$. The researchers are concerned about the presence of multicollinearity in the model. Explain what multicollinearity is, the problems it presents to the unwary regression analyst, and how it can be detected.

(11–13)   A naval base is considering modifying or adding to its fleet of 48 standard aircraft. The final decision regarding the type and number of aircraft to be added depends on a comparison of cost versus effectiveness of the modified fleet. Consequently, the naval base would like to model the projected percentage increase, y, in fleet effectiveness by the end of the decade as a function of the cost, x, of modifying the fleet (in million dollars). A first proposal is the straight-line model, $E(y) = \beta_0 + \beta_1 x$. The data provided in the table were collected on 10 naval bases of similar size that recently expanded their fleets.

	NAVAL BASE									
	1	2	3	4	5	6	7	8	9	10
PERCENT INCREASE IN EFFECTIVENESS y	18	32	9	37	6	3	30	10	25	2
COST OF MODIFICATION x	125	160	80	162	110	90	140	85	150	50

11. Estimate the values of β_0 and β_1. Interpret the results.
12. Conduct both a parametric and nonparametric test of zero slope. Interpret the results.
13. Calculate the residuals for the regression model and conduct a residual analysis. What are your recommendations for modifying the model, if any?

* Klassen, R. A. "The Application of Response Surface Methods to a Tablet Formulation Problem." Paper presented at Joint Statistical Meetings, American Statistical Association and Biometric Society, Aug. 1986, Chicago, IL.

(14–20) Refer to Questions 11–13. A second model considered is the quadratic model $E(y) = \beta_0 + \beta_1 x + \beta_2 x^2$. The SAS printout for the regression analysis is shown below:

Analysis of Variance

Source	DF	Sum of Squares	Mean Square	F Value	Prob>F
Model	2	1368.77501	684.38750	33.079	0.0003
Error	7	144.82499	20.68928		
C Total	9	1513.60000			

Root MSE	4.54855	R-square	0.9043	
Dep Mean	17.20000	Adj R-sq	0.8770	
C.V.	26.44504			

Parameter Estimates

Variable	DF	Parameter Estimate	Standard Error	T for H0: Parameter=0	Prob > |T|
INTERCEP	1	10.659036	14.55009061	0.733	0.4876
X	1	-0.281606	0.28087588	-1.003	0.3494
XX	1	0.002672	0.00125383	2.131	0.0706

Obs	X	Dep Var Y	Predict Value	Std Err Predict	Lower95% Predict	Upper95% Predict	Residual
1	125	18.0000	17.2073	2.063	5.3973	29.0173	0.7927
2	160	32.0000	34.0037	2.652	21.5528	46.4546	-2.0037
3	80	9.0000	5.2310	2.060	-6.5764	17.0384	3.7690
4	162	37.0000	35.1612	2.840	22.4815	47.8409	1.8388
5	110	6.0000	12.0128	2.218	0.0469	23.9788	-6.0128
6	90	3.0000	6.9572	2.083	-4.8731	18.7875	-3.9572
7	140	30.0000	23.6042	1.847	11.9957	35.2126	6.3958
8	85	10.0000	6.0273	2.049	-5.7695	17.8241	3.9727
9	150	25.0000	28.5367	2.007	16.7806	40.2929	-3.5367
10	50	2.0000	3.2586	4.192	-11.3682	17.8854	-1.2586

Obs	X	Std Err Residual	Student Residual	-2-1-0 1 2	Cook's D	Rstudent
1	125	4.054	0.196	| * |	0.003	0.1815
2	160	3.695	-0.542	*| |	0.051	-0.5129
3	80	4.055	0.929	| * |	0.074	0.9190
4	162	3.553	0.518	| * |	0.057	0.4886
5	110	3.971	-1.514	***| |	0.238	-1.7093
6	90	4.043	-0.979	*| |	0.085	-0.9753
7	140	4.157	1.539	| ***	0.156	1.7511
8	85	4.061	0.978	| * |	0.081	0.9748
9	150	4.082	-0.866	*| |	0.060	-0.8490
10	50	1.765	-0.713	*| |	0.955	-0.6854

Obs	X	Hat Diag H	Cov Ratio	Dffits	INTERCEP Dfbetas	X Dfbetas	XX Dfbetas
1	125	0.2057	1.9665	0.0924	-0.0594	0.0657	-0.0639
2	160	0.3401	2.1156	-0.3682	-0.1192	0.1505	-0.1871
3	80	0.2051	1.3457	0.4669	0.0286	0.0632	-0.1088
4	162	0.3898	2.3148	0.3904	0.1473	-0.1817	0.2199
5	110	0.2377	0.6336	-0.9545	0.5920	-0.7014	0.7211
6	90	0.2098	1.2924	-0.5025	0.1474	-0.2357	0.2724
7	140	0.1649	0.5511	0.7780	-0.3140	0.3143	-0.2585
8	85	0.2030	1.2818	0.4919	-0.0653	0.1582	-0.2007
9	150	0.1947	1.4030	-0.4174	0.0129	0.0093	-0.0503
10	50	0.8494	8.4082	-1.6276	-1.4594	1.2838	-1.1539

14. Find the value of s in the printout and interpret it.
15. Find the value of R_a^2 in the printout and interpret its value. Explain why R_a^2 is a better descriptive measure of model adequacy than R^2.

16. Perform a test of overall adequacy of the quadratic model. Use $\alpha = .05$.
17. Is there sufficient evidence to conclude that the percentage improvement, y, increases more quickly for more costly fleet modifications than for less costly fleet modifications? Test with $\alpha = .05$.
18. In the printout, find a 95% prediction interval for percentage improvement, y, when modification cost is $x = \$140$ million, and interpret the result.
19. Interpret the influence diagnostics shown in the printout.
20. Now consider the model $E(y) = \beta_0 + \beta_1 x_1 + \beta_2 x_1^2 + \beta_3 x_2 + \beta_4 x_1 x_2$, where

$$x_1 = \text{Cost of modifying the fleet}$$

$$x_2 = \begin{cases} 1 & \text{if American base} \\ 0 & \text{if foreign base} \end{cases}$$

The model is fit to the $n = 10$ data points and results in SSE $= 97.645$. Is there sufficient evidence to indicate that type of base (American or foreign) is a useful predictor of percentage improvement, y? Test using $\alpha = .05$.

(21–22) An insurance company is experimenting with three different training programs, A, B, and C, for its salespeople. The following first-order model is proposed:

$$E(y) = \beta_0 + \beta_1 x_1 + \beta_2 x_2 + \beta_3 x_3$$

where

$$y = \text{Monthly sales (in thousand dollars)}$$

$$x_1 = \text{Number of months experience}$$

$$x_2 = \begin{cases} 1 & \text{if training program B was used} \\ 0 & \text{otherwise} \end{cases}$$

$$x_3 = \begin{cases} 1 & \text{if training program C was used} \\ 0 & \text{otherwise} \end{cases}$$

Training program A is the base level.

21. What hypothesis would you test to determine whether the mean monthly sales differ for salespeople trained by the three programs?
22. After experimentation with 50 salespeople over a 5 year period, the first-order model is fit, with the following results:

$$\hat{y} = 10 + .5x_1 + 1.2x_2 - .4x_3 \qquad \text{SSE} = 140.5$$

Then the reduced model, $E(y) = \beta_0 + \beta_1 x_1$, is fit to the same data, with the following results:

$$\hat{y} = 11.4 + .4x_1 \qquad \text{SSE} = 183.2$$

Test the hypothesis formulated in Question 21. Use $\alpha = .05$.

(23–25) Most investment firms provide estimates, called *betas*, of systematic risks of securities. A stock's beta measures the relationship between its rate of return and the average rate of return for the market as a whole. Stocks with beta values greater than 1 are considered "aggressive" securities; stocks with beta values less than 1 are called "defensive" securities; and a stock with a beta value near 1 is called a "neutral" security. Does a stock's beta value depend on the length of the horizon (time period) over which the rates of return are calculated? The relationship between length of horizon (in months) and average beta value for each of the three types of stocks was investigated in the *Financial Analysts Journal* (Mar.–Apr. 1984). Varying the length of horizon from 1 to 30 months, rates of return were calculated for 144 stocks over the years 1946–1975. The stocks were divided into 38 aggressive, 38 defensive, and 68 neutral stocks based on their beta values. The table gives the average beta value for different horizons for each of the stock types.

| LENGTH OF HORIZON | BETA VALUES (y) | | |
x, Months	Aggressive Stocks	Defensive Stocks	Neutral Stocks
1	1.37	.50	.98
3	1.42	.44	.95
6	1.53	.41	.94
9	1.69	.39	1.00
12	1.83	.40	.98
15	1.67	.38	1.00
18	1.78	.39	1.02
24	1.86	.35	1.14
30	1.83	.33	1.22

23. The SAS printout of the simple linear regression equation relating average beta value, y, to length of horizon, x, for (1) aggressive stocks, (2) defensive stocks, and (3) neutral stocks are shown below. Give the least squares prediction equation for each type of stock.

```
----------------------------- STOCK=Aggresiv -----------------------------
Dependent Variable: BETA

                        Analysis of Variance

                              Sum of         Mean
        Source        DF     Squares        Square      F Value     Prob>F

        Model          1     0.19893       0.19893       19.156      0.0032
        Error          7     0.07269       0.01038
        C Total        8     0.27162

            Root MSE        0.10191     R-square        0.7324
            Dep Mean        1.66444     Adj R-sq        0.6941
            C.V.            6.12251

                        Parameter Estimates

                      Parameter      Standard     T for H0:
        Variable  DF   Estimate         Error    Parameter=0    Prob > |T|

        INTERCEP   1   1.450757    0.05947774       24.392         0.0001
        HORIZON    1   0.016298    0.00372383        4.377         0.0032


----------------------------- STOCK=Defensiv -----------------------------
Dependent Variable: BETA

                        Analysis of Variance

                              Sum of         Mean
        Source        DF     Squares        Square      F Value     Prob>F
        Model          1     0.01598       0.01598       30.115      0.0009
        Error          7     0.00371       0.00053
        C Total        8     0.01969

            Root MSE        0.02303     R-square        0.8114
            Dep Mean        0.39889     Adj R-sq        0.7845
            C.V.            5.77406

                        Parameter Estimates

                      Parameter      Standard     T for H0:
        Variable  DF   Estimate         Error    Parameter=0    Prob > |T|

        INTERCEP   1   0.459445    0.01344278       34.178         0.0001
        HORIZON    1  -0.004619    0.00084164       -5.488         0.0009
```

(continued)

```
------------------------------ STOCK=Neutral ------------------------------
Dependent Variable: BETA

                        Analysis of Variance

                            Sum of        Mean
       Source        DF    Squares       Square     F Value     Prob>F
       Model          1    0.05702      0.05702      32.172     0.0008
       Error          7    0.01241      0.00177
       C Total        8    0.06942

           Root MSE       0.04210    R-square      0.8213
           Dep Mean       1.02556    Adj R-sq      0.7958
           C.V.           4.10492

                       Parameter Estimates

                     Parameter    Standard    T for H0:
       Variable  DF   Estimate       Error    Parameter=0    Prob > |T|

       INTERCEP   1   0.911154    0.02457080      37.083      0.0001
       HORIZON    1   0.008726    0.00153835       5.672      0.0008
```

24. For each type of stock, test the hypothesis that length of horizon is a useful linear predictor of average beta value. Test using $\alpha = .05$.

25. For each type of stock, construct a 95% confidence interval for the slope of the line. Which stocks have beta values that increase linearly as length of horizon increases? Which stocks have beta values that decrease linearly as length of horizon increases?

CHAPTER 12

TIME SERIES ANALYSIS AND FORECASTING

CONTENTS

To operate effectively, power companies must be able to accurately predict daily peak demand for electricity. Consequently, they are continually developing and refining statistical models of daily peak demand. This chapter is an introduction to the very complex and voluminous body of material concerned with data collected over time—**time series**. The problem of modeling and forecasting the daily peak demand time series at Florida Power Corporation is addressed in the chapter case study.

TIME SERIES COMPONENTS

12.1

In many business and economic studies, the dependent variable y is measured sequentially in time. For example, we might record the number, y, of new housing starts for each month in a particular region. This collection of data is called a **time series**. Other examples of time series are data collected on the daily production for a manufacturing company, the annual sales for a corporation, and the recorded month-end values of the prime interest rate.

DEFINITION 12.1

A **time series** is a collection of data obtained by observing a response variable at periodic points in time.

DEFINITION 12.2

If repeated observations on a variable produce a time series, the variable is called a **time series variable**. We use y_t to denote the value of the variable at time t.

Researchers often approach the problem of describing the nature of a time series y_t by identifying four kinds of change, or variation, in the time series values. These four components are commonly known as (1) **secular trend**, (2) **cyclical effect**, (3) **seasonal variation**, and (4) **residual effect**.

The components of a time series are most easily identified and explained pictorially in a **time series plot**. A time series plot is a sequence plot with the time series variable, y_t, on the vertical axis and time, t, on the horizontal axis.

Figure 12.1a shows a secular trend in the time series values. The secular component describes the tendency of the value of the variable to increase or decrease over a long period of time. Thus, this type of change or variation is also known as the **long-term trend**. In Figure 12.1a, the long-term trend is of an increasing nature. However, this does not imply that the time series has always moved upward from month to month and from year to year. You can see that the series fluctuates, but that the trend has been an increasing one over that period of time.

FIGURE 12.1
The Components of a Time Series

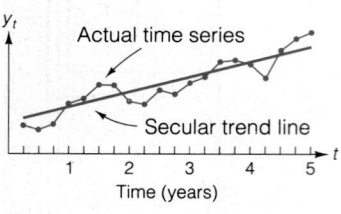

a.

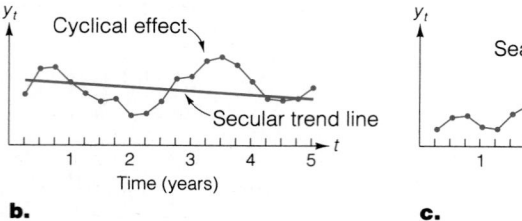

b.

c.

The cyclical effect in a time series, as shown in Figure 12.1b, generally describes the fluctuation about the secular trend that is attributable to business and economic conditions at the time. These fluctuations are sometimes called **business cycles**.

During a period of general economic expansion, the business cycle lies above the secular trend, while during a recession, when business activity is likely to slump, the cycle lies below the secular trend. You can see that the cyclical variation does not follow any definite trend, but moves rather unpredictably.

The seasonal variation in a time series describes the fluctuations that recur during specific portions of each year (eg, monthly or seasonally). In Figure 12.1c, you can see that the pattern of change in the time series within a year tends to be repeated from year to year, producing a wavelike, or oscillating, curve.

The final component, the residual effect, is what remains after the secular, cyclical, and seasonal components have been removed. This component is not systematic and may be attributed to unpredictable influences such as wars, hurricanes, presidential assassination, and randomness of human actions. Thus, the residual effect represents the random error component of a time series.

DEFINITION 12.3

The **secular trend** (T_t) of a time series is the tendency of the series to increase or decrease over a long period of time. It is also known as the **long-term trend**.

DEFINITION 12.4

The **cyclical fluctuation** (C_t) of a time series is the wavelike, or oscillating, pattern about the secular trend that is attributable to business and economic conditions at the time. It is also known as a **business cycle**.

DEFINITION 12.5

The **seasonal variation** (S_t) of a time series describes the fluctuations that recur during specific portions of the year (eg, monthly or seasonally).

DEFINITION 12.6

The **residual effect** (R_t) of a time series is what remains after the secular, cyclical, and seasonal components have been removed.

In many practical applications of time series, one of the objectives is to **forecast** (predict) some future value of the series. To obtain forecasts, some type of model that can be projected into the future must be used to describe the time series. One of the most widely used models is the **additive model**[*]

$$y_t = T_t + C_t + S_t + R_t$$

where T_t, C_t, S_t, and R_t represent the secular trend, cyclical effect, seasonal variation, and residual effect, respectively, of the time series variable, y_t. Various methods exist for estimating the components of the model and forecasting the time series. These range from simple **descriptive techniques**, which rely on smoothing the pattern of the time series, to complex **inferential models**, which combine regression analysis with specialized time series models.

Several descriptive techniques are presented in Sections 12.3 and 12.4, and forecasting using the general linear regression model of Chapters 10 and 11 is discussed in Section 12.5. The remainder of the chapter is devoted to the more complex and more powerful time series models. First, we discuss how to collect time series data.

COLLECTING TIME SERIES DATA

12.2

Since time series data are data collected sequentially on a regular chronological basis, this implies that the data should be equally spaced—every year, every 3 months, every other day, etc. In most business applications, we satisfy this requirement by recording the value of the variable of interest each time period (eg, day, month, or year) for *n consecutive* time periods.

For example, if we are interested in forecasting the annual price of gold (dollars per troy ounce), our sample might consist of annual gold prices for the past $n = 22$ years, as shown in Table 12.1. Note that we do not select a random sample of 22 years from the population of all years for which gold prices have been recorded. Rather, we observe the annual gold prices for 22 consecutive years, say 1971–1992, in the hopes of detecting a trend in the time series that can be used to forecast prices in future years.

TABLE 12.1

Gold Prices (Dollars Per Ounce) from 1971 to 1992

YEAR	PRICE	YEAR	PRICE	YEAR	PRICE
1971	41.25	1979	307.80	1986	367.87
1972	58.61	1980	606.01	1987	408.91
1973	97.81	1981	450.63	1988	436.93
1974	159.70	1982	374.18	1989	381.28
1975	161.40	1983	449.03	1990	384.07
1976	124.80	1984	360.29	1991	362.04
1977	148.30	1985	317.30	1992	344.50
1978	193.50				

Source: Survey of Current Business, U.S. Department of Commerce.

---

[*] Another useful model is the **multiplicative model**, $y_t = T_t C_t S_t R_t$. Note that this model can be written in the form of an additive model by taking natural logarithms:

$$\log y_t = \log T_t + \log C_t + \log S_t + \log R_t$$

This characteristic of time series—data recorded at n consecutive points in time—makes it easy to collect the data. The problem is in deciding how many consecutive time periods to include in the sample. A rule of thumb used by some time series forecasters is that the number of time periods, n, in the sample should be at least twice as large as the forecast horizon (ie, the number of time periods into the future for which you want to obtain a forecast). For example, if we wanted to forecast annual gold price 5 years into the future, we would need to include in our sample, at minimum, gold prices for the past 10 years. On the other hand, some time series analysts will not make forecasts, short-term or long-term, without at least 40 data points in the sample.

Although there is merit for selecting a large n, keep in mind that most forecasting models give more weight to the most recent values of the time series. Intuitively, you would expect the future 1995 gold price to be much closer to \$344.50 (the 1992 price) than to \$41.25 (the 1971 price). We will see that for some simple forecasting methods, the key is selecting n large enough to capture the most recent trend in the series. Other, more complex regression-based forecasting models require a larger sample. Thus, the size n will vary with the forecasting method you use.

INDEX NUMBERS

12.3 Various descriptive methods are available for identifying and characterizing a time series. A popular descriptive technique employs **index numbers**. Index numbers are used to measure how much a variable changes over time, relative to a **base period**. For example, we may be interested in comparing the prime interest rate charged by U.S. banks in 1993 with the prime rate in 1981, a year in which a major recession occurred. An index number will allow us to make this comparison.

DEFINITION 12.7

An **index number** is a number that measures the relative change in a variable over time. Index numbers are often used to characterize time series phenomena.

Index numbers may be computed from a single time series variable (eg, world share of oil production), or they may be a composite of several time series variables. For example, an index familiar to everyone is the Consumer Price Index (CPI). The CPI, compiled monthly by the U.S. Bureau of Labor, measures overall price changes of a variety of consumer goods (including food, clothing, television equipment, housing, and transportation) relative to the base year of 1972. The CPI combines the prices of approximately 400 items into a single index that is often used to gauge the increase in the cost of living. Two other important business indexes that combine or aggregate several variables are the Dow Jones Average (DJA) and the Wholesale Price Index.

In this section we present two different types of index numbers, **simple index numbers** and **composite index numbers**, found to be useful in describing time series.

SIMPLE INDEX NUMBERS

DEFINITION 12.8

A **simple index number** is based on the relative changes over time in the value of a single time series variable.

EXAMPLE 12.1 The 1971–1992 gold prices of Table 12.1 are reproduced in Table 12.2. Calculate simple index numbers for the gold price series using 1972 as the base period. Interpret the results.

TABLE 12.2
Gold Prices, Revisited

YEAR	PRICE	YEAR	PRICE	YEAR	PRICE
1971	41.25	1979	307.80	1986	367.87
1972	58.61	1980	606.01	1987	408.91
1973	97.81	1981	450.63	1988	436.93
1974	159.70	1982	374.18	1989	381.28
1975	161.40	1983	449.03	1990	384.07
1976	124.80	1984	360.29	1991	362.04
1977	148.30	1985	317.30	1992	344.50
1978	193.50				

Source: Survey of Current Business, U.S. Department of Commerce.

Solution The first step in calculating an index number is to select the base period—that is, the time period (month, year, etc.), upon which the index is to be based. In this example, since the price of gold is measured each year, we have chosen 1972 as the base period. The base period is selected with some purpose in mind, since all comparisons of the price of gold will be made relative to the price in the base year. Usually, an economist will choose a year during which price levels are "normal," that is, undisturbed by unusual or extenuating factors (defining price normality is a complex, if not impossible, problem). Many current business and economic indexes, including the CPI, use 1972 as a base period, and for this example, we will also.

After the base period is selected, the next step is to compare the value of the time series variable at two different times—the time being indexed, say t, and the base period, say t_0. In our example, $t_0 = 1972$; thus, we will compare the price of gold in year t with the price of gold in 1972. In general, index numbers are expressed as percentages. We shall use the percentage

$$\left(\frac{\text{Price of gold in year } t}{\text{Price of gold in base year 1972}} \right) \times 100$$

as a simple index of the price of gold at year t. This percentage will then be computed for all years 1971–1992.

Let us start with year $t = 1971$. To compute the gold price index for 1971, say I_{1971}, first form the ratio

$$\frac{\text{Price of gold in 1971}}{\text{Price of gold in 1972}} = \frac{41.25}{58.61} = .704$$

Expressing this ratio as a percentage, we have

$$I_{1971} = \left(\frac{41.25}{58.61}\right) \times 100 = (.704)(100) = 70.4$$

Thus, the gold price index for the year 1971 is 70.4%. Notice that the gold price index for the base year $t_0 = 1972$ is

$$I_{1972} = \left(\frac{\text{Price of gold in 1972}}{\text{Price of gold in 1972}}\right) \times 100$$

$$= \left(\frac{58.61}{58.61}\right) \times 100 = 100.00$$

It is always true that **the index number for the base period is 100%**. The complete gold price index for 1971–1992 is shown in Table 12.3.

TABLE 12.3
Simple Index for Gold Prices of Example 12.1

YEAR	INDEX	YEAR	INDEX	YEAR	INDEX
1971	70.4	1979	525.2	1986	627.7
1972	100.0	1980	1,034.0	1987	697.7
1973	166.9	1981	768.9	1988	745.5
1974	272.5	1982	638.4	1989	650.5
1975	275.4	1983	766.1	1990	593.9
1976	212.9	1984	614.7	1991	617.7
1977	253.0	1985	541.4	1992	587.8
1978	330.1				

The index numbers of Table 12.3 reflect relative price changes in gold from the base year of 1972. Since the indexes are percentages, they represent the percentage change in gold price relative to the base year of 1972. For example, the index for 1971 is 70.4. Thus, we say that the price of gold in 1971 was 70.4% of the price in the base year 1972. Or, equivalently, the 1971 price was 29.6% less than the 1972 price. Now consider the 1987 gold price index of 697.7. This value implies that the price of gold in 1987 was 697.7% of the price in 1972; that is, the price of gold increased 597.7% relative to the base year of 1972. The remaining index values are interpreted similarly.

The graph of the gold price index for 1971–1992 is shown in Figure 12.2. Notice that the plot makes it easy to identify the highly inflationary period beginning in 1974 and the extreme jump in gold prices in 1980. This is one of the primary values of simple indexes—they make price fluctuations and trends easier to identify and compare.

STEPS IN CALCULATING A SIMPLE INDEX NUMBER FOR A TIME SERIES

STEP 1 Select the base period, that is, the time t_0 upon which the index is to be based.

STEP 2 Letting y_t represent the value of the time series variable at time t, compute the ratio

$$\frac{y_t}{y_{t_0}}$$

STEP 3 The simple index I_t for the time series variable at time t is the ratio in step 2 expressed as a percentage, that is,

$$I_t = \left(\frac{y_t}{y_{t_0}}\right) 100$$

STEP 4 Repeat steps 2 and 3 for each value y_t of the time series.

FIGURE 12.2
Graph of Gold Price Index for
Example 12.1

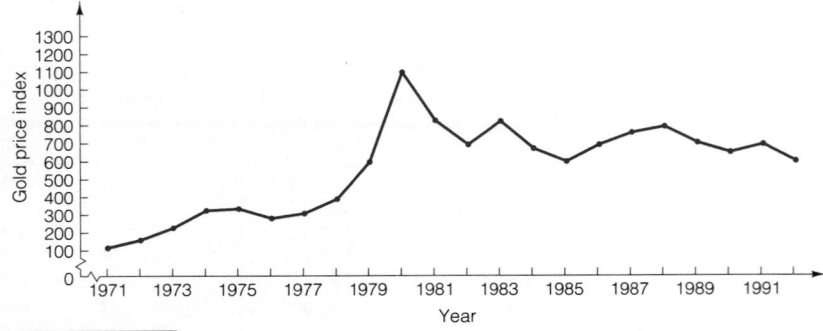

As previously stated, simple index numbers will always be based on a single time series variable. However, business and economic time series analysts are frequently more interested in examining index numbers for a composite of several variables, such as a combination of wholesale prices of manufactured goods.

**COMPOSITE INDEX
NUMBERS**

Index numbers computed from a combination of several time series variables or commodities are called **composite index numbers**. The construction of a composite index requires choosing a method of combining the commodities that compose the index. The simplest method of combining these time series variables is to sum them. A composite index based on this sum is called a **simple composite index**.*

---

* Another set of composite index numbers is the **weighted composite index**. The time series values are weighted before being summed, where the weights are multipliers chosen to reflect the relative importance of each value. Consult the references for details on how to compute weighted composite index numbers.

EXAMPLE 12.2 The total annual personal consumption expenditures (in billion dollars) of U.S. citizens for food, transportation, and medical care for 1983–1991 are given in Table 12.4. Calculate the simple composite index for total annual expenditures for these three commodities using the base period $t_0 = 1980$. Interpret the index.

TABLE 12.4

Annual Personal Consumption Expenditures for Example 12.2

YEAR	FOOD	TRANSPORTATION	MEDICAL	TOTALS
1980	394.9	77.4	200.6	672.9
1983	414.0	71.4	222.3	707.7
1984	422.8	75.9	232.0	730.7
1985	435.5	82.1	240.9	758.5
1986	447.1	86.2	251.5	784.8
1987	452.7	89.6	266.8	809.1
1988	460.0	94.5	278.2	832.7
1989	497.1	98.2	309.0	904.3
1990	523.8	102.6	329.8	956.2
1991	543.7	109.3	351.6	1,004.6

Source: Statistical Abstract of the United States, U.S. Bureau of the Census, 1992.

Solution   To compute a simple composite index, we first need to sum the values of the respective time series variables. In this example, we sum the annual personal consumption expenditures for food, transportation, and medical care. The sums of these annual expenditures are given in the column labeled TOTALS in Table 12.4. It is this column of numbers that is used to compute the simple composite index.

If we let y_t represent the total annual expenditures during year t, the simple composite index (using 1980 as a base) is

$$I_{1983} = \left(\frac{y_{1983}}{y_{1980}}\right) \times 100 = \left(\frac{707.7}{672.9}\right) \times 100 = 105.2$$

$$I_{1984} = \left(\frac{y_{1984}}{y_{1980}}\right) \times 100 = \left(\frac{730.7}{672.9}\right) \times 100 = 108.6$$

$$I_{1985} = \left(\frac{y_{1985}}{y_{1980}}\right) \times 100 = \left(\frac{758.5}{672.9}\right) \times 100 = 112.7$$

and so forth. The complete simple composite index for total annual personal consumption expenditures from 1983 to 1991 is given in Table 12.5.

TABLE 12.5

Simple Composite Index for Total Annual Personal Consumption Expenditures for Example 12.2

YEAR	INDEX	YEAR	INDEX
1983	105.2	1988	123.7
1984	108.6	1989	134.4
1985	112.7	1990	142.1
1986	116.6	1991	149.3
1987	120.2		

Our interpretation of the simple composite index is identical to that of the simple index. For example, the 1991 index value of 149.3 represents a 49.3% increase (relative to the base year of 1980) in total annual personal consumption expenditures for food, transportation, and medical care in the United States.

We conclude this section with a warning. There is little doubt that index numbers provide useful descriptive summaries of the degree of relative change in business and economic activity. However, there is a danger of using index numbers for more than they are intended. For example, the Consumer Price Index (CPI) measures how prices of a market basket of goods, *purchased by moderate-income, urban Americans*, have changed. But the CPI is frequently used to gauge the cost of living for *all Americans*. While the CPI does reflect the cost of living to some degree, all Americans certainly do not purchase the same goods in the same quantities as urban Americans with moderate incomes. Thus, using the CPI to measure the cost of living of, say, low-income, inner-city families would be improper.

PROBLEMS

12.1 Since the energy shortage, the price of foreign crude oil has skyrocketed. Consequently, crude oil imports into the United States have declined. The data in the table are the amounts of crude oil (million barrels) imported into the United States from the Organization of Petroleum Exporting Countries (OPEC) for the years 1973–1990. Using 1975 as the base period (a year when oil prices skyrocketed), calculate the simple index for OPEC imports from 1973 to 1990.

YEAR	t	IMPORTS y_t	YEAR	t	IMPORTS y_t
1973	1	767	1982	10	633
1974	2	926	1983	11	540
1975	3	1,171	1984	12	553
1976	4	1,663	1985	13	479
1977	5	2,058	1986	14	771
1978	6	1,892	1987	15	876
1979	7	1,866	1988	16	987
1980	8	1,414	1989	17	1,232
1981	9	1,067	1990	18	1,282

Source: *Statistical Abstracts of the United States*, U.S. Bureau of the Census, 1992.

12.2 The Gross National Product (GNP) is a measure of total U.S. output and is therefore an important indicator of the U.S. economy. The GNP is the sum of several components. One of these is personal consumption expenditures, which is itself the sum of durable goods, nondurable goods, and services. The amounts (in billion dollars) spent on durable goods, nondurable goods, and services in the United States for the period 1980–1992 are given in the table at the top of the next page.

YEAR	GNP Durable Goods	GNP Nondurable Goods	GNP Services
1980	211.6	674.3	785.3
1981	236.1	733.9	887.1
1982	245.1	757.5	982.2
1983	279.8	801.7	1,074.4
1984	335.5	867.3	1,128.7
1985	368.7	913.1	1,347.5
1986	402.4	939.4	1,458.0
1987	413.6	974.4	1,568.3
1988	455.2	1,052.3	1,727.6
1989	474.6	1,130.0	1,845.5
1990	480.3	1,193.7	1,983.3
1991	446.1	1,251.5	2,190.1
1992	480.3	1,290.5	2,324.0

Source: Survey of Current Business, U.S. Department of Commerce, Bureau of Economic Analysis.

a. Using 1980 as a base period, construct a simple composite index for personal consumption for the years 1980–1992.

b. Graph the entire simple composite index of part **a**.

c. Interpret the value of the index for 1992.

12.3 The table records the monthly number of mortgage applications (in thousands) for new home construction processed by the Federal Housing Administration (FHA) for the period 1990–1992.

	MORTGAGE APPLICATIONS (THOUSANDS)		
	1990	1991	1992
January	9.0	8.0	7.2
February	9.4	6.7	7.5
March	11.6	8.2	10.1
April	10.3	9.4	9.4
May	12.8	10.5	7.9
June	10.4	8.8	7.7
July	9.0	10.1	8.8
August	10.2	7.4	7.5
September	9.3	7.1	7.1
October	9.5	8.7	—
November	8.1	6.6	—
December	5.8	6.5	—

Source: Survey of Current Business, U.S. Department of Commerce, Bureau of Economic Analysis.

a. Using January 1990 as the base period, calculate and plot the simple index for monthly number of mortgage applications between January 1990 and September 1992.

b. Interpret the value of the index you obtained for July 1992.

12.4 The table on p. 634 lists the total number of automobiles (in thousands) sold by each of three major U.S. manufacturers (GM, Ford, and Chrysler) from 1980 to 1990. Using 1980 as the base period, construct a simple composite index for the total number of sales of the three major automobile manufacturers in the United States. Graph and interpret the index.

Data for Problem 12.4

	AUTOS SOLD (THOUSANDS)		
YEAR	GM	Ford	Chrysler
1980	7,101	4,328	1,225
1981	6,762	4,313	1,283
1982	6,244	4,255	1,182
1983	7,769	4,934	1,494
1984	8,256	5,584	2,034
1985	9,305	5,550	2,157
1986	8,576	5,916	2,198
1987	7,765	6,051	2,260
1988	8,108	6,441	2,567
1989	7,946	6,336	2,382
1990	7,451	4,395	1,946

Source: Moody's Industrial Manual, 1991.

FORECASTING USING SMOOTHING TECHNIQUES

12.4 Our discussion of forecasting begins with descriptive methods. Generally, these methods attempt to remove the rapid fluctuations in a time series so that the secular trend can be seen. For this reason, they are sometimes called **smoothing techniques**. Once the secular trend is identified, forecasts for future values of the time series are easily obtained. In this section we present three of the more popular smoothing techniques.

MOVING AVERAGE METHOD

A widely used smoothing technique is the **moving average method**. A moving average M_t at time t is formed by averaging the time series values over adjacent time periods. Moving averages aid in identifying the secular trend of a time series because the averaging tends to modify the effect of short-term (cyclical or seasonal) variation. That is, a plot of the moving averages yields a smooth time series curve that clearly depicts the long-term trend.

For example, consider Table 12.6, where we list the 1990–1993 quarterly power loads for a utility company located in a southern part of the United States.

The graph of the quarterly time series in Figure 12.3 shows the pronounced seasonal variation, that is, the fluctuation that recurs from year to year. The quarterly power loads tend to be highest in the summer months (quarter III), with another smaller peak in the winter months (quarter I), and lowest during the spring and fall (quarters II and IV, respectively). To clearly identify the long-term trend of the series, we need to average, or "smooth out," these seasonal fluctuations. We will apply the moving average method for this purpose.

The first step in calculating a moving average for quarterly data is to sum the observed time values, y_t—in this example, quarterly power loads—for the four quarters during the initial year 1990. Summing the values from Table 12.6, we have

$$y_1 + y_2 + y_3 + y_4 = 103.5 + 94.7 + 118.6 + 109.3$$
$$= 426.1$$

This sum is called a **4-point moving total**, which we denote by the symbol S_t. It is customary to use a subscript t to represent the time period at the midpoint of

TABLE 12.6
Quarterly Power Loads, 1990–1993

YEAR	QUARTER	TIME t	POWER LOAD y_t, Megawatts
1990	I	1	103.5
	II	2	94.7
	III	3	118.6
	IV	4	109.3
1991	I	5	126.1
	II	6	116.0
	III	7	141.2
	IV	8	131.6
1992	I	9	144.5
	II	10	137.1
	III	11	159.0
	IV	12	149.5
1993	I	13	166.1
	II	14	152.5
	III	15	178.2
	IV	16	169.0

FIGURE 12.3
Graph of Quarterly Power Loads, Table 12.6

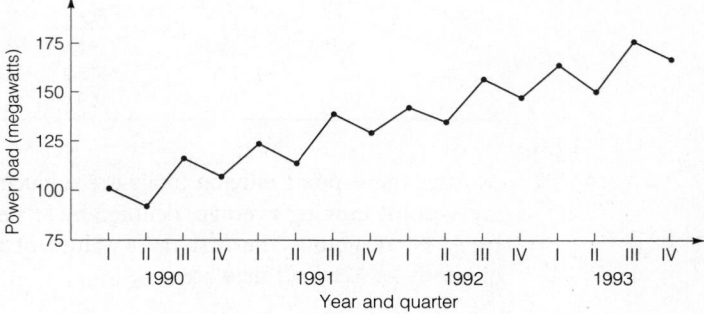

the four quarters in the total. Since the midpoint for this sum is between $t = 2$ and $t = 3$, we will use the conventional procedure of "dropping it down one line" to $t = 3$. Thus, our first 4-point moving total is $S_3 = 426.1$.

We find the next moving total by eliminating the first quantity in the sum, $y_1 = 103.5$, and adding the next value in the time series sequence, $y_5 = 126.1$. This enables us to keep four quarters in the total of adjacent time periods. Thus, we have

$$S_4 = y_2 + y_3 + y_4 + y_5 = 94.7 + 118.6 + 109.3 + 126.1 = 448.7$$

Continuing this process of moving the 4-point total over the time series until we have included the last value, we find

$$S_5 = y_3 + y_4 + y_5 + y_6 \quad = 118.6 + 109.3 + 126.1 + 116.0 = 470.0$$
$$S_6 = y_4 + y_5 + y_6 + y_7 \quad = 109.3 + 126.1 + 116.0 + 141.2 = 492.6$$
$$\vdots \qquad\qquad \vdots \qquad\qquad\qquad\qquad\qquad\qquad \vdots$$
$$S_{15} = y_{13} + y_{14} + y_{15} + y_{16} = 166.1 + 152.5 + 178.2 + 169.0 = 665.8$$

The complete set of 4-point moving totals is given in Table 12.7. Notice that three data points will be "lost" in forming the moving totals.

TABLE 12.7
4-Point Moving Average for the Quarterly Power Load Data

YEAR	QUARTER	TIME t	POWER LOAD y_t	4-POINT MOVING TOTAL S_t	4-POINT MOVING AVERAGE M_t	RATIO y_t/M_t
1990	I	1	103.5	—	—	—
	II	2	94.7	—	—	—
	III	3	118.6	426.1	106.5	1.113
	IV	4	109.3	448.7	112.2	.974
1991	I	5	126.1	470.0	117.5	1.073
	II	6	116.0	492.6	123.2	.942
	III	7	141.2	514.9	128.7	1.097
	IV	8	131.6	533.3	133.3	.987
1992	I	9	144.5	554.4	138.6	1.043
	II	10	137.1	572.2	143.1	.958
	III	11	159.0	590.1	147.5	1.078
	IV	12	149.5	611.7	152.9	.978
1993	I	13	166.1	627.1	156.8	1.059
	II	14	152.5	646.3	161.6	.944
	III	15	178.2	665.8	166.5	1.071
	IV	16	169.0	—	—	—

After the 4-point moving totals are calculated, the second step is to determine the **4-point moving average**, denoted by M_t, by dividing each of the moving totals by 4. For example, the first three values of the 4-point moving average for the quarterly power load data are

$$M_3 = \frac{y_1 + y_2 + y_3 + y_4}{4} = \frac{S_3}{4} = \frac{426.1}{4} = 106.5$$

$$M_4 = \frac{y_2 + y_3 + y_4 + y_5}{4} = \frac{S_4}{4} = \frac{448.7}{4} = 112.2$$

$$M_5 = \frac{y_3 + y_4 + y_5 + y_6}{4} = \frac{S_5}{4} = \frac{470.0}{4} = 117.5$$

All the 4-point moving averages are given in Table 12.7.

Both the original power load time series and the 4-point moving average are graphed in Figure 12.4. Notice that the moving average has "smoothed" the time series; that is, the averaging has modified the effects of the short-term or seasonal variation. The plot of the 4-point moving average clearly depicts the secular (long-term) trend component of the time series.

In addition to identifying a long-term trend, moving averages provide us with a measure of the seasonal effects in a time series. The ratio between the observed power load, y_t, and the 4-point moving average, M_t, for each quarter measures the seasonal effect (primarily attributable to temperature differences) for that quarter.

FIGURE 12.4

Quarterly Power Loads and 4-Point
Moving Average

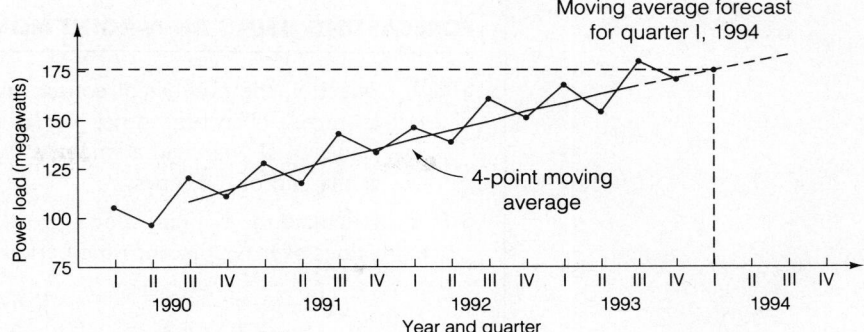

The ratios y_t/M_t are shown in the last column of Table 12.7. Note that the ratio is always greater than 1 in quarters I and III, and always less than 1 in quarters II and IV. The average of the ratios for a particular quarter, multiplied by 100, can be used to form a **seasonal index** for that quarter. For example, the seasonal index for quarter I is

$$(100)\frac{1.073 + 1.043 + 1.059}{3} = 105.8$$

implying that the time series value in quarter I is, on the average, 105.8% of the moving average value for that time period.

To forecast a future value of the time series, simply extend the moving average M_t on the graph to the future time period. For example, a graphical extension of the moving average for the quarterly power loads to quarter I of 1994 ($t = 17$) yields a moving average of approximately $M_{17} = 172$ (see Figure 12.4). Thus, if there were no seasonal variation in the time series, we would expect the power load for quarter I of 1994 to be approximately 172 megawatts. To adjust the forecast for seasonal variation, multiply the future moving average value $M_{17} = 172$ by the seasonal index for quarter I, and then divide by 100:

$$F_{17} = M_{17}\left(\frac{\text{Seasonal index for quarter I}}{100}\right)$$

$$= 172\left(\frac{105.8}{100}\right) \approx 182$$

where F_{17} is the forecast of y_{17}. Therefore, the moving average forecast for the power load in quarter I of 1994 is approximately 182 megawatts.

Moving averages are not restricted to 4 points. You may wish, for example, to calculate a 7-point moving average for daily data, a 12-point moving average for monthly data, or a 5-point moving average for yearly data. The choice of the number of points, N, is an important one. Large values of N yield a smoother series than small values of N. However, more data points are retained at the end of a series with a smaller N. Consequently, you should search for the number N that yields a smooth series, but is not so large that many points at the end of the series are lost. The method of forecasting with a general N-point moving average is outlined in the box on the next page.

FORECASTING USING AN *N*-POINT MOVING AVERAGE

STEP 1 Select N, the number of consecutive time series values that will be averaged. (The time series values must be equally spaced.) Larger values of N will yield a smoother series, but will retain fewer points at the end of the series.

STEP 2 Calculate the N-point moving total, S_t, by summing the time series values over N adjacent time periods, where

$$S_t = \begin{cases} y_{t-(N-1)/2} + \cdots + y_t + \cdots + y_{t+(N-1)/2} & \text{if } N \text{ is odd} \\ y_{t-N/2} + \cdots + y_t + \cdots + y_{t+N/2} & \text{if } N \text{ is even} \end{cases}$$

STEP 3 Compute the N-point moving average, M_t, by dividing the corresponding moving total by N:

$$M_t = \frac{S_t}{N}$$

STEP 4 Graph the moving average, M_t, on the vertical axis with time, t, on the horizontal axis. (This plot should reveal a smooth curve that identifies the long-term trend of the time series.*) Extend the graph to a future time period to obtain the forecast value of M_t.

STEP 5 For a future time period, t, the forecast of y_t is

$$F_t = \begin{cases} M_t & \text{if little or no seasonal variation exists in the time series} \\ M_t \cdot \left(\dfrac{\text{Seasonal index}}{100} \right) & \text{otherwise} \end{cases}$$

where the seasonal index for a particular quarter (or month) is the average of past values of the ratios

$$\frac{y_t}{M_t}(100)$$

for that quarter (or month).

EXPONENTIAL SMOOTHING

One problem with using a moving average to forecast future values of a time series is that values at the ends of the series are lost, thereby requiring that we subjectively extend the graph of the moving average into the future. No exact calculation of a forecast is available, since predicting the moving average at a future time period, t, requires that we know one or more future values of the series. A technique leading to forecasts that can be explicitly calculated is called **exponential smoothing**. Like the moving average method, exponential smoothing tends to de-emphasize

---

* When the number, N, of points is small, the plot may not yield a very smooth curve. However, the moving average will be smoother (or less variable) than the plot of the original time series values.

(or smooth) most of the residual effects. However, exponential smoothing averages only past and current values of the time series.

To obtain an exponentially smoothed time series, we first need to choose a weight, w, between 0 and 1 called the **exponential smoothing constant**. The exponentially smoothed series, denoted E_t, is then calculated as follows:

$$E_1 = y_1$$
$$E_2 = wy_2 + (1 - w)E_1$$
$$E_3 = wy_3 + (1 - w)E_2$$
$$\vdots$$
$$E_t = wy_t + (1 - w)E_{t-1}$$

You can see that the exponentially smoothed value at time t is simply a weighted average of the current time series value, y_t, and the exponentially smoothed value at the previous time period, E_{t-1}. Smaller values of w give less weight to the current value, y_t, while larger values give more weight to y_t. Consequently, the smaller the value of the smoothing constant w, the smoother the series, E_t.

For example, suppose we want to smooth the quarterly power loads given in Table 12.6 using an exponential smoothing constant of $w = .7$. Then we have

$$E_1 = y_1 = 103.5$$
$$E_2 = .7y_2 + (1 - .7)E_1 = .7(94.7) + .3(103.5) = 97.3$$
$$E_3 = .7y_3 + (1 - .7)E_2 = .7(118.6) + .3(97.3) = 112.2$$
$$\vdots$$

The exponentially smoothed values (using $w = .7$) for all the quarterly power loads are given in Table 12.8. Both the actual and the smoothed time series values are graphed in Figure 12.5.

TABLE 12.8
Quarterly Power Loads with Exponential Smoothing

YEAR	QUARTER	TIME t	POWER LOAD y_t	EXPONENTIALLY SMOOTHED POWER LOAD E_t
1990	I	1	103.5	103.5
	II	2	94.7	97.3
	III	3	118.6	112.2
	IV	4	109.3	110.2
1991	I	5	126.1	121.3
	II	6	116.0	117.6
	III	7	141.2	134.1
	IV	8	131.6	132.4
1992	I	9	144.5	140.9
	II	10	137.1	138.2
	III	11	159.0	152.8
	IV	12	149.5	150.5
1993	I	13	166.1	161.4
	II	14	152.5	155.2
	III	15	178.2	171.3
	IV	16	169.0	169.7

FIGURE 12.5

Plot of Exponentially Smoothed
Power Loads

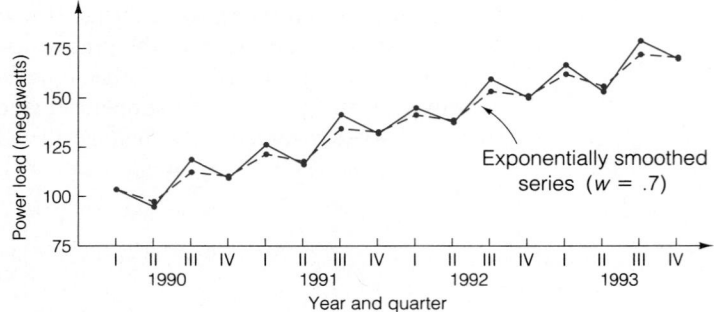

Exponentially smoothed
series ($w = .7$)

Exponential smoothing forecasts are obtained by taking a weighted average of the most recent value of the time series, y_t, and the most recent exponentially smoothed value, E_t. If n is the last time period in which y_t is observed, then the forecast for a future time period t is given by

$$F_t = wy_n + (1 - w)E_n \quad \text{See the box}$$

Note that the right-hand side of the forecast equation does not depend on t; hence, F_t is used to forecast all future values of y_t.

FORECASTING USING EXPONENTIAL SMOOTHING

STEP 1   The data consist of n equally spaced time series values, $y_1, y_2, ..., y_n$.

STEP 2   Select a smoothing constant, w, between 0 and 1. (Smaller values of w give less weight to the current value of the series and yield a smoother series. Larger values of w give more weight to the current value of the series and yield a more variable series.)

STEP 3   Calculate the exponentially smoothed series, E_t, as follows:

$$E_1 = y_1$$
$$E_2 = wy_2 + (1 - w)E_1$$
$$E_3 = wy_3 + (1 - w)E_2$$
$$\vdots$$
$$E_n = wy_n + (1 - w)E_{n-1}$$

STEP 4   Calculate the forecast for any future time period, t, as follows:

$$F_t = wy_n + (1 - w)E_n \qquad t = n + 1, n + 2, ...$$

For example, the forecast for the power load in quarter I of 1994 ($t = 17$) is calculated as follows:

$$F_{17} = wy_{16} + (1 - w)E_{16}$$
$$= .7(169.0) + .3(169.7) = 169.2$$

The forecasts for quarter II of 1994 ($t = 18$), quarter III of 1994 ($t = 19$), and all other future time periods will be the same:

$$F_{18} = 169.2$$
$$F_{19} = 169.2$$
$$F_{20} = 169.2$$
$$\vdots$$

This points out one disadvantage of the exponential smoothing forecasting technique. Since the exponentially smoothed forecast is constant for all future values, any changes in trend and/or seasonality are not taken into account. Therefore, exponentially smoothed forecasts are appropriate only when the trend and seasonal components of the time series are relatively insignificant.

HOLT–WINTERS FORECASTING MODEL

One drawback to the exponential smoothing forecasting method is that the secular trend and seasonal components of a time series are not taken into account. The **Holt–Winters forecasting model** is an extension of the exponential smoothing method that explicitly recognizes the trend and seasonal variation in a time series.

Consider a time series with a trend component, but little or no seasonal variation. Then the Holt–Winters model for y_t is

$$E_t = wy_t + (1 - w)(E_{t-1} + T_{t-1})$$
$$T_t = v(E_t - E_{t-1}) + (1 - v)T_{t-1}$$

where E_t is the exponentially smoothed series, T_t is the trend component, and w and v are smoothing constants between 0 and 1. Note that the trend component, T_t, is a weighted average of the most recent change in the smoothed value (measured by the difference $E_t - E_{t-1}$) and the trend estimate of the previous time period (T_{t-1}). When seasonal variation is present in the time series, the Holt–Winters model takes the form

$$E_t = w\left(\frac{y_t}{S_{t-P}}\right) + (1 - w)(E_{t-1} + T_{t-1})$$
$$T_t = v(E_t - E_{t-1}) + (1 - v)T_{t-1}$$
$$S_t = u\left(\frac{y_t}{E_t}\right) + (1 - u)S_{t-P}$$

where S_t is the seasonal component, u is a constant between 0 and 1, and P is the number of time periods in a cycle (usually a year). The seasonal component, S_t, is a weighted average of the ratio y_t/E_t (ie, the ratio of the actual time series value to the smoothed value) and the seasonal component for the previous cycle. For example, for the quarterly power loads, $P = 4$ (four quarters in a year) and the seasonal component for, say, quarter III of 1991 ($t = 7$) is a weighted average of the ratio y_7/E_7 and the seasonal component for quarter III of 1989 ($t = 3$). That is,

$$S_7 = u\left(\frac{y_7}{E_7}\right) + (1 - u)S_3$$

Forecasts for future time periods, $t = n + 1, n + 2, ...,$ using the Holt–Winters models are obtained by summing the most recent exponentially smoothed component with an estimate of the expected increase (or decrease) attributable to trend. For seasonal models, the forecast is multiplied by the most recent estimate of the seasonal component (similar to the moving average method).

The Holt–Winters forecasting methodology is summarized in the box.

FORECASTING USING THE HOLT–WINTERS MODEL

TREND COMPONENT ONLY

1. The data consist of n equally spaced time series values, $y_1, y_2, ..., y_n$.
2. Select smoothing constants w and v, where $0 \le w \le 1$ and $0 \le v \le 1$.
3. Calculate the exponentially smoothed component, E_t, and the trend component, T_t, for $t = 2, 3, ..., n$ as follows:

$$E_t = \begin{cases} y_2 & \text{if } t = 2 \\ wy_t + (1 - w)(E_{t-1} + T_{t-1}) & \text{if } t > 2 \end{cases}$$

$$T_t = \begin{cases} y_2 - y_1 & \text{if } t = 2 \\ v(E_t - E_{t-1}) + (1 - v)T_{t-1} & \text{if } t > 2 \end{cases}$$

Note: E_1 and T_1 are not defined.

4. The forecast for a future time period, t, is given by

$$F_t = \begin{cases} E_n + T_n & \text{if } t = n + 1 \\ E_n + 2T_n & \text{if } t = n + 2 \\ \vdots \\ E_n + kT_n & \text{if } t = n + k \end{cases}$$

TREND AND SEASONAL COMPONENTS

1. The data consist of n equally spaced time series values, $y_1, y_2, ..., y_n$.
2. Select smoothing constants w, v, and u, where $0 \le w \le 1$, $0 \le v \le 1$, and $0 \le u \le 1$.
3. Determine P, the number of time periods in a cycle. Usually, $P = 4$ for quarterly data and $P = 12$ for monthly data.
4. Calculate the exponentially smoothed component, E_t, the trend component, T_t, and the seasonal component, S_t, for $t = 2, 3, ..., n$ as follows:

$$E_t = \begin{cases} y_2 & \text{if } t = 2 \\ wy_t + (1 - w)(E_{t-1} + T_{t-1}) & \text{if } t = 3, 4, ..., P + 2 \\ w\left(\dfrac{y_t}{S_{t-P}}\right) + (1 - w)(E_{t-1} + T_{t-1}) & \text{if } t > P + 2 \end{cases}$$

(continued)

$$T_t = \begin{cases} y_2 - y_1 & \text{if } t = 2 \\ v(E_t - E_{t-1}) + (1 - v)T_{t-1} & \text{if } t > 2 \end{cases}$$

$$S_t = \begin{cases} \dfrac{y_t}{E_t} & \text{if } t = 2, 3, ..., P + 2 \\ u\left(\dfrac{y_t}{E_t}\right) + (1 - u)S_{t-P} & \text{if } t > P + 2 \end{cases}$$

Note: E_1, T_1, and S_1 are not defined.

5. The forecast for a future time period, t, is given by

$$F_t = \begin{cases} E_n + T_n(S_{n+1-P}) & t = n + 1 \\ E_n + 2T_n(S_{n+2-P}) & t = n + 2 \\ \vdots \\ E_n + kT_n(S_{n+k-P}) & t = n + k \end{cases}$$

EXAMPLE 12.3 Refer to the 1990–1993 quarterly power loads from Table 12.6, repeated here in Table 12.9. Use the Holt–Winters forecasting model with both trend and seasonal components to forecast the utility company's quarterly power loads in 1994. Use the smoothing constants $w = .7$, $v = .5$, and $u = .5$.

TABLE 12.9
Holt–Winters Components for Quarterly Power Load Data

YEAR	QUARTER	TIME t	POWER LOAD y_t	E_t $w = .7$	T_t $v = .5$	S_t $u = .5$
1990	I	1	103.5	—	—	—
	II	2	94.7	94.7	−8.8	1.000
	III	3	118.6	108.8	2.6	1.090
	IV	4	109.3	109.9	1.9	.994
1991	I	5	126.1	121.8	6.9	1.035
	II	6	116.0	119.8	2.5	.968
	III	7	141.2	127.4	5.1	1.100
	IV	8	131.6	132.3	5.0	.995
1992	I	9	144.5	138.9	5.8	1.038
	II	10	137.1	142.6	4.8	.965
	III	11	159.0	145.4	3.8	1.097
	IV	12	149.5	149.9	4.2	.996
1993	I	13	166.1	158.2	6.3	1.044
	II	14	152.5	160.0	4.1	.959
	III	15	178.2	162.9	3.5	1.095
	IV	16	169.0	168.7	4.7	.999

Solution First, note that $P = 4$ for the quarterly time series. Following the formulas for E_t, T_t, and S_t given in the box, we calculate

$$E_2 = y_2 = 94.7$$

$$T_2 = y_2 - y_1 = 94.7 - 103.5 = -8.8$$

$$S_2 = \frac{y_2}{E_2} = \frac{94.7}{94.7} = 1$$

$$E_3 = .7y_3 + (1 - .7)(E_2 + T_2) = .7(118.6) + .3(94.7 - 8.8) = 108.8$$

$$T_3 = .5(E_3 - E_2) + (1 - .5)T_2 = .5(108.8 - 97.4) + .5(-8.8) = 2.6$$

$$S_3 = \frac{y_3}{E_3} = \frac{118.6}{108.8} = 1.090$$

$$E_4 = .7y_4 + (1 - .7)(E_3 + T_3) = .7(109.3) + .3(108.8 + 2.6) = 109.9$$

$$T_4 = .5(E_4 - E_3) + (1 - .5)T_3 = .5(109.9 - 108.8) + .5(2.6) = 1.9$$

$$S_4 = \frac{y_4}{E_4} = \frac{109.3}{109.9} = .994$$

$$\vdots$$

(Remember that beginning with $t = P + 3 = 7$, the formulas for E_t and S_t shown in the box are slightly different.) All the values of E_t, T_t, and S_t are given in Table 12.9. The forecast for quarter I of 1994 (y_{17}) is given by

$$F_{17} = (E_{16} + T_{16})S_{17-4} = (168.7 + 4.7)(1.044) = 181.0$$

Similarly, the forecasts for y_{18}, y_{19}, and y_{20} (quarters II, III, and IV, respectively) are

$$F_{18} = (E_{16} + 2T_{16})S_{18-4} = [168.7 + 2(4.7)](.959) = 170.8$$

$$F_{19} = (E_{16} + 3T_{16})S_{19-4} = [168.7 + 3(4.7)](1.095) = 200.2$$

$$F_{20} = (E_{16} + 4T_{16})S_{20-4} = [168.7 + 4(4.7)](.999) = 187.3$$

We conclude this section with a comment. A major disadvantage of forecasting with smoothing techniques (the moving average method, exponential smoothing, or the Holt–Winters model) is that no measure of the forecast error (or reliability) is known. Although forecast errors can be calculated *after* the future values of the time series have been observed, we prefer to have some measure of the accuracy of the forecast *before* the actual values are observed. For this reason, smoothing techniques are generally regarded as descriptive rather than as inferential procedures.

WARNING

Many forecasting methods based on smoothing techniques have been proposed. There are usually no measures of reliability for these forecasts, and thus the risk associated with making decisions based on them cannot be assessed. These forecasting techniques should be used with care.

On the other hand, forecasts with inferential models (such as regression models) are accompanied by measures of the *standard error of the forecast*, which allow us to construct prediction intervals for the future time series value. We discuss inferential time series forecasting models in the remaining sections of this chapter.

PROBLEMS

12.5 Consider the gold price time series recorded in Table 12.1. The gold prices, given in dollars per troy ounce, are reproduced below.

YEAR	PRICE	YEAR	PRICE	YEAR	PRICE
1971	41.25	1979	307.80	1986	367.87
1972	58.61	1980	606.01	1987	408.91
1973	97.81	1981	450.63	1988	436.93
1974	159.70	1982	374.18	1989	381.28
1975	161.40	1983	449.03	1990	384.07
1976	124.80	1984	360.29	1991	362.04
1977	148.30	1985	317.30	1992	344.50
1978	193.50				

Source: Survey of Current Business, U.S. Department of Commerce.

a. Calculate a 3-point moving average for the gold price time series. Plot the gold prices and the 3-point moving average on the same graph. Can you detect the long-term trend and any cyclical patterns in the time series?

b. Use the 3-point moving averages from part **a** to forecast the price of gold in 1993.

c. Calculate and plot the exponentially smoothed gold price series using a smoothing constant of $w = .8$.

d. Use the exponentially smoothed series from part **c** to forecast the price of gold in 1993.

e. Use the Holt–Winters forecasting model with trend to forecast the price of gold in 1993. Use smoothing constants $w = .8$ and $v = .4$.

12.6 The quarterly Gross National Product (GNP) values (in billion dollars) from 1983 to 1992 are given in the table. Let y_t be the GNP in quarter t, $t = 1, 2, 3, ..., 40$.

YEARS	QUARTER I	II	III	IV
1983	3,172	3,272	3,362	3,432
1984	3,677	3,758	3,812	3,853
1985	3,909	3,965	4,031	4,088
1986	4,149	4,176	4,241	4,268
1987	4,389	4,476	4,567	4,648
1988	4,736	4,831	4,918	5,010
1989	5,101	5,174	5,239	5,289
1990	5,375	5,523	5,560	5,561
1991	5,586	5,658	5,713	5,753
1992	5,840	5,902	5,979	6,082

Source: Standard & Poor's Trade and Securities Statistics (Annual). New York: Standard & Poor's Corp.

a. Plot the quarterly time series. Can you detect a long-term trend? Can you detect any seasonal variation?

b. Calculate the 4-point moving average for the quarterly GNP.

c. Graph the 4-point moving average on the same set of axes you used for the graph in part **a**. Is the long-term trend more evident? What effects has the moving average method removed, or "smoothed"?

d. Calculate the seasonal index for the GNP in quarter IV.

e. Use the moving average method to forecast the GNP in quarter I of 1993.

12.7 Refer to the quarterly GNP data given in Problem 12.6.

a. Calculate the exponentially smoothed series for GNP using a smoothing constant of $w = .2$.

b. Use the exponentially smoothed series from part **a** to forecast the quarterly GNP in 1993.

c. Use the Holt–Winters forecasting model with both trend and seasonal components to forecast the quarterly GNP in 1993. Use smoothing constants $w = .2$, $v = .5$, and $u = .7$.

12.8 The table lists the total monthly retail sales (in billion dollars) in the United States for the period January 1990–December 1992.

	1990	1991	1992
January	136.1	134.7	142.1
February	130.7	131.8	143.1
March	152.4	152.9	154.7
April	149.1	151.9	159.1
May	158.7	163.7	165.8
June	158.3	157.7	164.6
July	153.7	158.5	166.0
August	162.2	163.6	166.3
September	150.0	150.0	160.6
October	155.2	155.7	168.7
November	159.7	159.3	167.2
December	183.6	185.5	204.1

Source: Standard & Poor's Trade and Securities Statistics (Annual). New York: Standard & Poor's Corp.

a. Calculate and plot a 12-point moving average for the total retail sales time series. Can you detect the secular trend? Does there appear to be a seasonal pattern?

b. Use the moving average from part **a** to forecast retail sales in January 1993.

c. Calculate and plot the exponentially smoothed series using $w = .6$.

d. Obtain the forecast for January 1993 using the exponential smoothing technique.

e. Obtain the forecast for January 1993 using the Holt–Winters model with trend and seasonal components and smoothing constants $w = .6$, $v = .7$, and $u = .5$.

12.9 The Consumer Price Index (CPI) measures the increase (or decrease) in the prices of goods and services relative to a base year. The CPI for the years 1980–1992 (using 1967 as a base period) is shown in the table.

YEAR	CPI	YEAR	CPI	YEAR	CPI
1980	246.8	1985	322.2	1989	353.8
1981	272.4	1986	328.4	1990	372.3
1982	289.1	1987	330.5	1991	379.8
1983	298.4	1988	337.7	1992	387.3
1984	311.1				

Source: Survey of Current Business, U.S. Department of Commerce.

a. Graph the time series. Do you detect a long-term trend?

b. Calculate and plot a 5-point moving average for the CPI. Use the moving average to forecast the CPI in 1993.

c. Calculate and plot the exponentially smoothed series for the CPI using a smoothing constant of $w = .4$. Use the exponentially smoothed values to forecast the CPI in 1993.

d. Use the Holt–Winters forecasting model with trend to forecast the CPI in 1993. Use smoothing constants $w = .4$ and $v = .5$.

FORECASTING USING REGRESSION

12.5 Many firms use past sales to forecast future sales. Suppose a wholesale distributor of sporting goods is interested in forecasting its sales revenue for each of the next 5 years. Since an inaccurate forecast may have dire consequences to the distributor, some measure of the forecast's reliability is required. To make such forecasts and assess their reliability, an **inferential time series forecasting model** must be constructed. The familiar general linear regression model of Chapters 10 and 11 represents one type of inferential model, since it allows us to calculate prediction intervals for the forecasts.

To illustrate the technique of forecasting with regression, consider the data in Table 12.10. The data are annual sales (in thousand dollars) for a firm (say, the sporting goods distributor) in each of its 35 years of operation. A plot of the data (Figure 12.6, p. 648) reveals a linearly increasing trend, so the first-order (straight-line) model

$$E(y_t) = \beta_0 + \beta_1 t$$

seems plausible for describing the secular trend.

TABLE 12.10
A Firm's Yearly Sales Revenue (Thousand Dollars)

t	y_t	t	y_t	t	y_t
1	4.8	13	48.4	25	100.3
2	4.0	14	61.6	26	111.7
3	5.5	15	71.4	27	108.2
4	15.6	16	83.4	28	115.5
5	23.1	17	93.6	29	119.2
6	23.3	18	94.2	30	125.2
7	31.4	19	85.4	31	136.3
8	46.0	20	86.2	32	146.8
9	46.1	21	89.9	33	146.1
10	41.9	22	89.9	34	151.4
11	45.5	23	89.2	35	150.9
12	53.5	24	99.1		

The SAS printout for the regression analysis of this model is shown in Figure 12.7. Note that the model apparently provides an excellent fit to the data, with $R^2 = .98$, $F = 1,615.72$ (p-value $< .0001$), and $s = 6.39$. The least squares prediction equation (coefficients are shaded in Figure 12.7) is

$$\hat{y}_t = \hat{\beta}_0 + \hat{\beta}_1 t = .4015 + 4.2956t$$

We can obtain sales forecasts and corresponding 95% prediction intervals for years 36–40 by employing the method of Section 10.3. These values are given in the bottom portion of the SAS printout shown in Figure 12.7. For example, the forecast for $t = 36$ is $F_{36} = 155.0$ (using the notation of Section 12.4) and the

FIGURE 12.6

Plot of Sales Data

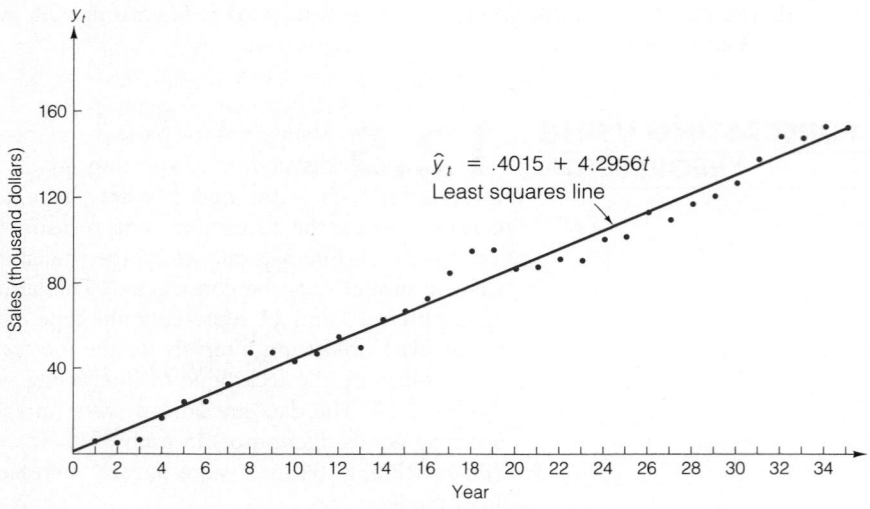

$\hat{y}_t = .4015 + 4.2956t$
Least squares line

FIGURE 12.7

SAS Printout for the Straight-Line Model

Analysis of Variance

Source	DF	Sum of Squares	Mean Square	F Value	Prob>F
Model	1	65875.20817	65875.20817	1615.724	0.0001
Error	33	1345.45355	40.77132		
C Total	34	67220.66171			

Root MSE	6.38524	R-square	0.9800
Dep Mean	77.72286	Adj R-sq	0.9794
C.V.	8.21540		

Parameter Estimates

Variable	DF	Parameter Estimate	Standard Error	T for H0: Parameter=0	Prob > |T|
INTERCEP	1	0.401513	2.20570829	0.182	0.8567
T	1	4.295630	0.10686692	40.196	0.0001

Obs	T	Dep Var Y	Predict Value	Std Err Predict	Lower95% Predict	Upper95% Predict	Residual
36	36	.	155.0	2.206	141.3	168.8	.
37	37	.	159.3	2.300	145.5	173.1	.
38	38	.	163.6	2.394	149.8	177.5	.
39	39	.	167.9	2.490	154.0	181.9	.
40	40	.	172.2	2.587	158.2	186.2	.

corresponding 95% prediction interval is (141.3, 168.8). Thus, we predict that sales revenue in year $t = 36$ will fall between \$141,300 and \$168,800 with 95% confidence.

Note that the prediction intervals for $t = 36, 37, ..., 40$ widen slightly as we attempt to forecast further into the future. Intuitively, we know that the farther into the future we forecast, the less certain we are of the accuracy of the forecast, since some unexpected change in business and economic conditions may make the model inappropriate. Since we have less confidence in the forecast for $t = 40$ than for $t = 36$, it follows that the prediction interval for $t = 40$ must be wider in order to attain a 95% level of confidence. For this reason, time series forecasting (regardless of the forecasting method) is generally confined to the short term.

Multiple regression models also can be used to forecast future values of a time series with seasonal variation. We illustrate with an example.

EXAMPLE 12.4   Refer to the 1990–1993 quarterly power loads listed in Table 12.6 (p. 635).

a. Propose a model for quarterly power load, y_t, that will account for both the secular trend and seasonal variation present in the series.

b. Fit the model to the data, and use the least squares prediction equation to forecast the utility company's quarterly power loads in 1994. Construct 95% prediction intervals for the forecasts.

Solution

a. A common way to describe seasonal differences in a time series is with dummy variables.* For quarterly data, a model that includes both trend and seasonal components is

$$E(y_t) = \beta_0 + \underbrace{\beta_1 t}_{\substack{\text{Secular} \\ \text{trend}}} + \underbrace{\beta_2 Q_1 + \beta_3 Q_2 + \beta_4 Q_3}_{\text{Seasonal component}}$$

where

t = Time period, ranging from $t = 1$ for quarter I of 1990 to $t = 16$ for quarter IV of 1993

y_t = Power load (megawatts) in time t

$Q_1 = \begin{cases} 1 & \text{if quarter I} \\ 0 & \text{if not} \end{cases}$

$Q_2 = \begin{cases} 1 & \text{if quarter II} \\ 0 & \text{if not} \end{cases}$

$Q_3 = \begin{cases} 1 & \text{if quarter III} \\ 0 & \text{if not} \end{cases}$

Base level = Quarter IV

The β coefficients associated with the seasonal dummy variables determine the mean increase (or decrease) in power load for each quarter, relative to the base level quarter, quarter IV.

b. The model is fit to the data from Table 12.6 using SAS. The resulting SAS printout is shown in Figure 12.8. Note that the model appears to fit the data quite well: $R^2 = .997$, indicating that the model accounts for 99.7% of the sample variation in power loads over the 4-year period; $F = 968.96$ strongly supports the hypothesis that the model has predictive utility (p-value = .0001); and the standard

---

* Another way to account for seasonal variation is with trigonometric (sine and cosine) terms. Consult the references for details on how to incorporate these trigonometric terms into the model.

FIGURE 12.8

SAS Printout of Least Squares Fit to Quarterly Power Loads

Analysis of Variance

Source	DF	Sum of Squares	Mean Square	F Value	Prob>F
Model	4	9101.67800	2275.41950	968.962	0.0001
Error	11	25.83138	2.34831		
C Total	15	9127.50938			

Root MSE	1.53242	R-square	0.9972	
Dep Mean	137.30625	Adj R-sq	0.9961	
C.V.	1.11606			

Parameter Estimates

Variable	DF	Parameter Estimate	Standard Error	T for H0: Parameter=0	Prob > |T|
INTERCEP	1	90.206250	1.14931396	78.487	0.0001
T	1	4.964375	0.08566480	57.951	0.0001
Q1	1	10.093125	1.11364246	9.063	0.0001
Q2	1	-4.846250	1.09704478	-4.418	0.0010
Q3	1	14.364375	1.08696452	13.215	0.0001

Obs	QUARTER	Dep Var Y	Predict Value	Std Err Predict	Lower95% Predict	Upper95% Predict	Residual
1	1990_I	103.5	105.3	0.923	101.3	109.2	-1.7637
2	1990_II	94.7	95.3	0.923	91.3518	99.2	-0.5887
3	1990_III	118.6	119.5	0.923	115.5	123.4	-0.8637
4	1990_IV	109.3	110.1	0.923	106.1	114.0	-0.7637
5	1991_I	126.1	125.1	0.785	121.3	128.9	0.9788
6	1991_II	116.0	115.1	0.785	111.4	118.9	0.8538
7	1991_III	141.2	139.3	0.785	135.5	143.1	1.8788
8	1991_IV	131.6	129.9	0.785	126.1	133.7	1.6788
9	1992_I	144.5	145.0	0.785	141.2	148.8	-0.4787
10	1992_II	137.1	135.0	0.785	131.2	138.8	2.0963
11	1992_III	159.0	159.2	0.785	155.4	163.0	-0.1787
12	1992_IV	149.5	149.8	0.785	146.0	153.6	-0.2787
13	1993_I	166.1	164.8	0.923	160.9	168.8	1.2637
14	1993_II	152.5	154.9	0.923	150.9	158.8	-2.3612
15	1993_III	178.2	179.0	0.923	175.1	183.0	-0.8363
16	1993_IV	169.0	169.6	0.923	165.7	173.6	-0.6362
17	1994_I	.	184.7	1.149	180.5	188.9	.
18	1994_II	.	174.7	1.149	170.5	178.9	.
19	1994_III	.	198.9	1.149	194.7	203.1	.
20	1994_IV	.	189.5	1.149	185.3	193.7	.

deviation, $s = 1.53$, implies that the model predictions will usually be accurate to within approximately $\pm 2(1.53)$, or about ± 3.06 megawatts.

Forecasts and corresponding 95% prediction intervals for the 1994 power loads are reported in the bottom portion of the printout in Figure 12.8. For example, the forecast for power load in quarter I of 1994 ($t = 17$) is $F_{17} = 184.7$ megawatts with 95% prediction interval (180.5, 188.9). Therefore, using a 95% prediction interval, we expect the power load in quarter I of 1994 to fall between 180.5 and 188.9 megawatts.

Many descriptive forecasting techniques have proved their merit by providing good forecasts for particular applications. Nevertheless, the advantage of forecasting using the regression approach is clear: Regression analysis provides us with a measure of reliability for each forecast through prediction intervals. However, there are two problems associated with forecasting time series using a multiple regression model.

FORECASTING USING REGRESSION

STEP 1   Hypothesize a model for the deterministic component:

$$E(y_t) = \beta_0 + \beta_1 x_{1t} + \beta_2 x_{2t} + \cdots + \beta_k x_{kt}$$

(You may consider time t as one of the independent variables in the model.)

STEP 2   Collect the time series data (in equally spaced data points).

STEP 3   Obtain the least squares prediction equation,

$$\hat{y}_t = \hat{\beta}_0 + \hat{\beta}_1 x_{1t} + \hat{\beta}_2 x_{2t} + \hat{\beta}_k x_{kt}$$

STEP 4   Assess the adequacy of the model.

STEP 5   If the model is deemed adequate, the forecast for a future time period t ($t = n + 1, n + 2, ...$) is

$$F_t = \hat{y}_t$$

Corresponding prediction intervals for the forecast also should be obtained.

PROBLEM 1   We are using the least squares prediction equation to forecast values outside the region of observation of the independent variable, t. For example, in Example 12.4, we are forecasting for values of t between 17 and 20 (the four quarters of 1994), even though the observed power loads are for t-values between 1 and 16. As noted in Section 10.3, it is risky to use a least squares regression model for prediction outside the range of the observed data, because some unusual change, economic or political, may make the model inappropriate for predicting future events. Because forecasting always involves predictions about future values of a time series, this problem obviously cannot be avoided. However, it is important that the forecaster recognize the dangers of this type of prediction.

PROBLEM 2   Recall the standard assumptions made about the random error component of a multiple regression model (Chapter 10). We assume that the errors have mean 0, constant variance, and normal probability distributions, and that they are *independent*. The latter assumption is often violated in time series that exhibit short-term trends. As an illustration, refer to the plot of the sales revenue data shown in Figure 12.6. Notice that the observed sales tend to deviate about the least squares line in positive and negative runs. That is, if the difference between the observed sales and predicted sales in year t is positive (or negative), the difference in year $t + 1$ tends to be positive (or negative). Since the variation in the yearly sales is systematic, the implication is that the errors are correlated. (We give a formal statistical test for correlated errors in the next section.) Violation of this standard regression assumption could lead to unreliable forecasts.

Time series models have been developed specifically for the purpose of making forecasts when the errors are known to be correlated. These models include an autoregressive term for the correlated errors that result from cyclical, seasonal, or other short-term effects. Time series autoregressive models are the subject of Sections 12.7 and 12.8.

PROBLEMS

12.10 Information on intercity passenger traffic (excluding travel by private automobiles) since 1940 is given in the table. The data are recorded as percentages of total passenger–miles traveled.

YEAR	TIME	RAILROADS	BUSES	AIR CARRIERS
1940	1	67.1	26.5	2.8
1945	2	74.3	21.4	2.7
1950	3	46.3	37.7	14.3
1955	4	36.5	32.4	28.9
1960	5	28.6	25.7	42.1
1965	6	17.9	24.2	54.7
1970	7	7.3	16.9	73.1
1975	8	5.8	14.2	77.7
1980	9	4.7	11.4	83.9
1985	10	3.6	7.9	88.4

Source: Statistical Abstract of the United States, 1987. Interstate Commerce Commission, Civil Aeronautics Board.

a. Let y_t be the percentage of total passenger–miles at time t for a particular mode of transportation. Consider the linear model $E(y_t) = \beta_0 + \beta_1 t$. Which modes of transportation do you think have a secular trend adequately represented by this model?

b. Fit the model in part **a** to the data for each mode of transportation.

c. Plot the data and the least squares line for each mode of transportation. Which models adequately describe the secular trend of percentage of total passenger–miles traveled? Does this agree with your answer to part **a**?

d. Refer to your answer for part **c**. Use the least squares prediction equations to forecast the percentage of total passenger–miles to be traveled for the respective modes of transportation in 1990. Support your answers with 95% prediction intervals. What are the risks associated with the forecast procedure?

12.11 The Employee Retirement Income Security Act (ERISA) of 1974 was originally established to enhance retirement security income. J. Ledolter (University of Iowa) and M. L. Power (Iowa State University) investigated the effects of ERISA on the growth in the number of private retirement plans (*Journal of Risk and Insurance*, Dec. 1983). Using quarterly data from 1956 through the third quarter of 1982 ($n = 107$ quarters), Ledolter and Power fit quarterly time series models for the number of pension qualifications and the number of profit-sharing plan qualifications. One of several models investigated was the quadratic model,

$$E(y_t) = \beta_0 + \beta_1 t + \beta_2 t^2$$

where y_t is the natural logarithm of the dependent variable, number of pension or number of profit-sharing qualifications, in quarter t. (The natural logarithm transformation was used to satisfy the regression assumption of constant error variance.) The results (modified for the purpose of this exercise) are summarized below:

Pension plan qualifications: $\quad \hat{y}_t = 6.19 + .039t - .00024t^2$
$\qquad\qquad\qquad\qquad\qquad\qquad t \text{ (for } H_0: \beta_2 = 0) = -1.39$

Profit-sharing plan qualifications: $\quad \hat{y}_t = 6.22 + .035t - .00021t^2$
$\qquad\qquad\qquad\qquad\qquad\qquad\qquad t \text{ (for } H_0: \beta_2 = 0) = -1.61$

a. Is there evidence that the quarterly number of pension plan qualifications increases at a decreasing rate over time? Test using $\alpha = .05$. [*Hint:* Test $H_0: \beta_2 = 0$ against $H_a: \beta_2 < 0$.]

b. Forecast the number of pension plan qualifications for the fourth quarter of 1982 ($t = 108$). [*Hint:* Since y_t is the logarithm of the number of pension plan qualifications, to obtain the forecast you must take the antilogarithm of $\hat{y}_{108}$, that is, $e^{\hat{y}_{108}}$.]

c. Is there evidence that the quarterly number of profit-sharing plan qualifications increase at a decreasing rate over time? Test using $\alpha = .05$. [*Hint:* Test $H_0: \beta_2 = 0$ against $H_a: \beta_2 < 0$.]

d. Forecast the number of profit-sharing plan qualifications for the fourth quarter of 1982 ($t = 108$). (See the hint in part **b**.)

12.12 Refer to the quarterly GNP data in Problem 12.6 (p. 645). The model $E(y_t) = \beta_0 + \beta_1 t$ was fit to the data using the method of least squares, where y_t = GNP in quarter t. Analyze the results shown in the MINITAB printout below. Do you recommend using the model for forecasting quarterly GNP? Explain.

```
The regression equation is
Y = 3213 + 72.6 T

Predictor       Coef       Stdev     t-ratio        p
Constant     3213.29       21.26      151.17    0.000
T            72.6140      0.9035       80.37    0.000

s = 65.96        R-sq = 99.4%      R-sq(adj) = 99.4%

Analysis of Variance

SOURCE        DF         SS           MS         F        p
Regression     1   28103970     28103970   6459.23    0.000
Error         38     165337         4351
Total         39   28269308

Unusual Observations
Obs.      T          Y       Fit  Stdev.Fit  Residual  St.Resid
 30     30.0     5523.0    5391.7       13.5     131.3     2.03R

R denotes an obs. with a large st. resid.
```

12.13 Refer to the Consumer Price Index data in Problem 12.9 (p. 646). Propose a regression model for predicting annual CPI, y_t. Use the least squares model to forecast the CPI in 1993, and obtain a 95% prediction interval for the forecast.

TESTING FOR AUTOCORRELATION

12.6

As pointed out in the previous section, the standard regression assumption of independent errors is often violated with time series data. The reason is that *time series residuals* tend to be correlated with one another.

Recall that a time series residual is computed as the difference between the observed value of the time series, y_t, and the corresponding predicted value, $\hat{y}_t$, that is, $(y_t - \hat{y}_t)$. For most business and economic time series, there is a tendency for the residuals to have positive and negative runs over time (Section 11.6). That is, neighboring residuals tend to have the same sign, and appear to be correlated. We call the correlation among the time series residuals at different points in time **autocorrelation**.

A special case of autocorrelation that has many applications to business and economic phenomena is the case in which neighboring residuals one time period apart (at times t and $t + 1$) are correlated. This type of correlation is called **first-order autocorrelation**. The more general type of autocorrelation (non–first-order autocorrelation) is beyond the scope of this text.* Therefore, whenever we use the term *autocorrelation*, we are referring to the first-order case.

---

* In general, correlation between time series residuals m time periods apart is **mth-order autocorrelation**.

Due to seasonality and economic trends, most time series models exhibit positively autocorrelated errors. Consequently, a test for first-order autocorrelation among residuals usually involves testing the null hypothesis

H_0: No residual autocorrelation

against the alternative hypothesis

H_a: Positive residual autocorrelation

The appropriate test statistic is the **Durbin–Watson d statistic**. Since most statistical software packages include a regression routine that calculates d, we are concerned more with the interpretation of d than with its computation.*

It can be shown (proof omitted) that the value of d always falls in the interval from 0 to 4 (ie, $0 \leq d \leq 4$). If the residuals are *uncorrelated*, then d is approximately equal to 2; if the residuals are *positively autocorrelated*, d is less than 2; and if the residuals are *negatively autocorrelated*, d is greater than 2. The closer d gets to 0 or 4, the stronger the autocorrelation (positive or negative, respectively). The interpretation of the d statistic is summarized in the box.

INTERPRETATION OF THE DURBIN–WATSON d STATISTIC

Range of d: $0 \leq d \leq 4$

Uncorrelated residuals: $d \approx 2$

Positive autocorrelation: $d < 2$

  (*Strong positive autocorrelation:* $d \approx 0$)

Negative autocorrelation: $d > 2$

  (*Strong negative autocorrelation:* $d \approx 4$)

For a test for positive autocorrelation, then, we will reject the null hypothesis in favor of the alternative if the d statistic is "too small"—that is, significantly less than 2. Durbin and Watson (1951) provided tables for the lower-tail values of the d statistic. A reproduction of part of Table 17, Appendix A, taken from Durbin and Watson, is shown in Table 12.11. The table gives critical values of the Durbin–Watson d statistic for $\alpha = .05$. (Critical values based on $\alpha = .01$ are given in Table 18,

---

* The formula for d is $d = \sum_{t=2}^{n}(\hat{R}_t - \hat{R}_{t-1})^2 / \sum_{t=1}^{n} \hat{R}_t^2$, where n is the number of observations (time periods) and R_t is the residual at time t, that is, $\hat{R}_t = (y_t - \hat{y}_t)$.

Appendix A.) You can see that the table values depend on two parameters: n, the sample size, and k, the number of independent variables in the time series model. Unlike the z, t, F, and other test statistics, however, the complexity of the sampling distribution of d prevents us from specifying a single point, d_α, that acts as a boundary between the rejection and nonrejection regions. Instead, upper and lower bounds on the critical value of d are specified.

TABLE 12.11

Reproduction of Part of Table 17, Appendix A ($\alpha = .05$)

n	$k = 1$		$k = 2$		$k = 3$		$k = 4$		$k = 5$	
	d_L	d_U	d_L	d_U	d_L	d_U	d_L	d_U	d_L	d_U
31	1.36	1.50	1.30	1.57	1.23	1.65	1.16	1.74	1.09	1.83
32	1.37	1.50	1.31	1.57	1.24	1.65	1.18	1.73	1.11	1.82
33	1.38	1.51	1.32	1.58	1.26	1.65	1.19	1.73	1.13	1.81
34	1.39	1.51	1.33	1.58	1.27	1.65	1.21	1.73	1.15	1.81
35	1.40	1.52	1.34	1.58	1.28	1.65	1.22	1.73	1.16	1.80
36	1.41	1.52	1.35	1.59	1.29	1.65	1.24	1.73	1.18	1.80
37	1.42	1.53	1.36	1.59	1.31	1.66	1.25	1.72	1.19	1.80
38	1.43	1.54	1.37	1.59	1.32	1.66	1.26	1.72	1.21	1.79
39	1.43	1.54	1.38	1.60	1.33	1.66	1.27	1.72	1.22	1.79
40	1.44	1.54	1.39	1.60	1.34	1.66	1.29	1.72	1.23	1.79

For example, for $\alpha = .05$, $n = 35$, and $k = 1$, the upper bound is given by $d_U = 1.52$ and the lower bound is $d_L = 1.40$. Since small values of d provide sufficient evidence of positive autocorrelation, we can *definitely reject H_0 if d is smaller than the lower bound, d_L*, that is, if $d < 1.40$. Similarly, there is *insufficient evidence to reject H_0 if d is greater than the upper bound, d_U*, that is, if $d > 1.52$. If d falls between the bounds, that is, if $1.40 < d < 1.52$, then more information is needed before we can reach any conclusion about the presence of autocorrelation. For this reason, the interval (d_L, d_U) is sometimes called the **inconclusive region**. A graphical depiction of the rejection region for the Durbin–Watson d test is shown in Figure 12.9.

FIGURE 12.9

Rejection Region for the Durbin–Watson d Test

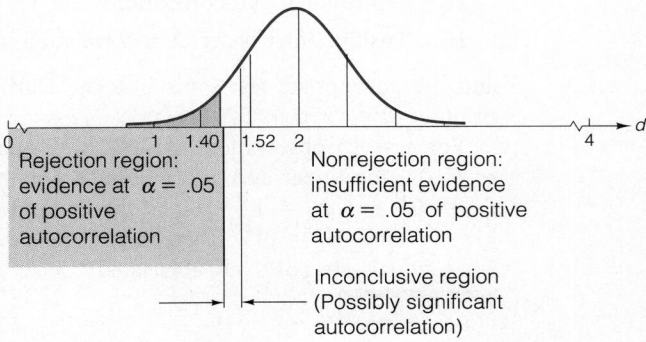

EXAMPLE 12.5 A leading pharmaceutical company that produces a hypertension medication would like to model annual revenue generated by this product. Company

researchers utilized data collected over the years 1979–1993 to fit the model

$$E(y_t) = \beta_0 + \beta_1 x_t + \beta_2 t$$

where

$$y_t = \text{Revenue in year } t \text{ (in million dollars)}$$
$$x_t = \text{Cost per pill in year } t$$
$$t = \text{Year } (1, 2, ..., 15)$$

The SAS printout for the regression analysis appears in Figure 12.10. A company statistician suspects that the assumption of independent errors may be violated and that, in fact, the regression residuals are positively autocorrelated. Test this claim using $\alpha = .05$.

FIGURE 12.10

SAS Printout for Example 12.5

Analysis of Variance

Source	DF	Sum of Squares	Mean Square	F Value	Prob>F
Model	2	48.82325	24.41163	206.187	0.0001
Error	12	1.42075	0.11840		
C Total	14	50.24400			

Root MSE	0.34409	R-Square	0.9717	
Dep Mean	7.32000	Adj R-Sq	0.9670	
C.V.	4.70064			

Parameter Estimates

Variable	DF	Parameter Estimate	Standard Error	T for H0: Parameter=0	Prob > |T|
INTERCEP	1	3.261191	1.87880228	1.736	0.1082
T	1	0.391588	0.07045937	5.558	0.0001
X	1	1.587609	4.12905034	0.384	0.7073

Durbin-Watson D	0.776
(For Number of Obs.)	15
1st Order Autocorrelation	0.485

Solution The null and alternative hypotheses for the test are given by

H_0: No residual autocorrelation

H_a: Positive (first-order) autocorrelation

and the appropriate test statistic is the Durbin–Watson d statistic from the SAS printout, $d = .776$.

For $n = 15$ observations (years), $k = 2$ independent variables (x_t and t), and $\alpha = .05$, the upper and lower bounds obtained from Table 17, Appendix A, are $d_L = .95$ and $d_U = 1.54$. Since the computed value ($d = .776$) is less than the lower bound ($d_L = .95$), there is sufficient evidence at $\alpha = .05$ to conclude that the residuals are positively correlated.

Two-tailed tests and tests for negative autocorrelation (although rare in practice) are similar to the test for positive autocorrelation. These tests, which are based on the symmetry of the sampling distribution of d, are outlined in the box.

```
┌──────────────────────────────────────────────────────────────────────────┐
│  DURBIN–WATSON d TEST                                                       │
│  ─────────────────────────────────────────────────────────────────────── │
│                                                                            │
│           ONE-TAILED TEST                      TWO-TAILED TEST             │
│                                                                            │
│  H₀:  No autocorrelation            H₀:  No autocorrelation               │
│                                                                            │
│  Hₐ:  Positive autocorrelation      Hₐ:  Positive or negative             │
│       [or Hₐ:  Negative                  autocorrelation                   │
│        autocorrelation]                                                    │
│                                                                            │
│  Test statistic:  d (obtained       Test statistic:  d (obtained          │
│  from a regression printout)        from a regression printout)           │
│                                                                            │
│  Rejection region:                  Rejection region:                     │
│                                                                            │
│  d < d_{L,α} [or (4 − d) < d_{L,α}] d < d_{L,α/2} or (4 − d) < d_{L,α/2}   │
│  where d_{L,α} is the lower table   where d_{L,α/2} is the lower table     │
│  value corresponding to k           value corresponding to k in-          │
│  independent variables              dependent variables and               │
│  and n observations                 n observations                        │
│                                                                            │
│  Caution:  If d_{L,α} < d < d_{U,α},  Caution: If d_{L,α/2} < d < d_{U,α/2},│
│  the test is inconclusive (ie,      the test is inconclusive (ie,          │
│  "possibly significant").           "possibly significant").              │
└──────────────────────────────────────────────────────────────────────────┘
```

If strong evidence of autocorrelation is detected, as in Example 12.5, then the least squares results and any inferences drawn from them are suspect. In the following section we present a time series forecasting model that accounts for (first-order) autocorrelation in the random errors.

PROBLEMS

12.14   Forecasts of automotive vehicle sales in the United States provide the basis for financial and strategic planning of large automotive corporations. S. J. Olson and J. Janakiraman developed a forecasting model for y, total monthly passenger car and light truck sales (in thousands):

$$E(y) = \beta_0 + \beta_1 x_1 + \beta_2 x_2 + \beta_3 x_3 + \beta_4 x_4 + \beta_5 x_5$$

where

x_1 = Average monthly retail price of regular gasoline

x_2 = Annual percentage change in GNP per quarter

x_3 = Monthly Consumer Confidence Index (CCI)

x_4 = Total number of vehicles scrapped (millions) per month

x_5 = Vehicle seasonality

The model was fit to monthly data collected over a 12 year period ($n = 144$ months) with the following results:[*]

$$\hat{y} = -676.42 - 1.93x_1 + 6.54x_2 + 2.02x_3 + .08x_4 + 9.82x_5$$

$R^2 = .856$ Durbin–Watson $d = 1.01$

* Olson, S. J., and Janakiraman, J. "Proposed U.S. Passenger Car and Light Truck Sales Forecast Model." Paper presented at SAS Users Group International Conference, Reno, NV, 1985.

a. Is there sufficient evidence to indicate that the model contributes information for the prediction of y? Test using $\alpha = .05$.

b. Is there sufficient evidence to indicate that the regression errors are positively correlated? Test using $\alpha = .05$.

c. Comment on the validity of the inference concerning model adequacy in light of the result of part **b**.

12.15 T. C. Chiang considered several time series forecasting models of future foreign exchange rates for U.S. currency (*The Journal of Financial Research*, Summer 1986). One popular theory among financial analysts is that the forward (90 day) exchange rate is a useful predictor of the future spot exchange rate. Using monthly data on exchange rates for the British pound for $n = 81$ months, Chiang fit the model

$$E(y_t) = \beta_0 + \beta_1 x_{t-1}$$

where

$$y_t = \text{Natural logarithm of spot rate in month } t$$

$$x_t = \text{Natural logarithm of forward rate in month } t$$

The method of least squares yielded the following results:

$$\hat{y} = -.009 + .986 x_{t-1} \qquad (t = 47.9)$$

$$s = .0249 \qquad R^2 = .957 \qquad \text{Durbin–Watson } d = .962$$

a. Is the model useful for predicting future spot exchange rates for the British pound? Test using $\alpha = .05$.

b. Interpret the values of $\hat{\beta}_1$ and R^2.

c. Is there evidence of positive autocorrelation among the residuals? Test using $\alpha = .05$.

d. Based on the results of parts **a–c**, would you recommend using the least squares model to forecast spot exchange rates?

12.16 The MINITAB printout of the straight-line regression for quarterly GNP from Problem 12.12 is reproduced below.

```
The regression equation is
Y = 3213 + 72.6 T

Predictor       Coef      Stdev     t-ratio        p
Constant     3213.29      21.26      151.17    0.000
T            72.6140     0.9035       80.37    0.000

s = 65.96      R-sq = 99.4%      R-sq(adj) = 99.4%

Analysis of Variance

SOURCE        DF          SS          MS         F        p
Regression     1    28103970    28103970   6459.23    0.000
Error         38      165337        4351
Total         39    28269308

Unusual Observations
Obs.       T        Y     Fit Stdev.Fit   Residual   St.Resid
 30     30.0   5523.0   5391.7      13.5      131.3      2.03R

R denotes an obs. with a large st. resid.
Durbin-Watson statistic = 0.36
```

a. Construct a residual plot over time (quarters). Is there visual evidence of autocorrelation?

b. Conduct a test for first-order autocorrelation using $\alpha = .05$. What are the consequences of this result?

12.17 Refer to the least squares regression for annual CPI discussed in Problem 12.13. Use a computer to find the Durbin–Watson d statistic and interpret the result.

FORECASTING USING AUTOREGRESSIVE MODELS

12.7 Once you have determined that the time series residuals are autocorrelated, you should avoid using the fitted least squares model for forecasting. When the standard regression assumption of independent errors is violated, the forecasts will have larger errors than expected. However, if the autocorrelated residuals can be accounted for in the time series model, then better forecasts can be obtained.

A time series model can be written as

$$y_t = E(y_t) + R_t$$

where $E(y_t)$ is the deterministic component and R_t is the residual component of the model. In time series analysis, the secular, seasonal, and cyclical variations discussed in Section 12.1 are usually incorporated into the deterministic component, $E(y_t)$, while it is assumed that the R_t's are autocorrelated. Thus, a pair of models is proposed—one model for the deterministic component, $E(y_t)$, and one model for the autocorrelated residuals, R_t.

A useful model for autocorrelated residuals is the **first-order autoregressive model**,

$$R_t = \phi R_{t-1} + \epsilon_t$$

where ϕ (the Greek letter "phi") is a constant coefficient that lies between -1 and 1, and the random error term, ϵ_t, has mean 0, constant variance, and is normally distributed and *independent*. This model implies that the values of R_t are autocorrelated with the constant ϕ as the correlation coefficient. When ϕ is positive, the residuals are positively autocorrelated; when ϕ is negative, the residuals are negatively autocorrelated; and when ϕ is 0, the residuals are uncorrelated. The closer ϕ is to 1 or -1, the stronger the autocorrelation (either positive or negative, respectively).

FIRST-ORDER AUTOREGRESSIVE MODEL

$$R_t = \phi R_{t-1} + \epsilon_t$$

where R_t is the time series residual at time t, $-1 \le \phi \le 1$, and ϵ_t is uncorrelated random error.

Since positive autocorrelations generate cyclic behavior in the time series residuals, first-order autoregressive models used for business and economic time series generally have positive values for ϕ.

EXAMPLE 12.6 The Dow Jones Industrial Average (DJA) is a widely followed stock market indicator. The values of the DJA from 1970 to 1989 are given in Table 12.12. Suppose we want to model the yearly DJA, y_t, as a function of t, where t is the number of years since 1969 (ie, $t = 1$ for 1970, $t = 2$ for 1971, ..., $t = 20$

TABLE 12.12
Dow Jones Industrial Average (DJA)

YEAR	DJA	YEAR	DJA
1970	839	1980	964
1971	885	1981	899
1972	951	1982	1,047
1973	924	1983	1,259
1974	759	1984	1,187
1975	802	1985	1,501
1976	975	1986	1,926
1977	835	1987	1,939
1978	805	1988	2,169
1979	839	1989	2,753

Source: Standard & Poor's Trade and Securities Statistics (Annual).
New York: Standard & Poor's Corp.

for 1989). Propose and fit a time series model that includes a long-term trend and autocorrelated residuals. Interpret the results.

Solution   The appropriate time series model can be written as

$$y_t = E(y_t) + R_t$$

where the long-term trend, $E(y_t)$, is given by

$$E(y_t) = \beta_0 + \beta_1 t$$

and the autocorrelated residuals, R_t, are represented by the autoregressive model,

$$R_t = \phi R_{t-1} + \epsilon_t$$

Combining the two components into one model, we have

$$y_t = \beta_0 + \beta_1 t + \phi R_{t-1} + \epsilon_t$$

Note that the model contains three unknown parameters: β_0, β_1, and ϕ. In order to estimate these parameters, a modification of the least squares method is used. The mathematical details of this technique are beyond the scope of this text. However, several statistical software packages are available that compute the estimates using the modified least squares method (eg, the AUTOREG procedure in SAS). The SAS printout for the data of Table 12.12 is shown in Figure 12.11.

The format of the SAS printout for the autoregression is different from that of the standard SAS regression printout. The estimates of the β's in the deterministic component, $E(y_t)$, appear at the bottom of the printout under the column heading B Value. These values (rounded) are $\hat{\beta}_0 = 402.95$ and $\hat{\beta}_1 = 85.52$.

The estimate of the first-order autoregressive parameter ϕ is given in the middle portion of the printout titled Estimates of the Autoregressive Parameters under the column heading Coefficient. The value shown (rounded) is $-.64$. However, the SAS autoregressive model is defined so that ϕ *has the opposite sign from the value contained in our model*. As a result, we must multiply the estimate of ϕ shown in

```
                              Autoreg Procedure

Dependent Variable = DJA

                      Ordinary Least Squares Estimates

            SSE            2031167    DFE                 18
            MSE           112842.6    Root MSE       335.9206
            SBC          293.3168     AIC            291.3253
            Reg Rsq        0.6543     Total Rsq        0.6543
            Durbin-Watson  0.3308


        Variable    DF      B Value    Std Error   t Ratio Approx Prob

        Intercept    1   414.568421      156.05      2.657      0.0161
        T            1    76.031579       13.03      5.837      0.0001


                     Estimates of Autocorrelations

   Lag  Covariance   Correlation -1 9 8 7 6 5 4 3 2 1 0 1 2 3 4 5 6 7 8 9 1

    0    101558.4     1.000000  |                    |********************|
    1    65007.01     0.640095  |                    |*************       |


                       Preliminary MSE = 59947.68
                  Estimates of the Autoregressive Parameters

            Lag    Coefficient      Std Error        t Ratio
             1     -0.64009517      0.18633906      -3.435110


                         Yule-Walker Estimates

            SSE           838942.2    DFE                 17
            MSE          49349.54     Root MSE       222.1476
            SBC          279.1552     AIC            276.168
            Reg Rsq        0.5495     Total Rsq        0.8572


        Variable    DF      B Value    Std Error   t Ratio Approx Prob

        Intercept    1   402.948499      234.67      1.717      0.1041
        T            1    85.523569       18.78      4.553      0.0003
```

the SAS printout by -1 to obtain the estimate for our model. Therefore, we have $\hat{\phi} = (-.64)(-1) = .64$.

The fitted time series models are

$$\hat{y}_t = 402.95 + 85.52t + \hat{R}_t \qquad \hat{R}_t = .64\hat{R}_{t-1}$$

or

$$\hat{y}_t = 402.95 + 85.52t + .64\hat{R}_{t-1}$$

The value $\hat{\beta}_1 = 85.52$ is positive and significant at $\alpha = .10$ (p-value $\approx .00015$ for a one-tailed test), indicating that the DJA is increasing over time. The value $\hat{\phi} = .64$ is also positive, implying that the time series residuals may be positively autocorrelated. Our forecasts should be more reliable because we have included an autoregressive component in our model to account for possible residual autocorrelation. Note the value of MSE shown in the lower portion of the printout, MSE = 49,349.54. The estimate of σ is then ROOT MSE = 222. Thus, we expect to predict the yearly DJA to within 2(222), or about 444, points of the actual value.

The ultimate objective of fitting a time series model is to forecast future values of the series. Suppose we use the data for n time periods to fit the time series model

$$y_t = \beta_0 + \beta_1 x_1 + R_t \qquad R_t = \phi R_{t-1} + \epsilon_t$$

and we now want to forecast the value of y_{n+1}. From the model,

$$y_{n+1} = \beta_0 + \beta_1 x_{n+1} + R_{n+1}$$

where

$$R_{n+1} = \phi R_n + \epsilon_{n+1}$$

Combining these two equations, we obtain

$$y_{n+1} = \beta_0 + \beta_1 x_{n+1} + \phi R_n + \epsilon_{n+1}$$

The forecast of y_{n+1} is obtained by estimating each of the unknown quantities in this equation.* Using the forecast notation of previous sections, we have

$$F_{n+1} = \hat{y}_{n+1} = \hat{\beta}_0 + \hat{\beta}_1 x_{n+1} + \hat{\phi} \hat{R}_n$$

where $\hat{\beta}_0$, $\hat{\beta}_1$, and $\hat{\phi}$ are the parametric estimates obtained from a computer printout, and ϵ_{n+1} is estimated by its expected value 0. The estimate $\hat{R}_n$ of the residual R_n is obtained by noting that

$$R_n = y_n - (\beta_0 + \beta_1 x_n)$$

so that

$$\hat{R}_n = y_n - (\hat{\beta}_0 + \hat{\beta}_1 x_n)$$

The forecast of y_{n+2} is similarly obtained. The true value of y_{n+2} is

$$y_{n+2} = \beta_0 + \beta_1 x_{n+2} + R_{n+2}$$
$$= \beta_0 + \beta_1 x_{n+2} + \phi R_{n+1} + \epsilon_{n+2}$$

and the forecast at $t = n + 2$ is

$$F_{n+2} = \hat{y}_{n+2} = \hat{\beta}_0 + \hat{\beta}_1 x_{n+2} + \hat{\phi} \hat{R}_{n+1}$$

The residual R_{n+1} (and all future residuals) can now be obtained from the recursive relation

$$R_{n+1} = \phi R_n + \epsilon_{n+1}$$

so that

$$\hat{R}_{n+1} = \hat{\phi} \hat{R}_n$$

Thus, the forecasting of future y-values is an iterative process, with each new forecast making use of the previous residual to obtain the estimated residual for the future time period. The general forecasting procedure using time series models with first-order autoregressive residuals is outlined in the box.

---

* Note that the forecast requires the value of x_{n+1}. When x_t is itself a time series, the future value x_{n+1} will generally be unknown and also must be estimated. Often, $x_t = t$ (as shown in the first example in Section 12.5). In this case, the future time period ($t = n + 1$) is known, and no estimate is required.

FORECASTING USING TIME SERIES MODELS WITH FIRST-ORDER AUTOREGRESSIVE RESIDUALS

$$y_t = \beta_0 + \beta_1 x_{1t} + \beta_2 x_{2t} + \cdots + \beta_k x_{kt} + R_t$$
$$R_t = \phi R_{t-1} + \epsilon_t$$

STEP 1   Use a statistical software package to obtain the estimated model:

$$\hat{y}_t = \hat{\beta}_0 + \hat{\beta}_1 x_{1t} + \hat{\beta}_2 x_{2t} + \cdots + \hat{\beta}_k x_{kt} + \hat{R}_t \qquad t = 1, 2, \ldots, n$$
$$\hat{R}_t = \hat{\phi}\hat{R}_{t-1}$$

STEP 2   Compute the estimated residual for the last time period in the data $(t = n)$ as follows:

$$\hat{R}_n = y_n - \hat{y}_n$$
$$= y_n - (\hat{\beta}_0 + \hat{\beta}_1 x_{1n} + \hat{\beta}_2 x_{2n} + \cdots + \hat{\beta}_k x_{kn})$$

STEP 3   Forecasts of future values are obtained as follows:

$$F_{n+1} = \hat{\beta}_0 + \hat{\beta}_1 x_{1,n+1} + \hat{\beta}_2 x_{2,n+1} + \cdots + \hat{\beta}_k x_{k,n+1} + \hat{\phi}\hat{R}_n$$
$$F_{n+2} = \hat{\beta}_0 + \hat{\beta}_1 x_{1,n+2} + \hat{\beta}_2 x_{2,n+2} + \cdots + \hat{\beta}_k x_{k,n+2} + \hat{\phi}^2\hat{R}_n$$
$$F_{n+3} = \hat{\beta}_0 + \hat{\beta}_1 x_{1,n+3} + \hat{\beta}_2 x_{2,n+3} + \cdots + \hat{\beta}_k x_{k,n+3} + \hat{\phi}^3\hat{R}_n$$
$$\vdots$$
$$F_{n+m} = \hat{\beta}_0 + \hat{\beta}_1 x_{1,n+m} + \hat{\beta}_2 x_{2,n+m} + \cdots + \hat{\beta}_k x_{k,n+m} + \hat{\phi}^m\hat{R}_n$$

(where $\hat{R}_n$ is obtained from step 2).

EXAMPLE 12.7   Refer to the DJA model discussed in Example 12.6. Use the fitted model to forecast the DJA for the years 1990, 1991, and 1992 (ie, $t = 21, 22,$ and 23, respectively).

Solution   The fitted model of Example 12.6 is given by

$$\hat{y}_t = 402.95 + 85.52t + .64\hat{R}_{t-1}$$

Consider first the forecast for 1990 ($t = 21$). Substituting $t = 21$ into the estimated model, we have

$$\hat{y}_{21} = 402.95 + 85.52(21) + .64\hat{R}_{20}$$

To complete the calculation of the forecast, however, we require an estimate of the residual for 1990, $\hat{R}_{20}$. By definition, the residual in year t is equal to the difference between the observed DJA in year t and its corresponding predicted value, that is, $\hat{R}_t = y_t - \hat{y}_t$, or

$$\hat{R}_t = y_t - (402.95 + 85.52t)$$

Substituting $t = 20$, we obtain

$$\hat{R}_{20} = y_{20} - [402.95 + 85.52(20)]$$
$$= 2{,}753 - 2{,}113.35$$
$$= 639.65$$

Thus, our forecast for 1990 is

$$\hat{y}_{21} = 402.95 + 85.52(21) + .64\hat{R}_{20}$$
$$= 402.95 + 85.52(21) + .64(639.65)$$
$$= 2{,}608.2$$

The forecasts for the remaining years are obtained by using the recursive relation

$$\hat{y}_t = 402.95 + 85.52t + .64\hat{R}_{t-1}$$

For 1991, $t = 22$ and

$$\hat{y}_{22} = 402.95 + 85.52(22) + .64\hat{R}_{21}$$

where

$$\hat{R}_{21} = .64\hat{R}_{20}$$
$$= .64(639.65)$$
$$= 409.38$$

Then the forecast for 1991 is

$$\hat{y}_{22} = 402.95 + 85.52(22) + .64(409.38)$$
$$= 2{,}546.4$$

Similarly, for 1992, $t = 23$ and

$$\hat{y}_{23} = 402.95 + 85.52(23) + .64\hat{R}_{22}$$

where

$$\hat{R}_{22} = .64\hat{R}_{21} = .64(409.38) = 262.0$$

Then the forecast for 1992 is

$$\hat{y}_{23} = 402.95 + 85.52(23) + .64(262) = 2{,}537.6$$

APPROXIMATE 95% FORECASTING LIMITS USING TIME SERIES MODELS WITH FIRST-ORDER AUTOREGRESSIVE RESIDUALS

FORECAST	FORECASTING LIMITS
F_{n+1}	$\pm 2\sqrt{\text{MSE}}$
F_{n+2}	$\pm 2\sqrt{\text{MSE}(1 + \hat{\phi}^2)}$
F_{n+3}	$\pm 2\sqrt{\text{MSE}(1 + \hat{\phi}^2 + \hat{\phi}^4)}$
$\vdots$	$\vdots$
F_{n+m}	$\pm 2\sqrt{\text{MSE}(1 + \hat{\phi}^2 + \hat{\phi}^4 + \cdots + \hat{\phi}^{2(m-1)})}$

How reliable are the DJA forecasts obtained in Example 12.7? To assess this, we need to place prediction limits on their values. The formulas for computing approximate prediction limits are given in the box on p. 664.

EXAMPLE 12.8 Refer to Example 12.7. Construct approximate 95% prediction limits for the DJA forecasts for 1990–1992. Comparisons with the actual DJA for these years are shown in Table 12.13.

TABLE 12.13
Comparisons of Forecast and Actual DJAs: 1990–1992

	FORECAST DJA (EXAMPLE 12.7)	ACTUAL DATA
1990	$\hat{y}_{21} = 2{,}608.2$	$y_{21} = 2{,}761$
1991	$\hat{y}_{22} = 2{,}546.4$	$y_{22} = 3{,}015$
1992	$\hat{y}_{23} = 2{,}537.6$	$y_{23} = 3{,}296$

Solution For the forecast $\hat{y}_{n+1}$ (ie, the DJA forecast for 1990), the 95% prediction interval is given by

$$\hat{y}_{n+1} \pm 2\sqrt{\text{MSE}}$$

where MSE is the mean square error obtained from the printout shown in Figure 12.11: MSE = 49,349.54. The approximate 95% prediction interval for the 1990 DJA is then obtained by substitution into the formula:

$$\hat{y}_{21} \pm 2\sqrt{\text{MSE}} = 2{,}608.2 \pm 2\sqrt{49{,}349.54}$$
$$= 2{,}608.2 \pm 444.3 \quad \text{or} \quad (2{,}163.9, 3{,}052.5)$$

For the forecast $\hat{y}_{n+2}$ (ie, the DJA forecast for 1991), the 95% prediction interval is given by

$$\hat{y}_{n+2} \pm 2\sqrt{\text{MSE}(1 + \hat{\phi}^2)}$$

where $\hat{\phi}$ is the estimated first-order autocorrelation coefficient obtained from the printout. Since $\hat{\phi} = .64$, the approximate 95% prediction interval for the DJA forecast for 1991 is

$$\hat{y}_{22} \pm 2\sqrt{\text{MSE}(1 + \hat{\phi}^2)} = 2{,}546.4 \pm 2\sqrt{49{,}349.54(1 + .64^2)}$$
$$= 2{,}546.4 \pm 527.5 \quad \text{or} \quad (2{,}018.9, 3{,}073.9)$$

The approximate 95% prediction interval for the forecast $\hat{y}_{n+3}$ is

$$\hat{y}_{n+3} \pm 2\sqrt{\text{MSE}(1 + \hat{\phi}^2 + \hat{\phi}^4)} = \hat{y}_{23} \pm 2\sqrt{\text{MSE}(1 + \hat{\phi}^2 + \hat{\phi}^4)}$$
$$= 2{,}537.6 \pm 2\sqrt{49{,}349.54(1 + .64^2 + .64^4)}$$
$$= 2{,}537.6 \pm 558.0 \quad \text{or} \quad (1{,}979.6, 3{,}095.6)$$

Notice that the actual DJAs for 1990 and 1991 fall within their respective 95% prediction intervals. However, the actual DJA for 1992 falls above its 95% prediction interval. Probably the best measure of the usefulness of a forecasting technique is a comparison of the forecasts against the future values of the time series. The fact that the 1992 forecast interval missed the actual DJA casts some doubt on the usefulness of the forecasting model. The coefficient of determination for the model (shown in the printout in Figure 12.11 as Total Rsq) is only $R^2 = .8572$. This implies that nearly 15% of the variation in the observed DJAs is left unexplained by the model.

Note also that the prediction intervals get wider as we forecast further into the future. This is because we are extrapolating outside the range of the time period containing the data. The further ahead we forecast, the less confidence we have that the structure of the fitted model will not change during the forecasting period; consequently, the forecasts are less reliable. For this reason, forecasts should be confined to the short term whenever possible.

The forecasting techniques outlined in this section apply to time series models with first-order autoregressive residuals. The more complex the autoregressive model, the more complex the forecasting process becomes. For details on forecasting using a more general autoregressive time series model, consult the references at the end of this chapter.

PROBLEMS

12.18 Suppose you are interested in buying gold on the commodities market. Your broker has advised you that your best strategy is to sell back the gold at the first substantial jump in price. Hence, you are interested in a short-term investment. Before buying, you would like to model the closing price of gold, y_t, over time (in days), t.

    a. Write a first-order model for the deterministic portion of the model, $E(y_t)$.

    b. If a plot of the daily closing prices for the past months reveals a quadratic trend, write a plausible model for $E(y_t)$.

    c. Since the closing price of gold on day $(t + 1)$ is very highly correlated with the closing price on day t, your broker suggests that the random error components of the model are correlated. Given this information, postulate a model for the error term, R_t.

12.19 Numerous studies have been conducted to examine the relationship between seniority and productivity in business. A problem encountered in such studies is that individual output is often difficult to measure. G. A. Krohn developed a technique for estimating the experience–productivity relationship when such a measure is available (*Journal of Business & Economic Statistics*, Oct. 1983). Krohn modeled the batting average of a major league baseball player in year $t(y_t)$ as a function of the player's age in year $t(x_t)$ and an autoregressive error term (R_t).

    a. Write a model for $E(y_t)$ that hypothesizes, as did Krohn, a curvilinear relationship with x_t.

    b. Write a first-order autoregressive model for R_t.

    c. Use the models from parts **a** and **b** to write the full time series autoregressive model for y_t.

12.20 Refer to the analysis of GNP in Problems 12.12 and 12.16 (p. 653 and p. 658).

    a. Hypothesize a time series model for quarterly GNP that includes a straight-line long-term trend and autocorrelated residuals.

    b. The SAS AUTOREG printout for the time series model

$$y_t = \beta_0 + \beta_1 t + \phi R_{t-1} + \epsilon_t$$

follows. Write the least squares prediction equation.

Autoreg Procedure

Dependent Variable = Y

Ordinary Least Squares Estimates

SSE	165337.1	DFE	38
MSE	4350.977	Root MSE	65.96194
SBC	453.9673	AIC	450.5896
Reg Rsq	0.9942	Total Rsq	0.9942
Durbin-Watson	0.3613		

Variable	DF	B Value	Std Error	t Ratio	Approx Prob
Intercept	1	3213.28846	21.256	151.168	0.0001
T	1	72.61398	0.904	80.369	0.0001

Estimates of Autocorrelations

Lag	Covariance	Correlation	-1 9 8 7 6 5 4 3 2 1 0 1 2 3 4 5 6 7 8 9 1
0	4133.428	1.000000	|********************|
1	3208.525	0.776238	|**************** |

Preliminary MSE = 1642.849

Estimates of the Autoregressive Parameters

Lag	Coefficient	Std Error	t Ratio
1	-0.77623822	0.10364365	-7.489491

Yule-Walker Estimates

SSE	56588.47	DFE	37
MSE	1529.418	Root MSE	39.10777
SBC	415.6916	AIC	410.625
Reg Rsq	0.9761	Total Rsq	0.9980

Variable	DF	B Value	Std Error	t Ratio	Approx Prob
Intercept	1	3186.70102	46.348	68.755	0.0001
T	1	73.37105	1.888	38.870	0.0001

c. Interpret the estimates of the model parameters β_0, β_1, and ϕ.

d. Interpret the value of R^2 and Root MSE.

e. Use the fitted autoregressive model to forecast the GNP for the four quarters of 1993. Calculate approximate 95% prediction limits for the forecasts.

12.21 Refer to Problem 12.11 (p. 652) and the study on the long-term effects of the Employee Retirement Income Security Act. Ledolter and Power also fit quarterly time series models for the number of pension plan terminations and the number of profit-sharing plan terminations from the first quarter of 1956 through the third quarter of 1982 ($n = 107$ quarters). To account for residual correlation, they fit straight-line autoregressive models of the form

$$y_t = \beta_0 + \beta_1 t + \phi R_{t-1} + \epsilon_t$$

The results were as follows:

Pension plan terminations: $\hat{y}_t = 3.54 + .039t + .40\hat{R}_{t-1}$ MSE = .0440

Profit-sharing terminations: $\hat{y}_t = 3.45 + .038t + .22\hat{R}_{t-1}$ MSE = .0402

a. Interpret the estimates of the model parameters for pension plan terminations.

b. Interpret the estimates of the model parameters for profit-sharing plan terminations.

c. Forecast the number of pension plan terminations for quarter IV of 1982 ($t = 108$). Assume that $y_{107} = 7.5$. [*Hint:* Recall that y_t is the logarithm of the number of pension plan terminations. Therefore, to obtain the forecast value, you must take the antilogarithm of $\hat{y}_{108}$; that is, the forecast number of pension plan terminations is $e^{\hat{y}_{108}}$.]

d. Place approximate 95% confidence bounds on the forecast obtained in part **c**. [*Hint:* First, calculate upper and lower confidence limits for y_{108}; then take antilogarithms.]

e. Repeat parts **c** and **d** for the number of profit-sharing plan terminations in quarter IV of 1982. Assume that $y_{107} = 7.6$.

FORECASTING USING LAGGED VALUES OF THE DEPENDENT VARIABLE

12.8

In previous examples we discussed a variety of choices for the deterministic component $E(y_t)$ of the time series models. All these models were functions of independent variables, such as t, x_t, x_{t-1}, and seasonal dummy variables. Often, the forecast of y_t can be improved by adding **lagged values of the dependent variable** to the model. For example, since the price y_t of a stock on day t is highly correlated with the price on the previous day (ie, on day $t - 1$), a useful model for $E(y_t)$ is

$$E(y_t) = \beta_0 + \beta_1 y_{t-1}$$

Models with lagged values of y_t tend to violate the standard regression assumptions outlined in Section 10.3; thus, they must be fit using specialized methods.

Box and Jenkins (1977) developed a method of analyzing time series models based on past values of y_t and past values of the random error ϵ_t. The general model, called an **autoregressive moving average model** and denoted **ARMA(p, q)**, takes the form

$$y_t + \phi_1 y_{t-1} + \phi_2 y_{t-2} + \cdots + \phi_p y_{t-p} = \epsilon_t + \theta_1 \epsilon_{t-1} + \theta_2 \epsilon_{t-2} + \cdots + \theta_q \epsilon_{t-q}$$

Note that the left side of the equation is a **pth-order autoregressive model** for y_t (see Section 12.7), while the right side of the equation is a **qth-order moving average model** for the random error ϵ_t.

The analysis of an ARMA (p, q) model is divided into three stages: (1) identification, (2) estimation, and (3) forecasting. In the identification stage, the values of p and q are determined from the sample data. That is, the order of both the autoregressive portion and the moving average portion of the model are identified.[*] For example, the analyst may find the best fit to be an ARMA model with $p = 2$ and $q = 0$. Substituting $p = 2$ and $q = 0$ into the previous equation, we obtain the ARMA(2, 0) model

$$y_t + \phi_1 y_{t-1} + \phi_2 y_{t-2} = \epsilon_t$$

Note that since $q = 0$, there is no moving average component to the model.

Once the model is identified, the second stage involves obtaining estimates of the model's parameters. In the case of the ARMA(2, 0) model, we require estimates of the autoregressive parameters ϕ_1 and ϕ_2. Tests for model adequacy are conducted, and, if the model is deemed adequate, the estimated model is used to forecast future values of y_t in the third stage.

---

[*] This step involves a careful examination of a plot of the sample autocorrelations. Certain patterns in the plot allow the analyst to identify p and q.

Analysis of ARMA(p, q) models for y_t requires a level of expertise that is beyond the scope of this text. Even with this level of expertise, the analyst cannot hope to proceed without the aid of a sophisticated computer program. Procedures for identifying, estimating, and forecasting with ARMA(p, q) models are available in SAS, SPSS, and MINITAB. Before attempting to run these procedures, however, you should consult the references provided at the end of this chapter.

COMPUTER LAB

TIME SERIES METHODS

All three of the statistical software packages discussed throughout this text have commands for calculating the Durbin–Watson test statistic. However, SAS is the only one that has a routine for fitting time series models with autoregressive error terms. The sample programs shown here give the commands for producing the Durbin–Watson statistic, and, if available, the commands for fitting a time series model with first-order autoregressive errors using the Dow Jones Industrial data from Table 12.12.

SAS

Command
Line

```
1    DATA DJA;                ⎫
2    INPUT YEAR Y;            ⎬  Data entry instructions
3    T=YEAR - 1969;          ⎭
4    CARDS;
     1970    839             ⎫
     1971    885             ⎪
       .       .             ⎬  Input data observations
       .       .             ⎪  (1 observation per line)
       .       .             ⎪
     1989    2753            ⎭
5    PROC REG;                ⎫  Durbin–Watson test statistic
6    MODEL Y=T/DW;           ⎭
7    PROC AUTOREG;            ⎫  Autoregressive model
8    MODEL Y=T/NLAG=1;       ⎭
```

COMMAND 6   Specify DW as an option of the REG procedure to produce the Durbin–Watson d statistic.

COMMAND 7   The AUTOREG procedure in SAS fits time series models with autoregressive errors.

COMMAND 8 In the MODEL statement, specify the dependent variable to the left of the equals (=) sign and the independent variables in the deterministic portion of the model to the right. The option NLAG = 1 following the slash (/) specifies a first-order autoregressive model for the random (correlated) error component.

NOTE The output for this SAS program is displayed in Figure 12.12.

SPSS

```
Command
   Line
    1      DATA LIST FREE/YEAR Y.⎤
    2      COMPUTE T=YEAR-1969.  ⎬  Data entry instructions
    3      BEGIN DATA.           ⎦
           1970    839⎤
           1971    885⎥
             .      . ⎬  Input data observations
             .      . ⎥  (1 observation per line)
             .      . ⎥
           1989   2753⎦
    4      END DATA.
    5      REGRESSION VARIABLES=Y T/      ⎤
    6          DEPENDENT=Y/METHOD=ENTER/  ⎬  Durbin–Watson test statistic
    7          RESIDUALS=DURBIN.          ⎦
```

COMMAND 7 Specify DURBIN as an option of the RESIDUALS subcommand in the REGRESSION procedure to produce the Durbin–Watson d statistic.

GENERAL Time series models with autoregressive error terms are unavailable in SPSS.

NOTE The output for this SPSS program is displayed in Figure 12.13 (p. 672).

MINITAB

```
Command
   Line
    1      READ C1 C2    Data entry instruction
           1970    839⎤
           1971    885⎥
             .      . ⎬  Input data observations
             .      . ⎥  (1 observation per line)
             .      . ⎥
           1989   2753⎦
```

(continued)

```
2      LET C3=C1-1969
3      NAME C1='YEAR' C2='Y' C3='T'
4      REGRESS C2 1 C3;⎫
5         DW.         ⎬  Durbin–Watson test statistic
                       ⎭
```

COMMAND 5   Specify DW as a subcommand in the REGRESS command to produce the Durbin–Watson d statistic.

GENERAL   Time series models with autoregressive error terms are unavailable in MINITAB.

NOTE   The output for this MINITAB program is displayed in Figure 12.14 (p. 673).

FIGURE 12.12
SAS Printout for Computer Lab

```
Dependent Variable = Y
                            Analysis of Variance

                             Sum of          Mean
            Source      DF   Squares        Square      F Value    Prob>F

            Model        1 3844232.6632 3844232.6632     34.067    0.0001
            Error       18 2031167.1368  112842.61871
            C Total     19 5875399.8000

            Root MSE      335.92055    R-square      0.6543
            Dep Mean     1212.90000    Adj R-sq      0.6351
            C.V.           27.69565

                         Parameter Estimates

                         Parameter     Standard    T for H0:
            Variable DF   Estimate       Error    Parameter=0   Prob > |T|

            INTERCEP  1   414.568421  156.04566415    2.657       0.0161
            T         1    76.031579   13.02644036    5.837       0.0001

Durbin-Watson D              0.331
(For Number of Obs.)            20
1st Order Autocorrelation    0.640
```

```
                          Autoreg Procedure
Dependent Variable = Y

                   Ordinary Least Squares Estimates

            SSE            2031167    DFE               18
            MSE          112842.6    Root MSE     335.9206
            SBC          293.3168    AIC          291.3253
            Reg Rsq        0.6543    Total Rsq      0.6543
            Durbin-Watson  0.3308

            Variable  DF   B Value    Std Error   t Ratio Approx Prob

            Intercept  1  414.568421    156.05     2.657     0.0161
            T          1   76.031579     13.03     5.837     0.0001
```

(continued)

FIGURE 12.12
(Continued)

```
                         Estimates of Autocorrelations

  Lag   Covariance   Correlation -1 9 8 7 6 5 4 3 2 1 0 1 2 3 4 5 6 7 8 9 1

   0     101558.4     1.000000  |                    |********************|
   1     65007.01     0.640095  |                    |*************       |

                       Preliminary MSE = 59947.68

                 Estimates of the Autoregressive Parameters

            Lag     Coefficient      Std Error        t Ratio
             1      -0.64009517     0.18633906       -3.435110

                       Yule-Walker Estimates

            SSE          838942.2    DFE                 17
            MSE          49349.54    Root MSE       222.1476
            SBC          279.1552    AIC             276.168
            Reg Rsq        0.5495    Total Rsq        0.8572


        Variable      DF      B Value    Std Error    t Ratio Approx Prob

        Intercept     1    402.948499      234.67      1.717      0.1041
        T             1     85.523569       18.78      4.553      0.0003
```

FIGURE 12.13
SPSS Printout for Computer Lab

```
Multiple R              .80888
R Square                .65429
Adjusted R Square       .63509
Standard Error      335.92055

Analysis of Variance
                    DF      Sum of Squares      Mean Square
Regression           1      3844232.66316     3844232.66316
Residual            18      2031167.13684      112842.61871

F =      34.06721      Signif F =   .0000


------------------ Variables in the Equation ------------------

Variable             B          SE B         Beta        T   Sig T

T            76.031579    13.026440      .808884     5.837  .0000
(Constant)  414.568421   156.045664                  2.657  .0161


Residuals Statistics:

                   Min           Max       Mean   Std Dev    N

*PRED         490.6000     1935.2000  1212.9000  449.8089   20
*RESID       -427.9474      817.8000     .0000   326.9611   20
*ZPRED         -1.6058        1.6058     .0000     1.0000   20
*ZRESID        -1.2740        2.4345     .0000      .9733   20

Total Cases =        20


Durbin-Watson Test =     .33078
```

FIGURE 12.14
MINITAB Printout for Computer Lab

```
The regression equation is
Y = 415 + 76.0 T

Predictor      Coef      Stdev     t-ratio      p
Constant       414.6     156.0      2.66      0.016
T              76.03     13.03      5.84      0.000

s = 335.9      R-sq = 65.4%      R-sq(adj) = 63.5%

Analysis of Variance

SOURCE         DF        SS         MS         F         p
Regression     1      3844233    3844233    34.07     0.000
Error          18     2031167     112843
Total          19     5875400

Unusual Observations
Obs.      T         Y       Fit  Stdev.Fit  Residual   St.Resid
 20     20.0     2753.0   1935.2    144.8     817.8       2.70R

R denotes an obs. with a large st. resid.
Durbin-Watson statistic = 0.33
```

CHAPTER NOTES

- A **time series** is a collection of data obtained by observing a response variable on a regular chronological basis. The response at time t, denoted y_t, is called a **time series variable**.

- Time series are often modeled as a function of four components: **secular trend**, **cyclical effect**, **seasonal variation**, and **residual variation**.

- The secular component describes the **long-term trend** of the time series; the cyclical effect describes the fluctuation about the secular trend that is due to **business cycles**; the seasonal variation describes the fluctuations that recur from month to month (or season to season) in a year; and, the residual effect describes unexplainable, or random, error.

- **Index numbers** are descriptive measures of the relative change in a variable over time, relative to a **base period**.

- A **simple index number** is based on relative changes over time in the value of a single time series variable.

- A **composite index number** is based on relative changes over time in the sum of two or more time series variables.

- Three **smoothing techniques** used for describing time series are (1) **moving averages**, (2) **exponential smoothing**, and (3) **Holt–Winters smoothing**.

- The moving average method uses estimates of the secular and seasonal components to forecast the time series. To obtain the forecasts, you must extrapolate the moving average into the future.

- Exponential smoothing is an adaptive forecasting method that leads to explicit forecasts for time series with slight secular or seasonal trends.

- The Holt–Winters method is an extension of exponential smoothing that allows for trend and seasonal components.

- A drawback to forecasting with smoothing methods is that no measure of reliability is provided along with the forecast. Consequently, the risk associated with making decisions based on these forecasts cannot be assessed.

- A regression model is an **inferential time series model** that allows you to construct prediction intervals for the forecasts. The deterministic portion of the model can account for secular and seasonal trends.
- Two potential problems associated with forecasting using regression are:

  1. **The least squares prediction equation is often used to forecast for values of the independent variables outside the range of the sample data.**
  2. **The assumption of independent errors is very likely to be violated.**

- **Autocorrelation** describes the correlation between time series residuals at different points in time.
- **First-order autocorrelation** occurs when neighboring residuals one time period apart (ie, at times t and $t + 1$) are correlated.
- The **Durbin–Watson d test** is used to test for first-order autocorrelation among the time series residuals. The test statistic has the following properties:

  1. $0 \le d \le 4$
  2. If the residuals are uncorrelated, $d \approx 2$.
  3. If the residuals are positively correlated, $d \approx 0$.
  4. If the residuals are negatively correlated, $d \approx 4$.

- One way to account for residual correlation in the time series is to incorporate an **autoregressive model** for the random error component.
- A **first-order autoregressive model** takes the form

$$R_t = \phi R_{t-1} + \epsilon_t$$

  where R_t is the time series residual at time t, $-1 \le \phi \le 1$, and ϵ_t is uncorrelated random error.
- Approximate 95% prediction limits around the forecast F_{n+m}, based on a time series model with first-order autoregressive residuals, are given by the formula

$$\hat{y}_{n+m} \pm 2\sqrt{\text{MSE}(1 + \hat{\phi}^2 + \hat{\phi}^4 + \cdots + \hat{\phi}^{2(m-1)})}$$

- Some time series models utilize **lagged (or past) values of the dependent variable** as independent variables to improve fit.
- Models that use only past values of y or ϵ in the deterministic and error components are called **autoregressive moving average (ARMA)** models.
- The general **ARMA(p, q)** model takes the form

$$y_t + \phi_1 y_{t-1} + \phi_2 y_{t-2} + \cdots + \phi_p y_{t-p} = \epsilon_t + \theta_1 \epsilon_{t-1} + \theta_2 \epsilon_{t-2} + \cdots + \theta_q \epsilon_{t-q}$$

LOOKING AHEAD

The final chapter of the text deals with analyzing designed experiments. Once the data have been collected, the general linear model of Chapters 10 and 11 can be employed to analyze the data.

FORECASTING AND BACK-CASTING PEAK ELECTRICITY DEMAND

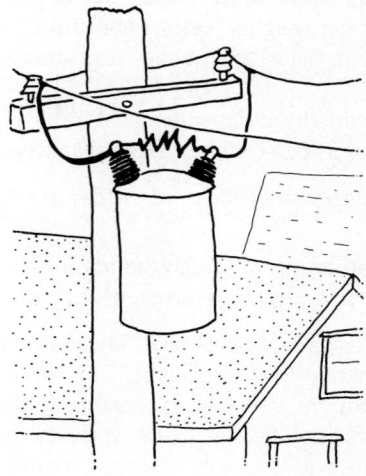

Power companies are continually developing and refining statistical models of daily peak demand. *Demand* (or *load*) is defined as the rate (measured in megawatts) at which electric energy is delivered to customers. Since demand is normally recorded hourly, daily peak demand refers to the maximum hourly demand in a 24 hour period.

Time series models of daily peak demand serve a twofold purpose. First, the models provide short-term *forecasts* that will assist in the economic planning and dispatching of electric energy. Second, models that relate peak demand to one or more weather variables provide estimates of historical peak demands under a set of alternative weather conditions. That is, since changing weather conditions represent the primary source of variation in peak demand, the model can be used to answer the often-asked question, "What would the peak daily demand have been had normal weather prevailed?" This second application, commonly referred to as *weather normalization*, is mainly an exercise in *back-casting* (ie, adjusting historical data) rather than forecasting.

Consider a study designed to compare several alternative methods of modeling daily peak demands for the Florida Power Corporation (FPC).* The data consist of daily observations on peak demand recorded by the FPC for the period beginning November 1, 1982, and ending October 31, 1983, and several factors that are known to influence demand. It is typically assumed that demand consists of two components, a non–weather-sensitive "base" demand that is not influenced by temperature changes, and a weather-sensitive demand component that is highly responsive to changes in temperature.

The principal factor that affects the usage of non–weather-sensitive appliances (such as refrigerators, generators, lights, and computers) is the day of the week. Typically, Saturdays have lower peak demands than weekdays due to decreased commercial and industrial activity, while Sundays and holidays exhibit even lower peak demands as commercial and industrial activity declines even further. Consequently, a useful predictor of demand is the qualitative independent variable "day of the week" at three levels: (1) weekday, (2) Saturday, and (3) Sunday/holiday.

The single most important factor affecting the usage of weather-sensitive appliances (such as heaters and air conditioners) is temperature. During the winter months, as temperatures drop below comfortable levels, customers begin to operate their electric heating units, thereby increasing the level of demand placed on the system. Similarly, during the summer months, as temperatures climb above comfortable levels, the use of air-conditioning drives demand upward. Since the FPC serves 32 counties along west-central and northern Florida, it was necessary to gather temperature data from multiple weather stations. This was accomplished by identify-

---

* Jacob, M. F. "A Time Series Approach to Modeling Daily Peak Electricity Demands." Paper presented at the SAS Users Group International Annual Conference, Reno, NV, 1985.

ing three primary weather stations within the FPC service area and recording the temperature at the hour of peak demand each day at each station. A weighted average of these three daily temperatures was used to represent the quantitative independent variable "coincident temperature" (ie, temperature at the hour of peak demand) for the entire FPC service area, where the weights were proportional to the percentage of total electricity sales attributable to the weather zones surrounding each of the three weather stations.

To summarize, the dependent variable (y_t) and the independent variables recorded for each of the 365 days of the November 1982–October 1983 year were:

Dependent variable: y_t = Peak demand (in megawatts) observed on day t

Independent variables:
 Qualitative: Day of the week (weekday, Saturday, or Sunday/holiday)
 Quantitative: Temperature (coincident temperature, in degrees, on day t)

Figure 12.15 shows a graph of the daily peak demand (y_t) over time. The seasonal weather impacts on peak demand are readily apparent from the figure. One way to account for this seasonal variation is to include dummy variables for months in the model. However, since temperature is such a strong indicator of the weather, the FPC opted for a simpler model with temperature as the sole seasonal weather variable.

FIGURE 12.15

Daily Peak Demand (Megawatts) Plotted in Time Order

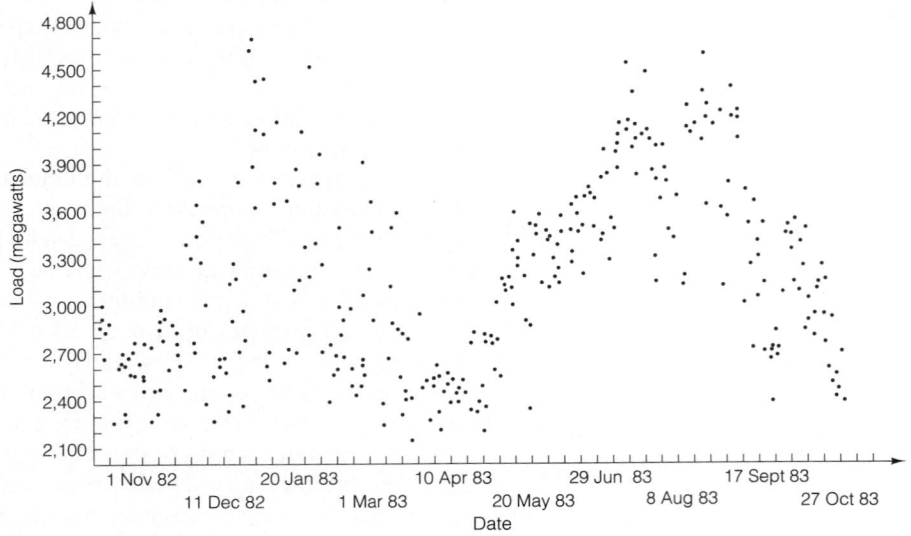

Source: Florida Power Corp.

Figure 12.16 presents a scatterplot of daily peak demand versus coincident temperature. Note the nonlinear relationship that exists between the two variables. During the cool winter months, peak demand is inversely related to temperature; lower temperatures cause increased usage of heating equipment, which, in turn, causes higher peak demands. In contrast, the summer months reveal a positive

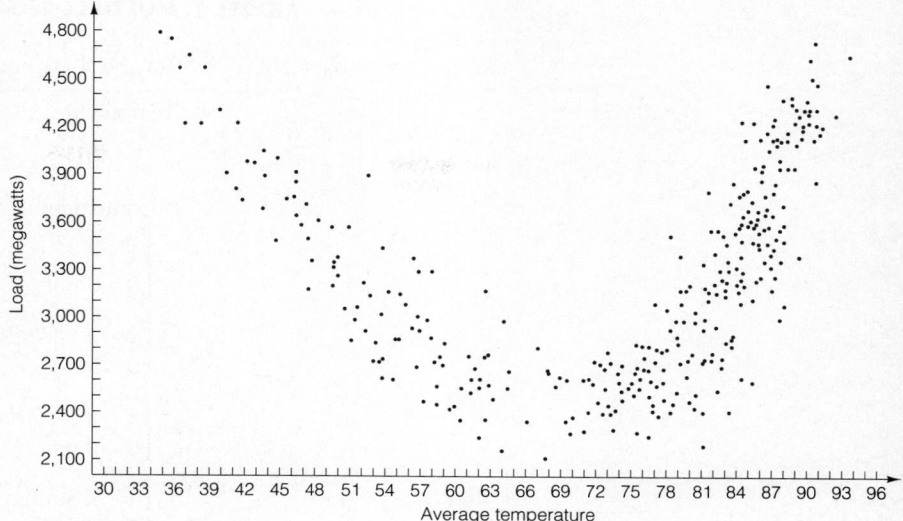

Source: Florida Power Corp.

relationship between peak demand and temperature; higher temperatures yield higher peak demands due to greater usage of air-conditioners. You might think that a second-order (quadratic) model would be a good choice to account for the U-shaped distribution of peak demands shown in Figure 12.16. The FPC, however, rejected such a model for two reasons:

1. A quadratic model yields a symmetrical shape (ie, a parabola) and would, therefore, not allow independent estimates of the winter and summer peak demand–temperature relationship.

2. In theory, there exists a mild temperature range where peak demand is assumed to consist solely of the non–weather-sensitive base demand component. For this range, a temperature change will not spur any additional heating or cooling and, consequently, has no impact on demand. The lack of linearity in the bottom portion of the U-shaped parabola fit by the quadratic model would tend to yield overestimates of peak demand at the extremes of the mild temperature range and underestimates for temperatures in the middle of this range (see Figure 12.17).

The solution was to model daily peak demand with a **piecewise linear regression** model.* This approach has the advantage of allowing the peak demand–temperature relationship to vary between some prespecified temperature ranges, as well as providing a mechanism for joining the separate pieces.

With the piecewise linear specification as the basic model structure, the following multiple regression model of daily peak demand was proposed:

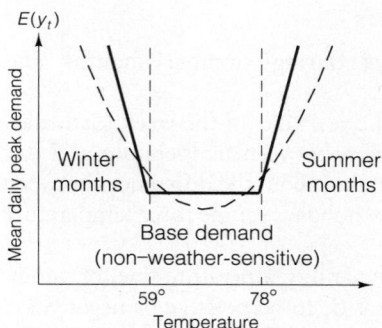

FIGURE 12.17

Theoretical Relationship Between Daily Peak Demand and Temperature

---

* Consult the references given at the end of Chapter 10 to learn more about piecewise linear regression.

MODEL 1: MULTIPLE REGRESSION MODEL

$$y_t = \beta_0 + \underbrace{\beta_1(x_{1t} - 59)x_{2t} + \beta_2(x_{1t} - 78)x_{3t}}_{\text{Temperature}} + \underbrace{\beta_3 x_{4t} + \beta_4 x_{5t}}_{\text{Day of the week}} + \epsilon_t$$

where

$$x_{1t} = \text{Coincident temperature on day } t$$

$$x_{2t} = \begin{cases} 1 & \text{if } x_{1t} < 59 \\ 0 & \text{if not} \end{cases}$$

$$x_{3t} = \begin{cases} 1 & \text{if } x_{1t} > 78 \\ 0 & \text{if not} \end{cases}$$

$$x_{4t} = \begin{cases} 1 & \text{if Saturday} \\ 0 & \text{if not} \end{cases}$$

$$x_{5t} = \begin{cases} 1 & \text{if Sunday or holiday} \\ 0 & \text{if not} \end{cases}$$

Base level = Weekday

a. Show that model 1 proposes three different straight-line relationships between peak demand (y_t) and coincident temperature (x_{1t}), one for each of the three temperature ranges corresponding to winter months (less than 59°), non–weather-sensitive months (between 59° and 78°), and summer months (greater than 78°). [*Hint:* For winter months ($x_{1t} < 59$), we have $x_{2t} = 1$ and $x_{3t} = 0$, while for weekdays, $x_{4t} = x_{5t} = 0$. Substituting $x_{2t} = 1$, $x_{3t} = 0$, $x_{4t} = 0$, and $x_{5t} = 0$ into the model, we obtain the equation of the demand–temperature line for weekdays during winter months:

$$\begin{aligned} E(y_t) &= \beta_0 + \beta_1(x_{1t} - 59)(1) + \beta_2(x_{1t} - 78)(0) + \beta_3(0) + \beta_4(0) \\ &= \beta_0 + \beta_1(x_{1t} - 59) \\ &= (\beta_0 - 59\beta_1) + \beta_1 x_{1t} \end{aligned}$$

Perform similar calculations for weekdays during summer months and non–weather-sensitive months.]

b. Model 1 also allows for variations in demand due to day of the week (Saturday, Sunday/holiday, or weekday). Since interaction between temperature and day of the week is omitted, what is the model assuming about the differences between mean peak demand for weekdays or weekends/holidays for the three temperature ranges?

c. Refer to part **a**. Show that the slope of the demand–temperature line for winter months (when $x_{1t} < 59$) is β_1. Do you expect β_1 to be positive or negative? [*Hint:* Use Figure 12.17.]

d. Refer to part **a**. Show that the slope for summer months (when $x_{1t} > 78$) is β_2. Do you expect β_2 to be positive or negative?

Model 1 is a multiple regression model that relies on the standard regression assumptions of independent errors (ie, errors uncorrelated). This may be a serious shortcoming since the data are in the form of a time series. To account for possible autocorrelated residuals, the following time series model was proposed:

MODEL 2:   TIME SERIES MODEL

$$y_t = \beta_0 + \beta_1(x_{1t} - 59)x_{2t} + \beta_2(x_{1t} - 78)x_{3t} + \beta_3 x_{4t} + \beta_4 x_{5t} + R_t$$
$$R_t = \phi R_{t-1} + \epsilon_t$$

Model 2 proposes a multiple regression–autoregressive pair of models for daily peak demand (y_t). The deterministic component, $E(y_t)$, is identical to the deterministic component of model 1; however, a first-order autoregressive model is chosen for the random error component.

e. What type of autocorrelation (positive or negative) occurs when ϕ in model 2 is positive? Negative?

f. The SAS multiple regression computer printout for model 1 is shown in Figure 12.18, and a plot of the least squares fit is shown in Figure 12.19. Interpret the values of R^2, F, and Root MSE in the printout.

g. Refer to the model 1 printout shown in Figure 12.18. Test the hypotheses

$$H_0: \quad \phi = 0$$
$$H_a: \quad \phi > 0$$

using the Durbin–Watson test. (Use $\alpha = .05$.) Interpret the results.

h. The SAS AUTOREG printout for model 2 is shown in Figure 12.20. Find and interpret the values of R^2 (TOTAL RSQ) and ROOT MSE in the printout. Compare these values to the values obtained in part f. Do these results support the conclusion reached by the Durbin–Watson test in part g?

FIGURE 12.18

SAS Printout: Model 1

Analysis of Variance

Source	DF	Sum of Squares	Mean Square	F Value	Prob>F
Model	4	106565982	26641495.5	441.729	0.0001
Error	360	21712247	60311.8		
C Total	364	128278229			

Root MSE	245.585	R-Square	0.8307	
Dep Mean	3191.863	Adj R-Sq	0.8289	
C.V.	7.694			

Parameter Estimates

Variable	DF	Parameter Estimate	Standard Error	T for H0: Parameter=0	Prob > |T|
INTERCEP	1	2670.171	21.251829	125.644	0.0001
AVTW	1	-82.038953	2.941928	-27.886	0.0001
AVTS	1	114.443	3.050468	37.516	0.0001
SAT	1	-164.932	37.990216	-4.341	0.0001
SUN	1	-285.114	35.328293	-8.070	0.0001

Durbin-Watson d	0.705
(For number of obs.)	365
1st Order Autocorrelation	0.648

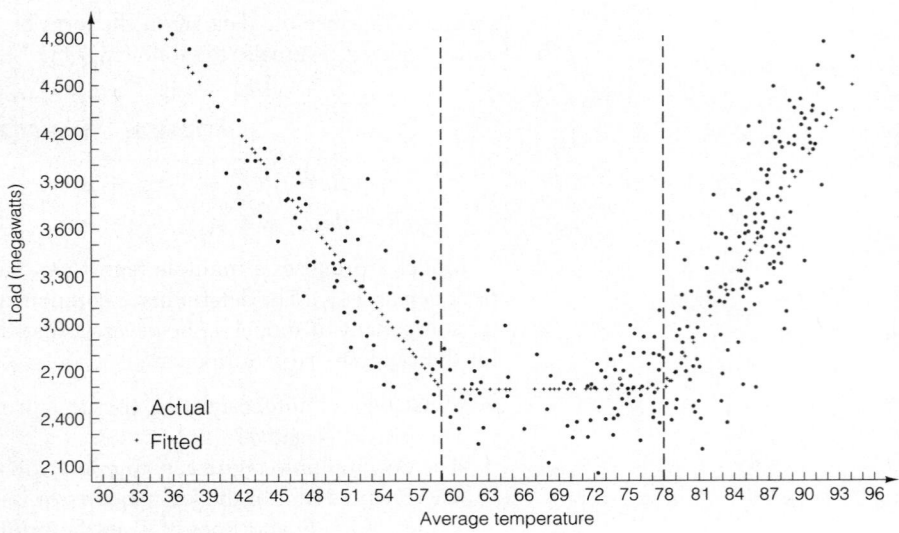

Source: Florida Power Corp.

FIGURE 12.20
SAS Printout: Model 2

DEPENDENT VARIABLE = LOAD

ORDINARY LEAST SQUARES ESTIMATES

SSE	21712247	DFE	360
MSE	60311.8	ROOT MSE	245.585
REG RSQ	0.8307	TOTAL RSQ	0.8307
DURBIN-WATSON	0.7052		

VARIABLE	DF	B VALUE	STD ERROR	T RATIO	APPROX PROB
INTERCEP	1	2670.171	21.251829	125.644	0.0001
AVTW	1	-82.038953	2.941928	-27.886	0.0001
AVTS	1	114.443	3.050468	37.516	0.0001
SAT	1	-164.932	37.990216	-4.341	0.0001
SUN	1	-285.114	35.328293	-8.070	0.0001

ESTIMATES OF THE AUTOCORRELATIONS

LAG	COVARIANCE	CORRELATION	-1 9 8 7 6 5 4 3 2 1 0 1 2 3 4 5 6 7 8 9 1
0	59485.6	1.000000	|********************|
1	38519.4	0.647541	|************ |

PRELIMINARY MSE=   35542.75

ESTIMATES OF THE AUTOREGRESSIVE PARAMETERS
LAG	COEFFICIENT	STD ERROR	T RATIO
1	-0.64754083	0.039887	-16.23458

YULE-WALKER ESTIMATES

SSE	9939789	DFE	359
MSE	26787.44	ROOT MSE	166.3943
REG RSQ	0.7626	TOTAL RSQ	0.9225

VARIABLE	DF	B VALUE	STD ERROR	T RATIO	APPROX PROB
INTERCEP	1	2812.967	29.879088	94.145	0.0001
AVTW	1	-65.337453	2.663925	-24.527	0.0001
AVTS	1	83.455	3.853199	21.659	0.0001
SAT	1	-130.828	22.413602	-5.837	0.0001
SUN	1	-275.551	21.373678	-12.892	0.0001

TABLE 12.14

Actual Peak Demand for the First 7 Days of November 1983

DATE	t	ACTUAL DEMAND y_t	ACTUAL TEMPERATURE x_{1t}
Tues., Nov. 1	366	2,799	76
Wed., Nov. 2	367	2,784	77
Thurs., Nov. 3	368	2,845	77
Fri., Nov. 4	369	2,701	76
Sat., Nov. 5	370	2,512	72
Sun., Nov. 6	371	2,419	71
Mon., Nov. 7	372	2,749	68

i. Use model 2 and the information provided in Table 12.14 to forecast daily peak demand for the first 7 days in November 1983. The estimated model,* obtained from Figure 12.20, is given by

$$\hat{y}_t = 2{,}812.967 - 65.337(x_{1t} - 59)x_{2t} + 83.455(x_{1t} - 78)x_{3t}$$
$$- 130.828x_{4t} - 275.551x_{5t} + R_t$$
$$\hat{R}_t = .6475\hat{R}_{t-1}$$

j. Construct approximate 95% prediction intervals for the forecasts of part i. Determine whether actual demand (see Table 12.14) falls within the corresponding prediction interval for each of the 7 days.

k. Consider the problem of using model 2 for weather normalization (or backcasting). Suppose the temperature on Saturday, March 5, 1983 ($t = 125$), was $x_{1,125} = 25°$, which was unusually cold for that day. Normally, temperatures range from 40° to 50° on March 5 in the FPC service area. Substitute $x_{1,125} = 45°$ into the prediction equation to obtain an estimate of the peak demand expected if normal weather conditions had prevailed on March 5, 1983. Calculate an approximate 95% prediction interval for the estimate. [Hint: Use $\hat{y}_{125} \pm 2\sqrt{\text{MSE}}$.]

REFERENCES

Anderson, T. W. *The Statistical Analysis of Time Series.* New York: Wiley, 1971.

Box, G. E. P., and Jenkins, G. M. *Time Series Analysis: Forecasting and Control*, 2d ed. San Francisco: Holden-Day, 1977.

Durbin, J., and Watson, G. S. "Testing for Serial Correlation in Least Squares Regression, I," *Biometrika*, 1950, *37*, pp. 409–428.

---

* Remember that the estimate of ϕ is obtained by multiplying the value reported in the SAS printout by (-1).

Durbin, J., and Watson, G. S. "Testing for Serial Correlation in Least Squares Regression, II," *Biometrika*, 1951, *38*, pp. 159–178.

Durbin, J., and Watson, G. S. "Testing for Serial Correlation in Least Squares Regression, III," *Biometrika*, 1971, *58*, pp. 1–19.

Fuller, W. A. *Introduction to Statistical Time Series*. New York: Wiley, 1976.

Granger, C. W. J., and Newbold, P. *Forecasting Economic Time Series*. Princeton, NJ: Princeton University Press, 1964.

Makridakis, S., et al. *The Forecasting Accuracy of Major Time Series Methods*. New York: Wiley, 1984.

Mendenhall, W., and Sincich, T. *A Second Course in Business Statistics: Regression Analysis*, 4th ed. New York: Dellen/Macmillan, 1993.

Nelson, C. R. *Applied Time Series Analysis for Managerial Forecasting*. San Francisco: Holden-Day, 1973.

SAMPLE EXAM QUESTIONS: CHAPTER 12

(1–8) The table lists the yearly outlays for the Federal Space Program (in million dollars) from 1971 through 1989.

YEAR	OUTLAY	YEAR	OUTLAY
1971	4,471	1981	9,978
1972	4,575	1982	12,091
1973	4,825	1983	15,564
1974	4,640	1984	17,449
1975	4,914	1985	20,167
1976	5,320	1986	21,659
1977	5,983	1987	26,448
1978	6,509	1988	26,373
1979	7,419	1989	30,196
1980	8,689		

Source: Statistical Abstract of the United States, U.S. Department of Commerce, Bureau of the Census.

1. Calculate a simple index for the federal space outlay in 1989 using 1980 as a base period.
2. Interpret the simple index for 1989 calculated in the previous question.
3. Calculate the first value in a 5-point moving average of the yearly federal space outlays.
4. Which leads to a smoother series, a 3-point, 5-point, or 7-point moving average? Explain.
5. Calculate the exponentially smoothed forecast of the 1993 federal space outlay. (Use only the years 1987–1989 to compute the forecast.)
6. Give at least one drawback to using a smoothing technique for forecasting the yearly space outlay series.
7. The SAS printout for the simple linear regression, $y_t = \beta_0 + \beta_1 t + \epsilon_t$, where y_t = space outlay in year t, follows. Interpret the results.

Dependent Variable: **OUTLAY**

Analysis of Variance

Source	DF	Sum of Squares	Mean Square	F Value	Prob>F
Model	1	1198804930.1	1198804930.1	127.226	0.0001
Error	17	160185305.68	9422665.0401		
C Total	18	1358990235.8			

(*continued*)

```
        Root MSE        3069.63598    R-square        0.8821
        Dep Mean       12487.89474    Adj R-sq        0.8752
        C.V.              24.58089

                       Parameter Estimates

                     Parameter      Standard    T for H0:
    Variable   DF     Estimate         Error    Parameter=0    Prob > |T|

    INTERCEP    1   -2014.403509   1465.9566395     -1.374        0.1873
    T           1    1450.229825    128.57290266     11.279        0.0001


    Durbin-Watson D              0.223
    (For Number of Obs.)            19
    1st Order Autocorrelation    0.742
```

8. Hypothesize a time series model that accounts for residual autocorrelation in the yearly series.

(9–10) In 1974 Congress adopted the Federal-Aid Highway Amendments, which reduced the highway speed limit to 55 miles per hour (mph). Since that time, controversy over the social efficiency of the decision has grown. T. H. Forester, R. F. McNown, and L. D. Singell conducted an analysis to estimate the effect of the 55 mph speed limit on traffic fatalities (*Southern Economic Journal*, Jan. 1984). Time series data for the United States from 1952 to 1979 ($n = 28$ years) were used to fit a regression model relating traffic fatalities, y_t, to $k = 7$ independent variables:

$$x_{1t} = \text{Real earned income}$$
$$x_{2t} = \text{Vehicle miles}$$
$$x_{3t} = \text{Ratio of number of youths to number of adults}$$
$$x_{4t} = \text{Percentage of all car purchases that are imported cars}$$
$$x_{5t} = \text{Average highway speed}$$
$$x_{6t} = \text{Percentage of cars traveling between 45 and 60 mph}$$
$$x_{7t} = \begin{cases} 0 & \text{if 55 mph speed limit imposed} \\ 1 & \text{otherwise} \end{cases}$$

The results of the multiple regression are summarized as follows:

$$\hat{y}_t = -20{,}016.4 + 7{,}544.85x_{1t} - .01046x_{2t} - 36{,}758.0x_{3t} - 117.609x_{4t} + 1{,}325.22x_{5t}$$
$$- 415.742x_{6t} + 9{,}678.08x_{7t}$$
$$R^2 = .987 \qquad F = 217.23 \qquad d = 1.97$$

9. Is there evidence that the model is useful for predicting annual traffic fatalities? Test using $\alpha = .05$.

10. Is there evidence that the regression residuals are positively autocorrelated? Test using $\alpha = .05$.

(11–15) In May 1978, the first casino (Resorts International Hotel and Casino) opened in Atlantic City, New Jersey. In the first 3 years following the casino's opening, employment in hotels and other lodging places accelerated along Atlantic City's boardwalk, as shown in the table on the next page.

A model that accounts for the secular, seasonal, and residual variation in employment is

$$y_t = \beta_0 + \beta_1 t + \beta_2 Q_1 + \beta_3 Q_2 + \beta_4 Q_3 + \phi R_{t-1} + \epsilon_t$$

YEAR	QUARTER	EMPLOYMENT
1	I	1,711
	II	4,065
	III	5,787
	IV	5,019
2	I	5,459
	II	9,184
	III	12,168
	IV	11,842
3	I	13,730
	II	14,964
	III	18,058
	IV	21,393

Source: Federal Reserve Bank of Philadelphia, *Business Review*, Jan.–Feb. 1982.

where

$$y_t = \text{Unemployment in quarter } t$$

$$Q_1 = \begin{cases} 1 & \text{if quarter I} \\ 0 & \text{if not} \end{cases}$$

$$Q_2 = \begin{cases} 1 & \text{if quarter II} \\ 0 & \text{if not} \end{cases}$$

$$Q_3 = \begin{cases} 1 & \text{if quarter III} \\ 0 & \text{if not} \end{cases}$$

$$R_t = \text{Correlated residual in quarter } t$$

$$\epsilon_t = \text{Uncorrelated random error in quarter } t$$

The time series model was fit to the $n = 12$ data points in the table, with the following results:

$$\hat{y}_t = -173.933 + 1{,}623.684t - 859.249Q_1 - 141.867Q_2 + 826.733Q_3 + .1702R_{t-1}$$
$$\text{MSE} = 2{,}125{,}312$$

11. Interpret the estimates of the model parameters.
12. Interpret the value of MSE.
13. Use the model to forecast the employment in Atlantic City hotels and motels in quarter I of the 4th year. Place approximate 95% confidence limits around the forecast.
14. Now consider the lagged dependent variable model,

$$y_t = \beta_0 + \beta_1 t + \beta_2 Q_1 + \beta_3 Q_2 + \beta_4 Q_3 + \beta_5 y_{t-1} + \epsilon_t$$

What problems occur if we use the method of least squares to fit the model?
15. Write an ARMA(2, 1) model for y_t.

CHAPTER 13

EXPERIMENTAL DESIGN: ANALYSIS OF VARIANCE

CONTENTS

Duke University students participated in a planned study designed to determine what factors influence their reluctance to deliver bad news (called the "MUM" effect). The students were equally divided into four groups, and each group was treated under a different experimental condition. Then the length of time it took each to deliver the bad news was recorded. How would you decide whether the data indicate differences among the four groups in the mean length of time required to deliver the bad news? In this chapter we present methods for analyzing data collected from a planned (designed) experiment. The technique, called **analysis of variance**, enables us to compare the means of three or more populations. The results of the MUM effect experiment are discussed in the chapter case study.

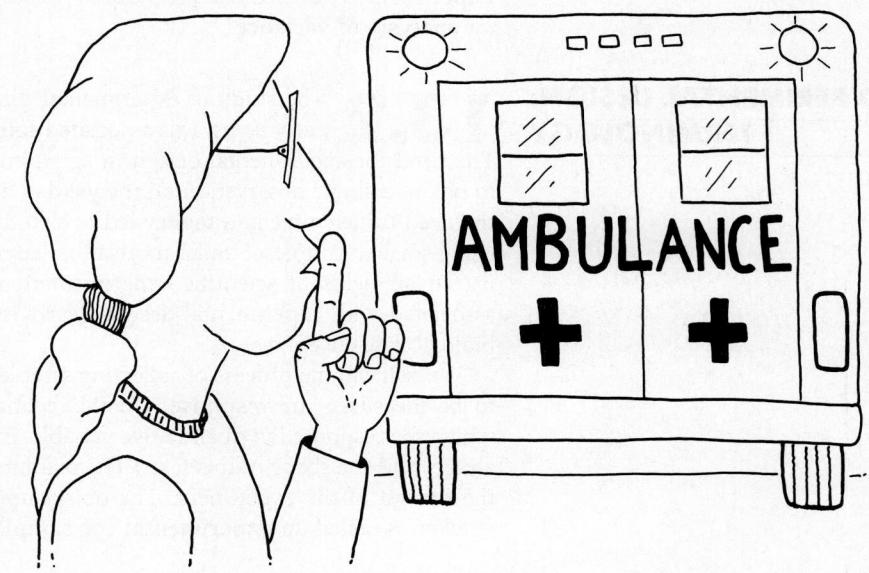

13.1

Recall (Section 10.2) that the data for regression can be either *observational* (where the values of the independent variables are uncontrolled) or *experimental* (where the x's are controlled via a designed experiment). Most data collected in business-related studies are observational for practical reasons. With observational data, however, there is a caveat:

> A statistically significant relationship between a response, y, and a predictor variable, x, does not imply a cause-and-effect relationship.

Since the values of other relevant independent variables—both those in the model and those omitted from the model—are uncontrolled, we are unsure whether it is these other variables or x that is causing the increase (or decrease) in y.

To illustrate, consider the data in Table 13.1 on monthly new home sales, y, of a residential builder and the number, x, of salespeople on staff. Obviously, sales (y) increases with number of salespeople (x) on staff. But does this imply that the builder need only hire more salespeople to increase new home sales? Common sense says no. More likely, there are other (unrecorded) variables that are causing the increase in new home sales (eg, lower interest rates, lower sale prices) and the builder is hiring more salespeople to keep up with monthly demand. In other words, an unmeasured variable, "demand," is causing both y and x to increase.

This caveat can be overcome by controlling the values of all the relevant x's via a planned experiment. With experimental data, we usually select the x's so that we can compare the mean responses, $E(y)$, for several different combinations of the x-values. The procedure for selecting the sample data is called the **design of the experiment**. The statistical procedure for comparing the population means is called an **analysis of variance**.

TABLE 13.1
New Home Sales Data

MONTH	SALES y	NUMBER OF SALESPEOPLE x
1	2	1
2	4	2
3	8	3
4	11	5
5	12	6
6	15	8

EXPERIMENTAL DESIGN: TERMINOLOGY

13.2

The study of experimental design originated in England, and in its early years, was associated solely with agricultural experimentation. The need for experimental design in agriculture was very clear: It takes a full year to obtain a single observation on the yield of a new variety of wheat. Consequently, the need to save time and money led to a study of ways to obtain more information using smaller samples. Similar motivation led to its subsequent acceptance and wide use in all fields of scientific experimentation. Despite this fact, the terminology associated with experimental design clearly indicates its early association with the biological sciences.

We will call the process of collecting sample data an **experiment** and the variable to be measured the **response**. (In this chapter we consider only experiments in which the response is a quantitative variable. Experiments with qualitative responses are beyond the scope of this text.) The planning of the sampling procedure is called the **design** of the experiment. The object upon which the response measurement is taken is called an **experimental (or sampling) unit**.

DEFINITION 13.1

The process of collecting sample data is called an **experiment**.

DEFINITION 13.2

The plan for collecting the sample is called the **design** of the experiment.

DEFINITION 13.3

The variable measured in the experiment is called the **response variable**. (In this chapter all response variables will be quantitative variables.)

DEFINITION 13.4

The object upon which the response variable is measured is called an **experimental (or sampling) unit**.

Variables that may be related to a response variable are called **factors**. The value—that is, the intensity setting—assumed by a factor in an experiment is called a **level**. The combinations of levels of factors for which the response will be observed are called **treatments**.

EXAMPLE 13.1 A marketing study is conducted to investigate the effects of brand and shelf location on weekly coffee sales. Coffee sales are recorded for each of the two brands (brand A and brand B) and for three shelf locations (bottom, middle, and top) each week for a period of 20 weeks. For this experiment, identify:

a. The experimental unit   **b.** The response
c. The factors   **d.** The factor levels
e. The treatments

Solution

a. Since our data will be collected each week for a period of 20 weeks, the experimental unit is 1 week.
b. The variable of interest—that is, the response—is weekly coffee sales. Note that weekly coffee sales is a quantitative variable.
c. Since we are interested in investigating the effect of brand and shelf location on sales, brand and shelf location are the factors. Note that both factors are qualitative.
d. For this experiment, brand is measured at two levels (A and B) and shelf location at three levels (bottom, middle, and top).
e. Since coffee sales are recorded for each of the six brand–shelf location combinations (brand A, bottom), (brand A, middle), (brand A, top), (brand B, bottom), (brand B, middle), and (brand B, top), the experiment involves six treatments.

The term **treatments** is used to describe the factor level combinations to be included in an experiment because many experiments involve treating, or doing something to alter the nature of, the experimental unit. Thus, we might view the six brand–shelf location combinations as treatments on the experimental units in the marketing study involving coffee sales.

DEFINITION 13.5

The variables, quantitative or qualitative, that are related to a response variable are called **factors**.

DEFINITION 13.6

The intensity setting of a factor (ie, the value assumed by a factor in an experiment) is called a **factor level**.

DEFINITION 13.7

A **treatment** is a particular combination of levels of the factors involved in an experiment.

Now that you understand some of the terminology, it is helpful to think of the design of an experiment in four steps:

STEP 1   Select the factors to be included in the experiment and identify the parameters that are the object of the study. Usually, the target parameters are the population means associated with the factor level combinations (ie, treatments).

STEP 2   Choose the treatments (the factor level combinations) to be included in the experiment.

STEP 3   Determine the number of observations (sample size) to be made for each treatment. [This will usually depend on the desired standard error(s). See Section 13.10.]

STEP 4   Plan how the treatments will be assigned to the experimental units. That is, decide on which design to employ.

Entire texts are devoted to properly executing these steps for various experimental designs. (See the references given at the end of this chapter.) The main objective of this chapter, however, is to show how to analyze the data that are collected in a designed experiment.

In Sections 13.4–13.6, we consider three popular experimental designs and demonstrate how to analyze the data for each. First, in Section 13.3, we present a short discussion of the logic behind the analysis of data collected from such experiments.

THE LOGIC BEHIND AN ANALYSIS OF VARIANCE

13.3 Once the data for a designed experiment have been collected, we will want to use the sample information to make inferences about the population means associated with the various treatments. The method used to compare the treatment means is known as **analysis of variance**, or **ANOVA**. The concept behind an analysis of variance can be explained using the following simple example.

EXAMPLE 13.2 Suppose we want to compare the means (μ_1 and μ_2) of two populations using independent random samples of size $n_1 = n_2 = 5$ from each of the populations. The sample observations and the sample means are listed in Table 13.2 and shown on a line plot in Figure 13.1.

a. Do you think the data provide sufficient evidence to indicate a difference between the population means μ_1 and μ_2?

b. Now look at two more samples of $n_1 = n_2 = 5$ measurements from the populations, as listed in Table 13.3 and plotted in Figure 13.2. Do the data appear to provide evidence of a difference between μ_1 and μ_2?

TABLE 13.2
Data for Example 13.2

SAMPLE FROM POPULATION 1	SAMPLE FROM POPULATION 2
6	8
−1	1
0	3
4	7
1	6
$\bar{y}_1 = 2$	$\bar{y}_2 = 5$

FIGURE 13.1
Dot Plot of Data in Table 13.2

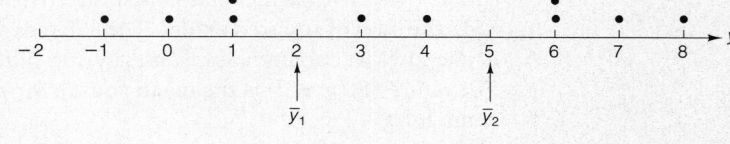

TABLE 13.3
Data for Example 13.2b

SAMPLE FROM POPULATION 1	SAMPLE FROM POPULATION 2
2	5
3	5
2	5
2	4
1	6
$\bar{y}_1 = 2$	$\bar{y}_2 = 5$

FIGURE 13.2
Dot Plot of Data in Table 13.3

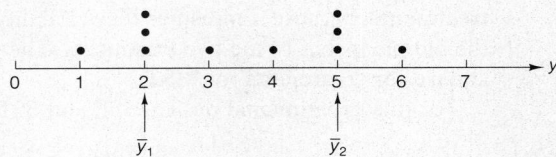

Solution

a. One way to determine whether a difference exists between the population means μ_1 and μ_2 is to examine the spread (or variation) *between* the sample means $\bar{y}_1$ and $\bar{y}_2$, and to compare it to a measure of variability *within* the samples. The greater the difference in the variations, the greater will be the evidence to indicate a difference between μ_1 and μ_2.

For the data of Table 13.2, you can see in Figure 13.1 that **the difference between the sample means is small relative to the variability within the sample observations**. Thus, we think you will agree that the difference between $\bar{y}_1$ and $\bar{y}_2$ is not large enough to indicate a difference between μ_1 and μ_2.

b. Notice that the difference between the sample means for the data of Table 13.3 is identical to the difference shown in Table 13.2. However, since there is now very little variability within the sample observations (see Figure 13.2), **the difference between the sample means is large compared to the variability within the sample observations**. Thus, the data appear to give clear evidence of a difference between μ_1 and μ_2.

In order to conduct a formal test of hypothesis, we need to quantify these two measures of variation. The variation within samples is measured by the pooled s^2 we computed for the independent random samples t test of Section 6.2, namely,

$$\text{Within-sample variation:} \quad s^2 = \frac{\sum_{i=1}^{n_1} (y_{i1} - \bar{y}_1)^2 + \sum_{i=1}^{n_2} (y_{i2} - \bar{y}_2)^2}{n_1 + n_2 - 2}$$

$$= \frac{\text{SSE}}{n_1 + n_2 - 2} = \frac{\text{SSE}}{n - 2}$$

where y_{i1} is the ith observation in sample 1, y_{i2} is the ith observation in sample 2, and $n = (n_1 + n_2)$ is the total sample size. The quantity in the numerator of s^2 is the **SSE, the sum of squared errors**. The SSE measures unexplained variability—that is, it measures variability *unexplained* by the differences between the sample means. The ratio $\text{SSE}/(n - 2)$ is the **mean square for error**, or **MSE**. Thus, MSE is another name for s^2.

A measure of the between-sample variation is given by the weighted sum of squares of deviations of the individual sample means about the mean for all n observations, $\bar{y}$, divided by the number of samples minus 1, that is,

$$\text{Between-sample variation:} \quad \frac{n_1(\bar{y}_1 - \bar{y})^2 + n_2(\bar{y}_2 - \bar{y})^2}{2 - 1} = \frac{\text{SST}}{1}$$

The quantity in the numerator is often denoted **SST, the sum of squares for treatments**, because it measures the variability *explained* by the differences between the sample means of the two treatments. The ratio $\text{SST}/(2 - 1)$ is also called **mean square for treatments**, or **MST**.

For this experimental design, SSE and SST sum to a known total, namely,

$$\text{SS(Total)} = \Sigma(y_i - \bar{y})^2$$

In the next section we will see that

$$F = \frac{\text{Between-sample variation}}{\text{Within-sample variation}} = \frac{\text{MST}}{\text{MSE}}$$

has an F distribution with $\nu_1 = 1$ and $\nu_2 = n_1 + n_2 - 2$ degrees of freedom and therefore can be used to test the null hypothesis of no difference between the treatment means. Large values of F lead us to conclude that a difference between the treatment (population) means exists.

The additivity property of the sums of squares led early researchers to view this analysis as a *partitioning* of SS(Total) $= \Sigma(y_i - \bar{y})^2$ into sources corresponding to the factors included in the experiment and to SSE. The simple formulas for computing the sums of squares, the additivity property, and the form of the test statistic made it natural for this procedure to be called an **analysis of variance**. We demonstrate the analysis of variance procedures for the general problem of comparing k population means for three special types of experimental designs in Sections 13.4–13.6.

COMPLETELY RANDOMIZED DESIGNS

13.4 The most common experimental design employed in practice is called a **completely randomized design**. This experiment involves a comparison of the means for a number, say k, of treatments, based on independent random samples of n_1, n_2, ..., n_k observations, drawn from populations associated with treatments 1, 2, ..., k, respectively.

> **DEFINITION 13.8**
>
> A **completely randomized design** to compare k treatment (population) means is one in which the treatments are randomly assigned to the experimental units, or in which independent random samples are drawn from each of the k target populations.

After collecting the data from a completely randomized design, our goal is to make inferences about k population means, where μ_i is the mean of the population of measurements associated with treatment i, for $i = 1, 2, ..., k$. The null hypothesis to be tested is that the k treatments are equal, that is,

$$H_0: \quad \mu_1 = \mu_2 = \cdots = \mu_k$$

and the alternative hypothesis is that at least two of the treatment means differ.

PARAMETRIC METHOD

An analysis of variance provides an easy way to analyze the data from a completely randomized design. This analysis partitions SS(Total) into two components, SSE and SST (see Figure 13.3). Recall that the quantity SST denotes the sum of squares for treatments and measures the variation explained by the differences between the treatment means. The sum of squares for error, SSE, is a measure of the unexplained variability, obtained by calculating a pooled measure of the variability within the k

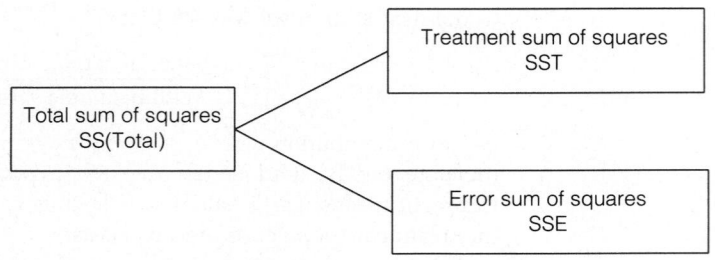

samples. If the treatment means truly differ, then SSE should be substantially smaller than SST. We compare the two sources of variability by forming an F statistic:

$$F = \frac{\text{SST}/(k-1)}{\text{SSE}/(n-k)} = \frac{\text{MST}}{\text{MSE}}$$

where n is the total number of measurements.

Under certain conditions, the F statistic has a repeated sampling distribution known as the **F distribution**. Recall that the F distribution depends on ν_1 numerator degrees of freedom and ν_2 denominator degrees of freedom. For the completely randomized design, F is based on $\nu_1 = (k-1)$ and $\nu_2 = (n-k)$ degrees of freedom. If the computed value of F exceeds the upper critical value, F_α, we reject H_0 and conclude that at least two of the treatment means differ.

TEST TO COMPARE k POPULATION MEANS FOR A COMPLETELY RANDOMIZED DESIGN

H_0: $\quad \mu_1 = \mu_2 = \cdots = \mu_k$ There is no difference in the treatment (population) means.

H_a: At least two treatment means differ.

Test statistic: $F = \dfrac{\text{MST}}{\text{MSE}}$

Rejection region: $F > F_\alpha$

where the distribution of F is based on $(k-1)$ numerator df and $(n-k)$ denominator df, and F_α is the F-value found in Tables 7–10, Appendix A, such that $P(F > F_\alpha) = \alpha$.

Assumptions:

1. All k population probability distributions are normal.
2. The k population variances are equal.
3. The samples from each population are random and independent.

The results of an analysis of variance are usually summarized and presented in an **analysis of variance (ANOVA) table**. Such a table shows the sources of variation, their respective degrees of freedom, sums of squares, mean squares, and the computed F statistic, as shown in the box.

ANALYSIS OF VARIANCE TABLE FOR
A COMPLETELY RANDOMIZED DESIGN

SOURCE	df	SS	MS	F
Treatments	$k-1$	SST	$MST = \dfrac{SST}{k-1}$	$F = \dfrac{MST}{MSE}$
Error	$n-k$	SSE	$MSE = \dfrac{SSE}{n-k}$	
Total	$n-1$	SS(Total)		

Virtually all statistical software packages currently available have routines that perform both parametric and nonparametric analyses of data collected from a designed experiment. In this chapter our emphasis is on the interpretation of results of the ANOVA rather than the tedious calculations that generate the results. For those who are interested, the parametric computational formulas for each design are provided in Appendix B.

EXAMPLE 13.3 Consider the problem of comparing the mean 1990 sale prices of residential properties contained in seven different neighborhoods (A, B, C, D, E, F, and G) of Tampa, Florida. Many of these properties were not sold, so we will never know their sale prices, but we can still imagine that a sale price exists for each property in a neighborhood and that the totality of these prices constitutes a population that characterizes property values in that neighborhood. Thus, we want to compare the mean sale prices corresponding to the seven neighborhood sale price populations; that is, we wish to test

H_0: $\mu_A = \mu_B = \mu_C = \mu_D = \mu_E = \mu_F = \mu_G$

H_a: At least two means are different.

To perform the comparison, independent random samples of sale prices were selected from the actual sale prices for the seven neighborhoods obtained from the data files of the city's property appraiser. The data (recorded in thousand dollars and listed in Table 13.4) were subjected to an analysis of variance using SAS. A portion of the SAS printout is reproduced in Figure 13.4 (p. 694). Interpret the results.

Solution You can see that the SAS printout (Figure 13.4) presents the results in the form of an ANOVA table. The source of variation attributable to treatments, that is, to the variability among the sample means for the seven neighborhoods, is labeled Model, and the source of variation attributable to error, that is, to the within-

TABLE 13.4
Sale Prices (in Thousand Dollars) of Properties in the Seven Neighborhoods

			NEIGHBORHOOD			
A	B	C	D	E	F	G
191.5	100.5	35.3	86.0	69.9	46.0	14.5
208.5	147.5	50.0	140.0	159.5	42.0	50.0
255.0	115.0	160.0	120.0	84.5	48.0	39.0
375.0	210.0	59.9	72.9	57.7	57.0	20.0
205.0	155.0	38.5	72.0	45.4	34.5	32.2
191.5	127.5	105.9	68.7	43.9	74.5	54.0
189.0	115.0	312.0	90.0	205.0	66.9	21.5
139.0	110.0	84.5	100.0	59.9	54.5	55.0
138.0	183.0	68.5	97.0	37.0	46.8	43.0
162.0	107.5	160.0	84.0	68.0	6.9	13.3

Source: Hillsborough County (FL) property appraiser's office, 1990.

FIGURE 13.4
SAS Printout of the ANOVA for Example 13.3

```
                          Analysis of Variance Procedure

Dependent Variable: SALEPRIC
                                  Sum of            Mean
Source                  DF        Squares          Square    F Value    Pr > F

Model                    6     199341.2469      33223.5411    13.34     0.0001
Error                   63     156930.9230       2490.9670
Corrected Total         69     356272.1699

                R-Square           C.V.         Root MSE       SALEPRIC Mean

                0.559520        49.33797        49.90959          101.158571

Source                  DF       Anova SS     Mean Square    F Value    Pr > F

NBRHOOD                  6     199341.2469      33223.5411    13.34     0.0001
```

sample variability, is labeled Error. Their corresponding sum of squares and mean squares are

$$SST = 199,341.2469$$
$$SSE = 156,930.9230$$
$$MST = 33,223.5411$$
$$MSE = 2,490.9670$$

The computed value of the test statistic, given under the column heading F Value, is

$$F = 13.34$$

To determine whether to reject the null hypothesis

$$H_0: \quad \mu_A = \mu_B = \cdots = \mu_G$$

in favor of the alternative

H_a: At least two population means are different.

we may consult Appendix A for tabulated values of the F distribution corresponding to an appropriately chosen significance level α. However, since the SAS printout gives the observed significance level (p-value) of the test, we will use this quantity to assist us in reaching a conclusion.

The observed significance level of the test is under the column headed Pr > F. This value, .0001, implies that H_0 will be rejected at any chosen level of α larger than .0001. Thus, there is very strong evidence of a difference among the mean 1990 sale prices of residential properties in the seven neighborhoods. The probability that this procedure will lead to a Type I error (conclude that there is a difference among the means when in fact they are all equal) is .0001.

The proper application of the parametric ANOVA procedure used in Example 13.3 requires that certain assumptions be satisfied—that is, all seven populations of sale prices are approximately normal with equal variances. In Section 13.10 we provide details on how to use residuals to determine whether these assumptions are satisfied to a reasonable degree. If the residual analysis, for example, reveals that one of the population variances is much larger than the others, then any inferences derived from the parametric ANOVA of the data are suspect. In this case, we can apply a nonparametric technique.

NONPARAMETRIC METHOD

The **Kruskal–Wallis H test** provides a nonparametric alternative to the ANOVA F test for the completely randomized design. Rather than compare population means, the Kruskal–Wallis test compares the *location* of two or more probability distributions, and no assumptions regarding the shapes or variances of the distributions are required.

THE KRUSKAL–WALLIS H TEST FOR COMPARING k POPULATION RELATIVE FREQUENCY DISTRIBUTIONS: COMPLETELY RANDOMIZED DESIGN

H_0: The k population relative frequency distributions are identical.

H_a: At least two of the population relative frequency distributions differ in location (shifted either to the left or to the right of one another).

Test statistic: $H = \dfrac{12}{n(n+1)} \sum_{i=1}^{k} \dfrac{T_i^2}{n_i} - 3(n+1)$

where

n_i = Number of observations in sample i

T_i = Rank sum of sample i

n = Total sample size = $n_1 + n_2 + \cdots + n_k$

Rejection region: $H > \chi_\alpha^2$, where χ_α^2 is based on $(k-1)$ degrees of freedom.

(continued)

Assumptions:

1. The k samples have been independently and randomly selected from their respective populations.

2. For the chi-square approximation to be adequate, there should be five or more observations in each sample.

3. Tied observations are assigned ranks equal to the average of the ranks that would have been assigned to the observations had they not been tied.

In this nonparametric test, the sample observations are ranked from the smallest to the largest, and the rank sums are calculated for each sample. For example, if you had three samples with $n_1 = 8$, $n_2 = 6$, and $n_3 = 7$, you would rank the $n_1 + n_2 + n_3 = 21$ observations from the smallest (rank 1) to the largest (rank 21) and then calculate the rank sums, T_1, T_2, and T_3, for the three samples. The Kruskal–Wallis H test uses these rank sums to calculate an H statistic that possesses an approximate χ^2 sampling distribution.

EXAMPLE 13.4 Refer to the residential sales data for seven neighborhoods from Example 13.3. Use a nonparametric test to analyze the data in Table 13.4. (Use $\alpha = .05$.)

Solution We want to test the following null and alternative hypotheses:

H_0: The sales price distributions for the seven neighborhoods are identical.

H_a: At least two of the sales price distributions differ in location.

To obtain the test statistic, we first rank all 70 observations in Table 13.4 from 1 to 70. Next, we sum the ranks for each of the seven neighborhoods to obtain the rank sums T_1, T_2, ..., T_7. Finally, we substitute these rank sums into the formula for H in the box. Rather than perform these computations, we resort to a computer.

The MINITAB printout of the nonparametric ANOVA is shown in Figure 13.5. The test statistic, shaded at the bottom of the printout, is $H = 45.86$. The observed significance level (also shaded) is $p \approx 0$. Since $\alpha = .05$ exceeds this p-value, we

FIGURE 13.5

MINITAB Printout: Nonparametric ANOVA of Data in Table 13.4

LEVEL	NOBS	MEDIAN	AVE. RANK	Z VALUE
1	10	191.50	61.7	4.39
2	10	121.25	51.5	2.69
3	10	76.50	36.0	0.08
4	10	88.00	39.8	0.72
5	10	63.95	30.9	-0.78
6	10	47.40	18.0	-2.94
7	10	35.60	10.8	-4.15
OVERALL	70		35.5	

$H = 45.85$ d.f. = 6   p = 0.000
$H = 45.86$ d.f. = 6   p = 0.000 (adj. for ties)

reject H_0. There is sufficient evidence (at $\alpha = .05$) to conclude that the sale price distributions differ for at least two of the seven neighborhoods. Note that this conclusion agrees with that of the parametric F test in Example 13.3.

PROBLEMS

13.1 When marketing its products in a foreign country, should a company use its own salespeople or salespeople from the target market country? To research this question, a study was designed to investigate the effect of salesperson nationality on buyer attitudes (*Journal of Business Research*, Vol. 22, 1991). A sample of American MBA students was divided into two groups and shown a videotape of an advertisement for forklift trucks made in India. For group 1, an Indian sales representative made the presentation; for group 2, an American sales representative made the presentation. After viewing the tape, the subjects were asked whether the salesperson was trustworthy (measured on a 5-point scale). The mean scores were compared using an ANOVA.

   a. Identify the treatments in this experiment.
   b. Give the null hypothesis of interest to the researchers.
   c. The ANOVA resulted in an F-value of 2.32, with an observed significance level of .13. Is there evidence of a difference between the mean trustworthiness scores of the two groups of MBA students? Use $\alpha = .10$.
   d. The sample mean scores for the two groups are $\bar{y}_1 = 3.12$ and $\bar{y}_2 = 3.49$. Suppose you were to test $H_0: \mu_1 = \mu_2$ against $H_a: \mu_1 < \mu_2$ at $\alpha = .10$. Use the result from part **a** to make the proper conclusion. [*Hint:* The p-value for a two-tailed t test is double the p-value for a one-tailed test.]

13.2 As oil drilling costs rise at unprecedented rates, the task of measuring drilling performance becomes essential to a successful oil company. One method of lowering drilling costs is to increase drilling speed. Researchers at Cities Service Co. have developed a drill bit, called the PD-1, which they believe penetrates rock at a faster rate than any other bit on the market. It was decided to compare the speed of the PD-1 with the two fastest drill bits known, the IADC 1-2-6 and the IADC 5-1-7, at 12 drilling locations in Texas. Four drilling sites were randomly assigned to each bit, and the rate of penetration (ROP) in feet per hour (fph) was recorded after drilling 3,000 feet at each site. The data are given in the table, followed by a MINITAB ANOVA printout.

PD-1	IADC 1-2-6	IADC 5-1-7
35.2	25.8	14.7
30.1	29.7	28.9
37.6	26.6	23.3
34.3	30.1	16.2

```
ANALYSIS OF VARIANCE ON ROP
SOURCE      DF        SS         MS        F        P
DRILLBIT     2      366.6      183.3      9.50    0.006
ERROR        9      173.7       19.3
TOTAL       11      540.2
                                   INDIVIDUAL 95 PCT CI'S FOR MEAN
                                   BASED ON POOLED STDEV
LEVEL        N       MEAN      STDEV    --------+---------+---------+---------
    1        4     34.300     3.127                             (------*------)
    2        4     28.050     2.167                   (------*------)
    3        4     20.775     6.589      (------*------)
                                   --------+---------+---------+---------
POOLED STDEV =     4.393            21.0      28.0      35.0
```

   a. Based on this information, can Cities Service Co. conclude that the mean ROP differs for at least two of the three drill bits? Test at $\alpha = .05$.

b. In the printout, locate a 95% confidence interval for μ_1, the mean ROP for the new PD-1 drill bit. Interpret the interval.

13.3 Data on total cash compensation for CEOs in four industry groups, extracted from *Business Week's* 1990 Executive Compensation Scoreboard, are listed in the table. Assume that the data represent independent random samples of 1990 total cash compensations (in thousand dollars) for eight corporate executives in each of the four industries, and that the experiment is a completely randomized design. The SPSS printout of the analysis is shown below.

CONSUMER PRODUCTS	UTILITIES	INDUSTRIAL–HIGH TECH	FINANCIAL SERVICES
1,567	1,862	2,925	3,125
3,313	1,390	3,409	4,143
2,058	1,115	1,767	4,013
25,216	1,105	4,097	6,583
4,634	1,272	3,196	3,169
5,214	2,849	4,042	5,217
20,795	1,723	2,601	3,447
9,162	1,474	8,286	4,469

Source: "Executive Compensation Scoreboard." *Business Week*, May 7, 1990, pp. 65–108. Reprinted from May 7, 1990 issue of *Business Week* by special permission, copyright © 1990 by McGraw-Hill, Inc. Used with permission.

```
* * *  A N A L Y S I S   O F   V A R I A N C E  * * *

          CASHCOMP
    BY    INDUSTRY

                            Sum of              Mean            Signif
Source of Variation         Squares      DF     Square      F    of F

Main Effects             232505651.844    3 77501883.948  3.556   .027
    INDUSTRY             232505651.844    3 77501883.948  3.556   .027

Explained                232505651.844    3 77501883.948  3.556   .027

Residual                 610272515.125   28 21795446.969

Total                    842778166.969   31 27186392.483

      32 Cases were processed.
       0 Cases (   .0 PCT) were missing.
```

a. Identify the response, the treatments, and the experimental units in this design.

b. Is there evidence of a difference among the means of the 1990 total cash compensations for the three groups of corporate executives? Test using $\alpha = .01$.

13.4 Researchers have found that in U.S. business, setting specific and difficult goals improves individual output more than no goals, "do best" goals, or easy goals. A study was conducted to investigate whether this goal-setting theory can be generalized to other cultures, especially in less developed countries. A sample of 92 rural women from a small eastern Caribbean island took part in an experiment in which they worked at home smocking children's clothing for pay. Workers were free to complete any quantity and were paid on a piece-rate basis. Before beginning work, each subject was randomly assigned to one of three goal groups: Group 1 consisted of $n_1 = 30$ workers with a specific difficult goal, 20% above the individual's previous high production; group 2 workers ($n_2 = 27$) were asked to "do their best"; and group 3 workers ($n_3 = 35$) received no goal instructions. The earnings per day were recorded for each worker, and the data subjected to an analysis of variance for a completely randomized design. A partial ANOVA summary table is reproduced at the top of the next page.

SOURCE	df	SS	MS	F
Groups	2	—	7.3	—
Error	89	—	1.265	
Total	91			

Source: Punnett, B. J. "Goal Setting: An Extension of the Research." *Journal of Applied Psychology*, Vol. 71, No. 1, 1986, p. 172.

a. Fill in the missing entries in the ANOVA table.

b. Is there a significant difference among the mean earnings per day of the three groups? Use $\alpha = .01$.

13.5 The display consoles of modern computer-based systems use many abbreviated words in order to accommodate the large volume of information to be displayed. *Human Factors* reported on a Navy experiment to determine the optimal method for abbreviating any specific set of words on sonar consoles. Of the 20 Navy and civilian personnel who took part in the study, 5 were highly familiar with the sonar system. The 15 subjects unfamiliar with the system were randomly divided into three groups of five. The experienced group and one inexperienced group (denoted TE and TI, respectively) were assigned to learn the simple method of abbreviation. One of the remaining inexperienced groups was assigned the conventional single abbreviation method (denoted CS), while the other was assigned the conventional multiple abbreviation method (denoted CM). Each subject was given a list of 75 abbreviations to learn, one at a time, through the display console of a minicomputer. The number of trials until the subject accurately decoded at least 90% of the words on the list is recorded in the table. Both a parametric and nonparametric analysis of the data are provided in the SAS printout. Interpret the results.

CM	CS	TE	TI
4	6	5	8
7	9	5	4
5	5	7	8
6	7	8	10
8	6	7	3

Source: Data are simulated values based on the group means reported in *Human Factors*, Feb. 1984. Copyright 1984 by the Human Factors Society, Inc. Reproduced by permission.

```
                Analysis of Variance for Variable TRIALS
                     Classified by Variable GROUP


GROUP       N        Mean                  Among MS      Within MS
                                          0.400000000    3.85000000
CM          5    6.00000000
CS          5    6.60000000                F Value       Prob > F
TE          5    6.40000000                 0.104         0.9566
TI          5    6.60000000
                Average Scores were used for Ties

            Wilcoxon Scores (Rank Sums) for Variable TRIALS
                     Classified by Variable GROUP


                      Sum of       Expected       Std Dev         Mean
GROUP       N         Scores       Under H0       Under H0        Score

CM          5     46.0000000     52.5000000     11.3046916    9.2000000
CS          5     55.0000000     52.5000000     11.3046916   11.0000000
TE          5     52.5000000     52.5000000     11.3046916   10.5000000
TI          5     56.5000000     52.5000000     11.3046916   11.3000000
                Average Scores were used for Ties


        Kruskal-Wallis Test (Chi-Square Approximation)
         CHISQ= 0.37853    DF= 3    Prob > CHISQ=    0.9446
```

13.6 Davis and Mount conducted a study to evaluate the effectiveness of performance appraisal training in an organizational setting (*Personnel Psychology*, Autumn 1984). Each of a sample of middle-level managers was randomly assigned to one of three training conditions: no training, computer-assisted training, or computer-assisted training plus a behavior-modeling workshop. Six months after the formal training, the managers were administered a 25 question, multiple-choice test of managerial knowledge, and the number of correct answers was recorded for each. The data in the table are adapted from summary information provided in the article. Is there sufficient evidence to indicate that the relative frequency distributions of scores differ in location for the three types of performance appraisal training? Test using $\alpha = .01$.

NO TRAINING	COMPUTER-ASSISTED TRAINING	COMPUTER TRAINING PLUS WORKSHOP
16	19	12
18	22	19
11	13	18
14	15	22
23	20	16
	18	25
	21	

RANDOMIZED BLOCK DESIGNS

BLOCKS (MANAGERS)

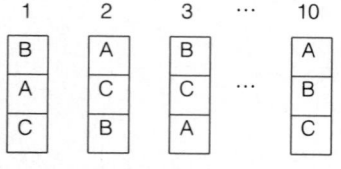

FIGURE 13.6

Diagram for a Randomized Block Design Containing $b = 10$ Blocks (Managers) and $k = 3$ Treatments (Training Programs)

13.5 In Section 6.4 we learned that for the same number of observations, paired samples often provide more information on the difference between a pair of population means than do independent samples. In Example 6.7 we compared the managerial assertiveness scores of two training methods. Now, suppose we want to compare three training programs, A, B, and C. We can use the same type of matching procedure as in the paired samples design, except that we match the experimental units in groups of 3. For the managerial assertiveness example, we match 30 managers according to experience, education, personality, etc., and form 10 groups (or **blocks**) of 3. One manager from each block is randomly assigned to training program A, one to B, and one to C (see Figure 13.6). In the language of analysis of variance, this matched sample design is called a **randomized block design**, consisting of $b = 10$ blocks and $k = 3$ treatments. A treatment is what makes the experimental units in one population differ from those in another population. The blocks always contain matched groups of k experimental units, one unit for each treatment.

> **DEFINITION 13.9**
>
> A **randomized block design** is a design in which k treatments (or populations) are compared within each of b blocks. Each block contains k matched experimental units, and the k treatments are randomly assigned, one to each of the units within each block.

PARAMETRIC METHOD

The data collected from matched samples can be analyzed using a parametric ANOVA *F* test. The analysis of variance partitions SS(Total) into three portions: the sum of squares for treatments (SST), the sum of squares for blocks (SSB), and the sum of squares for error (SSE). The analysis of variance is shown diagrammatically in Figure 13.7.

FIGURE 13.7

Partitioning of the Total Sum of Squares for the Randomized Block Design

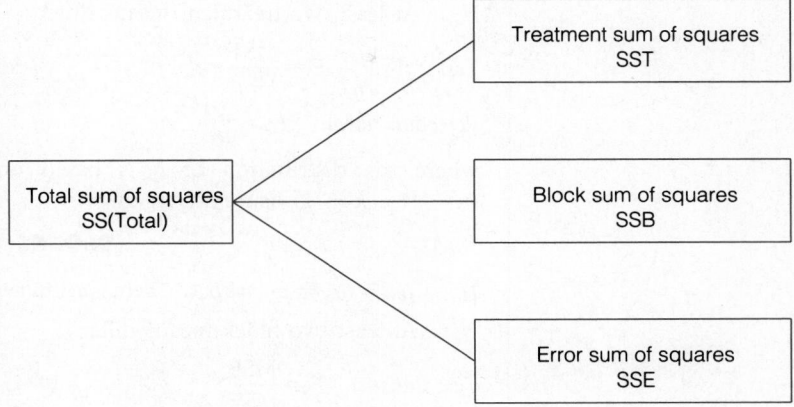

The sum of squares for treatments measures the variation between sample means. As in the case of the analysis of variance for a completely randomized design, we compare the mean square for treatments,

$$MST = \frac{SST}{k - 1}$$

with the mean square for error,

$$MSE = \frac{SSE}{n - b - k + 1} \qquad (n = bk)$$

using an *F* statistic. Although our main objective is to compare treatment (or population) means, we can also test to determine whether the data provide sufficient evidence to indicate differences among block means by comparing the mean square for blocks (MSB) with MSE. A summary of the ANOVA *F* tests and the general form of an ANOVA summary table for a randomized block design are given on p. 702. (The formulas for computing the sum of squares are given in Appendix B.)

EXAMPLE 13.5   A recent supermarket advertisement in the *Gainesville Sun* states: "You'll save up to 21% with Albertson's lower prices." To substantiate the claim, Albertson's supermarket compared the price of 49 grocery items at three competing supermarkets with its prices on a given day. The survey results for 7 items randomly selected from the 49 are shown in Table 13.5 (p. 703). Determine whether the mean prices of grocery items differ among the four supermarkets. Test using $\alpha = .05$.

TESTS TO COMPARE k TREATMENT AND b BLOCK MEANS FOR A RANDOMIZED BLOCK DESIGN

TREATMENTS

H_0: $\mu_1 = \mu_2 = \cdots = \mu_k$ There is no difference in the treatment means.

H_a: At least two treatment means differ.

Test statistic: $F = \dfrac{\text{MST}}{\text{MSE}}$

Rejection region: $F > F_\alpha$

where the distribution of F is based on $(k - 1)$ numerator df and $(n - b - k + 1)$ denominator df.

BLOCKS

H_0: $\mu_1 = \mu_2 = \cdots = \mu_b$ There is no difference in block means.

H_a: At least two block means differ.

Test statistic: $F = \dfrac{\text{MSB}}{\text{MSE}}$

Rejection region: $F > F_\alpha$

where the distribution of F is based on $(b - 1)$ numerator df and $(n - b - k + 1)$ denominator df.

Assumptions:

1. The population probability distribution of the differences between pairs of treatment observations within a block is approximately normal.

2. The variance of this probability distribution is constant and the same for all pairs of observations.

3. The treatments are randomly assigned to the experimental units within each block.

ANALYSIS OF VARIANCE TABLE FOR A RANDOMIZED BLOCK DESIGN

SOURCE	df	SS	MS	F
Treatments	$k - 1$	SST	$\text{MST} = \dfrac{\text{SST}}{k - 1}$	$F = \dfrac{\text{MST}}{\text{MSE}}$
Blocks	$b - 1$	SSB	$\text{MSB} = \dfrac{\text{SSB}}{b - 1}$	$F = \dfrac{\text{MSB}}{\text{MSE}}$
Error	$n - b - k + 1$	SSE	$\text{MSE} = \dfrac{\text{SSE}}{n - b - k + 1}$	
Total	$n - 1$	SS(Total)		

TABLE 13.5
Supermarket Survey Results

GROCERY ITEM	ALBERTSON'S	KASH 'N KARRY	PUBLIX	FOOD 4 LESS
Cheerios cereal	$1.10	$1.18	$1.39	$1.18
Jell-O gelatin	.24	.24	.31	.26
Dial soap	.52	.60	.63	.55
Crisco oil	1.26	1.70	2.27	1.29
Kleenex	.67	.70	.79	.70
Star-Kist tuna	.63	.66	.79	.63
Del Monte peas	.43	.47	.65	.47

Solution To determine whether the mean prices charged at the supermarkets differ, we will need to conduct an analysis of variance for a randomized block design. The columns of Table 13.5 correspond to the $k = 4$ treatments (ie, the supermarkets), and the rows correspond to $b = 7$ blocks of grocery items, each consisting of $k = 4$ observations. The observations within a block are matched because all prices within a block are for the same item on the same day. (A randomized block design is necessary to ensure that the same items are compared at the four supermarkets.)

Since the supermarkets represent the treatments, we want to test

H_0: $\mu_1 = \mu_2 = \mu_3 = \mu_4$

H_a: At least two of the treatment means differ.

where μ_1 = mean price charged at Albertson's, μ_2 = mean price at Kash 'n Karry, μ_3 = mean price at Publix, and μ_4 = mean price at Food 4 Less.

A MINITAB printout for the ANOVA is shown in Figure 13.8. The MINITAB printout shows the partitioning of SS(Total) into its three sources, SUPERMKT (Treatments), ITEM (Blocks), and ERROR, with the associated degrees of freedom, sum of squares, and mean squares given under the column headings DF, SS, and MS, respectively. Unlike some other software packages with ANOVA routines (eg, SAS and SPSS), MINITAB does not give the F statistics for testing differences in treatment means and block means—these must be calculated by hand.

FIGURE 13.8
MINITAB Printout for Matched
Samples ANOVA

```
ANALYSIS OF VARIANCE   PRICE

SOURCE        DF        SS          MS
SUPERMKT       3     0.3352      0.1117
ITEM           6     5.2311      0.8718
ERROR         18     0.4433      0.0246
TOTAL         27     6.0096
```

The test statistic, $F = \text{MST/MSE}$, is found by substituting the values of MST = .1117 and MSE = .0246 obtained from the printout:

$$F = \frac{\text{MST}}{\text{MSE}} = \frac{.1117}{.0246} = 4.540$$

The F statistic will have the numerator degrees of freedom $(k - 1) = 3$ (df for MST) and denominator degrees of freedom $(n - b - k + 1) = 18$ (df for MSE). From Table 8, Appendix A, the tabulated value of $F_{.05}$ with 3 and 18 df is 3.16. Therefore, we will reject H_0 if the calculated value of F is $F > 3.16$ (see Figure 13.9). Since the computed value of the test statistic, $F = 4.54$, exceeds 3.16, we have sufficient evidence to reject H_0 at $\alpha = .05$. There appear to be significant differences among the mean prices of grocery items at the four supermarkets.

FIGURE 13.9

Rejection Region for the F Test (Numerator df = 3, Denominator df = 18)

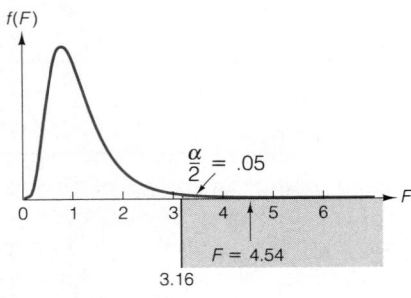

EXAMPLE 13.6 Refer to Example 13.5. Was blocking on grocery items effective in reducing item-to-item variation in prices? To answer this question, test the null hypothesis that there is no difference among the block (grocery item) means against the alternative hypothesis that at least two of the block means differ. Use $\alpha = .05$.

Solution   The F statistic for testing block means is $F = $ MSB/MSE. Substituting the values of MSB and MSE found in the MINITAB printout (Figure 13.8), we have

$$F = \frac{\text{MSB}}{\text{MSE}} = \frac{.8718}{.0246} = 35.40$$

The F statistic will have numerator degrees of freedom $(b - 1) = 6$, and the denominator degrees of freedom will be the df associated with MSE—namely, 18. Therefore, the rejection region for the test is

$$\text{Reject } H_0 \text{ if } F > F_{.05} = 2.66$$

where $F_{.05} = 2.66$ is obtained from Table 8, Appendix A. Since the F value of 35.40 falls well within the rejection region, there is sufficient evidence at $\alpha = .05$ to conclude that the block (item) means differ. It appears that blocking was effective in removing the item-to-item variation in prices.

As with a completely randomized design, you should always check to determine whether the assumptions required to properly conduct a parametric ANOVA for a randomized block design are satisfied. In situations where one or more of the assumptions are clearly violated, you will want to employ the nonparametric method discussed next.

NONPARAMETRIC METHOD

A nonparametric test appropriate for analyzing data collected from a randomized block design is the **Friedman F_r test**. This test detects shifts in location of the k population relative frequency distributions by ranking the k observations *in each block* from the smallest (rank 1) to the largest (rank k). The rank sums, T_1, T_2, ..., T_k, are then calculated for each of the k treatments and used to compute the Friedman F_r statistic. This statistic, like the Kruskal–Wallis H statistic, has a sampling distribution that can be approximated by a chi-square distribution with $(k-1)$ degrees of freedom. The test procedure is specified in the box and illustrated in Example 13.7.

THE FRIEDMAN F_r TEST FOR A RANDOMIZED BLOCK DESIGN

H_0: The relative frequency distributions for the k populations are identical.

H_a: At least two of the k populations differ in location (shifted either to the left or to the right of one another).

Test statistic:

Rank each of the k observations within each block from the smallest (rank 1) to the largest (rank k). Calculate the treatment rank sums, T_1, T_2, ..., T_k. Then the test statistic is

$$F_r = \frac{12}{bk(k+1)} \sum_{i=1}^{k} T_i^2 - 3b(k+1)$$

where

b = Number of blocks employed in the experiment
k = Number of treatments
T_i = Sum of the ranks for the ith treatment

Rejection region: $F_r > \chi_\alpha^2$
where χ_α^2 is based on $(k-1)$ degrees of freedom.

Assumptions:

1. The k treatments were randomly assigned to the k experimental units within each block.

2. For the chi-square approximation to be adequate, either the number b of blocks or the number k of treatments should exceed 5.

3. Tied observations are assigned ranks equal to the average of the ranks that would have been assigned to the observations had they not been tied.

EXAMPLE 13.7 A food products company conducted a *single-blind experiment* to compare the tastes of three similarly priced brands of coffee. Each of six experienced taste testers was presented three cups of coffee (one of each brand) in random order, and asked to rate the coffee from the poorest taste (rank 1) to the best taste (rank 3). The experiment is called *single-blind* because the brands contained in the cups were unknown to the taste testers, thereby eliminating the possibility of a bias, (ie, that the testers might favor one particular brand if the brands were known). The results of the taste test are shown in Table 13.6. Do the data provide sufficient evidence to indicate differences in taste appeal among the three brands of coffee? Test using the Friedman F_r test with $\alpha = .05$.

TABLE 13.6
Taste Tester Rankings for Three Brands of Coffee

TASTE TESTER	BRANDS		
	A	B	C
1	1	3	2
2	2	3	1
3	1	2	3
4	1	3	2
5	2	3	1
6	1	3	2
Rank sums	$T_A = 8$	$T_B = 17$	$T_C = 11$

Solution   This experiment was conducted according to a randomized block design. Comparisons of the taste of the three brands of coffee were made by each taste tester (a block) with the cups assigned for tasting in random order.

The null hypothesis is that there are no differences in taste among the three brands of coffee. The alternative hypothesis is that at least one brand is preferred over the others. The rank sums for the three brands, shown in Table 13.6, are $T_A = 8$, $T_B = 17$, and $T_C = 11$. Substituting these values along with $b = 6$ and $k = 3$ into the formula for the test statistic, we obtain

$$F_r = \frac{12}{bk(k + 1)} \sum_{i=1}^{3} T_i^2 - 3b(k + 1)$$

$$= \frac{12}{(6)(3)(3 + 1)} [(8)^2 + (17)^2 + (11)^2] - 3(6)(3 + 1)$$

$$= \frac{12}{72} (64 + 289 + 121) - 72$$

$$= 7.0$$

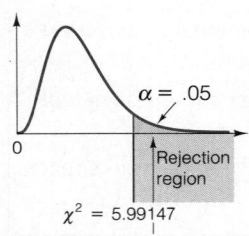

$\chi^2 = 5.99147$
Observed value of test statistic
$F_r = 7.0$

FIGURE 13.10
Rejection Region for the Friedman F_r Test

The rejection region for the test contains all values of F_r larger than χ_α^2 with $(k - 1)$ degrees of freedom. The value of $\chi_{.05}^2$ (given in Table 6, Appendix A) that corresponds to $\alpha = .05$ and $(k - 1) = (3 - 1) = 2$ degrees of freedom is 5.99147. Therefore, the rejection region for the test contains all values of F_r larger than $\chi_{.05}^2 = 5.99147$ (see Figure 13.10). Since the value of F_r computed for this test, $F_r = 7.0$, falls in the rejection region, we reject the null hypothesis and conclude that at least one of the brands of coffee is preferred over the others.

PROBLEMS

13.7 Refer to the comparison of prices of 60 food items at Winn-Dixie and Publix supermarkets given in Problems 6.21 and 6.22 (pp. 275–276). In addition to the prices at Winn-Dixie and Publix, the newspaper advertisement also reported the prices for the same 60 grocery items at a third supermarket, Kash 'N Karry. The data for all three supermarkets are provided in the table.

ITEM	WINN-DIXIE	PUBLIX	KASH 'N KARRY	ITEM	WINN-DIXIE	PUBLIX	KASH 'N KARRY
Big Thirst Towel	1.21	1.49	1.59	Keb Graham Crust	.79	1.29	1.28
Camp Crm/Broccoli	.55	.67	.67	Spiffits Glass	1.98	2.19	2.59
Royal Oak Charcoal	2.99	3.59	3.39	Prog Lentil Soup	.79	1.13	1.12
Combo Chdr/Chz Snk	1.29	1.29	1.39	Lipton Tea Bags	2.07	2.17	2.17
Sure Sak Trash Bag	1.29	1.79	1.89	Carnation Hot Coco	1.59	1.89	1.99
Dow Handi Wrap	1.59	2.39	2.29	Crystal Hot Sauce	.70	.87	.89
White Rain Shampoo	.96	.97	1.39	C/F/N/ Coffee Bag	1.17	1.15	1.55
Post Golden Crisp	2.78	2.99	3.35	Soup Start Bf Veg	1.39	2.03	1.94
Surf Detergent	2.29	1.89	1.89	Camp Pork & Beans	.44	.49	.58
Sacramento T/Juice	.79	.89	.99	Sunsweet Pit Prune	.98	1.33	1.10
SS Prune Juice	1.36	1.61	1.48	DM Vgcls Grdn Duet	1.07	1.13	1.29
V-8 Cocktail	1.18	1.29	1.28	Argo Corn Starch	.69	.89	.79
Rodd Kosher Dill	1.39	1.79	1.79	Sno Drop Bowl Clnr	.53	1.15	.99
Bisquick	2.09	2.19	2.09	Cadbury Milk Choc	.79	1.29	1.28
Kraft Italian Drs	.99	1.19	1.00	Andes Crm/De Ment	1.09	1.30	1.09
BC Hamburger Helper	1.46	1.75	1.75	Combat Ant & Roach	2.33	2.39	2.79
Comstock Chrry Pie	1.29	1.69	1.69	Joan/Arc Kid Bean	.45	.56	.38
Dawn Liquid King	2.59	2.29	2.58	La Vic Salsa Pican	1.22	1.75	1.49
DelMonte Ketchup	1.05	1.25	.59	Moist N Beef/Chz	2.39	3.19	2.99
Silver Floss Kraut	.77	.81	.69	Ortega Taco Shells	1.08	1.33	1.09
Trop Twist Beverag	1.74	2.15	2.25	Fresh Step Cat Lit	3.58	3.79	3.81
Purina Kitten Chow	1.09	1.05	1.29	Field Trial Dg/Fd	3.49	3.79	3.49
Niag Spray Starch	.89	.99	1.39	Tylenol Tablets	5.98	5.29	5.98
Soft Soap Country	.97	1.19	1.19	Rolaids Tablets	1.88	2.20	2.49
Northwood Syrup	1.13	1.37	1.37	Plax Rinse	2.88	3.14	2.53
Bumble Bee Tuna	.58	.65	.65	Correctol Laxative	3.44	3.98	3.59
Mueller Elbow/Mac	2.09	2.69	2.69	Tch Scnt Potpourri	1.50	1.89	1.89
Kell Nut Honey Crn	2.95	3.25	3.23	Chld Enema 2.250	.98	1.15	1.19
Cutter Spray	3.09	3.95	3.69	Gillette Atra Plus	5.00	5.24	5.59
Lawry Season Salt	2.28	2.97	2.85	Colgate Shave	.94	1.10	1.19

a. Suppose we want to use the data to compare the mean prices of grocery items at the three supermarkets. Identify the treatments and blocks for this randomized block design.

b. The data were subjected to an ANOVA using SAS. Use the information in the SAS printout shown on p. 708 to construct an ANOVA table for the data.

c. Test to determine whether the mean prices of grocery items differ among the three supermarkets. Use $\alpha = .01$.

d. Construct a 95% confidence interval for the difference between the mean prices per item at Winn-Dixie and Kash 'N Karry.

e. Does the interval obtained in part **d** provide evidence of a significant difference in mean prices per item between Winn-Dixie and Kash 'N Karry?

Analysis of Variance Procedure

Dependent Variable: PRICE

Source	DF	Sum of Squares	Mean Square	F Value	Pr > F
Model	61	218.2361989	3.5776426	106.27	0.0001
Error	118	3.9725322	0.0336655		
Corrected Total	179	222.2087311			

R-Square	C.V.	Root MSE	PRICE Mean
0.982123	9.989324	0.183482	1.83677778

Source	DF	Anova SS	Mean Square	F Value	Pr > F
SUPERMKT	2	2.6412678	1.3206339	39.23	0.0001
ITEM	59	215.5949311	3.6541514	108.54	0.0001

Level of SUPERMKT	N	------------PRICE------------ Mean	SD
KNKarry	60	1.92533333	1.14118503
Publix	60	1.91950000	1.10339142
WinnDix	60	1.66550000	1.09622376

13.8 The Perth (Australia) Metropolitan Water Authority recently completed construction of an overland pipeline for transporting domestic wastewater from a primary treatment plant. During construction, the cement mortar lining of the pipeline was tested for cracking to determine whether autogeneous healing would seal the cracks. Otherwise, expensive epoxy filling repairs would be necessary. After cracks were observed in the pipeline, it was kept full of water for a period of 14 weeks. At each of 12 crack locations, crack widths were measured (in millimeters) after 2, 6, and 14 weeks of the wet period, as shown in the table. The data were subjected to an analysis of variance using SPSS. The SPSS printout follows. Conduct a test to determine whether the mean crack widths differ for the four time periods. Test using $\alpha = .05$.

CRACK LOCATION	CRACK WIDTH AFTER WETTING			
	0 Weeks	2 Weeks	6 Weeks	14 Weeks
1	.50	.20	.10	.10
2	.40	.20	.10	.10
3	.60	.30	.15	.10
4	.80	.40	.10	.10
5	.80	.30	.05	.05
6	1.00	.40	.05	.05
7	.90	.25	.05	.05
8	1.00	.30	.05	.10
9	.70	.25	.10	.10
10	.60	.25	.10	.05
11	.30	.15	.10	.05
12	.30	.14	.05	.05

Source: Cox, B. G., and Kelsall, K. J. "Construction of Cape Peron Ocean Outlet Perth, Western Australia." Proceedings of Civil Engineers, Part 1, Vol. 80, Apr. 1986, p. 479 (Table 1).

```
               * * *   A N A L Y S I S   O F   V A R I A N C E   * * *
            WIDTH
       BY   PERIOD
            LOCATION

                                Sum of                  Mean              Signif
    Source of Variation         Squares      DF         Square      F      of F

    Main Effects                 2.962       14          .212     13.708    .000
        PERIOD                   2.685        3          .895     57.988    .000
        LOCATION                  .277       11          .025      1.632    .135

    Explained                    2.962       14          .212     13.708    .000

    Residual                      .509       33          .015

    Total                        3.471       47          .074
```

13.9   Early full-screen video display terminals presented the viewer with white characters on a black background. Initially, viewers found the high degree of contrast easy on the eyes. However, after an extended period of use, black and white displays were frequently found to cause temporary eye irritation. Later, researchers found that yellow/amber displays may be the easiest on the eyes. In one German study, video display terminals were produced with white/black, yellow/amber, and five different symbol colors. Ten test subjects were asked to specify which color combination they preferred by ranking each of the seven color combinations on a scale from 0 (no preference) to 10. The individual preference scores for the ten subjects are listed in the table, followed by a MINITAB printout of the analysis of variance. Do the data provide sufficient evidence of a difference among the mean preference scores for the seven video display color combinations? Test using $\alpha = .05$.

SUBJECT	GREEN/ BLACK	WHITE/ BLACK	YELLOW/ WHITE	ORANGE/ WHITE	YELLOW	YELLOW/ AMBER	YELLOW/ ORANGE
1	7	6	7	2	8	9	3
2	8	6	9	4	9	8	1
3	5	5	7	1	6	8	2
4	3	4	2	0	2	6	0
5	9	8	8	3	9	9	2
6	7	5	6	2	7	7	1
7	6	7	8	4	6	9	5
8	6	5	8	1	8	9	1
9	9	9	8	2	9	8	0
10	9	8	8	3	9	10	1

Source: Adapted from Solomon, L., and Burawa, A. "Maximize Your Computing Comfort and Efficiency." *Computers & Electronics*, Apr. 1983, pp. 35–40.

```
ANALYSIS OF VARIANCE  SCORE

SOURCE     DF        SS        MS
COLOR       6     421.34     70.22
SUBJECT     9     114.30     12.70
ERROR      54      71.80      1.33
TOTAL      69     607.44
```

13.10 Due to the growing concern over problems related to alcohol consumption, the Federal Trade Commission (FTC) has considered banning alcohol advertising. It is unclear, however, whether alcohol advertising actually increases alcohol consumption. A study was undertaken to examine the effect of price advertising on sales of beer in Lower Michigan. [The state of Michigan was selected because it has prohibited retailers from advertising the price of beer products since 1975, except for the brief period (March 1982–May 1983) when the ban was temporarily lifted.] The data in the table are the bimonthly total sales of brewed beverages (in thousands of 31 gallon barrels) over the period May 1981–April 1984. The data were used to compare mean sales of beer in three periods, before (period 1), during (period 2), and after (period 3) the lifting of the price advertising restrictions. Treating this as a completely randomized design, the data were subjected to an ANOVA using MINITAB.

| PERIOD 1: RESTRICTED | PERIOD 2: NO RESTRICTIONS | PERIOD 3: RESTRICTED |
May/June 1981–Jan./Feb. 1982	Mar./Apr. 1982–May/June 1983	July/Aug. 1983–Mar./Apr. 1984
462	522	433
417	508	470
516	427	609
605	477	442
654	603	446
	692	
	584	
	496	

Source: Wilcox, G. B. "The Effect of Price Advertising on Alcoholic Beverage Sales." *Journal of Advertising Research*, Vol. 25, No. 5, Oct./Nov. 1985, pp. 33–37.

MINITAB Completely Randomized ANOVA Printout

```
ANALYSIS OF VARIANCE ON SALES
SOURCE     DF       SS         MS        F        p
PERIOD      2     11358      5679      0.78    0.476
ERROR      15    109153      7277
TOTAL      17    120510
```

a. Is there sufficient evidence to indicate differences in the average total sales of beer in the three periods? Test using $\alpha = .10$.

b. The fact that the experimental unit is a month (actually, a pair of successive months since we are measuring total bimonthly beer sales) could introduce an unwanted source of variation into the analysis—namely, the month-to-month variation in beer sales. Explain how to set up a randomized block design to reduce this unwanted source of variation.

c. The data have been reorganized in the following table. Notice that the months in which the beer sales are recorded are now identified for each period. A MINITAB randomized block ANOVA was conducted on only the data for those months that appear across all three periods. Based on the MINITAB results that follow, is there sufficient evidence to indicate that mean total bimonthly beer sales differ among the three periods? Test using $\alpha = .10$.

MONTHS	PERIOD 1	PERIOD 2	PERIOD 3
Jan./Feb.	654	692	442
Mar./Apr.	—	522, 584	446
May/June	462	508, 496	—
July/Aug.	417	427	433
Sept./Oct.	516	477	470
Nov./Dec.	605	603	609

Source: Wilcox, G. B. "The Effect of Price Advertising on Alcoholic Beverage Sales." *Journal of Advertising Research*, Vol. 25, No. 5, Oct./Nov. 1985, pp. 33–37.

```
ANALYSIS OF VARIANCE   SALES

SOURCE       DF        SS         MS
PERIOD       2        9726       4863
MONTH        3       68258      22753
ERROR        6       27947       4658
TOTAL       11      105932
```

d. Compare the MSE for the randomized block ANOVA to the MSE for the completely randomized ANOVA. Does it appear that blocking on months was effective in reducing month-to-month variation in beer sales?

e. Conduct a test for blocks using $\alpha = .10$. Does the result support your answer to part d?

13.11 A study was conducted to explore the sources of occupational stress for engineers (*IEEE Transactions on Engineering Management*, Feb. 1986). One of the objectives was to determine "if there are consistent and significant differences among engineers at different levels of the organizational hierarchy in the degree to which they consider the different factors as sources of stress." A sample of male engineers from different types of organizations in Ontario, Canada, was administered the Stress Diagnostic Survey (SDS). The SDS provides stress ratings for each of 15 categories of work stressors. The researchers ranked 15 stress categories from 1 (highest stress) to 15 (lowest stress) for each of four groups of engineers—nonsupervisors, first-level supervisors, second-level supervisors, and third-level supervisors—as shown in the table. Conduct a test to determine whether the rank orderings of the stress categories differ among the four groups of engineers. Test using $\alpha = .01$.

STRESS CATEGORY	NONSUPERVISORS	1ST LEVEL	2ND LEVEL	3RD LEVEL
Politics	5	6	4	7
Underutilization	3	5	7	5
Human Resources Development	4	3	2	3
Supervisory Style	6	7	8	8
Rewards	1	1	1	4
Organizational Structure	9	9	10	12
Participation	2	4	5	6
Role Ambiguity	10	13	12	14
Overload/Quantitative	15	15	15	15
Overload/Qualitative	12	8	6	2
Time Pressure	8	2	3	1
Role Conflict	13	10	13	10
Career Progression	7	10	9	13
Job Scope	11	12	14	11
Responsibility for People	14	14	11	9

Source: Saleh, S. D., and Desai, K. "Occupational Stress for Engineers." *IEEE Transactions on Engineering Management*, Vol. EM-33, No. 1, Feb. 1986, p. 8 (Table II). © 1986 IEEE.

13.12 The in-tray (or in-basket) exercise, developed 25 years ago as a training tool for officers in the U.S. Air Force, is a simulation representing the typical contents of an executive's in-tray with a variety of everyday problems in a written form (letters, memoranda, notes, reports, and telephone messages)—both expected and unexpected, and requiring decisions and action. After completing the tasks, the trainees' performances are assessed by one or more expert raters on a scale of 1 (high performance) to 6 (low performance). However, the reliability of assessors' ratings should be determined before using the in-tray results as a measure of managerial effectiveness. The phenomenon of rater reliability was investigated in the *Journal of Occupational Psychology*. Seven subjects, all candidates for a general management position in a manufacturing company in the British motor industry, were given the in-tray test. Overall in-tray performance of each candidate was assessed by three different raters. The results are given in the table.

CANDIDATE	RATER 1	RATER 2	RATER 3
A	4.5	4.5	5.0
B	2.5	4.5	4.5
C	5.0	3.0	4.0
D	4.0	4.5	4.5
E	1.5	2.0	4.5
F	3.5	4.5	4.5
G	4.0	4.0	4.0

Source: Gill, R. W. T. "The In-Tray (In-Basket) Exercise As a Measure of Management Potential."
Journal of Occupational Psychology, Vol. 52, 1979, pp. 185–195.

a. The SPSS parametric ANOVA printout for the data follows. Is there evidence of a difference among the mean performance scores assessed by the three raters? Use a significance level of $\alpha = .05$.
b. Use the following SPSS printout to conduct a nonparametric analysis of the data. Compare these results to those obtained in part **a**. Which procedure would you recommend?

SPSS Printouts for Problem 13.12

```
* * * A N A L Y S I S   O F   V A R I A N C E * * *

          SCORE
     BY   RATER
          CANDATE

                              Sum of                Mean              Signif
Source of Variation           Squares     DF        Square      F     of F

Main Effects                   9.786       8         1.223    1.797    .174
   RATER                       2.667       2         1.333    1.959    .184
   CANDATE                     7.119       6         1.187    1.743    .194
Explained                      9.786       8         1.223    1.797    .174
Residual                       8.167      12          .681
Total                         17.952      20          .898


- - - - - Friedman Two-way ANOVA


   Mean Rank    Variable

     1.50       RATER1
     2.00       RATER2
     2.50       RATER3


     Cases          Chi-Square        D.F.     Significance
       7             3.5000             2          .1738
```

13.6

A **factorial experiment** is one conducted to investigate the effect of two or more variables (**factors**) on the mean value of a response variable. Experimental units are measured for various combinations of **factor levels** (values assumed by the factors). If an experiment involves two factors, with one at three levels and the other at two levels, the response can be measured for each of the $2 \times 3 = 6$ factor level combinations. If one observation on the response variable is taken for each of the six factor level combinations, we say that we have conducted one **replication** of a 2×3 factorial experiment. Stating that we conducted one replication of the experiment means that we obtained one measurement on the response variable for each of the six factor level combinations.

The data for a two-factor factorial experiment are presented in a two-way table, with rows corresponding to the levels of one factor and columns corresponding to the levels of the other factor. For each combination of factor levels, the data fall in one of the row–column cells of the table. To illustrate, consider the following example.

EXAMPLE 13.8 A company that stamps gaskets out of sheets of rubber, plastic, and cork wants to compare the mean number of gaskets produced per hour for two different types of stamping machines. Practically, the manufacturer wants to determine whether one machine is more productive than the other and, even more important, whether one machine is more productive in producing rubber gaskets while the other is more productive in producing plastic or cork gaskets. To answer these questions, the manufacturer decides to conduct an experiment using three types of gasket material, B_1, B_2, and B_3, with each of the two types of stamping machines, A_1 and A_2. Each machine is operated for three 1 hour time periods for each of the gasket materials, with the eighteen 1 hour time periods assigned to six machine–material combinations in random order. The purpose of the randomization is to eliminate the possibility that uncontrolled environmental factors might bias the results. The data for the experiment, the number of gaskets (in thousands) produced per hour, are shown in Table 13.7. Identify the factors and treatments (factor level combinations) in the experiment.

TABLE 13.7
Data for the 2 × 3 Factorial Experiment of Example 13.8

STAMPING MACHINE	GASKET MATERIAL			Totals
	Cork, B_1	Rubber, B_2	Plastic, B_3	
A_1	4.31 4.27 4.40	3.36 3.42 3.48	4.01 3.94 3.89	35.08
A_2	3.94 3.81 3.99	3.91 3.80 3.85	3.48 3.53 3.42	33.73
Totals	24.72	21.82	22.27	68.81

Solution Since the company will produce gaskets using three types of material with each of two types of stamping machine, the experiment involves two factors, machine (A) and material (B), with factor A at two levels (A_1, A_2) and factor B at three levels (B_1, B_2, B_3). Each of the $2 \times 3 = 6$ combinations of machine and material (A_1B_1, A_1B_2, A_1B_3, A_2B_1, A_2B_2, A_2B_3) represents the treatments in the experiment. For this reason the experiment is referred to as a 2×3 factorial experiment.

The two-way tables for a randomized block design and a factorial experiment differ in one very obvious way. The table for a randomized block design contains only one observation per cell. The cells for a factorial experiment contain equal numbers of observations, almost always more than one. (Table 13.7 contains three observations per cell.) Furthermore, the tables differ in their interpretation. For the randomized block design, one direction of classification corresponds to the k treatments included in the experiment. In a factorial experiment, **each cell of the table corresponds to a treatment**. Thus, each combination of machine and material in Table 13.7 represents a treatment, and the objective of the experiment is to compare the means for the six treatments.

EXAMPLE 13.9 Refer to the data of Table 13.7. Suppose that we have calculated the six cell (treatment) means. Consider two possible outcomes. Figure 13.11 shows two hypothetical plots of the six means. For both plots, the three means for stamping machine A_1 are connected by color line segments. The corresponding three means for machine A_2 are connected by black line segments. What do these plots imply?

Solution Figure 13.11a suggests that machine A_1 produces a larger number of gaskets per hour, regardless of the gasket material, and is therefore superior to machine A_2. On the average, machine A_1 stamps more cork (B_1) gaskets per hour than rubber or plastic, but the *difference* in the mean numbers of gaskets produced by the two machines remains approximately the same, regardless of the gasket material. Thus, the difference between the mean numbers of gaskets produced by the two machines is *independent* of the gasket material used in the stamping process.

FIGURE 13.11
Hypothetical Plot of the Means for the Six Machine–Material Combinations

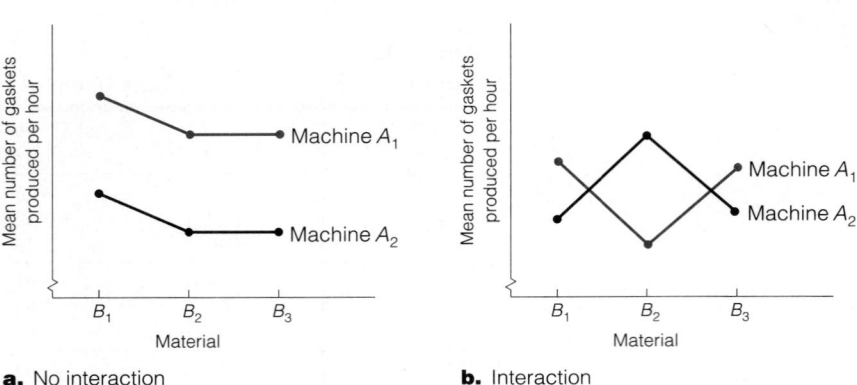

a. No interaction   **b.** Interaction

In contrast to Figure 13.11a, Figure 13.11b shows the productivity of machine A_1 to be larger than the productivity for machine A_2 when the gasket material is cork (B_1) or plastic (B_3). But the means are reversed for rubber (B_2) gasket material. For this material, machine A_2 produces, on the average, more gaskets per hour than machine A_1. Thus, Figure 13.11b illustrates a situation where the mean value of the response variable *depends* on the combination of the factor levels. When this situation occurs, we say that the factors **interact**. Thus, one of the most important objectives of a factorial experiment is to detect factor interaction, if it exists.

DEFINITION 13.12

In a factorial experiment, when the difference between the mean levels of factor A depends on the different levels of factor B, we say that the factors A and B **interact**. If the difference is independent of the levels of B, then there is **no interaction** between factors A and B.

The analysis of variance for a two-factor factorial experiment is very similar to the analysis of variance for a randomized block design. The sums of squares for the qualitative variables, blocks and treatments in the randomized block design, are now replaced by the sums of squares for the two factors, **SS(A)** and **SS(B)**, called **main effects sums of squares**. The failure of the difference in the mean levels of factor A to be the same for all levels of factor B is reflected in the **interaction sum of squares, SS(AB)**. Finally, because we have more than one observation per cell for the two-way table, we calculate a sum of squares designated as SSE. The partitioning of SS(Total) into its parts is shown in Figure 13.12.

FIGURE 13.12

Partitioning of the Total Sum of Squares for a Two-Factor Factorial Experiment

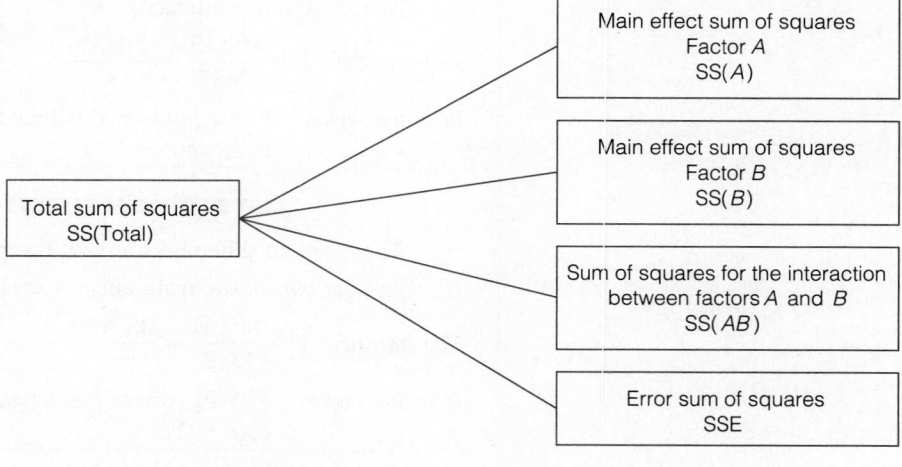

The formulas for the sums of squares and the corresponding mean squares for a factorial experiment are given in Appendix B. As in the previous two sections, we will resort to one of the many statistical software packages available to perform the analysis of the data, and we will summarize the ANOVA results in a table. In general, the ANOVA table for a two-factor factorial experiment, with factor A at a levels, factor B at b levels, and with r replications, appears as shown in the box.

ANALYSIS OF VARIANCE TABLE FOR A TWO-FACTOR FACTORIAL EXPERIMENT

SOURCE	df	SS	MS	F
Main effect, A	$a - 1$	SS(A)	$MS(A) = \dfrac{SS(A)}{a - 1}$	$F = \dfrac{MS(A)}{MSE}$
Main effect, B	$b - 1$	SS(B)	$MS(B) = \dfrac{SS(B)}{b - 1}$	$F = \dfrac{MS(B)}{MSE}$
AB interaction	$(a - 1)(b - 1)$	SS(AB)	$MS(AB) = \dfrac{SS(AB)}{(a - 1)(b - 1)}$	$F = \dfrac{MS(AB)}{MSE}$
Error	$ab(r - 1)$	SSE	$MSE = \dfrac{SSE}{ab(r - 1)}$	
Totals	$abr - 1$	SS(Total)		

ANOVA F TESTS FOR TWO-FACTOR FACTORIAL EXPERIMENT

TEST FOR FACTOR INTERACTION

H_0: No interaction between factors A and B

H_a: Factors A and B interact.

Test statistic: $F = \dfrac{MS(AB)}{MSE} = \dfrac{MS(AB)}{s^2}$

Rejection region: $F > F_\alpha$, where F is based on $\nu_1 = (a - 1)(b - 1)$ and $\nu_2 = ab(r - 1)$ df

TEST FOR MAIN EFFECTS FOR FACTOR A

H_0: There are no differences among the means for main effect A.

H_a: At least two of the main effect A means differ.

Test statistic: $F = \dfrac{MS(A)}{MSE} = \dfrac{MS(A)}{s^2}$

Rejection region: $F > F_\alpha$, where F is based on $\nu_1 = (a - 1)$ and $\nu_2 = ab(r - 1)$ df

TEST FOR MAIN EFFECTS FOR FACTOR *B*

H_0: There are no differences among the means for main effect *B*.

H_a: At least two of the main effect *B* means differ.

Test statistic: $F = \dfrac{MS(B)}{MSE} = \dfrac{MS(B)}{s^2}$

Rejection region: $F > F_\alpha$, where F is based on $\nu_1 = (b - 1)$ and $\nu_2 = ab(r - 1)$ df

---

Assumptions:

1. The population probability distribution of the observations for any factor level combination is approximately normal.

2. The variance of the probability distribution is constant and the same for all factor level combinations.

3. The treatments (factor level combinations) are randomly assigned to the experimental units.

4. The observations for each factor level combination represent independent random samples.

WARNING

When the assumptions for analyzing data collected from a factorial experiment (see above) are violated, any inferences derived from the ANOVA are suspect. Nonparametric methods are available for analyzing factorial experiments, but they are beyond the scope of this text. Consult the references given at the end of this chapter if you want to learn about such techniques.

EXAMPLE 13.10 Refer to Examples 13.8 and 13.9. The SAS printout for the 2 × 3 factorial ANOVA of the data in Table 13.7 is shown in Figure 13.13 (p. 718).

a. Use the information in the printout to construct an ANOVA summary table.
b. Conduct the appropriate ANOVA *F* test for interaction.
c. Interpret the results from part **b**.

Solution

a. The degrees of freedom, sums of squares, mean squares, and *F* statistic for the ANOVA main effects and interaction are shaded at the bottom of the SAS printout in Figure 13.13. The SS, MS, and df for ERROR are shaded in the top portion of the printout. These values enable us to construct the ANOVA summary table shown in Table 13.8.

Analysis of Variance Procedure

Dependent Variable: NUMBER

Source	DF	Sum of Squares	Mean Square	F Value	Pr > F
Model	5	1.68122778	0.33624556	76.52	0.0001
Error	12	0.05273333	0.00439444		
Corrected Total	17	1.73396111			

	R-Square	C.V.	Root MSE	NUMBER Mean
	0.969588	1.734095	0.066291	3.82277778

Source	DF	Anova SS	Mean Square	F Value	Pr > F
MACHINE	1	0.10125000	0.10125000	23.04	0.0004
MATERIAL	2	0.81194444	0.40597222	92.38	0.0001
MACHINE*MATERIAL	2	0.76803333	0.38401667	87.39	0.0001

TABLE 13.8
ANOVA Table for the Two-Factor Factorial Experiment of Example 13.10

SOURCE	df	SS	MS	F
Machines, A	1	.10125	.10125	23.04
Materials, B	2	.81194	.40597	92.38
AB interaction	2	.76803	.38402	87.39
Error	12	.05273	.00439	
Totals	17	1.73396		

b. We want to test

H_0: No interaction between machine and material

H_a: The two factors, machine and material, interact.

From the printout, the test statistic is $F = 87.39$, with a p-value of .0001. Consequently, for any reasonable α (say, $\alpha = .05$), we reject H_0. There is sufficient evidence to indicate that machine and material interact.

c. Insight into this interaction can be obtained by plotting the six sample means associated with the six machine–material combinations. This plot is shown in Figure 13.14. Consider the difference between the mean number of gaskets produced per hour by machines A_1 and A_2. Note that the magnitude and sign of this difference depends on the type of material being stamped. That is, the (machine × material) interaction implies that the effect of machine on the mean number of gaskets produced per hour depends on material.

FIGURE 13.14

Plot of the Means for the Six Machine–Material Combinations

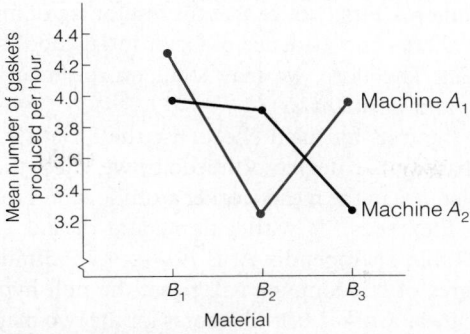

Tests for differences in the mean levels of the main effects in a factorial experiment are relevant *only when the factors do not interact*. When there is no factor interaction, the differences in the mean levels of factor *A* are the same for all levels of factor *B*. The test for main effect *A* tests the significance of these differences. In the presence of interaction, however, the main effect test is irrelevant since the differences in the mean levels of factor *A* are not the same at each level of factor *B*. The following example demonstrates the mechanics of the tests for main effects and discusses the practical implications of the tests.

EXAMPLE 13.11   A 2×2 factorial experiment was conducted to determine the effects of work scheduling (factor *A*) and method of payment (factor *B*) on attitude toward the job. Two types of scheduling were employed, the standard 8:00 A.M.–5:00 P.M. work day and a modification whereby the worker was permitted to vary the starting time and the length of the lunch hour. The two methods of payment were a standard hourly rate and a reduced hourly rate with an added piece rate based on worker production. Four workers were randomly assigned to each of the four scheduling–payment combinations, and each completed an attitude test after 1 month on the job. An analysis of variance table for the test scores data is shown in Table 13.9. Interpret the results of the ANOVA.

TABLE 13.9

ANOVA Table for the Two-Factor Factorial Experiment of Example 13.11

SOURCE	df	SS	MS	F
Schedule (*A*)	1	361	361	7.37
Payment (*B*)	1	1,444	1,444	29.47
Schedule–Payment (*AB*) interaction	1	1	1	.02
Error	12	588	49	
Totals	15	2,394		

Solution First, notice that the test for factor interaction is not statistically significant (ie, there is no evidence of factor interaction) since the value of F, .02, is extremely small. Therefore, we may focus on the main effects for the two factors, schedule (A) and payment (B).

The tests for main effects use the F statistics shown in Table 13.9. Since MS(A) is based on 1 degree of freedom, we reject the null hypothesis (at $\alpha = .05$) of no difference in the mean worker attitude scores for the two schedules if the corresponding F exceeds $F_{.05}$ with 1 numerator df and 12 denominator df. This value, found in Table 8, Appendix A, is $F_{.05} = 4.75$. Similarly, since MS(B) is also based on 1 degree of freedom, we will reject the null hypothesis that there is no difference in the mean worker attitude scores for the two methods of payment if the corresponding F exceeds $F_{.05} = 4.75$.

Note that the F values for main effect A (schedule) and main effect B (payment) both exceed the critical value. Thus, there is evidence (at $\alpha = .05$) of differences in the mean levels of the respective main effects. Practically, this implies that the mean worker attitude scores differ for the two schedules, but that this difference does not depend on method of payment (due to lack of interaction). Similarly, the mean worker attitude scores for the two methods of payment differ, but the difference does not depend on work schedule.

WARNING

In a factorial experiment, the F test for factor interaction should always be conducted first, because the F tests for factor main effects are usually relevant *only when factor interaction is not significant*. If interaction is detected, *do not* perform the F tests for main effects.

To conclude, we will comment about the number r of replications required for a factorial experiment. Some experimenters do conduct factorial experiments consisting of a single replication (ie, $r = 1$). Their logic is that if they assume the factors do not interact, then MS(AB) can be used as an estimate of σ^2 and the tests for main effects can be conducted in the same manner as for a randomized block design. Since factorial experiments are conducted primarily to detect factor interaction, if it exists, we do not recommend single-replication factorial experiments.

PROBLEMS

13.13 The *Accounting Review* (Jan. 1991) reported on a study of the effect of two factors, confirmation of accounts receivable and verification of sales transactions, on account misstatement risk by auditors. Both factors were held at the same two levels: completed or not completed. Thus, the experimental design is a 2 × 2 factorial design.

a. Identify the factors, factor levels, and treatments for this experiment.

b. Explain what factor interaction means for this experiment.

c. A graph of the hypothetical mean misstatement risks for each of the $2 \times 2 = 4$ treatments is displayed here. In this hypothetical case, does it appear that interaction exists?

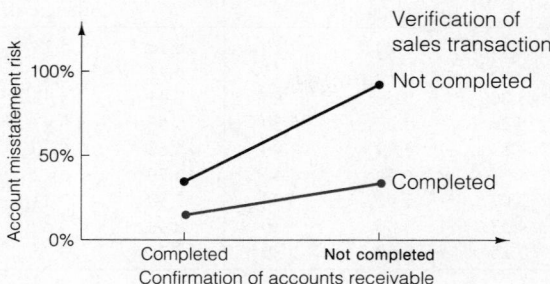

Source: Brown, C. E., and Solomon, I. "Configural Information Processing in Auditing: The Role of Domain-Specific Knowledge." *The Accounting Review*, Vol. 66, No. 1, Jan. 1991, p. 105 (Fig. 1).

13.14 Computer-based management information systems (MIS) comprise one of the fastest growing industries in the United States, yet little is known about the ethical decision-making processes of persons involved in creating and maintaining these systems. An empirical investigation was conducted to determine whether MIS majors, on average, exhibit ethical decision-making processes that differ from other business students (*Journal of Business Ethics*, Vol. 10, 1991). A large sample of business students was divided into two groups based on their major (MIS or non-MIS). Within each group, half of the students were administered the regular form of the Defining Issues Test (DIT) and the other half were given a form of the DIT modified to incorporate MIS. Thus, a 2×2 factorial experiment design was used, with major and form as the two factors. The dependent (response) variable measured was the "principled morality," or *P* score, expressed as a percentage. (High scores are indicative of morally conscious decisions.) Interpret the results of the ANOVA summarized in the table.

SOURCE	df	SS	MS	F	p-VALUE
Form	1	0.13	0.13	0.00	0.98
Major	1	1,290.10	1,290.10	6.25	0.01
Form × Major	1	56.38	56.38	0.27	0.60
Error	233	48,120.15	206.52		
Totals	236	49,466.76			

Source: Paradice, D. B., and Dejoie, R. M. "The Ethical Decision-Making Processes of Information Systems Workers." *Journal of Business Ethics,* Vol. 10, 1991, p. 9 (Table V).

13.15 A trade-off study regarding the inspection and test of transformer parts was conducted by the quality control department of a major defense contractor. The investigation was structured to examine the effects of varying inspection levels and incoming test times in detecting early parts failure or fatigue. The levels of inspection selected were full military specification (*A*), reduced military specification level (*B*), and commercial grade (*C*). Operational burn-in test times chosen for this study were at 1 hour increments from 1 hour to 9 hours. The response was failures per 1,000 pieces obtained from samples taken from lot sizes inspected to a specified level and burned-in over a prescribed time length. Three replications were randomly sequenced under each condition, making this a complete 3×9 factorial experiment (a total of 81 observations). The data for the study, shown in the table on p. 722, were subjected to an ANOVA using SAS. The SAS printout follows. Analyze and interpret the results.

BURN-IN Hours	INSPECTION LEVELS								
	Full Military Specification, A			Reduced Military Specification, B			Commercial, C		
1	7.60	7.50	7.67	7.70	7.10	7.20	6.16	6.13	6.21
2	6.54	7.46	6.84	5.85	6.15	6.15	6.21	5.50	5.64
3	6.53	5.85	6.38	5.30	5.60	5.80	5.41	5.45	5.35
4	5.66	5.98	5.37	5.38	5.27	5.29	5.68	5.47	5.84
5	5.00	5.27	5.39	4.85	4.99	4.98	5.65	6.00	6.15
6	4.20	3.60	4.20	4.50	4.56	4.50	6.70	6.72	6.54
7	3.66	3.92	4.22	3.97	3.90	3.84	7.90	7.47	7.70
8	3.76	3.68	3.80	4.37	3.86	4.46	8.40	8.60	7.90
9	3.46	3.55	3.45	5.25	5.63	5.25	8.82	9.76	9.52

Source: Danny La Nuez, College of Business Administration, graduate student, University of South Florida, 1989–1990.

```
                     Analysis of Variance Procedure

Dependent Variable: FAILURES
                                 Sum of        Mean
Source                  DF       Squares       Square    F Value    Pr > F

Model                   26     168.6120667    6.4850795   101.31    0.0001
Error                   54       3.4565333    0.0640099
Corrected Total         80     172.0686000

                R-Square          C.V.       Root MSE        FAILURE Mean

                0.979912        4.405990     0.253002         5.74222222


Source                  DF       Anova SS    Mean Square   F Value    Pr > F

BURNIN                   8     27.97440000   3.49680000     54.63    0.0001
INSLEVEL                 2     43.08411852  21.54205926    336.54    0.0001
BURNIN*INSLEVEL         16     97.55354815   6.09709676     95.25    0.0001
```

13.16   Many television and radio commercials utilize high-intensity stimulation (eg, rapid changes in visual imagery, quick movements, bright lights, and loud sounds) to increase the general arousal of the viewer or listener. In theory, the more aroused the viewer, the more likely he or she is to remember the advertised product. *Psychology & Marketing* (Summer 1986) reported on a study designed to examine the effect of high-intensity advertising on the audience. Two groups of psychology students (10 introverts and 10 extroverts) at a small midwestern liberal arts college took part in the experiment. (Scores on the Eysenck Personality Questionnaire were used to classify the students according to the two groups.) Five subjects from each group were then randomly assigned to one of two experimental conditions: high-volume commercial or normal-volume commercial. Thus, the experiment consists of two factors, personality type and commercial volume, each at two levels. All students listened to a 5 minute tape-recorded "radio program" that included a commercial for a fictitious brand of chewing gum played at the assigned volume; each subject's attitude toward the product was measured on a 14 point scale (1 = strongly dislike, 14 = strongly like). Since five responses were recorded for each of the $2 \times 2 = 4$ factor level combinations, the factorial experiment includes five replicates of each treatment.

a. A partial ANOVA table for the experiment is shown here. Calculate as many of the missing entries as possible.

SOURCE	df	SS	MS	F
Personality (P)	1	—	—	—
Volume (V)	—	—	—	4.61
VP	—	—	—	11.39
Error	—	—	15	
Totals	—	—		

Source: Cetola, H., and Prinkley, K. "Introversion–Extroversion and Loud Commercials." *Psychology & Marketing*, Vol. 3, No. 2, Summer 1986, pp. 123–132. Copyright © 1986 *Psychology & Marketing*. Reprinted by permission of John Wiley & Sons, Inc.

b. The means for the four treatments are given in the table. Plot the means in a graph similar to Figure 13.14. Does it appear that the two factors, personality type and commercial volume, interact?

	HIGH VOLUME	NORMAL VOLUME
Extroverts	10.6	7.0
Introverts	7.2	6.0

c. Conduct a test to determine whether personality type interacts with commercial volume. Use $\alpha = .05$. Interpret the result.

13.17 The chemical element antimony is sometimes added to tin–lead solder to replace the more expensive tin and to reduce the cost of soldering. A factorial experiment was conducted to determine how antimony affects the strength of the tin–lead solder joint (*Journal of Materials Science*, May 1986). Tin–lead solder specimens were prepared using one of four possible cooling methods (water-quenched, WQ; oil-quenched, OQ; air-blown, AB; and furnace-cooled, FC) and with one of four possible amounts of antimony (0%, 3%, 5%, and 10%) added to the composition. Three solder joints were randomly assigned to each of the $4 \times 4 = 16$ treatments and the shear strength of each measured. The experimental results, shown in the table, were subjected to an ANOVA using SAS. The SAS printout is also reproduced at the top of the next page.

AMOUNT OF ANTIMONY % Weight	COOLING METHOD	SHEAR STRENGTH Millipascals	AMOUNT OF ANTIMONY % Weight	COOLING METHOD	SHEAR STRENGTH Millipascals
0	WQ	17.6, 19.5, 18.3	5	WQ	22.3, 19.5, 20.5
0	OQ	20.0, 24.3, 21.9	5	OQ	20.9, 22.9, 20.6
0	AB	18.3, 19.8, 22.9	5	AB	22.9, 19.7, 21.6
0	FC	19.4, 19.8, 20.3	5	FC	19.6, 16.4, 20.5
3	WQ	18.6, 19.5, 19.0	10	WQ	15.2, 17.1, 16.6
3	OQ	20.0, 20.9, 20.4	10	OQ	16.4, 19.0, 18.1
3	AB	21.7, 22.9, 22.1	10	AB	15.8, 17.3, 17.1
3	FC	19.0, 20.9, 19.9	10	FC	16.4, 17.6, 17.6

Source: Tomlinson, W. J., and Cooper, G. A. "Fracture Mechanism of Brass/Sn-Pb-Sb Solder Joints and the Effect of Production Variables on the Joint Strength." *Journal of Materials Science*, Vol. 21, No. 5, May 1986, p. 1731 (Table II). Copyright 1986 Chapman and Hall.

```
                         Analysis of Variance Procedure

Dependent Variable: STRENGTH
                                 Sum of             Mean
Source               DF          Squares           Square      F Value    Pr > F

Model                15      157.95250000       10.53016667      6.10      0.0001
Error                32       55.24666667        1.72645833
Corrected Total      47      213.19916667

                  R-Square             C.V.          Root MSE          STRENGTH Mean

                  0.740868          6.7195275        1.3139476          19.55416667


Source               DF         Anova SS       Mean Square     F Value    Pr > F

AMOUNT                3      104.194167        34.731389       20.12      0.0001
METHOD                3       28.627500         9.542500        5.53      0.0036
AMOUNT*METHOD         9       25.130833         2.792315        1.62      0.1523
```

a. Construct an ANOVA summary table for the experiment.
b. Conduct a test to determine whether the two factors, amount of antimony and cooling method, interact. Use $\alpha = .01$.
c. Interpret the result obtained in part **b**.
d. If appropriate, conduct the tests for main effects. Use $\alpha = .01$.

13.18   A field experiment was conducted at a not-for-profit research and development organization to examine the expectations, attitudes, and decisions of employees with regard to training programs (*Academy of Management Journal*, Sept. 1987). In particular, the study was aimed at determining the effect of prior information and degree of choice on how managers evaluate a training program. These two factors, prior information and degree of choice, were varied at two levels each. The prior information managers received about the training program was either a realistic preview of the program and its benefits or a traditional announcement that tended to exaggerate the workshop's benefits. Degree of choice was either low (mandatory attendance) or high (little pressure from supervisors to attend). Twenty-one managers were randomly assigned to each of the $2 \times 2 = 4$ experimental conditions; thus, a 2×2 factorial design was employed. At the end of the training program, each manager was asked to rate his or her satisfaction with the workshop on a 7 point scale (1 = no satisfaction, 7 = extremely satisfied). The ratings were subjected to an analysis of variance, with the results partially summarized in the table.

SOURCE	df	SS	MS	F
Prior information (P)	1	—	1.55	—
Degree of choice (D)	1	—	22.26	—
PD interaction	1	—	.61	—
Error	80	—	1.43	
Totals	83	—		

Source: Hicks, W. D., and Klimoski, R. J. "Entry into Training Programs and Its Effects on Training Outcomes: A Field Experiment." *Academy of Management Journal*, Vol. 30, No. 3, Sept. 1987, p. 548.

a. Complete the ANOVA summary table.
b. Conduct the appropriate ANOVA F tests (use $\alpha = .05$). Interpret the results.

FOLLOW-UP ANALYSIS: MULTIPLE COMPARISONS OF MEANS

13.7

Many designed experiments are conducted with the ultimate goal of determining the largest (or the smallest) mean in a set. For example, suppose a drug store manager is considering five floor displays for a new product. After conducting an ANOVA on the data and discovering differences among the mean weekly sales associated with the five displays, the manager would then want to determine which display yields the greatest mean weekly sales of the product.

Once differences among, say, five treatment means have been detected in an ANOVA, choosing the treatment with the largest mean might appear to be a simple matter. We could, for example, obtain the sample means, $\bar{y}_1, \bar{y}_2, ..., \bar{y}_5$, and compare them by constructing a $(1 - \alpha)100\%$ confidence interval for the difference between each pair of treatment means. However, there is a problem associated with this procedure:

A confidence interval for $\mu_i - \mu_j$, with its corresponding value of α, is valid only when the two treatments (i and j) to be compared are selected prior to experimentation.

After you have looked at the data, you cannot use a confidence interval to compare the treatments for the largest and smallest sample means because they will always be farther apart, on the average, than any pair of treatments selected at random. Furthermore, if you construct a series of confidence intervals, each with a chance α of indicating a difference between a pair of means if no difference exists, then the risk of making *at least one* Type I error in the series of inferences will be larger than the value of α specified for a single interval.

There are a number of procedures for comparing and ranking a group of treatment means as part of a *follow-up analysis* to the ANOVA. A general method that is useful in most experimental designs is called the **Bonferroni multiple comparisons procedure**.*

The Bonferroni approach is based on the following result (proof omitted). If g comparisons (ie, confidence intervals) are to be made, each with confidence coefficient $(1 - \alpha/g)$, then the overall probability of making one or more Type I error(s) is at most α. Or, equivalently, the set of intervals constructed using the Bonferroni method yields an overall confidence level of at least $(1 - \alpha)$.

EXAMPLE 13.12 Suppose you want to construct two confidence intervals with an overall Type I error rate of at most $\alpha = .05$. Use the Bonferroni method to determine the confidence level of each individual interval.

Solution For this example, $g = 2$ intervals are to be constructed with an overall α level of .05. Therefore, the confidence level of each interval will be

$$1 - \frac{\alpha}{g} = 1 - \frac{.05}{2} = 1 - .025 = .975$$

---

* Other procedures, such as Tukey and Tukey–Kramer, may be more powerful in certain sampling situations. Consult the references for details on how to use these multiple comparisons methods.

In other words, two 97.5% confidence intervals must be constructed to guarantee an overall Type I error rate of at most $\alpha = .05$.

When applied to pairwise comparisons of treatment means, the Bonferroni technique can be carried out by comparing the difference between two treatment means, $(\bar{y}_i - \bar{y}_j)$, to a critical difference B_{ij}, where B_{ij} depends on n_i, n_j, α, MSE, and the total number of treatments to be compared. If the difference between the sample means exceeds the critical difference, there is sufficient evidence to conclude that the population means differ. The steps to follow in carrying out the Bonferroni multiple comparisons procedure are described in the box.

BONFERRONI MULTIPLE COMPARISONS PROCEDURE FOR PAIRWISE COMPARISONS OF TREATMENT MEANS

STEP 1   Select the desired overall confidence level, $(1 - \alpha)$.

STEP 2   Calculate B_{ij} for each treatment pair (i, j):

$$B_{ij} = (t_{\alpha^*/2})(s)\sqrt{\frac{1}{n_i} + \frac{1}{n_j}}$$

where

k = Number of sample (treatment) means in the experiment

g = Number of pairwise comparisons [*Note:*   If all pairwise comparisons are to be made, then $g = k(k - 1)/2$.]

$\alpha^* = \alpha/g$

$s = \sqrt{\text{MSE}}$

n_i = Number of observations in sample for treatment i

n_j = Number of observations in sample for treatment j

ν = Number of degrees of freedom associated with MSE

$t_{\alpha^*/2}$ = Critical value of t distribution with ν df and tail area $\alpha^*/2$ (Table 3, Appendix A)

STEP 3   Calculate and rank the sample means.

STEP 4   Place a bar over any treatment mean pair (i, j) that differs by less than B_{ij}. Any pair of means not connected by an overbar implies a difference in the corresponding population means.

Note: The level of confidence associated with all inferences drawn from the analysis is at least $(1 - \alpha)$.

EXAMPLE 13.13   Refer to the ANOVA for the completely randomized design discussed in Example 13.3 (p. 693). Recall that we rejected the null hypothesis of no differences among the mean residential sale prices in the seven neighborhoods. Use Bonferroni's method to perform pairwise comparisons of the means for the seven neighborhoods. Use an overall Type I error rate of $\alpha = .02$.

Solution For these multiple comparisons, $\alpha = .02$, $k = 7$, and $g = 7(6)/2 = 21$. Thus, $\alpha^* = \alpha/g = .02/21 \approx .001$, $\alpha^*/2 = .0005$, and the critical t-value is $t_{.0005} \approx 3.46$ (based on $\nu = 63$ degrees of freedom).

Since the sample sizes for the neighborhoods are equal ($n_i = 10$), the Bonferroni critical difference used in all pairwise comparisons is

$$B_{ij} = (t_{.0005})s\sqrt{\frac{1}{n_i} + \frac{1}{n_j}}$$

From Example 13.3, $s = 49.9$; thus, we have

$$B_{ij} = (3.46)(49.9)\sqrt{\frac{1}{10} + \frac{1}{10}} = 77.2$$

Therefore, if the sample means for any two neighborhoods differ by more than $B_{ij} = 77.2$, the corresponding population means will be considered significantly different.

The sample sale price means for the seven neighborhoods are shown in the SAS printout, Figure 13.15 (p. 728). Note that the means are listed vertically in decreasing order of magnitude. This printout also shows the Bonferroni analysis of the seven means. The critical difference, B_{ij}, is shaded in the printout. This value (77.394) differs slightly from our hand-computed value due to rounding.

The left side of the SAS printout shows the Bonferroni groupings (rankings) of the seven means. Means with the same letter (A, B, or C) are not significantly different at an overall $\alpha = .02$. The information in the printout yields the rankings shown below. Our interpretation of these results for each neighborhood follows.

Sample means:	205.45	137.10	107.46	93.06	83.08	47.71	34.25
Neighborhood:	A	B	C	D	E	F	G

NEIGHBORHOOD A Note that the mean for neighborhood A is connected by a bar to the mean for neighborhood B. (The difference, $\bar{y}_A - \bar{y}_B$, is less than the critical difference, 77.2.) Thus, the means for these two neighborhoods are not significantly different. However, $\bar{y}_A = 205.45$ exceeds all other sample means by more than 77.2 (no other means are connected directly to A by a bar). Consequently, we say that μ_A, the population mean sale price for neighborhood A, is larger than the population means for the remaining five neighborhoods, that is, $\mu_A > (\mu_C, \mu_D, \mu_E, \mu_F, \mu_G)$.

NEIGHBORHOOD B Neighborhood B is connected by a bar to neighborhood A and by a bar to neighborhoods C, D, and E. Consequently, the mean for neighborhood B is not significantly different from the means for neighborhoods A, C, D, and E.

FIGURE 13.15

SAS ANOVA Printout with Bonferroni Analysis

```
                    Analysis of Variance Procedure
Dependent Variable: SALEPRIC
                                 Sum of             Mean
Source                DF         Squares           Square    F Value    Pr > F

Model                  6       199341.2469      33223.5411     13.34     0.0001
Error                 63       156930.9230       2490.9670
Corrected Total       69       356272.1699

               R-Square            C.V.        Root MSE        SALEPRIC Mean

               0.559520          49.33797      49.90959          101.158571


Source                DF        Anova SS     Mean Square    F Value    Pr > F

NBRHOOD                6       199341.2469    33223.5411      13.34     0.0001


               Bonferroni (Dunn) T tests for variable: SALEPRIC

   NOTE: This test controls the type I experimentwise error rate, but
         generally has a higher type II error rate than REGWQ.

               Alpha= 0.02   df= 63   MSE= 2490.967
                    Critical Value of T= 3.47
               Minimum Significant Difference= 77.394

   Means with the same letter are not significantly different.

           Bon Grouping           Mean     N   NBRHOOD

                      A          205.45    10   A
                      A
                 B    A          137.10    10   B
                 B
                 B    C          107.46    10   C
                 B    C
                 B    C           93.06    10   D
                 B    C
                 B    C           83.08    10   E
                      C
                      C           47.71    10   F
                      C
                      C           34.25    10   G
```

Since B is not directly connected by a bar to neighborhoods F and G, we say that $\mu_B > (\mu_F, \mu_G)$.

NEIGHBORHOOD C The middle bar implies that the mean for neighborhood C is not significantly different from the mean for neighborhood B; the top bar implies that the mean for neighborhood C is also not significantly different from the means for neighborhoods D, E, F, and G. Since no bar directly connects A to C, we have $\mu_C < \mu_A$.

NEIGHBORHOOD D Using the same reasoning as for neighborhood C, we have $\mu_D < \mu_A$.

NEIGHBORHOOD E Using the same reasoning as for neighborhood C, we have $\mu_E < \mu_A$.

NEIGHBORHOOD F   The top bar implies that the mean for neighborhood F is not significantly different from the means for neighborhoods C, D, E, and G. Since no bar directly connects either A or B to F, we have $\mu_F < (\mu_A, \mu_B)$.

NEIGHBORHOOD G   Using the same reasoning as for neighborhood F, we have $\mu_G < (\mu_A, \mu_B)$.

In summary, we conclude that neighborhoods A and B have the largest sale price means; the neighborhood A mean is significantly larger than the means for neighborhoods C, D, E, F, and G; while the neighborhood B mean is significantly larger than the means for neighborhoods F and G. The means for neighborhoods C, D, E, F, and G are the smallest and not significantly different. These inferences are made with an overall Type I error rate of $\alpha = .02$.

TABLE 13.10

Sample Means for the $k = 6$ Treatments of the Factorial Experiment, Example 13.14

MACHINE	MATERIAL		
	B_1	B_2	B_3
A_1	4.33	3.42	3.95
A_2	3.91	3.85	3.48

EXAMPLE 13.14   Refer to the 2×3 factorial experiment of Examples 13.8–13.10. The sample means for the six factor level combinations (treatments) are shown in Table 13.10. Use Bonferroni's method to perform pairwise comparisons of the six treatment means. Use $\alpha = .03$.

Solution   From Examples 13.9–13.10, we have $s = \sqrt{\text{MSE}} = .066$, $\nu = 12$ df for error, and $n_i = n_j = 3$ observations for all treatment pairs (i, j). For $k = 6$ means, the number of pairwise comparisons to be made is

$$g = \frac{k(k - 1)}{2} = \frac{6(5)}{2} = 15$$

Also, $\alpha^* = \alpha/15 = \frac{.03}{15} = .002$. Thus, we need to find the critical value, $t_{\alpha^*/2} = t_{.002/2} = t_{.001}$, for the t distribution based on $\nu = 12$ df. This value, shown in Table 3, Appendix A, is 3.930. Substituting $t_{.001} = 3.930$ into the equation for Bonferroni's critical difference B_{ij}, we have

$$B_{ij} = (t_{.001})s\sqrt{\frac{1}{n_i} + \frac{1}{n_j}} = (3.930)(.066)\sqrt{\frac{1}{3} + \frac{1}{3}} = .212$$

for any treatment pair (i, j). Therefore, population means corresponding to pairs of sample means that differ by more than .212 will be judged to be significantly diffierent. The six treatment means are ranked as follows:

Sample means:	3.42	3.48	3.85	3.91	3.95	4.33
Treatments $(A_i B_j)$:	$(A_1 B_2)$	$(A_2 B_3)$	$(A_2 B_2)$	$(A_2 B_1)$	$(A_1 B_3)$	$(A_1 B_1)$

Using $B_{ij} = .212$ as a yardstick to determine differences between pairs of treatments, we have placed connecting horizontal bars over those means that *do not* significantly differ.

You can see that the treatment corresponding to machine A_1 and material B_1 has a significantly higher mean number of gaskets produced per hour than the other five treatments. The bar over the three means for treatments (A_2B_2), (A_2B_1), and (A_1B_3) indicates that we are unable to detect differences between any pair of these treatments. However, these treatments have significantly larger means than those for treatments (A_1B_2) and (A_2B_3). In summary, the treatment means appear to fall into three groups, as shown here:

<table>
<tr><td></td><td></td><td>**TREATMENTS**</td></tr>
<tr><td>*Group 1:*</td><td>Highest mean number produced per hour</td><td>A_1B_1</td></tr>
<tr><td>*Group 2:*</td><td></td><td>A_2B_2, A_2B_1, A_1B_3</td></tr>
<tr><td>*Group 3:*</td><td>Lowest mean number produced per hour</td><td>A_1B_2, A_2B_3</td></tr>
</table>

Bonferroni's method guarantees that all inferences derived from this analysis can be made at an overall confidence level of at least $(1 - \alpha) = (1 - .03) = .97$.

In this section we have presented a multiple comparisons procedure that may be employed in a follow-up analysis to ANOVA. Keep in mind, however, that many other methods of making multiple comparisons are available, and one or more of these techniques may be more appropriate to use in your particular application. Consult the references given at the end of this chapter for details on other techniques.

In general, multiple comparisons of treatment means should be performed only as a follow-up analysis to the ANOVA, that is, only after we have conducted the appropriate analysis of variance F test(s) and determined that sufficient evidence exists of differences among the treatment means. Be wary of conducting multiple comparisons when the ANOVA F test indicates no evidence of a difference among a small number of treatment means—this may lead to confusing and contradictory results.*

WARNING

In practice, it is advisable to avoid conducting multiple comparisons of a small number of treatment means when the corresponding ANOVA F test is nonsignificant; otherwise, confusing and contradictory results may occur.

PROBLEMS

13.19 Videocassette recorders (VCRs) are currently being used in over half of American households, and the percentage is expected to reach 85% by 1995. Are all VCR users alike, or can they be segmented into subgroups with different motives and behaviors? This question was the topic of research reported in the *Journal of Advertising Research* (Apr./May 1988). A sample of 371 members of a large videotape rental club in a southeastern city were surveyed about their VCR use. Based on their responses, each member was categorized into one of five groups:

---

*When a large number of treatments are to be compared, a borderline, nonsignificant F value (eg, $.05 < p$-value $< .10$) may mask differences between some of the means. In this situation, it is better to ignore the F test and proceed directly to a multiple comparisons procedure.

GROUP		NUMBER IN SAMPLE
(1) *Videophile:*	Record TV programs often, and rent/buy videotapes often	61
(2) *Time shifter:*	Record TV programs often, rarely rent/buy videotapes	74
(3) *Source shifter:*	Rarely record TV programs, rent/buy videotapes often	50
(4) *Low user:*	Rarely record TV programs or rent/buy videotapes	58
(5) *Regular user:*	Periodically record TV programs and/or rent/buy videotapes	128
		Total 371

One of the dependent variables measured was degree to which the user "zipped" (ie, fast-forwarded) through commercials while replaying a taped TV program. This "ad avoidance" variable was measured on a 7 point scale, where 1 = almost always and 7 = never.

a. The F value for testing the hypothesis H_0: $\mu_1 = \mu_2 = \mu_3 = \mu_4 = \mu_5$ is $F = 5.4$. Interpret this value (use $\alpha = .05$).

b. The mean ad avoidance levels of the five groups are listed below, as well as the results of a multiple comparisons analysis (at $\alpha = .05$). Interpret the results.

Mean ad avoidance:	1.8	2.6	2.8	2.9	3.4
VCR user segment:	Time shifter	Videophile	Regular user	Low user	Source shifter

13.20 Refer to the video display terminals study of Problem 13.9 (p. 709). Use Bonferroni's method to rank the mean preference scores for the seven video display color combinations. Use $\alpha = .10$.

13.21 Refer to Problem 10.26 (p. 495) and the *Human Factors* (Apr. 1990) study of recognizer accuracy at three levels (90%, 95%, and 99%) and vocabulary size at three levels (75%, 87.5%, and 100%) on the performance of a computerized speech recognizer. The data on task completion times (minutes) were subjected to an analysis of variance for a 3×3 factorial design. The F test for accuracy–vocabulary interaction resulted in a p-value less than .003.

a. Interpret the result of the test for interaction.

b. As a follow-up to the test for interaction, the mean task completion times for the three levels of accuracy were compared under each level of vocabulary. Comment on this method of analysis.

c. Refer to part **b.** Bonferroni's multiple comparison method was used to compare the three accuracy means within each level of vocabulary at an overall error rate of $\alpha = .05$. The results are summarized in the table. Interpret these results.

Mean Task Completion Time

VOCABULARY SIZE	ACCURACY LEVEL		
	99%	95%	90%
75%	15.49	19.29	22.19
87.5%	12.77	14.31	16.48
100%	8.67	9.68	11.88

Source: Casali, S. P., Williges, B. H., and Dryden, R. D. "Effects of Recognition Accuracy and Vocabulary Size of a Speech Recognition System on Task Performance and User Acceptance." *Human Factors*, Vol. 32, No. 2, Apr. 1990, p. 190 (Fig. 2).

13.22 In business, the prevailing theory is that companies can be categorized into one of four types based on their strategic profile: reactors (marginal competitors, unstable, victims of industry forces); defenders (specialize in established products, lower costs while maintaining quality); prospectors (develop new/improved products); and analyzers (operate in two product areas—one stable, one dynamic). The *American Business Review* (Jan. 1990) reported on a study that proposes a fifth organization type, balancers, who operate in three product spheres—one stable and two dynamic. Each firm in a sample of 78 glassware firms was categorized into one of these five types and the level of performance (process research and development ratio) of each was measured.

a. A completely randomized design ANOVA of the data resulted in a significant (at $\alpha = .05$) F-value for treatments (organization types). Interpret this result.

b. Multiple comparisons of the five mean performance levels (using a procedure similar to Bonferroni, at $\alpha = .05$) are summarized below. Interpret the results.

Mean:	.138	.235	.820	.826	.911
Type:	Reactor	Prospector	Defender	Analyzer	Balancer

Source: Wright, P., et al. "Business Performance and Conduct of Organization Types: A Study of Select Special-Purpose and Laboratory Glassware Firms." *American Business Review*, Jan. 1990, p. 95 (Table 4).

13.23 Refer to the *Academy of Management Journal* study of Problem 13.18. The sample mean satisfaction ratings of managers for the four combinations of prior information and degree of choice are shown in the table. Use Bonferroni's method to rank the four means. Use $\alpha = .06$.

DEGREE OF CHOICE	PRIOR INFORMATION	
	Realistic Preview	Traditional Announcement
High	6.20	6.06
Low	5.33	4.82

Source: Hicks, W. D., and Klimoski, R. J. "Entry into Training Programs and Its Effects on Training Outcomes: A Field Experiment." *Academy of Management Journal*, Vol. 30, No. 3, Sept. 1987, p. 548.

THE RELATIONSHIP BETWEEN ANOVA AND REGRESSION

13.8 The preceding sections illustrated the analysis of variance approach to analyzing data collected from designed experiments. Although we utilized the computer to conduct the analysis, the ANOVA sum of squares can be computed with the aid of a pocket or desk calculator (see the formulas in Appendix B). By forming a ratio of mean squares, we are able to test the hypothesis that a set of population means (treatment means, block means, or factor main effect means) are equal.

The same analysis also can be conducted using a multiple regression analysis. Each experimental design is associated with a general linear model for the response y, called the **complete model**. The analysis of variance F test for testing a set of means is equivalent to either an overall F test of model utility or a partial F test in which the complete model is fit and compared to a **reduced model**. The proper test will depend on the specific design employed. Consequently, before you can apply regression analysis in an analysis of variance, you need to determine the appropriate complete and reduced models to fit for each type of experimental design.

The regression approach to analyzing data for all three designs covered in this chapter is summarized in the boxes.

ANOVA *F* TEST FOR A COMPLETELY RANDOMIZED DESIGN WITH *k* TREATMENTS: REGRESSION APPROACH

H_0: $\beta_1 = \beta_2 = \cdots = \beta_{k-1} = 0$ (ie, H_0: $\mu_1 = \mu_2 = \cdots = \mu_k$)

H_a: At least one of the β parameters listed in H_0 differs from 0 (ie, H_a: At least two means differ)

Complete model: $E(y) = \beta_0 + \beta_1 x_1 + \beta_2 x_2 + \cdots + \beta_{k-1} x_{k-1}$

where

$$x_1 = \begin{cases} 1 & \text{if treatment 2} \\ 0 & \text{if not} \end{cases}$$

$$x_2 = \begin{cases} 1 & \text{if treatment 3} \\ 0 & \text{if not} \end{cases}$$

$$\vdots$$

$$x_{k-1} = \begin{cases} 1 & \text{if treatment } k \\ 0 & \text{if not} \end{cases} \qquad \text{(Base level = Treatment 1)}$$

Test statistic: $F = \dfrac{[\text{SS(Total)} - \text{SSE}]/(k-1)}{\text{SSE}/(n-k)} = \dfrac{\text{MS(Model)}}{\text{MSE}}$

Rejection region: $F > F_\alpha$, where the distribution of F is based on $\nu_1 = k - 1$ and $\nu_2 = n - k$ degrees of freedom.

Note: The test statistic is the global F-value for a test of overall adequacy of the complete model.

ANOVA *F* TEST FOR A RANDOMIZED BLOCK DESIGN WITH *k* TREATMENTS AND *b* BLOCKS: REGRESSION APPROACH

H_0: $\beta_1 = \beta_2 = \cdots = \beta_{k-1} = 0$ (ie, H_0: The k treatment means are equal)

H_a: At least one of the β parameters listed in H_0 differs from 0 (ie, H_a: At least two treatment means differ)

Complete model: $E(y) = \beta_0 + \overbrace{\beta_1 x_1 + \cdots + \beta_{k-1} x_{k-1}}^{(k-1)\text{ treatment terms}} + \overbrace{\beta_k x_k + \cdots + \beta_{k+b-2} x_{k+b-2}}^{(b-1)\text{ block terms}}$

where

$$x_1 = \begin{cases} 1 & \text{if treatment 2} \\ 0 & \text{if not} \end{cases} \quad \cdots \quad x_{k-1} = \begin{cases} 1 & \text{if treatment } k \\ 0 & \text{if not} \end{cases} \quad \text{(Base level = Treatment 1)}$$

$$x_k = \begin{cases} 1 & \text{if block 2} \\ 0 & \text{if not} \end{cases} \quad \cdots \quad x_{k+b-2} = \begin{cases} 1 & \text{if block } b \\ 0 & \text{if not} \end{cases} \quad \text{(Base level = Block 1)}$$

Reduced model: $E(y) = \beta_0 + \beta_k x_k + \cdots + \beta_{k+b-2} x_{k+b-2}$

(continued)

Test statistic: $F = \dfrac{(SSE_R - SSE_C)/(k-1)}{SSE_C/(n-k-b+1)}$

where

SSE_R = SSE for reduced model

SSE_C = SSE for complete model

Rejection region: $F > F_\alpha$, where F is based on $\nu_1 = (k-1)$ and $\nu_2 = (n-k-b+1)$ degrees of freedom.

ANOVA *F* TEST FOR INTERACTION IN A TWO-FACTOR FACTORIAL EXPERIMENT WITH FACTOR *A* AT *a* LEVELS AND FACTOR *B* AT *b* LEVELS: REGRESSION APPROACH

H_0: $\beta_{a+b-1} = \beta_{a+b} = \cdots = \beta_{ab-1} = 0$ (ie, H_0: No interaction between factors A and B)

H_a: At least one of the β parameters listed in H_0 differs from 0 (ie, H_a: Factors A and B interact)

Complete model:
$$E(y) = \beta_0 + \overbrace{\beta_1 x_1 + \cdots + \beta_{a-1}x_{a-1}}^{\text{Main effect } A \text{ terms}} + \overbrace{\beta_a x_a + \cdots + \beta_{a+b-2}x_{a+b-2}}^{\text{Main effect } B \text{ terms}}$$

$$+ \overbrace{\beta_{a+b-1}x_1 x_a + \beta_{a+b}x_1 x_{a+1} + \cdots + \beta_{ab-1}x_{a-1}x_{a+b-2}}^{AB \text{ interaction terms}}$$

where*

$x_1 = \begin{cases} 1 & \text{if level 2 of factor } A \\ 0 & \text{if not} \end{cases}$ $\cdots$ $x_{a-1} = \begin{cases} 1 & \text{if level } a \text{ of factor } A \\ 0 & \text{if not} \end{cases}$ (Base level of factor A = Level 1)

$x_a = \begin{cases} 1 & \text{if level 2 of factor } B \\ 0 & \text{if not} \end{cases}$ $\cdots$ $x_{a+b-2} = \begin{cases} 1 & \text{if level } b \text{ of factor } B \\ 0 & \text{if not} \end{cases}$ (Base level of factor B = Level 1)

Reduced model:
$$E(y) = \beta_0 + \overbrace{\beta_1 x_1 + \cdots + \beta_{a-1}x_{a-1}}^{\text{Main effect } A \text{ terms}} + \overbrace{\beta_a x_a + \cdots + \beta_{a+b-2}x_{a+b-2}}^{\text{Main effect } B \text{ terms}}$$

Test statistic: $F = \dfrac{(SSE_R - SSE_C)/[(a-1)(b-1)]}{SSE_C/[ab(r-1)]}$

where

SSE_R = SSE for reduced model

SSE_C = SSE for complete model

r = Number of replications

Rejection region: $F > F_\alpha$, where F is based on $\nu_1 = (a-1)(b-1)$ and $\nu_2 = ab(r-1)$ df.

---

* The independent variables $x_1, x_2, ..., x_{a+b-2}$, are defined for an experiment in which both factors represent *qualitative* variables. When a factor is *quantitative*, you may choose to represent the main effects with quantitative terms such as x, x^2, x^3, and so forth.

EXAMPLE 13.15 Refer to Example 13.3 (p. 693), where we compared the mean sale prices of residential properties in seven neighborhoods. The experiment is a completely randomized design with $k = 7$ treatments (the seven neighborhoods). Analyze the data in Table 13.4 using a regression analysis.

Solution According to the first box above, the appropriate complete model for $k = 7$ treatments is

$$E(y) = \beta_0 + \beta_1 x_1 + \beta_2 x_2 + \beta_3 x_3 + \beta_4 x_4 + \beta_5 x_5 + \beta_6 x_6$$

where

$$x_1 = \begin{cases} 1 & \text{if neighborhood A} \\ 0 & \text{if not} \end{cases} \qquad x_4 = \begin{cases} 1 & \text{if neighborhood D} \\ 0 & \text{if not} \end{cases}$$

$$x_2 = \begin{cases} 1 & \text{if neighborhood B} \\ 0 & \text{if not} \end{cases} \qquad x_5 = \begin{cases} 1 & \text{if neighborhood E} \\ 0 & \text{if not} \end{cases}$$

$$x_3 = \begin{cases} 1 & \text{if neighborhood C} \\ 0 & \text{if not} \end{cases} \qquad x_6 = \begin{cases} 1 & \text{if neighborhood F} \\ 0 & \text{if not} \end{cases}$$

The MINITAB regression analysis for the complete model is shown in Figure 13.16. Note that the SSE shown in the printout, 156,931, agrees (except for rounding) with the value of SSE calculated in Example 13.3.

FIGURE 13.16

MINITAB Regression Printout for the Completely Randomized Design, Example 13.15

```
The regression equation is
Price = 34.3 + 171 x1 + 103 x2 + 73.2 x3 + 58.8 x4 + 48.8 x5 + 13.5 x6

Predictor        Coef        Stdev      t-ratio          p
Constant        34.25        15.78         2.17      0.034
x1             171.20        22.32         7.67      0.000
x2             102.85        22.32         4.61      0.000
x3              73.21        22.32         3.28      0.002
x4              58.81        22.32         2.63      0.011
x5              48.83        22.32         2.19      0.032
x6              13.46        22.32         0.60      0.549

s = 49.91       R-sq = 56.0%      R-sq(adj) = 51.8%

Analysis of Variance

SOURCE          DF          SS           MS          F          p
Regression       6      199341        33224      13.34      0.000
Error           63      156931         2491
Total           69      356272
```

The null hypothesis that the seven population means are equal, that is,

$$H_0: \quad \mu_A = \mu_B = \mu_C = \mu_D = \mu_E = \mu_F = \mu_G$$

is equivalent to the null hypothesis

$$H_0: \quad \beta_1 = \beta_2 = \beta_3 = \beta_4 = \beta_5 = \beta_6 = 0$$

[This is because (according to the 0–1 system of coding) $\beta_1 = \mu_A - \mu_G$, $\beta_2 = \mu_B - \mu_G$, ..., $\beta_6 = \mu_F - \mu_G$. Thus, when β_1, β_2, ..., β_6 are 0, all treatment mean differences equal 0.] According to the box, the test statistic for a completely randomized design is the global F-value for the complete model. This value, shaded in the MINITAB printout in Figure 13.16, is $F = 13.34$. This value is identical to the analysis of variance F statistic computed in Example 13.3. The observed significance level of the test, also shaded, is $p \approx 0$. Since the p-value is less than $\alpha = .05$, there is sufficient evidence to indicate that the means for the seven neighborhoods differ.

EXAMPLE 13.16 Refer to the machine–material 2×3 factorial experiment of Examples 13.8–13.10 (pp. 713–719).

a. Write the complete model for the experiment.
b. What hypothesis would you test to determine whether machine and material interact?

Solution

a. Since both factors are qualitative, we need to set up dummy variables as follows:

$$x_1 = \begin{cases} 1 & \text{if machine } A_2 \\ 0 & \text{if machine } A_1 \end{cases} \qquad x_2 = \begin{cases} 1 & \text{if material } B_2 \\ 0 & \text{if not} \end{cases} \qquad x_3 = \begin{cases} 1 & \text{if material } B_3 \\ 0 & \text{if not} \end{cases}$$

Then, according to the third box above, the complete factorial model is

$$E(y) = \beta_0 + \beta_1 x_1 + \beta_2 x_2 + \beta_3 x_3 + \beta_4 x_1 x_2 + \beta_5 x_1 x_3$$

where y = number of gaskets produced. Note that the interaction terms for the model are constructed by taking the products of the various main effect dummy variables, one from each factor.

b. To test the null hypothesis that machine and material do not interact, we must test the null hypothesis that the interaction terms are not needed in the complete model of part **a**, that is,

$$H_0: \quad \beta_4 = \beta_5 = 0$$

This requires that we fit the reduced model,

$$E(y) = \beta_0 + \beta_1 x_1 + \beta_2 x_2 + \beta_3 x_3$$

and perform the partial F test outlined in Section 11.5. The test statistic is

$$F = \frac{(SSE_R - SSE_C)/2}{MSE_C}$$

where

$$SSE_R = \text{SSE for reduced model}$$
$$SSE_C = \text{SSE for complete model}$$
$$MSE_C = \text{MSE for complete model}$$

PROBLEMS

13.24 Refer to Problem 13.2 (p. 697).

    a. Give the complete and reduced models for conducting the ANOVA.
    b. If you have access to a statistical software package, fit the models specified in part **a** and compute the value of the F statistic. The value you obtain should agree with the value calculated in Problem 13.2.

13.25 Refer to Problem 13.3 (p. 698).

    a. Give the complete and reduced models for conducting the ANOVA.
    b. If you have access to a statistical software package, fit the models specified in part **a** and compute the value of the F statistic. The value you obtain should agree with the value calculated in Problem 13.3.

13.26 Refer to Problem 13.7 (p. 707).

    a. Give the complete and reduced models for conducting the ANOVA.
    b. If you have access to a statistical software package, fit the models specified in part **a** and compute the value of the F statistic. The value you obtain should agree with the value calculated in Problem 13.7.

13.27 Refer to Problem 13.12 (p. 711).

    a. Give the complete and reduced models for conducting the ANOVA.
    b. If you have access to a statistical software package, fit the models specified in part **a** and compute the value of the F statistic. The value you obtain should agree with the value calculated in Problem 13.12.

13.28 Refer to Problem 13.15 (p. 721).

    a. Give the complete and reduced models for conducting the ANOVA.
    b. If you have access to a statistical software package, fit the models specified in part **a** and compute the value of the F statistic. The value you obtain should agree with the value calculated in Problem 13.15.

CHECKING ANOVA ASSUMPTIONS

13.9 For each of the experiments and designs discussed in this chapter, we listed in the relevant boxes the assumptions underlying the analysis in the terminology of ANOVA. For example, the assumptions for a completely randomized design are (1) the k probability distributions of the response y corresponding to the k treatments are normal and (2) the population variances of the k treatments are equal. Similarly, for randomized block designs and factorial designs, the data for the treatments must come from normal probability distributions with equal variances.

These assumptions are equivalent to those required for a regression analysis (see Section 10.3). The reason, of course, is that the probabilistic model for the response y that underlies each design is the familiar general linear regression model of Chapters 10 and 11. Consequently, checks on the ANOVA assumptions can be performed by examining the regression residuals. A brief overview of these techniques follows.

DETECTING NONNORMAL POPULATIONS

1. For each treatment, construct a histogram or stem-and-leaf display of the residuals. Look for highly skewed distributions. (Remember, ANOVA, like regression, is robust with respect to the normality assumption. That is, slight departures from normality will have little impact on the validity of the inferences derived from the analysis.) [*Note:* If the sample size for each treatment is small, then these graphs will probably be of limited use.]

2. Formal statistical tests of normality (such as the *Shapiro–Wilk test*) are also available. The null hypothesis is that the probability distribution of the response is normal. These tests, however, are sensitive to slight departures from normality. Since in most scientific applications the normality assumption will not be satisfied exactly, these tests will likely result in a rejection of the null hypothesis and, consequently, are of limited use in practice. Consult the references for more information on these formal tests.

3. If the distribution of the residuals departs greatly from normality, a *normalizing transformation* may be necessary. For example, for highly skewed distributions, transformations on the response *y* such as log *y* or $\sqrt{y}$ tend to normalize the data, since these functions "pull" the observations in the tail of the distribution back toward the mean.

DETECTING UNEQUAL VARIANCES

1. For each treatment, construct a *residual frequency plot* and look for differences in the spread (variability) of the residuals shown in the plots. Residual frequency plots (ie, dot plots) for the seven neighborhoods (treatments) in the completely randomized design ANOVA of Example 13.3 (p. 693) are shown in the MINITAB printout, Figure 13.17. Due to several outliers, it appears that the variability of the residuals may not be the same for the seven neighborhoods. Consequently, the residual plots cast doubt on the validity of the equal variances assumption.

2. When the sample sizes are small for each treatment, only a few points are plotted

FIGURE 13.17
MINITAB Dot Plots for ANOVA Residuals of Seven Neighborhoods

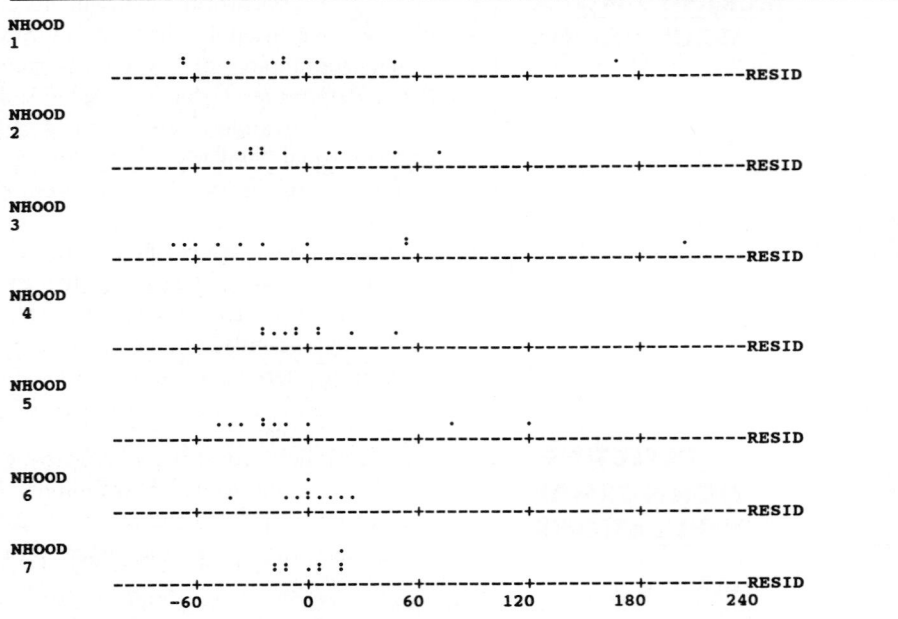

in the residual frequency plots, making it difficult to detect differences in variation. In this situation, you may want to use one of several formal statistical tests of homogeneity of variances that are available. For k treatments, the null hypothesis is H_0: $\sigma_1^2 = \sigma_2^2 = \cdots = \sigma_k^2$, where σ_i^2 is the population variance of the response y corresponding to the ith treatment. If all k populations are approximately normal, **Bartlett's test for homogeneity of variances** can be applied. The elements of the test are shown in the box. Note that the test statistic depends on whether the sample sizes are equal or unequal.

BARTLETT'S TEST OF HOMOGENEITY OF VARIANCE

H_0: $\sigma_1^2 = \sigma_2^2 = \cdots = \sigma_k^2$

H_a: At least two variances differ.

Test statistic (equal sample sizes): $B = \dfrac{(n-1)[k \log \bar{s}^2 - \Sigma \log s_i^2]}{1 + \dfrac{(k+1)}{3k(n-1)}}$

where

$\qquad n = n_1 = n_2 = \cdots = n_k$

$\qquad s_i^2$ = Sample variance for sample i

$\qquad \bar{s}^2$ = Average of the k sample variances = $(\Sigma s_i^2)/k$

$\quad \log x$ = Natural logarithm (ie, log to the base e) of the quantity x

Test statistic (unequal sample sizes):

$\qquad B = \dfrac{[\Sigma(n_i - 1)]\log \bar{s}^2 - \Sigma(n_i - 1)\log s_i^2}{1 + \dfrac{1}{3(k-1)}\left[\Sigma \dfrac{1}{(n_i - 1)} - \dfrac{1}{\Sigma(n_i - 1)}\right]}$

where

$\qquad n_i$ = Sample size for sample i

$\qquad s_i^2$ = Sample variance for sample i

$\qquad \bar{s}^2$ = Weighted average of the k sample variances = $\dfrac{\Sigma(n_i - 1)s_i^2}{\Sigma(n_i - 1)}$

$\quad \log x$ = Natural logarithm (ie, log to the base e) of the quantity x

Rejection region: $B > \chi_\alpha^2$, where χ_α^2 locates an area α in the upper tail of a χ^2 distribution with $(k-1)$ degrees of freedom.

Assumptions:

1. Independent random samples are selected from the k populations.

2. All k populations are normally distributed.

We apply Bartlett's test to the ANOVA of Example 13.3. The null hypothesis is

$$H_0: \quad \sigma_1^2 = \sigma_2^2 = \sigma_3^2 = \sigma_4^2 = \sigma_5^2 = \sigma_6^2 = \sigma_7^2$$

where $\sigma_1^2, \sigma_2^2, ..., \sigma_7^2$ are the true variances in sale prices for the seven neighborhoods. Since the sample sizes are the same ($n_1 = n_2 = \cdots = n_7 = 10$), the formula for the test statistic is

$$B = \frac{(n-1)[k \log \bar{s}^2 - \Sigma \log s_i^2]}{1 + \dfrac{k+1}{3k(n-1)}}$$

To obtain B, we first compute the sample variances, $s_1^2, s_2^2, ..., s_7^2$, and their average, $\bar{s}^2$. These sample variances are shaded in the MINITAB printout shown in Figure 13.18. From these values, we obtain

$$\bar{s}^2 = \frac{\sum_{i=1}^{7} s_i^2}{7} = \frac{(68.9)^2 + (36.3)^2 + (84.9)^2 + (22.6)^2 + (55.1)^2 + (18.5)^2 + (16.2)^2}{7}$$
$$= 2{,}489.2$$

Substituting these values into the formula, we obtain

$$B = \frac{(10-1)\{7 \log(2{,}489.2) - [\log(68.9^2) + \log(36.3^2) + \cdots + \log(16.2^2)]\}}{1 + \dfrac{7+1}{3(7)(10-1)}}$$

$$= \frac{9\{54.7 - 50.2\}}{1.042} = 39.25$$

FIGURE 13.18

MINITAB Descriptive Statistics for Residuals of Example 13.3

	NHOOD	N	MEAN	MEDIAN	TRMEAN	STDEV	SEMEAN
RESID	1	10	0.0	-13.9	-12.8	68.9	21.8
	2	10	0.0	-15.8	-4.5	36.3	11.5
	3	10	0.0	-31.0	-16.5	84.9	26.9
	4	10	0.00	-5.06	-2.82	22.55	7.13
	5	10	-0.0	-19.1	-9.5	55.1	17.4
	6	10	0.00	-0.31	1.75	18.54	5.86
	7	10	0.00	1.35	0.03	16.22	5.13

From Table 6, Appendix A, $\chi_{.05}^2 = 12.5916$ (based on $k-1 = 6$ degrees of freedom). Thus, the rejection region for the test is $B > 12.5916$. Since the test statistic, $B = 39.25$, exceeds the critical χ^2 value, we reject the null hypothesis of equal variances; there is sufficient evidence (at $\alpha = .05$) of differences among the variances in sale prices for the seven neighborhoods.

Bartlett's test works well when the data come from normal (or near normal) distributions. The results, however, can be misleading for nonnormal data. In this case, we can apply a test that is much less sensitive to nonnormality in the data. **Levene's test of homogeneity of variance** utilizes residuals calculated as absolute deviations, $|y_i - M|$, where M is the sample (treatment) median. The test is described in the box.

LEVENE'S TEST OF HOMOGENEITY OF VARIANCE

H_0: $\sigma_1^2 = \sigma_2^2 = \cdots = \sigma_k^2$

H_a: At least two variances differ.

1. For each sample measurement, calculate the absolute deviation

$$a_{ij} = |y_{ij} - M_j|$$

where y_{ij} is the ith response in treatment j and M_j is the median for treatment j ($j = 1, 2, ..., k$).

2. Perform an analysis of variance on the a_{ij}'s for a completely randomized design with k treatments (samples). Obtain the MST and MSE from the ANOVA.

Test statistic: $F = \dfrac{\text{MST}}{\text{MSE}}$

Rejection region: $F > F_\alpha$

where F_α locates an area α in the upper tail of an F distribution with $(k - 1)$ numerator degrees of freedom and $(n - k)$ denominator degrees of freedom. [*Note:* $n = n_1 + n_2 + \cdots + n_k$.]

Assumption: Independent random samples are collected from the k populations.

---

3. When unequal variances are detected, use one of the **variance-stabilizing transformations** of the response y discussed in Section 11.6.

In most business applications, the assumptions will not be satisfied exactly. These analysis of variance procedures are flexible, however, in the sense that slight departures from the assumptions will not significantly affect the analysis or the validity of the resulting inferences. On the other hand, gross violations of the assumptions (eg, a nonconstant variance) will cast doubt on the validity of the inferences. Therefore, you should make it standard practice to conduct an analysis of the residuals from the ANOVA to verify that the assumptions are (approximately) satisfied.

CHECKING ANOVA ASSUMPTIONS

DETECTING NONNORMAL POPULATIONS

1. For each treatment, construct a histogram or stem-and-leaf display of the residuals. Look for highly skewed distributions. (Remember, ANOVA, like regression, is robust with respect to the normality assumption. That is, slight departures from normality will have little impact on the validity of the inferences derived from the analysis.) [*Note:* If the sample size for each treatment is small, then these graphs will probably be of limited use.]

2. Formal statistical tests of normality are also available. The null hypothesis is that the probability distribution of the response is normal. These tests, however, are sensitive to slight departures from normality. Since in most scientific applications the normality assumption will not be satisfied exactly, these tests will likely result in a rejection of the null hypothesis and, consequently, are of limited use in practice. Consult the references for more information on these formal tests.

3. If the distribution of the residuals departs greatly from normality, a *normalizing transformation* may be necessary. For example, for highly skewed distributions, transformations on the response y such as $\log y$ or $\sqrt{y}$ tend to normalize the data since these functions "pull" the observations in the tail of the distribution back toward the mean.

DETECTING UNEQUAL VARIANCES

1. For each treatment, construct a **residual frequency (dot) plot** and look for differences in the spread (variability) of the residuals shown in the plots.

2. When the sample sizes are small for each treatment, only a few points are plotted in the residual frequency plots, making it difficult to detect differences in variation. In this situation, you may want to use one of several formal statistical tests of homogeneity of variances that are available. *Bartlett's test* is appropriate for normal data and *Levene's test* for nonnormal data.

3. When unequal variances are detected, use one of the *variance-stabilizing transformations* of the response y discussed in Section 11.6.

PROBLEMS

[*Note:* These exercises require the use of a computer to calculate and plot residuals.]

13.29 Check the assumptions for the completely randomized design ANOVA of Problem 13.3 (p. 698).

13.30 Check the assumptions for the completely randomized design ANOVA of Problem 13.6 (p. 700).

13.31 Check the assumptions for the randomized block design ANOVA of Problem 13.9 (p. 709). [*Hint:* For each block (subject), calculate and plot differences between all possible pairs of treatment residuals.]

13.32 Check the assumptions for the factorial design ANOVA of Problem 13.15 (p. 721).

13.10

In Chapter 6 we demonstrated how to select the sample size for estimating a single population mean or comparing two population means. We now show you how this problem can be solved for designed experiments.

As mentioned in Section 13.2, a measure of the quantity of information in an experiment that is pertinent to a particular population parameter is the standard error of the estimator of the parameter. A more practical measure is the half-width of the parameter's confidence interval, which will, of course, be a function of the standard error. For example, the half-width of a confidence interval for a population mean (as given in Section 6.4) is

$$(t_{\alpha/2})s_{\bar{y}} = (t_{\alpha/2})\left(\frac{s}{\sqrt{n}}\right)$$

Similarly, the half-width of a confidence interval for the slope β_1 of a straight-line model relating y to x (as given in Section 10.3) is

$$(t_{\alpha/2})s_{\hat{\beta}_1} = (t_{\alpha/2})\left(\frac{s}{\sqrt{SS_{xx}}}\right) = (t_{\alpha/2})\sqrt{\frac{SSE}{n-2}\left(\frac{1}{\sqrt{SS_{xx}}}\right)}$$

In both cases, the half-width is a function of the total number of data points in the experiment. Each interval half-width gets smaller as the total number of data points n increases. The same is true for a confidence interval for a parameter β_i of a general linear model, for a confidence interval for $E(y)$, and for a prediction interval for y. Since each designed experiment can be represented by a linear model, this result can be used to select, approximately, the number of replications (ie, the number of observations measured for each treatment) in the experiment.

For example, consider a designed experiment consisting of three treatments, A, B, and C. Suppose we want to estimate $(\mu_A - \mu_C)$, the difference between the treatment means for A and C. From our knowledge of linear models for designed experiments, we know this difference will be represented by one of the β parameters in the model, say β_2. The confidence interval for β_2 for a single replication of the experiment is

$$\hat{\beta}_2 \pm (t_{\alpha/2})s_{\hat{\beta}_2}$$

If we repeat exactly the same experiment r times (we call this r *replications*), it can be shown (proof omitted) that the confidence interval for β_2 will be

$$\hat{\beta}_2 \pm \underbrace{t_{\alpha/2}\left(\frac{s_{\hat{\beta}_2}}{\sqrt{r}}\right)}_{B}$$

To find r, we first set the half-width of the interval to the largest value, B, we are willing to tolerate. Then we approximate $t_{\alpha/2}$ and $s_{\hat{\beta}_2}$, and solve for the number of replications r.

EXAMPLE 13.17 Consider a 2 × 2 factorial experiment to investigate the effect of two factors on the light output y of flashbulbs used in cameras. The two factors (and their levels) are: x_1 = amount of foil contained in the bulb (100 and 200 milligrams) and x_2 = speed of sealing machine (1.2 and 1.3 revolutions per minute). The complete model for the 2 × 2 factorial experiment is

$$E(y) = \beta_0 + \beta_1 x_1 + \beta_2 x_2 + \beta_3 x_1 x_2$$

How many replicates of the 2 × 2 factorial are required to estimate β_3, the interaction β, to within .3 of its true value using a 95% confidence interval?

Solution To solve for the number of replicates r, we want to solve the equation

$$t_{\alpha/2}\left(\frac{s_{\hat{\beta}_3}}{\sqrt{r}}\right) = B$$

You can see that we need to have an estimate of $s_{\hat{\beta}_3}$, the standard error of $\hat{\beta}_3$ for a single replication. Suppose it is known from a previous experiment conducted by the manufacturer of the flashbulbs that $s_{\hat{\beta}_3} \approx .2$. For a 95% confidence interval, $\alpha = .05$ and $\alpha/2 = .025$. Since we want the half-width of the interval to be $B = .3$, we have

$$t_{.025}\left(\frac{.2}{\sqrt{r}}\right) = .3$$

The degrees of freedom for $t_{.025}$ will depend on the sample size $n = (2 \times 2)r = 4r$; consequently, we must approximate its value. In fact, since the model includes four parameters, the degrees of freedom for t will be df(Error) $= n - 4 = 4r - 4 = 4(r - 1)$. At minimum, we require two replicates; hence, we will have at least $4(2 - 1) = 4$ df. Searching Table 3, Appendix A, we find $t_{.025} = 2.776$ for df = 4. We will use this conservative estimate of t in our calculations.

Substituting $t = 2.776$ into the equation, we have

$$\frac{2.776(.2)}{\sqrt{r}} = .3$$

$$\sqrt{r} = \frac{(2.776)(.2)}{.3} = 1.85$$

$$r = 3.42$$

Since we can run either three or four replications (but not 3.42), we should choose four replications to be reasonably certain that we will be able to estimate the interaction parameter β_3 to within .3 of its true value. The 2 × 2 factorial with four replicates would be laid out as shown in Table 13.11.

TABLE 13.11

2 × 2 Factorial with Four Replicates

MACHINE SPEED, x_2	AMOUNT OF FOIL, x_1	
	100	200
1.2	4 observations on y	4 observations on y
1.3	4 observations on y	4 observations on y

13.11

All the basic designs presented in this chapter involve randomization of some sort. In a completely randomized design and a basic factorial experiment, the treatments are randomly assigned to the experimental units. In a randomized block design, the blocks are randomly selected and the treatments within each block are assigned in random order. Why randomize? The answer is related to the assumptions we make about the random error ϵ in the linear model. Recall (Section 10.3), that we assume that ϵ possesses a normal distribution with mean 0 and constant variance σ^2 for fixed settings of the independent variables (ie, for each of the treatments). Further, we assume that the random errors associated with repeated observations are independent of each other in a probabilistic sense.

The experimenter rarely knows all the important variables in a process and does not know the true functional form of the model. Hence, the functional form chosen to fit the true relation is only an approximation, and the variables included in the experiment form only a subset of the total. The random error, ϵ, is thus a composite error caused by the failure to include all the important factors as well as the error in approximating the function.

Although many unmeasured and important independent variables affecting the response y do not vary in a completely random manner during the conduct of a designed experiment, we hope their behavior is such that their cumulative effect varies in a random manner and satisfies the assumptions upon which our inferential procedures are based.

> The randomization in a designed experiment has the effect of randomly assigning these error effects to the treatments and assists in satisfying the assumptions on ϵ.

COMPUTER LAB

ANALYSIS OF VARIANCE

All three statistical software packages described in this text contain ANOVA routines for designed experiments, ranging from simple completely randomized designs to the more sophisticated factorial experiments. The key to using these packages is identifying the source(s) of variation for the experiment, that is, treatments for completely randomized designs, treatments and blocks for randomized designs, and main effects and factor interaction for factorial designs.

The programs in this section conduct both a parametric and nonparametric (if available) analysis of variance for the data in Table 13.4 (completely randomized design), Table 13.5 (randomized block design), and Table 13.7 (factorial design). [*Note:* Except for SAS variables, the data for all factors (eg, independent variables) must be input as *quantitative* levels.]

```
Command
  Line
    1     DATA TAB13_4;
    2     INPUT NHOOD $ SALEPRIC @@;     Data entry instructions
    3     CARDS;
          A 191.5   A 208.5   A 255.0   A 375.0   A 205.0
          .    .    .    .    .    .    .    .    .    .       Input data values
          .    .    .    .    .    .    .    .    .    .       (5 observations per line)
          .    .    .    .    .    .    .    .    .    .
          G  54.0   G  21.5   G  55.0   G  43.0   G  13.3
    4     PROC ANOVA;
    5     CLASSES NHOOD;               Parametric ANOVA: Completely randomized design
    6     MODEL SALEPRIC=NHOOD;
    7     MEANS NHOOD/BON;   Bonferroni multiple comparisons
    8     PROC NPAR1WAY WILCOXON;
    9     VAR SALEPRIC;                Nonparametric ANOVA: Completely randomized design
   10     CLASS NHOOD;

   11     DATA TAB13_5;
   12     INPUT ITEM MARKET $ PRICE @@;   Data entry instructions
   13     CARDS;
          1 ALB 1.10   1 KNK 1.18   1 PUB   1.39   1 F4L 1.18
          .    .    .    .    .    .    .    .    .    .       Input data values
          .    .    .    .    .    .    .    .    .    .       (4 observations per line)
          .    .    .    .    .    .    .    .    .    .
          7 ALB  .43   7 KNK  .47   7 PUB    .65   7 F4L  .47
   14     PROC ANOVA;
   15     CLASSES MARKET ITEM;          Parametric ANOVA: Randomized block design
   16     MODEL PRICE=MARKET ITEM;
   17     MEANS MARKET/BON;   Bonferroni multiple comparisons

   18     DATA TAB13_7;
   19     INPUT MACHINE $ MATERIAL $ NUMBER @@;   Data entry instructions
   20     CARDS;
          A1 CORK 4.31   A1 CORK 4.27   A1 CORK 4.40
          .    .    .    .    .    .    .    .    .       Input data values
          .    .    .    .    .    .    .    .    .       (3 observations per line)
          .    .    .    .    .    .    .    .    .
          A2 PLAS 3.48   A2 PLAS 3.53   A2 PLAS 3.42
   21     PROC ANOVA;
   22     CLASSES MACHINE MATERIAL;                        Parametric ANOVA:
   23     MODEL NUMBER=MACHINE MATERIAL MACHINE*MATERIAL;   Factorial design
   24     MEANS MACHINE*MATERIAL/BON;   Bonferroni multiple comparisons
```

COMMANDS 4, 14, 21   The ANOVA procedure is used to conduct a parametric analysis of variance.

COMMANDS 5, 15, 22   The CLASSES statement identifies the sources of variation (in addition to ERROR) for the experiment.

COMMANDS 6, 16, 23   The sources of variation are specified to the right of the equals sign (=) in the MODEL statement, the dependent (response) variable to the left.

COMMANDS 7, 17, 24   The MEANS command produces a multiple comparisons analysis of the means of the specified source. The BON option selects the Bonferroni multiple comparisons procedure.

COMMANDS 8–10   The WILCOXON option of the NPAR1WAY procedure is used to conduct the nonparametric Kruskal–Wallis test for a completely randomized design. (Nonparametric ANOVAs for randomized block designs and factorial designs are not available in SAS.)

NOTE   The output for this SAS program is displayed in Figure 13.19 (p. 751).

SPSS

Command Line		
1	`DATA LIST FREE/NHOOD SALEPRIC.`	Data entry instructions
2	`BEGIN DATA.`	
	`1 191.5   1 208.5   1 255.0   1 375.0   1 205.0` ⎫	
	`.   .   .   .   .   .   .   .   .   .` ⎬ Input data values	
	`.   .   .   .   .   .   .   .   .   .` ⎪ (5 observations per line)	
	`7 54.0   7 21.5   7 55.0   7 43.0   7 13.3` ⎭	
3	`END DATA.`	
4	`ONEWAY VARIABLES=SALEPRIC BY NHOOD(1,7)/` ⎫ Parametric ANOVA:	
5	`     RANGES=TUKEY.` ⎭ Completely randomized design	
6	`NPAR TESTS K-W=SALEPRIC BY NHOOD(1,7).` ⎫ Nonparametric ANOVA: Completely randomized design	
7	`DATA LIST FREE/ITEM MARKET PRICE.`	Data entry instructions
8	`BEGIN DATA.`	
	`1 1 1.10   1 2 1.18   1 3 1.39   1 4 1.18` ⎫	
	`.   .   .   .   .   .   .   .   .   .   .   .` ⎬ Input data values	
	`.   .   .   .   .   .   .   .   .   .   .   .` ⎪ (4 observations per line)	
	`7 1 .43   7 2 .47   7 3 .65   7 4 .47` ⎭	
9	`END DATA.`	
10	`ANOVA VARIABLES=PRICE BY MARKET(1,4) ITEM(1,7)/` ⎫ Parametric ANOVA:	
11	`     OPTIONS=3/` ⎬ Randomized block design	
12	`     STATISTICS=3.` ⎭	

(continued)

```
13      DATA LIST FREE/ITEM ALB KNK PUB F4L.        Data entry instructions
14      BEGIN DATA.
        1   1.10   1.18   1.39   1.18 ⎤
        .     .      .      .      .   ⎥      Input data values
        .     .      .      .      .   ⎬      (4 observations per line)
        .     .      .      .      .   ⎥
        7    .43    .47    .65    .47 ⎦
15      END DATA.
16      NPAR TESTS FRIEDMAN=ALB KNK PUB F4L. ⎤  Nonparametric ANOVA:
                                             ⎦  Randomized block design
```

```
17      DATA LIST FREE/MACHINE MATERIAL NUMBER.    Data entry instructions
18      BEGIN DATA
        1 1 4.31   1 1 4.27   1 1 4.40 ⎤
        . . .      . . .      . . .    ⎥     Input data values
        . . .      . . .      . . .    ⎬     (3 observations per line)
        . . .      . . .      . . .    ⎥
        2 3 3.48   2 3 3.53   2 3 3.42 ⎦
19      END DATA.

20      ANOVA VARIABLES=NUMBER BY MACHINE(1,2) MATERIAL(1,3)/ ⎤  Parametric ANOVA:
21            STATISTICS=3.                                   ⎦  Factorial design
```

COMMAND 4   The ONEWAY command conducts a parametric one-way ANOVA. The dependent variable is specified to the left of the key word BY and the treatments to the right. The numeric values (ie, levels) of the treatments are given in parentheses following the treatment variable.

COMMAND 5   The subcommand RANGES=TUKEY produces a multiple comparisons of the treatment means using $\alpha = .05$. (The Tukey procedure is similar to the Bonferroni method described in this chapter.)

COMMAND 6   The NPAR TESTS command with the K-W subcommand conducts a nonparametric Kruskal–Wallis H test for a completely randomized design.

COMMANDS 10, 20   The ANOVA command is used to carry out a parametric analysis of variance for any type of design, including randomized block designs and factorial designs. The dependent variable is listed to the left of the key word BY and the sources of variation (factors, treatments, etc.) to the right. The range of the coded values of the sources must be specified in parentheses after each source. By default, interactions are automatically included in the ANOVA.

COMMAND 11   To remove interactions from the ANOVA, specify OPTIONS=3.

COMMAND 12   The STATISTICS=3 subcommand generates a table of means for each treatment. This information can be used to perform a multiple comparisons test of means. (In general, multiple comparisons tests such as Bonferroni are not available in the SPSS ANOVA procedure.)

COMMAND 16   The NPAR TESTS command with subcommand FRIEDMAN conducts a Friedman F_r test for a randomized block design. The data are entered so that each row represents a block and each column represents a treatment. The treatment variables are specified after the equals sign in the FRIEDMAN subcommand.

NOTE   The output for this SPSS program is displayed in Figure 13.20 (p. 753).

MINITAB

Command Line		
1	`READ TAB13 4 IN C1 C2` Data entry instruction	

```
1 191.5 ⎫
1 208.5 ⎪
  .    .  ⎬  Input data values
  .    .  ⎪  (1 observation per line)
  .    .  ⎪
7  13.3 ⎭
```

2	`NAME C1='NHOOD' C2='SALEPRIC'` ⎫	
3	`ANOVA C2=C1;`	Parametric ANOVA: Completely randomized design
4	`MEANS C1.` ⎭	
5	`KRUSKAL-WALLIS C2 C1` Nonparametric ANOVA: Completely randomized design	

| 6 | `READ TAB13_5 IN C1 C2 C3`   Data entry instruction | |

```
1 1 1.10 ⎫
1 2 1.18 ⎪
 .  .  .  ⎬  Input data values
 .  .  .  ⎪  (1 observation per line)
 .  .  .  ⎪
7 4  .47 ⎭
```

7	`ANOVA C3=C2 C1;` ⎫	Parametric ANOVA:
8	`MEANS C2.` ⎭	Randomized block design
9	`FRIEDMAN C3 C2 C1` Nonparametric ANOVA: Randomized block design	

| 10 | `READ TAB13_7 IN C1 C2 C3`   Data entry instruction | |

```
1 1 4.31 ⎫
1 1 4.27 ⎪
 .  .  .  ⎬  Input data values
 .  .  .  ⎪  (1 observation per line)
 .  .  .  ⎪
2 3 3.42 ⎭
```

11	`NAME C1='MACHINE' C2='MATERIAL' C3='NUMBER'`	
12	`ANOVA C3=C1 C2 C1*C2;` ⎫	Parametric ANOVA: Factorial design
13	`MEANS C1*C2.` ⎭	

COMMANDS 3, 7, 12   The ANOVA procedure conducts a parametric analysis of variance. The dependent variable is listed to the left of the equals sign, the sources of variation (factors, treatments, etc.) to the right.

COMMANDS 4, 8, 13   The MEANS subcommand produces a table of means for each source of variation specified in the command. (Multiple comparisons procedures such as Bonferroni are not available in MINITAB.)

COMMAND 5   The KRUSKAL-WALLIS command performs a nonparametric AN-OVA for a completely randomized design. The column containing the dependent variable is listed first, followed by the column containing the levels of the treatments.

COMMAND 9   The FRIEDMAN command performs a nonparametric ANOVA for a randomized block design. The column containing the dependent variable is listed first, followed by the treatment and block columns.

NOTE   The output for this MINITAB program is displayed in Figure 13.21 (p. 755).

FIGURE 13.19

SAS Printout for Computer Lab

Analysis of Variance Procedure

Dependent Variable: SALEPRIC

Source	DF	Sum of Squares	Mean Square	F Value	Pr > F
Model	6	199341.2469	33223.5411	13.34	0.0001
Error	63	156930.9230	2490.9670		
Corrected Total	69	356272.1699			

R-Square	C.V.	Root MSE	SALEPRIC Mean
0.559520	49.33797	49.90959	101.158571

Source	DF	Anova SS	Mean Square	F Value	Pr > F
NHOOD	6	199341.2469	33223.5411	13.34	0.0001

Bonferroni (Dunn) T tests for variable: SALEPRIC

NOTE: This test controls the type I experimentwise error rate, but generally has a higher type II error rate than REGWQ.

Alpha= 0.05   df= 63   MSE= 2490.967
Critical Value of T= 3.17
Minimum Significant Difference= 70.669

Means with the same letter are not significantly different.

Bon Grouping			Mean	N	NHOOD
	A		205.45	10	A
	A				
B	A		137.10	10	B
B					
B	C		107.46	10	C
B	C				
B	C	D	93.06	10	D
B	C	D			
B	C	D	83.08	10	E
	C	D			
	C	D	47.71	10	F
		D			
		D	34.25	10	G

N P A R 1 W A Y   P R O C E D U R E

Wilcoxon Scores (Rank Sums) for Variable SALEPRIC
Classified by Variable NHOOD

NHOOD	N	Sum of Scores	Expected Under H0	Std Dev Under H0	Mean Score
A	10	616.500000	355.0	59.5782277	61.6500000
B	10	515.000000	355.0	59.5782277	51.5000000
C	10	359.500000	355.0	59.5782277	35.9500000
D	10	398.000000	355.0	59.5782277	39.8000000
E	10	308.500000	355.0	59.5782277	30.8500000
F	10	180.000000	355.0	59.5782277	18.0000000
G	10	107.500000	355.0	59.5782277	10.7500000

Average Scores were used for Ties

Kruskal-Wallis Test (Chi-Square Approximation)
CHISQ= 45.856   DF= 6   Prob > CHISQ=   0.0001

(continued)

FIGURE 13.19 (Continued)

Analysis of Variance Procedure

Dependent Variable: PRICE

Source	DF	Sum of Squares	Mean Square	F Value	Pr > F
Model	9	5.56626786	0.61847421	25.11	0.0001
Error	18	0.44334286	0.02463016		
Corrected Total	27	6.00961071			

R-Square	C.V.	Root MSE	PRICE Mean
0.926228	19.69664	0.156940	0.79678571

Source	DF	Anova SS	Mean Square	F Value	Pr > F
MARKET	3	0.33518214	0.11172738	4.54	0.0155
ITEM	6	5.23108571	0.87184762	35.40	0.0001

Bonferroni (Dunn) T tests for variable: PRICE

NOTE: This test controls the type I experimentwise error rate, but generally has a higher type II error rate than REGWQ.

Alpha= 0.05   df= 18   MSE= 0.02463
Critical Value of T= 2.96
Minimum Significant Difference= 0.2485

Means with the same letter are not significantly different.

Bon Grouping		Mean	N	MARKET
	A	0.9757	7	PUB
	A			
B	A	0.7929	7	KNK
B				
B		0.7257	7	F4L
B				
B		0.6929	7	ALB

Analysis of Variance Procedure

Dependent Variable: NUMBER

Source	DF	Sum of Squares	Mean Square	F Value	Pr > F
Model	5	1.68122778	0.33624556	76.52	0.0001
Error	12	0.05273333	0.00439444		
Corrected Total	17	1.73396111			

R-Square	C.V.	Root MSE	NUMBER Mean
0.969588	1.734095	0.066291	3.82277778

Source	DF	Anova SS	Mean Square	F Value	Pr > F
MACHINE	1	0.10125000	0.10125000	23.04	0.0004
MATERIAL	2	0.81194444	0.40597222	92.38	0.0001
MACHINE*MATERIAL	2	0.76803333	0.38401667	87.39	0.0001

Level of MACHINE	Level of MATERIAL	N	------------NUMBER------------ Mean	SD
A1	CORK	3	4.32666667	0.06658328
A1	PLAS	3	3.94666667	0.06027714
A1	RUBB	3	3.42000000	0.06000000
A2	CORK	3	3.91333333	0.09291573
A2	PLAS	3	3.47666667	0.05507571
A2	RUBB	3	3.85333333	0.05507571

FIGURE 13.20
SPSS Printout for Computer Lab

```
- - - - - - - - - - O N E W A Y - - - - - - - - - -
Variable  SALEPRIC
                    By Variable  NHOOD

        Analysis of Variance

                                Sum of        Mean          F      F
        Source          D.F.    Squares       Squares      Ratio  Prob.

Between Groups           6    199341.2469    33223.5411   13.3376  .0000
Within Groups           63    156930.9230     2490.9670
Total                   69    356272.1699
```

Multiple Range Test

Tukey-HSD Procedure
Ranges for the .050 level -

```
        4.31   4.31   4.31   4.31   4.31   4.31
```

The ranges above are table ranges.
The value actually compared with Mean(J)-Mean(I) is..
     35.2914 * Range * Sqrt(1/N(I) + 1/N(J))

(*) Denotes pairs of groups significantly different at the .050 level

```
                        G G G G G G G
                        r r r r r r r
                        p p p p p p p

     Mean      Group    7 6 5 4 3 2 1

   34.2500    Grp 7
   47.7100    Grp 6
   83.0800    Grp 5
   93.0600    Grp 4
  107.4600    Grp 3     *
  137.1000    Grp 2     * *
  205.4500    Grp 1     * * * * * *
```

```
- - - - - Kruskal-Wallis 1-way ANOVA

     SALEPRIC
 by NHOOD

    Mean Rank    Cases

        61.65      10     NHOOD =     1
        51.50      10     NHOOD =     2
        35.95      10     NHOOD =     3
        39.80      10     NHOOD =     4
        30.85      10     NHOOD =     5
        18.00      10     NHOOD =     6
        10.75      10     NHOOD =     7
                   --
                   70     Total


                                            Corrected for Ties
     CASES    Chi-Square  Significance    Chi-Square  Significance
       70       45.8499        .0000        45.8555        .0000
```

(continued)

FIGURE 13.20 (Continued)

* * * A N A L Y S I S O F V A R I A N C E * * *

PRICE
BY MARKET
ITEM

Source of Variation	Sum of Squares	DF	Mean Square	F	Signif of F
Main Effects	5.566	9	.618	25.110	.000
MARKET	.335	3	.112	4.536	.015
ITEM	5.231	6	.872	35.398	.000
Explained	5.566	9	.618	25.110	.000
Residual	.443	18	.025		
Total	6.010	27	.223		

- - - - - Friedman Two-way ANOVA

Mean Rank	Variable
1.14	ALB
2.57	KNK
4.00	PUB
2.29	F4L

Cases	Chi-Square	D.F.	Significance
7	17.4000	3	.0006

* * * A N A L Y S I S O F V A R I A N C E * * *

NUMBER
BY MACHINE
MATERIAL

Source of Variation	Sum of Squares	DF	Mean Square	F	Signif of F
Main Effects	.913	3	.304	69.269	.000
MACHINE	.101	1	.101	23.040	.000
MATERIAL	.812	2	.406	92.383	.000
2-way Interactions	.768	2	.384	87.387	.000
MACHINE MATERIAL	.768	2	.384	87.387	.000
Explained	1.681	5	.336	76.516	.000
Residual	.053	12	.004		
Total	1.734	17	.102		

FIGURE 13.21
MINITAB Printout for Computer Lab

```
Analysis of Variance for Price

Source      DF        SS         MS       F       P
Nhood        6     199341      33224    13.34   0.000
Error       63     156931       2491
Total       69     356272

     MEANS
Nhood   N     Price
  1    10    205.45
  2    10    137.10
  3    10    107.46
  4    10     93.06
  5    10     83.08
  6    10     47.71
  7    10     34.25


LEVEL    NOBS    MEDIAN   AVE. RANK   Z VALUE
  1       10     191.50     61.7        4.39
  2       10     121.25     51.5        2.69
  3       10      76.50     36.0        0.08
  4       10      88.00     39.8        0.72
  5       10      63.95     30.9       -0.78
  6       10      47.40     18.0       -2.94
  7       10      35.60     10.8       -4.15
OVERALL   70                35.5

H = 45.85   d.f. = 6   p = 0.000
H = 45.86   d.f. = 6   p = 0.000 (adj. for ties)
```

```
Analysis of Variance for Price

Source      DF        SS          MS       F       P
Market       3     0.33518     0.11173    4.54    0.015
Item         6     5.23109     0.87185   35.40    0.000
Error       18     0.44334     0.02463
Total       27     6.00961

     MEANS
Market   N      Price
  1      7     0.69286
  2      7     0.79286
  3      7     0.97571
  4      7     0.72571


Friedman test of Price by Market blocked by Item

S = 17.40   d.f. = 3   p = 0.001
S = 18.74   d.f. = 3   p = 0.000 (adjusted for ties)

                 Est.      Sum of
Market   N      Median     RANKS
  1      7      0.6225      8.0
  2      7      0.6575     18.0
  3      7      0.7925     28.0
  4      7      0.6475     16.0

Grand median  =   0.6800
```

(continued)

FIGURE 13.21 (Continued)

```
Analysis of Variance for Number

Source            DF        SS        MS       F      P
Machine            1    0.10125   0.10125   23.04  0.000
Material           2    0.81194   0.40597   92.38  0.000
Machine*Material   2    0.76803   0.38402   87.39  0.000
Error             12    0.05273   0.00439
Total             17    1.73396

        MEANS
Machine Material   N     Number
        1     1    3     4.3267
        1     2    3     3.4200
        1     3    3     3.9467
        2     1    3     3.9133
        2     2    3     3.8533
        2     3    3     3.4767
```

CHAPTER NOTES

- **Experimental design** is a plan (or strategy) for collecting the experimental data.
- **Factors** are the independent variables (quantitative or qualitative) that are related to a response y.
- The values assumed by a factor in an experiment are called **levels**. These levels are set in advance of observing y.
- A **treatment** is a particular combination of the levels of all factors involved in an experiment.
- One of the main objectives of a designed experiment is to compare the means of the treatments. The method used to compare the means is known as **analysis of variance (ANOVA)**.
- A **completely randomized design** involves a single factor in which the treatments (the levels of the factor) are randomly assigned to the experimental units. (Alternatively, independent random samples may be drawn from each of the treatment populations.)
- A **randomized block design** involves two factors; the levels of one factor are called **treatments** and the levels of the other factor are called **blocks**. The treatments are randomly assigned to the experimental units within each block, with one unit assigned per treatment.
- A **factorial design** is a method for selecting the treatments to be included in an experiment. A **complete factorial experiment** is one in which the treatments consist of all factor–level combinations.
- A **single replication** of a factorial experiment is one in which y is observed once for every possible factor–level combination.
- In a factorial experiment, when the difference between the mean levels of factor A depends on the level of factor B, we say that the factors A and B **interact**.
- The **parametric F tests** and **assumptions** for the three designs are summarized in the table.

DESIGN	NULL HYPOTHESIS	F VALUE	ASSUMPTIONS
Completely randomized	Equal treatment means	$\dfrac{\text{MS(Treatments)}}{\text{MSE}}$	Treatment populations are normal with equal variances.
Randomized block	Equal treatment means	$\dfrac{\text{MS(Treatments)}}{\text{MSE}}$	Differences between pairs of treatment observations within a block are normal with equal variances.
	Equal block means	$\dfrac{\text{MS(Blocks)}}{\text{MSE}}$	
Two-factor factorial	No interaction between factors A and B	$\dfrac{\text{MS}(AB)}{\text{MSE}}$	Treatment (factor–level combination) populations are normal with equal variances.
	Equal main effect A means	$\dfrac{\text{MS}(A)}{\text{MSE}}$	
	Equal main effect B means	$\dfrac{\text{MS}(B)}{\text{MSE}}$	

■ **Nonparametric tests** for the three designs are summarized below:

DESIGN	NULL HYPOTHESIS	TEST STATISTIC
Completely randomized	Treatment distributions are identical	Kruskal–Wallis H
Randomized block	Treatment distributions are identical	Friedman F_r
Factorial	Beyond the scope of this text	

■ **Regression models** appropriate for parametric analysis of the three designs are summarized in the table.

DESIGN	COMPLETE MODEL	REDUCED MODEL
Completely randomized (testing treatments)	$E(y) = \beta_0 + \beta_1 x_1 + \cdots + \beta_{k-1} x_{k-1}$ where $x_1, x_2, \ldots, x_{k-1}$ are dummy variables representing the k treatments	$E(y) = \beta_0$
Randomized block (testing treatments)	$E(y) = \beta_0 + \beta_1 x_1 + \cdots + \beta_{k-1} x_{k-1} + \beta_k x_k + \cdots + \beta_{k+b-2} x_{k+b-2}$ where $x_1, x_2, \ldots, x_{k-1}$ are dummy variables for the k treatments, and $x_k, x_{k+1}, \ldots, x_{k+b-2}$ are dummy variables for the b blocks	$E(y) = \beta_0 + \beta_k x_k + \cdots + \beta_{k+b-2} x_{k+b-2}$
Two-factor factorial (testing interaction)	$E(y) = \beta_0 + \beta_1 x_1 + \cdots + \beta_{a-1} x_{a-1} + \beta_a x_a + \cdots + \beta_{a+b-2} x_{a+b-2}$ $\qquad + \beta_{a+b-1} x_1 x_a + \cdots + \beta_{ab-1} x_{a-1} x_{a+b-2}$ where $x_1, \ldots, x_{a-1}$ are dummy variables for a levels of factor A and $x_a, \ldots, x_{a+b-2}$ are dummy variables for b levels of factor B	$E(y) = \beta_0 + \beta_1 x_1 + \cdots + \beta_{a-1} x_{a-1} + \beta_a x_a$ $\qquad + \cdots + \beta_{a+b-2} x_{a+b-2}$

■ The **Bonferroni multiple comparisons** procedure controls α, the probability of at least one Type I error, when comparing all pairs of treatment means.
■ The **Bonferroni critical difference** is

$$B_{ij} = (t_{\alpha*/2})(s) \sqrt{\frac{1}{n_i} + \frac{1}{n_j}}$$

where $\alpha^* = \alpha/g$, $g = k(k + 1)/2$, k = number of treatment means, $s = \sqrt{MSE}$, n_i and n_j are sample sizes associated with the two means, and the distribution of t is based on ν = degrees of freedom for error for the complete model.

- The **residuals** of an ANOVA are calculated as $y - \hat{y}$, where $\hat{y}$ is the predicted response for a particular treatment.

- **Nonnormal treatment populations** can be detected graphically by constructing and analyzing a histogram, stem-and-leaf display, or normal probability plot for the residuals of each treatment. Highly skewed distributions imply that the assumption of normality is likely to be violated.

- As in regression, ANOVA is **robust** with respect to the normality assumption; slight or moderate departures from normality will have little effect on the validity of the inferences derived from the analysis.

- Treatment populations with **unequal variances** can be detected graphically by constructing a **residual frequency plot** for each treatment. Large differences in spread imply that the assumption of equal variances is likely to be violated.

- **Bartlett's test of homogeneity of variance** is a parametric test of H_0: $\sigma_1^2 = \sigma_2^2 = \cdots = \sigma_k^2$, where σ_i^2 is the population variance of treatment i. The test results may be misleading if the treatment populations are nonnormal.

- **Levene's test of homogeneity of variance** is a nonparametric test of H_0: $\sigma_1^2 = \sigma_2^2 = \cdots = \sigma_k^2$. The test, which utilizes the absolute values of the ANOVA residuals, is very robust with respect to nonnormal populations.

- The **randomization** in a designed experiment has the effect of randomly assigning to the treatments the error caused by the failure to include all important factors. This assists in the complete ANOVA model satisfying the assumptions of the random error term, ϵ.

CASE STUDY

RELUCTANCE TO TRANSMIT BAD NEWS: THE MUM EFFECT

In a 1970 experiment, psychologists S. Rosen and A. Tesser found that people were reluctant to transmit bad news to peers in a nonprofessional setting. Rosen and Tesser termed this phenomenon the "MUM effect."* Since that time, numerous studies have investigated the impact of the MUM effect in a professional setting, for example, on doctor–patient relationships, organizational functioning, and group psychotherapy. The consensus: The reluctance to transmit bad news continues to be a major professional concern.

Why do people keep mum when given an opportunity to transmit bad news to others? Two theories have emerged from this research. The first maintains that the MUM effect is an *aversion to private discomfort*. To avoid discomforts such as empathy

---

* Rosen, S., and Tesser, A. "On Reluctance to Communicate Undesirable Information: The MUM Effect." *Journal of Communication*, Vol. 22, 1970, pp. 124–141.

with the victim's distress or guilt feelings for their own good fortune, would-be communicators of bad news keep mum. The second theory is that the MUM effect is a *public display*. People experience little or no discomfort when transmitting bad news, but keep mum to avoid an unfavorable impression or to pay homage to a social norm.

The subject of this case study is an article by C. F. Bond and E. L. Anderson (*Journal of Experimental Social Psychology*, Vol. 23, 1987). Bond and Anderson conducted a controlled experiment to determine which of the two explanations for the MUM effect is more plausible. "If the MUM effect is an aversion to private discomfort," they state, "subjects should show the effect whether or not they are visible [to the victim]. If the effect is a public display, it should be stronger if the subject is visible than if the subject cannot be seen."

Forty undergraduates (25 males and 15 females) at Duke University participated in the experiment to fulfill an introductory psychology course requirement. Each subject was asked to administer an IQ test to another student and then provide the test taker with his or her percentile score. Unknown to the subject, the test taker was a confederate student working with the researchers.

The experiment manipulated two factors, *subject visibility* and *confederate success*, each at two levels. Subject visibility was manipulated by written instructions that told some subjects that they were *visible* to the test taker through a glass plate and the others that they were *not visible* through a one-way mirror. Confederate success was manipulated by supplying the subject with one of two bogus answer keys. With one answer key, the confederate would always seem to succeed at the test, placing him or her in the top 20% of all Duke undergraduates; when the other answer key was used, the confederate would always seem to fail, ranking in the bottom 20%.

Ten subjects were randomly assigned to each of the $2 \times 2 = 4$ experimental conditions; thus, a 2×2 factorial design with 10 replications was employed. The design is outlined in Table 13.12.

One of several behavioral variables that were measured during the experiment was *latency to feedback*, defined as time (in seconds) between the end of the test and delivery of feedback (ie, the percentile score) from the subject to the test taker. This case focuses on an analysis of variance of the dependent variable, latency to feedback. Presumably, the longer it takes the subject to deliver the score, the greater the MUM effect. With this analysis, the researchers hope to determine whether either one of the two factors, subject visibility or confederate success, have an impact on the MUM effect, and, if so, whether the factors are independent.

a. Write the complete model for this 2×2 factorial experiment.
b. Write the reduced model appropriate for testing whether the two factors interact. Specify the null hypothesis of the test in terms of the β parameters in the model.

Although the raw data for the experiment were not provided in the journal article, a summary of the results was given in the form of an ANOVA table, as shown in Table 13.13 (p. 760).

c. Interpret the ANOVA results.
d. The sample means (in seconds) for each of the four experimental conditions

TABLE 13.12
2 × 2 Factorial Design

SUBJECT VISIBILITY	CONFEDERATE SUCCESS	
	Success	Failure
Visible	Subject 1 2 ⋮ 10	Subject 21 22 ⋮ 30
Not Visible	Subject 11 12 ⋮ 20	Subject 31 32 ⋮ 40

TABLE 13.13
ANOVA Table for the 2 × 2 Factorial Experiment

SOURCE	df	SS	MS	F
Subject visibility	1	1,380.24	1,380.24	4.26
Confederate success	1	1,325.16	1,325.16	4.09
Visibility × Success	1	3,385.80	3,385.80	10.45
Error	36	11,664.00	324.00	
Totals	39	17,755.20		

are provided below. Conduct an appropriate follow-up analysis (ie, multiple comparison of means) using $\alpha = .06$. Interpret the results.

SUBJECT VISIBILITY	CONFEDERATE SUCCESS	
	Success	Failure
Visible	73.1	147.2
Not Visible	89.6	72.5

e. Bond and Anderson conclude that "subjects appear reluctant to transmit bad news—but only when they are visible to the news recipient." Do you agree? [*Hint:* Use your answer to part **c**.]

REFERENCES

Cochran, W. G., and Cox, G. M. *Experimental Designs*, 2d ed. New York: Wiley, 1957.

Davies, O. L. *Statistical Methods in Research and Production*, 3d ed. London: Oliver and Boyd, 1958.

Davies, O. L. *The Design and Analysis of Industrial Experiments*, 2d ed. New York: Hafner, 1956.

Dunn, O. J., and Clark, V. *Applied Statistics: Analysis of Variance and Regression*. New York: Wiley, 1974.

Johnson, N., and Leone, F. *Statistics and Experimental Design in Engineering and the Physical Sciences*, Vol. II, 2d ed. New York: Wiley, 1977.

Mason, R. L., Gunst, R. F., and Hess, J. L. *Statistical Design and Analysis of Experiments*. New York: Wiley, 1989.

Mendenhall, W. *Introduction to Linear Models and the Design and Analysis of Experiments*. Belmont, CA: Wadsworth, 1968.

Mendenhall, W., Scheaffer, R., and Wackerly, D. *Mathematical Statistics with Applications*. 3d ed. Boston: Duxbury, 1989.

Neter, J., Wasserman, W., and Kutner, M. H. *Applied Linear Statistical Models*, 3d ed. Homewood, IL: Irwin, 1990.

Ott, L. *An Introduction to Statistical Methods and Data Analysis*. Boston: Duxbury, 1978.

Scheffé, H. *The Analysis of Variance*. New York: Wiley, 1959.

Snedecor, G. W., and Cochran, W. G. *Statistical Methods*, 7th ed. Ames: Iowa State University Press, 1980.

(1–13) A few weeks after the end of each academic semester, the Career Resource Center (CRC) at the University of Florida mails out questionnaires pertaining to the employment status and starting salary of all students graduating that particular semester. This information is used to compare the mean starting salaries of graduates of the various university colleges. The table lists the starting salaries of independent random samples of eight graduates selected from each of five colleges—Business Administration, Education, Engineering, Liberal Arts, and Sciences.

BUSINESS ADMINISTRATION	EDUCATION	ENGINEERING	LIBERAL ARTS	SCIENCES
$13,400	$12,400	$27,200	$ 9,600	$15,200
23,400	14,700	16,000	11,300	20,300
15,100	11,500	29,200	12,800	15,600
22,900	21,800	24,400	10,700	14,400
18,000	7,700	25,700	13,100	18,100
19,300	11,900	18,000	17,800	14,800
22,600	10,700	21,900	12,600	15,900
18,100	6,100	25,700	21,600	15.200

Source: Career Resource Center, University of Florida.

To perform the comparison, the data were subjected to an analysis of variance using SPSS. The SPSS printout appears below.

```
- - - - - - - - - O N E W A Y - - - - - - - - - -

    Variable  SALARY

 By Variable  COLLEGE

                        Analysis of Variance

                        Sum of        Mean          F      F
       Source      D.F.  Squares      Squares      Ratio  Prob.

Between Groups       4  659451500.0  164862875.0  10.6550  .0000

Within Groups       35  541546250.0  15472750.00

Total               39  1200997750
```

1. Identify the type of experimental design employed to collect the data.
2. Identify the treatments in the experiment.
3. Give the null and alternative hypotheses appropriate for this analysis.
4. Find the value of the test statistic.
5. Do the data provide evidence of a difference in mean starting salaries among the five colleges? (Interpret the p-value for the test.)
6. Write a linear model that will allow you to conduct the ANOVA.
7. Answer Question 3 in terms of the β parameters of the linear model.
8. Find the critical t-value used to conduct a Bonferroni follow-up analysis of the five means. Assume the overall confidence level is 90%.

9. Interpret the results of the Bonferroni analysis shown in the SAS printout below:

```
                    Analysis of Variance Procedure

Dependent Variable: SALARY
                              Sum of              Mean
Source              DF        Squares            Square    F Value    Pr > F

Model                4      659451500.0      164862875.0     10.66     0.0001
Error               35      541546250.0       15472750.0
Corrected Total     39     1200997750.0

              R-Square            C.V.         Root MSE          SALARY Mean

              0.549086         23.25132        3933.542           16917.5000


Source              DF       Anova SS      Mean Square    F Value    Pr > F

COLLEGE              4      659451500.0     164862875.0     10.66     0.0001


            Bonferroni (Dunn) T tests for variable: SALARY

     NOTE: This test controls the type I experimentwise error rate, but
           generally has a higher type II error rate than REGWQ.

             Alpha= 0.05  df= 35  MSE= 15472750
                   Critical Value of T= 3.00
             Minimum Significant Difference= 5892.5

     Means with the same letter are not significantly different.

        Bon Grouping             Mean      N   COLLEGE

                     A           23513      8   ENG
                     A
               B     A           19100      8   BUS
               B
               B     C           16188      8   SC
               B     C
               B     C           13688      8   LA
                     C
                     C           12100      8   ED
```

10. Examine and interpret the MINITAB residual frequency plots shown below:

```
College
1
                      .       .       :   .       ...
         -----+---------+---------+---------+---------+---------+-Resids

College
2
                      .   .        . . .      .                  .
         -----+---------+---------+---------+---------+---------+-Resids

College
3
                 .      .         .      . :        .
         -----+---------+---------+---------+---------+---------+-Resids

College
4
                    .  . .   :.          .           .
         -----+---------+---------+---------+---------+---------+-Resids

College
5
                          ..:..      .      .
         -----+---------+---------+---------+---------+---------+-Resids
             -7000     -3500       0      3500      7000     10500
```

11. Examine and interpret the MINITAB residual stem-and-leaf displays shown below:

```
Stem-and-leaf of Resids     College = 1     N = 8
Leaf Unit = 1000

    2    -0 54
    2    -0
    4    -0 11
    4     0 0
    3     0 33
    1     0 4


Stem-and-leaf of Resids     College = 2     N = 8
Leaf Unit = 1000

    1    -0 6
    2    -0 4
    2    -0
   (3)   -0 100
    3     0 0
    2     0 2
    1     0
    1     0
    1     0 9


Stem-and-leaf of Resids     College = 3     N = 8
Leaf Unit = 1000

    1    -0 7
    2    -0 5
    2    -0
    3    -0 1
    4     0 0
    4     0 223
    1     0 5


Stem-and-leaf of Resids     College = 4     N = 8
Leaf Unit = 1000

    1    -0 4
    3    -0 22
   (3)   -0 100
    2     0
    2     0
    2     0 4
    1     0 7


Stem-and-leaf of Resids     College = 5     N = 8
Leaf Unit = 1000

   (6)   -0 110000
    2     0 1
    1     0
    1     0 4
```

12. Based on your answers to Questions 10 and 11, would you recommend conducting a nonparametric ANOVA of the data? Explain.

13. Interpret the results of the nonparametric ANOVA shown in the MINITAB printout below:

LEVEL	NOBS	MEDIAN	AVE. RANK	Z VALUE
1	8	18700	26.4	1.59
2	8	11700	9.7	-2.92
3	8	25050	33.6	3.53
4	8	12700	12.4	-2.18
5	8	15400	20.4	-0.02
OVERALL	40		20.5	

$H = 22.66$ d.f. = 4 $p = 0.000$
$H = 22.67$ d.f. = 4 $p = 0.000$ (adj. for ties)

(14–18) Prior to submitting a bid for a construction job, companies prepare a detailed analysis of the estimated labor and materials costs required to complete the job. This estimate will depend on the estimator who performs the analysis. An overly large estimate will reduce the chance of acceptance of a company's bid price and, if too low, will reduce the profit or even cause the company to lose money on the job. A company that employs three cost estimators wanted to compare the mean level of the estimator's estimates. This was done by having each estimator estimate the cost of the same four jobs. The data (in hundred thousand dollars) are shown in the table.

| | JOB | | | | |
ESTIMATOR	1	2	3	4	Means
1	4.6	6.2	5.0	6.6	5.60
2	4.9	6.3	5.4	6.8	5.85
3	4.4	5.9	5.4	6.3	5.50
Totals	13.9	18.4	15.8	19.7	
Means	4.63	6.13	5.27	6.57	

14. Identify the type of experimental design employed to collect the data.
15. Identify the treatments in the experiment.
16. A partial ANOVA summary table for this experiment is provided below. Complete the table.

SOURCE	df	SS	MS	F
Estimators	2	—	.130	—
Jobs	—	6.763	—	—
Error	—	.187	.031	
Totals	11	7.210		

17. Do the estimates provide sufficient evidence to indicate that the means for at least two of the estimators differ? Use $\alpha = .05$.
18. Test to determine whether blocking on jobs was effective in reducing experimental error; that is, is there evidence that the mean estimates for the jobs differ? Use $\alpha = .05$.

(19–25) In social psychology, researchers have found that when individuals have positive attitudes about an issue, a less credible source has a higher impact on positive attitude change than a highly credible source. Does this phenomenon exist in a personal selling situation? The *Journal of Personal Selling & Sales Management* (Fall 1990) reported on a study to examine the effects of salesperson credibility on buyer persuasion. The experiment involved two factors, each at two levels: brand quality (high versus low) and salesperson credibility (high versus low). Each of 64 undergraduate students were randomly assigned to one of the $2 \times 2 = 4$ experimental treatments (16 students per treatment). After viewing a presentation on laptop computers, the students' intentions to buy were measured with a questionnaire.

19. Identify the type of experimental design employed to collect the data.
20. Identify the treatments in the experiment.
21. Treating intention to buy as the dependent variable, write the appropriate complete model for this experiment.
22. Write the reduced model appropriate for testing whether brand quality and salesperson credibility interact.

23. A portion of the ANOVA table for this experiment is shown below. Conduct the test for interaction.

SOURCE OF VARIATION	df	SS	MS	F	p-VALUE
Brand quality (A)	1	59.30	59.30	39.74	.001
Salesperson credibility (B)	1	3.51	3.51	2.35	.130
A × B	1	15.13	15.13	10.14	.002

Source: Sharma, A. "The Persuasive Effect of Salesperson Credibility: Conceptual and Empirical Examination." *Journal of Personal Selling & Sales Management*, Fall 1990, Vol. 10, pp. 71–80 (Table 2).

24. In the words of the problem, explain what it means to say that brand quality and salesperson credibility interact.

25. If appropriate, interpret the *p*-values for the main-effect tests. If not, explain why they should not be interpreted.

APPENDIX A   STATISTICAL TABLES

CONTENTS

TABLE 1

Cumulative Binomial Probabilities

a. n = 5

x							π						
	.01	.05	.1	.2	.3	.4	.5	.6	.7	.8	.9	.95	.99
0	.9510	.7738	.5905	.3277	.1681	.0778	.0313	.0102	.0024	.0003	.0000	.0000	.0000
1	.9990	.9774	.9185	.7373	.5282	.3370	.1875	.0870	.0308	.0067	.0005	.0000	.0000
2	1.0000	.9988	.9914	.9421	.8369	.6826	.5000	.3174	.1631	.0579	.0086	.0012	.0000
3	1.0000	1.0000	.9995	.9933	.9692	.9130	.8125	.6630	.4718	.2627	.0815	.0226	.0010
4	1.0000	1.0000	1.0000	.9997	.9976	.9898	.9687	.9222	.8319	.6723	.4095	.2262	.0490

b. n = 6

x							π						
	.01	.05	.1	.2	.3	.4	.5	.6	.7	.8	.9	.95	.99
0	.9415	.7351	.5314	.2621	.1176	.0467	.0156	.0041	.0007	.0001	.0000	.0000	.0000
1	.9985	.9672	.8857	.6554	.4202	.2333	.1094	.0410	.0109	.0016	.0001	.0000	.0000
2	1.0000	.9978	.9841	.9011	.7443	.5443	.3437	.1792	.0705	.0170	.0013	.0001	.0000
3	1.0000	.9999	.9987	.9830	.9295	.8208	.6562	.4557	.2557	.0989	.0158	.0022	.0000
4	1.0000	1.0000	.9999	.9984	.9891	.9590	.8906	.7667	.5798	.3446	.1143	.0328	.0015
5	1.0000	1.0000	1.0000	.9999	.9993	.9959	.9844	.9533	.8824	.7379	.4686	.2649	.0585

c. n = 7

x							π						
	.01	.05	.1	.2	.3	.4	.5	.6	.7	.8	.9	.95	.99
0	.9321	.6983	.4783	.2097	.0824	.0280	.0078	.0016	.0002	.0000	.0000	.0000	.0000
1	.9980	.9556	.8503	.5767	.3294	.1586	.0625	.0188	.0038	.0004	.0000	.0000	.0000
2	1.0000	.9962	.9743	.8520	.6471	.4199	.2266	.0963	.0288	.0047	.0002	.0000	.0000
3	1.0000	.9998	.9973	.9667	.8740	.7102	.5000	.2898	.1260	.0333	.0027	.0002	.0000
4	1.0000	1.0000	.9998	.9953	.9712	.9037	.7734	.5801	.3529	.1480	.0257	.0038	.0000
5	1.0000	1.0000	1.0000	.9996	.9962	.9812	.9375	.8414	.6706	.4233	.1497	.0444	.0020
6	1.0000	1.0000	1.0000	1.0000	.9998	.9984	.9922	.9720	.9176	.7903	.5217	.3017	.0679

d. n = 8

x							π						
	.01	.05	.1	.2	.3	.4	.5	.6	.7	.8	.9	.95	.99
0	.9227	.6634	.4305	.1678	.0576	.0168	.0039	.0007	.0001	.0000	.0000	.0000	.0000
1	.9973	.9423	.8131	.5033	.2553	.1064	.0352	.0085	.0013	.0001	.0000	.0000	.0000
2	.9999	.9942	.9619	.7969	.5518	.3154	.1445	.0498	.0113	.0012	.0000	.0000	.0000
3	1.0000	.9996	.9950	.9437	.8059	.5941	.3633	.1737	.0580	.0104	.0004	.0000	.0000
4	1.0000	1.0000	.9996	.9896	.9420	.8263	.6367	.4059	.1941	.0563	.0050	.0004	.0000
5	1.0000	1.0000	1.0000	.9988	.9887	.9502	.8555	.6346	.4482	.2031	.0381	.0058	.0001
6	1.0000	1.0000	1.0000	.9999	.9987	.9915	.9648	.8936	.7447	.4967	.1869	.0572	.0027
7	1.0000	1.0000	1.0000	1.0000	.9999	.9993	.9961	.9832	.9424	.8322	.5695	.3366	.0773

e. n = 9

x							π						
	.01	.05	.1	.2	.3	.4	.5	.6	.7	.8	.9	.95	.99
0	.9135	.6302	.3874	.1342	.0404	.0101	.0020	.0003	.0000	.0000	.0000	.0000	.0000
1	.9966	.9288	.7748	.4362	.1960	.0705	.0195	.0038	.0004	.0000	.0000	.0000	.0000
2	.9999	.9916	.9470	.7382	.4623	.2318	.0898	.0250	.0043	.0003	.0000	.0000	.0000
3	1.0000	.9994	.9917	.9144	.7297	.4826	.2539	.0994	.0253	.0031	.0001	.0000	.0000
4	1.0000	1.0000	.9991	.9804	.9012	.7334	.5000	.2666	.0988	.0196	.0009	.0000	.0000
5	1.0000	1.0000	.9999	.9969	.9747	.9006	.7461	.5174	.2703	.0856	.0083	.0006	.0000
6	1.0000	1.0000	1.0000	.9997	.9957	.9750	.9102	.7682	.5372	.2618	.0530	.0084	.0001
7	1.0000	1.0000	1.0000	1.0000	.9996	.9962	.9805	.9295	.8040	.5638	.2252	.0712	.0034
8	1.0000	1.0000	1.0000	1.0000	1.0000	.9997	.9980	.9899	.9596	.8658	.6126	.3698	.0865

TABLE 1 (Continued)

f. n = 10

x	.01	.05	.1	.2	.3	.4	.5	.6	.7	.8	.9	.95	.99
							π						
0	.9044	.5987	.3487	.1074	.0282	.0060	.0010	.0001	.0000	.0000	.0000	.0000	.0000
1	.9957	.9139	.7361	.3758	.1493	.0464	.0107	.0017	.0001	.0000	.0000	.0000	.0000
2	.9999	.9885	.9298	.6778	.3828	.1673	.0547	.0123	.0016	.0001	.0000	.0000	.0000
3	1.0000	.9990	.9872	.8791	.6496	.3823	.1719	.0548	.0106	.0009	.0000	.0000	.0000
4	1.0000	.9999	.9984	.9672	.8497	.6331	.3770	.1662	.0473	.0064	.0001	.0000	.0000
5	1.0000	1.0000	.9999	.9936	.9527	.8338	.6230	.3669	.1503	.0328	.0016	.0001	.0000
6	1.0000	1.0000	1.0000	.9991	.9894	.9452	.8281	.6177	.3504	.1209	.0128	.0010	.0000
7	1.0000	1.0000	1.0000	.9999	.9984	.9877	.9453	.8327	.6172	.3222	.0702	.0115	.0001
8	1.0000	1.0000	1.0000	1.0000	.9999	.9983	.9893	.9536	.8507	.6242	.2639	.0861	.0043
9	1.0000	1.0000	1.0000	1.0000	1.0000	.9999	.9990	.9940	.9718	.8926	.6513	.4013	.0956

g. n = 15

x	.01	.05	.1	.2	.3	.4	.5	.6	.7	.8	.9	.95	.99
							π						
0	.8601	.4633	.2059	.0352	.0047	.0005	.0000	.0000	.0000	.0000	.0000	.0000	.0000
1	.9904	.8290	.5490	.1671	.0353	.0052	.0005	.0000	.0000	.0000	.0000	.0000	.0000
2	.9996	.9638	.8159	.3980	.1268	.0271	.0037	.0003	.0000	.0000	.0000	.0000	.0000
3	1.0000	.9945	.9444	.6482	.2969	.0905	.0176	.0019	.0001	.0000	.0000	.0000	.0000
4	1.0000	.9994	.9873	.8358	.5155	.2173	.0592	.0093	.0007	.0000	.0000	.0000	.0000
5	1.0000	.9999	.9978	.9389	.7216	.4032	.1509	.0338	.0037	.0001	.0000	.0000	.0000
6	1.0000	1.0000	.9997	.9819	.8689	.6098	.3036	.0950	.0152	.0008	.0000	.0000	.0000
7	1.0000	1.0000	1.0000	.9958	.9500	.7869	.5000	.2131	.0500	.0042	.0000	.0000	.0000
8	1.0000	1.0000	1.0000	.9992	.9848	.9050	.6964	.3902	.1311	.0181	.0003	.0000	.0000
9	1.0000	1.0000	1.0000	.9999	.9963	.9662	.8491	.5968	.2784	.0611	.0022	.0000	.0000
10	1.0000	1.0000	1.0000	1.0000	.9993	.9907	.9408	.7827	.4845	.1642	.0127	.0006	.0000
11	1.0000	1.0000	1.0000	1.0000	.9999	.9981	.9824	.9095	.7031	.3518	.0556	.0055	.0000
12	1.0000	1.0000	1.0000	1.0000	1.0000	.9997	.9963	.9729	.8732	.6020	.1841	.0362	.0004
13	1.0000	1.0000	1.0000	1.0000	1.0000	1.0000	.9995	.9948	.9647	.8329	.4510	.1710	.0096
14	1.0000	1.0000	1.0000	1.0000	1.0000	1.0000	1.0000	.9995	.9953	.9648	.7941	.5367	.1399

h. n = 20

x	.01	.05	.1	.2	.3	.4	.5	.6	.7	.8	.9	.95	.99
							π						
0	.8179	.3585	.1216	.0115	.0008	.0000	.0000	.0000	.0000	.0000	.0000	.0000	.0000
1	.9831	.7358	.3917	.0692	.0076	.0005	.0000	.0000	.0000	.0000	.0000	.0000	.0000
2	.9990	.9245	.6769	.2061	.0355	.0036	.0002	.0000	.0000	.0000	.0000	.0000	.0000
3	1.0000	.9841	.8670	.4114	.1071	.0160	.0013	.0000	.0000	.0000	.0000	.0000	.0000
4	1.0000	.9974	.9568	.6296	.2375	.0510	.0059	.0003	.0000	.0000	.0000	.0000	.0000
5	1.0000	.9997	.9887	.8042	.4164	.1256	.0207	.0016	.0000	.0000	.0000	.0000	.0000
6	1.0000	1.0000	.9976	.9133	.6080	.2500	.0577	.0065	.0003	.0000	.0000	.0000	.0000
7	1.0000	1.0000	.9996	.9679	.7723	.4159	.1316	.0210	.0013	.0000	.0000	.0000	.0000
8	1.0000	1.0000	.9999	.9900	.8867	.5956	.2517	.0565	.0051	.0001	.0000	.0000	.0000
9	1.0000	1.0000	1.0000	.9974	.9520	.7553	.4119	.1275	.0171	.0006	.0000	.0000	.0000
10	1.0000	1.0000	1.0000	.9994	.9829	.8725	.5881	.2447	.0480	.0026	.0000	.0000	.0000
11	1.0000	1.0000	1.0000	.9999	.9949	.9435	.7483	.4044	.1133	.0100	.0001	.0000	.0000
12	1.0000	1.0000	1.0000	1.0000	.9987	.9790	.8684	.5841	.2277	.0321	.0004	.0000	.0000
13	1.0000	1.0000	1.0000	1.0000	.9997	.9935	.9423	.7500	.3920	.0867	.0024	.0000	.0000
14	1.0000	1.0000	1.0000	1.0000	1.0000	.9984	.9793	.8744	.5836	.1958	.0113	.0003	.0000
15	1.0000	1.0000	1.0000	1.0000	1.0000	.9997	.9941	.9490	.7625	.3704	.0432	.0026	.0000
16	1.0000	1.0000	1.0000	1.0000	1.0000	1.0000	.9987	.9840	.8929	.5886	.1330	.0159	.0000
17	1.0000	1.0000	1.0000	1.0000	1.0000	1.0000	.9998	.9964	.9645	.7939	.3231	.0755	.0010
18	1.0000	1.0000	1.0000	1.0000	1.0000	1.0000	1.0000	.9995	.9924	.9308	.6083	.2642	.0169
19	1.0000	1.0000	1.0000	1.0000	1.0000	1.0000	1.0000	1.0000	.9992	.9885	.8784	.6415	.1821

TABLE 1 (Continued)

i. $n = 25$

x	.01	.05	.1	.2	.3	.4	.5	.6	.7	.8	.9	.95	.99
							π						
0	.7778	.2774	.0718	.0038	.0001	.0000	.0000	.0000	.0000	.0000	.0000	.0000	.0000
1	.9742	.6424	.2712	.0274	.0016	.0001	.0000	.0000	.0000	.0000	.0000	.0000	.0000
2	.9980	.8729	.5371	.0982	.0090	.0004	.0000	.0000	.0000	.0000	.0000	.0000	.0000
3	.9999	.9659	.7636	.2340	.0332	.0024	.0001	.0000	.0000	.0000	.0000	.0000	.0000
4	1.0000	.9928	.9020	.4207	.0905	.0095	.0005	.0000	.0000	.0000	.0000	.0000	.0000
5	1.0000	.9988	.9666	.6167	.1935	.0294	.0020	.0001	.0000	.0000	.0000	.0000	.0000
6	1.0000	.9998	.9905	.7800	.3407	.0736	.0073	.0003	.0000	.0000	.0000	.0000	.0000
7	1.0000	1.0000	.9977	.8909	.5118	.1536	.0216	.0012	.0000	.0000	.0000	.0000	.0000
8	1.0000	1.0000	.9995	.9532	.6769	.2735	.0539	.0043	.0001	.0000	.0000	.0000	.0000
9	1.0000	1.0000	.9999	.9827	.8106	.4246	.1148	.0132	.0005	.0000	.0000	.0000	.0000
10	1.0000	1.0000	1.0000	.9944	.9022	.5858	.2122	.0344	.0018	.0000	.0000	.0000	.0000
11	1.0000	1.0000	1.0000	.9985	.9558	.7323	.3450	.0778	.0060	.0001	.0000	.0000	.0000
12	1.0000	1.0000	1.0000	.9996	.9825	.8462	.5000	.1538	.0175	.0004	.0000	.0000	.0000
13	1.0000	1.0000	1.0000	.9999	.9940	.9222	.6550	.2677	.0442	.0015	.0000	.0000	.0000
14	1.0000	1.0000	1.0000	1.0000	.9982	.9656	.7878	.4142	.0978	.0056	.0000	.0000	.0000
15	1.0000	1.0000	1.0000	1.0000	.9995	.9868	.8852	.5754	.1894	.0173	.0001	.0000	.0000
16	1.0000	1.0000	1.0000	1.0000	.9999	.9957	.9461	.7265	.3231	.0468	.0005	.0000	.0000
17	1.0000	1.0000	1.0000	1.0000	1.0000	.9988	.9784	.8464	.4882	.1091	.0023	.0000	.0000
18	1.0000	1.0000	1.0000	1.0000	1.0000	.9997	.9927	.9264	.6593	.2200	.0095	.0002	.0000
19	1.0000	1.0000	1.0000	1.0000	1.0000	.9999	.9980	.9706	.8065	.3833	.0334	.0012	.0000
20	1.0000	1.0000	1.0000	1.0000	1.0000	1.0000	.9995	.9905	.9095	.5793	.0980	.0072	.0000
21	1.0000	1.0000	1.0000	1.0000	1.0000	1.0000	.9999	.9976	.9668	.7660	.2364	.0341	.0001
22	1.0000	1.0000	1.0000	1.0000	1.0000	1.0000	1.0000	.9996	.9910	.9018	.4629	.1271	.0020
23	1.0000	1.0000	1.0000	1.0000	1.0000	1.0000	1.0000	.9999	.9984	.9726	.7288	.3576	.0258
24	1.0000	1.0000	1.0000	1.0000	1.0000	1.0000	1.0000	1.0000	.9999	.9962	.9282	.7226	.2222

TABLE 2

Normal Curve Areas

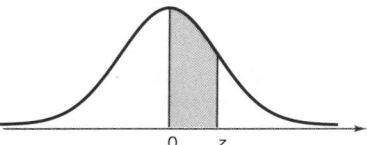

z	.00	.01	.02	.03	.04	.05	.06	.07	.08	.09
0.0	.0000	.0040	.0080	.0120	.0160	.0199	.0239	.0279	.0319	.0359
0.1	.0398	.0438	.0478	.0517	.0557	.0596	.0636	.0675	.0714	.0753
0.2	.0793	.0832	.0871	.0910	.0948	.0987	.1026	.1064	.1103	.1141
0.3	.1179	.1217	.1255	.1293	.1331	.1368	.1406	.1443	.1480	.1517
0.4	.1554	.1591	.1628	.1664	.1700	.1736	.1772	.1808	.1844	.1879
0.5	.1915	.1950	.1985	.2019	.2054	.2088	.2123	.2157	.2190	.2224
0.6	.2257	.2291	.2324	.2357	.2389	.2422	.2454	.2486	.2517	.2549
0.7	.2580	.2611	.2642	.2673	.2704	.2734	.2764	.2794	.2823	.2852
0.8	.2881	.2910	.2939	.2967	.2995	.3023	.3051	.3078	.3106	.3133
0.9	.3159	.3186	.3212	.3238	.3264	.3289	.3315	.3340	.3365	.3389
1.0	.3413	.3438	.3461	.3485	.3508	.3531	.3554	.3577	.3599	.3621
1.1	.3643	.3665	.3686	.3708	.3729	.3749	.3770	.3790	.3810	.3830
1.2	.3849	.3869	.3888	.3907	.3925	.3944	.3962	.3980	.3997	.4015
1.3	.4032	.4049	.4066	.4082	.4099	.4115	.4131	.4147	.4162	.4177
1.4	.4192	.4207	.4222	.4236	.4251	.4265	.4279	.4292	.4306	.4319
1.5	.4332	.4345	.4357	.4370	.4382	.4394	.4406	.4418	.4429	.4441
1.6	.4452	.4463	.4474	.4484	.4495	.4505	.4515	.4525	.4535	.4545
1.7	.4554	.4564	.4573	.4582	.4591	.4599	.4608	.4616	.4625	.4633
1.8	.4641	.4649	.4656	.4664	.4671	.4678	.4686	.4693	.4699	.4706
1.9	.4713	.4719	.4726	.4732	.4738	.4744	.4750	.4756	.4761	.4767
2.0	.4772	.4778	.4783	.4788	.4793	.4798	.4803	.4808	.4812	.4817
2.1	.4821	.4826	.4830	.4834	.4838	.4842	.4846	.4850	.4854	.4857
2.2	.4861	.4864	.4868	.4871	.4875	.4878	.4881	.4884	.4887	.4890
2.3	.4893	.4896	.4898	.4901	.4904	.4906	.4909	.4911	.4913	.4916
2.4	.4918	.4920	.4922	.4925	.4927	.4929	.4931	.4932	.4934	.4936
2.5	.4938	.4940	.4941	.4943	.4945	.4946	.4948	.4949	.4951	.4952
2.6	.4953	.4955	.4956	.4957	.4959	.4960	.4961	.4962	.4963	.4964
2.7	.4965	.4966	.4967	.4968	.4969	.4970	.4971	.4972	.4973	.4974
2.8	.4974	.4975	.4976	.4977	.4977	.4978	.4979	.4979	.4980	.4981
2.9	.4981	.4982	.4982	.4983	.4984	.4984	.4985	.4985	.4986	.4986
3.0	.4987	.4987	.4987	.4988	.4988	.4989	.4989	.4989	.4990	.4990

Source: Abridged from Table I of Hald, A. *Statistical Tables and Formulas.* New York: John Wiley & Sons, Inc., 1952. Reproduced by permission of A. Hald and the publisher.

TABLE 3
Critical Values for Student's *t*

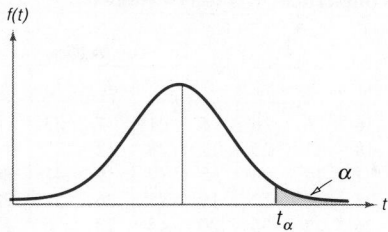

df	$t_{.100}$	$t_{.050}$	$t_{.025}$	$t_{.010}$	$t_{.005}$	$t_{.001}$	$t_{.0005}$
1	3.078	6.314	12.706	31.821	63.657	318.31	636.62
2	1.886	2.920	4.303	6.965	9.925	22.326	31.598
3	1.638	2.353	3.182	4.541	5.841	10.213	12.924
4	1.533	2.132	2.776	3.747	4.604	7.173	8.610
5	1.476	2.015	2.571	3.365	4.032	5.893	6.869
6	1.440	1.943	2.447	3.143	3.707	5.208	5.959
7	1.415	1.895	2.365	2.998	3.499	4.785	5.408
8	1.397	1.860	2.306	2.896	3.355	4.501	5.041
9	1.383	1.833	2.262	2.821	3.250	4.297	4.781
10	1.372	1.812	2.228	2.764	3.169	4.144	4.587
11	1.363	1.796	2.201	2.718	3.106	4.025	4.437
12	1.356	1.782	2.179	2.681	3.055	3.930	4.318
13	1.350	1.771	2.160	2.650	3.012	3.852	4.221
14	1.345	1.761	2.145	2.624	2.977	3.787	4.140
15	1.341	1.753	2.131	2.602	2.947	3.733	4.073
16	1.337	1.746	2.120	2.583	2.921	3.686	4.015
17	1.333	1.740	2.110	2.567	2.898	3.646	3.965
18	1.330	1.734	2.101	2.552	2.878	3.610	3.922
19	1.328	1.729	2.093	2.539	2.861	3.579	3.883
20	1.325	1.725	2.086	2.528	2.845	3.552	3.850
21	1.323	1.721	2.080	2.518	2.831	3.527	3.819
22	1.321	1.717	2.074	2.508	2.819	3.505	3.792
23	1.319	1.714	2.069	2.500	2.807	3.485	3.767
24	1.318	1.711	2.064	2.492	2.797	3.467	3.745
25	1.316	1.708	2.060	2.485	2.787	3.450	3.725
26	1.315	1.706	2.056	2.479	2.779	3.435	3.707
27	1.314	1.703	2.052	2.473	2.771	3.421	3.690
28	1.313	1.701	2.048	2.467	2.763	3.408	3.674
29	1.311	1.699	2.045	2.462	2.756	3.396	3.659
30	1.310	1.697	2.042	2.457	2.750	3.385	3.646
40	1.303	1.684	2.021	2.423	2.704	3.307	3.551
60	1.296	1.671	2.000	2.390	2.660	3.232	3.460
120	1.289	1.658	1.980	2.358	2.617	3.160	3.373
∞	1.282	1.645	1.960	2.326	2.576	3.090	3.291

Source: From Pearson, E. S., and Hartley, H. O., eds. *The Biometrika Tables for Statisticians*, Vol. 1, 3d ed., *Biometrika*, 1966. Reproduced by permission of the *Biometrika* Trustees.

TABLE 4
Critical Values for the Wilcoxon Rank Sum Test

a. $\alpha = .025$ **one-tailed;** $\alpha = .05$ **two-tailed**

n_2 \ n_1	3 T_L	3 T_U	4 T_L	4 T_U	5 T_L	5 T_U	6 T_L	6 T_U	7 T_L	7 T_U	8 T_L	8 T_U	9 T_L	9 T_U	10 T_L	10 T_U
3	5	16	6	18	6	21	7	23	7	26	8	28	8	31	9	33
4	6	18	11	25	12	28	12	32	13	35	14	38	15	41	16	44
5	6	21	12	28	18	37	19	41	20	45	21	49	22	53	24	56
6	7	23	12	32	19	41	26	52	28	56	29	61	31	65	32	70
7	7	26	13	35	20	45	28	56	37	68	39	73	41	78	43	83
8	8	28	14	38	21	49	29	61	39	73	49	87	51	93	54	98
9	8	31	15	41	22	53	31	65	41	78	51	93	63	108	66	114
10	9	33	16	44	24	56	32	70	43	83	54	98	66	114	79	131

b. $\alpha = .05$ **one-tailed;** $\alpha = .10$ **two-tailed**

n_2 \ n_1	3 T_L	3 T_U	4 T_L	4 T_U	5 T_L	5 T_U	6 T_L	6 T_U	7 T_L	7 T_U	8 T_L	8 T_U	9 T_L	9 T_U	10 T_L	10 T_U
3	6	15	7	17	7	20	8	22	9	24	9	27	10	29	11	31
4	7	17	12	24	13	27	14	30	15	33	16	36	17	39	18	42
5	7	20	13	27	19	36	20	40	22	43	24	46	25	50	26	54
6	8	22	14	30	20	40	28	50	30	54	32	58	33	63	35	67
7	9	24	15	33	22	43	30	54	39	66	41	71	43	76	46	80
8	9	27	16	36	24	46	32	58	41	71	52	84	54	90	57	95
9	10	29	17	39	25	50	33	63	43	76	54	90	66	105	69	111
10	11	31	18	42	26	54	35	67	46	80	57	95	69	111	83	127

Source: From Wilcoxon, F., and Wilcox, R. A. "Some Rapid Approximate Statistical Procedures." 1964, pp. 20–23. Reproduced with the permission of American Cyanamid Company.

TABLE 5
Critical Values for the Wilcoxon Signed Ranks Test

ONE-TAILED	TWO-TAILED	$n = 5$	$n = 6$	$n = 7$	$n = 8$	$n = 9$	$n = 10$
$\alpha = .05$	$\alpha = .10$	1	2	4	6	8	11
$\alpha = .025$	$\alpha = .05$		1	2	4	6	8
$\alpha = .01$	$\alpha = .02$			0	2	3	5
$\alpha = .005$	$\alpha = .01$				0	2	3
		$n = 11$	$n = 12$	$n = 13$	$n = 14$	$n = 15$	$n = 16$
$\alpha = .05$	$\alpha = .10$	14	17	21	26	30	36
$\alpha = .025$	$\alpha = .05$	11	14	17	21	25	30
$\alpha = .01$	$\alpha = .02$	7	10	13	16	20	24
$\alpha = .005$	$\alpha = .01$	5	7	10	13	16	19
		$n = 17$	$n = 18$	$n = 19$	$n = 20$	$n = 21$	$n = 22$
$\alpha = .05$	$\alpha = .10$	41	47	54	60	68	75
$\alpha = .025$	$\alpha = .05$	35	40	46	52	59	66
$\alpha = .01$	$\alpha = .02$	28	33	38	43	49	56
$\alpha = .005$	$\alpha = .01$	23	28	32	37	43	49
		$n = 23$	$n = 24$	$n = 25$	$n = 26$	$n = 27$	$n = 28$
$\alpha = .05$	$\alpha = .10$	83	92	101	110	120	130
$\alpha = .025$	$\alpha = .05$	73	81	90	98	107	117
$\alpha = .01$	$\alpha = .02$	62	69	77	85	93	102
$\alpha = .005$	$\alpha = .01$	55	61	68	76	84	92
		$n = 29$	$n = 30$	$n = 31$	$n = 32$	$n = 33$	$n = 34$
$\alpha = .05$	$\alpha = .10$	141	152	163	175	188	201
$\alpha = .025$	$\alpha = .05$	127	137	148	159	171	183
$\alpha = .01$	$\alpha = .02$	111	120	130	141	151	162
$\alpha = .005$	$\alpha = .01$	100	109	118	128	138	149
		$n = 35$	$n = 36$	$n = 37$	$n = 38$	$n = 39$	
$\alpha = .05$	$\alpha = .10$	214	228	242	256	271	
$\alpha = .025$	$\alpha = .05$	195	208	222	235	250	
$\alpha = .01$	$\alpha = .02$	174	186	198	211	224	
$\alpha = .005$	$\alpha = .01$	160	171	183	195	208	
		$n = 40$	$n = 41$	$n = 42$	$n = 43$	$n = 44$	$n = 45$
$\alpha = .05$	$\alpha = .10$	287	303	319	336	353	371
$\alpha = .025$	$\alpha = .05$	264	279	295	311	327	344
$\alpha = .01$	$\alpha = .02$	238	252	267	281	297	313
$\alpha = .005$	$\alpha = .01$	221	234	248	262	277	292
		$n = 46$	$n = 47$	$n = 48$	$n = 49$	$n = 50$	
$\alpha = .05$	$\alpha = .10$	389	408	427	446	466	
$\alpha = .025$	$\alpha = .05$	361	379	397	415	434	
$\alpha = .01$	$\alpha = .02$	329	345	362	380	398	
$\alpha = .005$	$\alpha = .01$	307	323	339	356	373	

Source: From Wilcoxon, F., and Wilcox, R. A. "Some Rapid Approximate Statistical Procedures," 1964, p. 28. Reproduced with the permission of American Cyanamid Company.

TABLE 6
Critical Values for the χ^2 Statistic

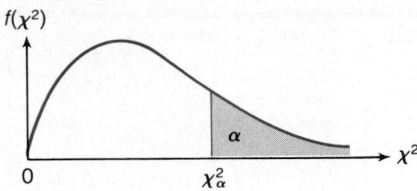

DEGREES OF FREEDOM	$\chi^2_{.995}$	$\chi^2_{.990}$	$\chi^2_{.975}$	$\chi^2_{.950}$	$\chi^2_{.900}$
1	.0000393	.0001571	.0009821	.0039321	.0157908
2	.0100251	.0201007	.0506356	.102587	.210720
3	.0717212	.114832	.215795	.351846	.584375
4	.206990	.297110	.484419	.710721	1.063623
5	.411740	.554300	.831211	1.145476	1.61031
6	.675727	.872085	1.237347	1.63539	2.20413
7	.989265	1.239043	1.68987	2.16735	2.83311
8	1.344419	1.646482	2.17973	2.73264	3.48954
9	1.734926	2.087912	2.70039	3.32511	4.16816
10	2.15585	2.55821	3.24697	3.94030	4.86518
11	2.60321	3.05347	3.81575	4.57481	5.57779
12	3.07382	3.57056	4.40379	5.22603	6.30380
13	3.56503	4.10691	5.00874	5.89186	7.04150
14	4.07468	4.66043	5.62872	6.57063	7.78953
15	4.60094	5.22935	6.26214	7.26094	8.54675
16	5.14224	5.81221	6.90766	7.96164	9.31223
17	5.69724	6.40776	7.56418	8.67176	10.0852
18	6.26481	7.01491	8.23075	9.39046	10.8649
19	6.84398	7.63273	8.90655	10.1170	11.6509
20	7.43386	8.26040	9.59083	10.8508	12.4426
21	8.03366	8.89720	10.28293	11.5913	13.2396
22	8.64272	9.54249	10.9823	12.3380	14.0415
23	9.26042	10.19567	11.6885	13.0905	14.8479
24	9.88623	10.8564	12.4011	13.8484	15.6587
25	10.5197	11.5240	13.1197	14.6114	16.4734
26	11.1603	12.1981	13.8439	15.3791	17.2919
27	11.8076	12.8786	14.5733	16.1513	18.1138
28	12.4613	13.5648	15.3079	16.9279	18.9392
29	13.1211	14.2565	16.0471	17.7083	19.7677
30	13.7867	14.9535	16.7908	18.4926	20.5992
40	20.7065	22.1643	24.4331	26.5093	29.0505
50	27.9907	29.7067	32.3574	34.7642	37.6886
60	35.5346	37.4848	40.4817	43.1879	46.4589
70	43.2752	45.4418	48.7576	51.7393	55.3290
80	51.1720	53.5400	57.1532	60.3915	64.2778
90	59.1963	61.7541	65.6466	69.1260	73.2912
100	67.3276	70.0648	74.2219	77.9295	82.3581
150	109.142	112.668	117.985	122.692	128.275
200	152.241	156.432	162.728	168.279	174.835
300	240.663	245.972	253.912	260.878	269.068
400	330.903	337.155	346.482	354.641	364.207
500	422.303	429.388	439.936	449.147	459.926

Source: From Thompson, C. M. "Tables of the Percentage Points of the χ^2-Distribution." *Biometrika*, 1941, 32, pp. 188–189. Reproduced by permission of the *Biometrika* trustees.

TABLE 6 (Continued)

DEGREES OF FREEDOM	$\chi^2_{.100}$	$\chi^2_{.050}$	$\chi^2_{.025}$	$\chi^2_{.010}$	$\chi^2_{.005}$
1	2.70554	3.84146	5.02389	6.63490	7.87944
2	4.60517	5.99147	7.37776	9.21034	10.5966
3	6.25139	7.81473	9.34840	11.3449	12.8381
4	7.77944	9.48773	11.1433	13.2767	14.8602
5	9.23635	11.0705	12.8325	15.0863	16.7496
6	10.6446	12.5916	14.4494	16.8119	18.5476
7	12.0170	14.0671	16.0128	18.4753	20.2777
8	13.3616	15.5073	17.5346	20.0902	21.9550
9	14.6837	16.9190	19.0228	21.6660	23.5893
10	15.9871	18.3070	20.4831	23.2093	25.1882
11	17.2750	19.6751	21.9200	24.7250	26.7569
12	18.5494	21.0261	23.3367	26.2170	28.2995
13	19.8119	22.3621	24.7356	27.6883	29.8194
14	21.0642	23.6848	26.1190	29.1413	31.3193
15	22.3072	24.9958	27.4884	30.5779	32.8013
16	23.5418	26.2962	28.8454	31.9999	34.2672
17	24.7690	27.5871	30.1910	33.4087	35.7185
18	25.9894	28.8693	31.5264	34.8053	37.1564
19	27.2036	30.1435	32.8523	36.1908	38.5822
20	28.4120	31.4104	34.1696	37.5662	39.9968
21	29.6151	32.6705	35.4789	38.9321	41.4010
22	30.8133	33.9244	36.7807	40.2894	42.7956
23	32.0069	35.1725	38.0757	41.6384	44.1813
24	33.1963	36.4151	39.3641	42.9798	45.5585
25	34.3816	37.6525	40.6465	44.3141	46.9278
26	36.5631	38.8852	41.9232	45.6417	48.2899
27	36.7412	40.1133	43.1944	46.9630	49.6449
28	37.9159	41.3372	44.4607	48.2782	50.9933
29	39.0875	42.5569	45.7222	49.5879	52.3356
30	40.2560	43.7729	46.9792	50.8922	53.6720
40	51.8050	55.7585	59.3417	63.6907	66.7659
50	63.1671	67.5048	71.4202	76.1539	79.4900
60	74.3970	79.0819	83.2976	88.3794	91.9517
70	85.5271	90.5312	95.0231	100.425	104.215
80	96.5782	101.879	106.629	112.329	116.321
90	107.565	113.145	118.136	124.116	128.299
100	118.498	124.342	129.561	135.807	140.169
150	172.581	179.581	185.800	193.208	198.360
200	226.021	233.994	241.058	249.445	255.264
300	331.789	341.395	349.874	359.906	366.844
400	436.649	447.632	457.305	468.724	476.606
500	540.930	553.127	563.852	576.493	585.207

TABLE 7
Critical Values for the F Statistic: $F_{.10}$

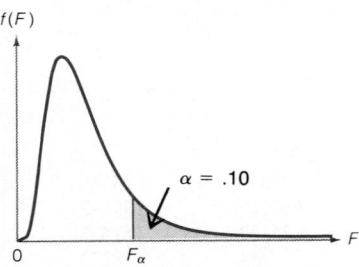

ν_1	NUMERATOR DEGREES OF FREEDOM								
ν_2	1	2	3	4	5	6	7	8	9
1	39.86	49.50	53.59	55.83	57.24	58.20	58.91	59.44	59.86
2	8.53	9.00	9.16	9.24	9.29	9.33	9.35	9.37	9.38
3	5.54	5.46	5.39	5.34	5.31	5.28	5.27	5.25	5.24
4	4.54	4.32	4.19	4.11	4.05	4.01	3.98	3.95	3.94
5	4.06	3.78	3.62	3.52	3.45	3.40	3.37	3.34	3.32
6	3.78	3.46	3.29	3.18	3.11	3.05	3.01	2.98	2.96
7	3.59	3.26	3.07	2.96	2.88	2.83	2.78	2.75	2.72
8	3.46	3.11	2.92	2.81	2.73	2.67	2.62	2.59	2.56
9	3.36	3.01	2.81	2.69	2.61	2.55	2.51	2.47	2.44
10	3.29	2.92	2.73	2.61	2.52	2.46	2.41	2.38	2.35
11	3.23	2.86	2.66	2.54	2.45	2.39	2.34	2.30	2.27
12	3.18	2.81	2.61	2.48	2.39	2.33	2.28	2.24	2.21
13	3.14	2.76	2.56	2.43	2.35	2.28	2.23	2.20	2.16
14	3.10	2.73	2.52	2.39	2.31	2.24	2.19	2.15	2.12
15	3.07	2.70	2.49	2.36	2.27	2.21	2.16	2.12	2.09
16	3.05	2.67	2.46	2.33	2.24	2.18	2.13	2.09	2.06
17	3.03	2.64	2.44	2.31	2.22	2.15	2.10	2.06	2.03
18	3.01	2.62	2.42	2.29	2.20	2.13	2.08	2.04	2.00
19	2.99	2.61	2.40	2.27	2.18	2.11	2.06	2.02	1.98
20	2.97	2.59	2.38	2.25	2.16	2.09	2.04	2.00	1.96
21	2.96	2.57	2.36	2.23	2.14	2.08	2.02	1.98	1.95
22	2.95	2.56	2.35	2.22	2.13	2.06	2.01	1.97	1.93
23	2.94	2.55	2.34	2.21	2.11	2.05	1.99	1.95	1.92
24	2.93	2.54	2.33	2.19	2.10	2.04	1.98	1.94	1.91
25	2.92	2.53	2.32	2.18	2.09	2.02	1.97	1.93	1.89
26	2.91	2.52	2.31	2.17	2.08	2.01	1.96	1.92	1.88
27	2.90	2.51	2.30	2.17	2.07	2.00	1.95	1.91	1.87
28	2.89	2.50	2.29	2.16	2.06	2.00	1.94	1.90	1.87
29	2.89	2.50	2.28	2.15	2.06	1.99	1.93	1.89	1.86
30	2.88	2.49	2.28	2.14	2.05	1.98	1.93	1.88	1.85
40	2.84	2.44	2.23	2.09	2.00	1.93	1.87	1.83	1.79
60	2.79	2.39	2.18	2.04	1.95	1.87	1.82	1.77	1.74
120	2.75	2.35	2.13	1.99	1.90	1.82	1.77	1.72	1.68
∞	2.71	2.30	2.08	1.94	1.85	1.77	1.72	1.67	1.63

Source: From Merrington, M., and Thompson, C. M. "Tables of Percentage Points of the Inverted Beta (F)-Distribution." *Biometrika*, Vol. 33, 1943, pp. 73–88. Reproduced by permission of the *Biometrika* Trustees.

TABLE 7 (Continued)

ν_1 / ν_2	NUMERATOR DEGREES OF FREEDOM									
	10	12	15	20	24	30	40	60	120	∞
1	60.19	60.71	61.22	61.74	62.00	62.26	62.53	62.79	63.06	63.33
2	9.39	9.41	9.42	9.44	9.45	9.46	9.47	9.47	9.48	9.49
3	5.23	5.22	5.20	5.18	5.18	5.17	5.16	5.15	5.14	5.13
4	3.92	3.90	3.87	3.84	3.83	3.82	3.80	3.79	3.78	3.76
5	3.30	3.27	3.24	3.21	3.19	3.17	3.16	3.14	3.12	3.10
6	2.94	2.90	2.87	2.84	2.82	2.80	2.78	2.76	2.74	2.72
7	2.70	2.67	2.63	2.59	2.58	2.56	2.54	2.51	2.49	2.47
8	2.54	2.50	2.46	2.42	2.40	2.38	2.36	2.34	2.32	2.29
9	2.42	2.38	2.34	2.30	2.28	2.25	2.23	2.21	2.18	2.16
10	2.32	2.28	2.24	2.20	2.18	2.16	2.13	2.11	2.08	2.06
11	2.25	2.21	2.17	2.12	2.10	2.08	2.05	2.03	2.00	1.97
12	2.19	2.15	2.10	2.06	2.04	2.01	1.99	1.96	1.93	1.90
13	2.14	2.10	2.05	2.01	1.98	1.96	1.93	1.90	1.88	1.85
14	2.10	2.05	2.01	1.96	1.94	1.91	1.89	1.86	1.83	1.80
15	2.06	2.02	1.97	1.92	1.90	1.87	1.85	1.82	1.79	1.76
16	2.03	1.99	1.94	1.89	1.87	1.84	1.81	1.78	1.75	1.72
17	2.00	1.96	1.91	1.86	1.84	1.81	1.78	1.75	1.72	1.69
18	1.98	1.93	1.89	1.84	1.81	1.78	1.75	1.72	1.69	1.66
19	1.96	1.91	1.86	1.81	1.79	1.76	1.73	1.70	1.67	1.63
20	1.94	1.89	1.84	1.79	1.77	1.74	1.71	1.68	1.64	1.61
21	1.92	1.87	1.83	1.78	1.75	1.72	1.69	1.66	1.62	1.59
22	1.90	1.86	1.81	1.76	1.73	1.70	1.67	1.64	1.60	1.57
23	1.89	1.84	1.80	1.74	1.72	1.69	1.66	1.62	1.59	1.55
24	1.88	1.83	1.78	1.73	1.70	1.67	1.64	1.61	1.57	1.53
25	1.87	1.82	1.77	1.72	1.69	1.66	1.63	1.59	1.56	1.52
26	1.86	1.81	1.76	1.71	1.68	1.65	1.61	1.58	1.54	1.50
27	1.85	1.80	1.75	1.70	1.67	1.64	1.60	1.57	1.53	1.49
28	1.84	1.79	1.74	1.69	1.66	1.63	1.59	1.56	1.52	1.48
29	1.83	1.78	1.73	1.68	1.65	1.62	1.58	1.55	1.51	1.47
30	1.82	1.77	1.72	1.67	1.64	1.61	1.57	1.54	1.50	1.46
40	1.76	1.71	1.66	1.61	1.57	1.54	1.51	1.47	1.42	1.38
60	1.71	1.66	1.60	1.54	1.51	1.48	1.44	1.40	1.35	1.29
120	1.65	1.60	1.55	1.48	1.45	1.41	1.37	1.32	1.26	1.19
∞	1.60	1.55	1.49	1.42	1.38	1.34	1.30	1.24	1.17	1.00

DENOMINATOR DEGREES OF FREEDOM

TABLE 8

Critical Values for the F Statistic: $F_{.05}$

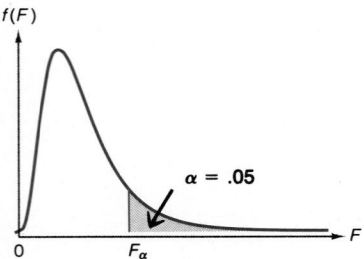

ν_1 ν_2	NUMERATOR DEGREES OF FREEDOM								
	1	2	3	4	5	6	7	8	9
1	161.4	199.5	215.7	224.6	230.2	234.0	236.8	238.9	240.5
2	18.51	19.00	19.16	19.25	19.30	19.33	19.35	19.37	19.38
3	10.13	9.55	9.28	9.12	9.01	8.94	8.89	8.85	8.81
4	7.71	6.94	6.59	6.39	6.26	6.16	6.09	6.04	6.00
5	6.61	5.79	5.41	5.19	5.05	4.95	4.88	4.82	4.77
6	5.99	5.14	4.76	4.53	4.39	4.28	4.21	4.15	4.10
7	5.59	4.74	4.35	4.12	3.97	3.87	3.79	3.73	3.68
8	5.32	4.46	4.07	3.84	3.69	3.58	3.50	3.44	3.39
9	5.12	4.26	3.86	3.63	3.48	3.37	3.29	3.23	3.18
10	4.96	4.10	3.71	3.48	3.33	3.22	3.14	3.07	3.02
11	4.84	3.98	3.59	3.36	3.20	3.09	3.01	2.95	2.90
12	4.75	3.89	3.49	3.26	3.11	3.00	2.91	2.85	2.80
13	4.67	3.81	3.41	3.18	3.03	2.92	2.83	2.77	2.71
14	4.60	3.74	3.34	3.11	2.96	2.85	2.76	2.70	2.65
15	4.54	3.68	3.29	3.06	2.90	2.79	2.71	2.64	2.59
16	4.49	3.63	3.24	3.01	2.85	2.74	2.66	2.59	2.54
17	4.45	3.59	3.20	2.96	2.81	2.70	2.61	2.55	2.49
18	4.41	3.55	3.16	2.93	2.77	2.66	2.58	2.51	2.46
19	4.38	3.52	3.13	2.90	2.74	2.63	2.54	2.48	2.42
20	4.35	3.49	3.10	2.87	2.71	2.60	2.51	2.45	2.39
21	4.32	3.47	3.07	2.84	2.68	2.57	2.49	2.42	2.37
22	4.30	3.44	3.05	2.82	2.66	2.55	2.46	2.40	2.34
23	4.28	3.42	3.03	2.80	2.64	2.53	2.44	2.37	2.32
24	4.26	3.40	3.01	2.78	2.62	2.51	2.42	2.36	2.30
25	4.24	3.39	2.99	2.76	2.60	2.49	2.40	2.34	2.28
26	4.23	3.37	2.98	2.74	2.59	2.47	2.39	2.32	2.27
27	4.21	3.35	2.96	2.73	2.57	2.46	2.37	2.31	2.25
28	4.20	3.34	2.95	2.71	2.56	2.45	2.36	2.29	2.24
29	4.18	3.33	2.93	2.70	2.55	2.43	2.35	2.28	2.22
30	4.17	3.32	2.92	2.69	2.53	2.42	2.33	2.27	2.21
40	4.08	3.23	2.84	2.61	2.45	2.34	2.25	2.18	2.12
60	4.00	3.15	2.76	2.53	2.37	2.25	2.17	2.10	2.04
120	3.92	3.07	2.68	2.45	2.29	2.17	2.09	2.02	1.96
∞	3.84	3.00	2.60	2.37	2.21	2.10	2.01	1.94	1.88

Source: From Merrington, M., and Thompson, C. M. "Tables of Percentage Points of the Inverted Beta (F)-Distribution." *Biometrika*, Vol. 33, 1943, pp. 73–88. Reproduced by permission of the *Biometrika* trustees.

TABLE 8 (Continued)

ν_1 / ν_2	NUMERATOR DEGREES OF FREEDOM									
	10	12	15	20	24	30	40	60	120	∞
1	241.9	243.9	245.9	248.0	249.1	250.1	251.1	252.2	253.3	254.3
2	19.40	19.41	19.43	19.45	19.45	19.46	19.47	19.48	19.49	19.50
3	8.79	8.74	8.70	8.66	8.64	8.62	8.59	8.57	8.55	8.53
4	5.96	5.91	5.86	5.80	5.77	5.75	5.72	5.69	5.66	5.63
5	4.74	4.68	4.62	4.56	4.53	4.50	4.46	4.43	4.40	4.36
6	4.06	4.00	3.94	3.87	3.84	3.81	3.77	3.74	3.70	3.67
7	3.64	3.57	3.51	3.44	3.41	3.38	3.34	3.30	3.27	3.23
8	3.35	3.28	3.22	3.15	3.12	3.08	3.04	3.01	2.97	2.93
9	3.14	3.07	3.01	2.94	2.90	2.86	2.83	2.79	2.75	2.71
10	2.98	2.91	2.85	2.77	2.74	2.70	2.66	2.62	2.58	2.54
11	2.85	2.79	2.72	2.65	2.61	2.57	2.53	2.49	2.45	2.40
12	2.75	2.69	2.62	2.54	2.51	2.47	2.43	2.38	2.34	2.30
13	2.67	2.60	2.53	2.46	2.42	2.38	2.34	2.30	2.25	2.21
14	2.60	2.53	2.46	2.39	2.35	2.31	2.27	2.22	2.18	2.13
15	2.54	2.48	2.40	2.33	2.29	2.25	2.20	2.16	2.11	2.07
16	2.49	2.42	2.35	2.28	2.24	2.19	2.15	2.11	2.06	2.01
17	2.45	2.38	2.31	2.23	2.19	2.15	2.10	2.06	2.01	1.96
18	2.41	2.34	2.27	2.19	2.15	2.11	2.06	2.02	1.97	1.92
19	2.38	2.31	2.23	2.16	2.11	2.07	2.03	1.98	1.93	1.88
20	2.35	2.28	2.20	2.12	2.08	2.04	1.99	1.95	1.90	1.84
21	2.32	2.25	2.18	2.10	2.05	2.01	1.96	1.92	1.87	1.81
22	2.30	2.23	2.15	2.07	2.03	1.98	1.94	1.89	1.84	1.78
23	2.27	2.20	2.13	2.05	2.01	1.96	1.91	1.86	1.81	1.76
24	2.25	2.18	2.11	2.03	1.98	1.94	1.89	1.84	1.79	1.73
25	2.24	2.16	2.09	2.01	1.96	1.92	1.87	1.82	1.77	1.71
26	2.22	2.15	2.07	1.99	1.95	1.90	1.85	1.80	1.75	1.69
27	2.20	2.13	2.06	1.97	1.93	1.88	1.84	1.79	1.73	1.67
28	2.19	2.12	2.04	1.96	1.91	1.87	1.82	1.77	1.71	1.65
29	2.18	2.10	2.03	1.94	1.90	1.85	1.81	1.75	1.70	1.64
30	2.16	2.09	2.01	1.93	1.89	1.84	1.79	1.74	1.68	1.62
40	2.08	2.00	1.92	1.84	1.79	1.74	1.69	1.64	1.58	1.51
60	1.99	1.92	1.84	1.75	1.70	1.65	1.59	1.53	1.47	1.39
120	1.91	1.83	1.75	1.66	1.61	1.55	1.50	1.43	1.35	1.25
∞	1.83	1.75	1.67	1.57	1.52	1.46	1.39	1.32	1.22	1.00

DENOMINATOR DEGREES OF FREEDOM

TABLE 9
Critical Values for the F Statistic: $F_{.025}$

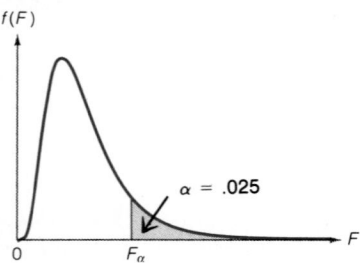

f(F)

$\alpha = .025$

F_α

F

0

ν_1 ν_2	NUMERATOR DEGREES OF FREEDOM								
	1	2	3	4	5	6	7	8	9
1	647.8	799.5	864.2	899.6	921.8	937.1	948.2	956.7	963.3
2	38.51	39.00	39.17	39.25	39.30	39.33	39.36	39.37	39.39
3	17.44	16.04	15.44	15.10	14.88	14.73	14.62	14.54	14.47
4	12.22	10.65	9.98	9.60	9.36	9.20	9.07	8.98	8.90
5	10.01	8.43	7.76	7.39	7.15	6.98	6.85	6.76	6.68
6	8.81	7.26	6.60	6.23	5.99	5.82	5.70	5.60	5.52
7	8.07	6.54	5.89	5.52	5.29	5.12	4.99	4.90	4.82
8	7.57	6.06	5.42	5.05	4.82	4.65	4.53	4.43	4.36
9	7.21	5.71	5.08	4.72	4.48	4.32	4.20	4.10	4.03
10	6.94	5.46	4.83	4.47	4.24	4.07	3.95	3.85	3.78
11	6.72	5.26	4.63	4.28	4.04	3.88	3.76	3.66	3.59
12	6.55	5.10	4.47	4.12	3.89	3.73	3.61	3.51	3.44
13	6.41	4.97	4.35	4.00	3.77	3.60	3.48	3.39	3.31
14	6.30	4.86	4.24	3.89	3.66	3.50	3.38	3.29	3.21
15	6.20	4.77	4.15	3.80	3.58	3.41	3.29	3.20	3.12
16	6.12	4.69	4.08	3.73	3.50	3.34	3.22	3.12	3.05
17	6.04	4.62	4.01	3.66	3.44	3.28	3.16	3.06	2.98
18	5.98	4.56	3.95	3.61	3.38	3.22	3.10	3.01	2.93
19	5.92	4.51	3.90	3.56	3.33	3.17	3.05	2.96	2.88
20	5.87	4.46	3.86	3.51	3.29	3.13	3.01	2.91	2.84
21	5.83	4.42	3.82	3.48	3.25	3.09	2.97	2.87	2.80
22	5.79	4.38	3.78	3.44	3.22	3.05	2.93	2.84	2.76
23	5.75	4.35	3.75	3.41	3.18	3.02	2.90	2.81	2.73
24	5.72	4.32	3.72	3.38	3.15	2.99	2.87	2.78	2.70
25	5.69	4.29	3.69	3.35	3.13	2.97	2.85	2.75	2.68
26	5.66	4.27	3.67	3.33	3.10	2.94	2.82	2.73	2.65
27	5.63	4.24	3.65	3.31	3.08	2.92	2.80	2.71	2.63
28	5.61	4.22	3.63	3.29	3.06	2.90	2.78	2.69	2.61
29	5.59	4.20	3.61	3.27	3.04	2.88	2.76	2.67	2.59
30	5.57	4.18	3.59	3.25	3.03	2.87	2.75	2.65	2.57
40	5.42	4.05	3.46	3.13	2.90	2.74	2.62	2.53	2.45
60	5.29	3.93	3.34	3.01	2.79	2.63	2.51	2.41	2.33
120	5.15	3.80	3.23	2.89	2.67	2.52	2.39	2.30	2.22
∞	5.02	3.69	3.12	2.79	2.57	2.41	2.29	2.19	2.11

DENOMINATOR DEGREES OF FREEDOM

Source: From Merrington, M., and Thompson, C. M. "Tables of Percentage Points of the Inverted Beta (F)-Distribution." *Biometrika*, Vol. 33, 1943, pp. 73–88. Reproduced by permission of the *Biometrika* Trustees.

TABLE 9 (Continued)

ν_1	NUMERATOR DEGREES OF FREEDOM									
ν_2	10	12	15	20	24	30	40	60	120	∞
1	968.6	976.7	984.9	993.1	997.2	1001	1006	1010	1014	1018
2	39.40	39.41	39.43	39.45	39.46	39.46	39.47	39.48	39.49	39.50
3	14.42	14.34	14.25	14.17	14.12	14.08	14.04	13.99	13.95	13.90
4	8.84	8.75	8.66	8.56	8.51	8.46	8.41	8.36	8.31	8.26
5	6.62	6.52	6.43	6.33	6.28	6.23	6.18	6.12	6.07	6.02
6	5.46	5.37	5.27	5.17	5.12	5.07	5.01	4.96	4.90	4.85
7	4.76	4.67	4.57	4.47	4.42	4.36	4.31	4.25	4.20	4.14
8	4.30	4.20	4.10	4.00	3.95	3.89	3.84	3.78	3.73	3.67
9	3.96	3.87	3.77	3.67	3.61	3.56	3.51	3.45	3.39	3.33
10	3.72	3.62	3.52	3.42	3.37	3.31	3.26	3.20	3.14	3.08
11	3.53	3.43	3.33	3.23	3.17	3.12	3.06	3.00	2.94	2.88
12	3.37	3.28	3.18	3.07	3.02	2.96	2.91	2.85	2.79	2.72
13	3.25	3.15	3.05	2.95	2.89	2.84	2.78	2.72	2.66	2.60
14	3.15	3.05	2.95	2.84	2.79	2.73	2.67	2.61	2.55	2.49
15	3.06	2.96	2.86	2.76	2.70	2.64	2.59	2.52	2.46	2.40
16	2.99	2.89	2.79	2.68	2.63	2.57	2.51	2.45	2.38	2.32
17	2.92	2.82	2.72	2.62	2.56	2.50	2.44	2.38	2.32	2.25
18	2.87	2.77	2.67	2.56	2.50	2.44	2.38	2.32	2.26	2.19
19	2.82	2.72	2.62	2.51	2.45	2.39	2.33	2.27	2.20	2.13
20	2.77	2.68	2.57	2.46	2.41	2.35	2.29	2.22	2.16	2.09
21	2.73	2.64	2.53	2.42	2.37	2.31	2.25	2.18	2.11	2.04
22	2.70	2.60	2.50	2.39	2.33	2.27	2.21	2.14	2.08	2.00
23	2.67	2.57	2.47	2.36	2.30	2.24	2.18	2.11	2.04	1.97
24	2.64	2.54	2.44	2.33	2.27	2.21	2.15	2.08	2.01	1.94
25	2.61	2.51	2.41	2.30	2.24	2.18	2.12	2.05	1.98	1.91
26	2.59	2.49	2.39	2.28	2.22	2.16	2.09	2.03	1.95	1.88
27	2.57	2.47	2.36	2.25	2.19	2.13	2.07	2.00	1.93	1.85
28	2.55	2.45	2.34	2.23	2.17	2.11	2.05	1.98	1.91	1.83
29	2.53	2.43	2.32	2.21	2.15	2.09	2.03	1.96	1.89	1.81
30	2.51	2.41	2.31	2.20	2.14	2.07	2.01	1.94	1.87	1.79
40	2.39	2.29	2.18	2.07	2.01	1.94	1.88	1.80	1.72	1.64
60	2.27	2.17	2.06	1.94	1.88	1.82	1.74	1.67	1.58	1.48
120	2.16	2.05	1.94	1.82	1.76	1.69	1.61	1.53	1.43	1.31
∞	2.05	1.94	1.83	1.71	1.64	1.57	1.48	1.39	1.27	1.00

DENOMINATOR DEGREES OF FREEDOM

TABLE 10
Critical Values for the F Statistic: $F_{.01}$

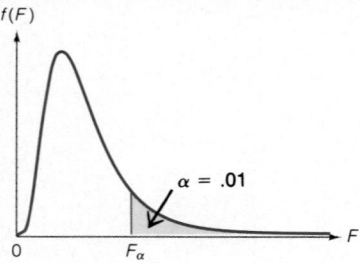

ν_2 \ ν_1	NUMERATOR DEGREES OF FREEDOM								
	1	2	3	4	5	6	7	8	9
1	4,052	4,999.5	5,403	5,625	5,764	5,859	5,928	5,982	6,022
2	98.50	99.00	99.17	99.25	99.30	99.33	99.36	99.37	99.39
3	34.12	30.82	29.46	28.71	28.24	27.91	27.67	27.49	27.35
4	21.20	18.00	16.69	15.98	15.52	15.21	14.98	14.80	14.66
5	16.26	13.27	12.06	11.39	10.97	10.67	10.46	10.29	10.16
6	13.75	10.92	9.78	9.15	8.75	8.47	8.26	8.10	7.98
7	12.25	9.55	8.45	7.85	7.46	7.19	6.99	6.84	6.72
8	11.26	8.65	7.59	7.01	6.63	6.37	6.18	6.03	5.91
9	10.56	8.02	6.99	6.42	6.06	5.80	5.61	5.47	5.35
10	10.04	7.56	6.55	5.99	5.64	5.39	5.20	5.06	4.94
11	9.65	7.21	6.22	5.67	5.32	5.07	4.89	4.74	4.63
12	9.33	6.93	5.95	5.41	5.06	4.82	4.64	4.50	4.39
13	9.07	6.70	5.74	5.21	4.86	4.62	4.44	4.30	4.19
14	8.86	6.51	5.56	5.04	4.69	4.46	4.28	4.14	4.03
15	8.68	6.36	5.42	4.89	4.56	4.32	4.14	4.00	3.89
16	8.53	6.23	5.29	4.77	4.44	4.20	4.03	3.89	3.78
17	8.40	6.11	5.18	4.67	4.34	4.10	3.93	3.79	3.68
18	8.29	6.01	5.09	4.58	4.25	4.01	3.84	3.71	3.60
19	8.18	5.93	5.01	4.50	4.17	3.94	3.77	3.63	3.52
20	8.10	5.85	4.94	4.43	4.10	3.87	3.70	3.56	3.46
21	8.02	5.78	4.87	4.37	4.04	3.81	3.64	3.51	3.40
22	7.95	5.72	4.82	4.31	3.99	3.76	3.59	3.45	3.35
23	7.88	5.66	4.76	4.26	3.94	3.71	3.54	3.41	3.30
24	7.82	5.61	4.72	4.22	3.90	3.67	3.50	3.36	3.26
25	7.77	5.57	4.68	4.18	3.85	3.63	3.46	3.32	3.22
26	7.72	5.53	4.64	4.14	3.82	3.59	3.42	3.29	3.18
27	7.68	5.49	4.60	4.11	3.78	3.56	3.39	3.26	3.15
28	7.64	5.45	4.57	4.07	3.75	3.53	3.36	3.23	3.12
29	7.60	5.42	4.54	4.04	3.73	3.50	3.33	3.20	3.09
30	7.56	5.39	4.51	4.02	3.70	3.47	3.30	3.17	3.07
40	7.31	5.18	4.31	3.83	3.51	3.29	3.12	2.99	2.89
60	7.08	4.98	4.13	3.65	3.34	3.12	2.95	2.82	2.72
120	6.85	4.79	3.95	3.48	3.17	2.96	2.79	2.66	2.56
∞	6.63	4.61	3.78	3.32	3.02	2.80	2.64	2.51	2.41

Source: From Merrington, M., and Thompson, C. M. "Tables of Percentage Points of the Inverted Beta (F)-Distribution." *Biometrika*, Vol. 33, 1943, pp. 73–88. Reproduced by permission of the *Biometrika* Trustees.

TABLE 10 (Continued)

ν_1 ν_2	NUMERATOR DEGREES OF FREEDOM									
	10	12	15	20	24	30	40	60	120	∞
1	6,056	6,106	6,157	6,209	6,235	6,261	6,287	6,313	6,339	6,366
2	99.40	99.42	99.43	99.45	99.46	99.47	99.47	99.48	99.49	99.50
3	27.23	27.05	26.87	26.69	26.60	26.50	26.41	26.32	26.22	26.13
4	14.55	14.37	14.20	14.02	13.93	13.84	13.75	13.65	13.56	13.46
5	10.05	9.89	9.72	9.55	9.47	9.38	9.29	9.20	9.11	9.02
6	7.87	7.72	7.56	7.40	7.31	7.23	7.14	7.06	6.97	6.88
7	6.62	6.47	6.31	6.16	6.07	5.99	5.91	5.82	5.74	5.65
8	5.81	5.67	5.52	5.36	5.28	5.20	5.12	5.03	4.95	4.86
9	5.26	5.11	4.96	4.81	4.73	4.65	4.57	4.48	4.40	4.31
10	4.85	4.71	4.56	4.41	4.33	4.25	4.17	4.08	4.00	3.91
11	4.54	4.40	4.25	4.10	4.02	3.94	3.86	3.78	3.69	3.60
12	4.30	4.16	4.01	3.86	3.78	3.70	3.62	3.54	3.45	3.36
13	4.10	3.96	3.82	3.66	3.59	3.51	3.43	3.34	3.25	3.17
14	3.94	3.80	3.66	3.51	3.43	3.35	3.27	3.18	3.09	3.00
15	3.80	3.67	3.52	3.37	3.29	3.21	3.13	3.05	2.96	2.87
16	3.69	3.55	3.41	3.26	3.18	3.10	3.02	2.93	2.84	2.75
17	3.59	3.46	3.31	3.16	3.08	3.00	2.92	2.83	2.75	2.65
18	3.51	3.37	3.23	3.08	3.00	2.92	2.84	2.75	2.66	2.57
19	3.43	3.30	3.15	3.00	2.92	2.84	2.76	2.67	2.58	2.49
20	3.37	3.23	3.09	2.94	2.86	2.78	2.69	2.61	2.52	2.42
21	3.31	3.17	3.03	2.88	2.80	2.72	2.64	2.55	2.46	2.36
22	3.26	3.12	2.98	2.83	2.75	2.67	2.58	2.50	2.40	2.31
23	3.21	3.07	2.93	2.78	2.70	2.62	2.54	2.45	2.35	2.26
24	3.17	3.03	2.89	2.74	2.66	2.58	2.49	2.40	2.31	2.21
25	3.13	2.99	2.85	2.70	2.62	2.54	2.45	2.36	2.27	2.17
26	3.09	2.96	2.81	2.66	2.58	2.50	2.42	2.33	2.23	2.13
27	3.06	2.93	2.78	2.63	2.55	2.47	2.38	2.29	2.20	2.10
28	3.03	2.90	2.75	2.60	2.52	2.44	2.35	2.26	2.17	2.06
29	3.00	2.87	2.73	2.57	2.49	2.41	2.33	2.23	2.14	2.03
30	2.98	2.84	2.70	2.55	2.47	2.39	2.30	2.21	2.11	2.01
40	2.80	2.66	2.52	2.37	2.29	2.20	2.11	2.02	1.92	1.80
60	2.63	2.50	2.35	2.20	2.12	2.03	1.94	1.84	1.73	1.60
120	2.47	2.34	2.19	2.03	1.95	1.86	1.76	1.66	1.53	1.38
∞	2.32	2.18	2.04	1.88	1.79	1.70	1.59	1.47	1.32	1.00

DENOMINATOR DEGREES OF FREEDOM

TABLE 11
Critical Values for the Ansari–Bradley Test, $2 \le n_2 \le n_1$, $(n_1 + n_2) \le 20$

$n_2 = 2$

x	$n_1=2$	$n_1=3$	$n_1=4$	$n_1=5$	$n_1=6$	$n_1=7$	$n_1=8$	$n_1=9$	$n_1=10$	$n_1=11$	$n_1=12$	$n_1=13$	$n_1=14$	$n_1=15$	$n_1=16$	$n_1=17$	$n_1=18$
2	1.0000	1.0000	1.0000	1.0000	1.0000	1.0000	1.0000	1.0000	1.0000	1.0000	1.0000	1.0000	1.0000	1.0000	1.0000	1.0000	1.0000
3	.8333	.9000	.9333	.9524	.9643	.9722	.9778	.9818	.9848	.9872	.9890	.9905	.9917	.9926	.9935	.9942	.9947
4	.1667	.5000	.6667	.7619	.8214	.8611	.8889	.9091	.9242	.9359	.9451	.9524	.9583	.9632	.9673	.9708	.9737
5		.2000	.3333	.5238	.6429	.7222	.7778	.8182	.8485	.8718	.8901	.9048	.9167	.9265	.9346	.9415	.9474
6			.0667	.2381	.3571	.5000	.6000	.6727	.7273	.7692	.8022	.8286	.8500	.8676	.8824	.8947	.9053
7				.0952	.1786	.3056	.4000	.5091	.5909	.6538	.7033	.7429	.7750	.8015	.8235	.8421	.8579
8					.0357	.1389	.2222	.3273	.4091	.5000	.5714	.6286	.6750	.7132	.7451	.7719	.7947
9						.0556	.1111	.2000	.2727	.3590	.4286	.5048	.5667	.6176	.6601	.6959	.7263
10							.0222	.0909	.1515	.2308	.2967	.3714	.4333	.5000	.5556	.6023	.6421
11								.0364	.0758	.1410	.1978	.2667	.3250	.3897	.4444	.5029	.5526
12									.0152	.0641	.1099	.1714	.2250	.2868	.3399	.3977	.4474
13										.0256	.0549	.1048	.1500	.2059	.2549	.3099	.3579
14											.0110	.0476	.0833	.1324	.1765	.2281	.2737
15												.0190	.0417	.0809	.1176	.1637	.2053
16													.0083	.0368	.0654	.1053	.1421
17														.0147	.0327	.0643	.0947
18															.0065	.0292	.0526
19																.0117	.0263
20																	.0053

$n_2 = 3$

x	$n_1=3$	$n_1=4$	$n_1=5$	$n_1=6$	$n_1=7$	$n_1=8$	$n_1=9$	$n_1=10$	$n_1=11$	$n_1=12$	$n_1=13$	$n_1=14$	$n_1=15$	$n_1=16$	$n_1=17$
4	1.0000	1.0000	1.0000	1.0000	1.0000	1.0000	1.0000	1.0000	1.0000	1.0000	1.0000	1.0000	1.0000	1.0000	1.0000
5	.9000	.9429	.9643	.9762	.9833	.9879	.9909	.9930	.9945	.9956	.9964	.9971	.9975	.9979	.9982
6	.7000	.8286	.8929	.9286	.9500	.9636	.9727	.9790	.9835	.9868	.9893	.9912	.9926	.9938	.9947
7	.3000	.5714	.7143	.8095	.8667	.9030	.9273	.9441	.9560	.9648	.9714	.9765	.9804	.9835	.9860
8	.1000	.3429	.5000	.6548	.7500	.8182	.8636	.8951	.9176	.9341	.9464	.9559	.9632	.9690	.9737
9		.1429	.2857	.4643	.5833	.6909	.7636	.8182	.8571	.8857	.9071	.9235	.9363	.9463	.9544
10		.0286	.1071	.2857	.4167	.5455	.6364	.7168	.7747	.8198	.8536	.8794	.8995	.9154	.9281
11			.0357	.1429	.2500	.3939	.5000	.5979	.6703	.7341	.7821	.8206	.8505	.8741	.8930
12			.0119	.0595	.1333	.2606	.3636	.4755	.5604	.6374	.6964	.7485	.7892	.8225	.8491
13				.0167	.0500	.1455	.2364	.3497	.4396	.5297	.6000	.6632	.7132	.7575	.7930
14					.0167	.0727	.1364	.2413	.3297	.4242	.5000	.5735	.6324	.6852	.7281
15						.0303	.0727	.1503	.2253	.3209	.4000	.4794	.5441	.6058	.6561
16						.0061	.0273	.0839	.1429	.2286	.3036	.3868	.4559	.5232	.5789
17							.0091	.0420	.0824	.1516	.2179	.2985	.3676	.4396	.5000
18								.0175	.0440	.0945	.1464	.2206	.2868	.3591	.4211
19								.0035	.0165	.0527	.0929	.1529	.2108	.2817	.3439
20									.0055	.0264	.0536	.1015	.1495	.2136	.2719
21										.0110	.0286	.0632	.1005	.1548	.2070
22										.0022	.0107	.0353	.0637	.1073	.1509
23											.0036	.0176	.0368	.0712	.1070
24												.0074	.0196	.0444	.0719
25												.0015	.0074	.0248	.0456
26													.0025	.0124	.0263

TABLE 11 (Continued)

$n_2 = 4$

x	$n_1 = 4$	$n_1 = 5$	$n_1 = 6$	$n_1 = 7$	$n_1 = 8$	$n_1 = 9$	$n_1 = 10$	$n_1 = 11$	$n_1 = 12$	$n_1 = 13$	$n_1 = 14$	$n_1 = 15$	$n_1 = 16$
6	1.0000	1.0000	1.0000	1.0000	1.0000	1.0000	1.0000	1.0000	1.0000	1.0000	1.0000	1.0000	1.0000
7	.9857	.9921	.9952	.9970	.9980	.9986	.9990	.9993	.9995	.9996	.9997	.9997	.9998
8	.9286	.9603	.9762	.9848	.9899	.9930	.9950	.9963	.9973	.9979	.9984	.9987	.9990
9	.8000	.8889	.9333	.9576	.9717	.9804	.9860	.9897	.9923	.9941	.9954	.9964	.9971
10	.6286	.7778	.8571	.9091	.9394	.9580	.9700	.9780	.9835	.9874	.9902	.9923	.9938
11	.3714	.6032	.7333	.8242	.8788	.9161	.9401	.9560	.9670	.9748	.9804	.9845	.9876
12	.2000	.4286	.5810	.7152	.7980	.8573	.8961	.9238	.9429	.9563	.9660	.9732	.9785
13	.0714	.2619	.4190	.5818	.6889	.7762	.8342	.8769	.9066	.9286	.9444	.9561	.9649
14	.0143	.1349	.2667	.4424	.5677	.6783	.7542	.8154	.8582	.8908	.9144	.9324	.9459
15		.0476	.1429	.3030	.4323	.5650	.6593	.7385	.7951	.8408	.8742	.9002	.9197
16		.0159	.0667	.1939	.3111	.4503	.5554	.6520	.7225	.7811	.8245	.8599	.8867
17			.0238	.1061	.2020	.3357	.4446	.5546	.6374	.7101	.7647	.8101	.8448
18			.0048	.0515	.1212	.2378	.3407	.4564	.5473	.6319	.6967	.7528	.7961
19				.0182	.0606	.1538	.2458	.3590	.4527	.5471	.6209	.6873	.7391
20				.0061	.0283	.0923	.1658	.2711	.3626	.4613	.5412	.6166	.6764
21					.0101	.0490	.1039	.1934	.2775	.3761	.4588	.5413	.6078
22					.0020	.0238	.0599	.1319	.2049	.2979	.3791	.4654	.5368
23						.0084	.0300	.0821	.1418	.2261	.3033	.3896	.4632
24						.0028	.0140	.0484	.0934	.1655	.2353	.3189	.3922
25							.0050	.0256	.0571	.1151	.1755	.2531	.3236
26							.0010	.0125	.0330	.0765	.1258	.1953	.2609
27								.0044	.0165	.0471	.0856	.1450	.2039
28								.0015	.0077	.0277	.0556	.1042	.1552
29									.0027	.0147	.0340	.0712	.1133
30									.0005	.0071	.0196	.0470	.0803
31										.0025	.0098	.0289	.0541
32										.0008	.0046	.0170	.0351
33											.0016	.0090	.0215
34											.0003	.0044	.0124
35												.0015	.0062

TABLE 11 (Continued)

$n_2 = 5$

x	$n_1 = 5$	$n_1 = 6$	$n_1 = 7$	$n_1 = 8$	$n_1 = 9$	$n_1 = 10$	$n_1 = 11$	$n_1 = 12$	$n_1 = 13$	$n_1 = 14$	$n_1 = 15$
9	1.0000	1.0000	1.0000	1.0000	1.0000	1.0000	1.0000	1.0000	1.0000	1.0000	1.0000
10	.9921	.9957	.9975	.9984	.9990	.9993	.9995	.9997	.9998	.9998	.9999
11	.9762	.9870	.9924	.9953	.9970	.9980	.9986	.9990	.9993	.9995	.9996
12	.9286	.9610	.9773	.9860	.9910	.9940	.9959	.9971	.9979	.9985	.9988
13	.8492	.9156	.9495	.9689	.9800	.9867	.9908	.9935	.9953	.9966	.9974
14	.7302	.8420	.9015	.9386	.9600	.9734	.9817	.9871	.9907	.9931	.9948
15	.5873	.7446	.8333	.8936	.9291	.9524	.9670	.9767	.9832	.9876	.9907
16	.4127	.6147	.7374	.8275	.8821	.9197	.9437	.9601	.9711	.9787	.9840
17	.2698	.4805	.6237	.7451	.8212	.8761	.9116	.9368	.9538	.9659	.9743
18	.1508	.3463	.5000	.6457	.7423	.8182	.8681	.9047	.9295	.9476	.9604
19	.0714	.2294	.3763	.5385	.6523	.7483	.8132	.8633	.8978	.9235	.9417
20	.0238	.1342	.2626	.4266	.5514	.6663	.7468	.8116	.8569	.8920	.9171
21	.0079	.0693	.1667	.3209	.4486	.5771	.6708	.7508	.8079	.8533	.8861
22		.0303	.0985	.2269	.3477	.4832	.5870	.6810	.7498	.8067	.8483
23		.0108	.0505	.1507	.2577	.3916	.5000	.6054	.6846	.7530	.8038
24		.0022	.0227	.0917	.1788	.3044	.4130	.5254	.6130	.6923	.7523
25			.0076	.0513	.1179	.2268	.3292	.4449	.5383	.6267	.6950
26			.0025	.0249	.0709	.1608	.2532	.3662	.4617	.5572	.6329
27				.0109	.0400	.1086	.1868	.2928	.3870	.4864	.5673
28				.0039	.0200	.0686	.1319	.2262	.3154	.4157	.5000
29				.0008	.0090	.0406	.0884	.1690	.2502	.3478	.4327
30					.0030	.0220	.0563	.1214	.1921	.2840	.3671
31					.0010	.0107	.0330	.0835	.1431	.2262	.3050
32						.0047	.0183	.0546	.1022	.1751	.2477
33						.0017	.0092	.0339	.0705	.1318	.1962
34						.0003	.0041	.0197	.0462	.0960	.1517
35							.0014	.0107	.0289	.0675	.1139
36							.0005	.0052	.0168	.0455	.0829
37								.0023	.0093	.0294	.0583
38								.0008	.0047	.0181	.0396
39								.0002	.0021	.0105	.0257
40									.0007	.0057	.0160

TABLE 11 (Continued)

$n_2 = 6$

x	$n_1 = 6$	$n_1 = 7$	$n_1 = 8$	$n_1 = 9$	$n_1 = 10$	$n_1 = 11$	$n_1 = 12$	$n_1 = 13$	$n_1 = 14$
12	1.0000	1.0000	1.0000	1.0000	1.0000	1.0000	1.0000	1.0000	1.0000
13	.9989	.9994	.9997	.9998	.9999	.9999	.9999	1.0000	1.0000
14	.9946	.9971	.9983	.9990	.9994	.9996	.9997	.9998	.9999
15	.9848	.9918	.9953	.9972	.9983	.9989	.9992	.9995	.9996
16	.9632	.9802	.9887	.9932	.9958	.9973	.9982	.9987	.9991
17	.9264	.9592	.9760	.9856	.9910	.9942	.9961	.9973	.9981
18	.8658	.9242	.9547	.9724	.9825	.9887	.9925	.9948	.9964
19	.7846	.8735	.9217	.9518	.9692	.9799	.9865	.9907	.9935
20	.6807	.8048	.8751	.9215	.9487	.9663	.9772	.9843	.9890
21	.5649	.7203	.8139	.8803	.9202	.9469	.9636	.9749	.9823
22	.4351	.6189	.7366	.8260	.8812	.9199	.9445	.9613	.9725
23	.3193	.5122	.6474	.7600	.8322	.8849	.9190	.9431	.9591
24	.2154	.4038	.5501	.6829	.7717	.8407	.8860	.9191	.9413
25	.1342	.3030	.4499	.5984	.7025	.7877	.8451	.8887	.9184
26	.0736	.2133	.3526	.5085	.6246	.7259	.7962	.8514	.8896
27	.0368	.1410	.2634	.4190	.5425	.6574	.7398	.8074	.8549
28	.0152	.0851	.1861	.3323	.4575	.5831	.6765	.7564	.8138
29	.0054	.0484	.1249	.2543	.3754	.5065	.6082	.6996	.7668
30	.0011	.0239	.0783	.1860	.2975	.4292	.5364	.6376	.7139
31		.0105	.0453	.1303	.2283	.3549	.4636	.5723	.6566
32		.0035	.0240	.0859	.1678	.2851	.3918	.5049	.5954
33		.0012	.0113	.0539	.1188	.2226	.3235	.4376	.5322
34			.0047	.0312	.0798	.1678	.2602	.3716	.4678
35			.0017	.0170	.0513	.1226	.2038	.3094	.4046
36			.0003	.0082	.0308	.0859	.1549	.2518	.3434
37				.0036	.0175	.0579	.1140	.2002	.2861
38				.0012	.0090	.0370	.0810	.1550	.2332
39				.0004	.0042	.0226	.0555	.1170	.1862
40					.0017	.0128	.0364	.0855	.1451
41					.0006	.0069	.0228	.0608	.1104
42					.0001	.0033	.0135	.0415	.0816
43						.0015	.0075	.0274	.0587
44						.0005	.0039	.0172	.0409
45						.0002	.0018	.0104	.0275
46							.0008	.0058	.0177
47							.0003	.0031	.0110
48							.0001	.0015	.0065
49								.0007	.0036
50								.0002	.0019
51								.0001	.0009
52									.0004
53									.0001
54									.0000

$n_2 = 7$

x	$n_1 = 7$	$n_1 = 8$	$n_1 = 9$	$n_1 = 10$	$n_1 = 11$	$n_1 = 12$	$n_1 = 13$
16	1.0000	1.0000	1.0000	1.0000	1.0000	1.0000	1.0000
17	.9994	.9997	.9998	.9999	1.0000	1.0000	1.0000
18	.9983	.9991	.9995	.9997	.9998	.9999	.9999
19	.9948	.9972	.9984	.9991	.9994	.9996	.9998
20	.9878	.9935	.9963	.9978	.9987	.9992	.9995
21	.9744	.9862	.9921	.9954	.9972	.9982	.9988
22	.9534	.9744	.9851	.9912	.9946	.9966	.9978
23	.9196	.9549	.9734	.9841	.9901	.9937	.9959
24	.8730	.9270	.9559	.9734	.9833	.9893	.9930
25	.8106	.8878	.9306	.9574	.9729	.9826	.9885
26	.7348	.8375	.8965	.9354	.9583	.9730	.9820
27	.6463	.7748	.8523	.9059	.9381	.9595	.9727
28	.5507	.7021	.7981	.8685	.9118	.9415	.9602
29	.4493	.6194	.7336	.8221	.8782	.9181	.9435
30	.3537	.5324	.6608	.7676	.8374	.8889	.9223
31	.2652	.4435	.5820	.7052	.7887	.8532	.8958
32	.1894	.3577	.5000	.6368	.7333	.8111	.8637
33	.1270	.2777	.4180	.5637	.6714	.7626	.8258
34	.0804	.2075	.3392	.4888	.6050	.7085	.7822
35	.0466	.1478	.2664	.4139	.5353	.6494	.7332
36	.0256	.1005	.2019	.3421	.4647	.5869	.6795
37	.0122	.0648	.1477	.2753	.3950	.5220	.6219
38	.0052	.0393	.1035	.2154	.3286	.4568	.5616
39	.0017	.0221	.0694	.1633	.2667	.3925	.5000
40	.0006	.0115	.0441	.1199	.2113	.3311	.4384
41		.0053	.0266	.0847	.1626	.2735	.3781
42		.0022	.0149	.0576	.1218	.2213	.3205
43		.0008	.0079	.0375	.0882	.1749	.2668
44		.0002	.0037	.0233	.0619	.1350	.2178
45			.0016	.0136	.0417	.1014	.1742
46			.0005	.0075	.0271	.0742	.1363
47			.0002	.0038	.0167	.0526	.1042
48				.0017	.0099	.0361	.0777
49				.0007	.0054	.0239	.0565
50				.0003	.0028	.0152	.0398
51				.0001	.0013	.0092	.0273
52					.0006	.0053	.0180
53					.0002	.0029	.0115
54					.0001	.0015	.0070
55						.0007	.0041
56						.0003	.0022
57						.0001	.0012
58						.0000	.0005
59							.0002
60							.0001
61							.0000

TABLE 11 (Continued)

$n_2 = 8$					
x	$n_1 = 8$	$n_1 = 9$	$n_1 = 10$	$n_1 = 11$	$n_1 = 12$
20	1.0000	1.0000	1.0000	1.0000	1.0000
21	.9999	1.0000	1.0000	1.0000	1.0000
22	.9996	.9998	.9999	.9999	1.0000
23	.9989	.9994	.9997	.9998	.9999
24	.9974	.9986	.9992	.9996	.9997
25	.9941	.9969	.9983	.9990	.9994
26	.9885	.9938	.9965	.9980	.9988
27	.9789	.9886	.9935	.9962	.9977
28	.9643	.9804	.9887	.9934	.9960
29	.9428	.9680	.9813	.9889	.9932
30	.9133	.9504	.9704	.9823	.9890
31	.8737	.9262	.9551	.9728	.9830
32	.8246	.8947	.9344	.9598	.9745
33	.7650	.8549	.9075	.9423	.9629
34	.6970	.8069	.8738	.9199	.9477
35	.6212	.7508	.8328	.8918	.9281
36	.5413	.6877	.7847	.8578	.9038
37	.4587	.6184	.7296	.8174	.8742
38	.3788	.5457	.6686	.7710	.8392
39	.3030	.4714	.6031	.7189	.7986
40	.2350	.3983	.5347	.6621	.7528
41	.1754	.3281	.4653	.6015	.7022
42	.1263	.2636	.3969	.5386	.6476
43	.0867	.2055	.3314	.4746	.5898
44	.0572	.1557	.2704	.4113	.5302
45	.0357	.1139	.2153	.3500	.4698
46	.0211	.0807	.1672	.2925	.4102
47	.0115	.0548	.1262	.2394	.3524
48	.0059	.0358	.0925	.1919	.2978
49	.0026	.0221	.0656	.1503	.2472
50	.0011	.0131	.0449	.1150	.2014
51	.0004	.0072	.0296	.0856	.1608
52	.0001	.0037	.0187	.0621	.1258
53		.0017	.0113	.0437	.0962
54		.0007	.0065	.0298	.0719
55		.0002	.0035	.0196	.0523
56		.0001	.0017	.0124	.0371
57			.0008	.0075	.0255
58			.0003	.0043	.0170
59			.0001	.0023	.0110
60			.0000	.0012	.0068
61				.0006	.0040
62				.0002	.0023
63				.0001	.0012

$n_2 = 9$			
x	$n_1 = 9$	$n_1 = 10$	$n_1 = 11$
25	1.0000	1.0000	1.0000
26	1.0000	1.0000	1.0000
27	.9999	.9999	1.0000
28	.9996	.9998	.9999
29	.9991	.9995	.9997
30	.9981	.9990	.9995
31	.9963	.9980	.9989
32	.9932	.9964	.9980
33	.9882	.9937	.9964
34	.9805	.9894	.9940
35	.9695	.9831	.9903
36	.9540	.9741	.9849
37	.9332	.9618	.9773
38	.9062	.9453	.9669
39	.8724	.9240	.9532
40	.8313	.8972	.9355
41	.7833	.8646	.9133
42	.7283	.8259	.8862
43	.6677	.7813	.8538
44	.6025	.7310	.8160
45	.5346	.6759	.7731
46	.4654	.6166	.7251
47	.3975	.5548	.6729
48	.3323	.4916	.6173
49	.2717	.4287	.5593
50	.2167	.3673	.5000
51	.1687	.3092	.4407
52	.1276	.2552	.3827
53	.0938	.2064	.3271
54	.0668	.1632	.2749
55	.0460	.1262	.2269
56	.0305	.0952	.1840
57	.0195	.0700	.1462
58	.0118	.0500	.1138
59	.0068	.0347	.0867
60	.0037	.0232	.0645
61	.0019	.0150	.0468
62	.0009	.0093	.0331
63	.0004	.0056	.0227
64	.0001	.0031	.0151
65	.0000	.0017	.0097
66		.0008	.0060
67		.0004	.0036
68		.0002	.0020
69		.0001	.0011
70		.0000	.0005
71			.0003
72			.0001
73			.0000
74			.0000

$n_2 = 10$	
x	$n_1 = 10$
30	1.0000
31	1.0000
32	1.0000
33	.9999
34	.9998
35	.9996
36	.9992
37	.9984
38	.9971
39	.9951
40	.9920
41	.9874
42	.9808
43	.9718
44	.9597
45	.9440
46	.9239
47	.8993
48	.8694
49	.8344
50	.7940
51	.7486
52	.6986
53	.6449
54	.5881
55	.5296
56	.4704
57	.4119
58	.3551
59	.3014
60	.2514
61	.2060
62	.1656
63	.1306
64	.1007
65	.0761
66	.0560
67	.0403
68	.0282
69	.0192
70	.0126
71	.0080
72	.0049
73	.0029
74	.0016
75	.0008
76	.0004
77	.0002
78	.0001
79	.0000
80	.0000

TABLE 12

Factors Used When Constructing Control Charts

NUMBER OF OBSERVATIONS IN SAMPLE	CHART FOR AVERAGES		CHART FOR RANGES		
n	A_2	d_2	d_3	D_3	D_4
2	1.880	1.128	.853	0	3.276
3	1.023	1.693	.888	0	2.575
4	.729	2.059	.880	0	2.282
5	.577	2.326	.864	0	2.115
6	.483	2.534	.848	0	2.004
7	.419	2.704	.833	.076	1.924
8	.373	2.847	.820	.136	1.864
9	.337	2.970	.808	.184	1.816
10	.308	3.078	.797	.223	1.777
11	.285	3.173	.787	.256	1.744
12	.266	3.258	.778	.284	1.719
13	.249	3.336	.770	.308	1.692
14	.235	3.407	.762	.329	1.671
15	.223	3.472	.755	.348	1.652
16	.212	3.532	.749	.364	1.636
17	.203	3.588	.743	.379	1.621
18	.194	3.640	.738	.392	1.608
19	.187	3.689	.733	.404	1.596
20	.180	3.735	.729	.414	1.586
21	.173	3.778	.724	.425	1.575
22	.167	3.819	.720	.434	1.566
23	.162	3.858	.716	.443	1.557
24	.157	3.895	.712	.452	1.548
25	.153	3.931	.709	.459	1.541

Source: ASTM *Manual on Quality Control of Materials*, American Society for Testing Materials, Philadelphia, PA, 1951. Copyright ASTM. Reprinted with permission.

TABLE 13

Values of K for Tolerance Limits for Normal Distributions

n	1 − α = .95			1 − α = .99		
γ	.90	.95	.99	.90	.95	.99
2	32.019	37.674	48.430	160.193	188.491	242.300
3	8.380	9.916	12.861	18.930	22.401	29.055
4	5.369	6.370	8.299	9.398	11.150	14.527
5	4.275	5.079	6.634	6.612	7.855	10.260
6	3.712	4.414	5.775	5.337	6.345	8.301
7	3.369	4.007	5.248	4.613	5.488	7.187
8	3.136	3.732	4.891	4.147	4.936	6.468
9	2.967	3.532	4.631	3.822	4.550	5.966
10	2.839	3.379	4.433	3.582	4.265	5.594
11	2.737	3.259	4.277	3.397	4.045	5.308
12	2.655	3.162	4.150	3.250	3.870	5.079
13	2.587	3.081	4.044	3.130	3.727	4.893
14	2.529	3.012	3.955	3.029	3.608	4.737
15	2.480	2.954	3.878	2.945	3.507	4.605
16	2.437	2.903	3.812	2.872	3.421	4.492
17	2.400	2.858	3.754	2.808	3.345	4.393
18	2.366	2.819	3.702	2.753	3.279	4.307
19	2.337	2.784	3.656	2.703	3.221	4.230
20	2.310	2.752	3.615	2.659	3.168	4.161
25	2.208	2.631	3.457	2.494	2.972	3.904
30	2.140	2.549	3.350	2.385	2.841	3.733
35	2.090	2.490	3.272	2.306	2.748	3.611
40	2.052	2.445	3.213	2.247	2.677	3.518
45	2.021	2.408	3.165	2.200	2.621	3.444
50	1.996	2.379	3.126	2.162	2.576	3.385
55	1.976	2.354	3.094	2.130	2.538	3.335
60	1.958	2.333	3.066	2.103	2.506	3.293
65	1.943	2.315	3.042	2.080	2.478	3.257
70	1.929	2.299	3.021	2.060	2.454	3.225
75	1.917	2.285	3.002	2.042	2.433	3.197
80	1.907	2.272	2.986	2.026	2.414	3.173
85	1.897	2.261	2.971	2.012	2.397	3.150
90	1.889	2.251	2.958	1.999	2.382	3.130
95	1.881	2.241	2.945	1.987	2.368	3.112
100	1.874	2.233	2.934	1.977	2.355	3.096
150	1.825	2.175	2.859	1.905	2.270	2.983
200	1.798	2.143	2.816	1.865	2.222	2.921
250	1.780	2.121	2.788	1.839	2.191	2.880
300	1.767	2.106	2.767	1.820	2.169	2.850
400	1.749	2.084	2.739	1.794	2.138	2.809
500	1.737	2.070	2.721	1.777	2.117	2.783
600	1.729	2.060	2.707	1.764	2.102	2.763
700	1.722	2.052	2.697	1.755	2.091	2.748
800	1.717	2.046	2.688	1.747	2.082	2.736
900	1.712	2.040	2.682	1.741	2.075	2.726
1,000	1.709	2.036	2.676	1.736	2.068	2.718
∞	1.645	1.960	2.576	1.645	1.960	2.576

Source: From *Techniques of Statistical Analysis* by C. Eisenhart, M. W. Hastay, and W. A. Wallis. Copyright 1947, McGraw-Hill Book Company, Inc. Reproduced with permission of McGraw-Hill.

TABLE 14

Sample Size n for Nonparametric Tolerance Limits

γ	$1 - \alpha$					
	.50	.70	.90	.95	.99	.995
.995	336	488	777	947	1,325	1,483
.99	168	244	388	473	662	740
.95	34	49	77	93	130	146
.90	17	24	38	46	64	72
.85	11	16	25	30	42	47
.80	9	12	18	22	31	34
.75	7	10	15	18	24	27
.70	6	8	12	14	20	22
.60	4	6	9	10	14	16
.50	3	5	7	8	11	12

Source: Tables A-25d of Wilfrid J. Dixon and Frank J. Massey, Jr., *Introduction to Statistical Analysis*, 3d ed., McGraw-Hill Book Company, New York, 1969. Used with permission of McGraw-Hill Book Company.

TABLE 15
Critical Values of Spearman's Rank
Correlation Coefficient

n	$\alpha = .05$	$\alpha = .025$	$\alpha = .01$	$\alpha = .005$
5	.900	—	—	—
6	.829	.886	.943	—
7	.714	.786	.893	—
8	.643	.738	.833	.881
9	.600	.683	.783	.833
10	.564	.648	.745	.794
11	.523	.623	.736	.818
12	.497	.591	.703	.780
13	.475	.566	.673	.745
14	.457	.545	.646	.716
15	.441	.525	.623	.689
16	.425	.507	.601	.666
17	.412	.490	.582	.645
18	.399	.476	.564	.625
19	.388	.462	.549	.608
20	.377	.450	.534	.591
21	.368	.438	.521	.576
22	.359	.428	.508	.562
23	.351	.418	.496	.549
24	.343	.409	.485	.537
25	.336	.400	.475	.526
26	.329	.392	.465	.515
27	.323	.385	.456	.505
28	.317	.377	.448	.496
29	.311	.370	.440	.487
30	.305	.364	.432	.478

Source: From Olds, E. G. "Distribution of Sums of Squares of
Rank Differences for Small Samples." *Annals of Mathematical Statis-
tics*, Vol. 9, 1938. Reproduced with the permission of the Editor,
Annals of Mathematical Statistics.

TABLE 16
Critical Values for the Theil Zero-Slope Test

c	4	5	8	9	12	13	16	17	20	21	24	25	28	29	32	33	36	37	40
0	.625	.592	.548	.540	.527	.524	.518	.516	.513	.512	.510	.509	.508	.507	.506	.506	.505	.505	.505
2	.375	.408	.452	.460	.473	.476	.482	.484	.487	.488	.490	.491	.492	.493	.494	.494	.495	.495	.495
4	.167	.242	.360	.381	.420	.429	.447	.452	.462	.464	.471	.472	.477	.478	.481	.482	.484	.484	.486
6	.042	.117	.274	.306	.369	.383	.412	.420	.436	.441	.451	.454	.461	.463	.468	.469	.473	.474	.477
8		.042	.199	.238	.319	.338	.378	.388	.411	.417	.432	.436	.446	.448	.455	.457	.462	.464	.468
10		.008	.138	.179	.273	.295	.345	.358	.387	.394	.413	.418	.430	.434	.442	.445	.452	.453	.459
12			.089	.130	.230	.255	.313	.328	.362	.371	.394	.400	.415	.419	.430	.433	.441	.443	.449
14			.054	.090	.190	.218	.282	.299	.339	.349	.375	.382	.400	.405	.417	.421	.430	.433	.440
16			.031	.060	.155	.184	.253	.271	.315	.327	.356	.364	.385	.390	.405	.409	.420	.423	.431
18			.016	.038	.125	.153	.225	.245	.293	.306	.338	.347	.370	.376	.392	.397	.409	.413	.422
20			.007	.022	.098	.126	.199	.220	.271	.285	.320	.330	.355	.362	.380	.385	.399	.403	.413
22			.002	.012	.076	.102	.175	.196	.250	.265	.303	.314	.341	.348	.368	.373	.388	.393	.404
24			.001	.006	.058	.082	.153	.174	.230	.246	.286	.297	.326	.334	.356	.362	.378	.383	.395
26			.000	.003	.043	.064	.133	.154	.211	.228	.270	.282	.312	.321	.344	.350	.368	.373	.386
28				.001	.031	.050	.114	.135	.193	.210	.254	.266	.298	.308	.332	.339	.358	.363	.377
30				.000	.022	.038	.097	.118	.176	.193	.238	.251	.285	.295	.320	.328	.347	.353	.369
32					.016	.029	.083	.102	.159	.177	.223	.237	.272	.282	.309	.317	.338	.344	.360
34					.010	.021	.070	.088	.144	.162	.209	.222	.259	.270	.298	.306	.328	.334	.351
36					.007	.015	.058	.076	.130	.147	.195	.209	.246	.257	.287	.295	.318	.325	.343
38					.004	.011	.048	.064	.117	.134	.181	.196	.234	.246	.276	.285	.308	.315	.334
40					.003	.007	.039	.054	.104	.121	.169	.183	.222	.234	.265	.274	.299	.306	.326
42					.002	.005	.032	.046	.093	.109	.156	.171	.211	.223	.255	.264	.290	.297	.318
44					.001	.003	.026	.038	.082	.098	.145	.159	.200	.212	.244	.254	.280	.288	.309
46					.000	.002	.021	.032	.073	.088	.134	.148	.189	.201	.234	.244	.271	.279	.301
48						.001	.016	.026	.064	.079	.123	.138	.178	.191	.224	.235	.262	.271	.293
50						.001	.013	.021	.056	.070	.113	.128	.168	.181	.215	.225	.254	.262	.285
52						.000	.010	.017	.049	.062	.104	.118	.158	.171	.206	.216	.245	.254	.277
54							.008	.014	.043	.055	.095	.109	.149	.162	.197	.207	.237	.245	.270
56							.006	.011	.037	.049	.087	.101	.140	.153	.188	.199	.228	.237	.262
58							.004	.009	.032	.043	.079	.093	.131	.144	.179	.190	.220	.229	.255
60							.003	.007	.027	.037	.072	.085	.123	.136	.171	.182	.212	.222	.247
62							.002	.005	.023	.032	.066	.078	.115	.128	.163	.174	.204	.214	.240
64							.002	.004	.020	.028	.059	.071	.108	.120	.155	.166	.197	.206	.233
66							.001	.003	.017	.024	.054	.065	.101	.112	.147	.158	.189	.199	.226
68							.001	.002	.014	.021	.048	.059	.094	.105	.140	.151	.182	.192	.219
70							.001	.002	.012	.018	.044	.054	.087	.099	.133	.144	.175	.185	.212
72							.000	.001	.010	.015	.039	.049	.081	.092	.126	.137	.168	.178	.205
74								.001	.008	.013	.035	.044	.075	.086	.119	.130	.161	.171	.199
76								.001	.007	.011	.031	.040	.070	.080	.113	.124	.155	.165	.192
78								.000	.006	.009	.028	.036	.065	.075	.107	.117	.148	.158	.186
80									.005	.008	.025	.032	.060	.070	.101	.111	.142	.152	.180
82									.004	.007	.022	.029	.055	.065	.095	.106	.136	.146	.174
84									.003	.005	.019	.026	.051	.060	.090	.100	.130	.140	.168
86									.002	.005	.017	.023	.047	.056	.085	.095	.124	.134	.162
88									.002	.004	.015	.021	.043	.052	.080	.090	.119	.129	.156
90									.002	.003	.013	.018	.039	.048	.075	.085	.114	.123	.151
92									.001	.002	.011	.016	.036	.044	.070	.080	.108	.118	.146
94									.001	.002	.010	.014	.033	.041	.066	.075	.103	.113	.140
96									.001	.002	.009	.013	.030	.037	.062	.071	.099	.108	.135
98									.001	.001	.007	.011	.027	.034	.058	.067	.094	.103	.130
100									.000	.001	.006	.010	.025	.031	.054	.063	.089	.098	.125

TABLE 16 (Continued)

c																		
	6	7	10	11	14	15	18	19	22	23	26	27	30	31	34	35	38	39
1	.500	.500	.500	.500	.500	.500	.500	.500	.500	.500	.500	.500	.500	.500	.500	.500	.500	.500
3	.360	.386	.431	.440	.457	.461	.470	.473	.478	.479	.483	.484	.486	.487	.488	.489	.490	.490
5	.235	.281	.364	.381	.415	.423	.441	.445	.456	.458	.465	.467	.472	.473	.477	.478	.480	.481
7	.136	.191	.300	.324	.374	.385	.411	.418	.434	.438	.448	.451	.458	.460	.465	.466	.470	.472
9	.068	.119	.242	.271	.334	.349	.383	.391	.412	.417	.431	.434	.444	.446	.453	.455	.460	.462
11	.028	.068	.190	.223	.295	.313	.354	.365	.390	.397	.414	.418	.430	.433	.442	.444	.450	.452
13	.008	.035	.146	.179	.259	.279	.327	.339	.369	.377	.397	.402	.416	.420	.430	.433	.440	.443
15	.001	.015	.108	.141	.225	.248	.300	.314	.348	.357	.380	.386	.402	.407	.418	.422	.431	.433
17		.005	.078	.109	.194	.218	.275	.290	.328	.338	.363	.371	.389	.394	.407	.411	.421	.424
19		.001	.054	.082	.165	.190	.250	.267	.308	.319	.347	.355	.375	.381	.396	.400	.411	.414
21		.000	.036	.060	.140	.164	.227	.245	.289	.301	.331	.340	.362	.368	.384	.389	.401	.405
23			.023	.043	.117	.141	.205	.223	.270	.283	.316	.325	.349	.355	.373	.378	.392	.396
25			.014	.030	.096	.120	.184	.203	.252	.265	.300	.310	.336	.343	.362	.368	.382	.387
27			.008	.020	.079	.101	.165	.184	.234	.248	.285	.296	.323	.331	.351	.357	.373	.377
29			.005	.013	.063	.084	.147	.166	.217	.232	.270	.281	.310	.318	.340	.347	.363	.368
31			.002	.008	.050	.070	.130	.149	.201	.216	.256	.268	.298	.306	.329	.336	.354	.359
33			.001	.005	.040	.057	.115	.133	.186	.201	.242	.254	.286	.295	.319	.326	.345	.350
35			.000	.003	.031	.046	.100	.119	.171	.187	.229	.241	.274	.283	.308	.316	.336	.341
37				.002	.024	.037	.088	.105	.157	.173	.216	.228	.262	.272	.298	.306	.327	.333
39				.001	.018	.029	.076	.093	.144	.160	.203	.216	.251	.261	.288	.296	.318	.324
41				.000	.013	.023	.066	.082	.131	.147	.191	.204	.239	.250	.278	.286	.309	.315
43					.010	.018	.056	.072	.120	.135	.179	.192	.228	.239	.268	.277	.300	.307
45					.007	.014	.048	.062	.109	.124	.168	.181	.218	.229	.259	.267	.291	.298
47					.005	.010	.041	.054	.099	.114	.157	.170	.208	.219	.249	.258	.283	.290
49					.003	.008	.034	.047	.089	.104	.147	.160	.198	.209	.240	.249	.274	.282
51					.002	.006	.029	.040	.080	.094	.137	.150	.188	.199	.231	.240	.266	.274
53					.002	.004	.024	.034	.072	.086	.127	.141	.178	.190	.222	.232	.258	.266
55					.001	.003	.020	.029	.064	.078	.118	.132	.169	.181	.213	.223	.250	.258
57					.001	.002	.016	.025	.058	.070	.110	.123	.160	.172	.205	.215	.242	.250
59					.000	.001	.013	.021	.051	.063	.102	.115	.152	.164	.196	.206	.234	.243
61						.001	.011	.017	.045	.057	.094	.107	.144	.155	.188	.198	.227	.235
63						.001	.009	.014	.040	.051	.087	.099	.136	.147	.180	.191	.219	.228
65						.000	.007	.012	.035	.046	.080	.092	.128	.140	.173	.183	.212	.221
67							.005	.010	.031	.041	.073	.085	.121	.132	.165	.176	.205	.214
69							.004	.008	.027	.036	.067	.079	.114	.125	.158	.168	.198	.207
71							.003	.006	.024	.032	.062	.073	.107	.118	.151	.161	.191	.200
73							.003	.005	.021	.028	.057	.067	.100	.112	.144	.154	.184	.193
75							.002	.004	.018	.025	.052	.062	.094	.105	.137	.148	.177	.187
77							.001	.003	.015	.022	.047	.057	.088	.099	.131	.141	.171	.180
79							.001	.003	.013	.019	.043	.052	.083	.093	.125	.135	.165	.174
81							.001	.002	.011	.017	.039	.048	.077	.088	.119	.129	.158	.168
83							.001	.002	.010	.015	.035	.044	.072	.082	.113	.123	.152	.162
85							.000	.001	.008	.013	.032	.040	.067	.077	.107	.117	.147	.156
87								.001	.007	.011	.029	.036	.063	.072	.102	.112	.141	.150
89								.001	.006	.009	.026	.033	.059	.068	.097	.107	.135	.145
91								.001	.005	.008	.023	.030	.054	.063	.092	.101	.130	.139
93								.000	.004	.007	.021	.027	.051	.059	.087	.096	.125	.134
95									.003	.006	.019	.025	.047	.055	.082	.092	.120	.129
97									.003	.005	.017	.022	.043	.052	.078	.087	.115	.124
99									.002	.004	.015	.020	.040	.048	.074	.083	.110	.119
101									.002	.004	.013	.018	.037	.045	.070	.078	.105	.114

TABLE 17
Critical Values for the Durbin–Watson d Statistic ($\alpha = .05$)

n	$k=1$ d_L	$k=1$ d_U	$k=2$ d_L	$k=2$ d_U	$k=3$ d_L	$k=3$ d_U	$k=4$ d_L	$k=4$ d_U	$k=5$ d_L	$k=5$ d_U
15	1.08	1.36	.95	1.54	.82	1.75	.69	1.97	.56	2.21
16	1.10	1.37	.98	1.54	.86	1.73	.74	1.93	.62	2.15
17	1.13	1.38	1.02	1.54	.90	1.71	.78	1.90	.67	2.10
18	1.16	1.39	1.05	1.53	.93	1.69	.82	1.87	.71	2.06
19	1.18	1.40	1.08	1.53	.97	1.68	.86	1.85	.75	2.02
20	1.20	1.41	1.10	1.54	1.00	1.68	.90	1.83	.79	1.99
21	1.22	1.42	1.13	1.54	1.03	1.67	.93	1.81	.83	1.96
22	1.24	1.43	1.15	1.54	1.05	1.66	.96	1.80	.86	1.94
23	1.26	1.44	1.17	1.54	1.08	1.66	.99	1.79	.90	1.92
24	1.27	1.45	1.19	1.55	1.10	1.66	1.01	1.78	.93	1.90
25	1.29	1.45	1.21	1.55	1.12	1.66	1.04	1.77	.95	1.89
26	1.30	1.46	1.22	1.55	1.14	1.65	1.06	1.76	.98	1.88
27	1.32	1.47	1.24	1.56	1.16	1.65	1.08	1.76	1.01	1.86
28	1.33	1.48	1.26	1.56	1.18	1.65	1.10	1.75	1.03	1.85
29	1.34	1.48	1.27	1.56	1.20	1.65	1.12	1.74	1.05	1.84
30	1.35	1.49	1.28	1.57	1.21	1.65	1.14	1.74	1.07	1.83
31	1.36	1.50	1.30	1.57	1.23	1.65	1.16	1.74	1.09	1.83
32	1.37	1.50	1.31	1.57	1.24	1.65	1.18	1.73	1.11	1.82
33	1.38	1.51	1.32	1.58	1.26	1.65	1.19	1.73	1.13	1.81
34	1.39	1.51	1.33	1.58	1.27	1.65	1.21	1.73	1.15	1.81
35	1.40	1.52	1.34	1.58	1.28	1.65	1.22	1.73	1.16	1.80
36	1.41	1.52	1.35	1.59	1.29	1.65	1.24	1.73	1.18	1.80
37	1.42	1.53	1.36	1.59	1.31	1.66	1.25	1.72	1.19	1.80
38	1.43	1.54	1.37	1.59	1.32	1.66	1.26	1.72	1.21	1.79
39	1.43	1.54	1.38	1.60	1.33	1.66	1.27	1.72	1.22	1.79
40	1.44	1.54	1.39	1.60	1.34	1.66	1.29	1.72	1.23	1.79
45	1.48	1.57	1.43	1.62	1.38	1.67	1.34	1.72	1.29	1.78
50	1.50	1.59	1.46	1.63	1.42	1.67	1.38	1.72	1.34	1.77
55	1.53	1.60	1.49	1.64	1.45	1.68	1.41	1.72	1.38	1.77
60	1.55	1.62	1.51	1.65	1.48	1.69	1.44	1.73	1.41	1.77
65	1.57	1.63	1.54	1.66	1.50	1.70	1.47	1.73	1.44	1.77
70	1.58	1.64	1.55	1.67	1.52	1.70	1.49	1.74	1.46	1.77
75	1.60	1.65	1.57	1.68	1.54	1.71	1.51	1.74	1.49	1.77
80	1.61	1.66	1.59	1.69	1.56	1.72	1.53	1.74	1.51	1.77
85	1.62	1.67	1.60	1.70	1.57	1.72	1.55	1.75	1.52	1.77
90	1.63	1.68	1.61	1.70	1.59	1.73	1.57	1.75	1.54	1.78
95	1.64	1.69	1.62	1.71	1.60	1.73	1.58	1.75	1.56	1.78
100	1.65	1.69	1.63	1.72	1.61	1.74	1.59	1.76	1.57	1.78

Source: From Durbin, J., and Watson, G. S. "Testing for Serial Correlation in Least Squares Regression, II." *Biometrika,* Vol. 38, 1951, pp. 159–178. Reproduced by permission of the *Biometrika* Trustees.

TABLE 18

Critical Values for the Durbin–Watson d Statistic ($\alpha = .01$)

	$k = 1$		$k = 2$		$k = 3$		$k = 4$		$k = 5$	
n	d_L	d_U	d_L	d_U	d_L	d_U	d_L	d_U	d_L	d_U
15	.81	1.07	.70	1.25	.59	1.46	.49	1.70	.39	1.96
16	.84	1.09	.74	1.25	.63	1.44	.53	1.66	.44	1.90
17	.87	1.10	.77	1.25	.67	1.43	.57	1.63	.48	1.85
18	.90	1.12	.80	1.26	.71	1.42	.61	1.60	.52	1.80
19	.93	1.13	.83	1.26	.74	1.41	.65	1.58	.56	1.77
20	.95	1.15	.86	1.27	.77	1.41	.68	1.57	.60	1.74
21	.97	1.16	.89	1.27	.80	1.41	.72	1.55	.63	1.71
22	1.00	1.17	.91	1.28	.83	1.40	.75	1.54	.66	1.69
23	1.02	1.19	.94	1.29	.86	1.40	.77	1.53	.70	1.67
24	1.04	1.20	.96	1.30	.88	1.41	.80	1.53	.72	1.66
25	1.05	1.21	.98	1.30	.90	1.41	.83	1.52	.75	1.65
26	1.07	1.22	1.00	1.31	.93	1.41	.85	1.52	.78	1.64
27	1.09	1.23	1.02	1.32	.95	1.41	.88	1.51	.81	1.63
28	1.10	1.24	1.04	1.32	.97	1.41	.90	1.51	.83	1.62
29	1.12	1.25	1.05	1.33	.99	1.42	.92	1.51	.85	1.61
30	1.13	1.26	1.07	1.34	1.01	1.42	.94	1.51	.88	1.61
31	1.15	1.27	1.08	1.34	1.02	1.42	.96	1.51	.90	1.60
32	1.16	1.28	1.10	1.35	1.04	1.43	.98	1.51	.92	1.60
33	1.17	1.29	1.11	1.36	1.05	1.43	1.00	1.51	.94	1.59
34	1.18	1.30	1.13	1.36	1.07	1.43	1.01	1.51	.95	1.59
35	1.19	1.31	1.14	1.37	1.08	1.44	1.03	1.51	.97	1.59
36	1.21	1.32	1.15	1.38	1.10	1.44	1.04	1.51	.99	1.59
37	1.22	1.32	1.16	1.38	1.11	1.45	1.06	1.51	1.00	1.59
38	1.23	1.33	1.18	1.39	1.12	1.45	1.07	1.52	1.02	1.58
39	1.24	1.34	1.19	1.39	1.14	1.45	1.09	1.52	1.03	1.58
40	1.25	1.34	1.20	1.40	1.15	1.46	1.10	1.52	1.05	1.58
45	1.29	1.38	1.24	1.42	1.20	1.48	1.16	1.53	1.11	1.58
50	1.32	1.40	1.28	1.45	1.24	1.49	1.20	1.54	1.16	1.59
55	1.36	1.43	1.32	1.47	1.28	1.51	1.25	1.55	1.21	1.59
60	1.38	1.45	1.35	1.48	1.32	1.52	1.28	1.56	1.25	1.60
65	1.41	1.47	1.38	1.50	1.35	1.53	1.31	1.57	1.28	1.61
70	1.43	1.49	1.40	1.52	1.37	1.55	1.34	1.58	1.31	1.61
75	1.45	1.50	1.42	1.53	1.39	1.56	1.37	1.59	1.34	1.62
80	1.47	1.52	1.44	1.54	1.42	1.57	1.39	1.60	1.36	1.62
85	1.48	1.53	1.46	1.55	1.43	1.58	1.41	1.60	1.39	1.63
90	1.50	1.54	1.47	1.56	1.45	1.59	1.43	1.61	1.41	1.64
95	1.51	1.55	1.49	1.57	1.47	1.60	1.45	1.62	1.42	1.64
100	1.52	1.56	1.50	1.58	1.48	1.60	1.46	1.63	1.44	1.65

Source: From Durbin, J., and Watson, G. S. "Testing for Serial Correlation in Least Squares Regression, II." *Biometrika*, Vol. 38, 1951, pp. 159–178. Reproduced by permission of the *Biometrika* Trustees.

APPENDIX B   CALCULATION FORMULAS FOR PARAMETRIC ANALYSIS OF VARIANCE

COMPLETELY RANDOMIZED DESIGN

1. CM = Correction for mean

$$= \frac{(\text{Total of all observations})^2}{\text{Total number of observations}} = \frac{(\Sigma y)^2}{n}$$

   k = Number of means (treatments) to be compared

   n_i = Number of observations for treatment i

   n = Total sample size = $n_1 + n_2 + \cdots + n_k$

2. SS(Total) = Total sum of squares

   = (Sum of squares of all observations) − CM

   = Σy^2 − CM

3. SST = Sum of squares for treatments

$$= \left(\begin{array}{c} \text{Sum of squares of treatment totals} \\ \text{with each square divided by the} \\ \text{number of observations in that treatment} \end{array} \right) - \text{CM}$$

$$= \frac{T_1^2}{n_1} + \frac{T_2^2}{n_2} + \cdots + \frac{T_k^2}{n_k} - \text{CM}$$

   where T_i is the total of all observations for treatment i, $i = 1, 2, \ldots, k$.

4. SSE = Sum of squares for error

   = SS(Total) − SST

5. MST = Mean square for treatments = $\dfrac{\text{SST}}{k-1}$

6. MSE = Mean square for error = $\dfrac{\text{SSE}}{n-k}$

7. F = Test statistic = $\dfrac{\text{MST}}{\text{MSE}}$

RANDOMIZED BLOCK DESIGN

1. CM = Correction for mean

$$= \frac{(\text{Total of all } n \text{ observations})^2}{n}$$

   where

$$n = bk$$
$$b = \text{Number of blocks}$$
$$k = \text{Number of treatments}$$

2. SS(Total) = (Sum of squares of all observations) − CM

3. $SST = \dfrac{T_1^2 + T_2^2 + \cdots + T_k^2}{b} - CM$

   where T_i is the total of all observations for treatment i, $i = 1, 2, ..., k$.

4. $SSB = \dfrac{B_1^2 + B_2^2 + \cdots + B_b^2}{k} - CM$

   where B_i is the total of all observations for block i, $i = 1, 2, ..., b$.

5. SSE = SS(Total) − SST − SSB

6. $MST = \dfrac{SST}{k-1}$, $\quad MSB = \dfrac{SSB}{b-1}$, $\quad$ and $\quad MSE = \dfrac{SSE}{n-b-k+1}$

7. F statistic for comparing treatment means: $\quad F = \dfrac{MST}{MSE}$

8. F statistic for comparing block means: $\quad F = \dfrac{MSB}{MSE}$

TWO-FACTOR FACTORIAL EXPERIMENT

1. CM = Correction for mean

   $= \dfrac{(\text{Total of all } n \text{ observations})^2}{n}$

   where

   $n = abr$

   $a =$ Number of levels of factor A

   $b =$ Number of levels of factor B

   $r =$ Number of replications of the factorial experiment

2. SS(Total) = (Sum of squares of all observations) − CM

3. Main effect sum of squares for factor A:

$$SS(A) = \frac{A_1^2 + A_2^2 + \cdots + A_a^2}{br} - CM$$

   where A_i is the total of all observations at level i for factor A.

4. Main effect sum of squares for factor B:

$$SS(B) = \frac{B_1^2 + B_2^2 + \cdots + B_b^2}{ar} - CM$$

   where B_i is the total of all observations at level i for factor B.

5. Interaction sum of squares:

$$SS(AB) = \sum_{i,j} \frac{(AB_{ij})^2}{r} - SS(A) - SS(B) - CM$$

where AB_{ij} is the sum of all observations in the cell corresponding to the ith level of factor A and the jth level of factor B.

[*Note:* To find SS(AB), square each cell total, sum the squares for all cell totals, divide by r, and then subtract SS(A), SS(B), and CM.]

6. $SSE = SS(\text{Total}) - SS(A) - SS(B) - SS(AB)$

7. $MS(A) = \dfrac{SS(A)}{a - 1}$

   $MS(B) = \dfrac{SS(B)}{b - 1}$

   $MS(AB) = \dfrac{SS(AB)}{(a - 1)(b - 1)}$

   $MSE = s^2 = \dfrac{SSE}{ab(r - 1)}$

8. F statistic for testing AB interaction: $\quad F = \dfrac{MS(AB)}{MSE}$

9. F statistic for testing A main effect: $\quad F = \dfrac{MS(A)}{MSE}$

10. F statistic for testing B main effect: $\quad F = \dfrac{MS(B)}{MSE}$

APPENDIX C   ASP TUTORIAL

This appendix provides an overview of the ASP program. It gives the minimal hardware requirements and start-up procedures necessary to begin an ASP session on a personal computer (PC). This tutorial is not intended to replace any of the ASP documentation manuals available from the publisher or DMC Software, Inc. (See the Preface.)

HARDWARE REQUIREMENTS   ASP must be run on an IBM-compatible PC with at least 512K of memory, two disk drives (either one hard drive and one floppy drive, or two floppy drives), and DOS 2.0 or higher. A blank formatted floppy disk is also required for data storage, unless your PC has a hard drive (ie, fixed disk) available for storing data.

GETTING STARTING   To use the ASP program, you must first load it into the memory of the computer. To accomplish this when starting ASP from a floppy disk:

1. Insert your copy of ASP (provided in the back cover pocket) into either of your two disk drives, drive A or drive B. (Assume drive A.)
2. Type A: and press ENTER to make drive A the current drive.

```
A:  <ENTER>
```

3. Type ASP and press ENTER to load the ASP program into memory.

```
ASP  <ENTER>
```

The ASP disk must remain in drive A for as long as you are using the program.

To start ASP from a fixed disk or hard drive (eg, drive C), it is first necessary to install ASP on the fixed disk. This is accomplished by placing your copy of the ASP disk into drive A and entering the following commands at the DOS prompt:

```
C:          <ENTER>
MD \ASP     <ENTER>
CD \ASP     <ENTER>
COPY A:*.*  <ENTER>
```

(This sequence of DOS commands assumes the drive letter of the fixed disk is C and that the subdirectory in which the ASP program resides is \ASP.) Once ASP has been installed on the fixed disk it need not be installed again. The ASP program can then be started at any point in the future by entering the following commands at the DOS prompt:

```
C:          <ENTER>
CD \ASP     <ENTER>
ASP         <ENTER>
```

THE MAIN MENU   The initial screen to appear as the ASP program is loaded into memory displays copyright and licensing information. After reading this information, press any key to obtain the Main Menu shown in Figure C.1.

FIGURE C.1

The ASP Main Menu

```
****************  MAIN MENU  ****************
   A Statistical Package for Business, Economics, and The Social Sciences
        Copyright 1992 by DMC Software, Inc. (Version 2.xx)

 A. Analysis of Variance    B. Regression Analysis    C. Correlation Matrix
 D. Summary Statistics      E. Probability Dists.     F. File Management Menu
 G. Time Series Analysis    H. Hypothesis Tests       I. INSTRUCTIONS
 J. Factor Analysis         K. Miscellaneous Plots    L. Crosstab/Contingency
 M. Auxiliary Programs      N. Enter a DOS Command    O. Scr./Data Dir. Dflts

 F1=ALT COMMANDS MENU       F2=CALCULATOR      F3=TOGGLE PRINT (OFF)     X=EXIT
```

The Main Menu is a typical ASP "bounce bar" menu. The highlighted bar can be moved from option to option by pressing the SPACE BAR, the cursor control keys ($\rightarrow$ $\leftarrow$ $\uparrow$ $\downarrow$), or the TAB key. Once your selection is made, press ENTER to display submenus associated with the option. (You can also make a selection by pressing the letter of the desired option.)

Table C.1 (p. A38) gives a brief description of each of the Main Menu options and the corresponding chapters in the text. Several of these options contain statistical procedures that are beyond the scope of the text. Only the statistical routines covered in the text are described in the table.

ALTERNATE COMMANDS MENU   All the statistical routines in ASP are accessible through the Main Menu. However, additional commands can be executed through the Alt Commands Menu. The Alt Commands Menu is called by pressing the F1 function key anytime within the ASP program. When F1 is pressed from the Main Menu, the Alt Commands Menu appears as shown in Figure C.2 (p. A39).

TABLE C.1

Options on the Main Menu

OPTION	DESCRIPTION	CHAPTER(S)
A. Analysis of Variance	One-way and two-way ANOVAs	13
B. Regression Analysis	Simple and multiple regression; residual analysis	10–11
C. Correlation Matrix	Bivariate correlations	10
D. Summary Statistics	Mean, median, standard deviation, etc.	3
E. Probability Dists.	Binomial and normal distributions	4
F. File Management Menu	Creating, saving, editing data	—
G. Time Series Analysis	Moving averages, exponential smoothing, simple linear forecasts	12
H. Hypothesis Tests	Confidence intervals and hypothesis tests for means, proportions, and variances; 1-way table χ^2 test; nonparametric tests	5–8
I. INSTRUCTIONS	A short tutorial on the use of ASP	—
J. Factor Analysis Menu	(Beyond the scope of this text)	—
K. Miscellaneous Plots	Stem-and-leaf display, box plot, normal probability plot, scatterplot	2, 3, 5
L. Crosstab/Contingency	Two-way (contingency) table χ^2 test	8
M. Auxiliary Programs	(Beyond the scope of this text)	—
N. Enter a DOS Command	Enter and execute DOS commands within an ASP session	—
O. Scr./Data Dir. Dflts.	Set the color scheme on the monitor; set the default directory and printer port	—

You can execute the commands on this menu by either moving the cursor to the desired option and pressing ENTER or by pressing the letter associated with the option. You will find this menu most useful for:

- Creating or editing data sets (option E)
- Listing data (option L)
- Getting data from an already created ASP data set (option G)
- Creating new variables for a data set (option T)
- Adding or deleting variables and/or cases (option A)
- Changing the names of variables (option I)
- Getting or saving data in an external ASCII file (option B)
- Saving an ASP data set (option S)

CREATING A DATA MATRIX   Typically, you will use ASP to analyze a data set. To do this, you must first create an ASP "data matrix." Select E = Edit Or Create Data Matrix on the Alt Commands Menu and ASP responds with a series of questions and prompts. The first question is

```
EDIT or CREATE? E
```

FIGURE C.2

The Alt Commands Menu

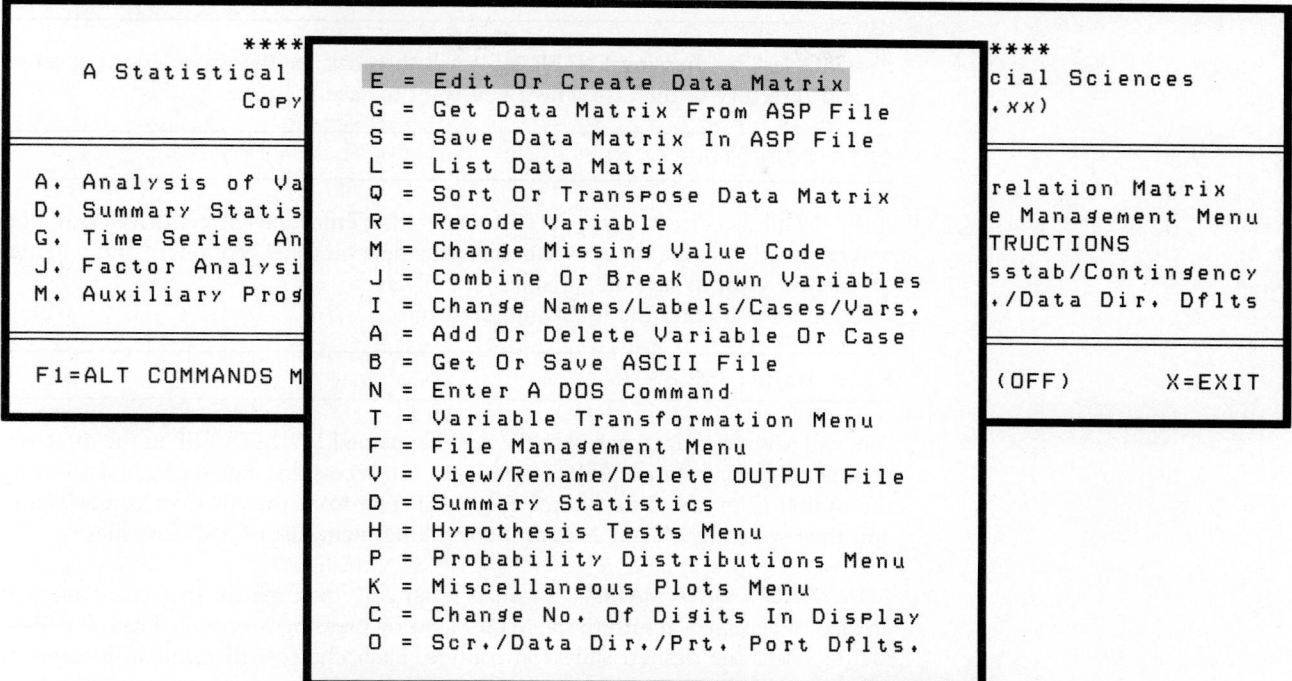

Note that the ASP default answer is E for EDIT. This is used when you want to edit an existing ASP data matrix. To create a data matrix, press the letter C (for CREATE). You are now prompted with the question:

Number of Variables? 1

Change the default to the correct number and press ENTER. ASP creates names for the variables using the convention Var1, Var2, Var3, etc., then asks:

Are Names OK? Y

To change the names, press N (for No). ASP will then ask you to enter the new name of each variable. Once this is completed, ASP will prompt you, one case (ie, one observation) and one variable at a time, to enter the data into the data matrix.

Important: The ASP data editor will not accept letters or special characters (eg, dollar sign, comma) as data. Only whole numbers or numbers with decimals should be entered into the data matrix.

When data entry is complete, press X to exit the numerical data editor. Several questions will be asked, the most important being:

`Do You Wish to Save the Data Matrix?  Y`

Answer "yes" by pressing ENTER. ASP will then ask for the drive letter (eg, drive A) and directory of the disk where you want to save the data:

`DATA DIRECTORY:  A:\`

If the default is correct, press ENTER. Otherwise, enter the correct drive/path. You will be asked to name the ASP data file, provide a file label (optional), and whether or not you want to save all variables and all cases.

Suppose you enter the following file name:

`File Name:  MYDATA`

ASP will save your data matrix in the ASP file named MYDATA.ASP in the directory specified earlier. In future ASP sessions, you can access this data set by first selecting the option G = Get Data Matrix From ASP File from the Alt Commands Menu, and then selecting MYDATA from the resulting menu-list of ASP data files.

ANALYZING A DATA MATRIX   To analyze an ASP data matrix that you have just created or accessed, return to the Main Menu by pressing X or ESC. From the Main Menu, select the desired statistical routine. Each choice will result in a series of submenus, prompts, and/or questions similar to those shown previously. After making your selections, ASP will perform the analysis and immediately display the results on the monitor screen. ASP menu selections at the bottom of the screen permit you to send the output directly to a printer or to save the output in a file for future use.

AVAILABLE DOCUMENTATION

- *ASP User's Manual* (by DMC Software, Inc.)—available free to adopters of the text from the publisher of the text, Macmillan/Dellen Publishing.
- *ASP Tutorial and Student Guide* (by George Blackford)—can be purchased directly from DMC Software, Inc., or from your campus book store (see the Preface).

SHORT ANSWERS TO PROBLEMS

CHAPTER 1

1.1. a. Qualitative   **b.** Quantitative   **c.** Qualitative   **d.** Quantitative   **e.** Quantitative   **f.** Qualitative   **1.2. a.** Qualitative
b. Qualitative   **c.** Quantitative   **1.3. a.** Hawaiian properties
b. Leased fee value: quantitative; lot size: quantitative; neighborhood: qualitative; lot location: qualitative
1.4. a. Canadian manufacturing workers
b. Behavior type: qualitative; age: quantitative; managerial level: qualitative; number of employees supervised: quantitative; performance rating: quantitative
1.5. a. New automobiles
b. Model: qualitative; manufacturer: qualitative; transmission: qualitative; engine size: quantitative; number of cylinders: quantitative; city mpg: quantitative; highway mpg: quantitative
1.6. a. Differences between the two SAT scores of all students who did not perform as well as they should have the first time they took the SAT, but took a beta blocker prior to the second test
b. The differences between the SAT scores for the 22 high school students
c. It appears that beta blockers are effective in reducing anxiety in test takers, and therefore, lead to a greater average increase in SAT scores than the national average.
1.7. a. Quality of all gear shifts produced   **b.** Status (defective or not) of each of the 50 gear shifts tested per hour
1.8. a. Enumerative   **b.** All regular TV viewers   **c.** Viewing status (watched *Seinfeld*, or not) of each of the 165 families
1.9. a. Analytic   **b.** Annual prime interest rates from 1987 to 1993   **c.** Prime interest rates for all years, past and present
1.10. a. Productivities of all high self-esteem students in the positive inequity condition; productivities of all high self-esteem students in the equity condition; productivities of all low self-esteem students in the positive inequity condition; productivities of all low self-esteem students in the equity condition
b. Productivities of the 20 high self-esteem students in the positive inequity condition; productivities of the 20 high self-esteem students in the equity condition; productivities of the 20 low self-esteem students in the positive inequity condition; productivities of the 20 low self-esteem students in the equity condition
c. Yes   **d.** Sample information   **1.11. a.** Merit increase; quantitative   **b.** Sample
1.12. Not every person will return the questionnaire   **1.14.** New product tested does not have benefit of advertising blitz
1.15. Sample of high school juniors was probably not selected at random and therefore, may not be representative of population, in general.
1.16. The 1936 election took place during the Depression; only the wealthy (a small percentage) could afford a telephone.

CHAPTER 2

2.1. a. Type of store where white bread is purchased
b. Convenience: .07; day-old/thrift: .12; neighborhood bakery: .03; supermarket bakery: .08; supermarket shelf: .67; other: .03
2.2. a. Qualitative   **b.** 6 day/48 hour; 5 day/40 hour; 4 day/40 hour; 3 day/40 hour   **c.** 3; 10; 8; 4   **d.** .12; .40; .32; .16
2.3. Relative frequencies: .147, .126, .101, .080, .045, .266, .234   **2.4. b.** Statement is true; 67% purchase off supermarket shelf.
2.5. b. 76.6%   **2.6.** PepsiCo has approx. 10,000 more restaurants than McDonald's, worldwide.
2.8. Energy use and production causes the most global warming ($\approx$ 57%)   **2.9.** Relative frequencies: .37, .18, .32, .07, .06   **2.10.** Yes
2.12. c. Population   **2.14.** Employed in service industry, has a bachelor's degree, is married   **2.16. a.** Brand of ketchup
2.17. Relative frequencies: .206; .175, .073, .320, .145, .081   **2.18. a.** Country that uses industrial robots
b. Cumulative proportions: Japan (.623), U.S. (.810), Germany (.863), Sweden (.900), Italy (.931), Poland (.954), Norway (.966), France (.979), Great Britain (.990), Finland (.998), Russia (1.000)
2.19. Upgraded cumulative proportions: 3 (.275), 0 (.464), 4 (.638), 2 (.783), 5 (.913), 7 (.942), 1 (.971), 9 (.986), 6 (1.000), 8 (1.000), 15 (1.000)
Downgraded cumulative proportions: 4 (.215), 2 (.430), 5 (.591), 3 (.753), 1 (.871), 0 (.968), 15 (.978), 7 (.989), 6 (1.000), 8 (1.000), 9 (1.000)
2.20. Cumulative proportions: LO (.266), NR (.500), LPR (.647), LGC (.773), LCOC (.874), LRC (.955), LRCC (1.000)
2.21. a. Transaction type depends on transaction timing   **b.** Purchase: .689, .311; sale: .541, .459   **d.** Yes

2.22.

SEX	EDUCATION DEGREE				Totals
	Associate	Bachelor's	Master's	PhD/Other	
Male	.015	.524	.426	.035	1.000
Female	.099	.492	.309	.099	1.000

2.23. a.

	Responses	Nonresponses	Totals
Typewritten/Small	86	57	143
Typewritten/Large	191	97	288
Typeset/Small	72	69	141
Typeset/Large	192	92	284

b. Typewritten/small: .601; typewritten/large: .663; typeset/small: .511; typeset/large: .676

2.24. a. Type of control contest; dissident shareholders' success

b.

	Dissidents Successful	Dissidents Unsuccessful	Totals
Full Control	32	63	95
Partial Control	28	19	47

c. Full control/successful: .337; full control/unsuccessful: .663; partial control/successful: .596; partial control/unsuccessful: .404

CHAPTER 3

3.6.

```
13 | 7  8  (8)  (9)
14 | (4) (5) (8)
15 |
16 | 0  (7)
17 | (9)
```

3.7. a. Stem is leftmost digit (6, 7, 8, or 9)   **b.** .923

3.8. a.

```
1 | 24 96
2 | 05 61 66
3 | 29 32 46 98 99
4 | 09 23 33
5 | 23 33 41 41 89
6 | 47
7 | 32
```

c. .35

3.9. Brand name

3.10.

```
1  | 1 4 4 5 5 6 6 7
2  | 2 2 4 6 9
3  | 0 6 8
4  |
5  |
6  | 2 4 7
7  |
8  |
9  |
10 |
11 |
12 | 7
```

3.12. a. 9   **b.** 5   **3.13. b.** Skewed right   **3.15. a.** Yes; rightward   **b.** 55

3.16. a. 2,550   **b.** .06   **c.** Yes; skewed left   **3.17. a.** Sample   **3.19. b.** Yes   **3.20. b.** Increasing trend
3.21. c. Specifications not being met for all bottles   **3.22. a.** Mean = 145, median = 138   **b.** Mean = 151.4, median = 145
3.23. Mean = 33,738.2, median = 23,710, no mode; median   **3.24. a.** Mean = 13,290.6, median = 15,900, mode = 16,500
b. Skewed left   **3.25.** Mean = 91.044, median = 92   **3.26. a.** Mean = 77,158.19, median = 59,900, mode = 50,000   **b.** Median
3.27. a. 8.36   **b.** Range = 36, variance = 79.94, std. dev. = 8.94   **c.** Approx. 95%   **d.** 92.9%
e. Mean = 6.23, range = 16, variance = 18.03, std. dev. = 4.24; 92.3%
3.28. a. 14.682   **b.** 199.974; 14.141   **c.** Approx. 95%   **d.** .909   **e.** Decrease; decrease   **f.** Mean = 13.736, std. dev. = 11.961
g. Approx. 95%, .908   **3.29.** (0, 222,311)   **3.30. a.** Empirical Rule   **b.** (1.66, 21.54)
3.31. b. Mean = 159.38, median = 77.4, std. dev. = 262.5   **c.** .967   **d.** Mean = 114.26, median = 76.0, std. dev. = 90.0

3.32. b. -1.56 **c.** -2.23 **3.33. a.** $Q_L = 13$, $M = 15$, $Q_U = 18$ **c.** 19 **3.34. a.** $\bar{x} = 6.03$, $s = 8.13$ **b.** $\bar{x} = 6.86$, $s = 8.47$
c. 1.72 **d.** 1.55 **e.** Fat tissue **3.35. a.** Range $= 26.9$, variance $= 60.214$, std. dev. $= 7.76$ **b.** $z = -1.93$ **3.36. a.** 41,800
b. 86,900 **c.** 191,000 **d.** $z = .039$ **3.37. a.** IQR $= 4$; inner fences: -4, 12; outer fences: -10, 18 **b.** Suspect outliers
c. Highly suspect outliers **d.** Yes **3.38. a.** 12.62; yes **b.** Measurement from a different population
3.39. a. Yes; city C, 82.0 **b.** $\bar{x} = 9.07$, $s = 15.69$; $z = 4.65$; yes **c.** No outliers detected; $\bar{x} = 6.00$, $s = 2.28$
3.40. a. $Q_L = 15,832$, $M = 23,710$, $Q_U = 38,005$ **c.** Highly suspect outlier: 127,002 **d.** Outlier: 127,002 ($z = 3.34$)
3.41. Outliers: 20 and 36 **3.42. a.** Yes; positive **b.** $r = .830$ **3.44. a.** Yes; positive **b.** .77
3.45. Moderate to low negative association between age and Machiavellianism score **3.46. a.** Yes; positive **b.** $r = .726$ **3.47.** $r = -.11$

CHAPTER 4

4.2. a. No **b.** $\dfrac{1}{17,000,000,000,000}$ **c.** Greater than .5 **4.3. a.** $\dfrac{1}{10}$ **b.** $\dfrac{8}{10}$ **4.4. a.** $\dfrac{21}{238} = .088$ **b.** $\dfrac{40}{240} = .167$
c. 1975-1982 **4.5. a.** .18 **b.** .28 **c.** .99 **d.** .58
4.6. a. Batch scheduling; JES queue space, C-to-C links; hardware errors; SMF management; quiesce and IPL; performance; background monitor

b. .254, .190, .124, .159, .046, .095, .075, .058 **c.** .283 **d.** .925 **4.7. a.** $\dfrac{228}{234} = .974$ **b.** $\dfrac{3}{25} = .12$

4.8. a. {Body, Bounciness}, {Body, Control}, {Body, Luster}, {Body, Dandruff protection}, {Bounciness, Control}, {Bounciness, Luster}
{Bounciness, Dandruff protection}, {Control, Luster}, {Control, Dandruff protection}, {Luster, Dandruff protection}

b. $\dfrac{1}{10}$ **c.** $\dfrac{4}{10}$ **4.9. a.** .97 **b.** .04 **c.** No **4.10. a.** $(.9)(.9)(.9) = .729$ **b.** $(.1)(.1)(.1) = .001$ **c.** Claim is likely false
4.11. a. .0000000055 **b.** .000000005 **c.** .0000000119 **4.12. a.** 3.27×10^{-25} **b.** .9999999776 **c.** .0000000224
4.13. a. .266 **b.** .94 **c.** No **4.14. a.** .85 **b.** .40
c. In thousands: {0, 0}, {0, 50}, {0, 100}, {0, 500}, {0, 1,000}, {50, 0}, {50, 50}, {50, 100}, {50, 500}, {50, 1,000}, {100, 0}, {100, 50}, {100, 100}, {100, 500}, {100, 1,000}, {500, 0}, {500, 50}, {500, 100}, {500, 500}, {500, 1,000}, {1,000, 0}, {1,000, 50}, {1,000, 100}, {1,000, 500}, {1,000, 1,000}
d. .36, .06, .09, .06, .03, .06, .01, .015, .01, .005, .09, .015, .0225, .015, .075, .06, .01, .015, .01, .005, .03, .005, .075, .005, .0025
e. .64 **4.15. b.** .0574 **c.** .9984 **4.16. a.** .8386 **b.** .002 **4.17. a.** Yes **b.** Hotel offers shampoo in its guest rooms
c. .86 **d.** .383 **e.** .853 **4.18. a.** .064 **b.** .432 **c.** .648 **4.19. a.** Yes **b.** .40 **c.** 100 **d.** 100 ± 15.5
e. $x = 69$ ($z = -4$) **4.20. a.** 2 **b.** 1.34 **4.21. a.** Yes **b.** .0173 **c.** .6167 **d.** .22 **4.22. a.** 20 **b.** 4.24
c. 20 ± 8.48 **d.** Not very likely **4.23. a.** Yes **b.** .00001 **c.** .0001 **d.** $1.00 **e.** $.10; yes **4.24. a.** 25,256.57
b. 152.27 **c.** 36.41 **d.** True percentage is higher than 8.2% **4.25. a.** .9406 **b.** .0068 **4.26. a.** .0351 **b.** .2578
c. .2119 **d.** Yes; IQR$/\sigma = 1.36$ **4.27.** No; $\bar{x} \pm 2s$ includes negative numbers **4.28. a.** .0571 **b.** Yes **4.29. a.** .0918 **b.** 0
c. 4.87 decibels **4.30. a.** .0228 **b.** Approx. 0 **c.** 30.08 **d.** EPA estimate is too high **4.31.** IQR$/s = 1.3$; approx. normal
4.32. a. .0869 **b.** .2743 **c.** z-score for 100 in mature group is $z = 1.00$ **d.** Immature: approx. normal; mature: nonnormal
4.33. a. 0 **b.** 1 **c.** 0 **d.** $-.67$ **e.** .67 **4.34. a.** .9678 **b.** .8729 **c.** .9946 **d.** Not well

CHAPTER 5

5.1. c. Mean $= 4.73$; std. dev. $= 1.275$ **5.2. c.** Mean $= 4.73$; std. dev. $= .827$ **d.** Sampling distribution with $n = 10$
5.3. a. Approx. normal with $\mu_{\bar{x}} = 17$ and $\sigma_{\bar{x}} = 2$ **b.** Approx. normal with $\mu_{\bar{x}} = 17$ and $\sigma_{\bar{x}} = 1$ **c.** $P(15 < \bar{x}_{100} < 19)$
d. .6826; .9544; yes **5.4. a.** $\mu_{\bar{x}} = 293$, $\sigma_{\bar{x}} = 119.78$ **c.** .0158 **5.5. a.** Approx. normal with $\mu_{\bar{x}} = 28.5$ and $\sigma_{\bar{x}} = 5.98$ **b.** .6203
c. .5987 **5.6. a.** Approx. normal with $\mu_{\bar{x}} = -7.02$ and $\sigma_{\bar{x}} = 3.49$ **b.** .9778 **c.** No; $z = -3.10$
5.7. a. Approx. normal with $\mu_{\bar{x}} = 71$ and $\sigma_{\bar{x}} = 1.70$ **b.** .6034 **c.** .0094 **d.** No **5.8. a.** 1.452; 2.548 **b.** .0026
5.9. a. .0062 **b.** Likely that mean of new surface exceeds 60 **5.10.** 95% of similarly constructed intervals will contain μ.
5.11. Proportion of similarly constructed intervals that capture μ **5.12. c.** .97 **5.13. a.** 84.84 **b.** 84.84 ± 4.03 **c.** .95
5.14. $29.07 \pm .86$ **5.15. a.** $1.94 \pm .13$ **b.** Increase n or decrease confidence coefficient
5.16. c. Increase n or decrease confidence coefficient **5.17. a.** H_0: $\pi_1 - \pi_2 = 0$; H_a: $\pi_1 - \pi_2 \neq 0$ **b.** H_0: $\mu = 60$; H_a: $\mu > 60$
c. H_0: $\mu_1 - \mu_2 = 0$; H_a: $\mu_1 - \mu_2 < 0$ **d.** H_0: $\pi = .04$; H_a: $\pi < .04$ **e.** H_0: $\mu_1 - \mu_2 = 0$; H_a: $\mu_1 - \mu_2 \neq 0$
5.18. a. Two-tailed **b.** One-tailed **c.** One-tailed **d.** One-tailed **e.** Two-tailed **5.19.** Value of $\beta = P(\text{Type II error})$ is unknown
5.20. a. No; $z = -1.82$ **b.** Type I error: conclude that $\mu \neq 60$ when $\mu = 60$; Type II error: conclude that $\mu = 60$ when $\mu \neq 60$
5.21. a. Yes; $z = 2.27$ **b.** .305 **5.22.** Yes; $z = -6.10$ **5.23. a.** Yes; $z = 6.67$
b. Type I error: conclude that $\mu > 60$ when $\mu = 60$; Type II error: conclude that $\mu = 60$ when $\mu > 60$
c. .01 **d.** .1587 **e.** Approx. 1 **5.24.** $\bar{x}$ may not be normally distributed; s may not be a good estimator of σ.
5.25. a. Reject H_0; $t = -3.46$ **b.** Distribution of overall scores of sleep-deprived students is approx. normal.

5.26. a. Distribution of number of victims in fire-resistive buildings is approx. normal.   **b.** 8.36 ± 6.33 **5.27. a.** $.188 \pm .102$
b. $.085 \pm .070$ **c.** Samples do not appear to come from normal populations.   **5.28.** $t = -1.39$; do not reject H_0
5.29. a. Yes; $t = 2.89$ **b.** Distribution of benzene levels in air samples is approx. normal.   **5.30. a.** $.025$ **b.** $.05$ **c.** $.0038$
d. $.1056$ **5.31. a.** $.01$ **b.** $.10 < p < .20$ **c.** $.05$ **d.** $.02 < p < .05$ **5.32. a.** Do not reject H_0 **b.** Reject H_0 **c.** Reject H_0
d. Do not reject H_0 **e.** Do not reject H_0 **5.33.** $.0688$ **5.34.** $.0116$ **5.35.** $.001 < p < .005$

CHAPTER 6

6.1. a. 5.4 **b.** 5.4 ± 1.09 **6.2. a.** 5.99 ± 3.14 **c.** Distribution of TCDD levels is normal.   **d.** Distribution is skewed right.
6.3. Reject H_0; p-value $= .0001$ **6.4. a.** No   **c.** $S = 7$; do not reject H_0 **6.5. c.** Increase n and/or decrease the confidence coefficient.
d. No   **6.6.** Reject H_0; $z = 8.82$ $(p \approx 0)$ **6.7. a.** No   **b.** $S = 17$; reject H_0 **6.8. b.** Distributions of five variables are all normal.
c. Assumption is likely to be violated for tuition.   **6.9.** $S = 14$; reject H_0 $(p = .0318)$ **6.10. a.** $.1$ **b.** $.1 \pm .27$ **d.** Increase n's
6.11. No; $t = .68$ $(p = .50)$; both populations normal   **6.12. a.** H_0: $\mu_1 - \mu_2 = 0$, H_a: $\mu_1 - \mu_2 > 0$ **b.** $z > 1.645$ **c.** Reject H_0
6.13. a. -3.82 ± 4.05 **b.** Yes   **6.14.** Do not reject H_0 **6.15. a.** $.13 \pm .14$ **b.** No
c. Distribution of win probabilities for the two groups are both approx. normal; variances are equal.
6.16. a. Yes; reject H_0; $z = 5.82$ **b.** Reject H_0; $t = 3.19$ **6.17.** No; $T_1 = 66$ **6.18. a.** t test
b. Normal populations; equal variances   **c.** No   **d.** Do not reject H_0 **e.** At $\alpha > .02$, evidence of a difference between the means
6.19. No; $T_2 = 126$ **6.20.** $T^- = 0$; reject H_0 **6.21. a.** Same items selected at each of the two stores
b. Evidence that Winn-Dixie mean is less than Publix mean   **6.22. a.** -7.18 **b.** $.0001$ **6.23.** Yes; p-value ≈ 0 **6.24.** $-.82 \pm 1.38$
6.25. Yes; $t = 2.48$ **6.26.** No; $t = .46$ **6.27.** -21.53 ± 3.64 **6.28. a.** Reject H_0; $t = -4.956$
b. Distribution of differences between ratings of the two options is approx. normal.
6.29. 95% confidence interval for mean difference: 7.18 ± 77.33; no evidence of a difference   **6.30. a.** 683 **b.** 246 **c.** 426
6.31. a. 57 **b.** 99 **c.** 596 **6.32.** 24 **6.33.** 66 **6.34.** 155 **6.35.** 86 **6.36.** 893

CHAPTER 7

7.1. $(1.453, 4.125)$ **7.2. a.** Nonparametric   **b.** $M = .258$, $S = 7$; do not reject H_0 **7.3.** $(.053, .102)$
7.4. a. H_0: $\sigma^2 = .54$, H_a: $\sigma^2 > .54$ **b.** $.7425$ **c.** $\chi^2 = 40.84$; do not reject H_0 **7.5.** $(.038, .054)$ **7.6.** Yes; $\chi^2 = 688$
7.7. No; $\chi^2 = 2.97$ **7.8.** Yes; $\chi^2 = 54$ **7.9.** $\chi^2 = 14.13$; do not reject H_0 **7.10.** $F = 2.43$; reject H_0 at $\alpha = .05$
7.11. Evidence of a difference between variances   **7.12.** Yes; $F = 1.75$
7.13. $.154 \le \sigma_{Canned}/\sigma_{Dry} \le .155$; 90% confident that $\sigma_{Canned} < \sigma_{Dry}$ **7.14. a.** No; $F = 1.09$
b. Populations of cracking torsion moments for both 70 cm beams and 100 cm beams are approximately normal.
7.15. Do not reject H_0; $W_c = 36$ **7.16.** $M_1 = 1.32$, $M_2 = 2.05$, so apply Moses rank test; $W_c = 8$ $(p = .6858)$; do not reject H_0

CHAPTER 8

8.1. a. $.075$ **b.** $.075 \pm .028$ **8.2. a.** H_0: $\pi = .20$, H_a: $\pi > .20$ **b.** $z = 11.00$; reject H_0 **c.** Approx. 0   **8.3.** $.43 \pm .012$
8.4. a. Yes; reject H_0; $z = -7.75$ **b.** Approx. 0   **8.5.** $.18 \pm .035$ **8.6.** $.33 \pm .072$ **8.7.** Reject H_0; $z = 9.80$
8.8. a. $.597 \pm .026$ **b.** Wider interval   **8.9. a.** $.11 \pm .026$ **b.** No   **8.10.** Do not reject H_0; $z = 1.18$ **8.11. a.** $.13 \pm .035$
b. Yes; white former smokers had more difficulty quitting   **8.12.** Reject H_0; $z = -2.55$ **8.13. a.** Yes; $z = -3.07$ **b.** $.0011$
8.14. a. $.195 \pm .137$ **8.15. a.** Reject H_0; $z = -2.62$ **b.** $.0088$ **8.16. a.** $.152 \pm .140$ **b.** Yes   **c.** Yes
8.17. $z = 4.74$; reject H_0 **8.18.** Yes; $z = -4.05$ **8.19. a.** $-.0000183 \pm .04$ **b.** Decrease; no   **8.20. a.** Yes; $z = 1.96$
b. No; results may be invalid   **8.21.** 354 **8.22.** 275 **8.23.** $4,802$ **8.24.** 160 **8.25.** 270 **8.26.** Yes; $\chi^2 = 40.7$
8.27. $\chi^2 = 303.38$; reject H_0 **8.28.** $\chi^2 = 4.411$; do not reject H_0 **8.29. a.** $\chi^2 = 39.78$; reject H_0 **b.** No   **c.** $z = 3.56$; reject H_0
8.30. $\chi^2 = 16.745$; reject H_0 **8.31.** Do not reject H_0; $\chi^2 = 2.6$ **8.32.** Yes; $\chi^2 = 508.74$ **8.33. a.** Yes
b.
     c. $\chi^2 = 12.9$ **d.** Yes; reject H_0 **e.** $.233 \pm .2$

	HIGH FAT		LOW FAT	
	No Fiber	Fiber	No Fiber	Fiber
Yes	20	20	20	20
No	10	10	10	10

8.34. No; $\chi^2 = 7.431$ **8.35.** Yes; $\chi^2 = 13.08$ **8.36. a.** Reject H_0; $\chi^2 = 16.06$ **b.** $-.28 \pm .11$ **8.37.** $\chi^2 = 6.114$; do not reject H_0
8.38. b. Reject H_0 **8.39. a.** H_0: The two directions of classification, "Most important value" and "U.S. nation," are independent.
b. Reject H_0; $\chi^2 = 68.758$ $(p$-value $= .033)$ **c.** $-.0001 \pm .0813$; no evidence of a difference between proportions

CHAPTER 9

9.1. $\bar{x} = 1.4985$, $s = .0085$, LCL = 1.4731, UCL = 1.5239   **9.2. b.** $\bar{x} = .13974$, $s = .002809$, LCL = .1313, UCL = .1482   **c.** Yes
9.3. a. $\bar{x} = 4.972$ **b.** LCL = 4.738, UCL = 5.206   **c.** Yes   **9.4. a.** $\bar{x} = 5.895$, $s = .35314$, LCL = 4.836, UCL = 6.954   **b.** Yes
9.5. Yes; LCL = .13565, UCL = .14565   **9.6.** Yes; LCL = 4.93923, UCL = 5.04305   **9.7.** Yes
9.8. No (LCL = .40300, UCL = .40371); LCL = .40296, UCL = .40371, yes   **9.9.** $\bar{R} = .00867$, LCL = 0, UCL = .01833
9.10. $\bar{R} = .13917$, LCL = .01893, UCL = .25941; yes   **9.11.** $\bar{R} = .074$, LCL = 0, UCL = .15651; yes
9.12. $\bar{R} = .00062$, LCL = 0, UCL = .00131; modified control limits: LCL = 0, UCL = .00107
9.13. Evidence of a trend in sequences **d** and **f**   **9.14.** No evidence of a trend   **9.15.** No evidence of a trend
9.16. No evidence of a trend   **9.17.** Evidence of a trend; run of 7   **9.18. b.** LCL = 0, UCL = .39   **c.** No   **9.19. b.** .0372
c. LCL = 0, UCL = .09398; no   **d.** No trends detected   **9.20.** Yes; $p = .11$ falls outside control limits   **9.21. b.** .2571
c. LCL = .0717, UCL = .4426   **d.** No; $\bar{p} = .247$, LCL = .064, UCL = .430   **e.** No trends   **9.22. a.** $.14065 \pm .00827$ **b.** (.132, .148)
9.23. $.9958 \pm .0665$ **9.24. a.** $.40336 \pm .00104$ **b.** Yes   **c.** $n = 93$; (.4023, .4043)   **9.25. a.** 26 ± 29.11; $1 - \alpha = 1.00$
b. Specific cause (93.12 falls outside interval)   **9.26. a.** $.512 \pm .00313$ **b.** $.5005 \pm .0047$ **c.** No   **d.** Yes

CHAPTER 10

10.1. b. $\hat{y} = 4.79 + .014x$ **e.** SSE = 30.768, $s^2 = 2.051$ **f.** 1.432   **h.** Yes; $t = 5.14$ **i.** .630   **j.** 9.106 ± 3.198
10.2. b. $\hat{\beta}_0 = 9.15$, $\hat{\beta}_1 = .481$ **d.** Yes; $t = 8.07$ **e.** $18.77 \pm .51$ **10.3.** Yes; $t = 10.59$ **10.4. b.** $\hat{y} = 3.306 + .014755x$
d. $t = 5.356$; reject H_0 **e.** $.014755 \pm .0127$ **f.** .6116   **g.** .3740   **h.** (1.9898, 10.5242)
10.5. a. $\hat{y} = -.1776 + .8991x$; $\hat{y} = 1.0179 + .9753x$ **b.** $t = 11.32$; reject H_0 **c.** $t = 11.32$; reject H_0 **10.6. a.** Yes; $t = 7.13$
b. Yes; $t = 5.98$ **c.** Yes; $t = 4.98$ **d.** 7.07   **e.** 35.86   **f.** 1,390.1   **10.7. b.** $\hat{y} = 130.69 - 7.26x$ **10.8.** Yes; $t = 3.877$
10.9. $\hat{y} = 1.192 + .987x$; $t = 6.90$; reject H_0 **10.10. c.** $t_{\text{Males}} = -5.81$, reject H_0; $t_{\text{Females}} = -.739$, do not reject H_0
10.11. a. $E(y) = \beta_0 + \beta_1 x$ **b.** $\hat{y} = -.7995 + .93205x$ **e.** 1.310   **f.** Reject H_0; $t = 8.30$ **g.** $.932 \pm .191$ **h.** .689   **i.** Yes
j. 15.98 ± 2.26 **10.12. a.** $F = 20.914$, reject H_0: $\beta_1 = \beta_2 = \cdots = \beta_{27} = 0$; $s = 6,544$; $R^2 = .814$; $R_a^2 = .7751$ **b.** (15.13, 29.67)
c. No; inflated α error; no higher-order terms in model   **10.13.** Reject H_0: $\beta_1 = \beta_2 = \cdots = \beta_7 = 0$
10.14. a. Reject H_0: $\beta_1 = 0$ in favor of H_a: $\beta_1 > 0$ (p-value ≈ 0)   **b.** Reject H_0: $\beta_2 = 0$ in favor of H_a: $\beta_2 > 0$ (p-value $\approx .003$)
c. $3,444.3 \pm 1,861.7$ **d.** $F = 72.11$; reject H_0: $\beta_1 = \beta_2 = \beta_3 = \beta_4 = 0$ (p-value ≈ 0)   **e.** $s = 894.6$ **f.** $R_a^2 = .890$
g. (1,449, 2,424)   **h.** (47, 3,825)   **10.15. a.** $\hat{y} = 648.023 + 104.839x_1 + 357.185x_2$ **b.** Yes; $F = 19.017$ **c.** 104.839 ± 37.368
d. No; $t = .917$ **10.16. a.** $F = 3,909.25$; reject H_0 **b.** H_0: $\beta_4 = 0$, H_a: $\beta_4 < 0$ **d.** No, since $\hat{\beta}_4$ is positive
10.17. a. β_1 = change in number of module defects for every additional unique operand; β_2 = change in number of module defects for every
additional conditional statement, loop, or Boolean operator
b. Yes; $F = 443.18$ **10.18. a.** Reject H_0: $\beta_1 = \beta_2 = \beta_3 = 0$; $F = 9.6893$ **b.** Reject H_0: $\beta_1 = 0$; $t = 1.444$
c. Estimate coupon redemption rate to decrease by .13134 for every 1 point increase in time value score.
10.19. a. Reject H_0; $F = 7.99$ **c.** Reject H_0: $\beta_3 = 0$; $t = 1.85$ **d.** No
10.20. a. Nuclear: $\hat{y} = -17.556 + .519x_1 + 10.889x_2 + .132x_1x_2$; nonnuclear: $\hat{y} = -44.682 + 2.879x_1 + 25.062x_2 - .959x_1x_2$
b. Yes, $F = 13.217$; Yes, $F = 60.851$ **c.** No, $t = .118$; no, $t = -1.388$ **d.** (7.4528, 26.8903)
f. No, $x_2 = 1.10$ is outside the range of sample data for nuclear stocks
10.21. a. $F = 2.56$; $.05 < p < .10$ **b.** $\hat{y} = 3.031 + .000498x_1$ **c.** $\hat{y} = 3.712 - .000485x_1$ **e.** Reject H_0; $t = -2.63$ **f.** 3.13
10.22. b. $\hat{y} = 54.5 + .0077x_1 + .554x_2 + .000113x_1x_2$ **d.** Reject H_0; $F = 44.67$ (p-value = .000)   **e.** No; $t = .68$ (p-value = .528)
f. $E(y) = \beta_0 + \beta_1 x_1 + \beta_2 x_2$ **10.23. b.** H_0: $\beta_3 = 0$, H_a: $\beta_3 \neq 0$ **c.** Reject H_0 **10.24. a.** $E(y) = \beta_0 + \beta_1 x + \beta_2 x^2$ **b.** $\beta_2 > 0$
10.25. a. Accountants: reject H_0, $F = 10.68$; truck drivers: reject H_0, $F = 22.07$ **b.** $\hat{\beta}_2$ **c.** Yes; $t = 3.23$ **d.** Yes; $t = 4.70$
10.26. a. $E(y) = \beta_0 + \beta_1 x_1 + \beta_2 x_2 + \beta_3 x_1 x_2 + \beta_4 x_1^2 + \beta_5 x_2^2$ **c.** $F = 40.114$; reject H_0 **10.27. a.** Quadratic
b. $t = -15.78$; reject H_0 **c.** .0001   **d.** 188.892   **10.28. a.** H_0: $\beta_1 = \beta_2 = \beta_3 = \beta_4 = \beta_5 = 0$ **b.** Reject H_0; $F = 18.24$
10.29. b. No; $t = -.15$ **10.30. a.** $\mu_{\text{Employed}} < \mu_{\text{Unemployed}}$ **10.31. a.** Yes; $F = 53.2$ (p-value = .001)
b. .187; expect to predict natural log of 1977 salary to within $2s \approx .374$ using the model
c. .677; model explains 67.7% of sample variation in natural log y
d. $-.046 \pm .072$; no evidence of a difference in mean natural log of 1977 salaries between white and black players

e. No; do not reject H_0: $\beta_6 = 0$ $\left(p\text{-value} = \dfrac{.10}{2} = .05 \right)$ **10.32.** $F = 14.42$; reject H_0: $\beta_1 = \beta_2 = \beta_3 = 0$

10.33. a. $E(y) = \beta_0 + \beta_1 x$, where $x = \begin{cases} 1 & \text{if Hispanic} \\ 0 & \text{if Anglo} \end{cases}$

b. $\beta_0 = \mu_{\text{Anglo}}$, $\beta_1 = \mu_{\text{Hispanic}} - \mu_{\text{Anglo}}$ **c.** $E(y) = \beta_0 + \beta_1 x_1 + \beta_2 x_2 + \beta_3 x_3$, where $x_1 = \begin{cases} 1 & \text{if NE,} \\ 0 & \text{if not} \end{cases}$ $x_2 = \begin{cases} 1 & \text{if NC,} \\ 0 & \text{if not} \end{cases}$ $x_3 = \begin{cases} 1 & \text{if S} \\ 0 & \text{if not} \end{cases}$
d. $\beta_0 = \mu_{\text{W}}$, $\beta_1 = \mu_{\text{NE}} - \mu_{\text{W}}$, $\beta_2 = \mu_{\text{NC}} - \mu_{\text{W}}$, $\beta_3 = \mu_{\text{S}} - \mu_{\text{W}}$

10.35. a. $\hat{y} = 66.97 + 4.03x_1 + 5.55x_2$ **b.** Test $H_0\colon \beta_1 = \beta_2 = 0$ using the F test   **10.36. a.** .9323   **b.** Yes; reject H_0 **c.** $C = 96$; reject H_0
10.37. Yes; $r_s = -.529$ **10.38. a.** $C = -13$ **b.** No; do not reject H_0 **10.39.** $C = 21$; reject H_0 **10.40.** Reject H_0; $r_s = .834$

CHAPTER 11

11.1. a. x_2; $t = -90$ **b.** Yes
c. Consider all models of the form $E(y) = \beta_0 + \beta_1 x_2 + \beta_2 x_i$; select the x_i associated with the largest t-value for testing β_2.
11.2. a. x_4, x_5, x_6 **b.** No, there may be other important variables, as yet unspecified.
c. $E(y) = \beta_0 + \beta_1 x_4 + \beta_2 x_5 + \beta_3 x_6 + \beta_4 x_4 x_5 + \beta_5 x_4 x_6 + \beta_6 x_5 x_6$
11.3. a. At $\alpha = .01$, all but size (acres) and farmland (yes–no) are useful predictors.
b. $E(y) = \beta_0 + \beta_1 x_1 + \beta_2 x_2 + \beta_3 x_3 + \beta_4 x_4 + \beta_5 x_1 x_2 + \beta_6 x_1 x_3 + \beta_7 x_1 x_4$
$\underbrace{+\ \beta_8 x_2 x_3 + \beta_9 x_2 x_4 + \beta_{10} x_3 x_4 + \beta_{11} x_1^2 + \beta_{12} x_2^2 + \beta_{13} x_3^2 + \beta_{14} x_4^2}_{\text{Quantitative terms}}$

$+\ \beta_{15} x_5 + \beta_{16} x_6 + \beta_{17} x_5 x_6\}$ Qualitative terms
$+\ (\text{Quantitative} \times \text{Qualitative})$ interaction terms

where $x_1 =$ seedlings and saplings, $x_2 =$ percent ponds, $x_3 =$ distance to state park, $x_4 =$ site index,
$x_5 = \begin{cases} 1 & \text{if residential land} \\ 0 & \text{if not} \end{cases}$, $x_6 = \begin{cases} 1 & \text{if branches or springs} \\ 0 & \text{if not} \end{cases}$
11.4. a. Keep variables $x_2, x_3, x_4, x_5,$ and x_6 **11.5. a.** $x = e^{-p}$ **b.** $\hat{y} = 234.04 + 17,170.1x$; $t = 24.38$, reject H_0

c. $t = -20$; reject $H_0\colon \beta_1 = 0$ **11.6. a.** Curvilinear   **b.** Straight-line   **c.** $\widehat{\log y} = 10.6364 - 2.16985(\log x)$; yes, $t = -13.44$
d. 25.95   **11.7.** No; multicollinearity exists; $F = 48.71$, reject $H_0\colon \beta_1 = \beta_2 = \beta_3 = 0$ **11.8. a.** Yes; $t = 15.92$ **b.** Yes; $t = 11.76$
c. Yes (at $\alpha = .05$); $t = 2.51$ **11.9.** The low variance inflation factors indicate that multicollinearity, if it exists, is not severe.
11.10. a. .0025; no   **b.** .4341; no   **c.** No
d. $\hat{y} = -45.154 + 3.097x_1 + 1.032x_2$; $F = 39,222.34$; $R^2 = .9998$ **e.** $-.8998$; x_1 and x_2 are highly correlated
f. No; $t = 252.31$ for β_1; $t = 280.08$ for β_2 **11.11.** No; $F = 3.59$, reject $H_0\colon \beta_3 = \beta_4 = \cdots = \beta_{30} = 0$
11.12. a. $H_0\colon \beta_5 = \beta_6 = \beta_7 = \beta_8 = 0$; $F > 2.45$ **b.** Yes   **c.** Reject H_0 for both genders.   **11.13. a.** Yes; $F = 2.94$
b. No; $F = 1.50$ **c.** $F = 5.73$; reject H_0
d. Rate of change of performance rating (y) with subordinate-related managerial score (x_6) is the same for both middle or upper-level and lower-level managers.
11.14. $F = 8.79$; reject $H_0\colon \beta_3 = 0$ **11.15. a.** $\beta_3, \beta_4, \ldots, \beta_{11}$ **b.** $H_0\colon \beta_3 = \beta_4 = \cdots = \beta_{11} = 0$ **c.** $H_0\colon \beta_2 = \beta_9 = \beta_{10} = \beta_{11} = 0$
11.16. a. $(1, 2), (1, 3), (1, 4), (2, 3), (3, 4)$ **b.** Model 3   **11.17. a.** Model lacks curvature (ie, x^2 term)
b. Nonconstant residual variance   **c.** Outlier   **d.** Nonconstant residual variance   **e.** Nonnormal error distribution
11.18. a. .796, $-.219$, -1.004, .077, -1.071, 1.116, .868, .827, .223, -1.612 **b.** No   **c.** Yes; needs curvature term ($\beta_3 x_2^2$)
11.19. a. Yes; assumption of equal variances is violated   **b.** Use transformation $y^* = \sqrt{y}$
11.20. a. 25.67, 18.57, -60.14, 13.41, -72.40, 64.06, -19.77, 57.93, -63.36, -75.62, 46.31, -1.43
c. Yes; model needs curvature term, $\beta_2 x^2$
11.21. a. -29.29, -8.05, -51.55, 0.16, 23.69, -1.09, -29.68, -11.83, 41.37, -3.57, 38.26, 18.08, 21.91, 0.46, 31.14, -13.92, 6.07, -9.14, -9.08, -13.92
b. Yes; evidence of unequal variances   **c.** Use transformation $y^* = \log y$ **11.22. a.** $F = 83.54$; reject H_0 **b.** Yes   **c.** No outliers
11.23. a. Model explains only 7.3% of sample variation in work-hours missed
b. -50.76, -47.44, -15.96, -33.72, -54.64, -78.24, 16.84, -46.52, 43.24, -64.96, -55.96, -50.52, 436.52, 37.88, -36.00; almost all residuals are negative, one large positive residual
c. Omit data for this employee from analysis   **d.** $\hat{y} = 191.26 - 9.58x$; $R^2 = .483$; model is adequate ($t = -3.35$)
11.24. a. Yes; $F = 21.772$ **b.** Yes; unusual observation for Boston   **c.** Yes   **11.25. a.** No   **b.** Observation (child) 24 is influential

CHAPTER 12

12.1. 65.5, 79.1, 100, 142, 175.7, 161.6, 159.3, 120.7, 91.1, 54.1, 46.1, 47.2, 40.9, 65.8, 74.8, 84.3, 105.2, 109.5
12.2. a. 100, 111.1, 118.8, 129, 139.5, 157.3, 167.5, 176.9, 193.6, 206.4, 218.8, 232.6, 245
12.3. a. 100, 104.4, 128.9, 114.4, 142.2, 115.6, 100, 113.3, 103.3, 105.6, 90, 64.4, 88.9, 74.4, 91.1, 104.4, 116.7, 97.8, 112.2, 82.2, 78.9, 96.7, 73.3, 72.2, 80, 83.3, 112.2, 104.4, 87.8, 85.6, 97.8, 83.3, 78.9
12.4. 100, 97.7, 92.3, 112.2, 125.4, 134.4, 131.9, 127, 135.3, 131.7, 109

12.5. **a.** 65.9, 105.4, 139.6, 148.6, 144.8, 155.5, 216.5, 369.1, 454.8, 476.9, 424.6, 394.5, 375.5, 348.5, 364.7, 404.6, 409.0, 400.8, 375.8, 363.5
b. 350
c. 41.3, 55.1, 89.3, 145.6, 158.2, 131.5, 144.9, 183.8, 283.0, 541.4, 468.8, 393.1, 437.8, 375.8, 329.0, 360.1, 399.1, 429.4, 390.9, 385.4, 366.7
d. 348.9   **e.** 332.4   **12.6.** **a.** Yes; yes
b. 3,309.5, 3,435.7, 3,557.2, 3,669.7, 3,775.0, 3,833.0, 3,884.7, 3.939.5, 3,998.2, 4,058.2, 4,111.0, 4,163.5, 4,208.5, 4,268.5, 4,343.5, 4,425.0, 4,520.0, 4,606.7, 4,695.5, 4,783.2, 4,873.7, 4,965.0, 5,050.7, 5,131.0, 5,200.7, 5,269.2, 5,356.5, 5,436.7, 5,504.7, 5,557.5, 5,591.2, 5,629.5, 5,677.5, 5,741.0, 5,802.0, 5,868.5
c. Yes   **d.** 100.4   **e.** 5,950
12.7. **a.** 3,172, 3,192, 3,226, 3,267, 3,349, 3,431, 3,507, 3,576, 3,643, 3,707, 3,772, 3,835, 3,898, 3,954, 4,011, 4,062, 4,128, 4,197, 4,271, 4,347, 4,425, 4,506, 4,588, 4,673, 4,758, 4,841, 4,921, 4,995, 5,071, 5,161, 5,241, 5,305, 5,361, 5,420, 5,479, 5,534, 5,595, 5,656, 5,721
b. 5,793   **c.** 6,481
12.8. **a.** 154.1, 154.0, 154.1, 154.2, 154.4, 154.8, 154.8, 155.2, 155.3, 155.3, 155.3, 155.3, 155.4, 156.1, 157.0, 157.2, 157.8, 157.9, 158.5, 159.1, 159.4, 160.2, 161.3, 162.0
b. 163.5
c. 136.1, 132.9, 144.6, 147.3, 154.1, 156.6, 154.9, 159.3, 153.7, 154.6, 157.7, 173.2, 150.1, 139.1, 147.4, 150.1, 158.3, 161.5, 154.6, 155.3, 157.7, 174.4, 155.0, 147.9, 152.0, 156.3, 162.0, 163.6, 165.0, 165.8, 162.7, 166.3, 166.8
d. 189.2   **e.** 205   **12.9.** **a.** Yes   **b.** 283.6, 298.6, 309.8, 318.1, 326.0, 334.5, 344.5, 354.8; forecast = 366
c. 246.8, 257, 269.9, 281.3, 293.2, 304.8, 314.2, 320.7, 327.5, 338, 351.7, 362.9; forecast = 372.7
d. 399.1   **12.10.** **b.** Railroads: $\hat{y}_t = 74.527 - 8.239t$; buses: $\hat{y}_t = 35.260 - 2.442t$; air carriers: $\hat{y}_t = -13.173 + 10.915t$
d. Railroads: -16.11, $(-40.82, 8.60)$; buses: 8.40, $(-8.69, 25.49)$; air carriers: 106.90, (90.78, 123.00)   **12.11.** **a.** No; $t = -1.39$
b. 2,003.48   **c.** No; $t = -1.61$ **d.** 1,901.81   **12.12.** Yes; $t = 80.37$ (p-value = .000), $R^2 = .994$
12.13. $E(y_t) = \beta_0 + \beta_1 t$; $\hat{y}_t = 250.73 + 10.66t$; 400, (382.1, 417.9)   **12.14.** **a.** $F = 164.07$; yes   **b.** $d = 1.01$; yes
c. Model may be overly optimistic   **12.15.** **a.** Yes; reject H_0: $\beta_1 = 0$; $t = 47.9$ **c.** Yes; $d = .962$
d. No; evidence of autocorrelated errors   **12.16.** **a.** Yes   **b.** Reject H_0; $d = .36$; model may be overly optimistic
12.17. $d = .89$; evidence of positive autocorrelation   **12.18.** **a.** $E(y_t) = \beta_0 + \beta_1 t$ **b.** $E(y_t) = \beta_0 + \beta_1 t + \beta_2 t^2$ **c.** $R_t = \phi R_{t-1} + \epsilon_t$
12.19. **a.** $E(y_t) = \beta_0 + \beta_1 x_t + \beta_2 x_t^2$ **b.** $R_t = \phi R_{t-1} + \epsilon_t$ **c.** $y_t = \beta_0 + \beta_1 x_t + \beta_2 x_t^2 + \phi R_{t-1} + \epsilon_t$
12.20. **a.** $y_t = \beta_0 + \beta_1 t + R_t$, $R_t = \phi R_{t-1} + \epsilon_t$ **b.** $\hat{y}_t = 3,186.7 + 73.37t + .776\hat{R}_{t-1}$
e. Qtr I, 1993: 6,164.2 ± 78.2; Qtr II, 1993: 6,244.4 ± 99.0; Qtr III, 1993: 6,323.1 ± 109.6; Qtr IV, 1993: 6,400.6 ± 115.6
12.21. **c.** 2,136.2   **d.** (1,404.3, 3,249.7)   **e.** 1,944.0; (1,301.8, 2,902.9)

CHAPTER 13

13.1. **a.** Groups 1 and 2   **b.** H_0: $\mu_1 = \mu_2$ **c.** No; do not reject H_0 **d.** Reject H_0; $p = \dfrac{.13}{2} = .065$

13.2. **a.** Yes, reject H_0; $F = 9.50$, $p = .006$
13.3. **a.** Response = total cash compensation; treatments = 4 industries; experimental units = corporate executives
b. No, do not reject H_0; $F = 3.556$, $p = .027$ **13.4.** **a.** SS(Groups) = 14.6, SSE = 112.585, SS(total) = 127.585, $F = 5.77$
b. Yes; reject H_0 **13.5.** Parametric: do not reject H_0, $F = .104$, $p = .9566$; nonparametric: do not reject H_0, $H = .37853$, $p = .9446$
13.6. No; do not reject H_0, $H = .98$ **13.7.** **a.** Treatments = 3 supermarkets; blocks = 60 grocery items
b.

SOURCE	df	SS	MS	F
Supermarket	2	2.641	1.321	39.23
Item	59	215.595	3.654	108.54
Error	118	3.972	.034	
Totals	179	222.208		

c. Reject H_0; $p = .0001$ **d.** $-.26 \pm .07$

e. Yes   **13.8.** Reject H_0; $F = 57.988$, $p = .000$ **13.9.** Yes, reject H_0; $F = 52.80$
13.10. **a.** No, do not reject H_0; $F = .78$ **c.** No, do not reject H_0; $F = 1.04$ **d.** Yes   **e.** Reject H_0; $F = 4.88$; yes
13.11 Do not reject H_0; $F_r = 1.18$ **13.12.** **a.** No, do no reject H_0; $F = 1.959$, $p = .184$ **b.** Do not reject H_0; $F_r = 3.5$, $p = .1738$
13.13. **a.** Factor (levels) are confirmation (completed, not completed) and verification (completed, not completed); treatments are CC, CN, VC, VN
b. Effect of confirmation on risk depends on verification level   **c.** Yes
13.14. Interaction: do not reject H_0 ($p = .60$); form main effects: do not reject H_0 ($p = .98$); major main effects: reject H_0 ($p = .01$)
13.15. Interaction: reject H_0 ($p = .0001$); do not conduct tests on main effects

13.16. a.

SOURCE	df	SS	MS	F
P	1	—	—	—
V	1	69.15	69.15	4.61
VP	1	170.85	170.85	11.39
Error	16	240.00	15.00	
Totals	19	—		

b. Yes   **c.** Reject H_0; $F = 11.39$

13.17. a.

SOURCE	df	SS	MS	F
Amount (A)	3	104.19	34.73	20.12
Method (M)	3	28.63	9.54	5.53
AM	9	25.13	2.79	1.62
Error	32	55.25	1.73	
Totals	47	213.20		

b. Do not reject H_0; $F = 1.62$, $p = .1523$

c. No evidence of interaction   **d.** A: reject H_0 ($p = .0001$); M: reject H_0 ($p = .0036$)

13.18. a.

SOURCE	df	SS	MS	F
P	1	1.55	1.55	1.08
D	1	22.26	22.26	15.57
PD	1	.61	.61	.43
Error	80	114.4	1.43	
Totals	83	138.82		

b. $P \times D$: do not reject H_0, $F = .43$; P: do not reject H_0, $F = 1.08$; D: reject H_0, $F = 15.57$ **13.19. a.** Reject H_0; $F_{.05} \approx 2.21$
b. $\mu_{TS} < (\mu_V, \mu_{RU}, \mu_{LU}, \mu_{SS})$ **13.20.** $(\mu_7, \mu_4) < (\mu_2, \mu_1, \mu_3, \mu_5, \mu_6)$; $\mu_2 < \mu_6$ **13.21. a.** Reject H_0 **b.** Proper analysis
c. V = 75%: $\mu_{99} < \mu_{95} < \mu_{90}$; V = 87.5%: $\mu_{99} < \mu_{95} < \mu_{90}$; V = 100%: $(\mu_{99}, \mu_{95}) < \mu_{90}$ **13.22. a.** Reject H_0
b. $\mu_R < \mu_P < (\mu_D, \mu_A, \mu_B)$; $\mu_D < \mu_B$ **13.23.** $B_{ij} = .98$; $\mu_{LT} < (\mu_{HT}, \mu_{HR})$

13.24. a. Complete: $E(y) = \beta_0 + \beta_1 x_1 + \beta_2 x_2$, where $x_1 = \begin{cases} 1 & \text{if PD-1} \\ 0 & \text{if not} \end{cases}$, $x_2 = \begin{cases} 1 & \text{if IADC 1-2-6} \\ 0 & \text{if not} \end{cases}$; reduced: $E(y) = \beta_0$

13.25. a. Complete: $E(y) = \beta_0 + \beta_1 x_1 + \beta_2 x_2 + \beta_3 x_3$, where $x_1 = \begin{cases} 1 & \text{if CP} \\ 0 & \text{if not} \end{cases}$, $x_2 = \begin{cases} 1 & \text{if U} \\ 0 & \text{if not} \end{cases}$, $x_3 = \begin{cases} 1 & \text{if IHT} \\ 0 & \text{if not} \end{cases}$; reduced: $E(y) = \beta_0$

13.26. a. Complete: $E(y) = \beta_0 + \beta_1 x_1 + \beta_2 x_2 + \beta_3 x_3 + \cdots + \beta_{61} x_{61}$, where $x_1 = \begin{cases} 1 & \text{if WD} \\ 0 & \text{if not} \end{cases}$, $x_2 = \begin{cases} 1 & \text{if PLX} \\ 0 & \text{if not} \end{cases}$,

$x_3 = \begin{cases} 1 & \text{if Big Thirst Towel} \\ 0 & \text{if not} \end{cases}$, ..., $x_{61} = \begin{cases} 1 & \text{if Gillette Atra Plus} \\ 0 & \text{if not} \end{cases}$; reduced (testing supermarkets): $E(y) = \beta_0 + \beta_3 x_3 + \cdots + \beta_{61} x_{61}$; reduced
(testing items): $E(y) = \beta_0 + \beta_1 x_1 + \beta_2 x_2$

13.27. a. Complete: $E(y) = \beta_0 + \beta_1 x_1 + \beta_2 x_2 + \beta_3 x_3 + \cdots + \beta_8 x_8$, where $x_1 = \begin{cases} 1 & \text{if rater 1} \\ 0 & \text{if not} \end{cases}$, $x_2 = \begin{cases} 1 & \text{if rater 2} \\ 0 & \text{if not} \end{cases}$, $x_3 = \begin{cases} 1 & \text{if A} \\ 0 & \text{if not} \end{cases}$, ...,

$x_8 = \begin{cases} 1 & \text{if G} \\ 0 & \text{if not} \end{cases}$; reduced (testing raters): $E(y) = \beta_0 + \beta_3 x_3 + \cdots + \beta_8 x_8$; reduced (testing candidates): $E(y) = \beta_0 + \beta_1 x_1 + \beta_2 x_2$

13.28. a. Complete: $E(y) = \beta_0 + \beta_1 x_1 + \beta_2 x_2 + \cdots + \beta_8 x_8 + \beta_9 x_9 + \beta_{10} x_{10} + \beta_{11} x_1 x_9 + \beta_{12} x_1 x_{10} + \cdots + \beta_{25} x_8 x_9 + \beta_{26} x_8 x_{10}$, where

$x_1 = \begin{cases} 1 & \text{if 1 hour} \\ 0 & \text{if not} \end{cases}$, $x_2 = \begin{cases} 1 & \text{if 2 hours} \\ 0 & \text{if not} \end{cases}$, ..., $x_8 = \begin{cases} 1 & \text{if 8 hours} \\ 0 & \text{if not} \end{cases}$, $x_9 = \begin{cases} 1 & \text{if A} \\ 0 & \text{if not} \end{cases}$, $x_{10} = \begin{cases} 1 & \text{if B} \\ 0 & \text{if not} \end{cases}$;
reduced model (testing interaction): $E(y) = \beta_0 + \beta_1 x_1 + \cdots + \beta_{10} x_{10}$
13.29. Equal variance assumption appears to be violated.   **13.30.** No assumptions required, since nonparametric test applied.
13.31. Equal variance assumption appears to be violated.   **13.32.** Equal variance assumption appears to be violated.

INDEX

Least squares line, 430
  intercept, 431, 434
  slope, 431, 434
Level, in experiment, 687–688
Level of significance, 213
Levene's test of homogeneity of variance, 741
Leverage, 581–582
Limits
  control, 382–384
  specification, 409
  tolerance, 406
Linear regression analysis, 428
  assumptions, 435
Long-term trend, 624–625
Lower control limit (LCL), 383–384
Lower quartile, 111

Main effects sum of squares, 716
Main effects term(s), 531
Matched pairs, 269
Mean, 93
  binomial, 170
  population, 93
  sample, 93
Mean square
  for blocks (MSB), 701
  for error (MSE), 436, 690
  for treatments (MST), 690
Measures of central tendency, 92
Measures of relative standing, 110
Measures of reliability, 13–14
Measures of variation, 92–93
Median, 93
  population, 94
  sample, 94
Median absolute deviation (MAD), 308
Method of least squares, 429
Mid-quartile, 111
Minimum variance unbiased estimator
    (MVUE), 201–202
MINITAB software package, 6, 10–11,
    21–22, 51, 86–87, 136, 186,
    289–291, 327–328, 369, 410–411,
    456, 508, 593–594, 670–671,
    749–750
Modal class, 95
Mode, 95
Model(s)
  additive, 626
  autoregressive model, 659
  building, 526
  complete, 555, 732
  deterministic, 424
  first-order, 428, 461
  general linear, 459–460
  inferential, 626

Model(s), (continued)
  inferential time series forecasting model,
    647
  interaction, 480
  linear, 428
  log, 541
  misspecified, 564, 575
  multiple regression, 459
  multiplicative, 568, 626
  nested, 555
  parsimonious, 559–560
  probabilistic, 422–423
  quadratic, 489, 493
  random error component, 460
  reduced, 555, 732
  second-order, 489, 493
  straight-line, 428
  utility of, 437, 440, 467, 472
  see also Regression models
Model building, 527–528
Moses rank test, 317, 321
Moving average method, 634
  autoregressive, 668
  N-point moving average, 638
Multicollinearity, 546
  detecting, 548
Multinomial experiment, 352–353
Multinomial proportions, 352
  confidence interval, 355
  one-way table, 352
  testing, 354
  two-way table, 359
Multiple regression analysis, 459
  estimator of variance, 466
  models, 459
Multiplicative model, 568
Multiplicative rule of probability, 156
Mutually exclusive events, 152

Nested models, 555
  F test for comparing, 557
Nonnormality, 570, 737
Nonparametric regression, 511
Nonparametric statistical tests, 233–234
  Ansari–Bradley rank test, 317–318
  Durbin–Watson d test, 657
  Friedman F_r test, 705
  Kruskal–Wallis H test, 695–696
  Levene's test of homogeneity of variance,
    741
  MAD, 309
  Moses rank test, 317, 321
  sign test for population median, 250
  Spearman's rank correlation coefficient,
    513
  test for location, 247
  Theil C test, 513–515

Nonparametric statistical tests, (continued)
  Wilcoxon rank sum test, 262
  Wilcoxon signed ranks test, 272–273
Nonresponse, 350
Normal curve, 174
Normal distribution, 174
  standard, 176
  table, A6
Normal probability plot, 179–181
  constructing, 181
Null hypothesis, 210
Numerical descriptive measures, 92

Observational data, 425, 686
Observed significance level, 230
One-tailed test, 211–212
One-way table, 352
Outer fences, 120
Outlier, 116, 571
  detecting, 117, 121, 571
  highly suspect, 120
  suspect, 120

p-chart, 401–402
  interpreting, 403
  location of center line and control limits,
    402
p-value, 230–231
Paired observations, 268
Parameter, 13
Parametric methods, 245
Pareto diagram, 40
  constructing, 42
Pearson product moment coefficient of corre-
    lation, 128–129
Percentile, 110–111
  finding, 112
Pie chart, 36
  constructing, 37
Point estimator, 201–202
Poisson random variable, 567
Pooled estimate, 258
Population, 12
  coefficient of correlation, 131
  mean, 93
  median, 94
  standard deviation, 103
  variance, 101
  z-score, 114
Population correlation coefficient, 131
Power of a test, 221–222
Prediction interval
  for an individual value of the dependent
    variable in a straight-line model, 445
Probabilistic model
  regression, 422–423
  straight-line, 428